MW00335035

MERRILL

# P·H·Y·S·I·C·S

## — PRINCIPLES AND PROBLEMS —

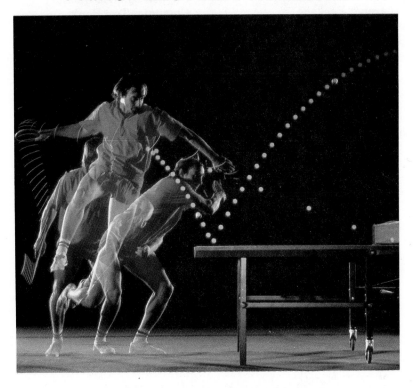

## CANADIAN EDITION

### AUTHORS

**Paul W. Zitzewitz**
Professor of Physics
Associate Dean of the College of
    Arts, Sciences, and Letters
University of Michigan-Dearborn
Dearborn, Michigan

**Robert F. Neff**
Physics Teacher
Suffern High School
Suffern, New York

**Mark Davids**
Physics Teacher
Grosse Pointe South
    High School
Grosse Pointe Farms,
    Michigan

**MAXWELL MACMILLAN CANADA**

# Merrill Physics: Principles & Problems

Student Edition (Canadian Edition)
Teacher Wraparound Edition
Problems and Solutions Manual
Teacher Resource Package
Transparency Package
Laboratory Manual:
   Student and Teacher Editions

Study Guide, Student Edition
Lab Software
Lesson Plan Booklet
English/Spanish Glossary
Computer Test Bank

## Canadian Edition Consultants

**Gerrit Cunningham**
Physics Teacher
John G. Diefenbaker High School
Calgary, Alberta

**Steve Sprysak**
Physics Teacher
Harry Ainlay Composite High School
Edmonton, Alberta

**Bill Paveley**
Gravimetric Specialist for Ontario
Department of Consumer and
Corporate Affairs

**Jim Wiese**
Science Consultant
Curriculum & Instructional
Services Centre
Surrey, British Columbia

**Canadian Cataloguing in Publication Data**
Zitzewitz, Paul W.
Physics : principles and problems

Canadian ed.
Includes index.
ISBN 0-02-954125-5

1. Physics. I. Neff, Robert F. II. Davids, Mark.
III. Title.

QC23.Z58 1992    530    C92-094479-5

Canadian Edition copyright © 1992 Maxwell Macmillan Canada Inc.
U.S. Edition copyright © 1990, 1992 by the Glencoe Division of
Macmillan/McGraw-Hill School Publishing Company.
Previously copyrighted by Merrill Publishing Company.

Pearson Education Canada
26 Prince Andrew Place
Don Mills, Ontario
M3C 2T8

Printed and bound in the U.S.A.
13    06

# TABLE OF Contents

# Physics Labs

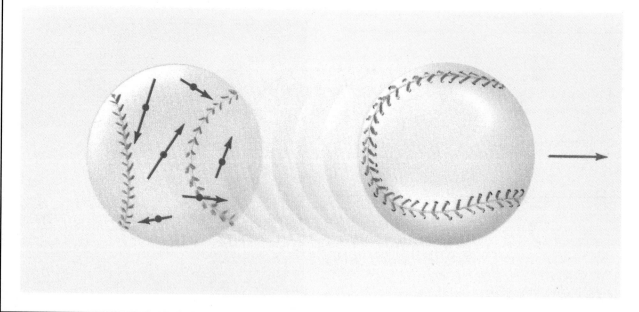

## STATES OF MATTER

## WAVES AND LIGHT

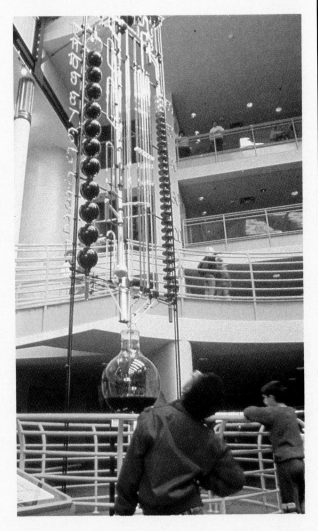

# Pocket Labs

# Features

## Problem Solving Strategies

## Using Your Calculator

## Using a Graphing Calculator

## MODERN PHYSICS

# Features

## Physics and Society

## Physics and Technology

# Features

## Connections

## Careers

Dear Students,

Physics is much more than equations and numbers. Physics is about what happens in the world all around you. It is about the colours in a rainbow, about the sparkle and hardness of a diamond. It is involved with walking, running, bicycling, driving a car, or directing an interplanetary probe. The principles of physics are evident in toys, in ball games, in musical instruments, and in giant electrical generators.

Look at the photos at the beginning of each chapter. They are examples of physics all around you. Physics, you will find, deals with the way nature behaves—with what are called natural laws. Many of the technological advances of civilization have resulted from understanding these laws. Studying physics might make it possible for you to help advance both science and technology. You may even find yourself in a career that uses the results of physics. In any case, as a citizen with a knowledge of physics, you will be better able to help solve the difficult questions that technology poses for our society.

You will find that physics is a human activity, an exciting adventure. You will learn a little about the men and women from many countries who, over the years, have helped us to understand the world around us. You can join the adventure as you begin to understand the world around you.

Paul W. Zitzewitz

# Get the Most out of Physics

Physics is all about the world around you. An example is popping the cork on a bottle of a carbonated beverage.

A question will be posed in each chapter. Do you know the answer to this one?

CHAPTER
## 13 States of Matter

◀ Bottled Cloud

Janet was helping her parents prepare for a dinner party. As she popped the cork on a bottle of sparkling grape juice, a small cloud formed around the bottle's mouth. The cloud surprised Janet's mother. What explanation did Janet give her mother?

You have lived with the three common states of matter all your life. You breathe air, drink and swim in water, and build with solid objects. In general, you are familiar with most of their properties. Yet, there can be some surprises. The photo shows a bottle that contained cold, sparkling grape juice. Carbon dioxide gas is dissolved in the liquid. When the cork is removed, the pressure in the bottle suddenly drops. The result is a beautiful display of the states of matter.

### Chapter Outline

**13.1 THE FLUID STATES**
· Pressure
· Fluids at Rest—Hydrostatics
· Fluids in Motion—
  Hydrodynamics
· Liquids vs Gases
· Surface Tension
· Evaporation and Condensation
· Plasma

**13.2 THE SOLID STATE**
· Solid Bodies
· Elasticity in Solids
· Thermal Expansion of Matter

### ✓ Concept Check

The following terms or concepts from earlier chapters are important for a good understanding of this chapter. If you are not familiar with them, you should review them before studying this chapter.
· force, Chapter 5
· work, kinetic energy, potential energy, Chapter 11
· temperature, thermal energy, heat, Chapter 12

265

The **Concept Check** is a reminder of what you should know before you start the new chapter. If you do not feel comfortable with the ideas listed, review them before starting the new chapter.

The answer will be somewhere in the chapter.

diameter. A cloud of these droplets is called a fog. Fogs often form when moist air is chilled by cold ground. Fogs can also be formed in your home. When a carbonated drink is opened, the sudden decrease in pressure causes the temperature to drop, condensing the water vapour and forming the fog seen when Janet opened the bottle of sparkling grape juice.

### Plasma

If you heat a solid, it melts to form a liquid. Further heating results in a gas. What happens if you increase the temperature still further? Collisions between the particles become violent enough to tear the particles

◀ Bottled Cloud

# Study for Mastery

## Objectives

- show an ability to add vectors by the graphical method; recognize that the order of vector addition does not matter.
- recognize the independence of perpendicular vector quantities.

The resultant i_____ ingle vector that could repres_____ um of several vectors.

> Physics involves ideas, or concepts. The list of **Objectives** will guide your study. Read the section quickly. Make note of all boldfaced terms. Skip equations and example problems. Don't worry if you don't understand the material now. The words and ideas will be more familiar the next time you read them.

## 6.1 GRAPHICAL METHOD OF VECTOR ADDITION

A vector quantity can be represented by an arrow-tipped line segment. The length of the line, drawn to scale, represents the magnitude of the quantity. The direction of the arrow indicates the direction of the quantity. This arrow-tipped line segment represents a vector. Just as we can represent a vector graphically, we can add vectors graphically. They may also be represented in the diagrams of this book in bold face, italic type, without arrows; for example, **A**, **B**.

### Vector Addition in One Dimension

Suppose a child walks 200 m east, pauses, and then continues 400 m east. To find the total displacement, or change in position of the child, we must add the two vector quantities. In Figure 6–1a, $\vec{A}$ and $\vec{B}$, drawn to scale, are vectors representing the two segments of the child's walk. The vectors are added by placing the tail of one vector at the head of the other vector. It is very important that neither the direction nor the length

## CONCEPT REVIEW

**1.1** The order in which you add vectors does not matter. Mathematicians say that vector addition is commutative. Which ordinary arithmetic operations are commutative? Which are not?

**1.2** Two boys push on a crate. One exerts a 400 N force, the other a 300 N force. The resultant force on the crate is 600 N. Explain.

**1.3** What is the largest resultant force the two boys in question 1.2 could exert on the crate? What is the smallest resultant force?

> Read the section again, more slowly this time. Pay attention to definitions. Use the **Concept Review** questions to check on your understanding. You may need to read the section again.

> Turn to the **Chapter Review.** Check the **Key Terms.** Review the **Summary** statements and compare them with the **Objectives** you read at the beginning of the section.

## CHAPTER 6 REVIEW

### SUMMARY

#### 6.1 Graphical Method of Vector Addition

- The resultant is the sum of two or more vectors.
- To add two vectors graphically, place the tail of the second vector at the head of the first vector. Draw th_____ vector t_____
- The res_____ be foun_____

- A vector can be resolved into two perpendi_____ components.
- Vectors at any angles may be added by fi_____ their components, adding all vertical and _____ zontal components separately, and then fi_____ the resultant.

### KEY TERMS

| | |
|---|---|
| resultant | components |
| trigonometry | vector resolution |
| sine (sin) | equilibrium |
| cosine (cos) | equilibrant force |
| tangent (tan) | |

### REVIEWING CONCEPTS

1. What method is used to add vectors graphically?
2. A vector is to be added graphically to a second vector. Which of th_____ to the first vector: mov_____ its length?
3. In your own words, w_____

12. A book is on an inclined plane.
    a. Describe two convenient compor_____ the weight of the book.
    b. How are the magnitudes of these _____ nents related to the angle of the in_____

### APPLYING CONCEPTS

1. A vector drawn 15 mm long represen_____ locity of 30 m/s. How long should you_____ vector to represent a velocity of 20 m_____
2. If a vector that is 1 cm long represents _____ of 5 N, how many newtons does a _____

> **Reviewing Concept** questions refer to the text. **Applying Concepts** questions require you to think of new ways to apply the ideas in the chapter. Extend your thinking by **Thinking Physic-ly!**

### THINKING PHYSIC-LY

Weight lifting or "pumping iron" has become very popular in the last few years. When lifting a barbell, which grip will exert less force on the lifter's arms: one in which the arms are extended straight upward from the body so they are at right angles to the bars, or one in which the arms are spread so that the bar is gripped

resultant _____ of 3 N ar_____ e resultant_____

# Solve Problems Successfully

Many ideas in physics are best described by using math. Most useful applications of physical principles often depend on quantitative relationships among variables.

Problem Solving Strategies are scattered throughout the book. They are helpful hints for working different kinds of problems. Example Problems use those hints to show you methods you can use to solve the Practice Problems. To help you be successful, complete solutions for all Practice Problems are in Appendix A. Problems in the Chapter Review will give you further practice.

## PROBLEM SOLVING STRATEGY

When solving problems, use an orderly procedure.

1. Read the problem carefully. Try to visualize the actual situation. Make a sketch if necessary.
2. Identify the quantities that are given in the problem.
3. Identify the quantity that is unknown, the one you have to find.
4. Select the equation or equations that will relate the given and unknown quantities.
5. Make sure the equations can be applied to the problem, that is, is the acceleration constant?
6. Rewrite equations as needed to solve for the unknown quantity.
7. Substitute the given values including proper units into the equation and solve. Be sure your answer is in the correct units.
8. Make a rough estimate to see if your answer is reasonable.

## Example Problem

### Flight of a Tennis Ball

A tennis ball is thrown straight up with an initial velocity of $+22.5$ m/s. It is caught at the same distance above ground from which it was thrown. **a.** How high does the ball rise? **b.** How long does the ball remain in the air?

**Given:** $\vec{v}_i = +22.5$ m/s,  **Unknowns: a.** $\vec{d}$  **b.** $t$

**Solution:**

**a.** At the top of its flight, the instantaneous velocity of the ball is zero. Thus, the final velocity for the upward part of the ball's flight will be zero. Therefore, we know $\vec{v}_i, \vec{g}$, and need $\vec{d}$. Use the equation $\vec{v}_f^2 = \vec{v}_i^2 + 2\vec{g}\vec{d}$, solving it for $\vec{d}$.

$= \vec{v}_i^2 + 2\vec{g}d$ or $2\vec{g}\vec{d} = -\vec{v}_i^2$.

$\dfrac{m/s)^2}{0\ m/s^2)} = +25.8$ m.

sitive), so $\vec{d} = +25.8$ m.

now that the times required for the rising and ht will be the same. That is, the time to rise Thus, we know $\vec{v}_f$ and $\vec{g}$ but need $t$. Use $_f = 0.0$, we solve for $t$, obtaining

$\dfrac{s}{^2} = +2.30$ s.

## Practice Problems

27. If you drop a golf ball, how far does it fall in 0.5 s?
28. A spacecraft travelling at a velocity of $+1210$ m/s is uniformly accelerated at $-150$ m/s². If the acceleration lasts for 8.68 s, what is the final velocity of the craft? Explain your results in words.
29. A man falls 1.0 m to the floor.

## Appendix A
### Solutions for Practice Problems

$IMA = \dfrac{d_e}{d_r} = \dfrac{33.0\ m}{16.5\ m} = 2.00$, so

efficiency $= \dfrac{1.74}{2.00} \times 100\% = 87\%$

**15.** $eff = \dfrac{W_o}{W_i} \times 100\% = \dfrac{F_r d_r}{F_e d_e} \times 100\%$, so

$d_e = \dfrac{F_r d_r(100\%)}{F_e(eff)}$

$= \dfrac{(125 \times 10^3\ N)(0.13\ m)(100\%)}{(225\ N)(88.7\%)}$

$= 0.81$ m

**4. a.** Since $W = \Delta E_k = \dfrac{1}{2}mv^2$, then $v = \sqrt{2W/m}$.

If $W' = \dfrac{1}{2}W$,

$v' = \sqrt{2W'/m}$

$= \sqrt{2\left(\dfrac{1}{2}W\right)/m} = \sqrt{\dfrac{1}{2}}\ v$

$= (0.707)(100\ km/h) = 71\ km/h$

**b.** If $W' = 2W$,

$v' = \sqrt{2}\ (100\ km/h)$

$= 140\ km/h$

You will find calculating tips and shortcuts in the Using Your Calculator features in the margin beside many of the Example Problems. If you like using a graphing calculator, you will enjoy the Using a Graphing Calculator excercises in some of the Chapter Reveiws.

### ▨ Using Your CALCULATOR

Calculators can be used to evaluate equations. Note that each of the factors in the denominator must be divided into the numerator.

$$d = -\dfrac{v_i^2}{2\ g}$$

| 22.5 | x² | +/− |   | −506. 25 |
| ÷ | 2 | ÷ | 9.80 | +/− | = | 25. 829082 |

$d = 25.8$ m

# Experiment with Physics

The ideas of physics must always be tested against the natural world. To find out how the world works, you must do some experiments.

Try the **Pocket Labs.** They are quick activities that give you hands-on experiences with new ideas introduced in a section of the chapter.

Pay attention to **Safety Symbols.** Look for them. They will alert you to possible dangers in your laboratory experiences.

The **Physics Labs** will help you develop valuable skills in gathering and analyzing data, of communicating your results to others, and of applying those results by answering questions.

## PHYSICS LAB : Heating Up

### Purpose

To discover how the temperature increases with a constant supply of thermal energy.

### Materials

- hot plate (or bunsen burner)
- 250-mL pyrex beaker
- water
- thermometer
- stopwatch
- goggles

### Procedure

1. Turn your hot plate to a medium setting (or as recommended by your teacher). Allow a few minutes for the plate to heat up. While heating water wear goggles.
2. Pour 150 mL of room temperature water into the 250-mL beaker.
3. Measure the initial temperature of the water. Keep the thermometer in the water.
4. Place the beaker on the hot plate and record the temperature every 1.0 min. Carefully stir the

### Analysis

1. What is the slope of the graph for the first

# *Think Physic-ly*

How does the study of Physics apply to the rest of your life? **Want Ads** describe careers that use some of the concepts you will learn in your study. **Connections** illustrate how the ideas of physics influence almost every area of your life. In an **FYI** you might find a poem, an amusing anecdote, or a bit of physics trivia. **Physics and Technology** features present an interesting application of physics. The **Physics and Society** features present a discussion of a social or environmental concern that involves some application of physics. You will find that Physics applies to all of your life.

## Physics and technology

### AERODYNAMIC HELMETS

In the 74th Indy 500, Arie Luyendyk drove an average speed of 297.5 km/h to win. His maximum speed was greater than 352 km/h. At these speeds, drivers complain that their heads are buffeted severely; their helmets lift up, impairing creating an area of low pressure; the higher pressure below the helmet pushes it upward. Simpson Race Products Company found a way to break up the airflow over the helmet through the use of pressure-relief ducts and stall strips. The Simpson helmet has two gill-like outlet ducts and two ripple strips on each side of the top of the helmet. The ducts allow low-energy airflow out of the helmet to mix with the faster moving air over the top, thus helmet won the 1990 Schwitzer Award given by the Society of Automotive Engineers for innovation and excellence in race car design. Besides its improved aerodynamic qualities, the helmet has a new liner that provides better protection and it improves airflow to cool the driver's head.

· What other applications might this improved helmet have?

## Physics and society

### WEAK ELECTROMAGNETIC FIELDS—A HEALTH CONCERN?

Alternating currents, such as those in household wiring, produce electric and magnetic fields. The very low AC frequency is call Extremely Low Frequency, or ELF. The many sources of ELF electric and magnetic fields include power lines, home wiring, electric

Recently, however, experiments have shown that cells are sensitive to even very weak ELF fields. They can affect flow of ions across cell membranes, synthesis of DNA, and the response of cells to hormones. Abnormal development of chick embryos has been seen. The experimental results, however, are very complex. Some effects of ELFs occur only at certain frequencies or amplitudes. Others occur only if the fields are turned on or off abruptly. Finally, for most environmental health hazards the larger the exposure, or dose,

ELF? Some studies found small increases in leukemia, breast cancer, and brain cancer. Studies of users of electric blankets have shown no effects on men, but increases in cancers and brain tumors in children whose mothers slept under electric blankets while pregnant. Studies to find the causes will take years and may not have conclusive results. In the meantime, what should be done?

### DEVELOPING A VIEWPOINT

Read articles about ELFs and

# CHAPTER
# 1 : What Is Physics?

◀ Super Ideas?

The floating block is a small magnet held up against the force of gravity by the disc of superconducting material under it. This disc is made of material that must be cooled well below 0°C by liquid nitrogen. Such a material was unknown only a few years ago. How did physicists discover superconductivity and develop these new materials?

What is physics? What do you think when you see the word *physics*? Do you see equations? Do you hear people saying how hard it is? The atomic bomb? Or do you see people? Albert Einstein with wild hair and no socks? Men in white coats?

Yes, physics has a certain reputation. Yes, physics does make use of mathematics as a powerful language. But, physics also involves concepts, ideas, and principles expressed in ordinary words. Yes, the atomic bomb was built with the aid of many physicists. But, the electricity that lights our homes and schools and brings us radio, television, CDs, and computers was also developed by physicists. Physics also helps athletes train more efficiently and have better equipment so that new records are set.

Of course, Albert Einstein was a physicist. But, so are many women and men who are not super-geniuses, who could easily be your next door neighbor—or you.

The goal of this course is not to make you a physicist. It is to give you an idea of the way physicists view the world; to have the satisfaction of understanding and even predicting the outcome of the activities occurring all around you; to know enough about physics so you can have a rewarding career in a technological world; to be able to make informed decisions as a citizen in an increasingly complex age; to learn to ask questions.

Someone once said, "Professional baseball players and physicists love their work. Others just go to work." We hope you will feel the same way about this class.

FIGURE 1–1. Shown here is the first operating cyclotron, used to study subatomic particles. It was built in 1930 by E.O. Lawrence. It has a circumference of about 33 cm. In contrast, the proposed superconducting Super Collider will be about 84 km in circumference, and can give particles 100 million times more energy.

# Physics: The Search for Understanding

**P**hysics is the branch of knowledge that studies the physical world. Physicists investigate objects as small as atoms and as large as galaxies. They study the natures of matter and energy and how they are related. How do they do this study? Physicists and other scientists are inquisitive people who look at the world around them with questioning eyes. Their observations lead them to search for the causes of what they see. What makes the sun shine? How do the planets move? Of what is matter made? More often than not, finding explanations to the original questions leads to more questions and experiments. What all scientists hope for are powerful explanations that describe more than one phenomenon and lead to a better understanding of the universe.

Sometimes the results of the work of physicists are only of interest to other physicists. Other times their work leads to devices, such as lasers, calculators, or computers, which change everyone's life. As an example of how physics works, let's look at the recent history of a field of physics which has produced some of the most important scientific advances of the last few years, "high temperature" superconductivity.

In September 1986, two Swiss scientists working for IBM Corporation announced that they had discovered a new superconducting material that worked at temperatures as "high" as $-243°C$, thirty degrees above absolute zero, the lowest possible temperature for matter. Until that time, materials were only superconducting at temperatures close to absolute zero, $-273°C$. This temperature is theoretically the lowest temperature possible. The new material was a ceramic, a glass-like material that does

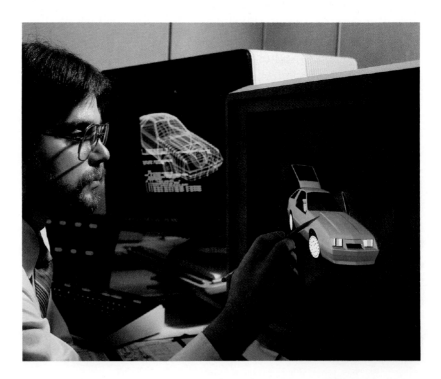

**FIGURE 1–2. Physicists don't always work in labs, and the results of their studies are important not just to other physicists.**

FIGURE 1–3. Superconducting materials are very quickly finding uses outside of physics. Medical diagnostic equipment is an example.

not normally conduct any electricity. Even though superconducting metals had been discovered in 1911, this development was exciting because earlier superconductors worked at temperatures very difficult to reach and maintain. In 1973, a metal alloy had been found that worked at twenty-three degrees above absolute zero, but in the next 13 years no further progress had been made.

Within weeks after the discovery was announced, researchers in the United States, China, and Japan had repeated the experiments. That fall, scientists tried different materials and increased the temperature to fifty degrees, then seventy-seven degrees, then ninety degrees, then, in February 1987, to ninety-eight degrees above absolute zero (−175°C). In March 1987, three thousand physicists jammed a hotel ballroom for eight hours to hear reports of experiments. By the end of the same year, high school students had made superconductors that worked at temperatures above −196°C.

Physicists and engineers have dreamed of many exciting applications for superconductors. Superconducting wires could carry electricity to cities from distant power plants without energy loss. They could be used in magnets that make nuclear fusion possible, that allow high-speed trains to "float" above the track, that could detect oil and minerals in Earth, or pinpoint diseased body tissue. Superconductors might make possible smaller, faster, more powerful computers. Until recently, the problem has been that superconductors worked at such low temperatures that they had to be cooled by liquid helium. Liquid helium is very expensive (more than $5.00/L) and difficult to store. The new superconductors can be cooled with liquid nitrogen, which costs about the same as soda pop. Now some of the dreams may be possible. But first the new materials, now as brittle as glass, must be modified so they can be made into flexible wires. Even more exciting would be the development of materials that are superconducting at room temperatures.

FIGURE 1–4. Wires made of superconducting materials. The ability to produce flexible materials will allow many exciting applications for superconductors.

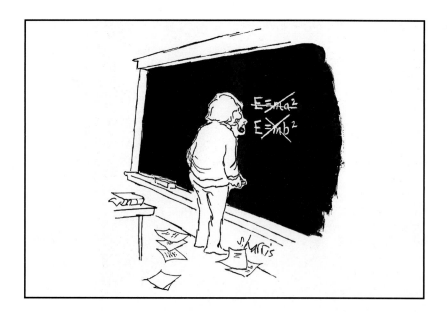

## POCKET LAB

### FALLING

Aristotle argued that heavy objects fall faster than light objects. Galileo stated that light and heavy objects fall at the same rate. What do you think? Tear a sheet of paper in half. Crumple one half so that it is in the shape of a ball. Hold the half sheet in one hand and the ball in the other. Drop them from the same height at the same time. Describe what you observed. Explain the results. Predict which will fall faster: four pennies taped together or a single penny. Try it. Was Aristotle correct? Explain.

How did these discoveries occur? The original discovery, in 1911, was made by the Dutch physicist Heike Kamerlingh Onnes. Kamerlingh Onnes was an experimental physicist, one who worked in a research laboratory, often inventing and building the equipment he needed to carry out his experiments, and then using insight, knowledge, and imagination to interpret the results. Many times the results had no immediate practical applications. Onnes had built new kinds of refrigerators that could reach previously unexplored low temperatures. He then studied the properties of gases, liquids, and solids at these new temperatures. He anticipated that mercury would become a better electrical conductor when the temperature was lowered. What totally surprised him was that *all* resistance disappeared when mercury reached four degrees above absolute zero!

For over forty years after 1911 no one had developed a complete explanation of how materials could conduct electricity without loss. That is, there was no theory of superconductivity. In 1957, three American theoretical physicists, John Bardeen, Leon Cooper, and Robert Schrieffer, presented a theory, called the BCS theory, that explained how superconductors work. Theoretical physicists use mathematics and, especially today, computers to construct a framework of explanations called a theory that explains experimental data and predicts new results. Theoreticians also need insight, imagination, and creativity. The work of theoreticians in superconductivity is not finished, because no theory can yet explain how the new superconducting materials work.

We still have much to learn about the interactions of matter and energy. Sometimes experimental results come before the theoretical explanations. In other cases, a theory predicts the result of an experiment that has not yet been done. Often physics has important applications to other sciences. Superconducting magnets are an important part of devices used by chemists to learn the structure of molecules, by biologists to trace molecules through cells, and by physicians to find brain tumors.

# Physics and society

## RESEARCH DOLLARS

How are scientific discoveries made? Although some important scientific discoveries are made "by chance," most are the result of years of carefully directed work called research. With the exception of a few people who study science as a hobby, most scientists get paid to do research in their scientific field. Some scientists are professors at universities. Teaching students is only part of their job. Much of their work consists of doing research—that is, exploring ideas, creating hypotheses, performing experiments, and publishing findings. Many other scientists also work for government-funded laboratories or for private companies.

Physicists call the current theory, or explanation, of the fundamental building blocks of matter the "Standard Model." According to this theory, the basic components from which all matter is made are the particles called quarks and leptons. Physicists at particle-accelerating facilities such as the University of British Columbia's TRIUMF complex and Fermilab, near Chicago, study the results of high-speed particle collisions to test predictions of the Standard Model.

Further research is needed to understand the nature of the quarks and leptons themselves. This new research, however, will require the construction of a larger, more powerful particle accelerator known as the Superconducting Super Collider (SSC). It is estimated that the SSC will cost more than 7 billion dollars to build.

It is difficult to measure the value of SSC research. Although it is expected to contribute significantly to our understanding of the natural world, SSC research offers no immediate practical application benefiting human society. Many people believe government money would be better spent improving the quality of human life in direct ways such as finding a cure for AIDS or reducing pollution. Some scientists are concerned that financing the SSC may take money away from important scientific research in other disciplines such as biology, medicine, chemistry, and other branches of physics.

## DEVELOPING A VIEWPOINT

1. Some of history's most important scientific discoveries had at first no apparent practical application. Can you think of some examples? What is the practical significance of understanding the essential composition of matter?

2. Should governments support basic research like the SSC project? Would money be better spent on applied research such as finding a cure for AIDS?

3. Earlier particle accelerators, built for basic physics research, led to new methods of treating cancer and to more advanced computers. What basic research in other areas of science has led to totally unexpected results?

## SUGGESTED READINGS

Dawson, John M. "Plasma Particle Accelerators." *Scientific American*, March 1989, pp. 54–61.

"The Supercostly Supercollider." *The Economist,* January 27, 1990, pp. 87–88.

Irvine, John and Ben R. Martin, Phoebe Isard. "Investing in the Future: How Much Governments Pay for Academic Research." *Physics Today,* September 1990, pp. 31–38.

# F.Y.I.

A strategy is an organized approach to a problem that breaks down the task of obtaining and organizing information into stages. Strategies can be the "bridge" in solving problems. Several strategies are listed below.

· List all possible solutions.
· Look for a pattern.
· Construct a table, graph, or figure.
· Make a model.
· Guess and check.
· Work backwards.
· Make a drawing.
· Solve a simpler or similar related problem.

Science and technology constantly interact. Often new equipment, such as the refrigerators Kamerlingh Onnes built, produce further scientific results. Other times science results in new products. For example, engineers have built giant magnets and small, efficient motors and generators using superconductors. The applications of science affect the lives of everyone more and more each year. For this reason, all of us need an understanding of physics, as well as the other sciences, to make informed decisions about problems involving our rapidly changing society.

Perhaps the most surprising aspect of physics is that its results can be described by a small number of relationships, or laws. These laws often can be expressed using mathematics, which has been called the language of physics.

· · · · · · · · · · · · · · · · · · · · · · · · · · · · · · · · · · · ·

# What and How, not Why: Scientific Methods

Starting in the fourth and fifth centuries B.C., Greek philosophers tried to determine what the world was made of. Chief among them was Aristotle, who lived around 340 B.C. Aristotle was a student of the philosopher Plato and tutored Alexander the Great, conqueror of much of the known world. Aristotle founded a school of philosophy and wrote many books, some on science. Aristotle and his followers made some observations of everyday occurrences, and then tried to draw all possible conclusions solely by logical argument. Unfortunately, they were not very interested in knowing exactly *what* happens or *how* it happens, or even *if* it happens, given different conditions. Their interests were mainly theorizing why the specific events that they observed occurred.

Aristotle believed that all matter within reach was made up of four elements: Earth, Water, Air, and Fire. Each element had a "natural place." The highest place belonged to Fire, then Air, then Water, and, at the bottom, Earth. Motion occurred because an element wanted to reach its own natural place. Thus Water bubbled up through springs on Earth. Adding Fire to Water produced steam, a form of Air, that rose. A stone (Earth) fell through both Air and Water to reach the ground. When a stone was tossed up, it was given "violent motion." When this motion ceased, natural motion took over and the stone fell.

**FIGURE 1–6. Aristotle believed that all "earthly" matter was composed of four elements. Each element had a particular quality associated with it.**

The writings of the early Greeks first came to Europe through Arabic translations in the twelfth century. Until the sixteenth century, Europeans accepted the Greek teachings as truth, with no need for verification. One of the first European scientists to claim publicly that knowledge must be based on observations and experiments rather than ancient books was Galileo Galilei (1564–1642). He questioned the belief that Earth is the center of the universe. He doubted Aristotle's views on physics, especially the idea that objects of large mass fall faster than objects of small mass. To prove Aristotle wrong, Galileo developed a systematic method of observation, experimentation, and analysis.

There is no single "scientific method." All scientists, however, study problems in an organized way. They combine systematic experimentation with careful measurement and analysis of results. From these analyses, conclusions are drawn. These conclusions are then subjected to additional tests to find out if they are valid. Since Galileo's time, scientists all over the world have used these techniques and methods to gain a better understanding of the universe. Knowledge, skill, luck, imagination, trial and error, educated guesses, and great patience—all play a part. For example, the two Swiss scientists who discovered the new superconductors said they "felt free to try something crazy." The leader of the University of Houston superconductor research group, Paul Chu, said, "We feel we have an advantage over some other groups because we are not confined to conventional thinking. We think wildly."

## CONCEPT REVIEW

**1.1** Did Heike Kamerlingh Onnes discover superconductivity trying to make a measurement agree with theory? Explain.

**1.2** What is a theory in physics?

**1.3** **Critical Thinking:** Which is a better model for scientific work, a student working in his or her basement on a project to enter in a competition, or a group of people with different talents cooperating to solve a problem?

## HISTORY CONNECTION

Historians of science relate cultural and political activities to the lives of scientists and their discoveries. For example, Henry Moseley, a brilliant English scientist studying X rays in Rutherford's laboratory, enlisted as a lieutenant in the Royal Engineers when World War I broke out. Rutherford tried, unsuccessfully, to get Moseley to resign to continue his research. Moseley was killed in the Battle of Gallipoli at the age of 27.

FIGURE 1–7. The University of Houston research team working on superconductors. A group of scientists with different areas of specialization often work together to produce spectacular results.

# PHYSICS LAB : The Paper Tower

## Purpose

To design and construct the tallest free standing tower from a single sheet of paper and 30 cm of tape.

## Materials

· 1 sheet white paper
· 1 sheet coloured paper
· 30-cm plastic tape
· scissors

## Procedure

1. Each student will receive 1 sheet of white paper. Use the white sheet to try out various design possibilities. Think wildly.
2. Each lab group will receive 1 sheet of coloured paper for their competition tower.

3. Before beginning with the coloured paper, examine the designs of each group member.
4. Decide which aspects of each design should be incorporated into your final design. The most important aspects of a winning team are communication and cooperation.
5. Plan ahead. Set a timetable for experimentation and for actual construction. Plan on finishing at least five minutes before the end of the period.
6. Watch your time. Do not fall too far behind schedule.
7. Your tower must be free standing for at least five seconds.
8. Measure your tower before it tips over.

## Observations and Data

1. Look at the designs from the other groups. Describe how they are similar.
2. Look at the designs from the other groups. Describe how they are different.

## Analysis

1. What were the limiting factors in your tower's construction?
2. Did your group work well as a team? What could you do differently to be more effective?

## Applications

1. What architectural elements have been incorporated into your design?

# CHAPTER
# 1 REVIEW · · · · · · · · · · · · · · · · · · · · · · · ·

## SUMMARY

· Physics is the study of matter and energy and their relationships.
· Physics is basic to all other sciences.
· A knowledge of physics makes us, as citizens, better able to make decisions about questions related to science and technology.
· Scientists study problems in an organized way, using many techniques.
· Scientists are interested in knowing what happens and how it happens, but not necessarily why.
· Much scientific work is done in groups, where people collaborate with one another.

## REVIEWING CONCEPTS

1. Define physics in your own words.
2. Why is mathematics important to science?
3. Which came first in superconductivity, the experimental physics or the theoretical physics?
4. Kamerlingh Onnes is considered an experimental physicist, while Bardeen, Cooper and Schrieffer are theoretical physicists. Explain the difference.
5. Assume Aristotle's four element theory is correct. How does the theory explain the motion of each of the elements?

## APPLYING CONCEPTS

1. Give some examples of applications of the result of work by physicists.
2. Give examples of applications of the result of work done by physicists on superconductivity.
3. Use a dictionary to find out what aspects of nature are investigated by each of the following scientists: astronomer, geophysicist, biophysicist, astrophysicist.

4. Some of the branches of physics you will study in this course will investigate motion, the properties of materials, sound, light, electricity and magnetism, properties of atoms, and nuclear physics. Give at least one example of an application of each branch.
5. What reason might the Greeks have had not to question the evidence that heavier objects fall faster than lighter objects? **Hint:** Did you ever question which fell faster?
6. Is the scientific method a clearly-defined set of steps and procedures? Support your answer.
7. Why will the work of a physicist never be finished?
8. Why does science tend to be self-correcting?
9. Aristotle believed wood was a combination of fire, water, and earth. Use his four-element theory to explain why a wooden boat floats on water.
10. In general, which comes first, the theory or the experiment?
11. Theories in science undergo change. Is this a strength or a weakness of science? Explain.

## THINKING PHYSIC-LY

It has been said that a fool can ask more questions than a wise person can answer. In science it is frequently the case that a wise person is needed to ask the right question rather than to answer it. Explain.

# CHAPTER 2

# A Mathematical Toolkit

◀ **A Graphic Display**

Identify the graph that shows a linear relationship.

Physics often uses mathematics as its language. This chapter presents a collection of mathematical techniques you will find useful throughout the course. You might think of the chapter as a collection of tools that can be used when needed later.

Central to the tools is the use of graphs and equations to represent the results of many observations and experiments. Probably the most famous physics equation is Einstein's $E = mc^2$. This simple equation describes one of the most powerful concepts of physics—the equivalence of mass and energy for a particle at rest.

How do you find an equation to describe experimental results? Frequently a graph of the data gives you a clue. In this chapter you will see how data describing the distance a car travels while braking to a stop can be expressed by an equation. Thus, you will learn that one of the most powerful ways of analyzing data is to display them as a graph.

## Chapter Outline

**2.1 THE MEASURE OF SCIENCE**
- The Metric System
- Scientific Notation
- Prefixes Used With SI Units
- Arithmetic Operations in Scientific Notation

**2.2 NOT ALL IS CERTAIN**
- Uncertainties of Measurement
- Accuracy and Precision
- Significant Digits
- Operations Using Significant Digits

**2.3 DISPLAYING DATA**
- Graphing Data
- Linear, Quadratic, and Inverse Relationships

**2.4 MANIPULATING EQUATIONS**
- Solving Equations Using Algebra
- Units in Equations

## ✓ Concept Check

The following terms or concepts are important for a good understanding of this chapter. If you are not familiar with them, you should review them before studying this chapter.
- algebra and graphing techniques

- state the fundamental SI units for time, length, and mass.
- demonstrate an ability to use scientific notation.
- identify and use common metric prefixes.
- be able to perform arithmetic operations using scientific notation.

The metric system is based on powers of ten.

The SI unit of time, the second, is based on the oscillation time of an atom.

FIGURE 2–1. Several countries have issued stamps to help the general public become familiar with SI units of measurement.

## 2.1 THE MEASURE OF SCIENCE

The science of physics is based on a few principles and involves the development of concepts. The application of these principles and concepts usually involves the measurement of one or more quantities. In almost every country except the United States, the metric system is used in everyday life. The world-wide scientific community uses an adaptation of the metric system, the SI, to make measurements.

### The Metric System

The **metric system** of measurement was created by French scientists in 1795. It is convenient to use because units of different sizes are related by powers of ten. An international committee determines the standards of the metric system. This committee has set up the Système International d'Unités (**SI**). The SI is used throughout the world. Because other quantities can be described using the three basic units of the SI—time, length, and mass—they are called **base units**.

The standard unit of time is the **second** (s). The second was first defined as 1/86 400 of the mean solar day. A mean solar day is the average length of the day over a period of one year. In 1967, the second was redefined in terms of the frequency of one type of radiation emitted by a cesium-133 atom.

The standard SI unit of length is the **metre** (m). The metre was first defined as one ten-millionth ($10^{-7}$) of the distance from the north pole to the equator, measured along a line passing through Lyons, France.

In the 20th century, physicists found that light could be used to make very precise measurements of distances. In 1960, the metre was rede-finded as a multiple of a wavelength of light emitted by krypton-86. By 1982, an even more precise length measurement defined the metre as the distance light travels in 1/229 792 458 second in a vacuum.

The third standard unit measures the mass of an object. The **kilogram** (kg) is the only unit not defined in terms of the properties of atoms. It is the mass of a platinum-iridium metal cylinder kept near Paris. A copy is kept at the National Institute of Standards and Technology in the United States.

Two other base units will be introduced as needed in the text. A wide variety of other units, called **derived units**, are combinations of the base units. A common derived unit is the metre per second, or m/s, used to measure speed.

The SI unit of length is the metre, defined as the distance light travels in a certain amount of time.

The SI unit of mass is the kilogram.

## Scientific Notation

Scientists often work with very large and very small quantities. For example, the mass of Earth is about

6 000 000 000 000 000 000 000 000 kg

and the mass of an electron is

0.000 000 000 000 000 000 000 000 000 000 911 kg.

Written in this form, the quantities take up much space and are difficult to use in calculations. To work with such numbers more easily, we write them in a shortened form by expressing decimal places as powers of ten. This method of expressing numbers is called exponential nota-tion. **Scientific notation** is based on exponential notation. In scientific notation, the numerical part of a measurement is expressed as a number between 1 and 10 multiplied by a whole-number power of 10.

$$M \times 10^n$$

In this expression, $1 \leq M < 10$ and $n$ is an integer. For example, 2 km can be written $2 \times 10^3$ m. The mass of a softball is about 180 g or $1.8 \times 10^{-1}$ kg.

FIGURE 2–3. Most countries now use the SI unit *joule* rather than calorie for energy.

# F.Y.I.

To write measurements using scientific notation, move the decimal point until only one non-zero digit remains on the left. Then count the number of places the decimal point was moved and use that number as the exponent of ten. Thus, the approximate mass of Earth can also be expressed as $6 \times 10^{24}$ kg. Note that the exponent becomes larger as the decimal point is moved to the left.

To write the mass of the electron in scientific notation, the decimal point is moved 31 places to the right. Thus, the mass of the electron can also be written as $9.11 \times 10^{-31}$ kg. Note that the exponent becomes smaller as the decimal point is moved to the right.

## Practice Problems

*Express the following measurements in scientific notation.*
**1. a.** 5800 m **b.** 450 000 m **c.** 302 000 000 m **d.** 86 000 000 000 m
**2. a.** 0.000 508 kg **b.** 0.000 000 45 kg **c.** 0.003600 kg **d.** 0.004 kg
▶ **3. a.** 300 000 000 s **b.** 186 000 s **c.** 93 000 000 s

A quantity written in scientific notation consists of a number between 1 and 10 followed by 10 raised to a power.

## Prefixes Used With SI Units

Like our number system, the metric system is a decimal system. **Prefixes** are used to change SI units by powers of ten. Thus, one tenth of a metre is a decimetre, one hundredth of a metre is a centimetre, and one thousandth of a metre is a millimetre. Each of these divisions can be found on a metre stick. The prefixes that change SI units by a power of one thousand are most common. Thus, one thousand metres is a kilometre. Figure 2–4 shows the vast range of lengths of objects in our universe. Commonly used length units are shown.

Metric prefixes differ from one another by a power of ten.

**FIGURE 2–4. Objects in the universe range from the very small to the unimaginably large.**

Length of whale

Diameter of Earth

Distance to known galaxy

$10^{-16}$  $10^{-12}$  $10^{-8}$  $10^{-4}$  $10^{0}$  $10^{4}$  $10^{8}$  $10^{12}$  $10^{16}$  $10^{20}$  $10^{24}$

1 pm    1 nm    1 μm    1 mm    1 m    1 km

Diameter of blood cell

Length of Canada

Distance of a light year

The metric units for all quantities use the same prefixes. One thousandth of a gram is a milligram, and one thousand grams is a kilogram. To use SI units effectively, it is important to know the meanings of the prefixes in Table 2–1.

Table 2–1

| Prefixes Used with SI Units | | | |
|---|---|---|---|
| Prefix | Symbol | Fractions | Example |
| pico | p | 1/1 000 000 000 000 or $10^{-12}$ | picometre (pm) |
| nano | n | 1/1 000 000 000 or $10^{-9}$ | nanometre (nm) |
| micro | $\mu$ | 1/1 000 000 or $10^{-6}$ | microgram ($\mu$g) |
| milli | m | 1/1 000 or $10^{-3}$ | milligram (mg) |
| centi | c | 1/100 or $10^{-2}$ | centimetre (cm) |
| deci | d | 1/10 or $10^{-1}$ | decimetre (dm) |
| | | Multiples | |
| tera | T | 1 000 000 000 000 or $10^{12}$ | terametre (Tm) |
| giga | G | 1 000 000 000 or $10^{9}$ | gigametre (Gm) |
| mega | M | 1 000 000 or $10^{6}$ | megagram (Mg) |
| kilo | k | 1000 or $10^{3}$ | kilometre (km) |
| hecto | h | 100 or $10^{2}$ | hectometre (hm) |
| deka | da | 10 or $10^{1}$ | decagram (dag) |

# Example Problem

**Conversion Between Units**

What is the equivalent of 500 mm in metres?

**Solution:** From Table 2–1, we see the conversion factor is

$$1 \text{ mm} = 1 \times 10^{-3} \text{ m}$$

Therefore,

$$(500 \text{ mm}) \frac{(1 \times 10^{-3} \text{ m})}{1 \text{ mm}} = 500 \times 10^{-3} \text{ m} = 5.00 \times 10^{-1} \text{ m}$$

# Practice Problems

4. Convert each of the following length measurements to its equivalent in metres.
   **a.** 1.1 cm   **b.** 76.2 pm   **c.** 2.1 km   **d.** 0.123 Mm
▶ 5. Convert each of these mass measurements to its equivalent in kilograms.
   **a.** 147 g   **b.** 11 $\mu$g   **c.** 7.23 Mg   **d.** 478 mg

# Arithmetic Operations in Scientific Notation

Suppose you need to add or subtract measurements expressed in scientific notation. If the numbers have the same exponent, simply add or subtract the values of $M$ and keep the same $n$.

Quantities to be added or subtracted must have the same exponents.

# POCKET LAB

## PAPER BLOCK

Look closely at the markings on a cm scale. Would you guess that a single sheet of paper has a volume of more or less than 1.0 cm³? Estimate the volume of a single sheet of paper to one significant digit. Record your estimate in correct scientific notation. Use the cm scale to measure the volume of a sheet of paper. (**Hint:** Measure the thickness of 10 or 20 sheets.) Record your measured value. Compare the measured value to your estimate.

CALCULATOR **U s i n g  Y o u r**

Using a calculator simplifies performing arithmetic operations on numbers in scientific notation.

$$4.0 \times 10^{-6} \text{ kg} - 3.0 \times 10^{-7} \text{ kg}$$

| Keys | Answer |
|------|--------|
| [4.0] [EXP] [6] [+/−] [−] | $4.^{-06}$ |
| [3.0] [EXP] [7] [+/−] [=] | $3.7^{-6}$ |

$$3.7 \times 10^{-6} \text{ kg}$$

$$\frac{8 \times 10^6 \text{ m}}{2 \times 10^{-2} \text{ s}}$$

| | |
|------|--------|
| [8] [EXP] [6] [÷] | $8.^{06}$ |
| [2] [EXP] [2] [+/−] [=] | $4.^{08}$ |

$$4 \times 10^8 \text{ m/s}$$

## Example Problem

### Adding and Subtracting with Like Exponents

**a.** $4 \times 10^8 \text{ m} + 3 \times 10^8 \text{ m} = 7 \times 10^8 \text{ m}$
**b.** $6.2 \times 10^{-3} \text{ m} - 2.8 \times 10^{-3} \text{ m} = 3.4 \times 10^{-3} \text{ m}$

If the powers of ten are not the same, they must be made the same before the numbers are added or subtracted. Move the decimal points until the exponents are the same.

## Example Problem

### Adding and Subtracting with Unlike Exponents

**a.** $4.0 \times 10^6 \text{ m} + 3 \times 10^5 \text{ m}$
   $= 4.0 \times 10^6 \text{ m} + 0.3 \times 10^6 \text{ m} = 4.3 \times 10^6 \text{ m}$
**b.** $4.0 \times 10^{-6} \text{ kg} - 3 \times 10^{-7} \text{ kg}$
   $= 4.0 \times 10^{-6} \text{ kg} - 0.3 \times 10^{-6} \text{ kg} = 3.7 \times 10^{-6} \text{ kg}$

Suppose you have to add a measurement made in metres to one made in kilometres. You first must convert the measurements to a common unit, then make the power of ten the same. Finally you add or subtract.

## Example Problem

### Adding and Subtracting with Unlike Units

**a.** $4.1 \text{ m} + 1.5468 \text{ km} = 4.1 \text{ m} + 1546.8 \text{ m}$
   $= 1550.9 \text{ m} = 1.5509 \text{ km}$
**b.** $2.31 \times 10^{-2} \text{ g} + 6.1 \text{ mg} = 23.1 \text{ mg} + 6.1 \text{ mg} = 29.2 \text{ mg}$
**c.** $2.03 \times 10^2 \text{ m} + 1.057 \text{ km} = 2.03 \times 10^2 \text{ m} + 10.57 \times 10^2 \text{ m}$
   $= 12.60 \times 10^2 \text{ m} = 1.260 \text{ km}$

## Practice Problems

*Solve the following problems. Express your answers in scientific notation.*

**6. a.** $5 \times 10^{-7} \text{ kg} + 3 \times 10^{-7} \text{ kg}$
   **b.** $4 \times 10^{-3} \text{ kg} + 3 \times 10^{-3} \text{ kg}$
   **c.** $1.66 \times 10^{-19} \text{ kg} + 2.30 \times 10^{-19} \text{ kg}$
   **d.** $7.2 \times 10^{-12} \text{ kg} - 2.6 \times 10^{-12} \text{ kg}$
**7. a.** $6 \times 10^{-8} \text{ m}^2 - 4 \times 10^{-8} \text{ m}^2$
   **b.** $3.8 \times 10^{-12} \text{ m}^2 - 1.90 \times 10^{-11} \text{ m}^2$
   **c.** $5.8 \times 10^{-9} \text{ m}^2 - 2.8 \times 10^{-9} \text{ m}^2$
   **d.** $2.26 \times 10^{-18} \text{ m}^2 - 1.80 \times 10^{-18} \text{ m}^2$
▶ **8. a.** $5.0 \times 10^{-7} \text{ mg} + 4 \times 10^{-8} \text{ mg}$
   **b.** $6.0 \times 10^{-3} \text{ mg} + 2 \times 10^{-4} \text{ mg}$
   **c.** $3.0 \times 10^{-2} \text{ pg} - 2 \times 10^{-6} \text{ ng}$
   **d.** $8.2 \text{ km} - 3 \times 10^2 \text{ m}$

**18**   A Mathematical Toolkit

Quantities expressed in scientific notation do not need to have the same exponents before they are multiplied or divided. Multiply the values of $M$, then add the exponents. The units are multiplied.

## Example Problem

**Multiplication Using Scientific Notation**

**a.** $(3 \times 10^6 \text{ m}) (2 \times 10^3 \text{ m}) = 6 \times 10^{6+3} \text{ m}^2 = 6 \times 10^9 \text{ m}^2$
**b.** $(2 \times 10^{-5} \text{ m}) (4 \times 10^9 \text{ m}) = 8 \times 10^{9-5} \text{ m}^2 = 8 \times 10^4 \text{ m}^2$
**c.** $(4 \times 10^3 \text{ kg}) (5 \times 10^{11} \text{ m}) = 20 \times 10^{3+11} \text{ kg·m}$
$$= 2 \times 10^{15} \text{ kg·m}$$

Quantities expressed in scientific notation with different exponents also can be divided. Divide the values of $M$, then subtract the exponent of the divisor from the exponent of the dividend.

## Example Problem

**Division Using Scientific Notation**

**a.** $\dfrac{8 \times 10^6 \text{ m}}{2 \times 10^3 \text{ s}} = 4 \times 10^{(6-3)} \text{ m/s} = 4 \times 10^3 \text{ m/s}$

**b.** $\dfrac{8 \times 10^6 \text{ kg}}{2 \times 10^{-2} \text{ m}^3} = 4 \times 10^{6-(-2)} \text{ kg/m}^3 = 4 \times 10^8 \text{ kg/m}^3$

## Practice Problems

*Find the value of each of the following quantities.*

**9. a.** $(2 \times 10^4 \text{ m}) (4 \times 10^8 \text{ m})$   **c.** $(6 \times 10^{-4} \text{ m})(5 \times 10^{-8} \text{ m})$
  **b.** $(3 \times 10^4 \text{ m})(2 \times 10^6 \text{ m})$   **d.** $(2.5 \times 10^{-7} \text{ m})(2.5 \times 10^{16} \text{ m})$

**10. a.** $\dfrac{6 \times 10^8 \text{ kg}}{2 \times 10^4 \text{ m}^3}$   **c.** $\dfrac{6 \times 10^{-8} \text{ m}}{2 \times 10^4 \text{ s}}$

  **b.** $\dfrac{6 \times 10^8 \text{ kg}}{2 \times 10^{-4} \text{ m}^3}$   **d.** $\dfrac{6 \times 10^{-8} \text{ m}}{2 \times 10^{-4} \text{ s}}$

▶ **11. a.** $\dfrac{(3 \times 10^4 \text{ kg})(4 \times 10^4 \text{ m})}{6 \times 10^4 \text{ s}}$   **b.** $\dfrac{(2.5 \times 10^6 \text{ kg})(6 \times 10^4 \text{ m})}{5 \times 10^{-2} \text{ s}^2}$

## · · · · · · · · · · · · · · · ·
## CONCEPT REVIEW

**1.1** Some calculators display large numbers as 1.574 E8. Express in normal scientific notation.
**1.2** Your height might be given either in terms of a small unit, like a millimetre, or a larger unit, like a metre. In which case would your height be a larger number?
**1.3** Describe in detail how you would measure the time in seconds needed to go from home to school.
**1.4** **Critical Thinking**: What additional steps would you need to time your trip, using one clock at home and one at school?

a

b

**FIGURE 2–5.** For extremely small measurements, such as the diameter of a red blood cell (a), and for very large measurements, such as the distance to the Andromeda galaxy (b), it is convenient to use scientific notation. Showing all the digits in numbers like these makes calculations difficult.

The product of two numbers written in scientific notation is the product of the values of $M$ times 10 raised to the sum of their exponents.

The quotient of two numbers is the quotient of the values of $M$ times 10 raised to the difference of their exponents.

# Physics and society

## THE SAGA OF THE SI

If you ask typical teenagers from Canada, or most other countries, for their height, you will probably receive answers like "160 cm" or "1.60 m". That is because Canada, like most other countries around the world, uses the Système International d'Unités (commonly abbreviated as SI), which is a metric system of measurement.

Scientists all over the world use the SI because it provides a common means of communicating data. Only the United States, Liberia, and Burma have yet to fully adopt and implement the SI.

For students raised and educated with the metric system since its inception, the SI has posed little problem. For people brought up using the Imperial system of measurement, however, "going metric" has required a substantial period of adjustment. Even today, many individuals still find it more convenient (and often necessary!) to convert metric units to, what is for them, the more familiar Imperial units.

Imagine, then, what it must be like across the border in the United States. In 1975, the American Congress passed the Metric Conversion Act, which called for voluntary conversion to the metric system. Some U.S. states immediately began incorporating kilometres on highway signs. Some schools began to teach the metric system along with Imperial units. The major

automobile makers started building "metric" cars.

In 1988, the United States Omnibus Trade and Competitiveness Act established the metric system as the preferred system of measurement for United States commerce. The bill required all federal agencies to adopt the metric system in all business dealings by 1992. One of the biggest initial holdouts, however, was the aerospace industry, which uses Imperial standards for building aircraft. Since the passage of the Trade Act, several aerospace companies have been in the process of converting to the SI. And in 1989, at least 60% of major American corporations manufactured at least some products bearing metric units on their labels.

"Going metric" in the United States hasn't resulted in complete consistency with other metric countries, however. For example, the American spelling of "metre" and "litre" reverses the last two letters. And many manufacturers of consumer products have not adjusted to the SI symbol for "litre", using a lowercase "l" instead of the more common capital "L". Even so, such inconsistencies are minor. More important is that many Americans believe that the use of the same units of

measurement all over the world will improve trade among nations, just as it has always facilitated "trade" among scientists.

## DEVELOPING A VIEWPOINT

Read some U.S.-based references on the subject so you can discuss the following questions:

1. What are some specific economic advantages to using the same measurement system as other countries? What about scientific advantages?

2. How will changing to metric affect such jobs as an auto mechanic, a plumber, and a bank teller? (To answer this, it might help to find out first how Canadian jobs in these fields were affected.)

3. Air traffic controllers and pilots in most countries still report altitude in Imperial units. Would safety be compromised if all pilots and controllers were required to report altitude in metric units instead?

## REFERENCES

Byrne, Gregory. "Going the Extra Meter." *Science*, 241(4872), September 16, 1988, p. 1437.

Feirre, John L. *SI Metric Handbook.* Charles Scribner's Sons, New York, 1971.

Sheets, Kenneth R. "A New Measure of Success." *U.S. News & World Report* 108(10), March 12, 1990, p. 61.

___ "The SI Unit of Pressure." *American Metric Journal* 16(5), September/ October 1988, pp. 34–35.

# 2.2 NOT ALL IS CERTAIN

O ften several scientists measure the same quantities and compare the data they obtain. Each scientist must know how trustworthy the data are. Every measurement, whether made by a student or a professional scientist, is subject to uncertainty.

The length of a ruler can change with changes of temperature. An electric measuring device can be affected by magnetic fields near it. In one way or another, all instruments are subject to external influences. Uncertainties in measurement cannot be avoided, although we try to make them as small as possible. For this reason, it is important to clearly describe the uncertainties in our measurements.

## Uncertainties of Measurements

In addition to uncertainties due to external causes, such as those listed above, the accuracy of a measurement is affected by the person making the reading. One common source of error comes from the angle at which an instrument is read. In a car, the passenger's reading of the gas gauge and the driver's reading of the same gauge can be quite different. From the passenger's viewpoint, Figure 2–6, the needle is on the second division. From the driver's seat, the needle is above the third division. The driver's reading is more correct. The difference in the readings is caused by parallax. **Parallax** (PAR uh laks) is the apparent shift in the position of an object when it is viewed from various angles. The relative positions of the object and a reference point behind it change. Gas gauges and laboratory instruments must be read at eye level and straight on to avoid parallax errors.

## Accuracy and Precision

**Precision** is the degree of exactness to which the measurement of a quantity can be reproduced. For example, a student was conducting an experiment to determine the speed of light. Several trials were made that yielded values ranging from $3.000 \times 10^8$ m/s to $3.002 \times 10^8$ m/s, with an average of $3.001 \times 10^8$ m/s. This led the student to report that the speed of light is $(3.001 \pm 0.001) \times 10^8$ m/s. According to the student's measurements, the speed of light might range from $3.000 \times 10^8$ m/s to $3.002 \times 10^8$ m/s. The precision of the measurement was $0.001 \times 10^8$ m/s.

## Objectives

· recognize that all measured quantities have uncertainties.
· distinguish between accuracy and precision.
· show you can use significant digits and that you understand their use in stating the precision of measured quantities.
· use significant digits correctly when recording measured data.

All measurements are subject to uncertainties.

Precision is the degree of exactness to which a measurement can be reproduced.

The precision of an instrument is limited by the smallest division on the measurement scale.

a

b

**FIGURE 2–6. A parallax example is shown when a car's gasoline gauge is viewed from the passenger's seat (a) and the driver's seat (b). Note the apparent difference in readings.**

FIGURE 2–7. The metre stick contains decimetre, centimetre, and millimetre divisions.

The precision of a measuring device is limited by the finest division on its scale. The smallest division on a metre stick, Figure 2–7, is a millimetre. Thus, a measurement of any smaller length with a metre stick can be only an estimate. Even on a micrometer, Figure 2–8a, you can make measurements to only 5 $\mu$m. There is a limit to the precision of even the best instruments.

The accuracy of a measurement describes how well the result agrees with an accepted value.

**Accuracy** is the extent to which a measured value agrees with the standard value of a quantity. In the experiment to measure the speed of light, the accuracy is the difference between the student's measurement and the defined value of the speed of light, quoted to the same precision: $2.998 \times 10^8$ m/s. Thus, the accuracy is $(3.001 \times 10^8$ m/s) $-$ $(2.998 \times 10^8$ m/s) $= 0.003 \times 10^8$ m/s. It would be possible to make a very precise measurement because the instrument is very sensitive, but have that measurement be inaccurate because the instrument was uncalibrated or because you made a reading error.

Significant digits are all the digits that are certain plus a digit that estimates the fraction of the smallest division of the measuring scale.

The accuracy of an instrument depends on how well its performance compares to a currently accepted standard. The accuracy of measuring devices should be checked regularly. They can be calibrated by using them to measure quantities whose values are accurately known. Uncertainties in measurement affect the accuracy of a measurement. Precision, however, is not affected because it is based on the smallest division on the instrument.

FIGURE 2–8. The micrometer (a) and analytical balance (b) are used to obtain very precise measurements of length and mass, respectively.

## Significant Digits

Because the precision of all measuring devices is limited, the number of digits that are valid for any measurement is also limited. The valid digits are called the **significant digits**. Suppose you measure the length

a

b

FIGURE 2–9. The accuracy of any measurement depends on both the instrument used and the observer. After a calculation, keep only those digits that truly reflect the accuracy of the original measurement.

of a strip of metal with a metre stick. The smallest division on the metre stick is a millimetre. You should read the scale to the nearest millimetre and then estimate any remaining length as a fraction of a millimetre. The metal strip in Figure 2–9 is somewhat longer than 5.6 cm (56 mm). Looking closely at the scale, you can see that the end of the metal strip is about four-tenths of the way between 56 and 57 mm. Therefore, the length of the strip is best stated as 56.4 mm. The last digit is an estimate. It might not be 4 but is likely not larger than 5 or smaller than 3. Your measurement, 56.4 mm, contains three significant digits. They are the two digits you are sure of, 5 and 6, and one, 4, that is an estimated digit.

Suppose that the end of the metal strip is exactly on the 56 mm mark. In this case, you should record the measurement as 56.0 mm. The zero indicates that the strip is not 0.1 mm more or less than 56 mm. The zero is a significant digit because it transmits information. It is the uncertain digit because you are estimating it. The last digit given for any measurement is the uncertain digit. *All non-zero digits in a measurement are significant.*

Zeros are often a problem. The zero mentioned in 56.0 mm is significant. However, a zero that only serves to locate the decimal point is not significant. Thus the value of 0.0026 kg contains two significant digits. The measurement of 0.002060 kg contains four significant digits. The final zero indicates a reasonable estimate.

There is no way to tell how many of the zeros in the measurement 186 000 m are significant. The 6 may have been the estimated digit and the three zeroes may be needed only to place the decimal point. Or, all three zeros may be significant because they were measured. To avoid confusion, such measurements are written in scientific notation. In the number that appears before the power of ten, all the digits are significant. Thus, $1.860 \times 10^5$ m has four significant digits. To summarize, these rules are used to determine the number of significant digits.

1. Nonzero digits are always significant.
2. All final zeros after the decimal point are significant.
3. Zeros between two other significant digits are always significant.
4. Zeros to the right of a whole number are considered to be ambiguous.

Write results in scientific notation to indicate clearly which zeros are significant.

# F.Y.I.

Any error that can creep in, will. It will be in the direction that will do most damage to the calculation.

Murphy's law

# Practice Problems

**12.** State the number of significant digits in each measurement.
- **a.** 2804 m
- **b.** 2.84 m
- **c.** 0.0029 m
- **d.** 0.003 068 m
- **e.** $4.6 \times 10^5$ m
- **f.** $4.06 \times 10^5$ m

▶ **13.** State the number of significant digits for each measurement.
- **a.** 75 m
- **b.** 75.00 mm
- **c.** 0.007 060 kg
- **d.** $1.87 \times 10^6$ ml
- **e.** $1.008 \times 10^8$ m
- **f.** $1.20 \times 10^{-4}$ m

## Operations Using Significant Digits

*The sum or difference of two values is as precise as the least precise value.*

When you are working in the laboratory it is extremely important to remember that *the result of any mathematical operation with measurements can never be more precise than the least precise measurement.* Suppose you measure the lengths 6.48 m and 18.2 m. You are asked to find the sum of the two lengths. The length 18.2 m is precise only to one-tenth of a metre. The result of any mathematical operation with measurements cannot be more precise than the least precise measurement. Therefore, the sum of the two lengths can be precise only to one-tenth of a metre. First add 6.48 m to 18.2 m to get 24.68 m. Then round off the sum to the nearest tenth of one metre. The correct value is 24.7 m. Subtraction is handled the same way. To add or subtract measurements, first perform the operation, and then round off the result to correspond to the least precise value involved.

## Example Problem

### Significant Digits—Addition and Subtraction

Add 24.686 m + 2.343 m + 3.21 m.

**Solution:**

| | |
|---|---|
| 24.686 m | Note that 3.21 m is the least precise |
| 2.343 m | measurement. Round off the result to |
| 3.21 m | the nearest hundredth of one metre. |
| 30.239 m | Follow the same rules for subtraction. |
| = 30.24 m | |

**FIGURE 2–10. When using a calculator in solving problems, it is important to note that your answers cannot be more precise than the least precise quantity involved.**

24   A Mathematical Toolkit

A different method is used to find the correct number of significant digits when multiplying or dividing measurements. After performing the calculation, note the factor with the least number of significant digits. Round the product or quotient to this number of digits.

## Example Problem

### Significant Digits—Multiplication

Multiply 3.22 cm by 2.1 cm.

**Solution:**
$$3.\,2\,\textcircled{2}\ cm$$
$$\underline{2.\,\textcircled{1}\ cm}$$
$$\textcircled{3}\ \textcircled{2}\ \textcircled{2}$$
$$\underline{6\ 4\ \textcircled{4}}$$
$$6.\textcircled{7}\ \textcircled{6}\ \textcircled{2}\ cm^2 \ \text{This is correctly stated as 6.8 cm}^2.$$

The less precise factor, 2.1 cm, contains two significant digits. Therefore the product has only two. Note that each circled digit is doubtful, either because it is an estimated measurement or is multiplied by an estimated measurement. Since the 7 in the product is doubtful, the 6 and 2 are certainly not significant. The answer is best stated as 6.8 cm$^2$.

The number of significant digits in a product or quotient is the number in the factor with the lesser number of significant digits.

## Example Problem

### Significant Digits—Division

Divide 36.5 m by 3.414 s.

**Solution:**

$$\frac{36.5\ m}{3.414\ s} = 10.69\ m/s \quad \text{This is correctly stated as 10.7 m/s.}$$

Be sure to record all measurements made during an experiment with the correct number of significant digits. The number of significant digits shows the precision of the instrument. When using a calculator, be particularly careful to record your answer with the proper number of significant digits, even though the calculator shows additional, meaningless digits, Figure 2–10.

It is important to understand that significant digits are only considered when calculating with measurements, not when counting. For example, if you add 2 pencils and 3 pencils, you will have exactly 5 pencils, with no uncertainty. Because of the uncertainty in all measurements, it is important to let anyone who is using your data know exactly how precise your values are.

## Practice Problems

**14.** Add 6.201 cm, 7.4 cm, 0.68 cm, and 12.0 cm.
**15.** Subtract
    **a.** 8.264 g from 10.8 g.
    **b.** 0.4168 m from 475 m.

## POCKET LAB

### HIGH AND LOW

Measure the height of the tallest person and the shortest person in your lab group to the nearest 0.1 cm. Estimate the uncertainty in each measurement. Predict how tall each person would be from heel to the top of the head when lying down on the lab table. Would the values be within the uncertainty of the first measurement? Try it. Explain the results.

**16.** Perform the following multiplications.
   **a.** 131 cm × 2.3 cm
   **b.** 3.2145 km × 4.23 km
▶ **17.** Perform the following divisions.
   **a.** 20.2 cm ÷ 7.41 s
   **b.** 3.1416 cm ÷ 12.4 s

## CONCEPT REVIEW

**2.1** If you have a micrometer that has been bent more than 1 mm out of alignment, how would it compare to a new, quality metre stick in precision? accuracy?

**2.2** Does parallax affect the precision of a measuring instrument? Explain.

**2.3** Explain in your own words the range in heights that would be implied if you reported a measurement as "His height is 182 cm."

**2.4** **Critical Thinking:** Poll takers often interview people and report "1000 people were interviewed for a margin of accuracy of ±3%." Is this a measure of the precision or accuracy of the poll? **Hint:** Suppose you were interviewed by your principal about your opinions about school rules.

## Objectives

- distinguish between dependent and independent variables.
- be able to graph data points.
- understand how smooth curves drawn through data points represent the relationship between independent and dependent variables.
- recognize linear and direct relationships and be able to find and interpret the slope of the curve.
- recognize quadratic and inverse relationships.

## 2.3 DISPLAYING DATA

A well-designed graph is more than a "picture worth a thousand words." It can give you more information than either words, columns of numbers, or equations. To be useful, however, a graph must be drawn properly. In this section we will develop the use of graphs to display data.

### Graphing Data

One of the most important skills to learn in driving a car is how to stop it safely. No car can "stop on a dime." The faster the car is going, the farther it travels before it stops. If you studied for a driver's licence, you probably found a table in the manual showing how far a car moves beyond the point at which the driver makes a decision to stop.

One manual shows that a car travels a certain distance between the time the driver decides to stop the car and the time the brakes are applied. This is called the "reaction distance." When the brakes are applied, the car slows down and travels the "braking distance." Table 2—2 and the bar graph, Figure 2—11, show these distances, together with the total stopping distance for various speeds.

**Stopping distance**

(a) Braking distance / Reaction distance — bar graph of Distance (m) vs Speed (m/s): values 18, 32, 49, 68, 92 at speeds 11, 16, 20, 25, 29.

(b) Reaction distance / Braking distance / Total distance — line graph of Distance (m) vs Speed (m/s): values 18, 32, 49, 68, 92.

**Table 2–2**

| Reaction and Braking Distances vs Speed | | | |
|---|---|---|---|
| Original speed m/s | Reaction distance m | Braking distance m | Total distance m |
| 11 | 8 | 10 | 18 |
| 16 | 12 | 20 | 32 |
| 20 | 15 | 34 | 49 |
| 25 | 18 | 50 | 68 |
| 29 | 22 | 70 | 92 |

**FIGURE 2–11. The total stopping distance is the sum of the reaction and braking distances. Graphs (a) and (b) display the same information in two different ways.**

The first step in analyzing data is to look at them carefully. Which variable did the experimenter (the driver) change? In our example, it was the speed of the car. Thus speed is the **independent variable**, or manipulated variable. The other two variables, reaction distance and braking distance, changed as a result of the change in the speed. These quantities are called **dependent variables**, or responding variables.

How do the distances change for a given change in the speed? Notice that the reaction distance increases by about the same amount for each increase in speed. The braking distance, however, increases much more as the speed increases. The relationship between the distances and speed can be seen more easily if the data are plotted on a graph. To avoid confusion, you should plot two graphs, one of reaction distance and the other of braking distance.

*The independent variable is the one the experimenter can control directly. The value of the dependent variable depends on the independent variable.*

# PROBLEM SOLVING STRATEGY

**Plotting Graphs**

These steps will help you plot graphs from data tables.

1. Identify the independent and dependent variables. The independent variable is plotted on the horizontal, or x-axis. The dependent variable is plotted on the vertical, or y-axis. In our example, speed is plotted on the x-axis, and distance is plotted on the y-axis.

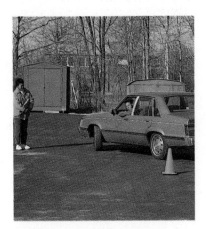

**FIGURE 2–12. Knowing when and how to apply brakes safely is an important part of a driver's test.**

# PHYSICS LAB

## Getting Straight

## Purpose

To create and use graphs to estimate the mass of objects.

## Materials

· 3 pieces of electrical wire with lengths between 5 cm - 30 cm
· 2 rectangular pieces of floor tile
· 1 triangular floor tile
· balance
· 30-cm ruler
· graph paper

## Procedure

1. Measure the length of the three wires to the nearest 0.1 cm.
2. Measure the mass of only the longest and shortest wires.
3. Make a graph of mass (vertical) versus length (horizontal). Include the units on the graph.
4. Use the graph to predict the mass of the middle length.
5. Calculate the area of both rectangular pieces of tile. Measure their masses.
6. Make a graph of mass (vertical) versus area (horizontal) for the rectangular pieces.
7. Measure the area of the triangular piece of tile and use the graph to predict the mass.

## Observations and Data

1. Does your graph of the wire mass versus length pass through the origin?
2. Does your graph of the area of the tiles versus mass pass through the origin?

## Analysis

1. Explain why your graphs should pass through the origin.
2. Calculate the slope of each graph (include the units).
3. Explain the meaning of each slope.

## Applications

1. In the pharmaceutical industry, how might the weight of compressed tablets be used to determine the quantity of finished tablets produced in a specific lot?

2. Determine the range of the independent variable to be plotted. In the example, data are given for speeds between 11 and 29 m/s. A convenient range for the x-axis might be 0–30 m/s.
3. Decide if the origin (0, 0) is a valid data point. When the speed is zero, reaction and stopping distances are obviously both zero. In this case then, your graph should include the origin. Spread out the data as much as possible. Let each space on the graph paper stand for a convenient unit. Choose 2, 5, or 10 spaces to represent 10 m/s.
4. Number and label the horizontal axis.
5. Repeat steps 2–4 for the dependent variable.
6. Plot your data points on the graph.
7. Draw the best straight line or smooth curve that passes through as many data points as possible. *Do not use a series of straight line segments that "connect the dots."*
8. Give the graph a title that clearly tells what the graph represents.

## Linear, Quadratic, and Inverse Relationships

The graph, Figure 2–13, of reaction distance versus speed is a straight line. That is, the dependent variable varies linearly with the independent variable; there is a **linear relationship** between the two variables.

The relationship of the two variables shown in this graph can be written as an equation

$$y = mx + b,$$

where $m$ and $b$ are constants called the slope and y-intercept, respectively. Each constant can be found from the graph. The **slope**, $m$, is the ratio of the vertical change to the horizontal change. To find the slope, select two points, **A** and **B**, as far apart as possible on the line. *They should not be data points.* The vertical change, or rise, $\Delta y$, is the difference in the vertical values of **A** and **B**. The horizontal change, or run, $\Delta x$, is the difference in the horizontal values of **A** and **B**. The slope of the graph is then calculated as

$$m = \frac{\text{rise}}{\text{run}} = \frac{\Delta y}{\Delta x} = \frac{(20 - 0)\ \text{m}}{(27 - 0)\ \text{m/s}} = \frac{20\ \text{m}}{27\ \text{m/s}} = 0.74\ \text{s}.$$

Notice that units have been kept with the variables.

◀ A Graphic Display

The independent variable is plotted on the x-axis. The dependent variable is plotted on the y-axis.

The slope of a graph is $\Delta y/\Delta x$.

**Reaction Distance Versus Speed**

FIGURE 2–13. The graph indicates a linear relationship between reaction distance and car speed.

**FIGURE 2–14.** The graph indicates a parabolic relationship; braking distance varies as the square of the original speed.

The *y*-intercept is the value of *y* when *x* is zero.

If the dependent variable decreases when the independent variable increases, then the slope is negative.

**POCKET LAB**

**JUICED UP**

Use a sharp pencil to make marks at 2.0 cm, 4.0 cm, and 6.0 cm on the insides of a juice can. Fill the can to the 2.0 cm mark and measure the mass of the can and water on a balance. Fill the can to the 6.0 cm mark and again measure the mass on a balance. Make a graph of mass (vertical) versus height (horizontal). Predict the mass when the can has 4.0 cm of water. (**Hint:** The graph should be a straight line.) Explain why the graph does not go through 0,0. What is the meaning of the slope of the graph?

The **y-intercept,** *b*, is the point at which the line crosses the y-axis, and is the *y* value when the value of *x* is zero. In this case, when *x* is zero, the value of *y* is 0 m. For special cases like this, when the y-intercept equals zero, the equation becomes $y = mx$. The quantity *y* varies directly with *x*.

The value of *y* does not always increase with increasing *x*. If *y* gets smaller as *x* gets larger, then $\Delta y/\Delta x$ is less than zero, and the slope is negative.

After drawing the graph and obtaining the equation, check to see if the results make sense. The slope indicates the increased reaction distance for an increase in speed. It has units of meters/(meters/second), or seconds. Thus it is a time, the reaction time. It is the time your body takes from the instant the message to stop the car registers in your brain until your foot hits the brake pedal. Thus, the slope is a *property* of the system the graph describes.

**FIGURE 2–15.** The graph shows the inverse relationship between the time required to travel a fixed distance and the speed.

Figure 2–14 is the graph of the braking distance versus speed, completed as suggested in the Problem Solving Strategy. Note that the relationship is not linear.

The smooth line drawn through all the data points curves upward. You cannot draw a straight line through all the points. Such graphs are frequently parabolas, indicating that the two variables are related by the equation

$$y = kx^2,$$

where $k$ is a constant. This equation shows that $y$ varies directly with the square of $x$. This equation is one form of a **quadratic relationship**. The constant $k$ shows how fast $y$ changes with $x^2$. In Chapters 4 and 5, we will discuss variables that are related by this equation, and learn why braking distance depends on speed in this way.

Some variables are related by the type of graph shown in Figure 2–15. In this case, a plot has been made of the time required to travel a fixed distance as the speed of travel is changed. When the speed is doubled, the time is reduced to one-half its original time. The relationship between speed and time is an inverse variation. The graph is a hyperbola, not a straight line. The general equation for an **inverse relationship** is

$$xy = k \text{ or } y = k \cdot \left(\frac{1}{x}\right) = kx^{-1}.$$

**Circumference Versus Diameter**

**FIGURE 2–16. Use with Concept Review 3.4.**

The parabolic relationship exists when one variable depends on the square of another.

# CONCEPT REVIEW

**3.1** What would be the meaning of a non-zero $y$-intercept to the graph of reaction distance versus speed?

**3.2** At what speed is the reaction distance 10 m?

**3.3** Explain in your own words the significance of a steeper line, or larger slope to the graph of reaction distance versus speed.

**3.4** Critical Thinking: Figure 2–16 shows the relationship between the circumference and the diameter of a circle. Could a different circle be described by a different straight line? What is the meaning of the slope?

A hyperbola results when one variable depends on the inverse of the other.

# 2.4 MANIPULATING EQUATIONS

The manner in which one quantity, such as the circumference of a circle, depends on another, such as the circle's diameter, can be represented symbolically by an equation, $C = \pi d$, as well as by a graph. If we want to find how the diameter depends on the circumference, we can use rules of algebra to rearrange the equation, $d = C/\pi$.

# Objectives

· **demonstrate the ability to manipulate algebraic equations.**
· **use dimensional analysis to test the validity of an equation.**

Solve equations for the required variable, the unknown, placing it on the left-hand side of the equals sign.

# F.Y.I.

"Mathematics is the door and the key to the sciences."
Roger Bacon

## Solving Equations Using Algebra

From your graph of the reaction distance versus speed, you can obtain an equation relating the two variables. If we represent the reaction distance by $d$, the speed of the car by $v$, and the slope, which we discovered had units of time, by $t$, the equation is

$$d = vt, \text{ or } d = tv.$$

Note that this last equation has the same form, but different symbols than $y = mx$. The distance, $d$, is the dependent variable. The speed, $v$, is the independent variable. The slope, $m$, is the reaction time, $t$. You can use this equation to find $d$ if you know $v$ and $t$. What if, however, you know $d$ and $t$ and want to find $v$? You can solve the equation above for $v$. First, place the term containing $v$ on the left side.

$$vt = d$$

To get $v$ alone on the left side, but not change the value of the relationship, divide both sides of the equation by $t$. Thus,

$$v = \frac{d}{t}.$$

That is, the speed of the car is equal to the reaction distance divided by the reaction time. If an equation contains several factors, the same process is followed until the unknown is isolated on the left side of the equation. The steps can be performed in any sequence; just be sure you perform the same operations on both sides of the equation.

# Example Problem

## Solving Equations

Solve the following equation for $x$.

$$\frac{ay}{x} = \frac{cb}{s}$$

**Solution:**
Multiply both sides by $x$.

$$ay = \frac{cbx}{s}$$

Rearrange to bring $x$ to the left side.

$$\frac{cbx}{s} = ay$$

Divide both sides by $cb$.

$$\frac{x}{s} = \frac{ay}{cb}$$

Multiply both sides by $s$.

$$x = \frac{asy}{cb}$$

## Example Problem

### Solving Equations

Solve the following equation for $x$.  $y = mx + b$

**Solution:**

Rearrange to bring $x$ to the left side.  $mx + b = y$

Subtract $b$ from both sides.  $mx = y - b$

Divide both sides by $m$.  $x = (y - b)/m$

## Practice Problems

**18.** Solve the following equation for $b$.  $y = mx + b$

**19.** Solve the following equations for $v$.

**a.** $d = vt$  **c.** $a = \dfrac{v^2}{2d}$

**b.** $t = \dfrac{d}{v}$  **d.** $\dfrac{v}{a} = \dfrac{b}{c}$

**20.** Solve each of these equations for $E$.

**a.** $f = \dfrac{E}{s}$  **b.** $m = \dfrac{2E}{v^2}$  **c.** $\dfrac{E}{c^2} = m$

**21.** Solve the equation $v^2 = v_0{}^2 + 2ad$ for $d$.

▶ **22.** Solve each of these equations for $a$.

**a.** $v = v_0 + at$  **c.** $v^2 = v_0{}^2 + 2ay$

**b.** $y = v_0 t + \frac{1}{2}at^2$  **d.** $v = \sqrt{2as}$

**FIGURE 2–17. Did somebody miscalculate?**

## Units in Equations

Suppose you want to find the area of a wood plank. The plank is 15.0 cm wide and 2.50 m long. If you simply multiply length times width, you get 37.5 cm · m. This is not very useful. You should first make sure all terms in an equation have the same units. In this case, change the width to 0.150 m. You will then obtain an area of 0.375 m².

Most physical quantities have units as well as numerical values. When you substitute a value into an equation, you must write both the value and the unit. If your answer has the wrong units, you have made an error in your solution. When a term has several units, you can operate on the units like any other mathematical quantity.

*All terms in an equation should have the same prefixes of the units.*

*Always write the units with the values in an equation.*

*Units provide a useful way of checking the correctness of an equation.*

## Example Problem

### Operating on Units

If $v$ = 11.0 m/s and $t$ = 6.00 s, find $d$ using $d = vt$. Find the units for $d$.

**Solution:**
$$d = vt = (11.0 \text{ m/s})(6.00 \text{ s}) = 66.0 \text{ (m/s) s} = 66.0 \text{ m}$$

Note that the units on the right, metres, are the units for distance. By inspecting the units, you will often be able to tell when you have set up the equation incorrectly.

## Practice Problems

**23.** Identify the answers to these exercises using consistent units.
  **a.** Find the area of a rectangle 2 mm by 30 cm.
  **b.** Find the perimeter of a rectangle 25 cm by 2.00 m.
▶ **24.** Find which of the following equations are incorrect.
  **a.** area = (length)(width)(height)   **c.** distance = (speed)(time)²
  **b.** time = distance/speed

## . . . . . . . . . . . . . . . . . .
# CONCEPT REVIEW

**4.1** Write a sentence that gives the same information as the equation $P = 4C$, where $P$ represents the number of people and $C$ represents the number of cars.

**4.2** Write a sentence giving the same information as the equation $C = 2\pi r$, where $C$ is the circumference of a circle and $r$ is its radius.

**4.3** Write an equation using the variables $S$ and $T$ to represent the following sentence: "There are twenty times as many students as teachers at this school."

**4.4** **Critical Thinking:** The radius of Earth at the equator is 6378 km. Imagine a stiff wire wrapped around the equator of a perfectly smooth Earth. Suppose we now increased the length of the wire by 15 m, and shaped the wire into a circle centered at the center of Earth. How far above Earth's surface would the wire be? Explain your reasoning. If any information that you did not need was given in the problem, indicate it.

## SUMMARY

### 2.1 The Measure of Science

· The metre, second, and kilogram are the fundamental units of length, time, and mass in the SI system.
· Derived units are a combination of fundamental units.
· Large and small measurements, often used in physics, are most clearly written using scientific notation.
· Prefixes are used to change SI units by powers of 10.
· To be added or subtracted, quantities written in scientific notation must be raised to the same power of 10.
· Quantities written in scientific notation need not have the same power of 10 to be multiplied or divided.

### 2.2 Not All Is Certain

· All measurements are subject to some uncertainty.
· Precision is the degree of exactness with which a quantity is measured.
· Accuracy is the extent to which the measured and accepted values of a quantity agree.
· For a given measurement, the number of significant digits is limited by the precision of the measuring device.
· The last digit in a measurement is always an estimate. Only one estimated digit is significant.
· The result of any mathematical operation made with measurements can never be more precise than the least precise measurement.

### 2.3 Displaying Data

· Data are plotted in graphical form to show the relationship between two variables.
· The independent variable is the one the experimenter changes. It is plotted on the $x$- or horizontal axis. The dependent variable, which changes as a result of the changes made by the experimenter, is plotted on the $y$- or vertical axis.

· A graph in which data lie in a straight line is a graph of a linear relationship.
· A linear relationship can be represented by the equation $y = mx + b$.
· The slope, $m$, of a straight-line graph is the vertical change (rise) divided by the horizontal change (run).
· The graph of a quadratic relationship is a parabolic curve. It represents an equation $y = kx^2$.
· The graph of an inverse relationship between $x$ and $y$ is a hyperbolic curve. It represents an equation $xy = k$.

### 2.4 Manipulating Equations

· When solving an equation for a quantity, you should add, subtract, multiply, or divide in order to put that quantity alone on the left side of the equation.
· Units must be included when solving problems. The units must be the same on both sides of the equation. If this is not true, the equation is wrong.

## KEY TERMS

| | |
|---|---|
| metric system | precision |
| SI | accuracy |
| base units | significant digits |
| second | independent variable |
| metre | dependent variables |
| kilogram | linear relationship |
| derived units | slope |
| scientific notation | $y$-intercept |
| prefixes | quadratic relationship |
| parallax | inverse relationship |

## REVIEWING CONCEPTS

1. Why is the SI important?
2. List the common base units in the SI system.
3. How are the base units and derived units related?

4. Give the proper name for each multiple of the metre listed.
   **a.** 1/100 m   **b.** 1/1000 m   **c.** 1000 m
5. What determines the precision of a measurement?
6. Give an example of a measurement that is
   **a.** accurate but not precise.
   **b.** precise but not accurate.
7. How does the last digit differ from the other digits in a measurement?
8. Rick recorded a measurement as 76 000 nm.
   **a.** Why is it difficult to tell how many significant digits there are?
   **b.** How can the number of significant digits in such a number be made clear?
9. How do you find the slope of a straight-line or linear graph.
10. A person who has consumed alcohol usually has longer reaction times than a person who has not. Thus, the time between seeing a stoplight and hitting the brakes would be longer for the drinker than for the nondrinker.
    **a.** For a fixed speed, would the "reaction distance" for such a driver be longer or shorter than for a nondrinking driver?
    **b.** Would the slope of the graph of reaction distance versus speed have a larger or smaller slope?
11. During a laboratory experiment, the temperature of the gas in a balloon is varied and the volume of the balloon is measured. Which quantity is the independent variable? Which quantity is the dependent variable?
12. When plotting a graph of the experiment in the previous question,
    **a.** what quantity is plotted as the abscissa (horizontally)?
    **b.** what quantity is plotted as the ordinate (vertically)?
13. A relationship between the independent variable $x$ and the dependent variable $y$ can be written using the equation $y = ax^2$, where $a$ is a constant.
    **a.** What is the shape of the graph of this equation?
    **b.** If $z = x^2$, what would be the shape of the graph $y = az$?
14. According to the formula $F = mv^2/r$, what relationship exists between
    **a.** $F$ and $r$?
    **b.** $F$ and $m$?
    **c.** $F$ and $v$?
15. For the previous question, what type of graph would be drawn for
    **a.** $F$ versus $r$?
    **b.** $F$ versus $m$?
    **c.** $F$ versus $v$?
16. How may units be used to check if an equation is written correctly?

## APPLYING CONCEPTS

1. The density of a substance is the mass per unit volume of that substance.
   **a.** List a possible metric unit for density.
   **b.** Does density have a fundamental or derived unit?
   **c.** What is the SI unit for density?
2. Locate the size of the following objects in Figure 2—4.
   **a.** The width of your thumb.
   **b.** The thickness of a page in this book.
   **c.** The height of your classroom.
   **d.** The distance from your home to school.
3. Make a chart of sizes of objects similar to Figure 2—4. Include only objects you have measured. Some should be less than one millimetre, others several kilometres.
4. Make a chart of time intervals similar to Figure 2—4. Include intervals like the time between heartbeats, the time between provincial elections, the average lifetime of a human, the age of Canada, and so forth. Find as many very short and very long examples as you can.
5. Two students use a metre stick to measure the width of a lab table. One records an answer of 84 cm and the other 83.78 cm. Explain why neither answer is recorded correctly.
6. Suppose Madelaine measures the speed of light to be $2.999 \times 10^8$ m/s with an uncertainty of $0.006 \times 10^8$ m/s.
   **a.** Is this measurement more or less precise than the example on page 21?
   **b.** Is it more or less accurate?
7. Why can quantities with different units never be added or subtracted but can be multiplied or divided? Give examples to support your answer.

8. Suppose you receive $5.00 at the beginning of a week and spend $1.00 each day for lunch. You prepare a graph of the amount you have left at the end of each day. Would the slope of this graph be positive, zero, or negative? Why?

9. Data are plotted on a graph and the value on the y-axis is the same for each value of the independent variable. What is the slope? Why?

10. The graph of braking distance versus car speed is part of a parabola. Thus we write the equation $d = kv^2$. The distance, $d$, has units, metres, and velocity, $v$, has units metres/second. How could you find the units of $k$? What would they be?

11. Think of a relationship between two variables. In baseball you might consider the relationship between the distance the ball is hit and the speed of the pitch. Determine which is the independent variable and which is the dependent variable. In this example, the speed of the pitch is the independent variable. Choose your own relationship. If you can, think of other possible independent variables for the same dependent variable.

12. Aristotle said that the quickness of a falling object varies inversely with the density of the medium in which it is falling.
    a. According to Aristotle, would a rock fall faster in water (density 1000 kg/m³), or in air (density 1 kg/m³)?
    b. How fast would a rock fall in a vacuum? Based on this, why did Aristotle say that there could be no such thing as a vacuum?

# PROBLEMS

## 2.1 The Measure of Science

1. Express the following numbers in scientific notation.
    a. 5 000 000 000 000 000 000 000 000 m
    b. 0.000 000 000 000 000 000 166 m
    c. 2 033 000 000 m
    d. 0.000 000 103 0 m

2. Convert each of the following measurements into meters.
    a. 42.3 cm       d. 0.023 mm
    b. 6.2 pm        e. 214 μm
    c. 21 km         f. 570 nm

▶ 3. Rank the following mass measurements from smallest to largest: 11.6 mg, 1021 μg, 0.000 006 kg, 0.31 mg.

4. Add or subtract as indicated.
    a. $5.80 \times 10^9$ s + $3.20 \times 10^8$ s
    b. $4.87 \times 10^{-6}$ m − $1.93 \times 10^{-6}$ m
    c. $3.14 \times 10^{-5}$ kg + $9.36 \times 10^{-5}$ kg
    d. $8.12 \times 10^7$ g − $6.20 \times 10^6$ g

## 2.2 Not All Is Certain

5. State the number of significant digits in the following measurements.
    a. 248 m        c.    64.01 m
    b. 0.000 03 m   d.    80.001 m

6. State the number of significant digits in the following measurements.
    a. $2.40 \times 10^6$ kg
    b. $6 \times 10^8$ kg
    c. $4.07 \times 10^{16}$ m

7. A consumer product manufacturer in the United States still uses Imperial units on labels, but also includes the metric equivalents. Examples are: 12 fluid ounces (9345.66 mL), 353 ft (107.59 m), 2.0 inch (50.80 mm). Report each metric equivalent using the correct number of significant digits.

8. Add or subtract as indicated and state the answer with the correct number of significant digits.
    a. 16.2 m + 5.008 m + 13.48 m
    b. 5.006 m + 12.0077 m + 8.0084 m
    c. 78.05 cm² − 32.046 cm²
    d. 15.07 kg − 12.0 kg

9. Multiply or divide as indicated watching significant digits.
    a. $(6.2 \times 10^{18}$ m$)(4.7 \times 10^{-10}$ m$)$
    b. $(5.6 \times 10^{-7}$ m$) \div (2.8 \times 10^{-12}$ s$)$
    c. $(8.1 \times 10^{-4}$ km$)(1.6 \times 10^{-3}$ km$)$
    d. $(6.5 \times 10^5$ kg$) \div (3.4 \times 10^3$ m³$)$

10. Tom did the following problems on his calculator, reporting the results shown. Give the answer to each using the correct number of significant digits.
    a. 5.32 mm + 2.1 mm = 7.4200000 mm
    b. 13.597 m × 3.65 m = 49.6290500 m²
    c. 83.2 kg − 12.804 kg = 70.3960000 kg

11. A rectangular floor has a length of 15.72 m and a width of 4.40 m. Calculate the area of the floor to the best possible value using these measurements.

12. A yard is 33.21 m long and 17.6 m wide.
    a. What length of fence must be purchased to enclose the entire yard?
    b. What area must be covered if the yard is to be fertilized?
13. The length of a room is 16.40 m, its width is 4.5 m, and its height is 3.26 m. What volume does the room enclose?
14. The sides of a quadrangular plot of land are 132.68 m, 48.3 m, 132.736 m, and 48.37 m. What is the perimeter of the plot as can best be determined from these measurements?
15. A water tank has a mass of 3.64 kg when empty and a mass of 51.8 kg when filled to a certain level. What is the mass of the water in the tank?

## 2.3 Displaying Data

▶ 16. Figure 2–18 shows the mass of three substances for volumes between 0 and 60 cm³.
    a. What is the mass of 30 cm³ of each substance?
    b. If you had 100 g of each substance, what would their volumes be?
    c. Describe the meaning of the steepness of the lines in this graph (a single word is not a sufficient answer!).

FIGURE 2-18. Use with Problem 16.

17. During an experiment, a student measured the mass of 10.0 cm³ of ethanol. The student then measured the mass of 20.0 cm³ of ethanol. In this way the data in Table 2–3 were collected.

### Table 2–3

| Volume (cm³) | Mass (g) |
|---|---|
| 10.0 | 7.9 |
| 20.0 | 15.8 |
| 30.0 | 23.7 |
| 40.0 | 31.6 |
| 50.0 | 39.6 |

a. Plot the values given in the table and draw the curve that best fits all points.
b. Describe the resulting curve.
c. Use the graph to write an equation relating the volume to the mass of the alcohol.
d. Find the units of the slope of the graph. What is the name given to this quantity?

▶ 18. During a class demonstration, an instructor placed a 1.0-kg mass on a horizontal table that was nearly frictionless. The instructor then applied various horizontal forces to the mass and measured the rate at which the mass gained speed (was accelerated) for each force applied. The results of the experiment are shown in Table 2–4.

### Table 2–4

| Force (N) | Acceleration (m/s²) |
|---|---|
| 5.0 | 4.9 |
| 10.0 | 9.8 |
| 15.0 | 15.2 |
| 20.0 | 20.1 |
| 25.0 | 25.0 |
| 30.0 | 29.9 |

a. Plot the values given in the table and draw the curve that best fits all points.
b. Describe, in words, the relationship between force and acceleration according to the graph.
c. Write the equation relating the force and the acceleration that results from the graph.
d. Find the units of the slope of the graph.

▶ 19. The teacher who performed the experiment in the previous problem then changed the procedure. The mass was varied while the force was kept constant. The acceleration of each mass was then recorded. The results are shown in Table 2–5.

### Table 2–5

| Mass (kg) | Acceleration (m/s²) |
|---|---|
| 1.0 | 12.0 |
| 2.0 | 5.9 |
| 3.0 | 4.1 |
| 4.0 | 3.0 |
| 5.0 | 2.5 |
| 6.0 | 2.0 |

**a.** Plot the values given in the table and draw the curve that best fits all points.

**b.** Describe the resulting curve.

**c.** According to the graph, what is the relationship between mass and the acceleration produced by a constant force?

**d.** Write the equation relating acceleration to mass given by the data in the graph.

**e.** Find the units of the constant in the equation.

### 2.4 Manipulating Equations

**20.** Each cubic centimetre of gold has a mass of 19.3 g. A cube of gold measures 4.23 cm on each edge.

    **a.** What is the volume of the cube?

    **b.** What is its mass?

**21.** Solve the equation

$$T = 2\pi\sqrt{l/g}$$

    **a.** for $l$.

    **b.** for $g$.

**22.** Each cubic centimetre of silver has a mass of 10.5 g.

    **a.** What is the mass of 65.0 cm$^3$ of silver?

    **b.** When placed on a beam balance, the 65.0-cm$^3$ piece of silver has a mass of only 616 g. What volume of the piece is hollow?

**23.** Assume that a small sugar cube has sides 1 cm long. If you had a box containing 1 mol of sugar cubes and lined them up side by side, how long would the line be? 1 mol = $6.02 \times 10^{23}$ units.

**24.** The average distance between Earth and the sun is $1.50 \times 10^8$ km.

    **a.** Calculate the average speed, in km/h, of Earth assuming a circular path about the sun. Use the equation $v = \dfrac{2\pi r}{T}$.

    **b.** Convert your answer from km/h to m/s. Show all units.

▶ **25.** The radius of Earth is $6.37 \times 10^3$ km.

    **a.** Find the speed, in km/h, resulting from the rotation of Earth, of a person standing on the equator.

    **b.** Convert your answer to m/s.

▶ **26.** A child rides a merry-go-round horse that is 5.4 m from the centre. The rides lasts 10 min. During this time, the ride makes 24 revolutions. Find the speed of the child in metres per second. Use the equation $v = \dfrac{2\pi r}{T}$.

**27.** Manipulate the equation $v = d/t$ and find the answers to these problems using consistent units.

    **a.** Find the distance a bike travels in 1.5 min, if it is travelling at a constant speed of 20 km/h.

    **b.** How long will it take a car to travel 6000 m if its speed is a constant 30 km/h?

**28.** Water drips from a faucet into a flask at the rate of two drops every 3 s. One cubic centimetre (cm$^3$) contains 20 drops. What volume of water, in cubic decimetres (dm$^3$), will be collected in 1 h?

▶ **29.** Tony's Pizza Shop ordered new 23-cm pizza pans. By mistake, 26-cm pans were delivered. Tony says that the difference is too small to worry about. As Tony's accountant, what would you say knowing materials cost about $0.25/cm$^2$?

**FIGURE 2–19.**

## THINKING PHYSIC-LY

Three students decide to buy a $20.51 gift for a friend. Sally divides $20.51 by 3 on her calculator and gets 6.83666667 as a result. Is this a reasonable amount for each student to pay? Explain.

# CHAPTER
# 3  Describing Motion: Velocity

◀ **How Fast?**

In the 1988 Summer Olympics, Florence Griffith-Joyner won the 100-m race in 10.54 s and the 200-m race in 21.34 s. In which race did she run faster?

Take a moment to think of things that move. People walk, run, and ride bikes. Earth rotates once each day and revolves about the sun once each year. The sun also rotates with the Milky Way, which itself is moving within its local group of galaxies. Because motion is common to everything in the universe, we begin our study of physics with a study of motion.

Two of the most exciting forms of motion to watch are the 100-m and 200-m dashes. Sprinters must blast out of the starting blocks, reaching peak speed in the shortest possible time. Sometimes the race seems over almost before it has begun.

We can describe motion in three ways. The first description uses common, ordinary words in sentences. The second uses an equation involving mathematical quantities. The third uses graphs that show how these quantities change in time.

## ✓ Concept Check

The following terms or concepts from earlier chapters are important for a good understanding of this chapter. If you are not familiar with them, you should review them before studing this chapter.
· units: fundamental (length and time) and derived (m/s), manipulation of algebraic equations, Chapter 2
· graphing techniques, Chapter 2

41

- define and give an example of a frame of reference.
- define the concept of average velocity in a way that shows you know how to calculate it.
- demonstrate the ability to calculate average velocity and to solve an equation involving velocity, distance, and time.
- interpret and plot position-time graphs for positive and negative positions.
- be able to determine the slope of a curve on a position-time graph and calculate the velocity.

Position is the separation between an object and a reference point.

A vector is a quantity that is represented by both a magnitude and a direction.

**Vector Conventions**

▶ Velocity vectors are red.

▶ Displacement vectors are green.

▶ Vectors appearing as labels for diagrams in this textbook are in boldface, italicized type. See page 110, first paragraph.

# 3.1 HOW FAR AND HOW FAST?

Before we can study how something moves, we have to know where it is. To simplify matters, we will set up a few ground rules. First, we will only describe motion, not try to explain its causes. Second, we will begin by studying objects that move only in straight lines. Third, we will study objects as if they were point objects, not three-dimensional bodies. For example, if we describe the motion of a bicycle, we will mentally step back until the bike and its rider look like a point.

## Position and Distance

Where is something? How do we locate it? Figure 3–1 is a drawing of two cars on a road. Where is car A? More precisely, what is the position of a very tiny dot on car A? First, put a scale on the drawing. To locate car A, we describe its position in terms of its relationship to some other point on the scale, like the zero mark. The scale shows the separation between the zero mark and car A is 8.0 m. That is, A is 8.0 m to the right of zero. What is the position of car B? It is 1.0 m to the left of zero.

In making zero the **reference point**, you have chosen a **frame of reference**. You could have chosen either car, some point to the left of both, to the right of both, or any other point between them. The separation between car A and the reference point would be different in each case. The **position** of an object is the separation between that object and a reference point.

**Distance**, on the other hand, needs no reference frame. You measure the distance between two objects by measuring their separation. Car A is 9.0 m from car B no matter where you put the reference point.

Distance differs from position in a second way. Both a distance and a direction are needed to describe position. Point **A** is 8.0 m to the right of "0." Although the direction can be described in terms of left and right, it will be more convenient for us to use plus (+) and minus (−) signs. Positive (+) directions are to the right of the reference point; negative (−) directions are to the left. Thus, the position of A is +8.0 m and the position of B is −1.0 m. Distance, on the other hand, involves only a length measurement, never direction.

A quantity, like distance, that has only a magnitude, or size, is called a **scalar** (scā-ler). Position, on the other hand, has both magnitude (size) and direction. Such a quantity is called a **vector.** We will identify many other quantities as either scalars or vectors.

**FIGURE 3–1. The position of these two automobiles is determined from a point of reference.**

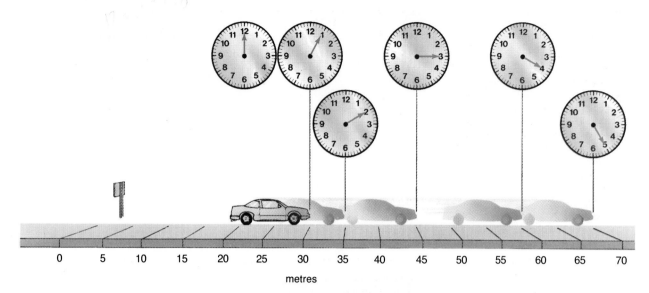

metres

**FIGURE 3–2. The change in position of car B over a 5 s period.**

## Average Velocity

Both car A and car B are moving, and Figure 3–1 shows their position at one particular instant. Figure 3–2 shows what would be seen if a series of photos of car B and a clock were made. We can identify the instant car B is at a certain position by the reading on a clock. We will give this **clock reading** the symbol $t$.

If the car continues to move, how long will it be at any one position? That is almost the same as asking "how long are the hands of the clock at any one position?" The clock reading lasts zero seconds. The moving car is located at 9.0 m at one and only one time. The position of the car is an **instantaneous position**. The moving car generates a series of pairs of instantaneous positions and clock readings, Table 3–1.

The numbers in this table can be used to find out how fast the car is moving. There is no question that between any two clock readings, a fast-moving car has a larger change in position than a slow-moving car. So first, we should define what we mean by change in position.

The change in position of an object is often called its **displacement**. To find the displacement of an object, take its position at one clock reading, $\vec{d_2}$, and subtract its position at an earlier clock reading, $\vec{d_1}$. We use the symbol $\Delta\vec{d}$ for the displacement or change in position, so $\Delta\vec{d} = \vec{d_2} - \vec{d_1}$. Displacement, the difference between two positions, is a vector quantity. It can either be positive or negative. In the same way, we find the **time interval** between two clock readings, $\Delta t = t_2 - t_1$.

Now, consider the ratio $\dfrac{\Delta\vec{d}}{\Delta t}$ between the times $t_1$ and $t_2$. For the moving car data given in Table 3–1, the denominator, the time interval, $\Delta t$, is always 1.0 s. The value of the ratio $\Delta\vec{d}/\Delta t$ varies from 0, between 0.0 and 1.0 s, to 15, between 3.0 and 4.0 s. Note that the ratio is larger when the car moves quickly than it is when the car moves slowly.

**Table 3–1**

| Clock readings, $t$, in s | Position $\vec{d}$, in m |
|:---:|:---:|
| 0.0 | 30 |
| 1.0 | 30 |
| 2.0 | 35 |
| 3.0 | 45 |
| 4.0 | 60 |
| 5.0 | 70 |

An instantaneous position is the location of an object at an instant, at a single time.

3.1 How Far and How Fast? **43**

The average velocity between two
times is the change in position divided
by the difference in the two times.

The ratio $\Delta\vec{d}/\Delta t$ is called **average velocity** and is indicated by the symbol $\vec{v}_{AVE}$. The average velocity over a given time interval is the change of position divided by the time interval over which the change occurred, or

$$\vec{v}_{AVE} = \frac{\Delta\vec{d}}{\Delta t} = \frac{\vec{d}_2 - \vec{d}_1}{t_2 - t_1}.$$

The units for average velocity are a distance unit divided by a time unit. Any distance unit and any time unit can be used to calculate speed. In this textbook, we will usually use kilometres or metres for distance and seconds or hours for time. For example, between 3.0 and 4.0 s, the average velocity of the car is 15 m/s.

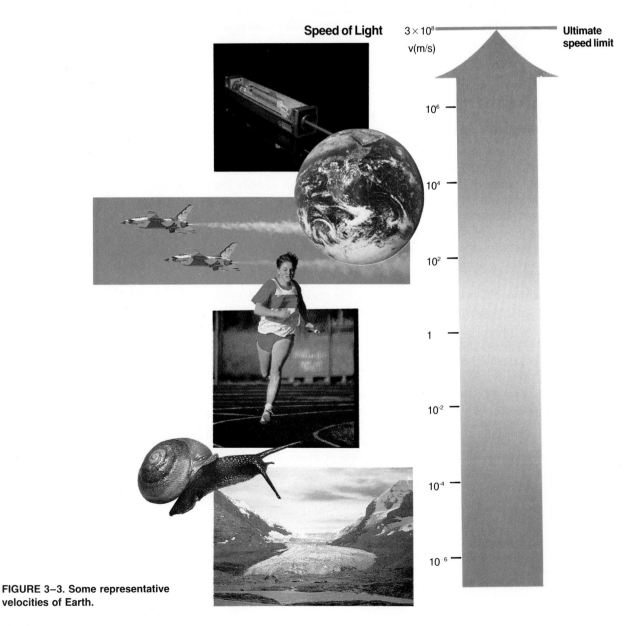

**FIGURE 3–3. Some representative velocities of Earth.**

# PROBLEM SOLVING STRATEGY

An easy way to change from one unit to another is by using conversion factors. To convert a velocity, given in kilometres per hour, km/h, to metres per second, m/s, you must first change kilometres to metres, then hours to seconds. The value of any quantity does not change when it is multiplied by 1. Any quantity divided by its equivalent equals one. Since 1000 m = 1 km and 3600 s = 1 h, we can make the following conversion factors.

$$\frac{1000 \text{ m}}{1 \text{ km}} = \frac{1 \text{ h}}{3600 \text{ s}} = 1$$

Therefore, to change a velocity in km/h to m/s, first multiply it by an appropriate distance conversion factor and then by a time conversion factor. For example, 100 km/h becomes

$$100\frac{\text{km}}{\text{h}} \cdot \left(\frac{1000 \text{ m}}{1 \text{ km}}\right) \cdot \left(\frac{1 \text{ h}}{3600 \text{ s}}\right) = 27.8\frac{\text{m}}{\text{s}}.$$

This method of converting one unit to another unit is called dimensional analysis, or the **factor-label method** of unit conversion. Unit labels are treated as mathematical factors and can be divided out. If the final units do not make sense, check your factors. You may find that a factor has either been inverted or stated incorrectly.

Units can be changed by multiplying by a factor of unit magnitude.

When solving problems, always include units with quantities.

## Example Problem

### Calculating Average Velocity

In the 1988 Summer Olympics, Florence Griffith-Joyner won the 100 m race in 10.54 s. Assuming the length of the race is measured to 10 cm, find her average velocity in m/s and km/h.

**Given:** displacement,
$$\Delta\vec{d} = +100.0 \text{ m}$$
time interval,
$$\Delta t = 10.54 \text{ s}$$

**Unknown:** average velocity, $\vec{v}_{AVE}$

**Basic equation:** $\vec{v}_{AVE} = \dfrac{\Delta\vec{d}}{\Delta t}$

**Solution:** $\vec{v} = \dfrac{\Delta\vec{d}}{\Delta t} = \dfrac{+100.0 \text{ m}}{10.54 \text{ s}} = +9.488 \text{ m/s}$

$$+9.488 \text{ m/s} \left(\frac{3600 \text{ s/h}}{1000 \text{ m/km}}\right) = +34.16 \text{ km/h}$$

That is, she ran at the rate of +9.488 m in 1 s, or +34.16 km in 1 h. In the 200 m race, Flo-Jo's average velocity was 200.0 m/21.34 s = +9.372 m/s, so her average velocity was greater in the 100 m race.

### POCKET LAB

**JOGGERS SPEED**

Take a stopwatch to a large field. Measure the time it takes to walk 50 m. Calculate your average speed. Measure the time it takes you to jog, or run, the same distance. What is your average speed?

◀ **How Fast?**

## Practice Problems

1. A high school athlete runs $1.00 \times 10^2$ m in 12.20 s. What is the velocity in m/s and km/h?
2. A person walks 13 km in 2.0 h. What is the person's average velocity in km/h and m/s?

3. Using the data in Table 3–1, during what one-second-long time interval is the car moving slowest? moving fastest?
▶ 4. Using the data in Table 3–1, find the average velocity of the car in the time interval between 0.0 and 2.0 s.

## Finding Displacement from Velocity and Time

Any one quantity in the equation for average velocity can be found if the other two are known. For example, if the average velocity and time interval are known, then the displacement can be found by rearranging the equation.

$$\vec{v}_{AVE} = \frac{\Delta \vec{d}}{\Delta t}, \text{ to the form, } \Delta \vec{d} = \vec{v}_{AVE}\Delta t.$$

You can quickly check your algebra by examining the units. The quantity $\Delta \vec{d}$ has units metres. The quantity $\vec{v}_{AVE}\Delta t$ has units (m/s)s = m. This is an indication that the equation is correct.

## Example Problem

### Distance Travelled with an Average Velocity

The high-speed train in Figure 3–4 travels from Paris to Lyons at an average velocity of +227 km/h. The trip takes 2.00 h. How far is Lyons from Paris?

**Given:** average velocity,
  $\vec{v}_{AVE} = +227$ km/h
  time interval,
  $\Delta t = 2.00$ h

**Unknown:** displacement, $\Delta \vec{d}$
**Basic equation:** $\vec{v}_{AVE} = \frac{\Delta \vec{d}}{\Delta t}$

**Solution:** $\Delta \vec{d} = \vec{v}_{AVE}\Delta t$
  $\Delta \vec{d} = (+227 \text{ km/h})(2.00\text{h}) = +454$ km

# Practice Problems

5. Suppose a car travels at a constant 10 m/s. How far would it move in 1 h? in 1 min? in 1 s? in 1 ms? in 1 $\mu$s? in 1 ns?

6. A train leaves the station at the 0.0-m marker travelling with a constant velocity of 36.0 m/s.
   a. How many seconds later will the train pass the 1620.0-m marker?
   b. What is the velocity of the train in km/h?

7. At 1:00 P.M., a car, travelling at a constant velocity of 94 km/h toward the west, is 17 km to the west of your school. Where will it be at 3:30 P.M.?

▶ 8. Suppose the car in Practice Problem 7 started 17 km east of your school at the same time, moving in the same direction at the same velocity.
   a. Where would it be at 3:30 P.M.?
   b. When would it be at your school?

If the average velocity of an object is the same for all time intervals, then the object moves at **constant velocity**. Constant velocity is often called uniform velocity. For all time intervals, no matter how long or short, the ratio $\Delta\vec{d}/\Delta t$ is constant. When describing motion with constant velocity, we can replace the time interval, $\Delta t$, by the clock reading, $t$. In the same way, we can replace the displacement, $\Delta\vec{d}$, by $\vec{d}$, the distance from the object's location at $t = 0$. For the special case of uniform velocity, then

$$\vec{v} = \frac{\Delta\vec{d}}{\Delta t}.$$

An object moves with constant velocity if its average velocity is the same for all time intervals.

# Physics and technology

## 3-D COMPUTER GRAPHING

While a table of numbers can record the results of scientific experiments, a graph can convey much more information. Graphing was developed by Rene Descartes in the mid-17th century.

A graph, a geometrical display, allows you to analyse data easily and to make a mental model of the data and test it. Interpolation between data points and extrapolation be-yond them can be used to see if the model makes sense. The ability to display a large amount of data geometrically is especially important in modern experiments when thousands of data points are measured by computerized instruments. Computer software lets the user try different graphical displays and pick the one that shows the data most clearly.

Two-dimensional graphs are used when there is only one independent variable. Often, however, a result depends on at least two variables. In these cases, a three-dimensional graph is needed. Because of the difficulty in making 3-D graphs by hand, a computer is almost

a necessity. Today, 3-D graphing programs are available for almost every popular microcomputer.

· Why, when computers can graph data in two or three dimensions, should students learn to make graphs by hand?

| Position versus Time | |
| --- | --- |
| Time | Position |
| (s) | (m) |
| 0 | 100 |
| 1 | 360 |
| 2 | 620 |
| 3 | 880 |
| 4 | 1140 |
| 5 | 1400 |

**FIGURE 3–5.** A position-time graph for an airplane travelling at a constant velocity.

**FIGURE 3–6.** Once a jetliner has reached cruising altitude, it moves with constant velocity. Its speed through the air and over the ground may be different, but they both will be uniform.

## Position-Time Graphs

A jet airplane travels at a constant velocity of $+260$ m/s. The equation describing the displacement $\Delta \vec{d}$, from its position at $t = 0$ for a constant velocity is $\Delta \vec{d} = \vec{v}\Delta t$. A graph that shows how position depends on clock reading, or time, is called a **position-time graph**. To make such a graph of the plane's motion, first make a table of clock readings (times) and corresponding positions of the plane. Figure 3–5 includes a table of positions for the first 5 s of travel, assuming the plane was located at the position 100 m from the reference position at $t = 0$ seconds. The data are then plotted on a graph with time as the independent variable and position as the dependent variable. A straight line best represents the data. This graph shows that there is a linear relationship between position and time. The y-intercept of the graph shows the position of the object at $t = 0$, in this case, 100 m.

An excellent way of learning about motion from graphs is to use your hand to model the moving object. Let the edge of your desk be the straight line along which the motion takes place. Choose the centre of the edge to be the reference point, with positive position numbers to the right. In the case of Figure 3–5, your hand should move smoothly, at a constant velocity, as you count off 5 s. Each second your hand moves a distance that represents 260 m.

## The Slope of a Position-Time Graph

The velocity of an object can be found from a position-time graph. On a position-time graph, the displacement is the vertical separation of two points. A time interval is the horizontal separation. The ratio of displacement to time interval is the average velocity. The ratio of the vertical separation of two points on a curve, or rise, to the horizontal separation of the points, or run, is the **slope** of the curve of a graph. That is,

$$slope = \frac{rise}{run} = \frac{\Delta \vec{d}}{\Delta t}$$

You can get a more accurate slope if you use the largest possible rise and run. In Figure 3–5, the slope of the line between points A and F is given by

$$slope = \frac{rise}{run} = \frac{1400\,m - 100\,m}{5.0\,s - 0\,s} = \frac{+1300\,m}{5.0\,s} = +260\frac{m}{s}.$$

You see that the slope is the velocity of the airplane we used to generate the graph.

## CONCEPT REVIEW

**1.1** Describe the position of the period in this sentence using three reference points: one on the book, the second on your desk, the third fixed in the room.

**1.2** For each of the position-time graphs in Figure 3–7 below,

  **a.** perform the indicated motions with your hand.

  **b.** write a description of the motion.

The slope of a line on a position-time graph is the average velocity, $\vec{v} = \frac{\Delta \vec{d}}{\Delta t}$.

**FIGURE 3–7. Use with Concept Review 1.2.**

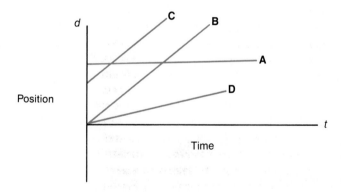

**1.3** Draw a position-time graph of a person who walks one block at a moderate speed, waits a short time for a "walk" light, walks the next block more slowly, then the final block very fast. All blocks are of equal length.

**1.4** **Critical Thinking:** Suppose that in your town positive house numbers are north of Main Street and negative numbers are south. You leave your house that is located at −800 at 9:00 A.M. You arrive at Main Street at 9:04, reach +800 at 9:08, and stop at +1600 at 9:14 A.M.

  **a.** Draw a position-time graph of your walk.

  **b.** Find your average velocity for your entire trip. (Use units of house number per minute.)

  **c.** Find your average velocities between 9:00 and 9:04, 9:04 and 9:08, 9:08 and 9:14. Which is largest? smallest?

# PHYSICS LAB

## The Car Race

## Purpose

To make and interpret a graph of the motion of a toy car.

## Materials

- battery-powered car (or bulldozer)
- marking pen
- 2.5 m length of wide paper
- masking tape
- 5 cm length of plastic straw
- 3.0-m fishing line
- metronome (or tape recorder with beeps recorded at 1.0 s intervals)

## Procedure

1. Tape the short length of the plastic straw to the underside of the car.
2. Thread the fishing line through the straw and tape both ends of the line as shown below. This will prevent the car from curving.
3. Mark a reference line near the end of the paper. (See sketch.)
4. Adjust the metronome or volume of the tape recorder so students can hear it.
5. Turn the car on and start it at the end of the paper. Note: The car must be moving at full speed before it reaches the reference line.

6. Mark the position of the back of the car at every beep.
7. You should have at least five marks after the car crosses the reference line.

## Observations and Data

1. Look at the spacing of the marks. What does this tell you about the motion?
2. Label the marks after the reference line 0 s, 1 s, and so on.
3. Measure each mark from the reference line.
4. Make a data table of times and displacements (measured from the reference line).
5. Make a graph of displacements (vertical axis) and times (horizontal axis).

## Analysis

1. Find the slope of the graph (include units). What does it mean?
2. Should all lab groups have the same type of graph? Explain.

## Applications

1. Look at the value of the slopes of at least two other lab groups. Can you predict which car is fastest?

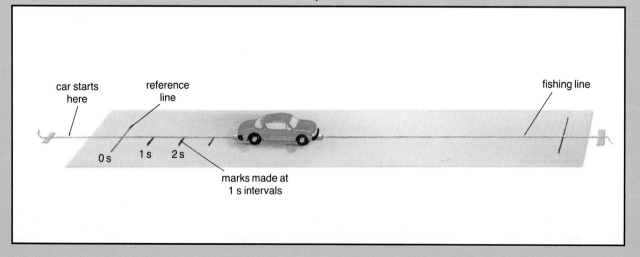

car starts here
reference line
fishing line
0 s   1 s   2 s
marks made at 1 s intervals

# 3.2 NEW MEANINGS FOR OLD WORDS

The concepts of position and velocity are not laws of nature that were discovered by scientists. Rather, they were invented or created by humans to help describe the motion of objects. We can choose a frame of reference and select a measuring scale. We can also decide which direction is positive and which is negative. In this section, we will use other tools that humans have invented to better understand motion.

## Positive and Negative Velocities

Positions, as we have described them, can be both positive and negative. When we first discussed positions, we chose positive positions to be to the right of a reference point and negative to the left. Displacements, or changes in position, can also be either positive or negative. Objects moving to the right have positive displacements. Motions to the left result in negative displacements. Time intervals, on the other hand, are always positive. No one has yet learned how to make time move backward!

Imagine a player on the +20-m line of a playing field. The player, running at a constant 10 m/s, could reach either the +10-m or +30-m line in 1 s. In either case, the magnitude of the velocity would be the same, but the algebraic sign would be different. **Speed** is the magnitude of the velocity. The **velocity** of an object, however, includes both its speed and the algebraic sign or direction. An object moving toward more positive positions has a positive velocity. Thus, a player moving from +20 m to +30 m would have an average velocity of +10 m/s, while a player moving from +20 m to +10 m would have $\vec{v} = -10$ m/s. As in Figure 3–8, an arrow can be used to indicate the velocity of an object. Arrows that point to the right show positive velocities; arrows pointing to the left indicate negative velocities.

Notice that an object can have a negative position but still have a positive velocity. A player running from −47 m to −27 m in 2.0 s would have an average velocity of +10 m/s.

Average velocity can be either positive or negative.

Speed is the size or magnitude of the velocity. Speed is always positive.

FIGURE 3–8. It is possible to arrive at a negative position with a positive velocity depending on the starting point.

# Example Problem

## Position-Time Graph for a Complete Trip

Figure 3–9 is a position-time graph for a short car trip. Find the velocity of the car for each part of the trip.

**Solution:** Between points **A** and **B**,

$$\vec{v} = \frac{\Delta \vec{d}}{\Delta t} = \frac{+200\,\text{m}}{10\,\text{s}} = +20\ \text{m/s}$$

Between point **B** and **C**, the line is horizontal.

$$\vec{v} = \frac{\Delta \vec{d}}{\Delta t} = \frac{+0\,\text{m}}{10\,\text{s}} = +0\ \text{m/s}$$

The car is at rest.

Between points **C** and **D**, the position of the car decreases; the displacement is negative.

$$\vec{v} = \frac{\Delta \vec{d}}{\Delta t} = \frac{-50\,\text{m}}{5.0\,\text{s}} = -10\ \text{m/s}$$

The slope and velocity are both negative; the car moves in a direction opposite to its original direction. Between points **D** and **E**,

$$\vec{v} = \frac{\Delta \vec{d}}{\Delta t} = \frac{-250\,\text{m}}{20\,\text{s}} = -13\ \text{m/s}$$

The slope and velocity are both more negative. The velocity has the same negative value for the entire segment, even though the position at point **E** is negative. That is, the car passed its starting point. Between points **E** and **F**,

$$\vec{v} = \frac{\Delta \vec{d}}{\Delta t} = \frac{+100\,\text{m}}{15\,\text{s}} = +6.7\ \text{m/s}$$

The velocity again is positive. The car is moving again in its original direction.

**FIGURE 3–9.** A position-time graph for a short car trip.

# Practice Problems

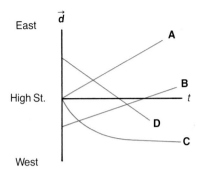

FIGURE 3–10. Use with Practice Problem 9.

9. Describe in words the motion of the four walkers shown in the four curves in Figure 3–10. Assume the positive direction is east and the reference point is the corner of High Street.

10. Sketch position-time graphs for these four motions:
   a. starting at a positive position with a positive velocity.
   b. starting at a negative position with a smaller positive velocity.
   c. remaining at a negative position.
   d. starting at a positive position with a negative velocity.

11. Find the average velocities shown in Figure 3–11.
   a. between $t = 10$ and 12 s      c. between $t = 20$ and 24 s
   b. between $t = 14$ and 18 s      d. between $t = 26$ and 30 s

FIGURE 3–11. Use with Practice Problem 11.

▶ 12. Draw a position-time graph of a moving elevator. Use the first floor as the reference point and up as positive. The elevator waits on the first floor for 30 s, rises to the third floor in 20 s, stops for 30 s, then goes to the basement, which it reaches in 40 s.

## Instantaneous Velocity

To find the velocity of a car, you use its speedometer. Suppose the speedometer needle swings upward from 70 to 90 km/h. What is the car doing? The car is obviously speeding up. If you glance at the speedometer and see the needle at 80 km/h, what does that mean? It means that at the instant you looked, the car's velocity was 80 km/h. Its instantaneous velocity was 80 km/h. That is, if the velocity had been constant, the car would have driven 80 km in 1 h.

A position-time graph can be used to find instantaneous velocity. Figure 3–12a is a position-time graph of a runner during a 100 m dash. Figure 3–12b shows the first 2.5 s of the dash. If the person had a speedometer, what would it read at 1.0 s? Start by finding the average velocity between 0.0 s and 2.0 s. The rise, the runner's displacement, is 12.5 m, while the run, the time interval, is 2.0 s. The slope of the line connecting these two points is the average velocity during this time interval, 6.3 m/s. Next, find the average velocity between 0.5 s and 1.5 s. Now the displacement is 6.8 m while the time interval is 1.0 s. The slope of the connecting line, the average velocity, is 6.8 m/s. We could continue this process, choosing the time interval smaller and smaller until the two clock readings are almost the same. We can no longer draw a line connecting the two points. We now draw a straight line that is the tangent to the curve at that point. The slope of the tangent is called the **instantaneous velocity** at that instant.

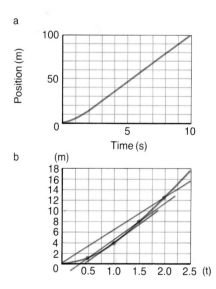

FIGURE 3–12. A position-time graph (a) can be used to find instantaneous velocities by determining the slope at various times (b).

## Position versus time

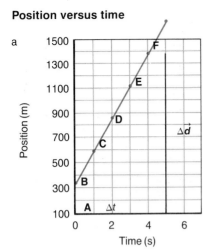

FIGURE 3–13. The velocity-time graph for an airplane moving with a constant velocity of 260 m/s.

The displacement between two times is the area under the curve of a velocity-time graph.

The instantaneous velocity is the tangent to a curve on a position-time graph.

b  **Velocity versus time**

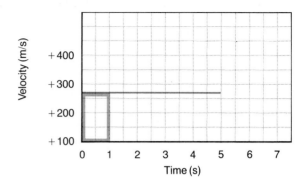

## Velocity-Time Graphs

A **velocity-time graph** is a useful new tool that can be used to describe motion with either constant or changing velocity. Again, model the motion shown in the graph with the motion of your hand along the edge of your desk. The data in Figure 3–5 were used to plot a position-time graph of an airplane flying at constant velocity. A plot of the velocity versus time is shown in Figure 3–13. Every point on the line has the same vertical value because the velocity is constant. The line is parallel to the t-axis.

How would you describe the motion of the runner shown in the velocity-time graph in Figure 3–14? The vertical value of any point is the instantaneous velocity at that time. During the first 5 s, the runner's instantaneous velocity increases. For the next 5 s, he runs at a constant 8 m/s, and over the last 3 s, he slows to a stop.

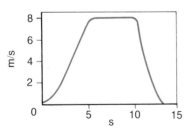

FIGURE 3–14. A velocity-time graph shows the instantaneous velocity of the runner at every instant.

## Example Problem

### Finding Displacement from a Velocity-Time Graph

Find the displacement of the plane whose velocity is shown in Figure 3–13 at **a.** 1.0 s. **b.** 3.0 s.

**Given:** $\vec{v}$-t graph, Figure 3–13b   **Unknown:** displacement, $\Delta\vec{d}$
time intervals,      **Basic equation:** area under graph,
**a.** 0.0 s to 1.0 s       $\Delta\vec{d} = \vec{v}\Delta t$
**b.** 0.0 s to 3.0 s

**Solution:**
Note shaded area under line in Figure 3–13b. The vertical side is velocity: $\vec{v} = +260$ m/s.
**a.** Horizontal side is time interval: $t = 1.0$ s;
the area of rectangle under the line is
$$\vec{v}\Delta t = (+260 \text{ m/s})(1.0 \text{ s}) = 2.6 \times 10^2 \text{ m}.$$
This quantity is the displacement in 1.0 s.
**b.** At the end of 3.0 s, the area under the line is
$$\vec{v}\Delta t = (+260 \text{ m/s})(3.0 \text{ s}) + 7.8 \times 10^2 \text{ m};$$
the displacement of the plane in 3.0 s.

Thus, the area under the line on a velocity-time graph is equal to the displacement of the object from its original position to its position at time *t*. When velocity is constant, displacement increases linearly with time. If you plot the displacement versus time, you will get a straight line with a slope equal to the velocity.

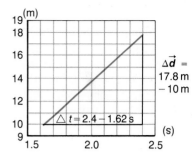

FIGURE 3–15. Use with Practice Problem 13.

## Practice Problems

13. Using Figure 3–15 find the sprinter's velocity at 2.0 s.
14. Use your hand on your desk to model the motion shown by the curves in Figure 3–16a below. Describe in words the motions.
15. Figure 3–16b is the velocity-time graph of an object. What is its velocity at
    **a.** 0 s?    **b.** 1 s?    **c.** 2 s?
16. Using the graph in Figure 3–16b, describe how the instantaneous velocity changes with time.
17. Sketch velocity-time graphs for the graphs in Figure 3–16c.
18. A car moves along a straight road at a constant velocity of +75 km/h for 4.0 h, stops for 2.0 h, and then drives in the reverse direction at the original speed for 3.0 h.
    **a.** Plot a velocity-time graph for the car.
    **b.** Find the area under the curve for the first 4.0 h. What does this represent?
    **c.** Explain how to use the graph to find the distance the car is from its starting point at the end of 9.0 h.

a

b

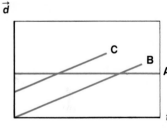

c

FIGURE 3–16. Use with Practice Problems 14, 15, 16, and 17.

▶19. A person drives a car at a constant +25 m/s for 10.0 min. The car runs out of gas, so the driver, carrying an empty gasoline can, walks at +1.5 m/s for 20.0 min to the nearest gas station. After the 10.0 min needed to fill the can, the driver walks back to the car at a slower −1.2 m/s. The car is then driven home at −25 m/s.
    **a.** Draw a velocity-time graph for the driver, using seconds as your time unit. You will have to calculate the distance the driver walked to the station in order to find the time needed to walk back to the car.
    **b.** Draw a position-time graph for the problem from the areas under the curves of the velocity-time graph.

# F.Y.I.

FIGURE 3–17. When the ship is travelling with constant velocity at sea, with nothing on the horizon to serve as a reference point, it is difficult to tell whether it is moving.

## Relativity of Velocity

If you have ever been a passenger on a large ship, you may have noticed that once the ship reached cruising speed, you have no sense of how fast the ship is moving. You could measure the velocity of passengers walking fore and aft, just as you could when the ship is moored at the pier. You might find that they were moving at $+2$ m/s or $-2$ m/s, depending on their direction. If a person on land could see into the ship, however, that person would see the situation differently. If the ship were moving at a typical velocity of 10 m/s, then the land observer would clock the passengers moving at 12 m/s or 8 m/s. Which observer is correct? The answer is either or both. When measuring either position or velocity, you must first define your reference frame. When on the ship, you used a reference frame with a reference point fixed to the ship. The viewer on land, however, used a reference frame that moved with Earth. The reference point was fixed with respect to Earth.

## Example Problem

### Finding Velocity from a Different Reference Frame

A ship is moving forward at 10.0 m/s. A passenger is walking on the deck. What are his velocities, as measured by an observer at rest on the shore, if the passenger walks a. with a velocity of $+2.0$ m/s toward the front of the ship? b. with a velocity of $-2.0$ m/s toward the rear?

**Given:** velocity of ship,
$\vec{v}_s = +10.0$ m/s
velocity of passenger,
a. $\vec{v}_p = +2.0$ m/s
b. $\vec{v}_p = -2.0$ m/s

**Unknown:** velocity of passenger relative to observer, $\vec{v}_o$
**Basic equation:** $\vec{v}_o = \vec{v}_p + \vec{v}_s$

**Solution:**
a. $\vec{v}_o = +2.0$ m/s $+ 10.0$ m/s $= +12$ m/s
b. $\vec{v}_o = -2.0$ m/s $+ 10.0$ m/s $= +8$ m/s

In 1905, Albert Einstein pointed out that this rule does not work when the velocities are near the "speed of light," $3 \times 10^8$ m/s. In fact, if the passengers and people on the ground measured the "speed of light" emitted by a lamp, even on a supersonic plane, both groups would measure exactly the same speed! This fact was central to Einstein's theory of relatively.

## Practice Problems

**20.** From the reference frame of a stationary observer, a car, travelling at a constant speed of 92 km/h, is passed by a truck moving at 105 km/h.
   **a.** From the point of view of the car, what is the truck's speed?
   **b.** From the point of view of the truck, what is the car's speed?
▶ **21.** As you travel at a constant 95 km/h, a car that you know to be 3.5 m long, passes you in 1.8 s. How fast is it going relative to Earth?

# CONCEPT REVIEW

**2.1** The hill people measure heights using the top of the highest peak as a reference point and down as the positive direction. Valley people use the river bottom as the reference point and up as the positive direction. If they both observed a stone falling, would they agree on its velocity? speed? displacement? distance?

**2.2** Draw a position-time graph for the motion of the particle shown on the velocity-time graph, Figure 3–18.

**2.3** Two people leave a lamppost at the same time. One walks east, the other west, both at the same speed. Describe the position-time and velocity-time graphs of the two people.

**2.4** **Critical Thinking:** A police officer clocked a driver going 20 km/h over the speed limit just as the driver passed a slower car. He arrested both drivers. The judge agreed, saying "If the two cars were next to each other, they must have been going the same speed." Is the judge correct? Explain in words and with a position-time graph.

**FIGURE 3–18. Use with Concept Review 2.2.**

# CHAPTER
# 3 REVIEW

## SUMMARY

### 3.1 How Far and How Fast?

- The position of an object is its separation from a reference point.
- Displacement is a vector quantity indicating the magnitude and direction of an object's charge of position.
- A scalar quantity is described completely by its magnitude, while a vector quantity requires both magnitude and direction.
- Average velocity is the displacement (change in position) divided by the time interval.
- The slope of a position-time graph is the velocity of the object.
- If the position-time graph is a straight line, the object is moving with constant velocity.

### 3.2 New Meanings for Old Words

- The area under the curve of a velocity-time graph is the displacement of the object.
- Instantaneous velocity is the velocity of an object at a given instant.
- A frame of reference defines a reference point from which positions are measured.

## KEY TERMS

| | |
|---|---|
| reference point | average velocity |
| frame of reference | factor-label method |
| position | constant velocity |
| distance | position-time graph |
| scalar | slope |
| vector | speed |
| clock reading | velocity |
| instantaneous position | instantaneous |
| displacement | velocity |
| time interval | velocity-time graph |

## REVIEWING CONCEPTS

1. List conditions under which a football may be treated as a point. When can it not be?
2. How does a vector differ from a scalar?
3. Is displacement a vector or a scalar?
4. Is average velocity a vector or a scalar?
5. What quantity can be obtained from the slope of a position-time graph?
6. A physics book is moving across a table. Can the book have a
   **a.** constant speed and a changing velocity?
   **b.** constant velocity and a changing speed?
   Explain your answers.

**7.** A walker and a runner leave your front door at the same time. They move in the same direction at different constant velocities. Describe the position-time graphs of each.

**8.** If you know the positions of a particle at two points along its path and also know the time it took to get from one point to the other, can you determine the particle's instantaneous velocity? its average velocity? Explain.

**9.** What quantity is represented by the area under a velocity-time curve?

**10.** Figure 3–19 shows a velocity-time graph for an automobile on a test track. Describe the changes in velocity with time.

**FIGURE 3–19. Use with Reviewing Concepts 10 and Problem 22.**

# APPLYING CONCEPTS

**1.** If the scale in Figure 3–1 was moved 3 m to the right, would the position of each car remain the same?

**2.** If the scale in Figure 3–1 was moved 3 m to the right, would the distance between the cars remain the same?

**3.** A NASA team oversees a space shuttle launch at Cape Kennedy in Florida and then travels to Edwards Air Force Base in California to supervise the landing. Which group of people, the astronauts or the NASA team, has the greater displacement?

**4.** Average velocity is $\Delta \vec{d}/t$. Consider the ratio $\Delta t/\vec{d}$. When is this new ratio large? When is it small? Can it ever be zero? Invent a reasonable name for it.

**5.** If the average velocity of a particle is zero in some time interval, what can you say about its displacement for that interval?

**6.** Look at Figure 3–20a.
  **a.** What kind of motion does this graph represent?
  **b.** What does the slope of the line represent?

**7.** Use the intervals marked on the graph in Figure 3–20b to describe the velocity of the object during each interval.

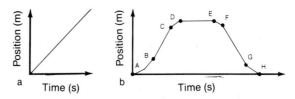

**FIGURE 3–20. Use with Applying Concepts 6 and 7 (b).**

**8.** Figure 3–21 is a position-time graph of two people running.
  **a.** Describe the position of runner A relative to runner B at the y-intercepts.
  **b.** Which runner is faster?
  **c.** What occurs at point **P** and beyond?

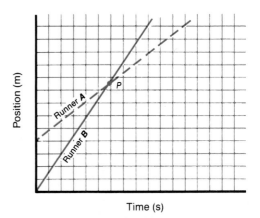

**FIGURE 3–21. Use with Applying Concepts 8.**

**9.** Figure 3–22 is a position-time graph of the motion of two cars on a road.
  **a.** At what time(s) does one car pass the other?
  **b.** Which car is moving faster at 7.0 s?
  **c.** At what time(s) do the cars have the same velocity?
  **d.** Over what time interval is car B speeding up all the time?
  **e.** Over what time interval is car B slowing down all the time?

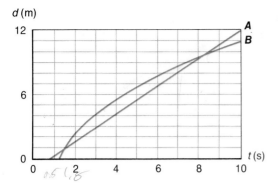

**FIGURE 3–22. Use with Applying Concepts 9 and Problem 21.**

10. Look at Figure 3–23a.
    a. What kind of motion does this graph represent?
    b. What does the area under the curve of the graph represent?
11. Look at Figure 3–23b.
    a. What kind of motion does this graph represent?
    b. What does the area under the curve of the graph represent?

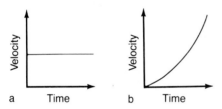

**FIGURE 3–23. Use (a) with Applying Concepts 10, (b) with Applying Concepts 11.**

## PROBLEMS

### 3.1 How Far and How Fast?

1. While John is travelling along a highway, he notices a 160-km marker as he passes through town. Later John passes another marker, 115 km.
   a. What is the distance between town and John's current location?
   b. What is John's current position?
2. While John is travelling along a straight highway, he notices that the marker reads 260 km. John travels until he reaches the 150-km marker and then retraces his path to the 175-km marker. What is John's resultant displacement from the 260-km marker?
3. A physics book is moved once around the perimeter of a table of dimensions 1.0 m by 2.0 m.
   a. If the book ends up at its initial position, what is its displacement?
   b. What is the distance travelled?
4. Light from the sun reaches Earth in 8.3 min. The speed of light is $3.00 \times 10^8$ m/s. How far is Earth from the sun?
5. You and a friend each drive 50 km. You travel at 90 km/h, your friend at 95 km/h. How long will your friend wait for you at the end of the trip?
6. From the list of winning times from the 1988 Summer Olympics track events in Table 3–2, calculate the average speeds for each race. Assume the length of each event is known to the nearest 0.1 m.

Table 3–2

| Length of event (m) | Time (min:s) | |
|---|---|---|
| | Men | Women |
| 100 | 0.09.92 | 0:10.54 |
| 200 | 0:19.75 | 0:21.34 |
| 400 | 0:43.87 | 0:48.65 |
| 800 | 1:44.06 | 1:56.10 |
| 1 500 | 3:35.96 | 3:53.96 |
| 3 000 | | 8:26.53 |
| 5 000 | 13:11.70 | |
| 10 000 | 27:21.46 | 31:05.21 |

7. Construct a table similar to Table 3–2 listing average speeds for track events in your school, school board, or province.
8. Construct an average speed table similar to Problem 6 for swimming events at your school, district, or state. Compare speeds for swimming to those for running. Explain.
9. Two cars approach each other; both cars are moving westward, one at 78 km/h, the other at 64 km/h.
   a. What is the velocity of the first car relative to (in the frame of reference of) the second car?
   b. After they pass, will their relative velocity change?

10. Ann is driving down a street at 55 km/h. Suddenly a child runs into the street. If it takes Ann 0.75 s to react and apply the brakes, how many metres will she have moved before she begins to slow down?

▶ 11. You plan a trip on which you want to average 90 km/h. You cover the first half of the distance at an average speed of only 48 km/h. What must your average speed be in the second half of the trip to meet your goal? Note that the velocities are based on half the distance, not half the time. Is this reasonable?

▶ 12. You drive a car 2.0 h at 40 km/h, then 2.0 h at 60 km/h.
   a. What is your average velocity?
   b. Do you get the same answer if you drive 100 km at each of the two speeds above?

13. The total distance a steel ball rolls down an incline at various times is given in Table 3–3.
   a. Draw a position-time graph of the motion of the ball. When setting up the axes, use five divisions for each 10 m of travel on the $\vec{d}$-axis. Use five divisions for each second of time on the t-axis.
   b. What type of curve is the line of the graph?
   c. What distance has the ball rolled at the end of 2.2 s?

**Table 3–3**

| Time (s) | Distance (m) |
|----------|--------------|
| 0.0 | 0.0 |
| 1.0 | 2.0 |
| 2.0 | 8.0 |
| 3.0 | 18.0 |
| 4.0 | 32.9 |
| 5.0 | 50.0 |

14. Use the position-time graph in Figure 3–24 to find how far the object travels
   a. between $t = 0$ s and $t = 40$ s.
   b. between $t = 40$ s and $t = 70$ s.
   c. between $t = 90$ s and $t = 100$ s.

FIGURE 3–24. Use with Problem 14 and 19.

▶ 15. Both car A and car B leave school when a clock reads zero. Car A travels at a constant 75 km/h, while car B travels at 85 km/h.
   a. Draw a position-time graph showing the motion of both cars.
   b. How far are the two cars from school when the clock reads 2.0 h? Calculate the distances using the equation of motion and show them on your graph.
   c. Both cars passed a gas station 100 km from the school. When did each car pass the station? Calculate the times and show them on your graph.

▶ 16. Draw a position-time graph for two cars driving to the beach, 50 km from school. Car A leaves a store 10 km from school closer to the beach at noon, and drives at 40 km/h. Car B starts from school at 12:30 P.M. and drives at 100 km/h. When does each get to the beach?

17. Plot the data in Table 3–1 on a position-time graph. Find the average velocity in the time interval between 0.0 s and 5.0 s.

18. A cyclist maintains a constant velocity of $+5.0$ m/s. At time $t = 0$, the cyclist is $+250$ m from point **A**.
   a. Plot a position-time graph of the cyclist's location from point **A** at 10.0-s intervals for 60.0 s.
   b. What is the cyclist's position from point **A** at 60.0 s?
   c. What is the displacement from the starting position at 60.0 s?

19. From the position-time graph, Figure 3–24, construct a table showing the average velocity of the object during each 10-s interval over the entire 100 s.

▶ 20. Two cars travel along a straight road. When a stopwatch reads $t = 0.00$ h, car A is at $\vec{d}_A = 48.0$ km moving at a constant 36.0 km/h. Later, when the watch reads $t = 0.50$ h, car B is at $\vec{d}_B = 0.00$ km moving at 48.0 km/h. Answer the following questions: first, graphically by creating a position-time graph; second, algebraically by writing down equations for the position $\vec{d}_A$ and $\vec{d}_B$ as a function of the stopwatch time, t.
   a. What will the watch read when car B passes car A?
   b. At what position will the passing occur?
   c. When the cars pass, how long will it have been since car A was at the reference point?

## 3.2 New Meaning for Old Words

**21.** Refer to Figure 3–22 to find the instantaneous speed for
   **a.** car B at 2.0 s.   **c.** car A at 2.0 s.
   **b.** car B at 9.0 s.

**22.** Find the instantaneous speed of the car at 15 s from Figure 3–19.

**23.** Plot a velocity-time graph using the information in Table 3–4.

### Table 3–4

| Time (s) | Velocity (m/s) | Time (s) | Velocity (m/s) |
|----------|----------------|----------|----------------|
| 0.0 | 4.0 | 7.0 | 12.0 |
| 1.0 | 8.0 | 8.0 | 8.0 |
| 2.0 | 12.0 | 9.0 | 4.0 |
| 3.0 | 14.0 | 10.0 | 0.0 |
| 4.0 | 16.0 | 11.0 | −4.0 |
| 5.0 | 16.0 | 12.0 | −8.0 |
| 6.0 | 14.0 | | |

**24.** Refer to Figure 3–25 to find the distance the moving object travels between
   **a.** $t = 0$ s and $t = 5$ s.
   **b.** $t = 5$ s and $t = 10$ s.
   **c.** $t = 10$ s and $t = 15$ s.
   **d.** $t = 0$ s and $t = 25$ s.

**FIGURE 3–25.**

**▶ 25.** The velocity of an automobile changes over an 8.0-s time period as shown in Table 3–5.
   **a.** Plot the velocity-time graph of the motion.
   **b.** Determine the distance the car travels during the first 2.0 s.
   **c.** What distance does the car travel during the first 4.0 s?
   **d.** What distance does the car travel during the entire 8.0 s?

### Table 3–5

| Time (s) | Velocity (m/s) | Time (s) | Velocity (m/s) |
|----------|----------------|----------|----------------|
| 0.0 | 0.0 | 5.0 | 20.0 |
| 1.0 | 4.0 | 6.0 | 20.0 |
| 2.0 | 4.0 | 7.0 | 20.0 |
| 3.0 | 8.0 | 8.0 | 20.0 |
| 4.0 | 16.0 | | |

## USING A GRAPHING CALCULATOR

Members of a physics class stood 25 m apart and used stopwatches to measure the time a car driving down the highway passed each person. They compiled their data into the following table:

### Table 3–6

| Time (s) | Position (m) | Time (s) | Position (m) |
|----------|--------------|----------|--------------|
| 0.0 | 0.0 | 5.9 | 125.0 |
| 1.3 | 25.0 | 7.0 | 150.0 |
| 2.7 | 50.0 | 8.6 | 175.0 |
| 3.6 | 75.0 | 10.3 | 200.0 |
| 5.1 | 100.0 | | |

Use a graphing calculator to fit a line to a position-time graph the data and to plot this line. Be sure to set the display range of the graph so that all the data fits on it. Find the slope of the line. What was the speed of the car?

## THINKING PHYSIC-LY

On some toll roads in the United States, the ticket is stamped with the time you enter the toll road and the time you exit. How can the toll taker determine if you were speeding?

# Describing Motion: Acceleration

◀ Demon Drop

The Demon Drop ride lasts only 1.5 s. How fast are you going when you are slowed to a halt? How far do you fall?

## ✓ Concept Check

The following terms or concepts from earlier chapters are important for a good understanding of this chapter. If you are not familiar with them, you should review them before studying this chapter.
· graphing, slopes, Chapter 2
· manipulating algebraic equations, Chapter 2
· position and velocity, Chapter 3
· graphs of motion at constant velocity, Chapter 3

A musement park rides thrill customers by changing the velocities of the riders quickly and in unexpected directions. The ride may be a gentle, circling carousel or a rapidly-swinging tilt-o-whirl. It may be the rapid ascents and descents of a roller coaster. For pure heart-stopping thrills, however, nothing beats the ride on the Demon Drop. Held down with shoulder bars, you stop for a moment at the top. The supports under the car are suddenly released, and you drop with close to the acceleration of gravity.

# Objectives

### Vector Conventions

- *Velocity vectors are red.*
- *Displacement vectors are green.*
▶ *Acceleration vectors are purple.*

# 4.1 WHAT IS ACCELERATION?

The faster that the velocity of a ride changes, the greater the thrill. How fast does velocity change? The rate at which velocity changes is such a useful concept that it is given a special name, acceleration. In this chapter, as in Chapter 3, we will consider motion in only one dimension. Changes in velocity can either be positive or negative; direction will be indicated by plus or minus.

## Average Acceleration

An airplane is at rest at the start of the runway, Figure 4–1; it has zero velocity. When cleared for takeoff by the tower, the pilot opens the plane's throttle. After 10 s, the airspeed indicator shows +30 m/s. After 20 s, it shows +60 m/s. When 30 s have elapsed, the airspeed is +90 m/s and the plane lifts off. In each 10 s interval the airplane's speed increased by 30 m/s. Thus, in each second, the velocity increased 3 m/s. The airplane has accelerated down the runway.

Let the change in velocity be $\Delta \vec{v}$, and the time interval during which the velocity changes be $\Delta t$. Consider the ratio $\dfrac{\Delta \vec{v}}{\Delta t}$. When is it large? The ratio is large when there is a large velocity change in a small time interval. The ratio is called the **average acceleration** between the two times.

Suppose an object has velocity $\vec{v}_1$ at time $t_1$ and velocity $\vec{v}_2$ at time $t_2$. The change in velocity is $\Delta \vec{v} = \vec{v}_2 - \vec{v}_1$. The change takes place during the time interval $\Delta t = t_2 - t_1$. Thus, the average acceleration, the change in velocity divided by the interval of time, is given by

$$\vec{a}_{AVE} = \frac{\vec{v}_2 - \vec{v}_1}{t_2 - t_1} = \frac{\Delta \vec{v}}{\Delta t}.$$

**FIGURE 4–1. The air speed indicators above the runway show the velocities at the times shown below the runway.**

Velocity is measured in metres per second, m/s, so acceleration is measured in (m/s)/s, or m/s/s. This unit is read "metres per second per second." More often the unit for acceleration is written as $m/s^2$ and read "metres per second squared." In either case, acceleration tells how many metres per second the velocity changes in each second.

Just as position and velocity are vectors, numbers with both magnitude and direction, so is acceleration. In straight-line motion, acceleration can be either positive or negative. When the velocity increases, its change is a positive number and the acceleration is positive; when velocity decreases, the change is negative, and so is the acceleration.

## Example Problem

### Calculating Average Acceleration

The velocity of a car increases from 2.0 m/s at 1.0 s to 16 m/s at 4.5 s. What is the car's average acceleration?

**Given:** first velocity,
$\vec{v}_1 = 2.0$ m/s
second velocity,
$\vec{v}_2 = 16$ m/s
time interval,
$t_1 = 1.0$ s; $t_2 = 4.5$ s

**Unknown:** acceleration, $\vec{a}_{AVE}$

**Basic equation:** $\vec{a}_{AVE} = \dfrac{\Delta \vec{v}}{\Delta t}$

**Solution:** Velocity change, $\Delta \vec{v} = \vec{v} = \vec{v}_2 - \vec{v}_1 = 16$ m/s $- 2.0$ m/s
= 14 m/s
time interval, $\Delta t = t_2 - t_1 = 4.5$ s $- 1.0$ s = 3.5 s
acceleration, $\vec{a}_{AVE} = \dfrac{\Delta \vec{v}}{\Delta t} = \dfrac{14\,\text{m/s}}{3.5\,\text{s}} = 4.0$ m/s$^2$

Does an object with a negative acceleration always slow down? Consider the following Example Problem.

The units of acceleration are usually m/s/s or m/s$^2$.

## Example Problem

### Acceleration of a Car Backing Up

A car goes faster and faster backwards down a long driveway. We define forward velocity as positive, so backward velocity is negative. The car's velocity changes from $-2.0$ m/s to $-9.0$ m/s in a 2.0 s time interval. Find its acceleration.

**Given:** first velocity,
$\vec{v}_1 = -2.0$ m/s
second velocity,
$\vec{v}_2 = -9$ m/s
$\Delta t = 2.0$ s

**Unknown:** acceleration, $\vec{a}_{AVE}$

**Basic equation:** $\vec{a}_{AVE} = \dfrac{\Delta \vec{v}}{\Delta t}$

**Solution:** Velocity change, $\Delta \vec{v} = -9.0$ m/s $- (-2$ m/s$)$
$= -7.0$ m/s

average acceleration, $\vec{a}_{AVE} = \dfrac{\Delta \vec{v}}{\Delta t} = \dfrac{-7.0\,\text{m/s}}{2.0\,\text{s}}$

$= -3.5$ m/s$^2$

FIGURE 4–2. The car backing down the driveway is increasing its velocity but in the negative direction.

Thus, the car's speed increases, but its acceleration is negative. When the car reaches the end of the driveway, the driver puts on the brakes and comes to a stop. Then, the final velocity will be less negative than the initial velocity. The acceleration will be positive, even though the car is moving slower.

## Practice Problems

1. A race car's velocity increases from +4.0 m/s to +36 m/s over a 4.0-s period. What is its average acceleration?
2. The same race car slows from +36 m/s to +15 m/s over 3.0 s. What is its average acceleration over this time interval?
3. A car is coasting backwards down a hill at −3.0 m/s when the driver gets the engine started. After 2.5 s, the car is moving uphill at a velocity of +4.5 m/s. What is the car's average acceleration?
▶ 4. A bus is moving at 25 m/s. The driver steps on the brakes, and the bus stops in 3.0 s.
   a. What is the average acceleration of the bus while braking?
   b. Suppose the bus took twice as long to stop. How would the acceleration compare to the acceleration you found above?

Acceleration is positive if the velocity change is positive.

Acceleration is the slope of a velocity-time graph.

## Average and Instantaneous Acceleration

In Chapter 3, velocity-time graphs were used to find the object's displacement. Now we will use them in another way. Figure 4–3 lists the velocities of a jet rolling down a runway for takeoff, and a graph of the data. As time increases, so does the velocity of the plane. The plane is accelerating. The change in velocity is the change in the ordinate, or *rise*, of the curve. The time interval is the change in the abscissa, or *run*. Average acceleration is the change in velocity divided by the time interval, so the average acceleration is given by the slope of the curve.

$$slope = \frac{rise}{run} = \frac{\Delta \vec{v}}{\Delta t} = \vec{a}_{AVE}$$

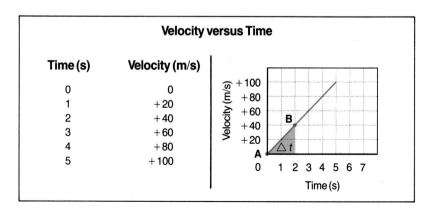

**Velocity versus Time**

| Time (s) | Velocity (m/s) |
|----------|----------------|
| 0 | 0 |
| 1 | +20 |
| 2 | +40 |
| 3 | +60 |
| 4 | +80 |
| 5 | +100 |

**FIGURE 4–3.** A velocity-time graph for uniformly accelerated motion.

**66** Acceleration

In this case, the curve on a velocity-time graph is a straight line, and so the change in velocity is the same in each time interval. The slope is constant, as is the acceleration of the object. For the airplane in Figure 4–3, the acceleration is 20 m/s². Its velocity increases 20 m/s for every second.

In many cases, however, acceleration changes in time. At a given time the instantaneous acceleration is the slope of the tangent to the curve at that time. Figure 4–4 shows the change in velocity with time of an automobile. In this case, the slope, and thus the acceleration, is greatest just as the car accelerates from rest. This car's acceleration is smallest when its velocity is largest.

**Velocity versus Time**

**FIGURE 4–4. The changes in velocity with time of a car accelerating as the driver shifts from first to fourth gear.**

# Example Problem

## Finding the Average Acceleration of a Runner

Figure 4–5 is a velocity-time graph of a sprinter during a 100 m dash. Find the sprinter's average acceleration between a. 0.0 s and 1.0 s. b. 2.0 s and 4.0 s.

**Given:** velocity-time graph

**Unknown:** average acceleration, $\vec{a}_{AVE}$

**Basic equation:** $\vec{a}_{AVE} = \dfrac{\Delta \vec{v}}{\Delta t} = \dfrac{rise}{run}$

**FIGURE 4–5. Use with the Example Problem.**

**Solution:** From the graph, we get Table 4–1.

Thus,

a. $\vec{a}_{AVE} = \dfrac{\Delta \vec{v}}{\Delta t} = \dfrac{rise}{run} = \dfrac{7.8 \text{ m/s}}{1.0 \text{ s}} = 7.8 \text{ m/s}^2$

b. $\vec{a}_{AVE} = \dfrac{\Delta \vec{v}}{\Delta t} = \dfrac{rise}{run} = \dfrac{0.8 \text{ m/s}}{2.0 \text{ s}} = 0.4 \text{ m/s}^2$

The **instantaneous acceleration** is given by the slope of a tangent to the curve on a velocity-time graph. You will find that a tangent to the curve as shown on Figure 4–5 at 1.0 s has a slope of 3.9 m/s².

Table 4–1

| Time (s) | Velocity (m/s) |
|---|---|
| 0.0 | 0.0 |
| 1.0 | 7.8 |
| 2.0 | 10.0 |
| 4.0 | 10.8 |

# Physics and technology

## CUSHIONING THE BLOW

The automobile has given people freedom, but over the years, its mass and speed have resulted in many deaths and serious injuries in collisions. To improve safety, manufacturers have installed devices either to avoid accidents or to protect occupants of a car in an accident. The latest passive restraint devices include shoulder straps that move into place automatically and air bags. These devices allow the car occupants to slow down gradually with the car instead of being thrown into the car body or into the air where their speed goes to zero very rapidly.

Air bags can be installed on both the driver and passenger sides of a car. A crash at 16 to 24 km/h with its sudden acceleration, triggers sensors that activate an igniter. This decomposes sodium azide pellets, producing nitrogen gas that rushes into the nylon bag, forcing it out of its storage compartment as it inflates. The whole process takes place in less than 40 ms. The air bag spreads the time over which the occupant's speed is brought to zero. Injuries to the head and chest are reduced or eliminated. The occupant forces the gas out of the cushion through holes in the bag. The bag deflates within 2 s, allowing the driver to maintain control of the car.

· Crash tests show that air bags dramatically reduce injury in frontal collisions. However, protection is poor in side impacts and in rollovers. Can you think of any other disadvantage?

## Practice Problems

5. Describe, in words, the velocity of the toy train shown in Figure 4–6 between 0 and 20 s.
6. Figure 4–6 shows a velocity-time graph of a toy train.
   a. During which time interval or intervals is the speed constant?
   b. During which interval or intervals is the train's acceleration positive?
   c. During which interval or intervals is its acceleration less than zero?
   d. During which time interval is the acceleration most negative?
7. For Figure 4–6, find the average acceleration during the given time intervals.
   a. 0 to 5 s     c. 15 to 20 s
   b. 0 to 10 s     d. 0 to 40 s
▶ 8. a. Draw a velocity-time graph for an object whose velocity is constantly decreasing from 10 m/s at $t = 0.0$ s to $-10$ m/s at $t = 2.0$ s. Assume it has constant acceleration.
   b. What is its average acceleration between 0.0 s and 2.0 s?
   c. What is its acceleration when its velocity is 0 m/s?

**FIGURE 4–6. Use with Practice Problems 5, 6, and 7.**

# Velocity of an Object With Constant Acceleration

Acceleration that does not change in time is **uniform** or **constant acceleration**. In this case, the velocity-time graph of constant acceleration is a straight line. The velocity when the clock reading, or time, is zero is called the **initial velocity**, $\vec{v}_i$. The slope of the line is the acceleration, $\vec{a}$, so the equation that describes the curve, and thus the velocity at $t$, is

$$\boxed{\vec{v}_f = \vec{v}_i + \vec{a}t.}$$

## Example Problem

### Final Velocity After Uniform Acceleration

If a car with a velocity of 2.0 m/s at $t = 0$ accelerates at a rate of $+4.0$ m/s$^2$ for 2.5 s, what is its velocity at time $t = 2.5$ s?

**Given:** $\vec{v}_i = +2.0$ m/s         **Unknown:** final velocity, $\vec{v}_f$
          $\vec{a} = +4.0$ m/s$^2$         **Basic equation:** $\vec{v}_f = \vec{v}_i + \vec{a}t$
          $t = 2.5$ s

**Solution:** $\vec{v}_f = \vec{v}_i + \vec{a}t$
          $= +2.0$ m/s $+ (+4.0$ m/s$^2)(2.5$ s$)$
          $= +12$ m/s

*If a velocity-time graph is a straight line, the acceleration is uniform or constant.*

## Practice Problems

9. A golf ball rolls up a hill toward a mini-golf hole.
    a. If it starts with a velocity of $+2.0$ m/s and accelerates at a constant rate of $-0.50$ m/s$^2$, what is its velocity after 2.0 s?
    b. If the acceleration occurs for 6.0 s, what is its final velocity?
    c. Describe, in words, the motion of the golf ball.
10. A bus traveling at $+30$ km/h accelerates at a constant $+3.5$ m/s$^2$ for 6.8 s. What is its final velocity in km/h?
11. If a car accelerates from rest at a constant 5.5 m/s$^2$, how long will be required to reach 28 m/s?
▶ 12. A car slows from 22 m/s to 3 m/s with a constant acceleration of $-2.1$ m/s$^2$. How long does it require?

......................
# CONCEPT REVIEW

1.1 Describe, in words, how you calculate average acceleration between two times.
1.2 a. If an object has zero acceleration, does that mean its velocity is zero? Give an example.
    b. If an object has zero velocity at some instant, does that mean its acceleration is zero? Give an example.
1.3 Is km/h/s a unit of acceleration? Is this unit the same as km/s/h? Explain the meaning of the two.
1.4 **Critical Thinking:** Figure 4–7 is a strobe photo of a horizontally moving ball. What information about the photo would you need and what measurements would you make to estimate the acceleration?

**FIGURE 4—7. Use with Concept Review 1.4.**

# PHYSICS LAB

## Ball and Car Race

## Purpose

To compare the motion of constant velocity to the motion of constant acceleration.

## Materials

- battery-powered car
- small steel ball
- 10 cm of tape
- 90 cm length of U channel
- short length of plastic straw
- 100 cm of fishing line
- stopwatch

## Procedure

1. Tape the straw to the bottom of the car. Thread the fishing line through the straw and securely tape *both* ends as shown below. (The car will now be constrained to move in a straight line.)
2. Place a piece of tape on the table to serve as a reference line.
3. Turn the car on and start it behind the reference line. (See sketch.)
4. Measure the average time needed for the car to travel from the reference line to the end of the ramp (at least 3 trials).
5. Place a book or wood blocks and so on under one end of the U channel and measure the time it takes for the ball to roll down the ramp when *starting from the reference line!*
6. Adjust the height of the end of the ramp until the time it takes the ball to roll is within the 0.1 s of the time needed for the car.

7. Place the ball on the ramp at the reference line. Start the car behind the reference line and release the ball as the cart reaches the reference line.
8. Which object won the race? Was it close?

## Observations and Data

1. Describe the motion of the car in words.
2. Describe the motion of the ball in words.
3. Did it appear that the objects ever had the same speed during the race? If so, then where?

## Analysis

1. Set up a graph of position (vertical axis) vs time (horizontal axis).
2. Assume that the car had a steady speed. Show this motion on the graph.
3. Place a marker at the halfway point for the ball. Measure the time needed for the ball to roll halfway.
4. Assume that the ball was gaining speed (accelerating) for the entire time. Draw a smooth curve to show the motion of the ball. (**Hint:** This curve should have the same starting and ending points as the car, but also include the data point for the halfway distance.)
5. Did the two graphs ever have equal slopes (equal velocities)? Where?

## Applications

1. Why does it take so long for someone in a parked car to catch up after you pass by?

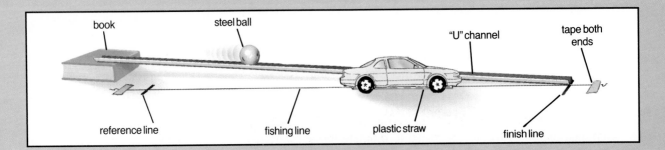

book · steel ball · "U" channel · tape both ends · reference line · fishing line · plastic straw · finish line

# 4.2 DISPLACEMENT DURING CONSTANT ACCELERATION

## Objectives

- be able to calculate the displacement of an object undergoing uniform acceleration when you know two out of the three quantities: acceleration, time, velocity.
- be able to solve problems of the motion of objects uniformly accelerated by gravity.
- learn to use an organized strategy for solving motion problems.

The displacement of a moving object is much easier to measure than its velocity. For that reason, we will develop three equations that relate the displacement to two of the three other quanities we use to describe motion—time, velocity, and acceleration. *These equations are correct only when acceleration is constant.* Fortunately, for many types of moving bodies, including those falling due to gravity, this condition is true when air resistance is ignored.

## Displacement When Velocity and Time Are Known

When an object is moving with constant velocity, its displacement can be found by multiplying its velocity by the time interval. To find the displacement if the object is uniformly accelerating, the velocity is replaced by the average velocity,

$$\vec{v}_{AVE} = \frac{1}{2}(\vec{v}_f + \vec{v}_i).$$

To show this, consider the velocity-time graph for an object with constant acceleration, Figure 4–8. The displacement is the total area under the curve. The total area is the sum of the area of the rectangle, $\vec{v}_i t$, and the area of the triangle, $\frac{1}{2}(\vec{v}_f - \vec{v}_i)t$. The total area is the displacement, $\vec{d} = \vec{v}_i t + \frac{1}{2}(\vec{v}_f - \vec{v}_i)t$, or

$$\boxed{\vec{d} = \frac{1}{2}(\vec{v}_f + \vec{v}_i)t.}$$

## Example Problem

### Displacement When Velocity and Time Are Known

What is the displacement of a train as it is accelerated uniformly from +11 m/s to +33 m/s in a 20.0-s interval?

**Given:** initial velocity,
    $\vec{v}_i = +11$ m/s
    final velocity,
    $\vec{v}_f = +33$ m/s
    time interval,
    $t = 20.0$ s

**Unknown:** displacement, $\vec{d}$
**Basic equation:** $\vec{d} = \frac{1}{2}(\vec{v}_f + \vec{v}_i)t$

**Solution:** $\vec{d} = \frac{1}{2}(\vec{v}_f + \vec{v}_i)t = \frac{1}{2}(+33$ m/s $+ 11$ m/s$)(20.0$ s$)$
        $= +4.4 \times 10^2$ m

# Practice Problems

**13.** A race car travelling at $+44$ m/s is uniformly accelerated to a velocity of $+22$ m/s over an 11 s interval. What is its displacement during this time?

**14.** A rocket travelling at $+88$ m/s is accelerated uniformly to $+132$ m/s over a 15-s interval. What is its displacement during this time?

**15.** A car accelerates at a constant rate from 15 m/s to 25 m/s while it travels 125 m. How long does this motion take?

▶ **16.** A bike rider accelerates constantly to a velocity of 7.5 m/s during 4.5 s. The bike's displacement is $+19$ m. What was the initial velocity of the bike?

## Displacement When Acceleration and Time Are Known

If the initial velocity, acceleration, and time interval are known, the displacement of the object can be found by combining equations already used. The final velocity of a uniformly accelerated object is $\vec{v}_f = \vec{v}_i + \vec{a}t$. The displacement of an object with uniform acceleration is $\vec{d} = \frac{1}{2}(\vec{v}_f + \vec{v}_i)t$.

Substitute the final velocity from the first equation into the second equation.

$$\vec{d} = \frac{1}{2}(\vec{v}_f + \vec{v}_i)t = \frac{1}{2}((\vec{v}_i + \vec{a}t) + \vec{v}_i)t = \frac{1}{2}(2\vec{v}_i + \vec{a}t)t$$

$$\boxed{\vec{d} = \vec{v}_i t + \frac{1}{2}\vec{a}t^2}$$

There are two terms in this equation. The first term, $\vec{v}_i t$, corresponds to the displacement of an object if it were moving with constant velocity, $\vec{v}_i$. The second term, $\frac{1}{2}\vec{a}t^2$, gives the displacement of an object starting from rest and moving with uniform acceleration. The sum of these two terms gives the displacement of an object that starts with an initial velocity and accelerates uniformly. For an object that starts from rest, the equation reduces to $\vec{d} = \frac{1}{2}\vec{a}t^2$.

You can see these relationships by looking at a velocity-time graph of uniformly accelerated motion. As you know, the area under the curve of a velocity-time graph is the displacement of the object.

Look at the coloured area under the curve between time $t_i = 0$ and time $t$, Figure 4–8. The coloured area is made up of a rectangle with a triangle on top. The area of the rectangle is its height, the initial velocity, $\vec{v}_i$, multiplied by its base, the time $t$. That is, area $= \vec{v}_i t$. This area is the displacement the object would have if it had the constant velocity $\vec{v}_i$.

The altitude of the triangle is the change in velocity of the uniformly accelerated object. Since $\vec{v}_f = \vec{v}_i + \vec{a}t$, $(\vec{v}_f - \vec{v}_i) = \vec{a}t$. The base is again the time $t$. The area of a triangle is half the base times the altitude, or $\frac{1}{2}(\vec{a}t)(t) = \frac{1}{2}\vec{a}t^2$. This area is the displacement the object would have if it were uniformly accelerated from rest.

The total displacement is the sum of the two areas under the curve, $\vec{d} = \vec{v}_i t + \frac{1}{2}\vec{a}t^2$.

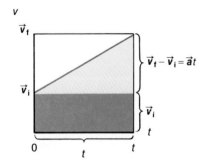

**FIGURE 4–8. A velocity-time graph of uniformly accelerated motion. The coloured area represents displacement.**

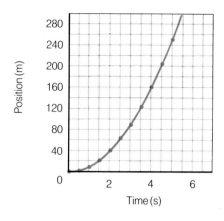

| Position versus Time | |
|---|---|
| Time (s) | Position (m) |
| 0 | +0 |
| 1 | +10 |
| 2 | +40 |
| 3 | +90 |
| 4 | +160 |
| 5 | +250 |

FIGURE 4–9. A position-time graph for uniformly accelerated motion.

What kind of curve is the position-time graph of an object accelerated from rest at a constant rate? Figure 4–9 includes a table of the positions of the jet plane for the first 5 s of its acceleration. The positions were found from the area under the curve of the velocity-time graph, Figure 4–3.

The data were then plotted to give the position-time graph shown. The curve of the position-time graph is half a parabola. When one quantity varies directly with the square of the other, a parabolic curve results.

As you have seen, the slope of a position-time graph is the velocity of the object. When an object's velocity is constant, its position changes the same amount each second. Therefore, the position-time graph is a straight line with a constant slope. If, however, the object is accelerated, during each second its displacement is different from the value it had the second before. The position-time graph for accelerated motion is a parabola, and the slope does change. Figure 4–10 again shows the position-time graph for the jet plane. Suppose you want to find the slope of the curve at point **P**. Draw a line tangent to the curve at point **P**. The slope of the tangent line is the instantaneous velocity at point **P**. Point **P** is at the time 3 s. A tangent line is drawn, and

$$\vec{v} = slope = \frac{rise}{run} = \frac{+270\,m - 0\,m}{6.0\,s - 1.5\,s}$$

$$= \frac{270\,m}{4.5\,s} = +60\,m/s.$$

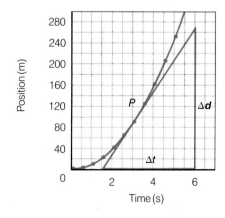

FIGURE 4–10. The slope at any point on a position-time graph indicates the velocity of the object.

The velocity at the end of 3 seconds for an object that accelerates at +20 m/s² is +60 m/s, which agrees with the velocity-time graph for the jet plane.

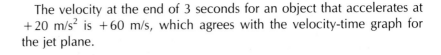
# Example Problem

## Calculating Displacement From Acceleration and Time

A car starting from rest accelerates uniformly at +6.1 m/s² for 7.0 s. How far does the car move?

**Given:** initial velocity,
$\vec{v}_i = 0.0$ m/s
acceleration,
$\vec{a} = +6.1$ m/s²
final time, $t = 7.0$ s

**Unknown:** displacement, $\vec{d}$
**Basic equation:** $\vec{d} = \vec{v}_i t + \frac{1}{2}\vec{a}t^2$

**Solution:** $\vec{d} = \vec{v}_i t + \frac{1}{2}\vec{a}t^2$
$= (0.0 \text{ m/s})(7.0 \text{ s}) + \frac{1}{2}(+6.1 \text{ m/s}^2)(7.0 \text{ s})^2$
$= 0.0 \text{ m} + 150 \text{ m} = 1.5 \times 10^2 \text{ m}$

# Practice Problems

17. An airplane starts from rest and accelerates at a constant +3.00 m/s² for 30.0 s before leaving the ground. What is its displacement during this time?

18. Starting from rest, a race car moves 110 m in the first 5.0 s of uniform acceleration. What is the car's acceleration?

19. A driver brings a car travelling at +22 m/s to a full stop in 2.0 s. Assume its acceleration is constant.
    a. What is the car's acceleration?
    b. How far does it travel before stopping?

▶ 20. A biker passes a lamppost at the crest of a hill at +4.5 m/s. She accelerates down the hill at a constant rate of +0.40 m/s² for 12 s. How far does she move down the hill during this time?

## Displacement When Velocity and Acceleration Are Known

We can combine the equations for final velocity and displacement to form an equation relating initial and final velocities, acceleration, and displacement in which time does not appear. First, recall the two motion equations,

$$\vec{d} = \frac{1}{2}(\vec{v}_f + \vec{v}_i)t \text{ and } \vec{v}_f = \vec{v}_i + \vec{a}t.$$

The second equation is now solved for $t$ and substituted in the first, resulting in

$$\vec{d} = \frac{1}{2}\frac{(\vec{v}_f + \vec{v}_i)(\vec{v}_f - \vec{v}_i)}{\vec{a}} = \frac{1}{2}\frac{\vec{v}_f^2 - \vec{v}_i^2}{\vec{a}}.$$

Solving for $\vec{v}_f^2$ yields

$$\boxed{\vec{v}_f^2 = \vec{v}_i^2 + 2\vec{a}\vec{d}.}$$

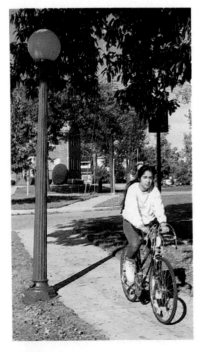

**FIGURE 4–11.**

## Example Problem

### Calculating Acceleration From Displacement and Velocity

An airplane must reach a velocity of 71 m/s for takeoff. If the runway is 1.0 km long, what must the constant acceleration be?

**Given:** initial velocity,
$$\vec{v}_i = 0.0 \text{ m/s}$$
final velocity,
$$\vec{v}_f = 71 \text{ m/s}$$
displacement,
$$\vec{d} = +1.0 \text{ km}$$
$$= +1.0 \times 10^3 \text{ m}$$

**Unknown:** acceleration, $\vec{a}$
**Basic equation:** $\vec{v}_f^2 = \vec{v}_i^2 + 2\vec{a}\vec{d}$

**Solution:** $\vec{v}_f^2 = \vec{v}_i^2 + 2\vec{a}\vec{d}$, so $\vec{a} = \dfrac{\vec{v}_f^2 - \vec{v}_i^2}{2\vec{d}}$

$$= \frac{(71 \text{ m/s})^2 - 0.0}{2\,(+1.0 \times 10^3 \text{ m})}$$

$$= +2.5 \text{ m/s}^2$$

Consider the reverse of this problem. The plane lands going 71 m/s. It slows to a halt with an acceleration of $-2.5$ m/s$^2$. How much runway does it require? We use the same basic equation, solved for the displacement,

$$\vec{d} = \frac{\vec{v}_f^2 - \vec{v}_i^2}{2\vec{a}}$$

$$= \frac{(0.0 \text{ m/s})^2 - (71 \text{ m.s})^2}{2\,(-2.5 \text{ m/s}^2)}$$

$$= +1.0 \times 10^3 \text{ m}.$$

Notice that the displacement is the same. The motion in these two cases is said to be symmetrical. The conditions at the beginning and end of the motion are reversed, and the solutions are equivalent. Symmetry often plays an important role in physics problems.

# Practice Problems

21. An airplane accelerates from a velocity of 21 m/s at the constant rate of 3.0 m/s$^2$ over $+535$ m. What is its final velocity?
22. The pilot stops the same plane in 484 m using a constant acceleration of $-8.0$ m/s$^2$. How fast was the plane moving before braking began?
23. A person wearing a shoulder harness can survive a car crash if the acceleration is smaller than $-300$ m/s$^2$. Assuming constant acceleration, how far must the front end of the car collapse if it crashes while going 101 km/h?
▶ 24. A car is initially sliding backwards down a hill at $-25$ km/h. The driver guns the car. By the time the car's velocity is $+35$ km/h, it is $+3.2$ m from its starting point. Assuming the car was uniformly accelerated, find the acceleration.

## Acceleration Due to Gravity

Galileo was the first to show that all objects fall to Earth with a constant acceleration. There is no evidence that he actually dropped two cannon balls from the leaning tower of Pisa, but he did conduct many experiments with balls rolling down inclined planes. He had previously shown that the inclined plane "diluted" gravity, slowing motion so he could make careful measurements.

We know from experiments that no matter what the mass of the object is, whether it is dropped from 1 m, 10 m, or 100 m, or whether it is dropped or thrown, as long as air resistance can be ignored, the acceleration due to gravity is the same for all objects at the same location on Earth.

**Acceleration due to gravity** is given a special symbol, $\vec{g}$. Since acceleration is a vector quantity, $\vec{g}$ must have both magnitude and direction. We will choose "up" as our positive direction, so a falling object has a negative velocity. The acceleration of a falling object is also negative. On the surface of Earth, a freely falling object has an acceleration, $\vec{g}$, of $-9.80$ m/s$^2$. Actually, $\vec{g}$ varies slightly, from location to location, depending (among other things) on the elevation above sea level. Typically, on a mountaintop its value can be as low as 9.780 m/s$^2$. We will use a typical value of $-9.80$ m/s$^2$. Thus, if a ball is dropped from the top of a building, it starts with zero velocity and in each second of fall gains a downward velocity of $-9.80$ m/s.

Strobe photos of a dropped ball are shown in Figure 4–12. The time interval between photos is 1/120 s. The distance between each pair of images increases. Since $\vec{v} = \Delta \vec{d}/\Delta t$, the speed is increasing. Because we have taken the upward direction to be positive, the velocity is becoming more and more negative.

Assuming no air resistance, all problems involving motion of falling objects can be solved by using the equations developed in this chapter with the acceleration, $\vec{a}$, replaced by $\vec{g}$.

$$\vec{v}_f = \vec{v}_i + \vec{g}t$$
$$\vec{v}_f^2 = \vec{v}_i^2 + 2\vec{g}\vec{d}$$
$$\vec{d} = \vec{v}_i t + \tfrac{1}{2}\vec{g}t$$

If you throw a ball straight up, it leaves your hand with a positive velocity of, say, $+20.0$ m/s. Positive velocity means it is rising. The acceleration of the ball is $-9.80$ m/s$^2$, so after 1 s its velocity is $+10.2$ m/s. After 2 s the velocity is $+0.40$ m/s. After 3 s, the velocity is $-9.40$ m/s. Now the velocity is no longer positive. The negative velocity indicates that the ball is no longer rising, it is falling. After 4 s, the velocity is $-19.20$ m/s, so it is falling faster and faster. See the velocity-time graph, Figure 4–13a. Let's examine what happens around 2 s, as shown in Figure 4–13b. The velocity changes smoothly from positive to negative at about 2.04 s. For just an instant, at the top of its flight, the ball has zero velocity.

How does the ball's position change? The position-time graph, Figure 4–13c, has a large positive slope at $t = 0$, when the velocity is large and positive. As time increases, the velocity and the slope decrease. When the slope (and velocity) is zero, the ball is at its maximum height, as shown in the detailed position-time graph, Figure 4–13d. On the

**FIGURE 4–12.** Strobe photograph of a ball in freefall. Images are at 1/120-s intervals.

a  Time (s)

b  Time (s)

c  Time (s)

d  Time (s)

FIGURE 4–13. Velocity-time and position-time graphs for a tennis ball thrown straight up.

way down, the ball's velocity and the slope of the position-time graph are negative and become more negative. After it has fallen 2.04 s, the ball will be once again in your hand. It spends as much time rising as falling. It rises the same distance during the first 2.04 s as it falls during the final 2.04 s. Note that, although the total distance the ball travels is the distance up plus the distance down, the total displacement, the change in position, is zero.

## Example Problem

### Freely Falling Objects

The time the Demon Drop ride at Cedar Point, Ohio is freely falling is 1.5 s. **a.** What is its velocity at the end of this time? **b.** How far does it fall?

**Given:** acceleration of gravity,
$\vec{g} = -9.80 \text{ m/s}^2$
initial velocity,
$\vec{v}_i = 0.0 \text{ m/s}$
time interval,
$t = 1.5 \text{ s}$

**Unknowns: a.** final velocity, $\vec{v}_f$
**b.** displacement, $d$
**Basic equations:**
**a.** $\vec{v}_f = \vec{v}_i + \vec{g}t$
**b.** $\vec{d} = \vec{v}_i t + \frac{1}{2}\vec{g}t^2$

**Solution:**
**a.** $\vec{v}_f = \vec{v}_i + \vec{g}t = 0.0 \text{ m/s} + (-9.80 \text{ m/s}^2)(1.5 \text{ s})$
$\vec{v}_f = -15 \text{ m/s}$
**b.** $\vec{d} = \vec{v}_i t + \frac{1}{2}\vec{g}t^2 = 0.0 \text{ m/s}(1.5 \text{ s}) + \frac{1}{2}(-9.80 \text{ m/s}^2)(1.5 \text{ s})^2$
$= \frac{1}{2}(-9.80 \text{ m/s}^2)(2.25 \text{ s}^2) = -11 \text{ m}$

Negative displacement means that the final position is lower than the initial position.

## Practice Problems

**25.** A brick falls freely from a high scaffold.
   **a.** What is its velocity after 4.0 s?
   **b.** How far does the brick fall during the first 4.0 s?
▶ **26.** Now that you know about acceleration, test your reaction time. Ask a friend to hold a ruler just even with the top of your fingers. Then have your friend drop the ruler. Taking the number of centimetres

Demon Drop

FIGURE 4–14. The thrill of the Demon Drop ride comes from being in freefall.

that the ruler falls before you can catch it, calculate your reaction time. An average of several trials will give more accurate results. The reaction time for most people is more than 0.15 s.

Several equations for solving problems of uniformly accelerated motion have been introduced in this chapter. How do you know which one(s) to use in solving a problem? The equations are listed in Table 4–2, together with a list of the quantities related by each equation.

Table 4–2

| Equations of Motion for Uniform Acceleration | | | | |
|---|---|---|---|---|
| **Equation** | | **Variables** | | |
| $\vec{v}_f = \vec{v}_i + \vec{a}t$ | $\vec{v}_i$ | $\vec{v}_f$ | $\vec{a}$ | $t$ |
| $\vec{d} = \frac{1}{2}(\vec{v}_f + \vec{v}_i)t$ | $\vec{v}_i$ $\vec{d}$ | $\vec{v}_f$ | | $t$ |
| $\vec{d} = \vec{v}_it + \frac{1}{2}\vec{a}t^2$ | $\vec{v}_i$ $\vec{d}$ | | $\vec{a}$ | $t$ |
| $\vec{v}_f^2 = \vec{v}_i^2 + 2\vec{a}\vec{d}$ | $\vec{v}_i$ $\vec{d}$ | $\vec{v}_f$ | $\vec{a}$ | |

Note that each equation has at least one of the four variables, $\vec{d}$, $\vec{v}_f$, $\vec{a}$, or $t$ missing. All include the initial velocity, $\vec{v}_i$, as well as the initial time (0) and initial position (also zero).

# PROBLEM SOLVING STRATEGY

When solving problems, use an orderly procedure.
1. Read the problem carefully. Try to visualize the actual situation. Make a sketch if necessary.
2. Identify the quantities that are given in the problem.
3. Identify the quantity that is unknown, the one you have to find.
4. Select the equation or equations that will relate the given and unknown quantities.
5. Make sure the equations can be applied to the problem, that is, is the acceleration constant?
6. Rewrite equations as needed to solve for the unknown quantity.
7. Substitute the given values including proper units into the equation and solve. Be sure your answer is in the correct units.
8. Make a rough estimate to see if your answer is reasonable.

## Example Problem

### Flight of a Tennis Ball

A tennis ball is thrown straight up with an initial velocity of +22.5 m/s. It is caught at the same distance above ground from which it was thrown. **a.** How high does the ball rise? **b.** How long does the ball remain in the air?

Given: $\vec{v}_i$ = +22.5 m/s, upward

$\vec{g}$ = −9.80 m/s², downward

Unknowns: a. $\vec{d}$  b. $t$
Basic equations: $\vec{v}_f = \vec{v}_i + \vec{g}t$

$\vec{d} = \vec{v}_it + \frac{1}{2}\vec{g}t^2$

$\vec{v}_f^2 = \vec{v}_i^2 + 2\vec{g}\vec{d}$

$\vec{d} = \frac{1}{2}(\vec{v}_f + \vec{v}_i)t$

**FIGURE 4–15. A tennis ball thrown up vertically.**

**Solution:**

**a.** At the top of its flight, the instantaneous velocity of the ball is zero. Thus, the final velocity for the upward part of the ball's flight will be zero. Therefore, we know $\vec{v}_i$, $\vec{g}$, and need $\vec{d}$. Use the equation $\vec{v}_f^2 = \vec{v}_i^2 + 2\vec{g}\vec{d}$, solving it for $\vec{d}$.

With $\vec{v}_f = 0.0$, $0.0 = \vec{v}_i^2 + 2\vec{g}\vec{d}$ or $2\vec{g}\vec{d} = -\vec{v}_i^2$.

Thus,

$$\vec{d} = \frac{-\vec{v}_i^2}{2\vec{g}} = \frac{-(22.5 \text{ m/s})^2}{2(-9.80 \text{ m/s}^2)} = +25.8 \text{ m}.$$

The direction is up (positive), so $\vec{d} = +25.8$ m.

**b.** From symmetry, we know that the times required for the rising and falling parts of the flight will be the same. That is, the time to rise is half the total time. Thus, we know $\vec{v}_f$ and $\vec{g}$ but need $t$. Use $\vec{v}_f = \vec{v}_i + \vec{g}t$. With $\vec{v}_f = 0.0$, we solve for $t$, obtaining

$$t = \frac{-\vec{v}_i}{\vec{g}} = \frac{-22.5 \text{ m/s}}{-9.80 \text{ m/s}^2} = +2.30 \text{ s}.$$

Thus, the total trip time is 4.60 s.

# Example Problem

## Finding Displacement When Velocities and Times Are Known

A spaceship far from any star or planet accelerates uniformly from $+65.0$ m/s to $+162.0$ m/s in 10.0 s. How far does it move?

**Given:** $\vec{v}_i = +65.0$ m/s
$\vec{v}_f = +162.0$ m/s
$t = 10.0$ s

**Unknown:** displacement, $\vec{d}$
**Basic equation:** $\vec{d} = \frac{1}{2}(\vec{v}_f + \vec{v}_i)t$

**Solution:** $\vec{d} = \frac{1}{2}(\vec{v}_f + \vec{v}_i)t$
$= \frac{1}{2}(+162.0 \text{ m/s} + 65.0 \text{ m/s})(10.0 \text{ s})$
$= +1.14 \times 10^3 \text{ m} = +1.14 \text{ km}$

**FIGURE 4–16. A spacecraft accelerates vertically at takeoff.**

# Practice Problems

**27.** If you drop a golf ball, how far does it fall in 0.5 s?

**28.** A spacecraft travelling at a velocity of $+1210$ m/s is uniformly accelerated at $-150$ m/s$^2$. If the acceleration lasts for 8.68 s, what is the final velocity of the craft? Explain your results in words.

**29.** A man falls 1.0 m to the floor.
  **a.** How long does the fall take?
  **b.** How fast is he going when he hits the floor?

**30.** On wet pavement, a car can be accelerated with a maximum acceleration $a = 0.20$ g before its tires slip.
  **a.** Starting from rest, how fast is it moving after 2.0 s?
  **b.** How far has it moved after 4.0 s?

| | |
|---|---|

## POCKET LAB

### A BALL RACE

Assemble an inclined ramp from a piece of U channel, or two metre sticks taped together along the edges, and a book. Mark a position 40 cm and 80 cm from the top. Start one ball at the top and one ball at the 40 cm position. When the balls are released at the same instant, will the balls get closer together or farther apart as they roll down the ramp? Why? Try it. Explain what happened in terms of the velocities. What does this tell you about the acceleration of each ball? Release one ball from the top. Release the other ball from the top as soon as the first ball reaches the 40 cm mark. Do the balls stay the same distance apart? As they roll down the hill, do they ever have the same velocities? Do they have the same acceleration?

31. A pitcher throws a baseball straight up with an initial speed of 27 m/s.
    a. How long does it take the ball to reach its highest point?
    b. How high does the ball rise above its release point?
▶ 32. A motor of a certain elevator gives it a constant upward acceleration of 46 m/(min·s). The elevator starts from rest, accelerates for 2.0 s, then continues with constant speed.
    a. Explain what this statement of acceleration means.
    b. What is the final speed after 2 s?
    c. Calculate speed after 0.5, 1.0, 1.5, 2.0, 3.0, 4.0, and 5.0 s. Sketch a graph showing speed v. time.
    d. How far has it risen 1.0, 2.0, 3.0, 4.0, and 5.0 s after start? Sketch the graph.

## CONCEPT REVIEW

**2.1** If you are given a table of velocities of an object at various times, how could you find out if the acceleration is constant?

**2.2** If initial and final velocities and constant acceleration are given and displacement is unknown, what equation would you use?

**2.3** The gravitational acceleration on Mars is about one-third that on Earth. If you could throw a ball up with the same velocity on Mars as on Earth,
    a. how would its maximum height compare to that on Earth?
    b. how would its flight time compare?

**2.4** Critical Thinking: When a ball is thrown vertically upward, it continues up until it reaches a certain point, then it falls down again. At the highest point, its velocity is instantaneously zero. It is not moving up or down. **a.** Is it accelerating? **b.** Give reasons. **c.** Devise an experiment to find out.

# CHAPTER 4 REVIEW

## SUMMARY

### 4.1 What Is Acceleration?

· Acceleration is the ratio of the change in velocity to the time interval over which it occurs.
· Constant acceleration is called uniform acceleration.
· The slope of the line on a velocity-time graph is the acceleration of the object.
· A velocity-time graph for a uniformly accelerated object is a straight line.

### 4.2 Displacement During Constant Acceleration

· Three equations relate the displacement of a uniformly accelerated object to velocity, time, and acceleration.
· A position-time graph for a uniformly accelerated object is half a parabola. Position varies with the square of the time.
· The acceleration of gravity is $-9.80$ m/s$^2$ near Earth.
· Problems of uniformly accelerated motion can be solved using one or more of the formulas in Table 4–2.

# KEY TERMS

average acceleration
instantaneous
  acceleration
constant or uniform
  acceleration

initial velocity
final velocity
acceleration due
  to gravity

# REVIEWING CONCEPTS

1. A car is travelling on a highway.
   a. Can the car have a negative velocity and a positive acceleration at the same time?
   b. Can the car change the direction of its velocity when travelling with a constant acceleration?
2. Can the velocity of an object change when its acceleration is constant? If you answer yes, give an example. If you answer no, explain why not.
3. What does the slope of the tangent to a velocity-time graph measure?
4. If a velocity-time curve is a straight line parallel to the $t$-axis, what can be deduced about the acceleration?
5. If you are given a table of velocities of an object at various times, how could you find out if the acceleration of the object is constant?
6. If initial and final velocities and acceleration are given, and the distance is unknown, what equation would you use?
7. Write a summary of the equations for displacement, velocity, and time of a body experiencing uniformly accelerated motion.
8. Explain why an aluminum ball and a steel ball of similar size and shape, dropped from the same height, reach the ground at the same time.
9. Give some examples of falling objects for which air resistance cannot be ignored.
10. Give some examples of falling objects for which air resistance can be ignored.

# APPLYING CONCEPTS

1. Figure 4–4 shows the velocity-time graph for an accelerating car. The three "notches" in the curve occur where the driver shifts gears.
   a. Describe the changes in velocity and acceleration of the car while it is in first gear.
   b. Is the acceleration just before a gear change larger or smaller than the acceleration just after the gear change? Explain your answer.
2. Study Figure 4–4. During what time interval is the acceleration largest? smallest?
3. Solve the equation $\vec{v}_f = \vec{v}_i + \vec{a}t$ for acceleration. What is the equation you get?
4. Look at Figure 4–17, which is a position-time graph of uniform acceleration.
   a. What type of curve does this graph represent?
   b. What does the slope of a tangent line taken at any point represent?
   c. How would slopes taken at higher points on the line differ from those taken at lower points?

**FIGURE 4–17. Use with Applying Concepts 4.**

5. An object shot straight up rises for 7.0 s before it reaches its maximum height. A second object falling from rest takes 7.0 s to reach the ground. Compare the displacements traveled by the objects during the 7.0-s period.
6. Describe the changes in the velocity of a ball thrown straight up into the air. Then describe the changes in its acceleration.
7. The value of $\vec{g}$ on the moon is one-sixth of its value on Earth.
   a. Will a ball dropped from the same height by an astronaut hit the ground with a smaller or larger speed than on Earth?
   b. Will the ball take more or less time to fall?
8. A ball is thrown vertically upward with the same initial velocity on Earth and on planet Alpha, which has three times the gravitational acceleration as Earth.
   a. How does the maximum height reached by the ball on Alpha compare with the maximum height on Earth?
   b. If the ball on Alpha were thrown with three times greater initial velocity, how would that change your answer to **a**?

9. Rock A is dropped from a cliff; rock B is thrown downward.
   a. When they reach the bottom, which rock has a greater velocity?
   b. Which has a greater acceleration?
   c. Which arrives first?

# PROBLEMS

## 4.1 What Is Acceleration?

1. Find the uniform acceleration that causes a car's velocity to change from 32 m/s to 96 m/s in an 8.0-s period.
2. Rocket-powered sleds are used to test the responses of humans to acceleration. Starting from rest, one sled can reach a speed of 444 m/s in 1.80 s and can be brought to a stop again in 2.15 s.
   a. Calculate the acceleration of the sled when starting and compare it to the acceleration due to gravity, 9.80 m/s².
   b. Find the acceleration of the sled when braking and compare it to the magnitude of the acceleration due to gravity.
3. Use Figure 4–18 to find the acceleration of the moving object
   a. during the first 5 s of travel.
   b. between the fifth and the tenth second of travel.
   c. between the tenth and the fifteenth second of travel.
   d. between the twentieth and twenty-fifth second of travel.

FIGURE 4–18. Use with Problem 3.

4. To accompany each of the graphs in Figure 4–19, draw
   a. a velocity-time graph.
   b. an acceleration-time graph.

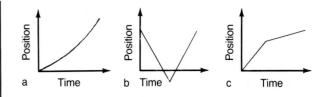

FIGURE 4–19. Use with Problem 4.

5. A car with a velocity of 22 m/s is accelerated uniformly at the rate of 1.6 m/s² for 6.8 s. What is its final velocity?
6. The velocity of an automobile changes over an 8.0-s time period as shown in Table 4–3.
   a. Plot the velocity-time graph of the motion.
   b. Determine the displacement of the car during the first 2.0 s.
   c. What displacement does the car have during the first 4.0 s?
   d. What displacement does the car have during the entire 8.0 s?
   e. Find the slope of the line between $t = 0$ s and $t = 4.0$ s. What does this slope represent?
   f. Find the slope of the line between $t = 5.0$ s and $t = 7.0$ s. What does this slope indicate?

Table 4–3

| Time (s) | Velocity (m/s) | Time (s) | Velocity (m/s) |
|---|---|---|---|
| 0.0 | 0.0 | 5.0 | 20.0 |
| 1.0 | 4.0 | 6.0 | 20.0 |
| 2.0 | 8.0 | 7.0 | 20.0 |
| 3.0 | 12.0 | 8.0 | 20.0 |
| 4.0 | 16.0 | | |

▶ 7. Figure 4–20 shows the position-time and velocity-time graphs of a karate expert using a fist to break wooden boards.
   a. Use the velocity-time graph to describe the motion of the expert's fist during the first 10 ms.
   b. Estimate the slope of the velocity-time graph to determine the acceleration of the fist when it suddenly stops.
   c. Express the acceleration as a multiple of the gravitational acceleration, $\vec{g} = 9.80$ m/s².
   d. Determine the area under the velocity-time curve to find the displacement of the fist in the first 6 ms. Compare with the position-time graph.

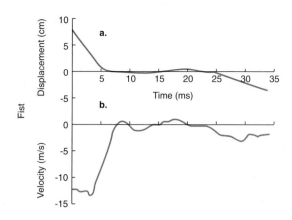

FIGURE 4–20. Use with Problem 7.

8. A supersonic jet flying at 145 m/s is accelerated uniformly at the rate of 23.1 m/s² for 20.0 s.
   a. What is its final velocity?
   b. The speed of sound in air is 331 m/s. How many times the speed of sound is the plane's final speed?
9. Determine the final velocity of a proton that has an initial velocity of $2.35 \times 10^5$ m/s, and then is accelerated uniformly in an electric field at the rate of $-1.10 \times 10^{12}$ m/s² for $1.50 \times 10^{-7}$ s.

## 4.2 Displacement During Constant Acceleration

10. Determine the displacement of a plane that is uniformly accelerated from 66 m/s to 88 m/s in 12 s.
11. How far does a plane fly in 15 s while its velocity is changing from 145 m/s to 75 m/s at a uniform rate of acceleration?
12. A car moves at 12 m/s and coasts up a hill with a uniform acceleration of $-1.6$ m/s².
    a. How far has it travelled after 6.0 s?
    b. How far has it gone after 9.0 s?
13. Four cars start from rest. Car A accelerates at 6.0 m/s²; car B at 5.4 m/s²; car C at 8.0 m/s², and car D at 12 m/s².
    a. In the first column of a table, show the velocity of each car at the end of 2.0 s.
    b. In the second column, show the displacement of each car during the same 2.0 s.
    c. What conclusion do you reach about the velocity attained and the displacement of a body starting from rest at the end of the first 2.0 s of acceleration?

14. An astronaut drops a feather from 1.2 m above the surface of the moon. If the acceleration of gravity on the moon is 1.62 m/s² down, how long does it take the feather to hit the surface?
▶ 15. Table 4–4 is a table of the displacements and velocities of a ball at the end of each second for the first 5.0 s of free-fall from rest.
    a. Use the data in the table to plot a velocity-time graph.
    b. Use the data in the table to plot a position-time graph.
    c. Find the slope of the curve at the end of 2.0 and 4.0 s on the position-time graph. What are the approximate slopes? Do the values agree with the table of velocity?
    d. Use the data in the table to plot a position versus time-squared graph. What type of curve is obtained?
    e. Find the slope of the line at any point. Explain the significance of the value.
    f. Does this curve agree with the equation $\vec{d} = \frac{1}{2}\vec{g}t^2$?

Table 4–4

| Time (s) | Displacement (m) | Velocity (m/s) |
|---|---|---|
| 0.0 | 0.0 | 0.0 |
| 1.0 | −4.9 | −9.8 |
| 2.0 | −19.6 | −19.6 |
| 3.0 | −44.1 | −29.4 |
| 4.0 | −78.4 | −39.2 |
| 5.0 | −122.5 | −49.0 |

16. A plane travels $5.0 \times 10^2$ m while being accelerated uniformly from rest at the rate of 5.0 m/s². What final velocity does it attain?
17. A race car can be slowed with a constant acceleration of $-11$ m/s².
    a. If the car is going 55 m/s, how many meters will it take to stop?
    b. Repeat for a car going 110 m/s.
18. An engineer must design a runway to accommodate airplanes that must reach a ground velocity of 61 m/s before they can take off. These planes are capable of being accelerated uniformly at the rate of 2.5 m/s².
    a. How long will it take the planes to reach takeoff speed?
    b. What must be the minimum length of the runway?

19. A rocket travelling at 155 m/s is accelerated at a rate of $-31.0$ m/s$^2$.
   a. How long will it take before the instantaneous speed is 0 m/s?
   b. How far will it travel during this time?
   c. What will be its velocity after 8.00 s?
20. Engineers are developing new types of guns that might someday be used to launch satellites as if they were bullets. One such gun can give a small object a velocity of 3.5 km/s moving it through only 2.0 cm.
   a. What acceleration does the gun give this object?
   b. Over what time interval does the acceleration take place?
21. An express train, travelling at 36.0 m/s, is accidentally sidetracked onto a local train track. The express engineer spots a local train exactly $1.00 \times 10^2$ m ahead on the same track and travelling in the same direction. The engineer jams on the brakes and slows the express at a constant rate of $-3.00$ m/s$^2$. The local engineer is unaware of the situation. If the speed of the local is 11.0 m/s, will the express be able to stop in time or will there be a collision? To solve this problem, take the position of the express when it first sights the local as a point of origin. Next, keeping in mind that the local has exactly a $1.00 \times 10^2$ m lead, calculate how far each train is from the origin at the end of the 12.0 s it would take the express to stop.
   a. On the basis of your calculations, would you conclude that there is or is not a collision?
   b. The calculations you made in part a do not allow for the possibility that a collision might take place before the end of the 12 s required for the express to come to a halt. To check on this, take the position of the express when it first sights the local as the point of origin and calculate the position of each train at the end of each second after sighting. Make a table showing the distance of each train from the origin at the end of each second. Plot these positions on the same graph and draw two lines.
   c. Use your graph to check your answer to part a.
22. Highway safety engineers build soft barriers so that cars hitting them will slow down at a safe rate. A person wearing a safety belt can withstand an acceleration of $-300$ m/s$^2$. How thick should barriers be to safely stop a car that hits a barrier at 110 km/h?
23. A baseball pitcher throws a fastball at a speed of 44 m/s. The acceleration occurs as the pitcher holds the ball in his hand and moves it through an almost straight-line distance of 3.5 m. Calculate the acceleration, assuming it is uniform. Compare this acceleration to the acceleration due to gravity, 9.80 m/s$^2$.
24. If a bullet leaves the muzzle of a rifle with a speed of 600 m/s, and the barrel of the rifle is 0.9 m long, what is the acceleration of the bullet while in the barrel?
▶ 25. A driver of a car going 90.0 km/h suddenly sees the lights of a barrier 40.0 m ahead. It takes the driver 0.75 s before she applies the brakes, and the average acceleration during braking is $-10.0$ m/s$^2$.
   a. Determine if the car hits the barrier.
   b. What is the maximum speed at which the car could be moving and not hit the barrier 40.0 m ahead? Assume the acceleration rate doesn't change.
▶ 26. Data in Table 4–5, taken from a driver's handbook, show the distance a car travels when it brakes to a halt from a specific initial velocity.

Table 4–5

| Initial velocity (m/s) | Braking distance (m) |
|---|---|
| 11 | 10 |
| 15 | 20 |
| 20 | 34 |
| 25 | 50 |
| 29 | 70 |

   a. Plot the braking distance versus the initial velocity. Describe the shape of the curve you obtain.
   b. Plot the braking distance versus the square of the initial velocity. Describe the shape of the curve you obtain.
   c. Calculate the slope of your graph from part b. Find the value and units of the quantity 1/slope of the curve.
   d. Does this curve agree with the equation $\vec{v_i}^2 = -2\vec{a}\vec{d}$? What is the value of $\vec{a}$?

27. A car moving with a constant acceleration covers the distance between two points 60 m apart in 6.0 s. Its velocity as it passes the second point is 15 m/s.
   a. What was the speed at the first point?
   b. What is the constant acceleration?
   c. How far behind the first point was the car at rest?

▶ 28. As a traffic light turns green, a waiting car starts with a constant acceleration of 6.0 m/s$^2$. At the instant the car begins to accelerate, a truck with a constant velocity of 21 m/s passes in the next lane. **Hint:** Set the two distance equations equal to each other.
   a. How far will the car travel before it overtakes the truck?
   b. How fast will the car be travelling when it overtakes the truck?

29. Use the information from the previous problem.
   a. Draw velocity-time and position-time graphs for the car and truck.
   b. Do the graphs confirm the answer you calculated for the exercise?

30. A stone falls freely from rest for 8.0 s.
   a. Calculate the stone's velocity after 8.0 s.
   b. What is the stone's displacement during this time?

31. A student drops a rock from a bridge to the water 12.0 m below. With what speed does the rock strike the water?

**FIGURE 4–21.**

32. Kyle is flying a helicopter when he drops a bag. When the bag has fallen 2.0 s,
   a. what is the bag's velocity?
   b. how far has the bag fallen?

▶ 33. Kyle is flying the same helicopter and it is rising at 5.0 m/s when he releases the bag. After 2.0 s,
   a. what is the bag's velocity?
   b. how far has the bag fallen?
   c. how far below the helicopter is the bag?

▶ 34. Kyle's helicopter now descends at 5.0 m/s as he releases the bag. After 2.0 s,
   a. what is the bag's velocity?
   b. how far has the bag fallen?
   c. how far below the helicopter is the bag?
   d. what is common to the answers to Problems 32, 33 and 34?

35. A weather balloon is floating at a constant height above Earth when it releases a pack of instruments.
   a. If the pack hits the ground with a velocity of −73.5 m/s, how far does the pack fall?
   b. How long does the pack fall?

36. During a baseball game, a batter hits a high pop-up. If the ball remains in the air for 6.0 s, how high does it rise? **Hint:** Calculate the height using the second half of the trajectory.

37. A tennis ball is dropped from 1.20 m above the ground. It rebounds to a height of 1.00 m.
   a. With what velocity does it hit the ground?
   b. With what velocity does it leave the ground?
   c. If the tennis ball were in contact with the ground for 0.010 s, find its acceleration while touching the ground. Compare to $g$.

## THINKING PHYSIC-LY

Which has the greater acceleration: a car that increases its speed from 50 to 60 km/h, or a bike that goes from 0 to 10 km/h in the same time? Explain.

# CHAPTER
# 5 Forces

◀ Going Down

A team of sky divers can form beautiful patterns as they plummet toward Earth at high speeds. How do the sky divers control their velocities?

Chapters 3 and 4 were limited to a discussion of the study of *how* objects move, **kinematics.** Galileo devised many ingenious experiments that allowed him to effectively describe motions but not to explain them. Chapter 5 introduces the subject of **dynamics.** The study of *why* objects move as they do. Dynamics can answer such questions as, "Why do the sky divers in the photograph accelerate rather than fall at a constant rate?"

The causes of acceleration were first studied by Sir Isaac Newton (1642–1727). The connection between acceleration and its cause can be summarized by three statements known, after the man who formulated them, as Newton's laws of motion.

## √ Concept Check

The following terms or concepts from earlier chapters are important for a good understanding of this chapter. If you are not familiar with them, you should review them before studying this chapter.
· dimensional analysis, Chapter 2
· velocity, Chapter 3
· acceleration, Chapter 4

· name the four basic forces, their relative strengths, and some familiar examples.
· state Newton's three laws of motion and display an understanding of their applications.
· be able to use Newton's second law in solving problems.
· understand the difference between net forces that cause acceleration and action-reaction pairs.

Forces are vector quantities.

# 5.1 NEWTON'S LAWS OF MOTION

Isaac Newton started work on his laws of motion in 1665, but did not publish them until 1687. More than three hundred years later, his three laws still summarize the relationship between acceleration, and its cause, force.

## Forces

What is a force? **Force** can be defined as a push or a pull. When you hang your jacket on a coat-hook, the hook pulls upward on your jacket. If you place a coin on your palm, the coin pushes downward on your hand. These forces occur when one object touches another. On the other hand, if you drop the coin, it will fall to the ground, pulled by a force called gravity. Gravity is a force that acts between objects even when they are not touching. Sometimes forces, like that of gravity on a coin, cause accelerations; other times forces stretch, bend, or squeeze an object. All forces are vectors—they not only have magnitude but they also have direction. In fact, we define "down" as the direction gravity pulls.

Although you can think of hundreds of different forces, physicists group them all into just four kinds. The force that Newton first described, the **gravitational force,** is an attractive force that exists between all objects. The gravitational force of Earth on the moon holds the moon in its orbit. The gravitational force of the moon on Earth causes tides. Despite its effects on our daily lives, the gravitational force is the weakest of the four forces.

The forces that give materials their strength, their ability to bend, squeeze, stretch, or shatter, are examples of the **electromagnetic force.** These forces result from a basic property of particles called electric charge. Charged particles at rest or in motion exert electric forces on each other. When charged particles are in motion they produce magnetic forces on each other. Electric and magnetic forces are both considered to be aspects of a single force, the electromagnetic force. It is very large compared to the gravitational force.

The two remaining forces are less familiar because they are evident mainly over distances the size of the nucleus of an atom. The third force is the **strong nuclear force** that holds the particles in the nucleus together. It is the strongest of the four forces—hundreds of times stronger than the electromagnetic force. But it only acts over distances the size of the nucleus.

The fourth force is called the **weak nuclear force**. It is actually a form of electromagnetic force, and is involved in the radioactive decay of some nuclei. Electricity and magnetism were unified into a single force in the 1870s. Recently the electromagnetic force has been linked with the weak force. This suggests to physicists that all forces are different aspects of a single force. They have constructed theories called Grand Unification Theories (GUTs) and Supersymmetric theories that try to demonstrate this unification. At this time, however, the theories are incomplete and do not fully agree with experiments.

**FIGURE 5–1. We take the interaction of forces for granted in everyday life. Electromagnetic forces between the bubble gum particles make this impressive bubble possible.**

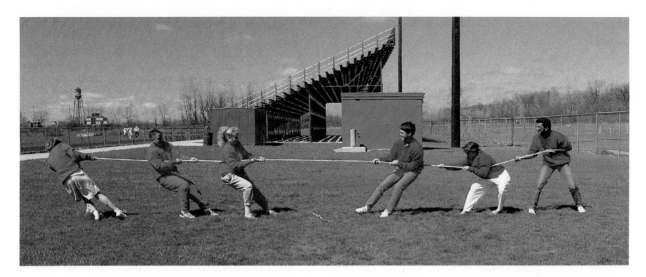

## Newton's First Law of Motion

Suppose you place a wooden block on a carpeted floor and give it a forward push. The carpeted floor pushes backwards on the block, and the block will stop moving almost as soon as you remove your hand. If you use a smooth wooden floor instead of the carpet, the smooth surface pushes back less, and the block will slide farther. If you have an extremely smooth block and a very slippery floor, almost no backward force is exerted on the block, and it may slide at almost constant speed for a long distance without any additional pushes from you. Galileo speculated that if a perfectly smooth object were on a perfectly smooth horizontal surface it might travel forever in a straight line.

It was left to Newton, however, to develop Galileo's idea more fully. Imagine an object with no force on it. If it is moving at constant speed in a straight line, it will continue to do so. If it is at rest, it will remain at rest, because rest is a special name for zero velocity. This behaviour of objects is described in **Newton's first law**. The law states that *an object with no force acting on it moves with constant velocity.*

Objects often have more than one force acting on them. Think of the rope used in a tug-of-war. The members of one team pull the rope one way, the people on the other team pull it in the opposite direction. If the two teams pull with equal strength, the rope will experience no net force, even though there are obviously forces acting on it. If one team pulls harder than the other, though, the rope will begin to accelerate.

To understand the effects of forces in two directions, we assign signs: positive for forces to the right, negative for forces to the left. All the forces pulling to the right combine to produce one large positive force. In the same way, forces to the left combine into a large negative force. If the team pulling to the right is stronger, the net force is positive. If the other team is stronger, the net force is negative. Thus, our method of finding the net force on an object is to sum all the forces, keeping track of signs. If the rope starts at rest, it does not begin to move if the net force is zero. It has a constant—zero—velocity. Thus, we state Newton's first law more carefully: *an object with no net force acting on it remains at rest or moves with constant velocity in a straight line.*

**FIGURE 5–2. If the red team exerts a greater force on the rope than the blue team, the rope will accelerate toward the red team.**

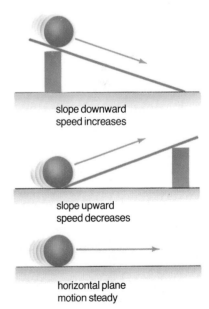

slope downward
speed increases

slope upward
speed decreases

horizontal plane
motion steady

**FIGURE 5–3. From observing the motion of objects on inclined planes, Galileo believed that if there were no friction, objects would continue in constant horizontal motion.**

# Newton's Second Law of Motion

Newton's first law states that if there is no net force on an object, there is no acceleration. In other words, the object moves at constant velocity. But how much will an object accelerate when there is a net force? Think about pushing a bowling ball. The harder you push, the faster the velocity of the ball will change. The larger the force, the larger the acceleration, the rate of change in velocity. Acceleration is found to be directly proportional to force.

Acceleration also depends on the mass of an object. Masses of bowling balls vary; some are small, others large. If you exert the same force on a less massive ball, its acceleration will be larger. In fact, if the mass is half as much, the acceleration will be twice as large. The acceleration is inversely proportional to the mass. These relationships are true in general and are stated in **Newton's second law:** *the acceleration of a body is directly proportional to the net force on it and inversely proportional to its mass.* Newton's second law may be summarized as

$$\vec{a} = \frac{\vec{F}}{m}, \text{ or, more commonly, } \vec{F} = m\vec{a}.$$

If an object has a net force exerted on it, it will accelerate. Force and acceleration both have direction as well as size. The acceleration is in the same direction as the force causing it. If the force is in the positive direction, so will be the acceleration. Similarly, if the force is in the negative direction, so will be the acceleration.

According to Newton's second law, a net force on an object causes it to accelerate. In addition, the larger the mass of the object, the smaller the acceleration. For this reason, we say that a massive body has more inertia than a less massive body.

Figure 5–4 pictures a simple experiment that demonstrates Newton's second law. Lay an index card over a drinking glass. Place a penny on the card, centred over the glass. With the flick of a finger, give the card a quick horizontal push. The card moves away, but the penny drops into the glass. Why doesn't the penny accelerate with the card? The penny has more mass (we say it has more inertia), and a horizontal force is needed to accelerate it. The card is too smooth to exert much horizontal force on the penny. With very little horizontal force on it, the penny has little sideways acceleration. As soon as the card is no longer under it, however, the upward force of the card is removed. There is mostly a net downward force, the force of gravity, so the penny accelerates downward, falling into the glass.

**FIGURE 5–4. A quick snap of a finger can knock the card from under a coin, allowing the coin to drop into the glass.**

a

b

c

## The Unit of Force

Newton's second law gives us a way to define the unit of force. A force that causes a mass of one kilogram to accelerate at a rate of one meter per second squared is defined as one newton (N). That is

$$\vec{F} = m\vec{a} = (1.00 \text{ kg})(1.00 \text{ m/s}^2) = 1.00 \text{ N}.$$

## Example Problem

### Using Newton's Second Law to Find the Net Force on an Accelerating Object

What net force is required to accelerate a 1500-kg race car at $+3.00 \text{ m/s}^2$?

**Given:** $m = 1500 \text{ kg}$      **Unknown:** force, $\vec{F}$
$\vec{a} = +3.00 \text{ m/s}^2$      **Basic equation:** $\vec{F} = m\vec{a}$

**Solution:**
Choose the positive direction to be in the direction of the acceleration.
Now, $\vec{F} = m\vec{a} = (1500 \text{ kg})(+3.00 \text{ m/s}^2)$
$\quad\quad = +4.5 \times 10^3 \text{ N}$, in the positive direction.

That is, a 4500-N force will accelerate a 1500-kg race car at a rate of $3.00 \text{ m/s}^2$. The force and acceleration are in the same direction.

**FIGURE 5–5.** By reducing the mass of a race car, car builders get maximum acceleration from the available force.

## Example Problem

### Finding Force When Acceleration Must Be Calculated

An artillery shell has a mass of 55 kg. The shell is fired from a gun, leaving the barrel with a velocity of $+770 \text{ m/s}$. The gun barrel is 1.5 m long. Assume that the force, and thus the acceleration, of the shell is constant while the shell is in the gun barrel. What is the force on the shell while it is in the gun barrel?

**Given:** $m = 55 \text{ kg}$      **Unknown:** force, $\vec{F}$
$\vec{v}_f = +770 \text{ m/s}$      **Basic equation:** $\vec{F} = m\vec{a}$
$\vec{v}_i = 0 \text{ m/s}$
$\vec{d} = +1.5 \text{ m}$

**Solution:**
You cannot use $\vec{F} = m\vec{a}$ directly because you don't know $\vec{a}$. You are given the final velocity and distance, and you know the initial velocity is zero. Since we assume that the acceleration is constant, we can find $\vec{a}$ using $\vec{v}_f^2 = \vec{v}_i^2 + 2\vec{a}\vec{d}$. The positive direction is along the gun barrel, in the direction of the velocity of the shell.

$$\vec{v}_f^2 = \vec{v}_i^2 + 2\vec{a}\vec{d}, \text{ or } \vec{a} = \frac{\vec{v}_f^2 - \vec{v}_i^2}{2\vec{d}} = \frac{(+770 \text{ m/s})^2 - 0}{2(+1.5 \text{ m})}$$

$$\vec{a} = +2.0 \times 10^5 \text{ m/s}^2 \text{ (in the direction of the velocity)}$$

$$\vec{F} = m\vec{a}$$

$$\vec{F} = 55 \text{ kg} (2.0 \times 10^5 \text{ m/s}^2)$$

$$= 1.1 \times 10^7 \text{ N}$$

That is, a forward force of $1.1 \times 10^7 \text{ N}$ acting on a shell will increase its speed from 0 to 770 m/s over a distance of 1.5 m.

Newton's second law defines the newton.

# F.Y.I.

When Newton was asked how he made so many important discoveries, he replied, "Nocte die-que incubando." ("By thinking about it night and day.")

# Practice Problems

1. When a shot-putter exerts a net force of 140 N on a shot, the shot has an acceleration of 19 m/s$^2$. What is the mass of the shot?
2. Together a motorbike and rider have a mass of 275 kg. The motorbike is slowed down with an acceleration of $-4.50$ m/s$^2$. What is the net force on the motorbike? Describe the direction of this force and the meaning of the negative sign.
3. A car, mass 1225 kg, travelling at 105 km/h, slows to a stop in 53 m. What is the size and direction of the force that acted on the car? What provided the force?
▶ 4. Imagine a spider with mass $7.0 \times 10^{-5}$ kg moving downward on its thread. The thread exerts a force that results in a net upward force on the spider of $1.2 \times 10^{-4}$ N.
   a. What is the acceleration of the spider?
   b. Explain the sign of the velocity and describe in words how the thread changes the velocity of the spider.

## Newton's Third Law of Motion

Forces always occur in pairs.

If you try to accelerate a bowling ball by kicking it, you may become painfully aware of Newton's third law. As you kick the ball, your toes will feel the equal force the ball is exerting on you. If you exert a force on a baseball to stop it, the ball also exerts a force on you. These are examples of the forces described in **Newton's third law:** *When one object exerts a force on a second object, the second exerts a force on the first that is equal in magnitude but opposite in direction.*

According to Newton's third law, if you exert a small force on the ball, it exerts a small force on you. The larger the force you exert on the ball, the stronger its force is on you. The magnitudes are always equal. These two forces are often called **action-reaction forces.**

FIGURE 5–6. Each pair of action-reaction forces is equal (a). However, there is a net upward force on the bowling ball, causing it to accelerate upward (b).

Let's analyze the forces involved when you pick up a bowling ball, as in Figure 5–6. When your hand exerts a force on the ball, the ball exerts a force on your hand that is the same size, but in the opposite direction. These two forces are action-reaction forces. In addition, Earth exerts a downward gravitational force on the ball, and the ball exerts an upward force of the same magnitude on Earth. As you examine the diagram, note the two equal but opposite forces acting on *two different* objects, your hand and the ball, the ball and Earth.

Why does the ball accelerate upward? After all, the force your hand exerts on the ball is the same magnitude as the force the ball exerts on your hand. Where is the net upward force that causes the acceleration? To answer that question, we need to isolate the bowling ball and examine only the forces that act on it. There are two forces acting on the ball, the force of your hand directed upward and the force of gravity pulling downward. When you lift the ball, the force exerted by your hand is greater than the force of gravity, so the ball accelerates upward. *Only the forces on the ball determine its acceleration.*

## CONCEPT REVIEW

**1.1** Suppose you exert a force on a black block and measure its acceleration. You then exert the same force on a brown block. Its acceleration is three times that of the black block. What can you conclude about the masses of the blocks?

**1.2** Describe the newton in words, without using the terms *equal, mass, accelerate,* or *acceleration.*

**1.3** Can you feel the inertia of a pencil? of this textbook? How?

**1.4** **Critical Thinking:** If you push forward on the back of an automobile, does that mean that its velocity has to be in the forward direction? Explain and give an example.

# 5.2 USING NEWTON'S LAW

A track can only exert force on a car through the tires. This force will be transmitted only if there is enough friction between track and tires. If you have ever tried to accelerate a car on icy or wet roads, you know that the existence of friction is not guaranteed. Among the applications of Newton's laws we will explore in this section is friction.

## Objectives

· **distinguish between weight and mass and use the second law to relate them.**

· **demonstrate an understanding of the nature of frictional forces and be able to use the coefficient of friction in solving problems.**

· **demonstrate an understanding of the meaning of net force and be able to calculate the acceleration that results.**

· **understand the definition of free-fall and the causes of air resistance and terminal velocity.**

**FIGURE 5–7. Drag racers "smoke" or "boil" their tires before a race to increase the friction between the tires and the track.**

**FIGURE 5–8. The weight of a medium-sized apple is about one newton.**

The weight of an object is proportional to its mass.

Weight is the gravitational force of an object.

## Mass and Weight

Walking home from school, you see a box on the ground and give it a good kick. If the box goes sailing, you know it has a small mass. If the box hardly accelerates at all, it must have a large mass. Suppose you pick up the box and then let it drop. It will accelerate downward. Thus, Earth must be exerting a downward force on it. The gravitational force exerted by a large body, usually Earth, is called **weight.** Weight is measured in newtons like all other forces. A medium-sized apple weighs about one newton.

The weight of an object can be found using Newton's second law of motion. On the surface of Earth, objects that have only the force of gravity acting on them fall downward with an acceleration of $9.80$ m/s². This acceleration is so important that we give it a special symbol and write $g = 9.80$ m/s² in the downward direction.

The force of gravity on an object is present whether the object is falling, resting on the ground, or being lifted. Earth still pulls downward on it. The force of gravity is given by the equation $\vec{F} = m\vec{g}$. This force is called the weight of an object and is given the symbol $\vec{W}$. Therefore, we write

$$\vec{W} = m\vec{g}.$$

On the surface of Earth, the weight of an object with a 1.00-kg mass is 9.80 N. The weight of any object is proportional to its mass. Weight is a vector quantity pointed toward the centre of Earth. If we assign "up" to be the positive direction, then weight would be negative. More often we will use the word "down" instead of a minus sign (−) when direction is needed.

## Example Problem

### Calculating Weight

Find the weight of a 2.26-kg bag of sugar.
$$\vec{W} = m\vec{g} = (2.26\,\text{kg})(9.80\,\text{m/s}^2)$$
$$= 22.1\,\text{kg·m/s}^2$$
$$= 22.1\,\text{N}.$$
The direction of the weight is down.

## Practice Problems

*In these problems use g = 9.80 m/s².*
5. What is the weight of each of the following objects?
   **a.** 0.113-kg hockey puck   **c.** 870-kg automobile
   **b.** 108-kg football player
6. Find the mass of each of these weights.
   **a.** 98 N     **b.** 80 N   **c.** 0.98 N
7. A 20-N stone rests on a table. What is the force the table exerts on the stone? in what direction?

**8.** An astronaut with mass 75 kg travels to Mars. What is his weight
  **a.** on Earth?
  **b.** What is his weight on Mars where $\vec{g} = 3.8$ m/s²?
  **c.** What is the value of a $\vec{g}$ on top of a mountain if the astronaut weighs 683 N?

You do not really "feel" your weight. What you do feel are the forces exerted on you by objects that touch you. When standing, you don't feel the force you exert on the floor, you feel the force the floor exerts on you. The larger your weight, the larger the force of the floor on you. When sitting, you feel the force of the chair. If you do a pull-up, you feel the force of the bar on your hands. When you are at rest, or moving at constant velocity, these forces are equal in magnitude to your weight, but in the opposite direction.

Mass and weight are not the same. Weight depends on the acceleration due to gravity, and thus may vary from location to location. A person weighs a very small amount less on top of a high mountain, even though he or she has the same mass. A bowling ball with a mass of 7.3 kg weighs 71 N on Earth, but only 12 N on the moon, where the acceleration due to gravity is 1.6 m/s². If you tried to kick a bowling ball across the surface of the moon, however, it would be just as hard to accelerate as on Earth because its mass would be the same.

## Two Kinds of Mass

We discussed one way of determining mass by measuring the amount of force necessary to accelerate it, that is, its inertia. The **inertial mass** of an object is the ratio of the net force exerted on the object and its acceleration,

$$m = \frac{\vec{F}}{\vec{a}}.$$

A second method of finding mass is to compare the gravitational forces exerted on two objects, one with an unknown mass, the other with a known mass. The object with the unknown mass is placed on one pan of a beam balance. The object with the known mass is placed

**FIGURE 5–9. A beam balance allows you to compare an unknown mass to a known mass. Using an inertial balance, you can calculate the mass from the back and forth motion of the mass.**

**FIGURE 5–10.** This photograph of a graphite crystal, magnified by a scanning tunneling microscope, reveals the surface irregularities of the crystal at the atomic level.

**FIGURE 5–11.** A greater and greater horizontal force, $\vec{F}_a$ is applied to a box (a-d). An equal force of static friction acts in the opposite direction to keep the box from moving. When $\vec{F}_a$ exceeds the force of static friction, the box accelerates (e). The box will move at a constant velocity if $\vec{F}_a$ is then reduced until it equals the force of sliding friction. (f).

on the pan at the other end of the beam. When the pans balance, the force of gravity is the same on each pan. Then the masses of the objects on either side of the balance must be the same. The mass measured this way is called the gravitational mass.

Suppose you apply the same force to two different objects and find that the acceleration of one object is twice that of the other. You would conclude that the mass of the first object is half that of the second. If you put the same objects on a pan balance, you would find the gravitational force on the first object is half the gravitational force on the second. Very precise experiments indicate that inertial mass and gravitational mass of objects are equal within the accuracy of the experiments. In 1916 Albert Einstein (1879–1955) used the equality of inertial and gravitational masses as one foundation for his general theory of relativity.

## Friction

Slide your hand across a tabletop. The force you feel opposing the movement of your hand is called friction. It acts when brakes slow a bike or car, when a sailboat moves through water, and when a sky diver falls through the air. If there was no friction, whenever you tried to walk, you would slip as if you were on ice. Without friction, tires would spin and cars would not move. An eraser could not grip your homework paper and remove a mistake.

**Friction** is the force that opposes the motion between two surfaces that are in contact. The direction of the force is parallel to the surface and in a direction that opposes the slipping of the two surfaces. To understand the cause of friction, you must recognize that on a microscopic scale, all surfaces are rough. When two surfaces rub, the high points of one surface temporarily bond to the high points of the other. The electromagnetic force causes this bonding.

If you try to push a heavy box along the floor, you will find it very hard to start it from rest, Figure 5–11. If two objects are not in relative motion, **static friction** is the force that opposes the start of motion. Static friction forces have maximum values. When the magnitude of your push on the box is greater than the maximum value of the static

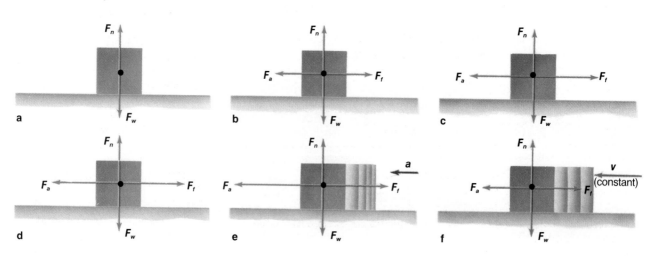

friction between the floor and the box, the box starts moving. When the box starts to move, the force of friction decreases. The force between surfaces in relative motion is called **sliding friction.** The force of sliding friction is less than that of static friction. Thus, a car will stop faster if the wheels are not skidding.

How large is the force of sliding friction? Slide your book across the desk. It slows down. To keep it moving at constant velocity, you must exert a constant force that is just the same size as the frictional force, but in the opposite direction. See Figure 5–12. By measuring the force you exert, called the applied force, $\vec{F}_A$, you can find the force of friction, $\vec{F}_f$.

Experimentally it has been found that the force of friction depends primarily on the force pushing the surfaces together, $\vec{F}_N$, and on the nature of the surfaces in contact. This result can be expressed as

$$\vec{F}_f = \mu \vec{F}_N.$$

In this equation $\mu$ (mu), called the **coefficient of friction,** is a constant that depends on the two surfaces in contact. $\vec{F}_N$ is the force pushing the surfaces together. It is called the normal force, where "normal" means perpendicular. In the example above, the normal force on the book is the force exerted by the table, perpendicular to its surface. When the book is resting on a horizontal surface, the normal force of the table on the book is numerically equal to the weight of the book ($\vec{W}$). The normal force of the table on the book is also equal to the force of the book on the table, since they are action-reaction forces. If you use your hands to exert an extra force, $\vec{F}$, down on the book, the force of the book on the table increases to $\vec{W} + \vec{F}$. By Newton's third law, the normal force of the table upward on the book also increases to $\vec{W} + \vec{F}$.

Notice that when we are studying the friction between two objects, such as a book lying on a horizontal table, there are two sets of forces. The first set is parallel to the surfaces that are touching. This set consists of the force that moves the object and the opposing frictional force. The second set of forces acts perpendicular to the two surfaces. The downward force may be just the object's weight, the downward force of gravity. Often, though, other forces are exerted on the object. A person might push the object down, or perhaps lift up on it. A second object might be placed on top of the first. The sum of all vertical forces is the total downward force. The other force in this set is the equal but upward force exerted on the object by the table. That force is the normal force on the object. In many cases, the coefficient of sliding friction for two surfaces in contact is very nearly independent of the amount of surface area in contact and the velocity of motion. Problems solved in this book will make this assumption.

# PROBLEM SOLVING STRATEGY

When solving problems involving more than one force on an object:
1. Always start by sketching a neat drawing of the object.
2. Then draw arrows representing all the forces acting on the object.
3. Label each force with the cause of the force. Be specific. Examples are "weight," "force of string," "normal force exerted by table," "force of friction."

**FIGURE 5–12. Four forces are shown acting on a book that is moving to the right at a constant velocity.**

# PHYSICS LAB

## The Elevator Ride

### Purpose

To determine why you feel heavier or lighter when riding in an elevator.

### Materials

· 1-kg mass
· 20 N spring scale
· 10 cm masking tape

### Procedure

1. Imagine you take an upward elevator ride. Write a few sentences describing when you feel normal, heavier (than normal), and lighter (than normal).
2. Imagine you take a downward elevator ride. Write a few sentences describing when you feel normal, heavier (than normal), and lighter (than normal).
3. Hold the 1-kg mass in your hand and give it an upward elevator ride. Describe when the mass feels normal, heavier than normal, and lighter than normal.
4. Hold the mass in your hand and give it a downward elevator ride. Describe when the mass feels normal, heavier than normal, and lighter than normal.
5. Securely tape the mass to the hook on the spring scale. Warning: A falling mass can cause serious damage to the foot or toe!
6. Start with the mass just above the floor and take it on an upward and downward elevator ride.

### Observations and Data

1. Carefully watch the spring scale and notice how the readings change for different parts of the ride. Record your observations.

### Analysis

1. Identify those places in the ride when the spring scale reads a normal value for the mass. Describe the motion of the mass. Are the forces balanced or unbalanced?

2. Identify those places in the ride when the spring scale reads a "heavier" value. Which direction is the $\vec{F}_{net}$? Which direction is the acceleration?
3. Identify those places in the ride when the spring scale reads a "lighter" value. When way is the $\vec{F}_{net}$? Which direction is the acceleration?

### Applications

1. Do you feel heavier or lighter when riding on an escalator? Explain your answer in terms of the motion and the forces.
2. Identify the places on a roller coaster ride where you feel heavier or lighter. Explain your answer in terms of the motion and the forces.

# Example Problem

## Sliding Friction

A smooth wooden block is placed on a smooth wooden tabletop. You find that you must exert a force of 14.0 N to keep the 40.0-N block moving at a constant velocity. **a.** What is the coefficient of sliding friction for the block and table? **b.** If a 20.0-N brick is placed on the block, what force will be required to keep the block and brick moving at constant velocity?

**FIGURE 5–13. Use with the Example Problem.**

**a. Given:** $\vec{F}_A = 14.0$ N     **Unknown:** coefficient of friction, $\mu$
            $W = 40.0$ N      **Basic equations:** $\vec{F} = m\vec{a}$
            $\vec{a} = 0.0$                            $\vec{F}_f = \mu \vec{F}_N$

**Solution:**
Draw a diagram showing the forces on the block, Figure 5–13. Because $\vec{a} = 0.0$, the force you exert, $\vec{F}_A$, must be equal in size to the frictional force, $\vec{F}_f$. In addition, because the block is resting on the table and there is no other vertical force on it, the normal force equals the weight, $\vec{F}_N = \vec{W}$. Thus, $\vec{F}_A = \vec{F}_f = \mu \vec{W}$ or

$$\mu = \frac{\vec{F}_A}{\vec{W}} = \frac{14.0 \text{ N}}{40.0 \text{ N}} = 0.350.$$

**b. Given:** weight of brick,     **Unknown:** new applied force, $\vec{F}_A$
            $W' = 20.0$ N      **Basic equation:** $\vec{F}_N = \vec{W} + \vec{W}'$

**Solution:**
The block exerts a larger force ($\vec{W} + \vec{W}'$) on the table, and so the normal force is also increased. This increases the frictional force.

$$\begin{aligned} \vec{F}_A &= \vec{F}_f \\ &= \mu \vec{F}_N \\ &= \mu(\vec{W} + \vec{W}') \\ &= (0.350)(40.0 \text{ N} + 20.0 \text{ N}) \\ &= 21.0 \text{ N}. \end{aligned}$$

Note that $\mu$ depends only on the surfaces in contact, and so is the same for the two parts of the Example Problem.

# Practice Problems

9. Suppose Joe, who weighs 625 N, stands on a bathroom scale calibrated in newtons.
   a. What force would the scale exert on Joe? in what direction?
   b. If Joe now holds a 50-N cat in his arms, what force would the scale exert on him?
   c. After Joe puts down the cat, his father comes up behind him and lifts upward on his elbows with a 72-N force. What force does the scale now exert on Joe?
10. a. A 52-N sled is pulled across a cement sidewalk at constant speed. A horizontal force of 36 N is exerted. What is the coefficient of sliding friction between the sidewalk and the metal runners of the sled?

Friction acts in a direction parallel to the surfaces in contact and opposes the motion.

**b.** Suppose the sled now runs on packed snow. The coefficient of friction is now only 0.12. If a person weighing 650 N sits on the sled, what force is needed to slide the sled across the snow at constant speed?

**11.** The coefficient of sliding friction between rubber tires and wet pavement is 0.50. The brakes are applied to a 750-kg car traveling 30 m/s, and the car skids to a stop.
   **a.** What is the size and direction of the force of friction that the road exerts on the car?
   **b.** What would be the size and direction of the acceleration of the car? Why would it be constant?
   **c.** How far would the car travel before stopping?

▶ **12.** If the tires of the car in Practice Problem 11 did not skid, the coefficient of friction would have been 0.70. Would the force of friction have been larger, smaller, or the same? Would the car have come to a stop in a shorter, the same, or a longer distance?

## The Net Force Causes Acceleration

In Newton's second law of motion, $\vec{F} = m\vec{a}$, the force, $\vec{F}$, that causes the mass to accelerate is the net force acting on the mass. In Figure 5–14a, a 10-kg mass rests on a frictionless, horizontal surface. A +100-N force is exerted horizontally on the mass. The resulting acceleration is

$$\vec{a} = \frac{\vec{F}}{m} = \frac{+100\,\text{N}}{10\,\text{kg}} = +10\,\text{m/s}^2.$$

If the same mass rests on a rough surface, friction will oppose the motion. In Figure 5–14b, the frictional force is −20 N. The negative sign indicates that the force acts in a direction opposite the positive applied force. The acceleration of any object is the result of the net force acting on it. The net force is the vector sum of the applied and frictional forces. When you sum forces, which are vectors, you must pay attention to the signs. That is,

$$\vec{F}_{net} = \vec{F}_{applied} + \vec{F}_f$$
$$= +100\,\text{N} + (-20\,\text{N}) = +80\,\text{N},$$

and the resulting acceleration is given by

$$\vec{a} = \frac{\vec{F}_{net}}{m} = \frac{+80\,\text{N}}{10\,\text{kg}} = +8.0\,\text{m/s}^2.$$

The direction of the acceleration is positive, in the direction of the applied force.

**FIGURE 5–14.** When acted upon by a 100 N force, the acceleration of a 10 kg mass on a frictionless surface (a) is greater than the acceleration of a 10 kg mass on a rough surface (b).

Other forces besides friction act on objects. Consider a 10.0-kg stone lying on the ground. The stone is at rest; the net force on it is zero. The weight of the stone, $\vec{W}$ is 98.0 N in a downward direction. The ground exerts an equal and opposite force, 98.0 N, upward. The net force is

$$\vec{F}_{net} = \vec{F}_{ground} + \vec{W}$$
$$= 98.0 \text{ N} + (-98.0 \text{ N})$$
$$= 0 \text{ N}.$$

How can the stone be given an upward acceleration? Suppose a person exerts a 148-N upward force on the stone. The net force is

$$\vec{F}_{net} = \vec{F}_{person} + \vec{W}$$
$$= +148.0 \text{ N} + (-98.0 \text{ N})$$
$$= +50.0 \text{ N}.$$

The net force acting on the stone is 50 N upward. The acceleration of the stone can now be found from Newton's second law:

$$\vec{a} = \frac{\vec{F}}{m} = \frac{+50 \text{ N}}{10 \text{ kg}} = +5.0 \text{ m/s}^2.$$

The stone will be accelerated upward at $+5.0$ m/s$^2$.

**FIGURE 5–15. A mass is accelerated upward if the total force exerted upward is greater than the weight.**

$F = 148$ N

10 kg

$W = 98$ N

# Example Problem

## Forces on an Accelerating Object

A spring scale hangs from the ceiling of an elevator. It supports a package that weighs 25 N. **a.** What upward force does the scale exert when the elevator is not moving? **b.** What force must the scale exert when the elevator and object accelerate upward at $+1.5$ m/s$^2$? Use Figure 5–16.

**Given:** weight of package,
    $\vec{W} = 25$ N
    acceleration,
    **a.** $\vec{a} = 0.0$ m/s$^2$
    **b.** $\vec{a} = +1.5$ m/s$^2$

**Unknown:** upward force, $\vec{F}_{scale}$
**Basic equations:** $\vec{F}_{net} = m\vec{a}$
    $\vec{F}_{net} = \vec{F}_{scale} + \vec{W}$
    $\vec{W} = m\vec{g}$

The net force is the vector sum of all forces acting on a body.

**Solution:**
**a.** Because $\vec{a} = 0.0$, $\vec{F}_{net} = 0.0$, so
    $\vec{F}_{scale} = -\vec{W} = -(-25 \text{ N}) = 25$ N (up).
    Weight is 25 N down, so the scale supplies 25 N up.

**b.** Now $\vec{a} = +1.5$ m/s$^2$. Therefore,
    $\vec{F}_{net} = m(+1.5 \text{ m/s}^2)$.
    We are not given the mass of the object, but we can find it from the weight, $\vec{W} = m\vec{g}$, so

$$m = \frac{\vec{W}}{\vec{g}} = \frac{25 \text{ N}}{9.80 \text{ m/s}^2} = 2.6 \text{ kg. Thus,}$$

$$\vec{F}_{net} = (2.6 \text{ kg})(+1.5 \text{ m/s}^2) = +3.9 \text{ N (up)}$$
$$\vec{F}_{net} = \vec{F}_{scale} + \vec{W}; \vec{F}_{scale} = \vec{F}_{net} - \vec{W}$$
$$= +3.9 \text{ N} - (-25 \text{ N}) = +29 \text{ N (up)}.$$

That is, the scale exerts a larger force and thus indicates a larger weight when the elevator accelerates upward.

**FIGURE 5–16. Use with the Example Problem.**

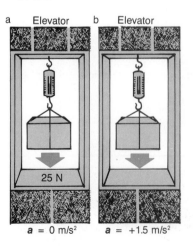

a    Elevator    b    Elevator

25 N

$a = 0$ m/s$^2$    $a = +1.5$ m/s$^2$

If you ride an elevator, you "feel" your inertial mass. When the elevator accelerates upward, you feel the added force of the floor on your feet, accelerating you up. You also feel the forces your muscles exert on your stomach; these forces may make your stomach feel strange.

## Practice Problems

13. A rubber ball weighs 49 N.
    a. What is the mass of the ball?
    b. What is the acceleration of the ball if an upward force of 69 N is applied?

14. A small weather rocket weighs 14.7 N.
    a. What is its mass?
    b. The rocket is carried up by a balloon. The rocket is released from the balloon and fired, but its engine exerts an upward force of 10.2 N. What is the acceleration of the rocket?

15. The space shuttle has a mass of $2.0 \times 10^6$ kg. At lift-off the engines generate an upward force of $30 \times 10^6$ N.
    a. What is the weight of the shuttle?
    b. What is the acceleration of the shuttle when launched?
    c. The average acceleration of the shuttle during its 10 min launch is 13 m/s$^2$. What velocity does it attain?
    d. As the space shuttle engines burn, the mass of the fuel becomes less and less. Assuming the force exerted by the engines remains the same, would you expect the acceleration to increase, decrease, or remain the same? Why?

▶ 16. A certain sports car accelerates from 0 to 100 km/h in 9.0 s (average acceleration = 3.0 m/s$^2$). The mass of the car is 1354 kg. The average backward force due to air drag during acceleration is 280 N. Find the forward force required to give the car this acceleration.

## The Fall of Bodies in the Air

Astronauts on the surface of the moon dropped a hammer and a feather together. These objects hit the surface at the same time. Without any air, all objects fall with the same acceleration. On Earth, the acceleration is 9.80 m/s$^2$; on the moon it is 1.60 m/s$^2$.

In air, however, an additional force acts on moving bodies. Try this experiment. Take two pieces of notebook paper. Crumple one into a ball. Now hold them side by side and drop them at the same time. The two pieces of paper obviously do not accelerate at the same rate. The flat paper encounters much more air resistance than the ball. Air resistance, sometimes called the drag force, is a friction-like force. As an object moves through the air, it collides with air molecules that exert a force on it. The force depends on the size and shape of the object, the density of the air, and the speed of motion.

Suppose you drop a ping-pong ball. Just after you drop it, it has very little velocity, and thus very small drag force. The downward force of gravity is larger than the upward drag force and the ball accelerates downward. As its velocity increases, so does the drag force. At some later time the drag force equals the force of gravity. The net force is now zero, and the velocity of the ball becomes constant. This constant velocity is called the **terminal velocity.**

An object in freefall (in a vacuum) has only the force of gravity acting on it. Its acceleration is equal to g.

The force of air molecules striking a moving object is called air resistance.

## FAST PEDALING

The forces that work against the speed of a bicycle racer are the weight of the bike and rider, friction with the road surface and within the wheel itself, and air resistance. The bike rider's biggest battle is with air resistance. About 70% of the air resistance, or drag, that a rider encounters is caused by his or her own body. That's why riders maintain a crouched position during a race. The rider can further cut air resistance by wearing tightfitting clothing made from smooth fabric. New aerodynamic designs for bikes, wheels, and helmets are also being used to reduce air resistance.

To reduce weight and make acceleration easier, lightweight alloys and composite materials containing carbon fibres are being used to build strong but very low mass frames. A bike made of titanium, for example, can have a mass of less than 9 kg.

The ball bearings in the wheels cause friction. This bearing friction can be reduced by using improved bearings and lubricants.

The total effect of all these efforts may be a gain of only a few metres per kilometre. However, even that small gain can mean a big difference in a race.
· What are some ways you could reduce the rolling friction between a bike and the riding surface?

The terminal velocity of a ping-pong ball in air is only 9 m/s. A basketball has a terminal velocity of 20 m/s, while a baseball can fall as fast as 42 m/s. Skiers increase their terminal velocities by decreasing drag force. They hold their bodies in an "egg" shape and wear very smooth clothing and streamlined helmets. A sky diver can control terminal velocity by changing body shape. A spread-eagle position gives the slowest terminal velocity, about 60 m/s. By opening the parachute, the sky diver has become part of a very large object with a correspondingly large drag force. The terminal velocity is now about 5 m/s.

◄ Going Down

# CONCEPT REVIEW

**2.1** A sky diver in the spread-eagle position opens the parachute. Is the diver accelerated? Which direction? Explain your answer.

**2.2** A weight lifter lifts a 115-kg barbell from the ground.
  **a.** How does the force exerted by the lifter compare with the weight of the barbell? Explain.
  **b.** How does the force exerted by the lifter on the barbell compare with the force exerted by the barbell on the lifter?

**2.3** Suppose you put a wooden block against a wall and push horizontally to keep it from falling. Draw a diagram showing the forces on the block and the causes of those forces. Pay special attention to the normal force and the weight of the block. Are they in the same direction? Are they equal?

**2.4** **Critical Thinking:** When a football defensive lineman wants to stop an opponent, he puts his shoulder into his opponent's body and lifts up. How does this affect the ability of his opponent to accelerate? Explain.

# CHAPTER
## 5 REVIEW
· · · · · · · · · · · · · · · · · · · · · ·

## SUMMARY

### 5.1 Newton's Laws of Motion

· All forces are vectors; they have both magnitude and direction.
· The four basic forces are the gravitational, electromagnetic, and strong and weak nuclear forces.
· Newton's first law states that an object with no net (unbalanced) force acting on it will either remain at rest or continue moving at constant speed in a straight line.
· Newton's second law states that when a net (unbalanced) force acts on an object, the resulting acceleration varies directly with the force and inversely with the mass of the object.
· Newton's third law states that forces always exist in pairs. When one object exerts a force on a second object, the second exerts an equal and opposite force on the first.
· The weight of a body is proportional to its mass.
· Weight is the gravitational force on a body.

### 5.2 Using Newton's Laws

· Gravitational mass and inertial mass are two essentially different concepts. The gravitational and inertial masses of a body, however, are numerically equal.
· Friction is a force that acts when two objects rub against each other.
· The magnitude of the sliding friction force is the product of the coefficient of friction and the normal force.
· Net force is the vector sum of forces acting on the body.
· A body falling in air reaches terminal velocity when the upward force of air resistance equals the downward force of gravity.

## KEY TERMS

| | |
|---|---|
| kinematics | Newton's third law |
| dynamics | action-reaction forces |
| force | weight |

gravitational force
electromagnetic force
strong nuclear force
weak nuclear force
Newton's first law
Newton's second law

inertial mass
friction
static friction
sliding friction
coefficient of friction
terminal velocity

## REVIEWING CONCEPTS

1. The text states that all forces can be grouped into just four kinds of forces. Name the force that best describes the following:
   a. the weakest force.
   b. the force that acts over the longest distance.
   c. the strongest force.
   d. the force that holds matter together.
2. A physics book is motionless on the top of a table. If you give it a hard push with your hand, it slides across the table and slowly comes to a stop. Use Newton's first law of motion to answer the following questions.
   a. Why does the book remain motionless before the force is applied?
   b. Why does the book move when the hand pushes on it?
   c. Why does the book eventually come to a stop?
   d. Under what conditions would the book remain in motion at a constant speed?
3. Why do you have to push harder on the pedals of a single-speed bicycle to start it moving than to keep it moving with a constant velocity?
4. Suppose you dropped a rock from a bridge into a valley below. Earth pulls on the rock and it accelerates downward. According to Newton's third law, the rock must also be pulling on Earth, yet we don't notice the Earth accelerating upward. Explain.
5. Let's say your textbooks have a total mass of 3.0 kg. What would be the mass of the books if they were taken to Jupiter where the acceleration due to gravity is 10 times that of Earth?
6. Compare the force needed to lift a 10-kg rock on Earth and on the moon. Now compare the

force needed to throw the same rock horizontally at the same speed in the two locations.

7. You place a carton of books on a hand cart. When you accelerate the cart, the carton also accelerates. What supplies the force that accelerates the carton?

8. Why does a package on the seat of a bus slide backward when the bus accelerates quickly from rest? Why does it slide forward when the driver applies the brakes?

9. Suppose the acceleration of an object is zero. Does this mean there are no forces acting on it? Give an example supporting your answer.

10. When a basketball player dribbles a basketball, it falls to the floor and bounces up. Is a force required to make it bounce? Why?

11. Before a skydiver opens her parachute, she may already be falling at a velocity higher than her terminal velocity with the parachute open.
    a. Describe what happens to her velocity as she opens her parachute.
    b. Describe her velocity from after her parachute has been open for a while until she is about to land.

## APPLYING CONCEPTS

1. Which of the four forces makes paint cling to a wall? Which force makes adhesive sticky? Which force makes wax stick to a car?

2. If you are in a car that is struck from behind, you can receive a serious neck injury called whiplash.
    a. Using Newton's laws of motion, explain what happens.
    b. How does a headrest reduce whiplash?

3. Should astronauts choose pencils with hard or soft lead when taking notes in space? Explain.

**FIGURE 5–17.**

4. According to legend, a horse learned Newton's laws. When it was told to pull a cart, it refused, saying that if it pulled the cart forward, according to Newton's third law there would be an equal force backwards. Thus, there would be balanced forces and, according to Newton's second law, the cart would

not accelerate. How would you reason with this rather weird horse?

5. When people go on a diet, most say they want to lose weight. Describe some methods that would allow them to decrease their weight without decreasing their mass.

6. Drag racers often set their tires on fire to soften the rubber and increase the coefficient of friction, $\mu$. What is the role friction plays?

7. Which creates a greater force of friction: sliding your physics book across a table on its back cover or along one of its edges?

8. Is the coefficient of friction the same between two identical surfaces in a lab on Earth and in a lab in a space colony on the moon? Explain.

9. Can the coefficient of friction ever be greater than one? less than one? Explain. What information would you need to calculate $\mu$ precisely?

10. The same object is dropped in a vacuum and then in air. Which of the parameters (distance, velocity, acceleration) vary and which remain constant during succeeding seconds of time
    a. in a vacuum?
    b. in air when terminal velocity from air resistance has been reached?

11. While riding in a helicopter, you drop two ping-pong balls, one filled with air and the other with water. Both experience air resistance as they fall. Which ball reaches terminal velocity first? Do both hit the ground at the same time? Explain.

## PROBLEMS

### 5.1 Newton's Laws of Motion

1. An 873-kg dragster, starting from rest, attains a speed of 26.3 m/s in 0.59 s.
    a. Find the average acceleration of the dragster during this time interval.
    b. What is the size of the average force on the dragster during this time interval?
    c. Assume the driver has a mass of 68 kg. What horizontal force does the seat exert on the driver?
    d. Is the driver's mass in part **c** an inertial mass or a gravitational mass?

2. The dragster in Problem 1 completed the 402.3 m run in 4.936 s. If the car had constant

acceleration, what would be its acceleration and final velocity?

▶ 3. The dragster crossed the finish line going 126.6 m/s. Is the assumption of constant acceleration good? What other piece of evidence could you use to see if the acceleration is constant?

4. In Chapter 4, you found that when a karate strike hits wooden blocks, the hand undergoes an acceleration of $-6500$ m/s$^2$. Medical data indicates the mass of the forearm and hand to be about 0.7 kg. What is the force exerted on the hand by the blocks? What is its direction?

5. After a day of testing race cars, you decide to take your own 1550-kg car onto the test track. While moving down the track at 10 m/s, you suddenly accelerate to 30 m/s in 10 s. What is the average net force that you have applied to the car during the 10-s interval?

▶ 6. A race car has a mass of 710 kg. It starts from rest and travels 40 m in 3.0 s. The car is uniformly accelerated during the entire time. What net force is applied to it?

▶ 7. A force of $-9000$ N is used to stop a 1500-kg car traveling at 20 m/s. What braking distance is needed to bring the car to a halt?

▶ 8. A 65-kg swimmer jumps off a 10-m tower.
   a. Find the swimmer's velocity when hitting the water.
   b. The swimmer comes to a stop 2 m below the surface. Find the net force exerted by the water.

9. When you drop a 400-g apple, Earth exerts a force on it that accelerates it at 9.8 m/s$^2$ toward Earth's surface. According to Newton's third law, the apple must exert an equal and opposite force on Earth. If the mass of Earth is $5.98 \times 10^{24}$ kg, what's the magnitude of Earth's acceleration?

10. A 60-kg boy and a 40-kg girl use an elastic rope while engaged in a tug-of-war on an icy frictionless surface. If the acceleration of the girl toward the boy is 3.0 m/s$^2$, determine the magnitude of the acceleration of the boy toward the girl.

## 5.2 Using Newton's Laws

11. A 95.0-kg boxer has his first match in the Canal Zone ($\vec{g} = 9.782$ m/s$^2$) and his second match at the North Pole ($\vec{g} = 9.832$ m/s$^2$).
   a. What is his mass in the Canal Zone?
   b. What is his weight in the Canal Zone?
   c. What is his mass at the North Pole?
   d. What is his weight at the North Pole?
   e. Does he "weigh-in" or does he really "mass-in"?

12. Your new motorcycle weighs 2450 N. What is its mass in kilograms?

13. You place a 7.50-kg television set on a spring scale. If the scale reads 78.4 N, what is the acceleration of gravity at that location?

14. In Chapter 4, you calculated the braking acceleration for a car based on data in a driver's handbook. The acceleration was $-12.2$ m/s$^2$. If the car has a mass of 925 kg, find the frictional force and state the direction.

15. If you use a horizontal force of 30.0 N to slide a 12.0-kg wooden crate across a floor at a constant velocity, what is the coefficient of sliding friction between crate and floor?

▶ 16. You are driving a 2500.0-kg car at a constant speed of 14.0 m/s along an icy, but straight and level road. While approaching a traffic light, it turns red. You slam on the brakes. Your wheels lock, the tires begin skidding, and the car slides to a halt in a distance of 25.0 m. What is the coefficient of sliding friction ($\mu$) between your tires and the icy roadbed? ·

17. A person fishing hooks a 2.0-kg fish on a line that can only sustain a maximum of 38 N of force before breaking. At one point while reeling in the bass, it fights back with a force of 40 N. What is the minimum acceleration with which you must play out the line during this time in order to keep the line from breaking?

18. A 4500-kg helicopter accelerates upward at 2 m/s$^2$. What lift force is exerted by the air on the propellers?

19. The maximum force a grocery bag can withstand and not rip is 250 N. If 20 kg of groceries are lifted from the floor to the table with an acceleration of 5 m/s$^2$, will the bag hold?

▶ 20. A student stands on a bathroom scale in an elevator at rest on the 64th floor of a building. The scale reads 836 N.
   a. As the elevator moves up, the scale reading increases to 935 N, then decreases back to 836 N. Find the acceleration of the elevator.
   b. As the elevator approaches the 74th floor, the scale reading drops as low as 782 N. What is the acceleration of the elevator?

**c.** Using your results from parts **a** and **b**, explain which change in velocity, starting or stopping, would take the longer time.

**d.** Explain the changes in the scale you would expect on the ride back down.

▶ **21.** A $2.1 \times 10^{-4}$-kg spider is suspended from a thin strand of spider web. The greatest tension the strand can withstand without breaking is $2.0 \times 10^{-3}$ N. What is the maximum acceleration with which the spider can safely climb up the strand?

**22.** A sled of mass 50 kg is pulled along snow-covered, flat ground. The static friction coefficient is 0.30, and the sliding friction coefficient is 0.10.

**a.** What does the sled weigh?

**b.** What force will be needed to start the sled moving?

**c.** What force is needed to keep the sled moving at a constant velocity?

**d.** Once moving, what total force must be applied to the sled to accelerate it $3.0 \text{ m/s}^2$?

**23.** A force of 40 N accelerates a 5.0-kg block at $6.0 \text{ m/s}^2$ along a horizontal surface.

**a.** How large is the frictional force?

**b.** What is the coefficient of friction?

**24.** A 200-kg crate is pushed horizontally with a force of 700 N. If the coefficient of friction is 0.20, calculate the acceleration of the crate.

**25.** Safety engineers estimate that an elevator can hold 20 persons of 75-kg average mass. The elevator itself has a mass of 500 kg. Tensile strength tests show that the cable supporting the elevator can tolerate a maximum force of $2.96 \times 10^4$ N. What is the greatest acceleration that the elevator's motor can produce without breaking the cable?

▶ **26.** The instruments attached to a weather balloon have a mass of 5.0 kg.

**a.** The balloon is released and exerts an upward force of 98 N on the instruments. What is the acceleration of the balloon and instruments?

**b.** After the balloon has accelerated for 10 s, the instruments are released. What is the velocity of the instruments at the moment of their release?

**c.** What net force acts on the instruments after their release?

**d.** When does the direction of their velocity first become downward?

▶ **27.** A 2.0-kg mass ($m_1$) and a 3.0-kg mass ($m_2$) are attached to a lightweight cord that passes over a frictionless pulley, Figure 5–18. The hanging masses are free to move. Assume the positive direction of motion to be when the smaller object moves upward and the larger mass moves downward.

**a.** Draw the situation, showing all forces.

**b.** In what direction does the smaller mass move?

**c.** What is its acceleration?

▶ **28.** You change the masses in Figure 5–18 to 1.00 kg and 4.00 kg.

**a.** What can you expect the acceleration of the 4.00-kg mass to be?

**b.** What is the tension force acting on the cord?

**FIGURE 5–18. Use with Problems 27, 28, and 29.**

▶ **29.** You then decide to replace the 1.00-kg object from Problem 28 with a 2.00-kg object.

**a.** What is the acceleration of the 2.00-kg object?

**b.** What is the new tension force acting on the cord?

# THINKING PHYSIC-LY

1. Suppose you are in a spaceship in freefall between Earth and the moon. How could you distinguish between a lead brick and an ordinary brick if you were blindfolded and wore gloves?

2. Cheetahs are bigger and faster than small gazelles, but more often than not gazelles escape a pursuing cheetah by zigzagging. Exactly why does this put the cheetah at a disadvantage?

# CHAPTER
# 6 Vectors

◄ A Weighty Subject

The slack wire supports the weight of the performer. How does the force exerted by the wire compare to the weight of the walker?

√ Concept Check

The following terms or concepts from earlier chapters are important for a good understanding of this chapter. If you are not familiar with them, you should review them before studying this chapter.
· velocity, Chapter 3
· acceleration, Chapter 4
· force, vectors, Newton's first and second laws, Chapter 5

**M**ake this challenge to some strong friends. Have them hold on to the ends of a light rope several metres long and pull until it is taut. Then challenge them to keep the rope from sagging as you hang a medium-sized bag of potatoes from its centre. After all, your friends claim to be strong, and the bag doesn't weigh much. Nevertheless, they will find it impossible to keep the rope perfectly straight. Why? You will discover the answer to this question as you understand the vector nature of forces.

The resultant is the single vector that could represent the sum of several vectors.

FIGURE 6–1. Vectors are added by placing the tail of one vector at the head of the other vector. The resultant, $\vec{R}$, represents the sum of $\vec{A}$ and $\vec{B}$ (a). The order of addition does not matter (b). The vectors can have different directions (c).

# 6.1 GRAPHICAL METHOD OF VECTOR ADDITION

A vector quantity can be represented by an arrow-tipped line segment. The length of the line, drawn to scale, represents the magnitude of the quantity. The direction of the arrow indicates the direction of the quantity. This arrow-tipped line segment represents a vector. Just as we can represent a vector graphically, we can add vectors graphically. They may also be represented in the diagrams of this book in bold face, italic type, without arrows; for example, **A**, **B**.

## Vector Addition in One Dimension

Suppose a child walks 200 m east, pauses, and then continues 400 m east. To find the total displacement, or change in position of the child, we must add the two vector quantities. In Figure 6–1a, $\vec{A}$ and $\vec{B}$, drawn to scale, are vectors representing the two segments of the child's walk. The vectors are added by placing the tail of one vector at the head of the other vector. It is very important that neither the direction nor the length of either vector is changed during the process. A third vector is then drawn connecting the tail of the first vector to the head of the second vector. This third vector represents the sum of the first two vectors. It is called the **resultant** of $\vec{A}$ and $\vec{B}$. The resultant is always drawn from the *tail* of the first vector to the *head* of the last vector.

When vectors are added, the order of addition does not matter. The tail of $\vec{A}$ could have been placed at the head of $\vec{B}$. Figure 6–1b shows that the same vector sum would result.

To find the magnitude of the resultant, $\vec{R}$, measure its length using the same scale used to draw $\vec{A}$ and $\vec{B}$. In this situation, the total change in position is 200 m east + 400 m east = 600 m east.

The two vectors can have different directions, Figure 6–1c. If the child had turned around after moving 200 m east and walked 400 m west, the change of position would have been 200 m east + 400 m west or 200 m west. Note that in both cases, the vectors are added head to tail, and the directions of the original vectors are not changed.

## Vector Addition in Two Dimensions

So far we have looked at motion in only one dimension. Vectors can also represent motion in two dimensions. In Figure 6–2, $\vec{A}$ and $\vec{B}$ represent the two displacements of a student who walked first 95 m east

FIGURE 6–2. The vector sum of $\vec{B} + \vec{A}$ is the same as the vector sum of $\vec{A} + \vec{B}$.

and then 55 m north. The vectors are added by placing the tail of one vector at the head of the other vector. The resultant of $\vec{A}$ and $\vec{B}$ is drawn from the tail of the first vector to the head of the second vector. To find the magnitude of the resultant, $\vec{R}$, measure its length using the same scale used to draw $\vec{A}$ and $\vec{B}$. Its direction can be found with a protractor. The direction is expressed as an angle measured counterclockwise from the horizontal. In Figure 6–2, the resultant displacement is 110 m at 30° north of east.

FIGURE 6–3. The resultant force of two forces acting on a point can be determined graphically.

The situation

A = 45 N, 60°

P

B = 65 N, 0°

Scale: 1 division = 10 N

The vector diagram

R = 96 N, 24°

A

θ = 24°

B

Force vectors are added in the same way as position or velocity vectors. In Figure 6–3, a force, $\vec{A}$, of 45 N and a force, $\vec{B}$, of 65 N are exerted on an object at point **P**. Force $\vec{A}$ acts in the direction of 60°, force $\vec{B}$ acts at 0°. The resultant, $\vec{R}$, is the sum of the two forces. Vectors representing forces $\vec{A}$ and $\vec{B}$ are drawn to scale. $\vec{R}$ is found by moving $\vec{A}$ without changing its direction or length until the tail of $\vec{A}$ is located at the head of $\vec{B}$. The resultant is drawn from the tail of the first vector, $\vec{B}$, to the head of the second vector, $\vec{A}$. As before, the magnitude of $\vec{R}$ is determined using the same scale used for $\vec{A}$ and $\vec{B}$. The angle is again found with a protractor. In this case, $\vec{R}$ is 96 N acting in a direction of 24°. A single force of 96 N acting in a direction of 24° will have exactly the same effect as two forces, 45 N at 60° and 65 N at 0°, acting at the same time.

## Addition of Several Vectors

Often, more than two forces act at the same time on the same object. To find the resultant of three or more vectors, follow the same procedure you used to add two vectors. Just be sure to place the vectors tail-to-head. The order of addition is not important. In Figure 6–4a, the three forces, $\vec{A}$, $\vec{B}$, and $\vec{C}$, are acting on point **P**. In Figures 6–4b and 6–4c, the vectors are added graphically. Note that the resultant is the same in both sketches although two different orders of addition are used. Remember, when placing vectors head-to-tail, the direction and length of each vector must not be changed.

## POCKET LAB

### MASS ON A STRING

Hang a 1.0-kg mass on a short string attached to a 20-N spring scale. What is the reading? Would the reading be larger or smaller if you use a longer string? Try it. What did you learn?

FIGURE 6–4. In (a) the three forces act concurrently on point P. In (b) and (c) the vectors are added graphically. The resultant is the same in both diagrams.

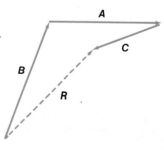

## Vector Conventions

- *Velocity vectors are red.*
- *Displacement vectors are green.*
- *Acceleration vectors are purple.*
- *Force vectors are blue.*
- ▶ **Vector resultants are dashed lines.**

# Practice Problems

*Draw vector diagrams to solve each problem.*

1. After walking 11 km due north from camp, a hiker then walks 11 km due east.
   a. What is the total distance walked by the hiker?
   b. Determine the total displacement from the starting point.
2. Two boys push on a box. One pushes with a force of 125 N to the east. The other exerts a force of 165 N to the north. What is the size and direction of the resultant force on the box?
▶ 3. An explorer walks 13 km due east, then 18 km north, and finally 3 km west.
   a. What is the total distance walked?
   b. What is the resulting displacement of the explorer from the starting point?

Scale: 1 division = 1 m/s

$v_R = 9.4$ m/s, 32°
$\theta = 32°$
$v_2 = 5.0$ m/s, 90°
$v_1 = 8.0$ m/s, 0°

Boat

**FIGURE 6–5. A boat traveling 9.4 m/s at 32° north of east can also be described as traveling both east at 8.0 m/s and north at 5.0 m/s at the same time.**

Perpendicular vector quantities can be treated independently of one another.

# Independence of Vector Quantities

Perpendicular vector quantities are independent of one another. A motorboat heads east at 8.0 m/s across a river that flows north at 5.0 m/s. Starting from the west bank, the boat will travel 8.0 m east in one second. In the same second, it also travels 5.0 m north. The velocity north does not change the velocity east. Neither does the velocity east change the velocity north. These two perpendicular velocities are independent of each other. *Perpendicular vector quantities can be treated independently of one another.*

In Figure 6–5, the two velocities of the boat are represented by vectors. When these vectors are added, the resultant velocity, $\vec{v}_R$, is 9.4 m/s at 32° north of east. You can also think of the boat as travelling, in each second, east 8.0 m and north 5.0 m at the same time. Both statements have the same meaning.

Suppose that the river is 80 m wide. Because the boat's velocity is 8 m/s east, it will take the boat 10 s to cross the river. During this 10 s the boat will also be carried 50 m downstream. In no way does the downstream velocity change the velocity of the boat across the river.

# Practice Problems

*Draw vector diagrams to solve each problem.*

4. A motorboat heads due east at 16 m/s across a river that flows due north at 9.0 m/s.
   a. What is the resultant velocity (speed and direction) of the boat?
   b. If the river is 136 m wide, how long does it take the motorboat to reach the other side?
   c. How far downstream is the boat when it reaches the other side of the river?
5. While flying due east at 120 km/h, an airplane is also carried northward at 45 km/h by the wind blowing due north. What is the plane's resultant velocity?

▶ **6.** Three teenagers push a heavy crate across the floor. Dion pushes horizontally with a force of 185 N at 0°. Shirley exerts a horizontal force of 165 N at 30°, while Joan pushes horizontally with 195 N of force at 300°. What is the resultant force on the crate?

## CONCEPT REVIEW

**1.1** The order in which you add vectors does not matter. Mathematicians say that vector addition is commutative. Which ordinary arithmetic operations are commutative? Which are not?

**1.2** Two boys push on a crate. One exerts a 400 N force, the other a 300 N force. The resultant force on the crate is 600 N. Explain.

**1.3** What is the largest resultant force the two boys in question 1.2 could exert on the crate? What is the smallest resultant force?

**1.4 Critical Thinking:** Two unequal forces are exerted on a box. Could the net force ever be zero? What if three unequal forces are exerted? Support your argument with a diagram.

# 6.2 ANALYTICAL METHOD OF VECTOR ADDITION

You have seen how a vector quantity can be represented by an arrow. A vector quantity in two dimensions can also be represented by two numbers. One gives its length and the second gives the angle between that vector and a reference direction. The sum of any two vectors can be determined using trigonometry. **Trigonometry** deals with the relationships among angles and sides of triangles.

Trigonometric functions are defined in terms of one of the non - 90° angles of a right triangle. The common trigonometric functions of an angle are the **sine** (sin), **cosine** (cos), and **tangent** (tan). For the triangle in Figure 6–6a,

$$\sin \theta = \frac{\text{opposite side}}{\text{hypotenuse}}$$

$$\cos \theta = \frac{\text{adjacent side}}{\text{hypotenuse}}$$

$$\tan \theta = \frac{\text{opposite side}}{\text{adjacent side}}$$

The numerical value of the trigonometry functions can be found with a calculator or from Table D–6 in the Appendix. For example, suppose you need to build a triangular form with the dimensions shown in Figure 6–6b. You know that the hypotenuse of the triangle is 7.6 m and the side adjacent to angle $\theta$ is 3.1 m. Therefore, by using the cosine function, you can determine what size you should make $\theta$.

$$\cos \theta = \frac{\text{adjacent side}}{\text{hypotenuse}} = \frac{3.1 \text{ m}}{7.6 \text{ m}} = 0.41$$

Therefore, from a calculator or trigonometry table, $\theta = 66°$.

**Objectives**

· **understand the addition of forces and be able to solve force vector addition problems.**
· **recognize the applications of elementary geometry and trigonometry to vector addition and be able to solve problems using these methods.**

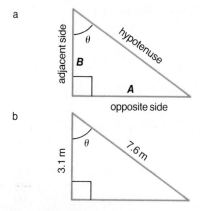

**FIGURE 6–6. Vector sums can be found using the trigonometric functions of right triangles.**

# PHYSICS LAB

# The Paper River

## Purpose

To discover how boats travel on a river.

## Materials

· small battery-powered car (or physics bulldozer)
· metre stick
· protractor
· stopwatch
· single sheet of paper about 1 m × 10 m-meat department butcher paper or from the art department

## Procedure

1. Your car will serve as the boat. Write a brief statement to explain how the boat's speed can be determined.
2. Your boat will start with all wheels on the paper river. Measure the width of the river and predict how much time is needed for your boat to go directly across the river. Show your data and calculations.
3. Determine the time needed to cross the river when your boat is placed on the edge of the river. Make three trials and record the times.
4. Do you think it will take more or less time to cross when the river is flowing? Explain your prediction.
5. Have a student (the hydro engineer) walk slowly, at a constant speed, while pulling the river along the floor. Each group should measure the time it takes for the boat to cross the flowing river. Compare the results with your prediction.
6. Devise a method to measure the speed of the river. Have the hydro engineer pull the river at a constant speed and collect the necessary data.

## Observations and Data

1. Does the boat move in the direction that it is pointing?
2. Did the motion of the water make the boat go faster?
3. Did the motion of the water affect the time needed when the boat was pointed straight across?
4. Which had more speed, the river or the boat? Explain your choice.

## Analysis

1. Calculate the speed of the river.
2. Using your results for the speed of the boat and river, calculate the speed of the boat, compared to the ground, when the boat is headed directly downstream.
3. Using the results for the speed of the boat and the river, calculate the speed of the boat, compared to the ground, when the boat is headed upstream.

## Applications

1. Do small propeller aircraft always move in the direction that they are pointing? Do they ever fly sideways?

## Adding Perpendicular Vectors

If two vectors are perpendicular, a right angle is formed when the tail of the second vector is placed at the head of the first. The resultant vector, drawn from the tail of the first to the head of the second, is the hypotenuse of the right triangle formed by the three vectors. The length of the resultant can be calculated using the Pythagorean theorem. You can find the interior angle, $\theta$, by using the trigonometric tangent function. In Figure 6–6, $\tan \theta = A/B$. Whenever solving vector addition analytically, draw a careful sketch of the vectors and check that your answer agrees with the sketch.

*The Pythagorean theorem can be used to calculate the resultant of perpendicular vectors.*

## Example Problem

### Finding a Resultant Velocity

An airplane flying toward 0° at 90.0 km/h is being blown toward 90° at 50.0 km/h, Figure 6–7. What is the resultant velocity of the plane?

**Given:** plane velocity
$$\vec{v}_p = 90.0 \text{ km/h at } 0°$$
wind velocity,
$$\vec{v}_w = 50.0 \text{ km/h at } 90°$$

**Unknown:** resultant velocity, $\vec{v}_R$
**Basic equation:** $R^2 = \vec{A}^2 + \vec{B}^2$
or $\vec{v}_R{}^2 = \vec{v}_p{}^2 + \vec{v}_w{}^2$

$$\tan \theta = \frac{\text{side opposite}}{\text{side adjacent}}$$

**Solution:** The vector $\vec{v}_R$ is the hypotenuse of a right triangle. Its magnitude is given by $\vec{v}_R{}^2 = \vec{v}_p{}^2 + \vec{v}_w{}^2$
$$\vec{v}_R{}^2 = (90.0 \text{ km/h})^2 + (50.0 \text{ km/h})^2$$
$$= \sqrt{1.06 \times 10^4 \text{ (km/h)}^2}$$
$$\vec{v}_R = 103 \text{ km/h}.$$

The angle, $\theta$, is found from
$$\tan \theta = \frac{\text{opposite side}}{\text{adjacent side}}$$
$$= \frac{50.0 \text{ km/h}}{90.0 \text{ km/h}}$$

so,
$$\tan \theta = 0.556.$$

A calculator, or Table D–6 in the Appendix, shows that 0.556 is the tangent of 29°. Therefore, $\theta$ is 29°. The resultant velocity is
$$\vec{v}_R = 103 \text{ km/h at } 29°.$$

**FIGURE 6–7. The vector diagram shows the approximate solution to the Example Problem.**

### Using Your CALCULATOR

Use your calculator to find the angle $\theta$ whose tangent is 50.0/90.0, called the arctan.

**Keys**         **Result**

50.0 ÷ 90.0 =    0.555...

shift tan       29.1

arctan 50.0/90.0 = 29.1°

## Practice Problems

**7.** A 110-N force and a 55-N force both act on an object point **P.** The 110-N force acts at 90°. The 55-N force acts at 0°. What is the magnitude and direction of the resultant force?

**8.** A motorboat travels at 8.5 m/s. It heads straight across a river 110 m wide.
  **a.** If the water flows downstream at a rate of 3.8 m/s, what is the boat's resultant velocity?
  **b.** How long does it take the boat to reach the opposite shore?

**9.** A boat heads directly across a river 41 m wide at 3.8 m/s. The current is flowing downstream at 2.2 m/s.
  **a.** What is the resultant velocity of the boat?
  **b.** How much time does it take the boat to cross the river?
  **c.** How far downstream is the boat when it reaches the other side?

▶ **10.** A 42-km/h wind blows toward 215°, while a plane heads toward 125° at 152 km/h. What is the resultant velocity of the plane?

## Components of Vectors

We have seen that two or more vectors acting in different directions from the same point may be replaced by a single vector, the resultant. The resultant has the same effect as the original vectors.

It is also possible to begin with a single vector and think of it as the resultant of two vectors. We usually choose two new vectors in directions that are perpendicular to each other. These two vectors are called the **components** of the vector.

**FIGURE 6–8. The force used to pull a sled can be resolved into its vertical and horizontal components.**

A vector quantity can be resolved into its perpendicular components.

The process of finding the magnitude of a component in a given direction is called **vector resolution**. Consider the sled being pulled in Figure 6–8. A 58 N force is exerted on a rope held at an angle of 30° with the horizontal. The rope pulls both forward and upward on the sled. The only force that pulls the sled forward is the horizontal component, $\vec{F}_h$. The vertical component, $\vec{F}_v$, pulls the sled upward.

The magnitudes of the horizontal and vertical components of $\vec{F}$ are found by first drawing a set of perpendicular axes, Figure 6–9. One axis is horizontal. The other axis is vertical. The vector that represents the force in the rope, $\vec{F}$, is then drawn to scale at the proper angle. To resolve the rope force into the components $\vec{F}_v$ and $\vec{F}_h$, draw perpendicular lines from each axis to the tip of the force vector. The magnitudes of the two components can then be measured using the scale used for $\vec{F}$. Note that we can reverse the process, and show that the resultant of $\vec{F}_v$ and $\vec{F}_h$ is $\vec{F}$, the original force.

Trigonometry can be used to find the magnitudes of perpendicular vector components.

a

$F = 58$ N

$\theta = 30°$

$F_h = 50$ N

$F_v = 29$ N

b

$F = 58$ N

$\theta = 60°$

$F_h = 29$ N

$F_v = 50$ N

**FIGURE 6–9. The magnitudes of horizontal and vertical components of a force depend on its direction.**

In Figure 6–9a, $\vec{F}_v$ and $\vec{F}_h$ are found using trigonometry. In this case,

$$\sin\theta = \frac{\vec{F}_v}{\vec{F}} \qquad \cos\theta = \frac{\vec{F}_h}{\vec{F}}$$

$$\vec{F}_v = \vec{F}\sin\theta \qquad \vec{F}_h = \vec{F}\cos\theta$$

The signs of $\vec{F}_v$ and $\vec{F}_h$ can be found from the vector diagram. If the value for either $\vec{F}_v$ or $\vec{F}_h$ is positive, then $\vec{F}_v$ acts upward and $\vec{F}_h$ acts to the right. If $\vec{F}_v$ is negative, it acts downward. A negative $\vec{F}_h$ acts to the left. If the angle $\theta$ is increased to 60° up from the horizontal, the new $\vec{F}_v$ and $\vec{F}_h$ forces are shown in Figure 6–9b.

Suppose the person pulling the sled keeps the force constant but lowers the rope. The angle, $\theta$, is decreased, and the horizontal component of the force is increased. The vertical component decreases. On the other hand, if the angle between the rope and the horizontal is increased, the horizontal component decreases, and the vertical component increases. Thus, the magnitude of the components change as the direction of the pulling force changes.

As the force becomes more nearly perpendicular to the direction of motion, the horizontal component approaches zero.

# Physics and technology

## SWAYING SKYSCRAPERS

The Sears Tower in Chicago is the world's tallest free-standing structure, rising 443 m above the pavement. There have been plans and models for taller buildings, to a height of more than 1.6 km. High-strength steel and concrete and new engineering designs make it possible to build tall buildings using lighter-weight structures. These less-massive buildings would be more vulnerable to wind buffeting than older buildings with heavy masonry and hundreds of steel columns.

High winds can cause upper floors of tall buildings to sway and elevators to jam. To counteract these effects, tuned mass dampers can be installed near the tops of buildings. Mass dampers may be huge blocks of concrete or large trays filled with lead. Using computer-controlled hydraulic systems, the dampers can be moved so that the resultant force of their motion dampens or reduces motion of the building. The force exerted on the building by the damper is opposite to the motion of the building. Thus the swaying of the building is reduced.

· What factor would you measure in order to determine when a mass damper system should be put into motion?

# PROBLEM SOLVING STRATEGY

In resolving force, velocity, or displacement vectors, choose the direction of the component axes according to the specifics of the problem. Since the choice of axes will not affect the results, choose the set that simplifies the solution. Quite often you will want one axis to represent a horizontal, or right-left direction, and the second axis a vertical, or up-down direction. In other problems, one component is in the east-west direction, while the other is in the north-south direction. Be sure to specify the positive direction for each axis.

The choice of axes does not affect the final solution of a problem.

## Example Problem

### Resolving a Velocity Vector Into Its Components

A wind with a velocity of 40.0 km/h blows toward 30.0°, Figure 6–10.
   **a.** What is the component of the wind's velocity toward 90°?
   **b.** What is the component of the wind's velocity toward 0°?

**Given:** $\vec{v}$ = 40.0 km/h, 30.0°    **Unknowns:** $\vec{v}_{90}$, $\vec{v}_{o}$

**Solution:**
Toward 0° and 90° are positive. Angles are measured from 0°. To find the component toward 90°, $\vec{v}_{90}$, use the relation

$$\sin 30° = \frac{\vec{v}_{90}}{\vec{v}}.$$

Then, $\vec{v}_{90} = \vec{v}(\sin 30.0°)$
             $= (40.0 \text{ km/h})(0.500)$
    $\vec{v}_{90} = 20.0 \text{ km/h at } 90.0°.$

To find the component from 0°, $\vec{v}_{o}$, use the relation

$$\cos 30° = \frac{\vec{v}_{o}}{\vec{v}}.$$

Then, $\vec{v}_{o} = \vec{v}(\cos 30°)$
             $= (40.0 \text{ km/h})(0.866)$
    $\vec{v}_{o} = 34.6 \text{ km/h at } 0.0°.$

**FIGURE 6–10. Use with the Example Problem.**

## Practice Problems

**11.** A heavy box is pulled across a wooden floor with a rope. The rope makes an angle of 60° with the floor. A force of 75 N is exerted on the rope. What is the component of the force parallel to the floor?

**12.** An airplane flies toward 149° at 525 km/h. What is the component of the plane's velocity
   **a.** toward 90°?     **b.** toward 180°?

**13.** A student exerts a force of 72 N along the handle of a lawn mower to push it across the lawn. Find the horizontal component of this force when the handle is held at an angle with the lawn of
   **a.** 60.0°.     **b.** 40.0°.     **c.** 30.0°.

▶ **14.** A hiker walks 14.7 km at an angle of 305° from east. Find the east-west and north-south components of this walk.

## Adding Vectors at Any Angle

Vector resolution can also be used to add two or more vectors that are not perpendicular to each other. First, each vector is resolved into its perpendicular components. Then the vertical components of all the vectors are added together to produce a single vector that acts in the vertical direction. Next, all of the horizontal components of the vectors are added together to produce a single horizontal vector. The resulting vertical and horizontal components can be added together to obtain the final resultant.

If two vectors are acting at angles other than 90° another way to determine the resultant mathematically is by using the law of cosines and the law of sines. These are discussed in Appendix E.

FIGURE 6–11. The resultant applied force on the log can be determined by adding the vertical and horizontal components of the rope forces.

## Example Problem

### Adding Non-Perpendicular Vectors

Two ropes are pulling on a log as shown in Figure 6–11. What is the net force on the log?

**Given:** $\vec{F}_1$ = 12.0 N at 10.0°  **Unknown:** $\vec{F}_{net}$
$\vec{F}_2$ = 8.0 N at 120°  **Basic equations:** $\vec{F}_x = \vec{F} \cos\theta$
$\qquad$ 14.0 N $\qquad$ 316 $\qquad\qquad\qquad$ $\vec{F}_y = \vec{F} \sin\theta$
$\qquad\qquad\qquad\qquad\qquad\qquad$ $\vec{F}_{net}^2 = \vec{F}_{net\,x}^2 + \vec{F}_{net\,y}^2$

**Solution:**
Find the perpendicular components of each force, Figure 6–12.

$$\vec{F}_{1x} = (12.0 \text{ N}) \cos 10.0° = 11.8 \text{ N}$$
$$\vec{F}_{1y} = (12.0 \text{ N}) \sin 10.0° = 2.1 \text{ N}$$
$$\vec{F}_{2x} = (8.0 \text{ N}) \cos 120.0° = -4.0 \text{ N}$$
$$\vec{F}_{2y} = (8.0 \text{ N}) \sin 120.0° = 6.9 \text{ N}$$

Sum x and y components.

$$\vec{F}_{net\,x} = \vec{F}_{1x} + \vec{F}_{2x} = 11.8 \text{ N} + (-4.0 \text{ N}) = 7.8 \text{ N}$$
$$\vec{F}_{net\,y} = \vec{F}_{1y} + \vec{F}_{2y} = 2.1 \text{ N} + 6.9 \text{ N} = 9.0 \text{ N}$$

Non-perpendicular vectors can be added by resolving each into its vertical and horizontal components and summing them.

Find the magnitude of the net force.

$$\vec{F}_{net} = \sqrt{\vec{F}_x^2 + \vec{F}_y^2} = \sqrt{(7.8 \text{ N})^2 + (9.0 \text{ N})^2} = 12 \text{ N}$$

Find the angle of the force.

$$\tan\theta = \frac{\vec{F}_y}{\vec{F}_x} = \frac{9.0 \text{ N}}{7.8 \text{ N}} = 1.15$$

$$= 49°$$

FIGURE 6–12. The forces on the log (a) are resolved into their horizontal and vertical components (b) (c) (d).

a

b

c

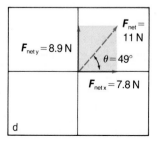

d

## Practice Problems

15. Find the resultant force on the log in the last Example Problem if $\vec{F}_1$ remains the same and $\vec{F}_2$ is changed to 14.0 N at 310.0°.

▶ 16. Three people are pulling on a tree. The first person pulls with 15 N at 65.0°; the second with 16 N at 135°; the third with 11 N at 195°. What is the magnitude and direction of the resultant force on the tree?

## CONCEPT REVIEW

2.1 Joanne pulls on a trunk with a 12-N force. Bev pulls at right angles to Joanne. How hard must Bev pull to make the resultant force on the trunk 13 N?

2.2 Could you ever have a resultant vector shorter than one of its components? equal to a component? Explain.

2.3 You have chosen axes with east and north positive. Angles are measured from the east axis. For what range of angles is the east-west component of a vector positive? For which angles is the east-west component of a vector negative?

2.4 **Critical Thinking:** You are piloting a boat that crosses a fast-moving river. You want to reach a pier directly across from your starting point. Describe how you would select your heading in terms of the components of your velocity.

## Objectives

· **state the requirements for equilibrium.**
· **state the meaning of equilibrant, differentiating between resultant and equilibrant.**
· **specify the proper method of resolving vectors into perpendicular components; be able to choose axes and resolve vectors graphically and analytically.**
· **be able to specify axes, resolve vectors, and solve inclined plane problems.**

# 6.3 APPLICATIONS OF VECTORS

Forces and accelerations are vector quantities, so it seems natural to think of Newton's laws in terms of vector equations. Newton, however, never used vectors. It was not until almost two hundred years later, in the 1880s, that Sir Oliver Heaviside, a British electrician, convinced sceptical physicists that Newton's laws were best understood using vectors. We can use the techniques for adding and resolving vectors to analyse the acceleration of objects that have several forces exerted on them.

FIGURE 6–13. When Darby and Spanky pull with equal force in opposite directions, the forces on the toy are in equilibrium, and the toy does not move. The resultant force is zero (a). Two equal forces exerted in opposite directions on the toy produce equilibrium (b).

a

Darby                    Toy                    Spanky

b                              P

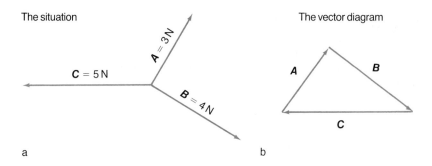

The situation

The vector diagram

**FIGURE 6–14. Forces in equilibrium give a resultant force of zero.**

a

b

## Equilibrium

When the net force—the net sum of all the forces acting—is zero, the object is in **equilibrium**. According to Newton's laws, the object will not be accelerated because there is no net force on it. A simple example of equilibrium is the case in which two equal forces act in opposite directions on an object, as shown in Figure 6–13. The resultant force is zero.

Equilibrium occurs when the net force acting on a point is zero.

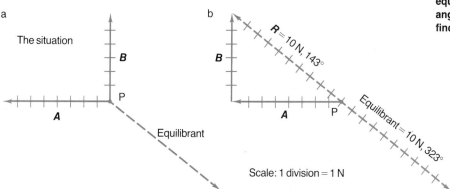

a

The situation

b

Scale: 1 division = 1 N

**FIGURE 6–15. To determine the equilibrant of two forces acting at an angle of 90° with each other, first find the resultant of the two forces.**

Figure 6–14a shows an object at point **P** with three forces acting on it. The 3-N force and the 4-N force are at right angles to each other. When the three vectors are added head-to-tail, they form a closed triangle, as in Figure 6–14b. The distance from the tail of the first vector to the head of the last vector is then zero, so the length of the resultant is zero. The length of the resultant is zero, so the vector sum is zero. Therefore, the three forces produce zero net force on point **P**. The object at point **P** is in equilibrium.

When the vector sum of forces acting at one point is not zero, a force can be applied that will produce equilibrium. This force is called the **equilibrant** (ee KWIL uh bruhnt) **force**. The equilibrant force is the single additional force that, if applied at the same point as the other forces, will produce equilibrium.

To find the equilibrant of two or more forces, first find the resultant force. The equilibrant force is equal in magnitude to the resultant, but opposite in direction. In Figure 6–15, the equilibrant force is a 10-N force whose direction is opposite to the direction of the resultant.

### POCKET LAB

#### FORCE VECTORS I

Choose two of the largest students in your class to pull on the opposite ends of a strong 10 m long rope. Does the rope appear to be straight? Now have the smallest student attempt to push down on the middle of the rope with one finger. Is it possible for the students to keep the rope taut and straight? Explain.

22.5°

22.5°

**168 N**

**FIGURE 6–16. Use with the Example Problem.**

Sometimes the equilibrant is exerted by two or more forces. For example, in the chapter-opening photo, the upward force that balances the weight of the performer is provided by the cable. The force exerted by the two ends of the cable can be found by following the method in the example below.

## Example Problem

### Finding Forces When Components Are Known

A sign that weighs 168 N is supported by ropes a and b, Figure 6–16, that make 22.5° angles with the horizontal. The sign is not moving. What forces do the ropes exert on the sign?

**Given:** The sign is in equilibrium.

weight of sign, $\vec{W}$ = 168.0 N (down)

angles ropes make with horizontal, 22.5°

**Unknowns:** forces of rope a, $\vec{A}$
forces of rope b, $\vec{B}$

**Basic equations:** In equilibrium, net force is zero,

$$\vec{A} + \vec{B} + \vec{W} = 0.$$

For any force, $\vec{F}$

$$\vec{F}_h = \vec{F}\cos\theta, \ \vec{F}_v = \vec{F}\sin\theta.$$

**Solution:**

Choose a coordinate system with horizontal and vertical axes. The direction of $\vec{W}$ is down, so the direction of $\vec{A} + \vec{B}$ is up.

The sum $\vec{A} + \vec{B}$ has no horizontal components, so the horizontal components of $\vec{A}$ and $\vec{B}$, $\vec{A}_h$ and $\vec{B}_h$, have equal magnitudes.

Now, $\vec{A}_h = \vec{A}\cos 22.5°$ and $\vec{B}_h = \vec{B}\cos 22.5°$.

Since $\vec{A}_h = \vec{B}_h$, the magnitudes of $\vec{A}$ and $\vec{B}$ must be equal.

The magnitude of the sum of the vertical components of $\vec{A}$ and $\vec{B}$ equals the magnitude of the weight of the sign, 168.0 N. That is,

$$\vec{A}_v + \vec{B}_v = 168.0 \text{ N}.$$

Since $\vec{A}_v = \vec{A}\sin 22.5°$ and $\vec{B}_v = \vec{B}\sin 22.5°$ and $\vec{A} = \vec{B}$,

$$\vec{A}_v = \vec{B}_v.$$

Thus,     $\vec{A}_v = \vec{B}_v = 1/2(168.0 \text{ N}) = 84.0 \text{ N}.$

and     $\vec{A} = \dfrac{\vec{A}_v}{\sin 22.5°} = 220 \text{ N}$

$$\vec{B} = \vec{A} = 220 \text{ N}$$

The force in each rope is larger than the weight of the sign. Try different angles. As the angle between the ropes and the horizontal increases, the horizontal components of the forces become smaller. When the ropes are vertical, the horizontal components are zero, and each rope exerts only half the weight of the sign, 84.0 N. Note that since the forces exerted by the ropes must always have vertical components adding to 168.0 N, the ropes can never be totally horizontal.

# Practice Problems

17. A net force of 55 N acts due west on an object. What added single force on the object produces equilibrium?

18. Two forces act on an object. One force is 6.0 N horizontally. The second force is 8.0 N vertically.
    a. Find the magnitude and direction of the resultant.
    b. If the object is in equilibrium, find the magnitude and direction of the force that produces equilibrium.

19. A 62-N force acts at 30.0° and a second 62-N force acts at 60.0°.
    a. Determine the resultant force.
    b. What is the magnitude and direction of the force that produces equilibrium?

20. Two forces act on an object. A 36-N force acts at 225°. A 48-N force acts at 315°. What would be the magnitude and direction of their equilibrant?

21. The sign in the last Example Problem is now hung by ropes that each make an angle of 42° with the horizontal. What force does each rope exert?

▶ 22. The people who hung the sign decided to raise it higher by pulling the two ropes more horizontal. They increase the force on each rope to 575 N and keep the angles equal. What angle does each rope make with the horizontal now?

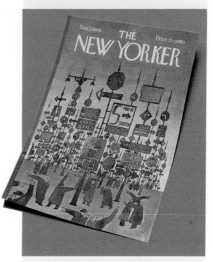
## Gravitational Force and Inclined Planes

The gravitational force acting on an object is directed toward the centre of Earth. The object's weight, $\vec{W}$, can be represented by a vector directed down. *Down* is the direction an object falls.

Figure 6–17 shows a trunk resting on an inclined plane. To analyse the forces acting on the trunk, the weight of the trunk, $\vec{W}$, is resolved into two components perpendicular to each other. When doing inclined plane problems, we may choose one axis along the incline, and the second axis perpendicular to it. Thus, we have one component, $\vec{F}_{\parallel}$, the parallel force, that acts parallel to the incline. The second component, $\vec{F}_{\perp}$, called the perpendicular force, acts perpendicular to the incline.

When solving inclined problems, it is convenient to choose a set of axes perpendicular and parallel to the plane.

**FIGURE 6–17. Using an inclined plane does not require less work, but often makes a job easier.**

**FIGURE 6–18.** The weight vector $\vec{W}$ is resolved into two components. One component acts parallel to the plane. The other acts perpendicular to the plane.

Look at the right triangle formed by the surface of the incline and its horizontal and vertical sides. It is similar to the right triangle formed by $\vec{W}$, $\vec{F}_\perp$, and $\vec{F}_\parallel$ because the corresponding sides are mutually perpendicular. Therefore the angles are equal. If $\theta$ and $\vec{W}$ are both known, a vector diagram similar to Figure 6–18 can be drawn, and the force $\vec{W}$ resolved into the components $\vec{F}_\parallel$ and $\vec{F}_\perp$. You can calculate the values of $\vec{F}_\parallel$ and $\vec{F}_\perp$ using either graphical or trigonometric methods.

## Example Problem

### Finding $\vec{F}_\perp$ and $\vec{F}_\parallel$

A trunk weighing 562 N is resting on a plane inclined at 30° from the horizontal, Figure 6–18. Find the components of the weight parallel and perpendicular to the plane.

**Given:** weight, $\vec{W}$ = 562 N
   plane angle with respect to horizontal, $\theta$ = 30.0°

**Unknowns:** perpendicular component, $\vec{F}_\perp$; parallel component, $\vec{F}_\parallel$

**Solution:**
Resolve weight into components perpendicular and parallel to plane.

$$\sin \theta = \frac{\vec{F}_\parallel}{\vec{W}}; \text{ so, } \vec{F}_\parallel = \vec{W} \sin \theta. \quad \cos \theta = \frac{\vec{F}_\perp}{\vec{W}}; \text{ so, } \vec{F}_\perp = \vec{W} \cos \theta.$$

$$\vec{F}_\parallel = +(562 \text{ N})(\sin 30.0°) \qquad \vec{F}_\perp = +(562 \text{ N})(\cos 30.0°)$$
$$= +(562 \text{ N})(0.500) \qquad\qquad = +(562 \text{ N})(0.866)$$
$$= +281 \text{ N} \qquad\qquad\qquad\quad = +487 \text{ N}$$

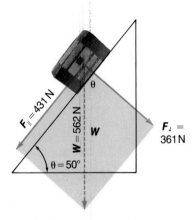

**FIGURE 6–19.** As the angle of the incline increases, the component of the weight acting parallel to the plane increases. The component that acts perpendicular to the plane decreases.

The directions of the two components are shown on Figure 6–18. Note that as the incline in Figure 6–19 becomes steeper, $\vec{F}_\parallel$ becomes greater and $\vec{F}_\perp$ becomes smaller.

What other forces act on the trunk besides the force of gravity? The inclined plane exerts an upward force perpendicular to its surface, the normal force, $\vec{F}_N$. Since the trunk has no acceleration perpendicular to the plane, all forces in that direction must be balanced. Therefore,

$$\vec{F}_N + \vec{F}_1 = 0$$
$$\vec{F}_N - \vec{W} \cos \theta = 0$$
$$\vec{F}_N = \vec{W} \cos \theta.$$

If there is no friction between the trunk and the plane, the only force on the trunk along the plane is the parallel component of its weight, $\vec{F}_\parallel = W \sin \theta$. According to Newton's second law, the acceleration,

$$\vec{a} = \frac{\vec{F}}{m} = \frac{W \sin \theta}{m}.$$

But, $W/m = \vec{g}$, so the acceleration of the trunk is $\vec{a} = \vec{g} \sin \theta$. As the plane becomes more horizontal, the acceleration approaches zero. When the plane is tilted more vertically, the acceleration approaches closer to $\vec{g} = 9.80 \text{ m/s}^2$.

## Example Problem

### Finding Acceleration Down a Plane

The 562 N trunk is on a frictionless plane inclined at 30.0° from the horizontal. Find the acceleration of the trunk. What is its direction?

**Given:** weight of trunk,
$W = 562$ N
angle of plane,
$\theta = 30.0°$

**Unknown:** acceleration down the plane, $a$

**Basic equations:** $\vec{F} = m\vec{a}$
$W = m\vec{g}$
$\vec{F}_\parallel = +W \sin \theta$

**Solution:**
Find net force on trunk.
$\vec{F}_\parallel = +W \sin \theta = +mg \sin \theta$
Find acceleration.
$$\vec{a} = \frac{\vec{F}}{m} = \frac{+W \sin \theta}{m} = +\vec{g} \sin \theta$$
$$= +(9.80 \text{ m/s}^2)(0.500)$$
$$\vec{a} = +4.90 \text{ m/s}^2$$

The acceleration is down the plane.

Usually there is friction between the inclined plane and the object on it. The resolution of weight on an inclined plane can be used to measure the force of friction or the coefficient of static friction between the two surfaces. Put a coin on one of your textbooks. Now slowly lift the cover. The coin will remain at rest until the cover reaches a certain angle. Then the coin begins to accelerate down the book.

The downward force along the cover is the parallel component of the coin's weight, proportional to sin $\theta$. As the cover angle is increased, the parallel component of the weight increases. It is balanced by the static friction force. Static friction can never be larger than $\mu \vec{F}_N$, so when the force along the cover exceeds the frictional force, the coin starts to move. Once the coin starts to move, static friction is replaced by sliding friction, which is a smaller force. The coin, with a non-zero net force on it, accelerates down the book. If you measure the angle of the cover when the coin first begins to move, you can determine the coefficient of static friction. Try different objects and books. Which combination has the greatest coefficient of static friction? the least?

FIGURE 6–20. By reducing friction between the slide and the slider, water adds excitement to a water slide.

**FIGURE 6–21. Use with Example Problem.**

# Example Problem

## Finding the Coefficient of Static Friction

A coin placed on the cover of a book just begins to move when the cover makes an angle of 38° with the horizontal, Figure 6–21. What is the coefficient of static friction between the cover and coin?

**Given:** angle of inclined plane,
$\theta = 38°$

**Unknown:** $\mu$

**Basic equations:** maximum static friction,
$$\vec{F_f} = \mu \vec{F_N}$$
$$\vec{F_\perp} = \vec{W} \cos \theta$$
$$\vec{F_\parallel} = \vec{W} \sin \theta$$

**Solution:**
Because the coin stays on the book cover, the forces perpendicular to the cover are equal in magnitude.
$$\vec{F_N} = \vec{F_\perp} = \vec{W} \cos \theta$$
As long as the coin is not moving, the forces parallel to the book cover are equal in magnitude.
$$\vec{F_f} = \vec{F_\parallel} = \vec{W} \sin \theta$$
When motion is just ready to start, friction is at its maximum.
$$\vec{F_f} = \mu \vec{F_N}$$
Thus, $\vec{W} \sin \theta = \mu \vec{W} \cos \theta$.

This means that $\mu = \sin \theta / \cos \theta = \tan \theta$. In this case, $\mu = \tan 38° = 0.78$.

# Practice Problems

**23.** The 562-N trunk is placed on an inclined plane that forms a 66° angle with the horizontal.
  **a.** Calculate the values of $\vec{F_\perp}$ and $\vec{F_\parallel}$.
  **b.** Compare your results with those given above for the same trunk on a 30° incline.

**24.** A car weighing $1.2 \times 10^4$ N is parked on a 36° slope.
  **a.** Find the force tending to cause the car to roll down the hill.
  **b.** What is the force the car exerts perpendicular to the hill?

**25.** The brakes in the car in Practice Problem 24 fail, and the car starts to roll down the hill. Assume there is no friction.
  **a.** What is the acceleration of the car?
  **b.** After it has moved 30 m, how fast is it moving?
  **c.** Could a sprinter run this fast?

▶ **26.** The roof on a house rises 1.00 m over a horizontal distance of 3.50 m. A 71.0-kg roofer stands on the roof. Is the frictional force that keeps the roofer from slipping equal in magnitude to $\vec{F_\perp}$ or $\vec{F_\parallel}$? What is its magnitude?

**FIGURE 6–22. Use with Concept Review 3.1.**

# CONCEPT REVIEW

**3.1** Figure 6–22 shows the shoe of a hiker who is climbing a hill. The two components of the force the person exerts on the shoe are shown. On a copy of the figure, draw the equilibrant force on the shoe that keeps the shoe in equilibrium. What exerts that force?

a          b

**FIGURE 6–23. Use with Concept Review 3.2.**

**3.2** Your mother asks you to hang a heavy painting. The frame has a wire across the back, and you plan to hook this wire over a nail in the wall. The wire will break if the force pulling on it is too big. You don't want it to break. Should it look like the Figure 6–23a or 6–23b? Explain.

**3.3** The snow under the skier in Figure 6–24 is so slippery that you can ignore friction. Copy the drawing and draw vectors showing the forces on the skier and the resultant force. Identify the cause of each force.

**3.4** **Critical Thinking:** The skier in the problem above suddenly runs into rough snow. As a result of the force of the snow, the skier moves with constant velocity. Add a vector representing this force on your drawing.

**FIGURE 6–24. Use with Concept Review 3.3, 3.4.**

# CHAPTER
## 6 REVIEW
. . . . . . . . . . . . . . . . . . . . .

## SUMMARY

### 6.1 Graphical Method of Vector Addition

· The resultant is the sum of two or more vectors.
· To add two vectors graphically, place the tail of the second vector at the head of the first vector. Draw the resultant vector from the tail of the first vector to the head of the second vector.
· The resultant of several concurrent vectors can be found by the same procedures used for adding two vectors.
· Perpendicular components of vector quantities are independent of each other.

### 6.2 Analytical Method of Vector Addition

· Perpendicular vectors may be added analytically by using the Pythagorean relation and the definition of the tangent of an angle.

· A vector can be resolved into two perpendicular components.
· Vectors at any angles may be added by finding their components, adding all vertical and horizontal components separately, and then finding the resultant.

### 6.3 Applications of Vectors

· When no net force acts on an object, it is in equilibrium.
· The equilibrant is the single force that is equal in magnitude and opposite in direction to the resultant of several forces acting on a point. This produces equilibrium.
· The weight of an object on an inclined plane can be resolved into two perpendicular components. One component, $\vec{F}_\parallel$, acts parallel to the plane; the other component, $\vec{F}_\perp$, acts perpendicular to the plane.

# KEY TERMS

resultant
trigonometry
sine (sin)
cosine (cos)
tangent (tan)

components
vector resolution
equilibrium
equilibrant force

# REVIEWING CONCEPTS

1. What method is used to add vectors graphically?
2. A vector is to be added graphically to a second vector. Which of the following may you do to the first vector: move it, rotate it, or change its length?
3. In your own words, write a clear definition of the resultant of two or more vectors. Do not tell how to find it, but tell what it represents.
4. Does anything happen to the forces that produce the resultant force? Do the original forces disappear?
5. How is the resultant force affected when force vectors are added in a different order?
6. Why are vectors $\vec{A}$ and $\vec{B}$ in Figure 6–25 considered to represent different forces?

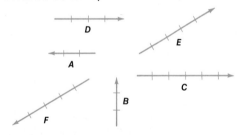

**FIGURE 6–25. Use with Reviewing Concepts 6 and Problems 2, 5, 6.**

7. We have often set up "vertical" and "horizontal" axes. How could you do this in the real world? How could you find the vertical when you are on a hill?
8. What is meant about the forces acting on a book if we state that the book is in a state of equilibrium?
9. How can the equilibrant of two or more forces be found?
10. Can an object in equilibrium be moving? Explain.
11. What is the sum of three vectors that form a triangle? Assuming that the vectors are forces, what does this imply about the object on which the forces act?

12. A book is on an inclined plane.
   a. Describe two convenient components of the weight of the book.
   b. How are the magnitudes of these components related to the angle of the incline?

# APPLYING CONCEPTS

1. A vector drawn 15 mm long represents a velocity of 30 m/s. How long should you draw a vector to represent a velocity of 20 m/s?
2. If a vector that is 1 cm long represents a force of 5 N, how many newtons does a vector 3 cm long, drawn to the same scale, represent?
3. What is the largest possible resultant force of two forces with magnitudes of 3 N and 4 N? What is the smallest possible resultant? Draw a sketch to demonstrate your answers.
4. Two dogs pull on a toy. One pulls with a force of 10 N, the other with a force of 15 N.
   a. In what relative directions can the dogs act to give the toy the smallest acceleration?
   b. Can they ever result in zero acceleration?
5. Two vectors are originally parallel. How does the resultant vector change as the angle between the two vectors increases to 180°?
6. A right triangle has two sides $A$ and $B$. If $\tan \theta = A/B$,
   a. which side of the triangle is longer if $\tan \theta$ is greater than one?
   b. which side of the triangle is longer if $\tan \theta$ is less than one?
   c. what does it mean if $\tan \theta$ equals one?
7. Gayle is pushing a lawn spreader across her lawn. Can she increase the horizontal component of the force without changing the force that she is applying to the spreader handle? Explain.
8. The transmitting tower of a TV station is held upright by guy wires that extend from the top of the tower to the ground. The wires make a 30.0° angle with the tower. The force along the guy wires can be resolved into two perpendicular components. Which one is larger?
9. What is the net force that acts on an object when it is in equilibrium?
10. When stretching a clothesline or a strand of wire between two posts, it is relatively easy to pull one end of the line hard enough to remove most of the slack. However, it is almost always necessary to resort to some mechani-

cal device that can exert a greater-than-human force to take out the last of the slack to make the line completely horizontal. Why is this true? Disregard any stretching of the line.

11. Bill is trying to get a car unstuck from mud using a long line of strong rope. Which method would allow the greater force to be exerted on the car? Why?
    a. Bill ties one end of the rope to the car and pulls on the other end.
    b. Bill ties one end on the car and the other to a tree, then stands about halfway between the two ends and pushes on the rope perpendicular to it.

12. The weight of a book sliding down a frictionless inclined plane can be broken into two vector components: one acting parallel to the plane, and the other acting perpendicular to the plane.
    a. At what angle are these two components equal?
    b. At what angle is the component parallel to the plane equal to zero?
    c. At what angle is the component parallel to the plane equal to the weight?

13. A student puts two objects on a physics book and carefully tilts the cover. At a small angle, one object starts to slide. At a large angle, the other begins to slide. Which has the greater coefficient of static friction?

# PROBLEMS

## 6.1 Graphical Method of Adding Vectors

1. What is the vector sum of a 65-N force acting due east and a 32-N force acting due west?
2. Graphically find the sum of the following pairs of vectors in Figure 6–25.
    a. $\vec{D}$ and $\vec{C}$
    b. $\vec{A}$ and $\vec{D}$
    c. $\vec{C}$ and $\vec{A}$
    d. $\vec{A}$ and $\vec{C}$
    e. $\vec{E}$ and $\vec{F}$
3. a. What is the resultant of a pair of forces, 100 N upward and 75 N downward?
    b. What is their resultant if they both act downward?
4. An airplane normally flies at 200 km/h. What is the resultant velocity of the airplane if
    a. it experiences a 50-km/h tail wind?
    b. it experiences a 50-km/h head wind?

5. Graphically add the following pairs of vectors in Figure 6–25.
    a. $\vec{C}$ and $\vec{D}$
    b. $\vec{C}$ and $\vec{E}$
    c. $\vec{D}$ and $\vec{E}$
6. Graphically add the following vectors in Figure 6–25.
    a. $\vec{A} + \vec{C} + \vec{D}$
    b. $\vec{D} + \vec{E} + \vec{B}$
    c. $\vec{B} + \vec{D} + \vec{F}$
7. Three forces act on point **P**. Force $\vec{A}$ has a magnitude of 80.0 N and is directed at 60.0°. Force $\vec{B}$ has a magnitude of 70.0 N and is directed at 0.0°. Force $\vec{C}$ has a magnitude of 40.0 N and is directed at 315°.
    a. Graphically add these three forces in the order $\vec{A} + \vec{B} + \vec{C}$.
    b. Graphically add these three forces in the order $\vec{C} + \vec{B} + \vec{A}$.
    c. What is noted about the solutions in each case?

## 6.2 Analytical Method of Adding Vectors

▶ 8. You head downstream on a river in a canoe. You can paddle at 5.0 km/h and the river is flowing at 2.0 km/h. How far downstream will you be in 30 min?

9. You walk 30 m south and 30 m east. Draw and add vectors for these two displacements. Compute the resultant.

▶ 10. A ship leaves its home port expecting to travel to a port 500 km due south. Before it can move, a severe storm comes up and blows the ship 100 km due east. How far is the ship from its destination? In what direction must the ship travel to reach its destination?

11. A hiker leaves camp and, using a compass, walks 4 km E, 6 km S, 3 km E, 5 km N, 10 km W, 8 km N, and 3 km S. At the end of three days, the hiker is lost. By drawing a diagram, compute how far the hiker is from camp and which direction should be taken to get back to camp.

▶ 12. Three forces act simultaneously on point **J**. One force is 10.0 N north; the second is 15.0 N west; the third is 15.0 N 30.0° east of north. Determine the magnitude and direction of the resultant force.

13. Diane rows a boat at 8.0 m/s directly across a river that flows at 6.0 m/s.
    a. What is the resultant speed of the boat?

**b.** If the stream is 240 m wide, how long will it take Diane to row across?

**c.** How far downstream will Diane be?

**14.** Dave rows a boat across a river at 4.0 m/s. The river flows at 6.0 m/s and is 360 m across.

**a.** In what direction, relative to the shore, does Dave's boat go?

**b.** How long does it take Dave to cross the river?

**c.** How far downstream is Dave's landing point?

**d.** How long would it take Dave to cross the river if there were no current?

**15.** Kyle is flying a plane due north at 225 km/h as a wind carries it due east at 55 km/h. Find the magnitude and direction of the plane's resultant velocity analytically.

**16.** Sue and Jenny kick a soccer ball at exactly the same time. Sue's foot exerts a force of 66 N north. Jenny's foot exerts a force of 88 N east. What is the magnitude and direction of the resultant force on the ball?

**17.** Kym is in a boat travelling 3.8 m/s straight across a river 240 m wide. The river is flowing at 1.6 m/s.

**a.** What is Kym's resultant velocity?

**b.** How long does it take Kym to cross the river?

**c.** How far is Kym downstream when she reaches the other side?

**18.** A weather station releases a weather balloon. The balloon's buoyancy accelerates it straight up at 15 m/s². At the same time, a wind accelerates it horizontally at 6.5 m/s². What is the magnitude and direction (with reference to the horizontal) of the resultant acceleration?

**19.** A descent vehicle landing on the moon has a vertical velocity toward the surface of the moon of 35 m/s. At the same time, it has a horizontal velocity of 55 m/s.

**a.** At what speed does the vehicle move along its descent path?

**b.** At what angle with the vertical is this path?

▶ **20.** Kyle wishes to fly to a point 450 km due south in 3.00 h. A wind is blowing from the west at 50 km/h. Compute the proper heading and speed that Kyle must choose in order to reach his destination on time.

**21.** Dan applies a force of 92 N on a heavy box by using a rope held at an angle of 45° with the horizontal. What are the vertical and horizontal components of the 92-N force?

**22.** Beth, a construction worker, attempts to pull a stake out of the ground by pulling on a rope that is attached to the stake. The rope makes an angle of 60.0° with the horizontal. Beth exerts a force of 125 N on the rope. What is the magnitude of the upward component of the force acting on the stake?

▶ **23.** A 40-kg crate is pulled across the ice with a rope. A force of 100 N is applied at an angle of 30° with the horizontal. Neglecting friction, calculate

**a.** the acceleration of the crate.

**b.** the upward force the ice exerts on the crate as it is pulled.

▶ **24.** Joe pushes on the handle of a 10-kg lawn spreader. The handle makes a 45° angle with the horizontal. Joe wishes to accelerate the spreader from rest to 1.39 m/s in 1.5 s. What force must Joe apply to the handle? Neglect friction.

**25.** Tammy leaves the office, drives 26 km due north, then turns onto a second highway and continues in a direction of 30.0° north of east for 62 km. What is her total displacement from the office?

**26.** Find the magnitude of the resultant of a 40-N force and a 70-N force acting concurrently when the angle between them is

**a.** 0.0°.   **b.** 30.0°.   **c.** 60.0°.   **d.** 90.0°.
**e.** 180.0°.

**27.** Three people attempt to haul a heavy sign to the roof of a building by using three ropes attached to the sign. Abby stands directly above the sign and pulls straight up on a rope. Eric and Kim stand on either side of Abby. Their ropes form 30.0° angles with Abby's rope. A force of 102 N is applied on each rope. What is the net upward force acting on the sign? See Figure 6-26.

**FIGURE 6-26. Use with Problem 27.**

**28.** A river flows toward 90°. Mark, a riverboat pilot, heads the boat at 297° and is able to go straight across the river at 6.0 m/s. See Figure 6–27.
  **a.** What is the velocity of the current?
  **b.** What is the velocity of the boat as seen from the river bank?

**FIGURE 6–27. Use with Problem 28.**

### 6.3 Applications of Vectors

**29.** An object in equilibrium has three forces exerted on it. A 33-N force acts at 90°, and a 44-N force acts at 60°. What is the magnitude and direction of the third force?

**30.** Five forces act on an object: the first, 60 N at 90°; the second, 40 N at 0°; the third, 80 N at 270°; the fourth, 40 N at 180°; and the fifth, 50 N at 60°. What is the magnitude and direction of a sixth force that produces equilibrium of the object?

**31.** A street lamp weighs 150 N. It is supported equally by two wires that form an angle of 120° with each other.
  **a.** What is the tension of each of these wires?
  **b.** If the angle between the wires is reduced to 90.0°, what new force does each wire exert?
  **c.** As the angle between the wires decrease, what happens to the force in the wire?

**32.** Joe wishes to hang a sign weighing 750 N so that cable A attached to the store makes a 30.0° angle as shown in Figure 6–28. Cable B is attached to an adjoining building. Calculate the necessary tension in cable B.

**FIGURE 6–28. Use with Problem 32.**

**33.** Rachel pulls her 18-kg suitcase at a constant speed by pulling on a handle that makes an angle $\theta$ with the horizontal. The frictional force on the suitcase is 27 N and Rachel exerts a 43-N force on the handle.
  **a.** What angle does the handle make with the horizontal?
  **b.** What is the normal force exerted on the suitcase?

**34.** You place a box weighing 215 N on an inclined plane that makes a 35.0° angle with the horizontal. Compute the component of the gravitational force acting down the inclined plane.

**35.** You slide a 325-N trunk up a 20.0° inclined plane with a constant velocity by exerting a force of 211 N parallel to the inclined plane.
  **a.** What is the component of the trunk's weight parallel to the plane?
  **b.** What is the sum of your applied force, friction, and the parallel component of the trunk's weight? Why?
  **c.** What is the size and direction of the friction force?
  **d.** What is the coefficient of friction?

**36.** What force would you have to exert on the trunk in Problem 35 so that it would slide down the plane with a constant velocity? What would be the direction of the force?

**37.** A 2.5-kg block slides down a 25° inclined plane with constant acceleration. The block starts from rest at the top. At the bottom, its velocity reaches 0.65 m/s. The length of the incline is 1.6 m.
  **a.** What is the acceleration of the block?
  **b.** What is the coefficient of friction between the plane and block?
  **c.** Does the result of either **a** or **b** depend on the mass of the block?

## THINKING PHYSIC-LY

Weight lifting or "pumping iron" has become very popular in the last few years. When lifting a barbell, which grip will exert less force on the lifter's arms: one in which the arms are extended straight upward from the body so they are at right angles to the bars, or one in which the arms are spread so that the bar is gripped closer to the weights? Explain.

# CHAPTER 7

# Motion in Two Dimensions

◀ $V_x + V_y$

After adjusting the strobe light, Jamahl and Stacey watched the water droplets spraying into a sink. Jamahl was surprised to see the drops spread apart as they fell into the sink. Stacey said she could explain it. What explanation would she give?

The graceful arch of the water drops in the photo on the facing page illustrates motion you have probably seen many times. The flight of baseballs, basketballs, and golf balls follows the same path. Mathematically, the curve is a parabola. Newton's laws of motion are all that are needed to understand how objects like water drops and golf balls move.

## ✓ Concept Check

The following terms or concepts from earlier chapters are important for a good understanding of this chapter. If you are not familiar with them, you should review them before studying this chapter
· velocity, Chapter 3
· acceleration, Chapter 4
· motion of falling objects, Chapter 5
· resolution of vectors, Chapter 6
· independence of vector quantities, Chapter 6

# Objectives

· show that you understand the independence of vertical and horizontal velocities of a projectile by solving problems of projectiles launched horizontally.
· find the maximum height and range of projectiles launched at an arbitrary angle if initial velocity and angle are given.

The path of a projectile is its trajectory.

The horizontal and vertical velocities of a projectile are independent.

# 7.1 PROJECTILE MOTION

Objects launched like the water drops are **projectiles.** The path they follow is called a **trajectory.** The motion of a projectile is described in terms of its position, velocity, and acceleration. These are all vector quantities, and we have seen that the perpendicular components of vector quantities are independent. How does this fact let us analyze the motion?

## Independence of Motion in Two Dimensions

Let's start with a simple trajectory. Figure 7–1 shows a photograph of two falling golf balls, taken with a strobe light that flashed 30 times each second. One ball was launched horizontally at 2.0 m/s, the other ball was simply dropped. Notice that the thrown ball moves the same distance to the right during each time interval. That is, its horizontal velocity is constant. The dropped ball also has a constant horizontal velocity, equal to zero. In each case, the force acting on the ball has no horizontal component, so there is no horizontal acceleration.

The golf ball photograph shows a remarkable property of motion. Look carefully at the height of the balls. At each flash, the vertical position of the dropped ball is the same as that of the thrown ball. This means that the vertical motion of the thrown ball and the dropped ball are the same. In addition, the change in vertical position between two successive flashes is the same for the two balls. This means that their average vertical velocities during these intervals also must be equal. The spaces between images grow larger because both balls are accelerated downward by the force of gravity. The photograph shows that the horizontal motion of the thrown ball does not affect its vertical motion at all.

FIGURE 7–1. A flash photograph of two golf balls released simultaneously. Both balls were allowed to fall freely, but one was projected horizontally with an initial velocity of 2.00 m/s. The light flashes are 1/30 s apart.

**FIGURE 7–2. To the passenger, the apple falls straight down. To the observer on the sidewalk, the path of the apple is a parabola.**

Suppose that a car slowly passes as you stand by the side of a road, Figure 7–2. A passenger in the car accidentally drops an apple out the window. Imagine that you can watch the apple only. What path will you see it take? Remember that the apple has the same horizontal velocity as the car. From your frame of reference, or point of view, the path will be curved like that of the launched golf ball. Will the passenger see the same path? The passenger and the apple both move with the same horizontal velocity. Thus, the passenger will see a straight vertical path like that of the dropped golf ball. The trajectory as seen by the two observers will be different, but both observers will agree that it takes the same time for the apple to hit the ground. Thus, the shape of the trajectory and the horizontal motion depend on the viewpoint, or frame of reference, of the observer. The vertical motion does not.

The shape of a trajectory depends on the viewpoint of the observer.

The independence of vertical and horizontal motion and our motion equations can be used to determine the position of thrown objects. If we call the horizontal displacement $\vec{x}$ and the initial horizontal velocity $\vec{v}_x$ then, at time $t$,

$$\vec{x} = \vec{v}_x t$$
$$\text{and } \vec{v}_{xf} = \vec{v}_i.$$

The equations for an object falling with constant acceleration, $\vec{g}$, describe the vertical motion. If $\vec{y}$ is the vertical displacement, the initial vertical velocity of the object is $\vec{v}_y$. At time $t$, the vertical displacement is

$$\vec{y} = \vec{v}_y t + \tfrac{1}{2}\vec{g}t^2$$
$$\text{also, } \vec{v}_{yf} = \vec{v}_y + \vec{g}t.$$

Using these equations, we can analyse the motion of projectiles. The simplicity of these calculations is due, in part, to the fact that for the golf ball, the force due to air resistance is negligible. For an object such as a feather, it could be a very important factor.

## POCKET LAB

### WHERE THE BALL BOUNCES

Place a golf ball in your hand and extend your arm sideways so the ball is at shoulder height. Drop the ball and have a lab partner start a stopwatch when the ball strikes the floor and stop it the next time the ball strikes the floor. Where would you expect the ball to hit when you walk at a steady speed and drop the ball? Would the ball take the same time to bounce? Try it. Where does it hit? Does it take more time?

**Trajectory of stone**

**FIGURE 7-3. The path of a projectile thrown horizontally.**

The horizontal velocity is constant. The vertical velocity is constantly changing because of gravity.

## Objects Launched Horizontally

We'll first look at the motion of objects that have an initial vertical velocity of zero.

## Example Problem

### Projectile Launched Horizontally

A stone is thrown horizontally at $+15$ m/s from the top of a cliff 44 m high, Figure 7-3. **a.** How long does the stone take to reach the bottom of the cliff? **b.** How far from the base of the cliff does the stone strike the ground? **c.** Sketch the trajectory of the stone.

**Given:** horizontal velocity,
$\vec{v}_x = +15$ m/s
initial vertical velocity,
$\vec{v}_y = 0$ m/s
vertical acceleration,
$\vec{g} = -9.80$ m/s$^2$
initial height, 44 m

**Unknowns: a.** time of flight, $t$
**b.** horizontal displacement, $x$
**Basic equations:** $\vec{x} = \vec{v}_x t$
$\vec{y} = \vec{v}_y t + \frac{1}{2}\vec{g}t^2$

**Solution:**
The cliff height is 44 m, so if we assign the initial position $y = 0.0$, then at the end of the flight (time $t$) the position is $\vec{y} = -44$ m.

**a.** We know all quantities in the equation $y = \vec{v}_y t + \frac{1}{2}\vec{g}t^2$ except the unknown, the time $t$. Since $\vec{v}_y = 0.0$, $y = \frac{1}{2}\vec{g}t^2$, or $t^2 = 2\frac{y}{\vec{g}}$.

$$t^2 = \frac{2(-44 \text{ m})}{-9.80 \text{ m/s}^2} = 9.0 \text{ s}^2$$
$$t = \sqrt{9.0 \text{ s}^2} = 3.0 \text{ s}$$

**b.** To find the horizontal displacement use
$$\vec{x} = \vec{v}_x t$$
$$= (+15 \text{ m/s})(3.0 \text{ s}) = +45 \text{ m}$$

**c.** See Figure 7-3.

## Practice Problems

1. A stone is thrown horizontally at a speed of $+5.0$ m/s from the top of a cliff 78.4 m high.
   **a.** How long does it take the stone to reach the bottom of the cliff?
   **b.** How far from the base of the cliff does the stone strike the ground?
   **c.** What are the horizontal and vertical components of the velocity of the stone just before it hits the ground?
2. How would the three answers to Practice Problem 1 change if
   **a.** the stone were thrown with twice the horizontal speed?
   **b.** the stone were thrown with the same speed but the cliff was twice as high?
3. A steel ball rolls with constant velocity across a tabletop 0.950 m high. It rolls off and hits the ground $+0.352$ m horizontally from the edge of the table. How fast was the ball rolling?

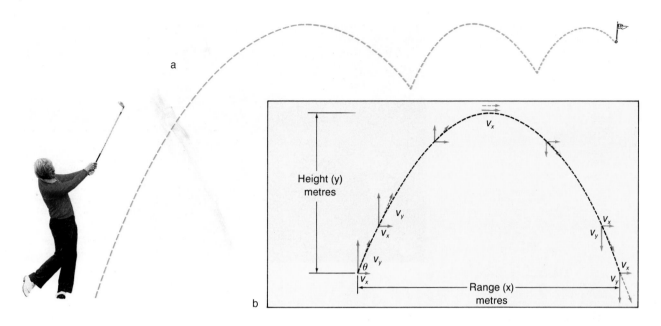

a

b

**FIGURE 7–4. The flight of a golf ball can be described in terms of horizontal and vertical components.**

▶ **4.** An auto, moving too fast on a horizontal stretch of mountain road, slides off the road, falling into deep snow 43.9 m below the road and 87.7 m beyond the edge of the road.
  **a.** How long did the auto take to fall?
  **b.** How fast was it going when it left the road? (in m/s and km/h)
  **c.** What was its acceleration 10 m below the edge of the road?

## Objects Launched at an Angle

Figure 7–4a shows what happens when a golf ball bounces off a hard surface. The vertical and horizontal velocity components during one of the bounces are shown in Figure 7–4b. The horizontal component, $\vec{v}_x$, is constant because very little force is exerted in the horizontal direction. Gravity, however, acts on the ball, giving it a downward acceleration. Thus, the vertical velocity component is large and positive at the beginning, decreases to zero at the top of the path, then increases in the negative direction as the projectile falls. When the object returns to its launch position, the vertical speed is the same as it was at launch, but its direction is reversed. The **range**, R, is the horizontal distance from the point of bounce until the porjectile returns to the surface height.

$$\vec{V}_x + \vec{V}_y$$

# PROBLEM SOLVING STRATEGY

When solving a projectile motion problem, first determine the horizontal and vertical components of the initial velocity. Then the parts of the problem involving either component can be solved separately. The symmetry of the trajectory can be used when the launching and landing locations are at equal height. Rising and falling times are equal, as are the horizontal distances moved in each half of the trajectory. We will ignore air resistance in projectile motion problems.

FIGURE 7–5. The time interval
between each position of the ball is
1/30 of a second.

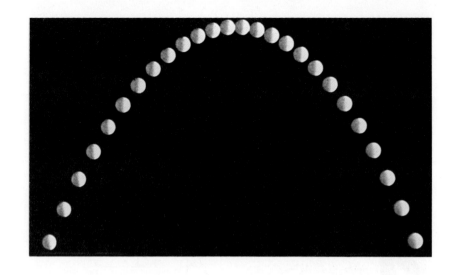

The trajectory of a projectile is a
parabola.

# Example Problem

## Flight of a Ball

In the strobe photo of the flight of the ball in Figure 7–5, the initial
velocity of the ball was 4.47 m/s at an angle of 66° above the horizontal. Find **a.** how long it took the ball to land, **b.** how high the ball
flew, **c.** what its range was.

**Given:** initial velocity,
$\vec{v}_i = +4.47$ m/s at 66.0°
initial angle,
$\theta = 66.0°$

**Unknowns: a.** time in flight, $t$
**b.** maximum vertical
displacement
(height), $\vec{y}$
**c.** range, $R$

**Basic equations:** $\vec{x} = \vec{v}_x t$
$\vec{y} = \vec{v}_y t + \frac{1}{2}\vec{g}t^2$

**Solution:** Find the components of initial velocity.
$$\vec{v}_x = \vec{v}_i \cos\theta = (+4.47 \text{ m/s})(\cos 66°) = (4.47 \text{ m/s})(0.407)$$
$$= +1.82 \text{ m/s}$$
$$\vec{v}_y = \vec{v}_i \sin\theta = (+4.47 \text{ m/s})(\sin 66°) = (4.47 \text{ m/s})(0.914)$$
$$= +4.08 \text{ m/s}$$

**a.** When it lands, the height is zero: $y = 0.0$, but

$$\vec{y} = \vec{v}_y t + \frac{1}{2}\vec{g}t^2 = 0.0. \text{ Therefore, } t = \frac{-2\vec{v}_y}{\vec{g}}.$$

$$t = \frac{-2(+4.08 \text{ m/s})}{-9.80 \text{ m/s}^2} = 0.833 \text{ s}$$

**b.** From the symmetry of the trajectory, the maximum height occurred at half the flight time, or 0.417 s after launch. At this
time,
$$\vec{y} = \vec{v}_y t + \frac{1}{2}\vec{g}t^2$$
$$= (+4.08 \text{ m/s})(0.417 \text{ s}) + \frac{1}{2}(-9.80 \text{ m/s}^2)(0.417 \text{ s})^2$$
$$\vec{y} = 1.70 \text{ m} - 0.852 \text{ m} = +0.85\text{m}$$

# F. Y. I.

**c.** The range is the horizontal distance travelled during the entire flight time, $t = 0.833$ s, or

$$R = \vec{v}_x t = (+1.82 \text{ m/s})(0.833 \text{ s}) = +1.52 \text{ m}$$

## PROBLEM SOLVING STRATEGY

Always check a problem to see if your answers are reasonable. In this case, you can use the photo and the knowledge that there were 30 flashes per second. The flight time was calculated to be 0.833 s. At 30 flashes per second this would be 25 flashes. You can count 25 flash intervals during this bounce, so the answer is fine. We don't know the photo scale, but the calculated maximum height is 0.85 m and the range is 1.5 m. The ratio of these two is 0.57/1. On the photo, the ratio of height to range is 57 mm/100 mm = 0.57/1, also in very good agreement.

## Practice Problems

**5.** A player kicks a football from ground level with a velocity of magnitude 27.0 m/s at an angle of 30.0° above the horizontal, Figure 7–6. Find
**a.** its "hang time," that is, the time the ball is in the air.
**b.** the distance the ball travels before it hits the ground.
**c.** its maximum height.

**6.** The kicker now kicks the ball with the same speed, but at 60.0° from the horizontal, or 30.0° from the vertical. Find
**a.** its "hang time," that is, the time the ball is in the air.
**b.** the distance the ball travels before it hits the ground.
**c.** its maximum height.

**7.** Using the results for Practice Problems 5 and 6, compare qualitatively the flight times, ranges, and maximum heights for projectiles launched with high and low trajectories, when the high angle is the complement of the low angle. (The complement of angle $\theta$ is (90° − $\theta$).)

▶ **8.** A rude tourist throws a peach pit horizontally with a 7.0 m/s velocity out of an elevator cage.
**a.** If the elevator is not moving, how long will the pit take to reach the ground, 17.0 m below?
**b.** How far (horizontally) from the elevator will the pit land?
**c.** He throws the next pit when the elevator is at the same height but moving upward at a constant 8.5 m/s velocity. How long will it take this pit to land?
**d.** How far away will this pit land?

## BIOLOGY CONNECTION

Have you ever watched a frog? The launch angle of a frog's jump is approximately 45°. This innate behaviour at this angle helps the frog cover maximum distance on flat ground.

The velocity of a projectile can be resolved into horizontal and vertical components.

**FIGURE 7–6. Use with Practice Problems 5, 6, and 7.**

# PHYSICS LAB

## The Softball Throw

## Purpose

To discover how fast you can throw a softball by measuring range and time.

## Materials

· *one* each—softball, stopwatch, paper, pencil, and calculator

## Procedure

1. Take all of your materials out to a football field (or a large open area with premeasured distances).
2. Select a thrower, a timer, and a marker from each group.
3. All throwers should toss the ball around to loosen up the arm muscles.
4. Set up a data table to record the distance the ball flies in the air and the time of flight.
5. The thrower should stand at the goal line. The marker should move downfield and stand at a place where she feels the ball might land.
6. Measure the time and use the lines on the field to estimate the range for two throws.
7. As soon as your group has estimated the range, give the softball to another group and *leave the area!*

## Calculations

1. Determine the initial values of $\vec{v}_x$ for each throw. **Hint:** Since

$$R = \vec{v}_x t, \text{ then } \vec{v}_x = \frac{R}{t}.$$

Sample calculation:

$$R = 60 \text{ m}, t = 4.0 \text{ s}; \vec{v}_x = \frac{60 \text{ m}}{4.0 \text{ s}} = 15 \text{ m/s}$$

2. Determine the initial value of $\vec{v}_y$. **Hint:** The ball spent an equal time moving up and down. Divide the time by 2 and then multiply by 9.8 m/s$^2$ to find the value of $\vec{v}_y$.
Sample calculation: $t = 4.0$ s indicates that the ball was at the top in 2.0 s. The initial value of $\vec{v}_y$:

$$\vec{v}_y = 9.8 \text{ m/s}^2 \times 2.0 \text{ s} = 19.6 \text{ m/s}$$

3. Draw a triangle as shown here. Record *your* values of $\vec{v}_x$ and $\vec{v}_y$.
4. Use the Pythagorean Theorem to find the value of $\vec{v}_i$.

## Observations and Data

1. Did each person throw at about the same range?
2. Did each person throw at about the same speed, $\vec{v}_y$?

## Analysis

1. Should the thrower try to throw with a larger $\vec{v}_x$ or $\vec{v}_y$? Explain.

## Applications

1. Why might a kickoff in a football game be made at a different angle than a punt?

# CONCEPT REVIEW

**1.1** Two baseballs are pitched horizontally from the same height but at different speeds. The faster ball crosses home plate within the strike zone, but the slower one is below the batter's knees. Why does the faster ball not fall as far as the slower one? After all, they travel the same distance and accelerate down at the same rate.

**1.2** A teflon hockey puck slides without friction across a table at constant velocity. When it reaches the end of the table, it flies off and lands on the ground.

   **a.** Draw the situation above, drawing vectors showing the force on the puck at two positions while it is on the table and at two more when it is in the air. Draw all vectors to scale.

   **b.** On a separate diagram, draw vectors showing the acceleration of the puck in the four locations.

**1.3** For the puck in question 1.2,

   **a.** draw vectors showing the horizontal and vertical components of the puck's velocity at the four points.

   **b.** using a different colored pen or pencil, draw the total velocity vector at the four points.

**1.4** **Critical Thinking:** Suppose an object is thrown with the same initial velocity and direction on the moon, where $g$ is one-sixth as large as on Earth. Will the following quantities change? If so, will they become larger or smaller?

   **a.** $v_x$ and $v_y$       **c.** maximum height

   **b.** time of flight       **d.** range

# 7.2 PERIODIC MOTION

Objectives

· **show an understanding of the centripetal acceleration of objects in circular motion and be able to apply Newton's laws to such motion.**
· **be able to characterize simple harmonic motion and apply Newton's laws to such motion.**
· **recognize resonance as a phenomenon often seen in daily life.**

Projectile motion is two dimensional, but the motion does not repeat. Projectiles move along their trajectories only once. On the other hand, if you swing a toy on a string, such as a yo-yo, horizontally around your head, its motion repeats itself at regular intervals. That is, its motion is periodic. An object bouncing on a spring or the pendulum of a clock is also periodic. Although different terms are used to describe this type of motion, Newton's laws can still be used to understand it.

**FIGURE 7–7. The regular up-and-down motion of a yo-yo is an example of periodic motion.**

FIGURE 7–8. Friction is the force
that holds people up. Centripetal
force keeps them from flying out.

## Circular Motion

Your body can't sense constant velocity, but it is a sensitive acceler-ometer. Your stomach can detect the acceleration of an elevator or of an airplane in rough weather. It can also feel acceleration in an amuse-ment park ride similar to the one in Figure 7–8. Except when the ride is starting or stopping, the speed is constant, but the velocity is changing because its direction is changing. The riders are moving with uniform circular motion.

A vector diagram like Figure 7–9a can help you find the acceleration of an object moving in a circle at constant speed. Points **A** and **B** are two successive positions of an object moving with uniform circular mo-tion. The radius of the circle is $r$. The radius and speed are constant, so the velocity is always perpendicular to the radius. That is, the velocity is tangent to the circle. The vector $\vec{v}_1$ represents the instantaneous velocity of the object at **A**. The vector $\vec{v}_2$ represents the instantaneous velocity of the object at **B**. Note that the two vectors have same length, but their directions are different.

Acceleration is the change in velocity, $\Delta\vec{v}$, divided by the time interval, $\Delta t$. The difference between the two vectors, $\vec{v}_1$ and $\vec{v}_2$, is $\Delta\vec{v}$. That is, $\Delta\vec{v} = \vec{v}_2 - \vec{v}_1$. You know how to find a vector sum, but not a difference. We can convert the equation into a sum by adding $\vec{v}_1$ to both sides of this equation to get $\vec{v}_2 = \vec{v}_1 + \Delta\vec{v}$. In Chapter 6, you found a vector sum by placing two vectors head to tail. Consider Figure 7–9b. The size of $\Delta\vec{v}$ can be found by using a ratio of the sides of similar triangles $ABC$ and $DEF$. The distance travelled by the object between point **A** and point **B** is the arc $AB$. If we choose **A** and **B** so they are close together, then arc $AB$ is approximately equal to chord $AB$. Thus,

$$\frac{\Delta\vec{v}}{\vec{v}} = \text{chord}\,\frac{AB}{r}.$$

a

b

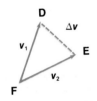

FIGURE 7–9. Vector diagrams can be used to analyse uniform circular motion.

But the distance travelled in the time interval $\Delta t$ is just $\vec{v}\Delta t$. Thus, we obtain

$$\frac{\Delta \vec{v}}{\vec{v}} = \frac{\vec{v}\Delta t}{r}.$$

Since acceleration is given by $a = \Delta \vec{v}/\Delta t$, we find

$$\vec{a} = \frac{\Delta \vec{v}}{\Delta t} = \frac{\vec{v}^2}{r}.$$

The direction of $\Delta \vec{v}$ can be seen in Figure 7–9b. As positions **A** and **B** become very close together, $\Delta \vec{v}$ becomes perpendicular to the two velocity vectors. That is, it is in the direction of the radius, pointing toward the centre of the circle. Newton originated the word *centripetal* (sen **TRIP** uht uhl) for a quantity that always points toward the centre of the circle. Centripetal means "centre seeking." For this reason, we call the acceleration just defined **centripetal acceleration** and write

$$\vec{a}_c = \frac{\Delta \vec{v}}{\Delta t} = \frac{\vec{v}^2}{r}.$$

Centripetal acceleration always points toward the centre of the circle. It is directly proportional to the square of the speed and inversely proportional to the radius of the circle.

It is often difficult to measure the speed of an object, but easier to measure the time needed to make a complete revolution, or the **period**, $T$. During this time, an object travels a distance equal to the circumference of the circle, $2\pi r$. The speed of the object is then

$$\vec{v} = \frac{2\pi r}{T}.$$

Centripetal acceleration is always toward the center of a circle.

**FIGURE 7–10.** In this projected rotating colony, "gravity" would actually be the centripetal force provided by the outer wall of the wheel. "Down" would be toward the outer circumference of the wheel.

This expression for $\vec{v}$ can be substituted into the equation for centripetal acceleration to yield.

$$\vec{a}_c = \frac{\left(\frac{2\pi r}{T}\right)^2}{r} = \frac{4\pi^2 r}{T^2}.$$

In circular motion, centripetal acceleration is at right angles to the instantaneous velocity.

Newton's second law tells us that an object does not accelerate unless a net force acts on it. The acceleration is in the same direction as the force. What exerts the force that gives a body its centripetal acceleration? In the case of the amusement park ride, the drum exerts a force against the backs of the riders. The force that causes the centripetal acceleration of a model plane flying in a circle is the force of the string on the plane. The moon orbits Earth with nearly uniform circular motion. Earth's gravity is the force that causes this acceleration. Because the force, as well as the acceleration, is toward the centre of the circle, these forces are often called **centripetal forces**. To understand centripetal acceleration, it is very important to identify the source of the force. For a body in uniform circular motion, Newton's second law can be written in the form

$$\vec{F}_{net} = \vec{F}_c = m\vec{a}_c = \frac{m\vec{v}^2}{r} = m\left(\frac{4\pi^2 r}{T^2}\right).$$

In what direction does an object fly if the force giving it centripetal acceleration suddenly disappears? Remember that with no net force, an object moves in a straight line at constant speed. Consider an Olympic hammer thrower. The "hammer" is a heavy ball on a chain that the thrower whirls in a circle. As he whirls it at greater and greater speeds, his arms and the chain supply the force that gives it centripetal acceleration. At the correct time, he lets go of the chain. The hammer flies off in a straight line tangent to the circle. After its release, only the gravitational force acts on it.

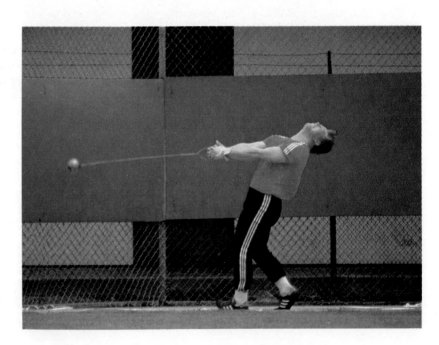

FIGURE 7–11. The force on the hammer is exerted toward the centre of the circle. When the thrower lets go, the hammer moves away in a straight line tangent to the point of release.

# Example Problem

## Uniform Circular Motion

A 0.013-kg rubber stopper is attached to a 0.93 m length of string. The stopper is swung in a horizontal circle, making one revolution in 1.18 s. **a.** Find the speed of the stopper. **b.** Find its centripetal acceleration. **c.** Find the force the string exerts on it.

**Given:** mass, $m = 0.013$ kg
circle radius, $r = 0.93$ m
period, $T = 1.18$ s

**Unknowns: a.** speed, $v$
**b.** acceleration, $\vec{a}_c$
**c.** force, $\vec{F}_c$

**Basic equations: a.** $v = \dfrac{2\pi r}{T}$

**b.** $\vec{a}_c = \dfrac{\vec{v}^2}{r}$

**c.** $\vec{F}_c = m\vec{a}_c$

## Solution:

**a.** From the period of the revolution, find the speed.

$$\text{speed} = \frac{\text{distance}}{\text{time}} = \frac{2\pi r}{T}$$

$$= \frac{2(3.14)(0.93 \text{ m})}{1.18 \text{ s}}$$

$$= \frac{5.8 \text{ m}}{1.18 \text{ s}} = 5.0 \text{ m/s}$$

**b.** acceleration, $\vec{a}_c = \dfrac{\vec{v}^2}{r} = \dfrac{(5.0 \text{ m/s})^2}{0.93 \text{ m}} = 27 \text{ m/s}^2$ (radially inward)

**c.** force, $\vec{F}_c = m\vec{a}_c = (0.013 \text{ kg})(27 \text{ m/s})^2$
$= 0.35$ N (radially inward)

# Practice Problems

9. **a.** Suppose the mass of the rubber stopper in the Example Problem above is doubled, but all other given quantities remain the same. How would the velocity, acceleration, and force change?
   **b.** If the radius in the Example Problem were twice as large, but all other given quantities remained the same, how would velocity, acceleration, and force change?
   **c.** If the stopper were swung in the same circle so it had a period half as large as in the example, how would the answers change?
10. A runner moving at a speed of 8.8 m/s rounds a bend with a radius of 25 m.
    **a.** Find the centripetal acceleration of the runner.
    **b.** What supplies the force needed to give this acceleration to the runner?
11. Racing on a flat track, a car going 32 m/s rounds a curve 56 m in radius.
    **a.** What is the car's centripetal acceleration?
    **b.** What would be the minimum coefficient of static friction between tires and road that would be needed for the car to round the curve without skidding?

**FIGURE 7–12. Not only the magnitude and direction of the applied force, but also its point of application affects the amount of torque produced.**

**12.** A racing car rounds a curve that is banked.
  **a.** Sketch the auto tire on the incline, drawing vectors representing all the forces on the tire.
  **b.** Components of what two forces provide the centripetal acceleration for the auto tire, and therefore, the auto?

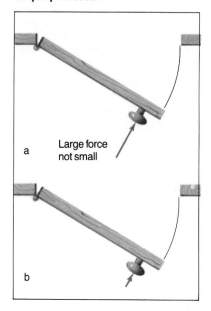

a   Large force
    not small

b

c   Far from hinges,
    not close

d

e   Perpendicular, not
    parallel to line
    from hinges

f

## Changing Circular Motion: Torque

As we have seen, if an object moves with constant circular motion its acceleration is always perpendicular to its velocity. In this case, the acceleration can change only the direction of the velocity, not its magnitude. How then can you start or stop circular motion? You have to apply another force on the object, one that has a component parallel to its velocity. But, changing the speed of circular motion is slightly more complicated.

Consider how you close a door, Figure 7–12. How do you make the door rotate rapidly about its axis of rotation, its hinges? First, you exert a large force. Second, you must exert the force as far from the hinges as possible. Pushing on the hinges does not start it rotating. Pushing halfway to the edge does some good, but pushing on the knob or the far edge gets the door rotating most rapidly. Third, you push perpendicular to the door, not toward the hinges. We combine the information about distance and direction into one concept, the lever arm. The lever arm, $\vec{d}$, Figure 7–13, is defined as the perpendicular distance from the axis of rotation to a line along which the force acts. The product of the force and the lever arm is called **torque**. The greater the torque, the greater the change in rotational motion. Thus, torque plays the role of force for rotational motion.

Torques can either stop, start, or change the direction of rotation. To stop the door from closing, or to open it, you exert a force in the opposite direction. Another example of torque is the seesaw. If a seesaw is balanced there is no net torque. If it is not rotating, it remains non-

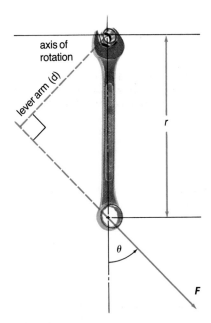

axis of rotation

lever arm (d)

$r$

$\theta$

$F$

**FIGURE 7–13. Torque is the product of the lever arm and the applied force.**

rotating. How do two children, one light, the other heavy, balance? Each child exerts a torque of the same magnitude, but in the opposite direction. The heavier one sits closer to the axis of the rotation, the pivot. Each torque is the product of the force, the child's weight, $m\vec{g}$, and the lever arm, $d$, the displacement to the pivot. That is, the seesaw is balanced if $m_1\vec{g}\vec{d}_1 = m_2\vec{g}\vec{d}_2$.

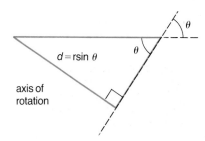

FIGURE 7–14. The lever arm is the perpendicular distance from a line along which the force acts and the axis of rotation.

## Simple Harmonic Motion

A playground swing moves back and forth over the same path. A vibrating guitar string, a pendulum, and a metal block on a spring are other examples of back and forth or vibrational motion.

In each case, the object has an equilibrium position. Whenever the object is pulled away from its equilibrium position, a force in the system pulls it back toward equilibrium. The force might be gravity, as in the case of the swing or pendulum. It could be the stretch of a guitar string or a spring. *If the restoring force varies linearly with the displacement, the motion that results is called **simple harmonic motion**.*

The motion of objects with SHM can be described by two quantities, period and amplitude. The **period**, $T$, is the time needed to repeat one complete cycle of motion. The **amplitude** of the motion is the maximum distance the object moves from its equilibrium position.

Let's look more closely at the motion of a metal block on a spring. The spring exerts a restoring force, a force that acts to oppose the force that stretched or compressed it. The force increases linearly with the amount the spring is stretched or compressed. An object that exerts a force in this way obeys a relationship called Hooke's law. Because the force dependence is linear, the movement of an object suspended on a spring is an example of simple harmonic motion.

When the block is at the equilibrium point, as shown in Figure 7–15a, the weight of the block is balanced by the force of the spring, $\vec{F}_1$. Suppose you start the motion as shown in Figure 7–15b by pulling the block down just a few centimetres and letting go. At first, the restoring force of the spring is more than the weight. There is a net upward force, so the block is accelerated upward. As the block rises, the spring is stretched less and less and the force it exerts gradually decreases. Thus, the net force decreases and the acceleration is less.

In simple harmonic motion, the restoring force varies linearly with displacement.

The period is the time required to complete a full complete cycle.

FIGURE 7–15. Simple harmonic motion can be shown by the vibration of a metal cylinder on a spring.

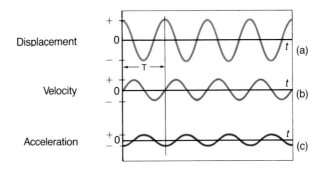

**FIGURE 7–16.** The graph in (a) shows the displacement, *d*, with respect to time, *t*. The velocity, *v*, and acceleration, *a*, with respect to time are shown in (b) and (c), respectively. Note how the amplitudes and the relative phases of the three curves are related.

When the block returns to its equilibrium position, the net force is again zero. Why doesn't the block stop? According to Newton's laws, a force is needed to change velocity. With no net force, the block continues with its upward motion. When the block is above the equilibrium position, the weight is larger than the force exerted by the spring. There is a net downward force and resulting downward acceleration. The speed of the block decreases. When the speed is zero, the block is as high as it will go. Even though the speed is zero, there is a net downward force, and the block accelerates down. When it again reaches the equilibrium position, there is no force, but the downward motion continues. When the block returns to its lowest location, one period, *T*, has elapsed, and the cycle of motion starts over. For a small displacement, the period depends on the mass of the block and stiffness of the spring. It does not depend on the amplitude of the motion.

Figure 7–16 shows graphs of the position, velocity, and acceleration of the block. At the vertical line, the block is at its largest distance from equilibrium. Its velocity is zero; it is momentarily at rest. Its acceleration is most negative, and thus the force pulling it back down to equilibrium is largest. Notice also that the speed is largest when the acceleration is zero, which occurs when the block is at the equilibrium position.

The swing of a pendulum also demonstrates SHM. A simple **pendulum** consists of an object (the bob) suspended by a string of length, *l*. The bob swings back and forth, as shown in Figure 7–17. The force on the bob when it is pulled away from the vertical is also shown. The gravitational force, the weight, $\vec{W}$, is resolved into two components. $\vec{F}_{\parallel}$ is along the direction of the string. The component $\vec{F}_{\perp}$ is at right angles to the direction of the string. When the bob is pulled to the right, $\vec{F}_{\perp}$ is to the left, and vice versa. That is, the component of the weight, $\vec{F}_{\perp}$, is a restoring force. Further, for small angles ($\theta$ less than 15°) the magnitude of $\vec{F}_{\perp}$ is proportional to the displacement of the bob. Thus, small-displacement pendulum motion is an example of SHM.

The period of the simple pendulum of length, *l*, is given by the equation

$$T = 2\pi\sqrt{l/|g|}.$$

Notice that for small-angle displacements, the period depends only on the length of the pendulum, not its mass or amplitude. By measuring the length and period of a pendulum, you can find the magnitude of the local value of the gravitational acceleration, $|g|$.

The frequency of a pendulum is the number of complete cycles of motion in one second. It can be found from the period using $f = 1/T$.

A pendulum making small swings undergoes simple harmonic motion.

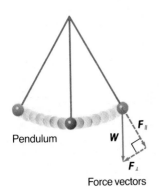

Pendulum    **W**        $F_{\parallel}$

$F_{\perp}$

Force vectors

**FIGURE 7–17.** The motion of a simple pendulum. The gravitational force on a pendulum can be resolved into two components.

## Example Problem

### The Pendulum

On top of a mountain a pendulum 1.55 m long has a period of 2.51 s. What is the acceleration due to gravity at this location?

**Given:** period of pendulum,    **Unknown:** $|g|$
$T = 2.51\ s$

length of pendulum,    **Basic equation:** $T = 2\pi\sqrt{\dfrac{l}{|g|}}$
$l = 1.55\ m$

**Solution:**

$$\vec{g} = \frac{4\pi^2}{T^2}\,l = \frac{4(3.14)^2}{(2.51\ s)^2}\,1.55\ m = 9.70\ m/s^2$$

# POCKET LAB

### TICK-TOCK

Use the pendulum equation to predict the length needed for a period of 1.00 s. Use a piece of string and a steel nut to build your pendulum. Test your pendulum for 30 complete swings. Note: The equation is accurate only for small displacements.

## Practice Problems

**13.** What is the length of a simple pendulum whose period is 1.00 s? Assume normal $\vec{g}$.

▶ **14.** A future astronaut lands on a planet with an unknown value of $\vec{g}$. She finds that the period of a pendulum 0.65 m long is 2.8 s. What is $\vec{g}$ for the surface of this planet?

# Physics and technology

## ELECTROMAGNETIC GUNS

Research is underway to develop electromagnetic guns that could be used to launch satellites into space and to provide the military with a new generation of battlefield weapons. The new technology uses electromagnetic induction to accelerate projectiles to extremely high velocities.

Working models of coil guns and rail guns have been tested successfully. A coil gun fires a projectile through a series of induction coils forming a barrel or flyway. The projectile consists of an aluminum armature plus a payload. A prototype coil gun has accelerated a 5-kg projectile to a speed of 335 m/s.

A rail gun uses a huge pulse of electricity that is applied to parallel metal rails and which produces a plasma, an electrically conducting gas. The resulting magnetic field propels the projectile at tremendous speeds.

To launch a satellite, these guns would fire a projectile containing the payload up through Earth's atmosphere. During this phase of the launch, the projectile follows the normal laws of projectile motion. Then at a specified height, a small rocket engine attached to the payload ignites and provides the final boost into orbit. These guns thus have the potential of launching small satellites at a fraction of the cost of large chemical rockets.

· What factors would you have to consider in designing the projectiles and payloads for these guns?

Aeroshell and Payload

Aeroshell Parts

Orbital Payload

The amplitude of any vibrating object can be greatly increased by applying small external forces at specific regular intervals of time. This effect is called **mechanical resonance.** You were probably first introduced to resonance when you learned to "pump" a playground swing. You found that you could increase the amplitude of the swing if your friend applied forces to it at just the right times. The time interval between the applied forces had to equal the period of the swing. Other familiar examples of mechanical resonance include rocking a car to free it from a snow bank and jumping up and down on a trampoline or diving board. Resonances can also cause damage. To avoid resonance, soldiers do not march across bridges in cadence. The rhythm of their steps could otherwise create large oscillations caused by their steps resonating with the natural period of the bridge.

The amplitude of a vibrating object can be increased by the application of small forces at specific intervals.

## CONCEPT REVIEW

**2.1** When you drive rapidly on a hilly road or ride in a roller coaster, you feel lighter as you go over the top of a hill, and heavier when you go through a valley. Sketch the situation, showing the forces that explain this sensation.

**2.2** Thanks to Earth's rotation, you move with uniform circular motion. What supplies the force that keeps you moving in this circle?

**2.3** The speed of a pendulum bob is largest when it is directly below the support. Give two ways you could increase this speed.

**2.4 Critical Thinking:** Is the rattle in a car ever an example of resonance? If so, how could you tell?

# CHAPTER 7 REVIEW

## SUMMARY

### 7.1 Projectile Motion

· The horizontal and vertical motions of a projectile are independent of one another, in the absence of air resistance.

· Ignoring air resistance, a projectile moves with constant velocity in the horizontal direction and constant acceleration in the vertical direction.

· The trajectory of a projectile depends on the horizontal and vertical components of its initial velocity.

### 7.2 Periodic Motion

· A body moving in uniform circular motion has a constant speed and is accelerated toward the center of the circle.

· Torque is the product of the force and the lever arm. Torque can either stop, start, or change the direction of rotation.

· An object moving with simple harmonic motion moves back and forth with a constant period.

· Mechanical resonance can greatly increase the amplitude of SHM when a small, periodic net force acts on an oscillating object at its natural frequency.

## KEY TERMS

projectiles
trajectory
range
centripetal acceleration
period
centripetal forces

torque
simple harmonic
    motion
amplitude
pendulum
mechanical resonance

## REVIEWING CONCEPTS

1. Consider the ball's trajectory in Figure 7–18.
   a. Where is the vertical velocity the greatest?
   b. Where is the greatest horizontal velocity?
   c. Where is the vertical velocity least?
   d. Name the curve traveled by the ball.

**FIGURE 7–18. Use with Reviewing Concepts 1.**

2. A student is playing with a radio-controlled race car on a balcony of a 6th-floor condominium. An accidental turn sends the car through the railing and off the edge of the balcony. Does the vertical distance the car falls depend on the velocity with which it speeds off the edge?

3. An airplane pilot flying at constant velocity and altitude drops a flare. Ignoring air resistance, where will the plane be relative to the flare when the flare hits the ground?

4. Can you go around a curve
   a. with zero acceleration? Explain.
   b. with constant acceleration? Explain.

5. What relationship must exist between an applied force and the velocity of a moving object if uniform circular motion is to result?

6. Sue whirls a yo-yo horizontally above her head. What is the direction of the force that acts on the yo-yo?

7. What is the direction of the force that acts on clothes in the spin cycle of a washing machine?

8. In general, a long-handled wrench is better to remove a stuck bolt than a short-handled wrench. Explain.

9. What is the difference between the period and the amplitude of a pendulum?

10. Describe a method of using a simple pendulum to find the value of g at a given location.

11. Sue is swinging her yo-yo as if it was a pendulum. At what point in the swing does the yo-yo have the greatest force acting on it?

12. When an object is vibrating on a spring and passes through the equilibrium position, there is no net force on it. Why is the velocity not zero at this point? What quantity is zero?

## APPLYING CONCEPTS

1. A batter hits a pop-up straight up over home plate at an initial velocity of 20 m/s. The ball is caught by the catcher at the same height that it was hit. At what velocity will the ball land in the catcher's mitt?

2. Sam throws a baseball horizontally from the top of a cliff. If Sam throws the baseball with higher speed,
   a. how will the time it takes to hit the ground be affected?
   b. how will the horizontal distance be affected?

3. A zoologist standing on a cliff aims a tranquilizer gun at a monkey hanging from a distant tree branch. The barrel of the gun is horizontal. Just as the zoologist pulls the trigger, the monkey lets go of the branch and begins to fall. Will the dart hit the monkey?

4. Bernie throws a football at a 45° angle. How long is the football in the air if it took 3.0 s to reach the top of its path?

5. A friend who is competing in the long jump asks you to explain the physics of this event. Does the height of the jump make any difference? What influences the length of the jump?

6. Sue is swinging a yo-yo around her head. What happens to the size of the centripetal acceleration if the mass of the yo-yo is doubled without changing the period or length of the string?

7. Imagine you are sitting in a car tossing a ball straight up into the air.
   a. If the car is moving with constant velocity, will the ball land in front of, behind, or in your hand?
   b. If the car rounds a curve at constant speed, where will the ball land?

8. Which is easier for turning a stuck screw, a screwdriver with a thick handle or one with a long handle?

9. Some doors in Europe have door knobs in the centre of the door rather than at the edge. Which door requires more force to produce the same torque to close the door?

10. If you find a pendulum clock running slightly fast, how can you adjust it to keep better time? Explain.

11. Suppose an astronaut carries a pendulum to the moon. Would the period of the pendulum be shorter, longer, or the same on the moon as on Earth?

# PROBLEMS

## 7.1 Projectile Motion

▶ 1. Assuming that the two baseballs in Figure 7-19 have the same velocity, 25 m/s, draw two separate graphs of $y$ as a function of $t$ and $x$ as a function of $t$ for each ball.

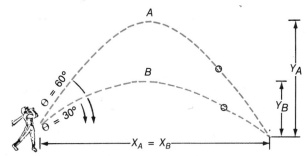

FIGURE 7–19. Use with Problem 1.

2. A stone is thrown horizontally at 8.0 m/s from a cliff 78.4 m high. How far from the base of the cliff does the stone strike the ground?

3. A toy car runs off the edge of a table that is 1.225 m high. If the car lands 0.400 m from the base of the table,
   a. how long does it take for the car to fall?
   b. what is the horizontal velocity of the car?

4. Janet jumps off a high-diving platform with a horizontal velocity of 2.8 m/s and lands in the water 2.6 s later. How high is the platform, and how far from the base of the platform does she land?

▶ 5. An airplane traveling 1001 m above the ocean at 125 km/h is to drop a box of supplies to shipwrecked victims below.
   a. How many seconds before being directly overhead should the box be dropped?
   b. What is the horizontal distance between the plane and the victims when the box is dropped?

▶ 6. Divers at Acapulco dive from a cliff that is 61 m high. If the rocks below the cliff extend outward for 23 m, what is the minimum horizontal velocity a diver must have to clear the rocks safely?

▶ 7. A dart player throws a dart horizontally at a speed of +12.4 m/s. The dart hits the board 0.32 m below the height from which it was thrown. How far away is the player from the board?

▶ 8. An arrow is shot at a 30.0° angle with the horizontal. It has a velocity of 49 m/s.
   a. How high will the arrow go?
   b. What horizontal distance will it travel?

▶ 9. A pitched ball is hit by a batter at a 45° angle. It just clears the outfield fence, 98 m away. Find the velocity of the ball when it left the bat. Assume the fence is the same height as the pitch.

▶ 10. Trailing by two points, and with only 2.0 s remaining in a basketball game, a player makes a jump-shot at an angle of 60° with the horizontal, giving the ball a velocity of 10 m/s. The ball is released at the height of the basket, 3.05 m above the floor. Yes! It's a score.
   a. How much time is left in the game when the basket is made?
   b. Shots made outside a semicircle of 6.02-m radius from a spot directly beneath the basket are awarded 3 points, while those inside score 2 points. Did the player tie the game or put the team ahead?

▶ 11. A basketball player tries to make a half-court jump-shot, releasing the ball at the height of the basket. Assuming the ball is launched at 51.0°, 14.0 m from the basket, what velocity must the player give the ball?

▶ 12. A baseball is hit at 30.0 m/s at an angle of 53.0° with the horizontal. Immediately an outfielder runs 4.00 m/s toward the infield and catches the ball at the same height it was hit. What was the original distance between the batter and the outfielder?

## 7.2 Periodic Motion

13. It takes a 615-kg racing car 14.3 s to travel at a uniform speed around a circular racetrack of 50.0 m radius.
   a. What is the acceleration of the car?
   b. What average force must the track exert on the tires to produce this acceleration?

14. An athlete whirls a 7.00-kg hammer tied to the end of a 1.3-m chain in a horizontal circle. The hammer moves at the rate of 1.0 r/s.
    a. What is the centripetal acceleration of the hammer?
    b. What is the tension in the chain?
15. Sue whirls a yo-yo in a horizontal circle. The yo-yo has a mass of 0.20 kg and is attached to a string 0.80 m long.
    a. If the yo-yo makes 1.0 complete revolution each second, what force does the string exert on it?
    b. If Sue increases the speed of the yo-yo to 2.0 revolutions per second, what force does the string now exert?
    c. What is the ratio of answer **b** to **a**? Why?
16. A coin is placed on a stereo record revolving at 33 1/3 revolutions per minute.
    a. In what direction is the acceleration of the coin, if any?
    b. Find the acceleration of the coin when it is placed 5.0, 10, and 15 cm from the centre of the record.
    c. What force accelerates the coin?
    d. At which of the three radii listed in **b** would the coin be most likely to fly off? Why?
17. According to the *Guinness Book of World Records*, (1990 edition, p. 169) the highest rotary speed ever attained was 2010 m/s. The rotating rod was 15.3 cm long. Assume the speed quoted is that of the end of the rod.
    a. What is the centripetal acceleration of the end of the rod?
    b. If you were to attach a 1.00-g object to the end of the rod, what force would be needed to hold it on the rod?
    c. What is the period of rotation of the rod?
▶ 18. Refer to Figure 7–8. The carnival ride has a 2.0-m radius and rotates 1.1 times per second.
    a. Find the speed of a rider.
    b. Find the centripetal acceleration of a rider.
    c. What produces this acceleration?
    d. When the floor drops down, riders are held up by friction. What coefficient of friction is needed to keep the riders from slipping?
▶ 19. An early major objection to the idea that Earth is spinning on its axis was that Earth would turn so fast at the equator that people would be thrown off into space. Show the error in this logic by calculating

a. the speed of a 97-kg person at the equator. The radius of Earth is about 6400 km.
    b. the centripetal force on the person.
    c. the weight of the person.
▶ 20. Friction provides the centripetal force necessary for a car to travel around a flat circular race track. What is the maximum speed at which a car can safely travel around a circular track of radius 80.0 m if the coefficient of friction between the tire and road is 0.30?
21. A pendulum has a length of 0.67 m.
    a. Find its period.
    b. How long would the pendulum have to be to double the period?
    c. Why is your answer to part **b** not just double the length?
▶ 22. Find the length of a pendulum oscillating on the moon that would have the same period as a 1.0-m pendulum oscillating on Earth. The moon's gravity is one-sixth of Earth's gravity.

## USING A GRAPHING CALCULATOR

A baseball player hits a belt-high (1.0 m) fastball down the left field line. The ball has an initial velocity of 46.0 m/s at an initial angle of 40°. The left field wall is 96.0 m away from home plate at the foul pole and is 14 m high. Use a graphing calculator to plot the path of the ball. Trace along the path of the ball to find how high above the ground the ball is at 96.0 m. Does the ball clear the wall?

## THINKING PHYSIC-LY

Two small, heavy objects are dropped simultaneously into a very deep and narrow canyon from opposite sides. One of them is given a shove in the horizontal direction toward the other object at the same instant they are dropped. Explain why, if air resistance is negligible, they will eventually collide if the canyon is deep enough.

# CHAPTER 8

# Universal Gravitation

◀ **Floating Freely**

Two astronauts, a satellite, and the space shuttle are seen in orbit about Earth. They appear to be floating weightless in space. Does Earth's gravitational force reach into space? Is this force the same strength as it is on Earth?

W hy do objects fall toward Earth? To ancient Greek scientists, certain things, like hot air or smoke, rose; others, like rocks and shoes, fell simply because they had some built-in desire to rise or fall. The Greeks gave the names "levity" and "gravity" to these properties. If you ask a child today why things fall, he or she will probably say "because of gravity." But, giving something a name does not explain it. Galileo and Newton gave the name *gravity* to the force that exists between Earth and objects. Newton showed that the same force exists between all bodies. In this century, Einstein gave a much different and deeper description of the gravitational attraction. But, we still know only how things fall, not why.

As Galileo wrote almost four hundred years ago in response to a statement that "gravity" is why stones fall downward,

> What I am asking you for is not the name of the thing, but its essence, of which essence you know not a bit more than you know about the essence of whatever moves the stars around. ...we do not really understand what principle or what force it is that moves stones downward.

The question of why objects attract each other is still not answered.

# ✓ Concept Check

The following terms or concepts from earlier chapters are important for a good understanding of this chapter. If you are not familiar with them, you should review them before studying this chapter.
· velocity, Chapter 3
· acceleration, Chapter 4
· Newton's second law, Chapter 5
· circular motion, Chapter 7
· centripetal acceleration, Chapter 7

# Objectives

- gain an understanding of need for precision and hard work in gathering data needed to understand how the universe works; list Kepler's laws and understand them.
- recognize how Kepler's laws resulted in Newton's law of gravitation; be able to calculate periods and velocities of orbiting objects.
- understand that gravitational force is proportional to both masses and the inverse square of the distance between the centers of spherical bodies.
- state the method used by Cavendish to measure G and understand the results of knowing G.

# 8.1 MOTION IN THE HEAVENS AND ON EARTH

We know how objects move on Earth. We can describe and even calculate projectile motion. Early humans could not do that, but they did notice that the motion of stars and other bodies in the heavens was quite different. Stars moved in regular paths. Planets, or wanderers, moved through the sky in much more complicated paths. Astrologers claimed that the motions of these bodies were able to control events in human lives. Comets were even more erratic. These mysterious bodies appeared without warning, spouting bright tails, and were considered bearers of evil omens. Because of the works of Galileo, Kepler, Newton, and others, we now know that all of these objects follow the same laws that govern the motion of golf balls and other objects on Earth.

## Kepler's Laws of Planetary Motion

As a boy of fourteen in Denmark, Tycho Brahe (1546–1601) observed an eclipse of the sun on August 21, 1560, and vowed to become an astronomer. In 1563, he observed two planets in conjunction, that is, located at the same point in the sky. The date of the event, predicted by all the books of that period, was off by two days, so Brahe decided to dedicate his life to making accurate predictions of astronomical events.

Brahe studied astronomy as he traveled throughout Europe for five years. In 1576, he persuaded King Frederick II of Denmark to give him the island of Hven as the site for the finest observatory of its time. Using huge instruments like those in Figure 8–1, he spent the next 20 years carefully recording the exact positions of the planets and stars.

Brahe was not known for his sunny disposition, so in 1597, out of favour with the new Danish king, Brahe moved to Prague. He became the astronomer to the court of Emperor Rudolph of Bohemia where, in 1600, a nineteen-year-old German Johannes Kepler (1571–1630) became one of his assistants. Although Brahe still believed strongly that Earth was the centre of the universe, Kepler wanted to use a sun-centred system to explain Brahe's precise data. He was convinced that geometry and mathematics could be used to explain the number, dis-

FIGURE 8–1. Some of the huge astronomical instruments Tycho Brahe had constructed to use at Hven: an astrolabe (a); a sextant (b); and a quadrant (c).

tance, and motion of the planets. By doing a careful mathematical analysis of Brahe's data, Kepler discovered three laws that still describe the behaviour of every planet and satellite. The theories he developed to explain his laws, however, are no longer considered correct. The three laws can be stated as follows:

1. The paths of the planets are ellipses with the centre of the sun at one focus.
2. An imaginary line from the sun to a planet sweeps out equal areas in equal time intervals. Thus, planets move fastest when closest to the sun, slowest when farthest away, Figure 8–2.
3. The ratio of the squares of the periods of any two planets revolving about the sun is equal to the ratio of the cubes of their average distances from the sun. Thus, if $T_a$ and $T_b$ are their periods and $r_a$ and $r_b$ their average distances, $\left(\dfrac{T_a}{T_b}\right)^2 = \left(\dfrac{r_a}{r_b}\right)^3$.

Notice that the first two laws apply to each planet, moon, or satellite individually. The third law relates the motion of several satellites about a single body. For example, it can be used to compare the distances and periods of the planets about the sun. It can also be used to compare distances and periods of the moon and artificial satellites around Earth.

Tycho Brahe made very accurate measurements of the positions of planets and stars that Kepler used to formulate his laws.

**FIGURE 8–2.** An imaginary line from Earth to the sun sweeps out equal areas each second whether Earth is close to or far from the sun.

# PROBLEM SOLVING STRATEGY

When working with equations that involve squares and square roots, or cubes and cube roots, your solution is more precise if you keep at least one extra digit in your calculations until you reach the end.

When you use Kepler's third law to find the radius of the orbit of a planet or satellite, first solve for the cube of the radius, then take the cube root. This is easier to do if your calculator has a cube-root key, $\sqrt[3]{x}$. If your calculator has a key $y^x$ or $x^y$, you can also find the cube root. Check the instructions of your calculator, but you usually enter the cube of the radius, press the $y^x$ key, then enter 0.3333333 and press $=$.

# PHYSICS LAB : The Orbit

## Purpose

To draw an ellipse and demonstrate how the force varies.

## Materials

- 2 thumbtacks
- 21 cm × 28 cm piece of cardboard or corkboard
- sheet of paper
- 30 cm of string or thread
- pencil

## Procedure

1. Push the thumbtacks into the paper and cardboard so that they are between 7 and 10 cm apart.
2. Make a loop with the string. Place the loop over the two thumbtacks. Keep the loop tight as you draw the ellipse. (See sketch.)
3. Remove the tacks and string. Draw a small star centred at one of the tack holes.

## Observations and Data

1. Draw the position of a planet in the orbit where it is farthest from the star.
2. Measure the distance from this position to the centre of the star.
3. Draw a 1 cm long force vector from the planet directly toward the star. Label this vector 1.0 $\vec{F}$.
4. Draw the position of the planet when it is nearest the star.
5. Measure the distance from this position to the star's centre.

## Analysis

1. Calculate the amount of force on the planet at the closest distance. Gravity is an inverse square

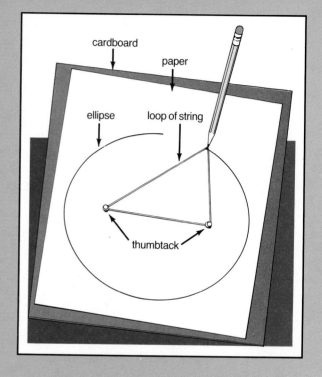

force. If the planet is 0.45 as far, the force is $1/(0.45)^2$ as much or 4.9 F. **Hint:** The force will be more than 1.0 $\vec{F}$.
2. Draw the force vector (correct length and direction) for this position. Use the scale of 1.0 $\vec{F}$ : 1.0 cm.
3. Draw the planet at two other positions in the orbit and draw the force vectors.

## Applications

1. Assume the planet moves in a clockwise pattern on the ellipse. Draw a velocity vector at each planet position to show the direction of motion. Remember that the planet moves faster when it is closer.
2. Look at the direction of velocity vectors and the direction of the force vectors. Identify the positions where the planet is gaining speed and also where it is losing speed.

Table 8–1

| Planetary Data | | | |
|---|---|---|---|
| Name | Average radius (m) | Mass (kg) | Mean distance from sun (m) |
| Sun | $696.0 \times 10^6$ | $1.991 \times 10^{30}$ | —— |
| Mercury | $2.43 \times 10^6$ | $3.2 \times 10^{23}$ | $5.80 \times 10^{10}$ |
| Venus | $6.073 \times 10^6$ | $4.88 \times 10^{24}$ | $1.081 \times 10^{11}$ |
| Earth | $6.3713 \times 10^6$ | $5.979 \times 10^{24}$ | $1.4957 \times 10^{11}$ |
| Mars | $3.38 \times 10^6$ | $6.42 \times 10^{23}$ | $2.278 \times 10^{11}$ |
| Jupiter | $69.8 \times 10^6$ | $1.901 \times 10^{27}$ | $7.781 \times 10^{11}$ |
| Saturn | $58.2 \times 10^6$ | $5.68 \times 10^{26}$ | $1.427 \times 10^{12}$ |
| Uranus | $23.5 \times 10^6$ | $8.68 \times 10^{25}$ | $2.870 \times 10^{12}$ |
| Neptune | $22.7 \times 10^6$ | $1.03 \times 10^{26}$ | $4.500 \times 10^{12}$ |
| Pluto | $1.15 \times 10^6$ | $1.2 \times 10^{22}$ | $5.9 \times 10^{12}$ |

# Example Problem

Kepler's laws can be used to calculate planetary orbits or periods.

## Using Kepler's Third Law to Find an Orbital Period

Galileo discovered four moons of Jupiter. Io, which he measured to be 4.2 units from the centre of Jupiter, has a period of 1.8 days. He measured the radius of Ganymede's orbit as 10.7 units. Use Kepler's third law to find the period of Ganymede.

**Given:** for Io
period, $T_b$ = 1.8 days
radius, $r_b$ = 4.2 units
for Ganymede
radius, $r_a$ = 10.7 units

**Unknown:** Ganymede's period, $T_a$

**Basic equation:** $\left(\dfrac{T_a}{T_b}\right)^2 = \left(\dfrac{r_a}{r_b}\right)^3$

**Solution:** $T_a{}^2 = T_b{}^2 \left(\dfrac{r_a}{r_b}\right)^3$

$= (1.8 \text{ days})^2 \left(\dfrac{10.7 \text{ units}}{4.2 \text{ units}}\right)^3$

$= (3.2 \text{ days}^2)(16.5) = 52.8 \text{ days}^2$

$T_a = 7.3 \text{ days}$

The observed period is 7.16 days.

Notice that when working problems that involve ratios, you do not need to convert all units to metres and seconds. You must, however, use the same units throughout the problem.

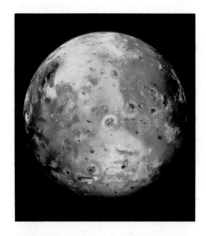

FIGURE 8–3. Io, one of Jupiter's moons, appears yellow because of sulfur deposits.

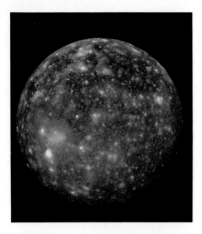

**FIGURE 8–4. Callisto, the fourth moon of Jupiter, is covered with ice.**

# Example Problem

## Using Kepler's Third Law to Find an Orbital Radius

The fourth moon of Jupiter, Callisto, has a period of 16.7 d. Find its distance from Jupiter using the same units Galileo used.

**Given:** for Io
    period, $T_b = 1.8$ d
    radius, $r_b = 4.2$ units
    for Callisto
    period, $T_a = 16.7$ d

**Unknown:** Callisto's radius, $r_a$

**Basic equation:** $\left(\dfrac{T_a}{T_b}\right)^2 = \left(\dfrac{r_a}{r_b}\right)^3$

**Solution:** $r_a{}^3 = r_b{}^3 \left(\dfrac{T_a}{T_b}\right)^2$

$$= (4.2 \text{ units})^3 \left(\frac{16.7 \text{ d}}{1.8 \text{ d}}\right)^2$$
$$= (74.1 \text{ units}^3)(86.1)$$
$$= 6.38 \times 10^3 \text{ units}^3$$
$$r_a = 18.5 \text{ units}$$

# Practice Problems

1. An asteroid revolves around the sun with a mean (average) orbital radius twice that of Earth's. Predict the period of the asteroid in Earth years.
2. From Table 8–1, you can calculate that, on the average, Mars is 1.52 times as far from the sun as is Earth. Predict the time required for Mars to circle the sun in Earth days.
3. The moon has a period of 27.3 d and has a mean distance of $3.90 \times 10^5$ km from the centre of Earth. Find the period of an artificial satellite that is $6.70 \times 10^3$ km from the centre of Earth.
▶ 4. From the data on the period and radius of revolution of the moon in Practice Problem 3, find the mean distance from Earth's centre to an artificial satellite that has a period of 1.00 d.

# Universal Gravitation

In 1666, some 45 years after Kepler's work, young Isaac Newton was living at home in rural England because the plague had closed all schools. Newton had used mathematical arguments to show that if the path of a planet were an ellipse, in agreement with Kepler's first law, then the magnitude of the net force, $F$, on the planet must vary inversely with the square of the distance between the planet and the sun. That is, he could write an equation,

$$F \propto \frac{1}{d^2},$$

where the symbol $\propto$ means "is proportional to," and $d$ is the average distance between the centres of the two bodies. He also showed that the force acted in the direction of a line connecting the centres. But, at this time, Newton could go no further because he could not measure the magnitude of the force, $F$.

Newton later wrote that the sight of a falling apple made him think of the problem of the motion of the planets. Newton recognized that the apple fell straight down because Earth attracted it. Might not this force extend beyond the trees, to the clouds, to the moon, and even beyond? Gravity could even be the force that attracts the planets to the sun. Newton recognized that the force on the apple must be proportional to its mass. Further, according to his own third law of motion, the apple would also attract Earth, so the force of attraction must be proportional to the mass of Earth as well. He was so confident the laws that governed motion on Earth would work anywhere that he assumed the same force of attraction acted between any two masses, $m_1$ and $m_2$. He proposed

$$F = G\frac{m_1 m_2}{d^2}$$

where $d$ is the distance between the centres of the spherical masses, and $G$ is a universal constant, one that is the same everywhere. According to Newton's equation, if the mass of a planet were doubled, the force of attraction would be doubled. Similarly, if the planet were attracted toward a star with twice the mass of the sun, the force would be twice as great. And, if the planet were twice the distance from the sun, the force would be only one-quarter as strong. Figure 8–5 illustrates these relationships. Because the force depends on $1/d^2$, it is called an **inverse square law**.

FIGURE 8–5. The gravitational force between any two bodies varies directly as the product of their masses and inversely as the square of the distance between them.

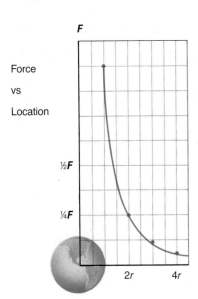

F

Force
vs
Location

½**F**

¼**F**

2r     4r

*Distance from Earth*

**FIGURE 8–6. The change in gravitational force with distance follows the inverse square law.**

**FIGURE 8–7. Cavendish verified the existence of gravitational forces between masses by using the apparatus shown.**

# Newton's Use of His Law of Universal Gravitation

Newton applied his inverse square law to the motion of the planets about the sun. He used the symbol $M_p$ for the mass of the planet, $M_s$ for the mass of the sun, and $r_{ps}$ for the radius of the planet's orbit. He then used his second law of motion, $F = ma$, with $F$ the gravitational force and $a$ the centripetal acceleration. That is, $F = M_p a$. For the sake of simplicity, we assume circular orbits.

$$G\frac{M_s M_p}{r_{ps}^2} = M_p \frac{4\pi^2 r_{ps}}{T_p^2},$$

where $T_p$ is the time required for the planet to make one complete revolution about the sun. He rearranged the equation in the form

$$T_p^2 = \left(\frac{4\pi^2}{GM_s}\right) r_{ps}^3.$$

This equation is Kepler's third law—the square of the period is proportional to the cube of the distance. The proportionality constant, $4\pi^2/GM_s$, depends only on the mass of the sun and Newton's universal gravitational constant $G$. It does not depend on any property of the planet. Thus, Newton's law of gravitation not only leads to Kepler's third law, but it also predicts the value of the constant. In our derivation of this equation, we have assumed the orbits of the planets are circles. Newton found the same result for elliptical orbits.

# Weighing Earth

As you know, the force of gravitational attraction between two objects on Earth is very small. You cannot feel the slightest attraction even between two massive bowling balls. In fact, it took 100 years after Newton's work to develop an apparatus that was sensitive enough to measure the force. In 1798, the English scientist Henry Cavendish (1731–1810) used equipment like that sketched in Figure 8–7. A rod about 20 cm long had two small lead balls attached. The rod was suspended by a thin wire so it could rotate. Cavendish measured the force on the spheres needed to rotate the rod through given angles. Then, he placed two large lead balls close to the small ones. The force of attraction between the balls caused the rod to rotate. By measuring the angle through which it turned, Cavendish was able to calculate the attractive force between the masses. He found that the force agreed with Newton's law of gravitation.

Cavendish measured the masses of the balls and the distance between their centres. Substituting these values for force, mass, and distance into Newton's law, he found the value of $G$.

Newton's law of universal gravitation says

$$F = G \frac{m_1 m_2}{d^2}.$$

When $m_1$ and $m_2$ are measured in kilograms, $d$ in metres, and $F$ in newtons, then $G = 6.67 \times 10^{-11}$ N·m²/kg². For example, the attractive gravitational force between two bowling balls, each of mass 7.26 kg, with their centres separated by 0.30 m is

$$F_g = \frac{(6.67 \times 10^{-11}\,\text{N·m}^2/\text{kg}^2)(7.26\,\text{kg})(7.26\,\text{kg})}{(0.30\,\text{m})^2} = 3.9 \times 10^{-8}\,\text{N}.$$

Cavendish's experiment is often called "weighing the earth." You know that on Earth's surface the weight of an object is a measure of Earth's gravitational attraction: $F = mg$. According to Newton, however,

$$F = \frac{GM_e m}{r^2}, \text{ so, } g = \frac{GM_e}{r^2}.$$

Because Cavendish measured the constant $G$, we can rearrange this equation as

$$M_e = \frac{g r_e^2}{G}.$$

Using modern values of the constants, we find

$$M_e = \frac{(9.80\,\text{m/s}^2)(6.37 \times 10^6\,\text{m})^2}{6.67 \times 10^{-11}\,\text{N·m}^2/\text{kg}^2} = 5.98 \times 10^{24}\,\text{kg}.$$

Comparing the mass of Earth to that of a bowling ball, you can see why the gravitational attraction of everyday objects is not easily sensed.

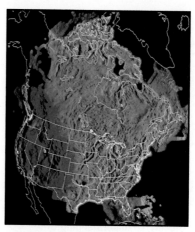

**FIGURE 8–8. This map shows variations in the force of gravity throughout North America.**

Cavendish tested the law of universal gravitation between small masses on Earth.

Cavendish was able to measure, experimentally, the constant, $G$, in Newton's law of universal gravitation.

· · · · · · · · · · · · ·
# CONCEPT REVIEW

**1.1** Earth is attracted to the sun by the force of gravity. Why doesn't Earth fall into the sun? Explain.

**1.2** If Earth began to shrink but its mass remained the same, predict what would happen to the value of $g$ on shrinking Earth's surface.

**1.3** Cavendish did his experiment using lead spheres. Suppose he had used equal masses of copper instead. Would his value of $G$ be the same or different? Explain.

**1.4** **Critical Thinking:** In a space colony on the moon, an astronaut can pick up a rock with less effort than on Earth. Is this also true when she throws the rock horizontally? If the rock drops on her toe, will it hurt more or less than on Earth? Explain your answers.

- recognize that the motion of
satellites in circular orbits about
Earth can be understood using
equations of uniform circular
motion; solve problems involving
orbital velocity and period.
- understand the use of the term
"weightlessness" in describing
objects in freefall near Earth and in
orbit.
- describe gravitational fields and
that the field concept does not
explain the origin of gravity.
- display an understanding of
Einstein's concept of gravity.

# 8.2 USING THE LAW OF UNIVERSAL GRAVITATION

The planet Uranus was discovered in 1781. By 1830, it appeared that Newton's law of gravitation didn't correctly predict its orbit. Some astronomers thought gravitational attraction from an undiscovered planet might be changing its path. In 1845, the location of such a planet was calculated, and astronomers at the Berlin Observatory searched for it. During the first evening, they found the giant planet now called Neptune.

## Motion of Planets and Satellites

Newton used a drawing similar to Figure 8–9 to illustrate a "thought experiment." Imagine a cannon, perched atop a high mountain, shooting a cannonball horizontally. The cannonball is a projectile and its motion has vertical and horizontal components. It follows a parabolic trajectory. During the first second the ball is in flight, it falls 4.9 m. If its speed increases, it will travel farther across the surface of Earth, but it will still fall 4.9 m in the first second of flight. Meanwhile, the surface of Earth is curved. If the ball goes just fast enough, after one second, it will reach a point where Earth has curved 4.9 m away from the horizontal. That is, the curvature of Earth will just match the curvature of the trajectory, and the ball will orbit Earth.

Figure 8–9 shows that Earth curves away from a line tangent to its surface at a rate of 4.9 m for every 8 km. That is, the altitude of the line tangent to Earth at **A** will be 4.9 m above Earth at **B.** If the cannonball in Figure 8–9 were given just enough horizontal velocity to travel from **A** to **B** in one second, it would also fall 4.9 m and arrive at **C.** The altitude of the ball in relation to Earth's surface would not have changed. The cannonball would fall toward Earth at the same rate that Earth's surface curves away. An object with a horizontal speed of 8 km/s will keep the same altitude and circle Earth as an artificial satellite.

**FIGURE 8–9.** If the cannonball travels 8 km horizontally in 1 s, it will fall the same distance toward Earth as Earth curves away from the cannonball.

Newton's thought experiment ignored air resistance. The mountain would have to be more than 150 km above Earth's surface to be above most of the atmosphere. A satellite at this altitude encounters little air resistance and can orbit Earth for a long time.

A satellite in an orbit that is always the same height above Earth moves with uniform circular motion. Its centripetal acceleration is $a_c = v^2/r$. Using Newton's second law, $F = ma$, with the gravitational force between Earth and the satellite, we obtain

$$\frac{GM_Em}{r^2} = \frac{mv^2}{r}.$$

Solving this for the velocity, $v$, we find

$$v = \sqrt{\frac{GM_E}{r}}.$$

By using Newton's law of universal gravitation, we have shown that the time for a satellite to circle Earth, its period, is given by

$$T = 2\pi\sqrt{\frac{r^3}{GM_E}}.$$

Note that the orbital velocity and period are independent of the mass of the satellite. Satellites are accelerated to the speeds needed to achieve orbit by large rockets, such as the shuttle booster rocket. The acceleration of any mass must follow Newton's law, $F = ma$, so a more massive satellite requires more force to put it into orbit. Thus, the mass of a satellite is limited by the capability of the rocket used to launch it.

Note that these equations for the velocity and period of a satellite can be used for any body in orbit about another. The mass of the central body, like the sun, would replace $M_E$ in the equations, and $r$ is the distance from the sun to the orbiting body.

**FIGURE 8–10.** This drawing by Rene Descartes illustrated his theory that space was filled with whirlpools of matter that moved the planets in their orbits.

The velocity of a satellite is independent of its mass.

## Example Problem

### Finding the Velocity of a Satellite

A satellite in low Earth orbit is 225 km above the surface. What is its orbital velocity?

**Given:** height above Earth, 225 km

**Unknown:** velocity, $v$

needed constants,

**Basic equation:** $v = \sqrt{\dfrac{GM_E}{r}}$

radius of Earth, $R_E = 6.37 \times 10^6$ m
mass of Earth, $M_E = 5.98 \times 10^{24}$ kg
$G = 6.67 \times 10^{-11}$ N·m²/kg²

**Solution:**

$$r = R_E + 225\,\text{km} = 6.60 \times 10^6\,\text{m}$$

$$v = \sqrt{\frac{(6.67 \times 10^{-11}\,\text{N·m}^2/\text{kg}^2)(5.98 \times 10^{24}\,\text{kg})}{6.60 \times 10^6\,\text{m}}}$$

$$= 7.77 \times 10^3\,\text{m/s} = 7.78\,\text{km/s}$$

Gravitational force diminishes as you go away from Earth, but it is never zero.

# Practice Problems

*Assume a near-circular orbit for all calculations.*

5. **a.** Calculate the velocity that a satellite shot from Newton's cannon must have in order to orbit Earth, 150 km above its surface.
   **b.** How long would it take for the satellite to return to the cannon in seconds and minutes?
6. Use the data in Table 8–1 for Mercury to find
   **a.** the speed of a satellite in orbit 265 km above the surface.
   **b.** the period of the satellite.
7. **a.** Find the velocity with which Mercury moves around the sun.
   **b.** Also, find the velocity of Saturn. Now, comment on whether or not it makes sense that Mercury is named after a speedy messenger of the gods, while Saturn is named after the father of Jupiter.

▶ 8. We can consider the sun to be a satellite of our galaxy, the Milky Way. The sun revolves around the centre of the galaxy with a radius of $2.2 \times 10^{20}$ m. The period of one rotation is $2.5 \times 10^8$ years.
   **a.** Find the mass of the galaxy.
   **b.** Assuming the average star in the galaxy has the mass of the sun, find the number of stars.
   **c.** Find the speed with which the sun moves around the centre of the galaxy.

# Weight and Weightlessness

The acceleration of objects due to Earth's gravitation can be found by using the inverse square law and Newton's second law. Since

$$F = \frac{GM_E M}{d^2} = ma, \text{ so } a = \frac{GM_E}{d^2},$$

but on Earth's surface, the equation can be written as

$$g = \frac{GM_E}{R_E^2}. \text{ Thus, } a = g\left(\frac{R_E}{d}\right)^2.$$

As we move farther from Earth's centre, the acceleration due to gravity is reduced according to this inverse square relationship.

**Floating Freely** ▶

You have probably seen astronauts on a space shuttle working and relaxing in "zero-g", or "weightlessness." The shuttle orbits Earth about 400 km above its surface. At that distance, $g = 8.7 \text{ m/s}^2$, only slightly less than on Earth's surface. Thus, Earth's gravitational force is certainly not zero in the shuttle. In fact, gravity causes the shuttle to circle Earth. Why, then, do the astronauts appear to have no weight? Just as with Newton's cannonball, the shuttle and everything in it are falling freely toward Earth as they orbit around it.

How do you measure weight? You either stand on a spring scale or hang an object from a scale. Weight is found by measuring the force the scale exerts in opposing the force of gravity. As we saw in Chapter 5, if you stand on a scale in an elevator that is accelerating downward, your weight is reduced. If the elevator is in freefall, that is, accelerating downward at $9.80 \text{ m/s}^2$, then the scale exerts no force on you. With no force on your feet, you feel weightless. So it is in an orbiting satellite. The satellite, the scale, you, and everything else in it are accelerating toward Earth.

Objects in freefall experience weightlessness.

**FIGURE 8–11. Astronauts in training experience a moment of weightlessness in a diving aircraft.**

**FIGURE 8–12. Vectors can be used to show Earth's gravitational field.**

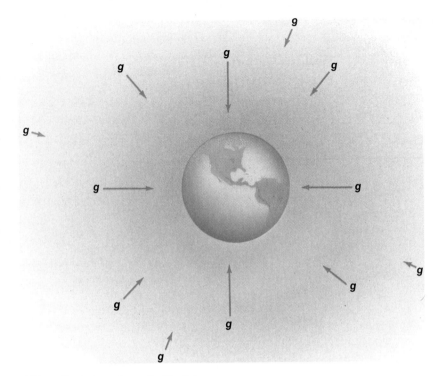

## The Gravitational Field

Many common forces are contact forces. Friction is exerted where two objects touch; the floor and your chair or desk push on you. Gravity is different. It acts on an apple falling from a tree and on the moon in orbit; it even acts on you in midair. In other words, gravity acts over a distance. Newton himself was uneasy with such an idea. How can the sun exert a force on Earth 150 000 000 km away?

In the nineteenth century, Michael Faraday invented the concept of the field to explain how a magnet attracts objects. Later, the field concept was applied to gravity. Anything that has mass is surrounded by a gravitational field. It is the field that acts on a second body, resulting in a force of attraction. The field acts on the second body at the location of that body. In general, the field concept makes the idea of a force acting across great distances unnecessary.

To find the strength of the gravitational field, place a small body of mass $m$ in the field and measure the force. We define the field strength, $g$, to be the force per unit mass, $F/m$. It is measured in newtons per kilogram. The direction of $g$ is in the direction of the force. Thus,

$$\vec{g} = \frac{\vec{F}}{m}.$$

Note that the field is numerically equal to the acceleration of gravity at the location of the mass. On Earth's surface, the strength of the gravitational field is 9.8 N/kg. It is independent of the size of the test mass. The field can be represented by a vector of length $g$ and pointing toward the object producing the field. We can picture the gravitational field of Earth as a collection of vectors surrounding Earth and pointing toward it, Figure 8–12. The strength of the field varies inversely with the square of the distance from the centre of Earth. To get a feeling for the field,

Einstein's concept of gravity agrees with every experimental test.

# F.Y.I.

Little Miss Muffet
Sits on her tuffet
in a nonchalant sort of a way.
With her force field around her
The spider, the bounder,
is not in the picture today.
—Frederick Winsor
The Space Child's
Mother Goose

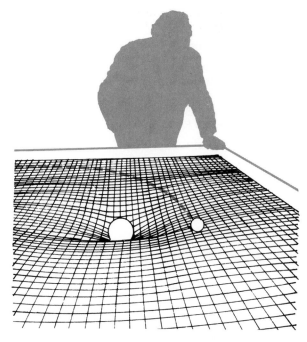

hold a heavy book in your hands and close your eyes. Imagine a spring pulling the book back toward the centre of Earth. As you lift the book, the spring stretches. Both the spring and gravitational field are invisible.

**FIGURE 8–13. Matter causes space to curve just as a mass on a rubber sheet curves the sheet around it. Moving bodies, near the mass, follow the curvature of space.**

## Einstein's Theory of Gravity

Newton's law of universal gravitation allows us to calculate the force that exists between two bodies because of their masses. The concept of a gravitational field allows us to picture the way gravity acts on bodies far away. Neither *explains* the origin of gravity.

Albert Einstein (1879–1955) proposed that gravity is not a force, but an effect of space itself. According to Einstein, a mass changes the space about it. Mass causes space to be curved, and other bodies are accelerated because they move in this curved space.

One way to picture how space is affected by mass is to compare it to a large two-dimensional rubber sheet, Figure 8–13. The yellow ball on the sheet represents a massive object. It forms an indentation. A marble rolling across the sheet simulates the motion of an object in space. If the marble moves near the sagging region of the sheet, its path will be curved. In the same way, Earth orbits the sun because space is distorted by the two bodies.

Einstein's theory, called the general theory of relativity, makes predictions that differ slightly from the predictions of Newton's laws. In every test, Einstein's theory has been shown to give the correct results.

Perhaps the most interesting prediction is the deflection of light by massive objects. In 1919, during an eclipse of the sun, astronomers found that light from distant stars that passed near the sun was deflected in agreement with Einstein's predictions. Astronomers have seen light from a distant, bright galaxy bent as it passed by a closer, dark galaxy.

**FIGURE 8–14. A black hole is so massive and of such unimaginable density, that light leaving it will be bent back to the black hole.**

The result is two or more images of the bright galaxy. Another result of general relativity is the effect on light of very massive objects. If the object is massive enough, light leaving it will be totally bent back to the object, Figure 8–14. No light ever escapes. Such an object, called a black hole, has been identified as a result of its effect on nearby stars.

Einstein's theory is not yet complete. It does not explain how masses curve space. Physicists are still working to understand the true nature of gravity.

## CONCEPT REVIEW

**2.1** What is the gravitational field strength on the surface of the moon?

**2.2** Two satellites are in circular orbits about Earth, one 150 km above the surface, the other 160 km.
   **a.** Which satellite has the larger orbital period?
   **b.** Which one has the larger velocity?

**2.3** What is *g*? Explain in your own words two different meanings for *g*. Be sure to use the correct units.

**2.4** **Critical Thinking:** It is easier to launch an Earth satellite into an orbit that circles eastward than one that circles westward. Explain.

# CHAPTER
# 8 REVIEW

## SUMMARY

### 8.1 Motion in the Heavens and on Earth

· Kepler's laws of planetary motion state that planets move in elliptical orbits, that they sweep out equal areas in equal times, and that the ratio of the square of the periods of any two planets is equal to the ratio of the cube of their distances to the sun.
· Newton's law of universal gravitation states that the force between two bodies depends on the product of their masses divided by the square of the distance between their centres. It is along a line connecting their centres.
· The mass of the sun can be found from the period and radius of a planet's orbit. The mass of the planet can be found only if it has a satellite orbiting it.
· Cavendish was the first to measure the gravitational attraction between two bodies on Earth.

### 8.2 Using the Law of Universal Gravitation

· A satellite in a circular orbit accelerates toward Earth at a rate equal to the acceleration of gravity at its orbital radius.
· All bodies have gravitational fields surrounding them that can be represented by a collection of vectors representing the force per unit mass at all locations.
· Einstein's theory of gravity describes gravitational attraction as a property of space itself.

## KEY TERMS

gravitational force
inverse square laws
Kepler's laws of planetary motion
satellite
weightlessness

# REVIEWING CONCEPTS

1. In 1610, Galileo looked through his telescope at Jupiter and saw four moons. The name of one of the moons is Io. Restate Kepler's first law for Io and Jupiter.

2. Earth moves more slowly in its orbit during summer than during winter. Is it closer to the sun in summer or in winter?

3. Is the area swept out per unit time by Earth moving around the sun equal to the area swept out per unit time by Mars moving around the sun?

4. Why did Newton think that a force must act on the moon?

5. The force of gravity acting on an object near Earth's surface is proportional to the mass of the object. Why does a heavy object not fall faster than a light object?

6. What information do you need to find the mass of Jupiter using Newton's version of Kepler's third law?

7. The mass of Pluto was not known until a satellite of the planet was discovered. Why?

8. How did Cavendish demonstrate that a gravitational force of attraction exists between two small bodies?

9. What provides the centripetal force that keeps a satellite in orbit?

10. How do you answer the question, "What keeps a satellite up?"

11. A satellite is going around Earth. On which of the following does the speed depend?
    **a.** mass of the satellite
    **b.** distance from Earth
    **c.** mass of Earth

12. Chairs in an orbiting spacecraft are weightless. If you were on board and barefoot, would you stub your toe if you kicked one? Explain.

13. During space flight, astronauts often refer to forces as multiples of the force of gravity on Earth's surface. What does a force of 5 $g$ mean to an astronaut?

14. Show that the dimensions of $g$ in the equation $\vec{g} = \vec{F}/m$ are m/s$^2$.

15. Newton assumed that the gravitational force acts directly between Earth and the moon. How does Einstein's view of the attraction between the two bodies differ from the view of Newton?

# APPLYING CONCEPTS

1. For each of the orbits shown in Figure 8–15, tell whether or not it is a possible orbit for a planet.

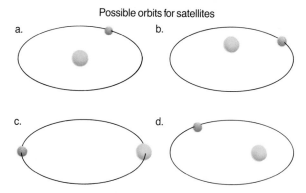

Possible orbits for satellites

a.          b.

c.          d.

**FIGURE 8–15. Use with Applying Concepts 1.**

2. What happens to the gravitational force between two masses when the distance between the masses is doubled?

3. The moon and Earth are attracted to each other by gravitational force. Does the more massive Earth attract the moon with a greater force than the moon attracts Earth? Explain.

4. According to Newton's version of Kepler's third law, how does the ratio $\left(\dfrac{T^2}{r^3}\right)$ change if the mass of the sun is doubled?

5. If Earth were twice as massive but remained the same size, what would happen to the value of $G$?

6. Examine the equation relating the speed of an orbiting satellite and the distance from the centre of Earth.
    **a.** Does a satellite with a large or small orbital radius have the greater velocity?
    **b.** When a satellite is too close to Earth, it can get into the atmosphere where there is air drag. As a result, its orbit gets smaller. Does its speed increase or decrease?

7. If a space shuttle goes into a higher orbit, what happens to the shuttle's period?

8. Mars has about half the mass of Earth. Satellite **M** orbits Mars with the same orbital radius as satellite **E** that orbits Earth. Which satellite has a smaller period?

9. A satellite is one earth radius above the surface of Earth. How does the acceleration due

to gravity at that location compare to the surface of Earth?

10. If Earth were twice as massive but remained the same size, what would happen to the value of $\vec{g}$.

11. Jupiter has about 300 times the mass of Earth and about 10 times earth's radius. Estimate the size of $\vec{g}$ on the surface of Jupiter.

12. If the mass in Earth's gravitational field is doubled, what will happen to the force exerted by the field upon it?

13. Yesterday, Sally had a mass of 50.0 kg. This morning she stepped on a scale and found that she gained weight.
    a. What happened, if anything, to Sally's mass?
    b. What happened, if anything, to the ratio of Sally's weight to her mass?

## PROBLEMS

### 8.1 Motion in the Heavens and on Earth

*Use* $G = 6.670 \times 10^{-11}$ Nm²/kg².

1. Jupiter is 5.2 times farther than Earth is from the sun. Find Jupiter's orbital period in earth years.

▶ 2. Uranus requires 84 years to circle the sun. Find Uranus' orbital radius as a multiple of Earth's orbital radius.

▶ 3. Venus has a period of revolution of 225 earth days. Find the distance between the sun and Venus, as a multiple of Earth's orbital radius.

4. If a small planet were located 8.0 times as far from the sun as Earth, how many years would it take the planet to orbit the sun?

▶ 5. A satellite is placed in an orbit with a radius that is half the radius of the moon's orbit. Find its period in units of the period of the moon.

6. An apparatus like the one Cavendish used to find G has a large lead ball that is 5.9 kg in mass and a small one that is 0.047 kg. Their centres are separated by 0.055 m. Find the force of attraction between them.

7. Use the data in Table 8–1 to compute the gravitational force the sun exerts on Jupiter.

8. Tom has a mass of 70.0 kg and Sally has a mass of 50.0 kg. Tom and Sally are standing 20.0 m apart on the dance floor. Sally looks up and she sees him. She feels an attraction. If the attraction is gravitation, find its size. Assume both can be replaced by spherical masses.

9. Two balls have their centres 2.0 m apart. One has a mass of 8.0 kg. The other has a mass of 6.0 kg. What is the gravitational force between them?

10. Two bowling balls each have a mass of 6.8 kg. They are located next to one another with their centres 21.8 cm apart. What gravitational force do they exert on each other?

11. Sally has a mass of 50.0 kg and Earth has a mass of $5.98 \times 10^{24}$ kg. The radius of Earth is $6.371 \times 10^6$ m.
    a. What is the force of gravitational attraction between Sally and Earth?
    b. What is Sally's weight?

12. The gravitational force between two electrons 1.00 m apart is $5.42 \times 10^{-71}$ N. Find the mass of an electron.

▶ 13. Two spherical balls are placed so their centres are 2.6 m apart. The force between the two balls is $2.75 \times 10^{-12}$ N. What is the mass of each ball if one ball is twice the mass of the other ball?

14. Using the fact that a 1.0-kg mass weighs 9.8 N on the surface of Earth and the radius of Earth is roughly $6.4 \times 10^6$ m,
    a. calculate the mass of Earth.
    b. calculate the average density of Earth.

▶ 15. The moon is $3.9 \times 10^5$ km from Earth's centre and $1.5 \times 10^8$ km from the sun's centre. If the masses of the moon, Earth, and sun are $7.3 \times 10^{22}$ kg, $6.0 \times 10^{24}$ kg, and $2.0 \times 10^{30}$ kg, respectively, find the ratio of the gravitational forces exerted by Earth and the sun on the moon.

▶ 16. A force of 40.0 N is required to pull a 10.0-kg wooden block at a constant velocity across a smooth glass surface on Earth. What force would be required to pull the same wooden block across the same glass surface on the planet Jupiter?

17. Use the information for Earth from Table 8–1 to calculate the mass of the sun using Newton's variations of Kepler's third law.

▶ 18. Mimas, a moon of Saturn, has an orbital radius of $1.87 \times 10^8$ m and an orbital period of about 23 h. Use Newton's version of Kepler's third law and these data to find the mass of Saturn.

▶ 19. Use Newton's version of Kepler's third law to find the mass of Earth. The moon is $3.9 \times 10^8$ m away from Earth and the moon has a period of 27.33 days. Compare this mass to the mass found in Problem 14.

## 8.2 Using the Law of Universal Gravitation

20. A geosynchronous satellite appears to remain over one spot on Earth. A geosynchronous satellite has an orbital radius of $4.23 \times 10^7$ m.
    a. Calculate its speed in orbit.
    b. Calculate its period.

▶ 21. On July 19, 1969, Apollo 11's orbit around the moon was adjusted to an average orbit of 111 km. The radius of the moon is 1785 km and the mass of the moon is $7.3 \times 10^{22}$ kg.
    a. How many minutes did it take to orbit once?
    b. At what velocity did it orbit the moon?

22. The asteroid Ceres has a mass $7 \times 10^{20}$ kg and a radius of 500 km.
    a. What is $\vec{g}$ on the surface?
    b. How much would a 85-kg astronaut weigh on Ceres?

23. The radius of Earth is about $6.40 \times 10^3$ km. A $7.20 \times 10^3$-N spacecraft travels away from Earth. What is the weight of the spacecraft at the following distances from Earth's surface?
    a. $6.40 \times 10^3$ km   b. $1.28 \times 10^4$ km

▶ 24. How high does a rocket have to go above Earth's surface until its weight is half what it would be on Earth?

▶ 25. The formula for the period of a pendulum, $T$, is $T = 2\pi\sqrt{l/g}$.
    a. What would be the period of a 2.0 m long pendulum on the moon's surface? The moon's mass is $7.34 \times 10^{22}$ kg and its radius is $1.74 \times 10^6$ m.
    b. What is the period of this pendulum on Earth?

26. A 1.25-kg book in space has a weight of 8.35 N. What is the value of the gravitational field at that location?

27. The moon's mass is $7.34 \times 10^{22}$ kg and it is $3.8 \times 10^8$ m away from Earth. Earth's mass can be found in Table 8–1.
    a. Calculate the gravitational force of attraction between the two.
    b. Find Earth's gravitational field at the moon.

28. Earth's gravitational field is 7.83 N/kg at the altitude of the space shuttle. What is the size of the force of attraction between a student, mass of 45.0 kg, and Earth?

 USING A GRAPHING CALCULATOR

Use Newton's universal gravitational equation and constant and the radius of Earth to find an equation where $x$ is equal to an object's distance from Earth's centre, and $y$ is equal to that object's acceleration due to gravity. The equation should be of the form $y = c(1/x^2)$. Use a graphing calculator to graph this equation, using 6400–6000 km as the range for $x$ and 10 m/s² – 8 m/s² as the range for $y$. Trace along this graph and find $a$: at sea level, 6400 km; on top of Mt. Everest, 6410 km; in a typical satellite orbit, 6500 km; and in a much higher orbit, 6600 km.

## THINKING PHYSIC-LY

1. As an astronaut in an orbiting space shuttle, how would you go about "dropping" an object down to Earth?

2. The weather pictures you see every day on TV come from a spacecraft in a stationary position 35 700 km above Earth's equator. Explain how it can stay exactly in position day after day. What would happen if it were closer in? farther out? **Hint:** A sketch may help.

# Momentum and Its Conservation

◀ **Air Force**

Some cars already have air bags. In a head-on crash of two air bag-equipped cars, both drivers walked away uninjured. How does an air bag help to reduce the injury to a person in a car crash?

I n the crash of a car moving at high speed, the passengers are brought to a stop very quickly. You have learned that force is needed to produce the acceleration of the passengers. We will now take a slightly different point of view. Rather than studying forces acting on an object, and the acceleration that results, we will look at a clearly defined collection of objects before and after an interaction takes place. We will look for properties that remain constant. Such properties are said to be conserved.

## √ Concept Check

The following terms or concepts from earlier chapters are important for a good understanding of this chapter. If you are not familiar with them, you should review them before studying this chapter.
· velocity, Chapter 3
· mass, force, Newton's second and third laws, Chapter 5
· vectors, Chapter 6

Momentum is the product of the mass and the velocity of a body. It is a vector quantity.

# POCKET LAB

## CART MOMENTUM

Attach a spring scale to a laboratory cart. First, pull the cart for 1.0 s exerting 1.0 N of force. Second, pull the cart for 2.0 s exerting about 0.50 N of force. Predict which trial will give the cart more acceleration. Explain. Predict which trial will give the cart more velocity. Explain. Try it. What happened? Which factor, $F$ or $\Delta t$, seems to be more important in changing the velocity of the cart?

FIGURE 9–1. The graph shows the force exerted by a moving ball colliding with a ball at rest.

# 9.1 IMPULSE AND CHANGE IN MOMENTUM

The word momentum is often used in everyday speech. A winning sports team is said to have the "big mo," momentum—as is a politician who rates high in opinion polls. In physics, however, momentum has a very special definition. Newton actually wrote his three laws of motion in terms of momentum, which he called the *quantity of motion*.

## Momentum and Impulse

Suppose a heavy truck and a compact car move down the road at the same velocity. If the two stop in the same time interval, it takes more force to stop the more massive truck. Now consider two cars of equal mass. If one car is moving faster than the other, a larger force is needed to stop the faster car in the same time interval. Obviously both the velocity and the mass of a moving object help determine what is needed to change its motion. The product of the mass and velocity of a body is called **momentum.** Momentum is a vector quantity that has the same direction as the velocity of the object.

Momentum is represented by $p$. The equation for momentum is

$$\vec{p} = m\vec{v}.$$

The unit for momentum is kilogram·metre/second (kg·m/s).

According to Newton's first law, if no net force acts on a body, its velocity is constant. If we consider only a single isolated object, then its mass cannot change. If its velocity is also constant, then so is its momentum, the product of its mass and velocity. In other words, if a single body has no net force acting on it, its momentum is constant. Its momentum is conserved.

Newton's second law describes how the velocity of a body is changed by a force acting on it, Figure 9–1. Let's rewrite Newton's second law using the definition of acceleration as the change in velocity divided by the time interval,

$$\vec{F} = m\vec{a} = \frac{m\Delta\vec{v}}{\Delta t}.$$

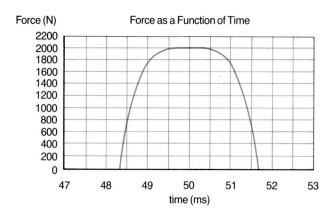

Force (N)    Force as a Function of Time

time (ms)

Multiplying both sides of the equation by $\Delta t$, we have the equation

$$\vec{F}\Delta t = m\Delta\vec{v}.$$

The left side of this equation, the product of the net force and the time interval over which it acts, is called the **impulse**. Impulse is a vector in the direction of the force. Impulse is measured in units of newton·second (N·s).

If the mass of an object is constant, then a change in its velocity results in a change in its momentum. Under these conditions,

$$\Delta\vec{p} = m\Delta\vec{v}.$$

Thus, we see that the impulse given to an object is equal to the change in its momentum,

$$\vec{F}\Delta t = \Delta\vec{p}.$$

This equation is called the **impulse-momentum theorem.** The equality of impulse and change in momentum is another way of writing Newton's second law. Often the force is not constant during the time it is exerted. In that case, the average force is used in the impulse-momentum theorem.

Impulse is the product of the average force and the time interval during which the force is exerted. A large change in momentum occurs only when there is a large impulse. A large impulse, however, can result from either a large force acting over a short time, or a smaller force acting over a longer time. What happens to the driver when a crash suddenly stops a car? An impulse is needed to bring the driver's momentum to zero. The steering wheel can exert a large force during a short length of time. An air bag reduces the force exerted on the driver by greatly increasing the length of time the force is exerted. The product of the average force and time interval of the crash would be the same.

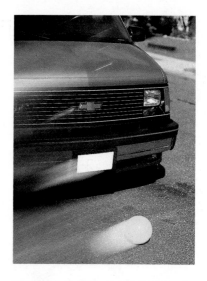

**FIGURE 9–2. With an equal amount of force, it will take longer to stop a truck than a compact car.**

◀ Air Force

# Example Problem

## Calculating Momentum

A baseball of mass 0.14 kg is moving at $+35$ m/s. **a.** Find the momentum of the baseball. **b.** Find the velocity at which a bowling ball, mass 7.26 kg, would have the same momentum as the baseball.

**a. Given:** mass, $m = 0.14$ kg          **Unknown:** momentum, $\vec{p}$
  velocity, $\vec{v} = +35$ m/s       **Basic equation:** $\vec{p} = m\vec{v}$

**Solution:** $\vec{p} = m\vec{v} = (0.14 \text{ kg})(+35 \text{ m/s}) = +4.9 \text{ kg·m/s}$
Note that the momentum is in the same direction ($+$) as the velocity.

**b. Given:** momentum,            **Unknown:** velocity, $\vec{v}$
  $\vec{p} = +4.9$ kg·m/s      **Basic equation:** $\vec{p} = m\vec{v}$
  mass, $m = 7.26$ kg

**Solution:** $\vec{p} = m\vec{v}$   $\vec{v} = \dfrac{\vec{p}}{m} = \dfrac{+4.9 \text{ kg·m/s}}{7.26 \text{ kg}} = +0.67 \text{ m/s}$

Note that the velocity is in the same ($+$) direction as the momentum.

Impulse is the product of a force and the time interval over which it acts.

$mv$
(Ball)

a

b

$F_{bat\ on\ ball}t$

$mv'$
(Ball)

c

**FIGURE 9–3.** The ball moves in the direction of the batter with momentum $mv$. The bat provides impulse $F_{bat\ on\ ball}t$ to the ball. The ball moves off with a change in momentum $mv'$ equal to the impulse from the bat.

# Example Problem

## Impulse and Momentum Change

A 0.144-kg baseball is pitched horizontally at $+38$ m/s. After it is hit by a bat, it moves horizontally at $-38$ m/s.
**a.** What impulse did the bat deliver to the ball?
**b.** If the bat and ball were in contact 0.80 ms, what was the average force the bat exerted on the ball?
**c.** Find the average acceleration of the ball during its contact with the bat.
Indicate the direction of the impulse, force, and acceleration.

**a. Given:** $m = 0.144$ kg      **Unknown:** impulse, $\vec{F}\Delta t$
initial velocity,      **Basic equation:** $\vec{F}\Delta t = \Delta\vec{p}$
$\vec{v}_i = +38$ m/s
final velocity,
$\vec{v}_f = -38$ m/s

**Solution:** $\vec{F}\Delta t = \Delta\vec{p} = m\vec{v}_f - m\vec{v}_i = m(\vec{v}_f - \vec{v}_i)$
$= (0.144\text{ kg})(-38\text{ m/s} - (+38\text{ m/s}))$
$= (0.144\text{ kg})(-76\text{ m/s})$
$= -11\text{ kg·m/s (in the direction of the batted ball)}$

**b. Given:** momentum change,      **Unknown:** average force, $\vec{F}$
$\Delta\vec{p} = 11$ kg·m/s      **Basic equation:** $\vec{F}\Delta t = \Delta\vec{p}$
time interval,
$\Delta t = 0.80$ ms $= 8.0 \times 10^{-4}$ s

**Solution:** $\vec{F}\Delta t = \Delta\vec{p}$, so $\vec{F} = \dfrac{\Delta\vec{p}}{\Delta t} = \dfrac{-11\text{ kg·m/s}}{0.80\text{ ms}} = \dfrac{-11\text{ kg·m/s}}{8.0 \times 10^{-4}\text{ s}}$
$= -1.4 \times 10^2\text{ N (in the direction of the batted ball)}$

**c. Given:** average force      **Unknown:** average acceleration, $\vec{a}$
$\vec{F} = -1.4 \times 10^4$ N      **Basic equation:** $\vec{F} = m\vec{a}$
mass,
$m = 0.144$ kg

**Solution:** $\vec{F} = m\vec{a}$, so
$\vec{a} = \dfrac{\vec{F}}{m}$
$= \dfrac{-1.4 \times 10^4\text{ N}}{0.144\text{ kg}}$
$= -9.7 \times 10^4\text{ m/s}^2,$
about 10 000 gs in the direction of the batted ball.

# Practice Problems

**1.** A compact car, mass 725 kg, is moving at $+100$ km/h.
  **a.** Find its momentum.
  **b.** At what velocity is the momentum of a larger car, mass 2175 kg, equal to that of the smaller car?

2. A snowmobile has a mass of $2.50 \times 10^2$ kg. A constant force is exerted on it for 60.0 s. The snowmobile's initial velocity is 6.00 m/s and its final velocity 28.0 m/s.
   a. What is its change in momentum?
   b. What is the magnitude of the force exerted on it?
3. The brakes exert a $6.40 \times 10^2$ N force on a car weighing 15 680 N and moving at 20.0 m/s. The car finally stops.
   a. What is the car's mass?
   b. What is its initial momentum?
   c. What is the change in the car's momentum?
   d. How long does the braking force act on the car to bring it to a halt?
▶ 4. Figure 9—1 shows, as a function of time, the force exerted by a ball that collided with a box at rest. The impulse, $\vec{F}\Delta t$, is the area under the curve.
   a. Find the impulse given to the box by the ball.
   b. If the box has a mass of 2.4 kg, what velocity did it have after the collision?

## Angular Momentum

As we have seen, the speed of an object moving in a circle changes only if a torque is applied to it. The quantity of angular motion that is similar to linear momentum is called **angular momentum.** Thus, if there is no torque on an object, its angular momentum is constant.

Momentum is the product of the object's mass and velocity. Angular momentum is the product of its mass, velocity, and distance from the center of rotation, and the component of velocity perpendicular to that distance. For example, the angular momentum of planets around the sun is constant. Therefore, when a planet's distance from the sun is larger, its velocity must be smaller. This is another statement of Kepler's second law.

Angular momentum is the product of an object's mass, velocity, and distance from centre of rotation.

FIGURE 9–4. This hurricane was photographed from space. The huge rotating mass of air possesses a large angular momentum.

- *Velocity vectors are red.*

- *Displacement vectors are green.*

- *Acceleration vectors are purple.*

- *Force vectors are blue.*

▶ **Momentum vectors are orange.**

- *Vector resultants are dashed lines.*

# Objectives

- state the law of conservation of momentum and use it, especially in collision problems.
- distinguish between external and internal forces and use this distinction.
- explain the extension of the law of conservation of momentum to two dimensions; solve collision problems using vectors.

The impulse-momentum theorem is another way of stating Newton's third law.

A system is isolated if no net external force acts on it.

## CONCEPT REVIEW

**1.1** Is the momentum of a car traveling south different from that of the same car moving north at the same speed? Explain.

**1.2** If you jump off a table, as your feet hit the floor you let your legs bend at the knees. Explain why.

**1.3** Which has more momentum, a supertanker tied at the dock or a falling raindrop?

**1.4** Critical Thinking: An archer shoots arrows at a target. Some arrows stick in the target while others bounce off. Assuming the mass and velocity are the same, which arrows give a bigger impulse to the target? **Hint:** Consider the change in momentum of the arrow.

# 9.2 THE CONSERVATION OF MOMENTUM

Suppose you place several sugar cubes in a box and close it. We can call the box and the sugar in it a **system,** a defined collection of objects. Shake the box hard for several minutes. When you open it, you find that the shapes of the cubes have changed. In addition, there are sugar grains in the box that were not there before. It would be almost impossible to apply Newton's laws to each of the forces that were acting while the box was being shaken. Instead, we can look for a property of the system that has remained constant. A balance would show that the mass of the sugar and the box remains the same. The mass is conserved. Over the past century, physicists have found that studying conserved properties has produced great success in solving problems and understanding the principles of the physical world.

## Newton's Third Law and Momentum

The example of a batted ball involved a type of collision. The baseball collided with the bat. In the collision, the momentum of the baseball changed as a result of the impulse given it by the bat. But, what happened to the bat? The bat exerted a force on the ball. By Newton's third law, the ball must have exerted a force on the bat of equal magnitude, but in the opposite direction. Thus, the bat also received an impulse. The direction of force on the bat is opposite the force on the ball, so the impulse given to the bat must also be in the opposite direction. By the impulse-momentum theorem, we know that the momentum of the bat must have changed. Its forward momentum was reduced as a result of its collision with the ball.

The momentum change of the bat may not be obvious because the bat is massive and is held by a batter who stands with his feet firmly planted on the ground, usually wearing spiked shoes for a firmer grip. In the ball and bat collision, as with almost all natural processes, many forces are exerted. We need to look at a much simpler system to really understand the impulses and changes in momentum.

To study momentum changes in collisions, we must use a **closed, isolated system.** Remember, a system can be any specified collection of

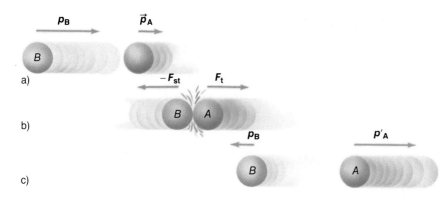

**FIGURE 9–5.** Ball A is moving with momentum $\vec{p}_A$ while ball B is moving with momentum $\vec{p}_B$ (a). When they collide, the impulses provided to the balls are equal in magnitude, but opposite in direction (b). After the collision, ball A moves with new momentum $\vec{p}'_A$, while ball B moves with new momentum $\vec{p}'_B$ (c).

objects. A system is closed if objects neither enter nor leave it. It is isolated if no net external force is exerted on it. Two balls on a billiard table are an isolated system as long as friction is small enough to be ignored, and as long as neither ball hits the bumper at the edge of the table.

In Figure 9–5, ball A is moving with momentum $\vec{p}_A$ and ball B with momentum $\vec{p}_B$. They collide, and ball B exerts force $+\vec{F}$ on ball A. The balls are in contact for a time $\Delta t$, so the impulse given ball A is $+\vec{F}\Delta t$. The momentum of ball A is changed by an amount equal to the impulse, $\Delta\vec{p} = +\vec{F}\Delta t$. The new momentum of ball A is

$$\vec{p}'_A = \vec{p}_A + \Delta\vec{p}.$$

During the collision, ball A also exerts a force on ball B. According to Newton's third law, the force ball A exerts on ball B is equal in magnitude but opposite in direction to the force B exerts on A. The time interval of the collision is the same, so the impulse given ball B is $-\vec{F}\Delta t$. The momentum of B is changed by an amount $-\Delta\vec{p}$ that is equal in size but opposite in direction to the momentum change of ball A; $-\Delta\vec{p} = -\vec{F}\Delta t$. Thus the new momentum of ball B is

$$\vec{p}'_B = \vec{p}_B + (-\Delta\vec{p}).$$

The momentum of ball B decreases while the momentum of ball A increases. The momentum lost by B equals the momentum gained by A. For the whole system consisting of the two balls, *the net change in momentum is zero*. That is, the final momentum of the system equals the initial momentum of the system; $\vec{p}_A + \vec{p}_B = \vec{p}'_A + \vec{p}'_B$. The total momentum before the collision is the same as the total momentum after the collision. That is, the momentum of the system is not changed; it is conserved. In summary:

**Table 9–1**

| Object | Ball A | Ball B | System |
|---|---|---|---|
| Initial momentum | $\vec{p}_A$ | $\vec{p}_B$ | $\vec{p}_A + \vec{p}_B$ |
| Impulse | $+\vec{F}\Delta t$ | $-\vec{F}\Delta t$ | 0 |
| Momentum change | $+\Delta\vec{p}$ | $-\Delta\vec{p}$ | 0 |
| Final momentum | $\vec{p}'_A$ | $\vec{p}'_B$ | $\vec{p}'_A + \vec{p}'_B$ |

# PHYSICS LAB

# The Explosion

## Purpose

To investigate and compare the forces and change in momentum acting on different masses during an explosion.

## Materials

· 2 laboratory carts (one with a spring mechanism)
· 2 C-clamps
· 2 blocks of wood
· 20-N spring balance
· 0.50-kg mass
· stopwatch
· masking tape

## Procedure

1. Securely tape the 0.50-kg mass to cart 2 and then use the balance to determine the mass of each cart.
2. Arrange the equipment as shown in the diagram.
3. Predict the starting position so that the carts will hit the blocks at the same instant when the spring mechanism is released.
4. Place pieces of tape on the table at the front of the carts. (See sketch.)

5. Depress the mechanism to release the spring mechanism and explode the carts.
6. Notice which cart hits the block first.
7. Adjust the starting position until the carts hit at the same instant. (Remember to move the tapes.)

## Observations and Data

1. Which cart moved farther?
2. Which cart moved faster? Explain.

## Analysis

1. Estimate the velocity of each cart. Which was greater?
2. Compare the change in momentum of each cart.
3. Suppose that the spring pushed on cart 1 for 0.05 s. How long did cart 2 push on the spring? Explain.
4. Using $\vec{F}\Delta t = m\Delta\vec{v}$, which cart had the greater force?

## Applications

1. Explain why a target shooter might prefer to shoot a more massive gun.

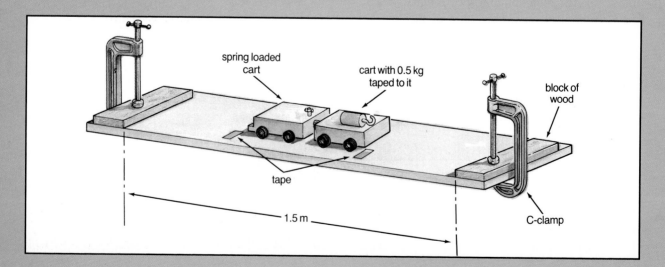

spring loaded cart

cart with 0.5 kg taped to it

block of wood

tape

C-clamp

1.5 m

## Law of Conservation of Momentum

The **law of conservation of momentum** states: *The momentum of any closed, isolated system does not change.* It doesn't matter how many objects are in the system. It is only necessary that no objects enter or leave the system and that there is no net external force on the system. Because all interactions can be classified as collisions in one form or another, the law of conservation of momentum is a very powerful tool.

As an example, imagine two freight cars, A and B, each with a mass of $3.0 \times 10^5$ kg, as seen in Figure 9–6. Car B is moving at $+2.2$ m/s while car A is at rest. The system is composed of the cars A and B. Assume that the cars roll without friction so there is no net external force. Thus, the two cars make up a closed, isolated system, and the momentum of the system is conserved. When the two cars collide, they couple and move away together. We can use conservation of momentum to find the velocity of the coupled cars.

The masses of the cars are equal, so we can write $m_A = m_B = m$. The initial velocity of A is zero, so $\vec{v}_A = 0$ and $\vec{p}_A = 0$. The initial velocity of B is $\vec{v}_B$. The initial momentum of B is $m\vec{v}_B$ or $\vec{p}_B$. Thus, the initial momentum of the system is

$$\vec{p}_A + \vec{p}_B = \vec{p}_B = m\vec{v}_B.$$

After the collision, the two coupled cars of course have the same velocity, $\vec{v}'_A = \vec{v}'_B = \vec{v}'$. Because their masses are also equal, $\vec{p}'_A = \vec{p}'_B = m\vec{v}'$. Therefore, the final momentum of the system is

$$\vec{p}'_A + \vec{p}'_B = 2m\vec{v}'.$$

By the law of conservation of momentum,

$$\vec{p}'_A + \vec{p}'_B = \vec{p}'_A + \vec{p}'_B$$

$$m\vec{v}_B = 2m\vec{v}'$$

$$\vec{v}_B = 2\vec{v}'$$

$$\text{or } \vec{v}' = \tfrac{1}{2}\vec{v}_B.$$

Since $\vec{v}_B = +2.2$ m/s, $\vec{v}' = \tfrac{1}{2}(+2.2 \text{ m/s}) = +1.1$ m/s.

After the collision, the two cars move together with half the velocity of the moving car B before the collision.

The total momentum of an isolated system always remains constant.

**FIGURE 9–6.** The total momentum of the freight car system after collision is the same as the total momentum of the system before collision.

2.2 m/s

B    A

B    A

1.1 m/s

B    A

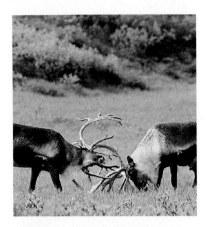

**FIGURE 9–7.** The horns of two elk fighting often become entangled, producing an inelastic collision.

The momentum of the two cars before the collision is given by

$$\vec{p}_A + \vec{p}_B = m_A\vec{v}_A + m_B\vec{v}_B$$
$$= (3.0 \times 10^5 \text{ kg})(0 \text{ m/s}) + (3.0 \times 10^5 \text{ kg})(+2.2 \text{ m/s})$$
$$= +6.6 \times 10^5 \text{ kg·m/s}.$$

The final momentum of the system is given by

$$\vec{p}'_A + \vec{p}'_B = m_A\vec{v}'_A + m_B\vec{v}'_B$$
$$= (3.0 \times 10^5 \text{ kg})(+1.1 \text{ m/s}) + (3.0 \times 10^5 \text{ kg})(+1.1 \text{ m/s})$$
$$= +6.6 \times 10^5 \text{ kg·m/s in the direction of car B's original motion.}$$

We can also look at the changes in momentum of individual parts of the system. The change in momentum of car A is

$$\Delta\vec{p}_A = \vec{p}'_A - \vec{p}_A$$
$$= m_A\vec{v}'_A - m_A\vec{v}_A$$
$$= (3.0 \times 10^5 \text{ kg})(1.1 \text{ m/s}) - (3.0 \times 10^5 \text{ kg})(0 \text{ m/s})$$
$$= +3.3 \times 10^5 \text{ kg·m/s.}$$

The change in momentum of car B is

$$\Delta\vec{p}_B = \vec{p}'_B - \vec{p}_B$$
$$= m_B\vec{v}'_B - m_B\vec{v}_B$$
$$= (3.0 \times 10^5 \text{ kg})(1.1 \text{ m/s}) - (3.0 \times 10^5 \text{ kg})(+2.2 \text{ m/s})$$
$$= -3.3 \times 10^5 \text{ kg·m/s.}$$

The magnitude of the momentum lost by car B ($-3.3 \times 10^5$ kg·m/s) is equal to the magnitude of the momentum gained by car A ($+3.3 \times 10^5$ kg·m/s).

The freight cars illustrate two important features of any collision. First, for the closed, isolated system as a whole, the total momentum is the same before and after the collision.

$$\vec{p}_A + \vec{p}_B = \vec{p}'_A + \vec{p}'_B$$

Second, the momentum gained by one part of the system is lost by the other part. Momentum is transferred,

$$\Delta\vec{p}_A = -\Delta\vec{p}_B.$$

**FIGURE 9–8.** Air tracks provide nearly frictionless surfaces to simplify the measurement of the change in momentum during collisions.

# Example Problem

## Conservation of Momentum—1

Glider A of mass 0.355 kg moves along a frictionless air track with a velocity of 0.095 m/s. It collides with glider B of mass 0.710 kg moving in the same direction at a speed of 0.045 m/s. After the collision, glider A continues in the same direction with a velocity of 0.035 m/s. What is the velocity of glider B after the collision?

**Given:** $m_A = 0.355\,kg$
$\vec{v}_A = +0.095\,m/s$
$m_B = 0.710\,kg$
$\vec{v}_B = +0.045\,m/s$
$\vec{v}'_A = +0.035\,m/s$

**Unknown:** $\vec{v}'_B$

**Basic equation:** $\vec{p}_A + \vec{p}_B =$
$$\vec{p}'_A + \vec{p}'_B$$

**Solution:** $\vec{p}_A + \vec{p}_B = \vec{p}'_A + \vec{p}'_B$, so
$$\vec{p}'_B = \vec{p}_B + \vec{p}_A - \vec{p}'_A$$
$$m_B\vec{v}'_B = m_B\vec{v}_B + m_A\vec{v}_A - m_A\vec{v}'_A$$

or

$$\vec{v}'_B = \frac{m_B\vec{v}_B + m_A\vec{v}_A - m_A\vec{v}'_A}{m_B}$$

$$= \frac{(0.710\,kg)(+0.045\,m/s) + (0.355\,kg)(+0.095\,m/s)}{0.710\,kg}$$

$$- \frac{(0.355\,kg)(+0.035\,m/s)}{}$$

$$= +0.075\,m/s$$

## Using Your CALCULATOR

Using the memory function of your calculator can simplify the evaluation of complex expressions. Note that, since the third term in the numerator is subtracted, the $+/-$ key is used to make the term negative before the subtotal is recalled from memory and added.

$$v'_B = \frac{m_B v_B + m_A v_A - m_A v'_A}{m_B}$$

# Practice Problems

5. A 0.105-kg hockey puck moving at 48 m/s is caught by a 75-kg goalie at rest. With what speed does the goalie slide on the ice?
6. A 35.0-g bullet strikes a 5.0-kg stationary wooden block and embeds itself in the block. The block and bullet fly off together at 8.6 m/s. What was the original velocity of the bullet?
7. A 35.0-g bullet moving at 475 m/s strikes a 2.5-kg wooden block. The bullet passes through the block, leaving at 275 m/s. The block was at rest when it was hit. How fast is it moving when the bullet leaves?
▶ 8. A 0.50-kg ball traveling at 6.0 m/s collides head-on with a 1.00-kg ball moving in the opposite direction at a velocity of −12.0 m/s. The 0.50-kg ball moves away at −14 m/s after the collision. Find the velocity of the second ball.

| | | | |
|---|---|---|---|
| $\boxed{.710}\boxed{\times}\boxed{.045}\boxed{=}\boxed{M_{in}}$ | | | $0.03195$ |
| $\boxed{AC}\boxed{.355}\boxed{\times}\boxed{.095}\boxed{=}$ | | | $0.033725$ |
| $\boxed{+}\boxed{MR}\boxed{=}\boxed{M_{in}}\boxed{AC}$ | | | $0.065675$ |
| $\boxed{.355}\boxed{\times}\boxed{.035}\boxed{=}\boxed{+/-}$ | | | $-0.012425$ |
| $\boxed{+}\boxed{MR}\boxed{=}$ | | | $0.05325$ |
| $\boxed{\div}\boxed{.710}\boxed{=}$ | | | $0.075$ |

$$v'_B = 0.075\,m/s$$

The momentum gained by one object in an interaction is equal to the momentum lost by the other object.

## Internal and External Forces

In the example of the collision of two railroad cars, the cars exerted forces on each other. The forces between objects within a system are called **internal forces.** The total momentum of a system is conserved, or stays the same, only when it is closed and isolated from external forces. What if we define the system as car A only? When car A collides with car B, a force is exerted by an object outside the system. An **external force** acts. Our system is no longer isolated, and the momentum of the system is not conserved. You see, it is very important to define the system carefully.

Consider the two roller bladers shown in Figure 9–9 as an isolated, closed system. That is, we will assume no external forces because the surface is so smooth that there is very little frictional force. Blader A has a mass of 60.0 kg; blader B has a mass of 45.0 kg. At first the bladers are standing still. The initial momentum of the system is zero. Blader A gives blader B a push. Now both bladers are moving. Only an internal force has been exerted, so the momentum of the system is conserved. We can find the relative velocities of the two bladers using conservation of momentum.

$$\vec{p}_A + \vec{p}_B = \vec{p}'_A + \vec{p}'_B$$
$$0 = \vec{p}'_A + \vec{p}'_B$$

or

$$\vec{p}'_A = -\vec{p}'_B$$
$$m_A\vec{v}'_A = -m_B\vec{v}'_B$$

Since the initial momentum of the system is zero, the vector sum of the momenta after the collision must also be zero. Therefore, the mo-

An internal force cannot change the total momentum of a system.

It is important to define a system carefully. A force may be either internal or external depending on the system definition.

FIGURE 9–9. The internal forces exerted by these bladers cannot change the total momentum of the system.

### RUNNING SHOE DESIGN

About $3 million a year are spent on athletic shoes in North America. Not only are athletic shoes big business, they are also "high-tech". Athletic shoes are now engineered to give the best performance for a specific use. Because running shoes take the most beating during use, they are the testing ground for other kinds of athletic shoes.

Each time an average runner's foot strikes the ground, the runner's body must absorb the force of two to four times its own weight. A goal of athletic shoe engineering is to reduce the stress of this load on the leg and foot. The vertical component of momentum goes to zero when the runner's foot hits the ground, requiring a large impulse. By using materials that lengthen the time of impact on the runner's foot, shoe engineers can reduce the force on the foot.

Therefore, the midsole, sandwiched between the insole and the outsole, becomes the most important part of the shoe. The midsole, which cushions the foot and absorbs part of the force on the runner's body, can be made of a wide variety of materials. One manufacturer uses a three-dimensional, woven-coil fabric developed by NASA for moonboots. Another uses an encapsulated silicone-based gel. Some midsoles consist of polyurethane that con-

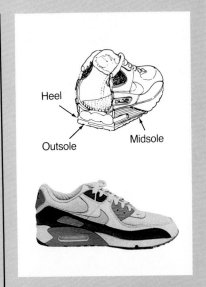

tains trapped bubbles of air or a freon-type gas. A recent design provides the runner with two sets of air cylinders that can be placed beneath the insole.
· What is the value of a design feature such as this?

menta of the two bladers are equal in magnitude and opposite in direction. Their velocities, however, are not equal. The more massive blader moves more slowly than the smaller one.

The system we defined included both bladers. Therefore, when one blader pushed on the other, the force was an internal force. The total momentum of the system remained the same. On the other hand, if we had defined the system as only blader B, there would have been an external force, and the total momentum of the system would have changed.

A system can contain more than two objects. For example, a stoppered flask filled with gas, Figure 9–10, is a system consisting of many particles. The gas particles are constantly colliding with each other and the walls of the flask. Their momenta are changing with every collision. In these collisions, the momentum gained by one particle is equal to the momentum lost by the other particle. Thus, the total momentum of the system does not change. The total momentum of any closed, isolated system is constant.

How does a rocket accelerate in space? This is another example of conservation of momentum. Fuel and oxidizer chemically combine, and the hot gases that result are expelled from the rocket's exhaust nozzle at high speed. Before combustion, the rocket with its unburned fuel

**FIGURE 9–10. The total momentum of an isolated system is constant.**

FIGURE 9–11. The Space Shuttle and its exhaust gases represent an isolated system in which momentum is conserved.

moves forward at some constant speed. It has a momentum $mv$. After the firing, the mass of the combustion gases moves backward with high relative velocity. In order to conserve momentum, the rocket, with its mass reduced by the burned fuel, must move with increased speed in the forward direction.

## Example Problem

### Conservation of Momentum—2

An astronaut at rest in space with mass 84 kg fires a thruster that expels 35 g of hot gas at 875 m/s. What is the velocity of the astronaut after firing the shot?

**Given:** before firing: $m_A = 84\,\text{kg}$
$\vec{v}_A = 0\,\text{m/s}$
$m_B = 0.035\,\text{kg}$
$\vec{v}_B = 0\,\text{m/s}$
after firing: $\vec{v}'_B = 875\,\text{m/s}$

**Unknown:** $\vec{v}'_A$
**Basic equation:** $\vec{p}_A + \vec{p}_B$
$= \vec{p}'_A + \vec{p}'_B$

**Solution:** $\vec{p}_A + \vec{p}_B = \vec{p}'_A + \vec{p}'_B$

But $\vec{v}_A = \vec{v}_B = 0$, so $\vec{p}_A = \vec{p}_B = 0$, and $\vec{p}'_A = -\vec{p}'_B$

$$m_A\vec{v}'_A = -m_B\vec{v}'_B \quad \vec{v}'_A = -\frac{m_B\vec{v}'_B}{m_A}$$

$$\vec{v}'_A = -\frac{(0.035\,\text{kg})(+875\,\text{m/s})}{84\,\text{kg}} = -0.36\,\text{m/s}$$

The astronaut recoils in a direction opposite that of the moving gas.

## Practice Problems

9. A 4.00-kg model rocket is launched, shooting 50.0 g of burned fuel from its exhaust at an average velocity of 625 m/s. What is the velocity of the rocket after the fuel has burned? (Ignore effects of gravity and air resistance.)

10. A thread holds two carts together on a frictionless surface as in Figure 9–12. A compressed spring acts upon the carts. After the thread is burned, the 1.5-kg cart moves with a velocity of 27 cm/s to the left. What is the velocity of the 4.5-kg cart?

1.5 kg          4.5 kg

FIGURE 9–12. Use with Practice Problem 10.

11. Two campers dock a canoe. One camper steps onto the dock. This camper has a mass of 80.0 kg and moves forward at 4.0 m/s. With what speed and direction do the canoe and the other camper move if their combined mass is 110 kg?

▶ 12. A gunner sets up his 225-kg cannon at the edge of the flat top of a high tower. It shoots a 4.5-kg cannon ball horizontally. The ball hits the ground 215 m from the base of the tower. The cannon also moves, on frictionless wheels, and falls off the back of the tower, landing on the ground.

    a. What is the horizontal distance of the cannon's landing, measured from the base of the back of the tower?

    b. Why do you not need to know the width of the tower?

## Conservation of Momentum in Two Dimensions

Until now we have looked at momentum in one dimension only. The law of conservation of momentum, however, holds for all isolated, closed systems. It is true regardless of the directions of the particles before and after they collide.

Figure 9–13a shows the result of billiard ball A striking stationary ball B. The momentum of the moving ball is represented by the vector $\vec{p}_A$. The momentum of the ball at rest is zero. Therefore, the total momentum of the system is the vector $\vec{p}_A$ going toward the right. After the collision, the momenta of the two balls are represented by the vectors $\vec{p}'_A$ and $\vec{p}'_B$. Figure 9–13b shows that the vector sum of $\vec{p}'_A$ and $\vec{p}'_B$ equals the original momentum, $\vec{p}_A$. The vertical and horizontal components of the vectors can also be added. The initial momentum has no vertical or y component, so the vector sum of the final vertical components of the two balls, $\vec{p}'_{Ay}$ and $\vec{p}'_{By}$, must be zero. They are equal in magnitude but opposite in direction. The sum of the final horizontal components, $\vec{p}'_{Ax}$ and $\vec{p}'_{Bx}$, must equal the original momentum, which is totally horizontal.

The total momentum of a system is the vector sum of the momenta of all the parts of the system.

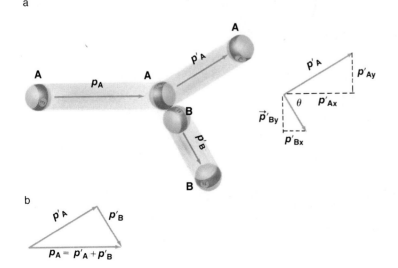

a

b

$p_A = p'_A + p'_B$

**FIGURE 9–13.** The law of conservation of momentum holds for all isolated, closed systems, regardless of the directions of objects before and after they collide (a). The vector sum of the momenta is constant (b).

**FIGURE 9–14. Use with the following Example Problem.**

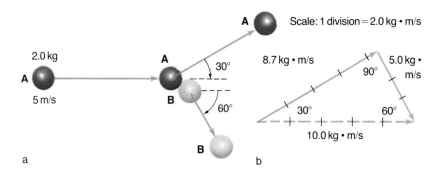

a                                        b

# Example Problem

## Conservation of Momentum in Two Dimensions

A 2.00-kg ball, A, is moving at a velocity of 5.00 m/s. It collides with a stationary ball, B, also of mass 2.00 kg, Figure 9–14. After the collision, ball A moves off in a direction 30.0° to the left of its original direction. Ball B moves off in a direction 90.0° to the right of ball A's final direction. **a.** Draw a vector diagram to find the momentum of ball A and of ball B after the collision. **b.** Find the velocities of the balls after the collision.

**Given:** $m_A = 2.00\,\text{kg}$      **Unknowns:** $\vec{p}_A, \vec{p}'_A, \vec{p}'_B, \vec{v}'_A, \vec{v}'_B$

$\qquad\quad \vec{v}_A = +5.00\,\text{m/s}$    **Basic equation:** $\vec{p} = \vec{p}'$, so $\vec{p}_A + \vec{p}_B$

$\qquad\quad m_B = 2.00\,\text{kg}$                            $= \vec{p}'_A + \vec{p}'_B$

$\qquad\quad \vec{v}_B = 0.00\,\text{m/s}$

**Solution:** Find the initial momenta.

$$\vec{p}_A = m_A\vec{v}_A = +10.0\,\text{kg·m/s} \qquad \vec{p}_B = 0$$

Therefore, $\vec{p} = \vec{p}_A + \vec{p}_B = +10.0\,\text{kg·m/s}$

The vector representing the initial momentum is an arrow to the right. The initial and final momenta are equal, $\vec{p} = \vec{p}'$, so $\vec{p}_A + \vec{p}_B = \vec{p}'_A + \vec{p}'_B$. Because the angle between the final directions of ball A and ball B is 90°, the vector triangle is a right triangle with the initial momentum as the hypotenuse. The vector $\vec{p}'_A$ is at 30.0°. We can use trigonometry to find the magnitudes of the vectors.

                  Ball A                                  Ball B

$\cos 30° = \dfrac{\vec{p}'_A}{\vec{p}'}$                        $\sin 30° = \dfrac{\vec{p}'_B}{\vec{p}'}$

$\qquad\quad \vec{p}'_A = \vec{p}'\cos 30°$           $\vec{p}'_B = \vec{p}'\sin 30°$

$\qquad\qquad = (1.0 \times 10^1\,\text{kg·m/s})$     $= (1.0 \times 10^1\,\text{kg·m/s})$

$\qquad\qquad\quad (0.87)$                          $(0.50)$

$\qquad\qquad = 8.7\,\text{kg·m.s}$            $= 5.0\,\text{kg·m/s}$

Now use the definition of momentum, $\vec{p} = m\vec{v}$, to find the magnitudes of the velocities.

$$\vec{p}'_A = m_A \vec{v}'_A \qquad\qquad \vec{p}'_B = m_B \vec{v}'_B$$

$$\vec{v}'_A = \frac{\vec{p}'_A}{m_A} \qquad\qquad\qquad \vec{v}'_B = \frac{\vec{p}'_B}{m_B}$$

$$= \frac{8.7\,\text{kg}\cdot\text{m/s}}{2.0\,\text{kg}} = 4.4\ \text{m/s} \qquad = \frac{5.0\,\text{kg}\cdot\text{m/s}}{2.0\,\text{kg}} = 2.5\ \text{m/s}$$

## Practice Problems

**13.** A 1325-kg car moving north at 27.0 m/s collides with a 2165-kg car moving east at 17.0 m/s. They stick together. Draw a vector diagram of the collision. In what direction and with what speed do they move after the collision?

**14.** A 6.0-kg object, A, moving at velocity 3.0 m/s, collides with a 6.0-kg object, B, at rest. After the collision, A moves off in a direction 40.0° to the left of its original direction. B moves off in a direction 50.0° to the right of A's original direction.
  **a.** Draw a vector diagram and determine the momenta of object A and object B after the collision.
  **b.** What is the velocity of each object after the collision?

▶**15.** A stationary billiard ball, mass 0.17 kg, is struck by an identical ball moving at 4.0 m/s. After the collision, the second ball moves off at 60° to the left of its original direction. The stationary ball moves off at 30° to the right of the second ball's original direction. What is the velocity of each ball after the collision?

· · · · · · · · · · · · · · · · · · · · · · ·

# CONCEPT REVIEW

**2.1** Two soccer players come from opposite directions. They leap in the air to try to hit the ball, but collide with each other instead, coming to rest in midair. What can you say about their original momenta?

**2.2** During a tennis serve, momentum gained by the ball is lost by the racket. If momentum is conserved, why doesn't the racket's speed change much?

**2.3** Someone throws a heavy ball to you when you are standing on a skateboard. You catch it and roll backward with the skateboard. If you were standing on the ground, however, you would be able to avoid moving. Explain both using momentum conservation.

**2.4** A pole vaulter runs toward the launch point with horizontal momentum. Where does the vertical momentum come from as the athlete vaults over the crossbar?

**2.5** Critical Thinking: A hockey player deflects a fast-moving puck through an angle of 90°. The puck's speed is not changed. By considering the two components of the impulse given the puck by the stick, tell in what direction the stick must have been moving when it deflected the puck.

**FIGURE 9–15. An inelastic collision.**

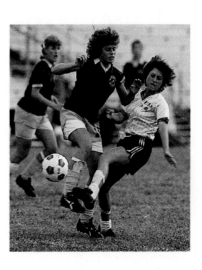

## SUMMARY

### 9.1 Impulse and Change in Momentum

· The momentum of an object is the product of its mass and velocity.

· The change in momentum of an object is equal to the impulse that acts on it.

· Impulse is the product of the average force and the time interval over which the force acts.

### 9.2 The Conservation of Momentum

· Newton's third law is another statement of the law of conservation of momentum.

· The law of conservation of momentum states: *In a closed, isolated system, the total momentum of the system does not change.*

· The momentum of a system changes when it is not isolated, that is, when a net external force acts on it.

## KEY WORDS

| | |
|---|---|
| momentum | closed, isolated |
| impulse | system |
| impulse-momentum | law of conservation |
| theorem | of momentum |
| angular momentum | internal forces |
| system | external force |

## REVIEWING CONCEPTS

1. Can a bullet have the same momentum as a truck? Explain.
2. A pitcher throws a fastball to the catcher. Assuming the speed of the ball does not change appreciably in flight,
   a. which player exerts the larger impulse on the ball?
   b. which player exerts the larger force on the ball?
3. Newton's second law says that if there is no net force exerted on a system, no acceleration is possible. Does it follow that no change in momentum can occur?

4. Why are cars made with bumpers that can be pushed in during a crash?
5. What is meant by an isolated system?
6. What is a conservation law?
7. A spacecraft in outer space increases velocity by firing its rockets. How can hot gases escaping from its rockets change the velocity of the craft when there is nothing in space for the gases to push against?
8. The white cue ball travels across a pool table and collides with the stationary eight-ball. The two balls have equal mass. After the collision the cue ball is at rest. What must be true of the speed of the 8-ball?
9. Consider a falling ball.
   a. Why is the momentum not conserved?
   b. Define a system including the falling ball in which the total momentum is conserved.
10. If only an external force can change the momentum of an object, how can the internal force of a car's brakes bring the car to a stop?

## APPLYING CONCEPTS

1. Is it possible for an object to obtain a larger impulse from a smaller force than it does from a larger force? How?
2. You are sitting at a baseball game when a foul ball comes in your direction. You prepare to catch it barehanded. In order to catch it safely, should you move your hands toward the ball, hold them still, or move them in the same direction as the moving ball? Why?
3. A 0.11-g bullet leaves a pistol at 323 m/s, while a similar bullet leaves a rifle at 396 m/s. Explain the difference in exit speeds of the bullets.
4. A baseball player slides into second base. What happens to his momentum?
5. During a "space walk", the tether connecting an astronaut to the space capsule breaks. Using a gas pistol, the astronaut manages to get back to the capsule. Explain.
6. A tennis ball bounces off a wall and its momentum is reversed. Explain this in view of the law of conservation of momentum.

**7.** You command Spaceship Zero, which is moving at high speed through interplanetary space. Using the law of conservation of momentum, explain how you would slow down your ship.

**FIGURE 9–16.**

**8.** Two trucks that look the same collide. One was originally at rest. The trucks stick together and move off at more than half the original speed of the moving truck. What can you say about the contents of the two trucks?

**9.** When you shoot a rifle for the first time, you quickly learn to place the butt of the rifle firmly against your shoulder. In terms of momentum, why is this good advice?

**10.** Two bullets of equal mass are shot at equal speeds at blocks of wood on a smooth ice rink. One bullet, made of rubber, bounces off the wood. The other bullet, made of aluminum, burrows into the wood. Which bullet makes the wood move faster? Why?

**11.** Which collision presents the greater possibility of danger to the passengers involved: (1) two cars colliding and remaining entangled, or (2) the same two cars colliding and rebounding off each other? Explain.

# PROBLEMS

## 9.1 Impulse and Change in Momentum

**1.** Jenny has a mass of 35.6 kg and her skateboard has a mass of 1.3 kg. What is the momentum of Jenny and her skateboard together if they are going 9.50 m/s?

**2.** A hockey player makes a slap shot, exerting a force of 30.0 N on the hockey puck for 0.16 s. What impulse is given to the puck?

**3.** The hockey puck shot in Problem 2 has a mass of 0.115 kg and was at rest before the shot. With what speed does it head toward the goal?

**4.** A force of 6.00 N acts on a 3.00-kg object for 10.0 s.
  **a.** What is the object's change in momentum?
  **b.** What is its change in velocity?

**5.** The velocity of a 600-kg auto is changed from +10.0 m/s to +44.0 m/s in 68.0 s by an applied, constant force.
  **a.** What change in momentum does the force produce?
  **b.** What is the magnitude of the force?

**6.** A 845-kg drag race car accelerates from rest to 100 km/h in 0.90 s.
  **a.** What is the change in momentum of the car?
  **b.** What average force is exerted on the car?

**7.** A sprinter with a mass of 76 kg accelerates from 0 to 9.4 m/s in 2.8 s. Find the average force acting on the runner.

**8.** A 0.25-kg soccer ball is rolling at 6.0 m/s toward a player. The player kicks the ball back in the opposite direction and gives it a velocity of $-14$ m/s. What is the average force during the interaction between the player's foot and the ball if the interaction lasts $2.0 \times 10^{-2}$ s.

**9.** A force of $1.21 \times 10^3$ N is needed to bring a car moving at $+22.0$ m/s to a halt in 20.0 s? What is the mass of the car?

▶ **10.** Small rockets are used to make small adjustments in the speed of satellites. One such rocket has a thrust of 35 N. If it is fired to change the velocity of a 72 000-kg spacecraft by 63 cm/s, how long should it be fired?

**11.** A 10 000-kg freight car is rolling along a track at 3.00 m/s. Calculate the time needed for a force of 1000 N to stop the car.

▶ **12.** A car moving at 10 m/s crashes into a barrier and stops in 0.25 m.
  **a.** Find the time required to stop the car.
  **b.** If a 20-kg child were to be stopped in the same time as the car, what average force must be exerted?
  **c.** Approximately what is the mass of an object whose weight equals the force from part **b?** Could you lift such a mass with your arm?
  **d.** What does your answer to part **c** say about holding an infant on your lap instead of using a separate infant restraint?

**13.** An animal-rescue plane flying due east at 36.0 m/s drops a bale of hay from an altitude of 60.0 m. If the bale of hay weighs 175 N, what is the momentum of the bale the moment it strikes the ground?

**14.** A 10-kg lead brick falls from a height of 2.0 m.
   **a.** Find its momentum as it reaches the ground.
   **b.** What impulse is needed to bring the brick to rest?
   **c.** The brick falls onto a carpet, 1.0 cm thick. Assuming the force stopping it is constant, find the average force the carpet exerts on the brick.
   **d.** If the brick falls onto a 5.0-cm foam rubber pad, what constant force is needed to bring it to rest?

**15.** A 60-kg dancer leaps 0.32 m high.
   **a.** With what momentum does the dancer reach the ground?
   **b.** What impulse is needed to make a stop?
   **c.** As the dancer lands, the knees bend, lengthening the stopping time to 0.050 s. Find the average force exerted on the body.
   **d.** Compare the stopping force to the performer's weight.

## 9.2 The Conservation of Momentum

**16.** A 95-kg fullback, running at 8.2 m/s, collides in midair with a 128-kg defensive tackle moving in the opposite direction. Both players end up with zero speed.
   **a.** What was the fullback's momentum before the collision?
   **b.** What was the change in the fullback's momentum?
   **c.** What was the change in the tackle's momentum?
   **d.** What was the tackle's original momentum?
   **e.** How fast was the tackle moving originally?

**17.** A glass ball, ball A, of mass 5.0 g, moves at a velocity of 20.0 cm/s. It collides with a second glass ball, ball B, of mass 10.0 g, moving along the same line with a velocity of 10.0 cm/s. After the collision, ball A is still moving, but with a velocity of 8.0 cm/s.
   **a.** What was ball A's original momentum?
   **b.** What is ball A's change in momentum?
   **c.** What is ball B's change in momentum?

**d.** What is the momentum of ball B after the collision?
   **e.** What is ball B's speed after the collision?

**18.** Before a collision, a 25-kg object is moving at +12 m/s. Find the impulse that acted on this object if after the collision it moves at
   **a.** +8 m/s.   **b.** −8 m/s.

**19.** A 2575-kg van runs into the back of a 825-kg compact car at rest. They move off together at 8.5 m/s. Assuming no friction with the ground, find the initial speed of the van.

**20.** A 15-g bullet is shot into a 5085-g wooden block standing on a frictionless surface. The block, with the bullet in it, acquires a velocity of 1.0 m/s. Calculate the velocity of the bullet before striking the block.

**21.** A hockey puck, mass 0.115 kg, moving at 35.0 m/s, strikes a rubber octopus thrown on the ice by a fan. The octopus has a mass of 0.265 kg. The puck and octopus slide off together. Find their velocity.

**FIGURE 9–17.**

**22.** A 50-kg woman, riding on a 10-kg cart, is moving east at 5.0 m/s. The woman jumps off the cart and hits the ground at 7.0 m/s eastward, relative to the ground. Calculate the velocity of the cart after she jumps off.

**23.** Two students on roller skates stand face-to-face, then push each other away. One student has a mass of 90 kg, the other 60 kg. Find the ratio of their velocities just after their hands lose contact. Which student has the greater speed?

**24.** A car with mass 1245 kg, moving at 29 m/s, strikes a 2175-kg car at rest. If the two cars stick together, with what speed do they move?

**25.** A 92-kg fullback, running at 5.0 m/s, attempts to dive across the goal line for a touchdown. Just as he reaches the goal line, he is met head-on in midair by two 75-kg linebackers, one moving at 2.0 m/s and the other at 4.0 m/s. If they all become entangled as one mass, with what velocity do they travel? Does the fullback score?

**26.** A 5.00-g bullet is fired with a velocity of 100 m/s toward a 10.00-kg stationary solid block resting on a frictionless surface.
   **a.** What is the change in momentum of the bullet if it is embedded in the block?
   **b.** What is the change in momentum of the bullet if it ricochets in the opposite direction with a speed of 99 m/s–almost the same speed as it had originally?

**27.** A 0.200-kg plastic ball moves with a velocity of 0.30 m/s. It collides with a second plastic ball of mass 0.100 kg, moving along the same line at a velocity of 0.10 m/s. After the collision, the velocity of the 0.100-kg ball is 0.26 m/s. What is the new velocity of the first ball?

**28.** Figure 9–18 shows a brick weighing 24.5 N being released from rest on a 1.00-m frictionless plane, inclined at an angle of 30.0°. The brick slides down the incline and strikes a second brick weighing 36.8 N.
   **a.** Calculate the speed of the brick at the bottom of the incline.
   **b.** If the two bricks stick together, with what initial speed will they move along?
   **c.** If the force of friction acting on the two bricks is 5.0 N, how much time will elapse before the bricks come to rest?
   **d.** How far will the two bricks slide before coming to rest?

**FIGURE 9–18. Use with Problem 28.**

**29.** Ball A, rolling west at 3.0 m/s, has a mass of 1.0 kg. Ball B has a mass of 2.0 kg and is stationary. After colliding with ball B, ball A moves south at 2.0 m/s. Calculate the momentum and velocity of ball B after the collision.

**30.** A cue ball, moving with 7.0 N·s of momentum strikes the nine-ball at rest. The nine-ball moves off with 2.0 N·s in the original direction of the cue ball and 2.0 N·s perpendicular to that direction. What is the momentum of the cue ball after the collision?

**31.** A 7600-kg space probe is traveling through space at 120 m/s. Mission control determines that a change in course of 30.0° is necessary and, by electronic communication, instructs the probe to fire rockets perpendicular to its present direction of motion. If the escaping gas leaves the craft's rockets at an average speed of 3200 m/s, what mass of gas should be expelled?

**32.** Figure 9–19, which is drawn to scale, shows two balls during an elastic collision. The balls enter from the left of the page, collide, and bounce away. The heavier ball at the bottom of the diagram has a mass of 600 g, while the ball on the top has a mass of 400 g. Using a vector diagram, determine if momentum is conserved in this collision. **Hint:** *Remember that the two masses are not equal.* Try to account for any discrepancy found in the total momentum before and after the collision.

**FIGURE 9–19. Use with Problem 32.**

**33.** The head of a 1.0-kg hammer, moving at 3.6 m/s, strikes a nail and drives it into hardwood.
   **a.** The head stays in contact 2.0 m/s and rebounds with negligible velocity. What is the average force exerted on the nail?
   **b.** When the same hammer hits a springy nail, it rebounds with its initial speed, 3.6 m/s. The contact time is the same. What force is exerted this time?

## THINKING PHYSIC-LY

You cannot throw a raw egg against a brick wall without breaking the egg, but you can throw it with the same speed into a sagging sheet without breaking the egg. Explain.

# CHAPTER
# 10

# Work, Energy, and Simple Machines

◀ A-Not-So-Simple Machine

How does a multispeed bicycle let a rider ride over any kind of terrain with the least effort?

What is energy? When you have a lot of energy you can run farther or faster; you can jump higher. Objects, as well as people, can have energy. A stone falling off a high ledge has enough energy to damage a car roof. One way to summarize the examples of energy above is to say that an object has energy if it can produce a change in itself or in its surroundings. This may not seem very exact, but there is no more precise definition.

In this chapter, we will concentrate on ways of producing changes in objects or their environment. The human race has developed many tools and machines that make it easier to produce such changes. A 10-speed bicycle is a machine that allows the rider to select the speed that makes the bike easiest to ride whether it is going uphill or along a level path. You will discover the physical principles that make this kind of machine work.

# ✓ Concept Check

The following terms or concepts from earlier chapters are important for a good understanding of this chapter. If you are not familiar with them, you should review them before studying this chapter.
· finding area under graph, Chapters 2, 3, 4
· force and force components, Chapter 5
· Newton's second and third laws, Chapter 5
· friction, Chapter 5
· cosine of an angle, Chapter 6

- display an ability to calculate work done by a force.
- identify the force that does the work.
- understand the relationship between work done and energy transferred.
- differentiate between work and power and correctly calculate power used.

# 10.1 WORK AND ENERGY

If you spend the morning lifting crates from the floor of a warehouse up onto a truck, you will get tired and hungry. You will need to eat food to "get more energy." Somehow, the energy in the food will be transferred into the energy in the raised crates. We use the word *work* to indicate the amount of energy that was transferred from food to you to the crates. The word work has both an everyday and a scientific meaning. In the case of lifting crates, everyone will agree that work was done. In everyday life, however, we use the word when talking about other activities. For example, everyone says that learning physics is hard work! But in physics, we reserve the term work to mean a very special form of physical activity.

FIGURE 10–1. In physics, work is done only when a force causes an object to move a certain distance.

## Work

When lifting crates, or any other object, we do more work when the crate is heavier. The task is even harder if the crate must be lifted higher. It seems reasonable to use the quantity force times distance to measure the amount of energy transferred when lifting. For cases where the force is constant, we define **work** as the product of the force exerted on an object and the distance the object moves in the direction of the force. In equation form,

$$W = Fd,$$

where $W$ is the work, $F$ is the magnitude of force, and $d$ is the magnitude of displacement in the direction of the force. Note that work is a scalar quantity; it has no direction. The SI unit of work is the **joule** [JOOL]. The joule is named after James Prescott Joule, a nineteenth century English physicist and brewer. If a force of one newton moves an object one metre, one joule of work is done.

$$1 \text{ joule (J)} = 1 \text{ newton} \cdot \text{metre (N} \cdot \text{m)}$$

Work is done on an object only if the object moves. If you hold a heavy banner at the same height for an hour, you may get tired, but you do no work on the banner. Even if you carry the banner at constant velocity and at a constant height, you do no work on it. The force you exert is upward while the motion is sideways, so the banner gains no energy. Work is only done when the force and displacement are in the same direction.

*Work is a product of a force and the displacement of an object in the direction of the force.*

**Force versus Displacement**

Displacement (m)

**FIGURE 10–2. A force-displacement graph of a rock being pushed horizontally.**

A force-displacement graph can give you a picture of the work done. Figure 10–2 shows the force-displacement graph of a rock being pushed horizontally. A net force of 20 N is needed to push the rock 1.5 m with constant velocity. The work done on the rock is the product of the force and the displacement, $W = Fd = (20 \text{ N})(1.5 \text{ m}) = 30 \text{ N} \cdot \text{m} = 30 \text{ J}$. The shaded area under the curve of Figure 10–2 is equal to 20 N × 1.5 m, or 30 J. The area under the curve of a force-displacement graph represents the work done. If you increase either the width of the rectangle (displacement) or the height (force), you increase the work done.

Work is done on an object only if it moves in the direction of the force.

## Example Problem

### Calculating Work

A student lifts a box of books that weighs 185 N. The box is lifted 0.800 m. How much work does the student do?

**Given:** $mg = 185 \text{ N}$      **Unknown:** work, $W$
       $d = 0.800 \text{ m}$      **Basic equation:** $W = Fd$

**Solution:** The student exerted enough force to lift the box, that is, enough to balance the weight of the box. Thus,

$$W = Fd = (185 \text{ N})(0.800 \text{ m}) = 148 \text{ N} \cdot \text{m} = 148 \text{ J}$$

## Practice Problems

1. A force of 825 N is needed to push a car across a lot. Two students push the car 35 m.
   **a.** How much work is done?
   **b.** After a rainstorm, the force needed to push the car doubled because the ground became soft. By what amount does the work done by the students change?
2. A delivery clerk carries a 34-N package from the ground to the fifth floor of an office building, a total height of 15 m. How much work is done by the clerk?
3. What work is done by a forklift raising a 583-kg box 1.2 m?
▶ 4. You and a friend each carry identical boxes to a room one floor above you and down the hall. You choose to carry it first up the stairs, then down the hall. Your friend carries it down the hall, then up another stairwell. Who does more work?

Direction of applied force

Direction of motion

**FIGURE 10–3. Work is done on the box only when it moves in the direction of the applied force.**

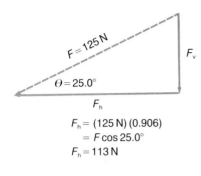

$F_h = (125\ \text{N})(0.906)$
$\quad = F \cos 25.0°$
$F_h = 113\ \text{N}$

a                                                                      b

**FIGURE 10–4. If a force is applied to the mower at an angle, the net force doing the work is the component that acts in the direction of the motion.**

Only the component in the direction of the motion does work.

## Work and Direction of Force

Work is done only if a force is exerted in the direction of motion. The person or object that exerts the force does the work. If a force is exerted perpendicular to the motion, no work is done. What if a force is exerted at some other angle to the motion? For example, if you push the lawn mower in Figure 10–4a, what work do you do? You know that any force can be replaced by its components. The 125-N force ($F$) you exert in the direction of the handle has two components, Figure 10–4b. The horizontal component ($F_h$) is 113 N; the vertical component ($F_v$) is −53 N (downward). The vertical component is perpendicular to the motion. It does no work. Only the horizontal component does work. The work you do when you exert a force at an angle to a motion is equal to the component of the force in the direction of the motion times the distance moved.

The magnitude of the component of the force $F$ acting in the direction of motion is found by multiplying the force $F$ by the cosine of the angle between $F$ and the direction of motion.

$$W = F(\cos \theta)d$$
$$= Fd \cos \theta$$

Other objects exert forces on the lawn mower. Which of these objects do work? Earth's gravity acts downward, and the ground exerts the normal force upward. Both are perpendicular to the direction of motion. That is, the angle between the force and direction of motion is 90°. Since $\cos 90° = 0$, no work is done.

The lawn exerts a force, friction, in the direction opposite the motion. In fact, if the lawn mower moves at a constant speed, the horizontal component of the applied force is balanced by the force of friction, $F_{\text{friction}}$. The angle between the force of friction and the direction of motion is 180°. Since $\cos 180° = -1$, the work done by the grass is $W = -F_{\text{friction}}d$. The work done by the friction of the grass is negative. The force is exerted in one direction, while the motion was in the opposite direction. Negative work indicates that work is being done on the grass by the mower. The positive sign of the work done by you exerting the force on the handle means you are doing work.

What is the effect of doing work? When you lift a box of books onto a shelf, you give the box a certain property. If the box falls, it can do work; it might exert forces that crush another object. If the box is on a cart and you push on it, you will start it moving. Again, the box could exert forces that crush another object. In this case too, you have given the box **energy**—the ability to produce a change in itself or its surroundings.

By doing work on the box, you have transferred energy from your body to the box. Thus, we say that *work is the transfer of energy by mechanical means.* You can think of work as energy transferred as the result of motion. When you lift a box, the work you do is positive. Energy is transferred from you to the box. When you lower the box, work is negative. The energy is transferred from the box to you.

## PROBLEM SOLVING STRATEGY

When doing work problems, you should:
1. Carefully check the forces acting on the object. Draw a diagram indicating all the force vectors.
2. Ask, "What is the displacement? What is the angle between force and displacement?"
3. Check the sign of the work by determining the direction energy is transferred. If the energy of the object increases, the work done on it is positive.

## Example Problem

### Work—Force and Displacement at an Angle

A sailor pulls a boat along a dock using a rope at an angle of 60.0° with the horizontal, Figure 10–5. How much work is done by the sailor if he exerts a force of 255 N on the rope and pulls the boat 30.0 m?

**Given:** $\theta = 60.0°$
$\quad\quad\quad F = 255$ N
$\quad\quad\quad d = 30.0$ m

**Unknown:** work, $W$
**Basic equation:** $W = Fd \cos \theta$

**Solution:** The work done by the sailor,
$$W = Fd \cos \theta = (255 \text{ N})(30.0 \text{ m})(\cos 60.0°)$$
$$= (255 \text{ N})(30.0 \text{ m})(0.500) = 3.83 \times 10^3 \text{ J}$$

**FIGURE 10–5. The force exerted by the sailor must exceed the force needed to move the boat because only the horizontal force changes the velocity.**

# Practice Problems

FIGURE 10–6. Use with Practice Problem 8.

5. How much work does the force of gravity do when a 25-N object falls a distance of 3.5 m?

6. An airplane passenger carries a 215-N suitcase up stairs, a displacement of 4.20 m vertically and 4.60 m horizontally.
   a. How much work does the passenger do?
   b. The same passenger carries the same suitcase back down the same stairs. How much work does the passenger do now?

7. A rope is used to pull a metal box 15.0 m across the floor. The rope is held at an angle of 46.0° with the floor and a force of 628 N is used. How much work does the force on the rope do?

▶ 8. A worker pushes a crate weighing 93 N up an inclined plane, pushing horizontally, parallel to the ground, Figure 10–6.
   a. The worker exerts a force of 85 N. How much work does he do?
   b. How much work is done by gravity? (Be careful of signs.)
   c. The coefficient of friction is $\mu = 0.20$. How much work is done by friction? (Be careful of signs.)

## Power

Power is the rate at which work is done.

Until now, none of the discussions of work have mentioned the time it takes to move an object. The work done lifting a box of books is the same whether the box is lifted in 2 s or if each book is lifted separately, so that it takes 20 min to put them all on the shelf. The work done is the same, but the power is different. **Power** is the rate of doing work. That is, *power is the rate at which energy is transferred.* Power is work done divided by the time it takes. Power can be calculated using

$$P = \frac{W}{t}.$$

Power is measured in watts (W). One **watt** is one joule of energy transferred in one second. A machine that does work at a rate of one joule per second has a power of one watt. A watt is a relatively small unit of power. For example, a glass of water weighs about 2 N. If you lift it 0.5 m to your mouth, you do 1 J of work. If you do it in one second, you are doing work at the rate of one watt. Because a watt is such a small unit, power is often measured in kilowatts (kW). A kilowatt is 1000 W.

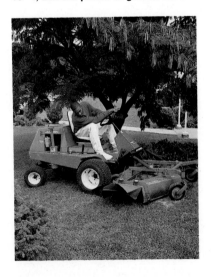

FIGURE 10–7. The same amount of work is being done as in Figure 10–4, but the power is greater here.

## Example Problem

### Power

An electric motor lifts an elevator that weighs $1.20 \times 10^4$ N a distance of 9.00 m in 15.0 s, Figure 10–8, **a.** What is the power of the motor in watts? **b.** What is the power in kilowatts?

**Given:** $F = 1.20 \times 10^4$ N
$\qquad\quad d = 9.00$ m
$\qquad\quad t = 15.0$ s

**Unknown:** power, $P$

**Basic equation:** $P = \dfrac{W}{t}$

**Solution:**

**a.** power of a motor,

$$P = \frac{W}{t} = \frac{Fd}{t} = \frac{(1.20 \times 10^4 \text{ N})(9.00 \text{ m})}{15.0 \text{ s}}$$
$$= 7.20 \times 10^3 \text{ N} \cdot \text{m/s} = 7.20 \times 10^3 \text{ J/s} = 7.20 \times 10^3 \text{ W}$$

**b.** $P = 7.20 \times 10^3 \text{ W}\left(\dfrac{1 \text{ kW}}{1000 \text{ W}}\right) = 7.20 \text{ kW}$

## Practice Problems

9. A box that weighs 575 N is lifted a distance of 20.0 m straight up by a rope. The job is done in 10.0 s. What power is developed in watts and kilowatts?

10. A rock climber wears a 7.50-kg knapsack while scaling a cliff. After 30.0 min, the climber is 8.2 m above the starting point.
    a. How much work does the climber do on the knapsack?
    b. If the climber weighs 645 N, how much work does she do lifting herself and the knapsack?
    c. What is the average power developed by the climber?

11. An electric motor develops 65 kW of power as it lifts a loaded elevator 17.5 m in 35.0 s. How much force does the motor exert?

▶ 12. Two cars travel the same speed, so that they move 105 km in 1 h. One car, a sleek sports car, has a motor that delivers only 35 kW of power at this speed. The other car needs its motor to produce 65 kW to move the car this fast. Forces exerted by friction from the air resistance cause the difference.
    a. For each car, list the external horizontal forces exerted on it, and give the cause of each force. Compare their magnitudes.
    b. By Newton's third law, the car exerts forces. What are their directions?
    c. Calculate the magnitude of the forward frictional force exerted by each car.
    d. The car engines did work. Where did the energy they transferred come from?

**FIGURE 10–8. If the elevator took 20.0 s instead of 15.0 s, would the work change? Would the power change?**

A watt, one joule/second, is a relatively small unit. A kilowatt, 1000 W, is commonly used.

## CONCEPT REVIEW

1.1 Explain in words, without the use of a formula, what work is.

1.2 When a bowling ball rolls down a level alley, does Earth's gravity do any work on the ball? Explain.

1.3 As you walk, there is a static frictional force between your shoes and the ground. Is any work done?

1.4 Critical Thinking: If three objects exert forces on a body, can they all do work at the same time? Explain.

## Purpose

To determine the work and power as you climb stairs.

## Materials

· Each lab group will need a metre stick, a stopwatch, and a climber.

## Procedure

1. Estimate the mass of the climber in kg. (**Hint:** 100 kg weighs approximately 1000 N.)
2. Measure the height (vertical distance) of the stairs.
3. The climber should approach the stairs with a steady speed.

   NOTE - Do NOT run. Do NOT skip stairs. Do NOT trip.

4. The timer will start the watch as the climber hits the first stair and stop the clock when the climber reaches the top.

5. Climbers and timers should rotate until all students have had the opportunity to climb.

## Observations and Data

1. Calculate the work and the power for yourself.
2. Compare your work and power calculations to others.

## Analysis

1. Which students did the most work? Explain.
2. Which students had the most power? Explain with examples.
3. Calculate your power in kilowatts.

## Applications

1. Your local electric company supplies you 1 kW of power for 1 h for 8¢. Assume that you could climb stairs continuously for 1 h. How much money would this climb be worth?

# 10.2 MACHINES

E veryone uses some machines every day. Some are simple tools like bottle openers and screwdrivers; others are complex objects such as bicycles and automobiles. Machines, whether powered by engines or people, make our tasks easier. A **machine** eases the load either by changing the magnitude or the direction of a force, but does not change the amount of work done.

## Objectives

· **demonstrate knowledge of why simple machines are useful.**
· **understand the concept of mechanical advantage in ideal and real machines and use it correctly in solving problems.**
· **recognize that complex machines are simple machines linked together; show an ability to calculate mechanical advantage for some complex machines.**

## Simple and Complex Machines

Consider the bottle opener in Figure 10–9. When you use the opener, you lift the handle, doing work on the opener. The opener lifts the cap, doing work on it. The work you do is called the input work, $W_i$. The work the machine does is called the output work, $W_o$.

Work, you remember, is the transfer of energy by mechanical means. You put work into the machine. That is, you transfer energy to the bottle opener. The machine does work on another object. The opener, in turn, transfers energy to the cap. The opener is not a source of energy, so the cap cannot receive more energy than you put into the opener. Thus, the output work can never be larger than the input work. The machine simply aids in the transfer of energy from you to the bottle cap.

## Energy Conservation and Mechanical Advantage

The force you exert on a machine is called the **effort force**, $F_e$. The force exerted by the machine is called the **resistance force**, $F_r$. The ratio of resistance force to effort force, $F_r/F_e$, is called the **mechanical advantage** (*MA*) of the machine. That is,

$$MA = \frac{F_r}{F_e}.$$

Many machines, like the bottle opener, have a mechanical advantage greater than one. When the mechanical advantage is greater than one, the machine increases the force you apply.

We can calculate the mechanical advantage of a machine using the definition of work. The input work is the product of the effort force you exert, $F_e$, and the displacement of your hand, $d_e$. In the same way, the output work is the product of the resistance force, $F_r$, and the displacement caused by the machine, $d_r$. A machine can increase force, but it cannot increase energy. An ideal machine transfers all the energy, so the output work equals the input work,

$$W_o = W_i \text{, or}$$
$$F_r d_r = F_e d_e \text{ .}$$

This equation can be rewritten $\frac{F_r}{F_e} = \frac{d_e}{d_r}$. We know that the mechanical advantage is given by $MA = F_r/F_e$. For an ideal machine, we also have $MA = d_e/d_r$. Because this equation is characteristic of an ideal machine,

**FIGURE 10–9. A bottle opener is an example of a simple machine. It makes opening a bottle easier, but not less work.**

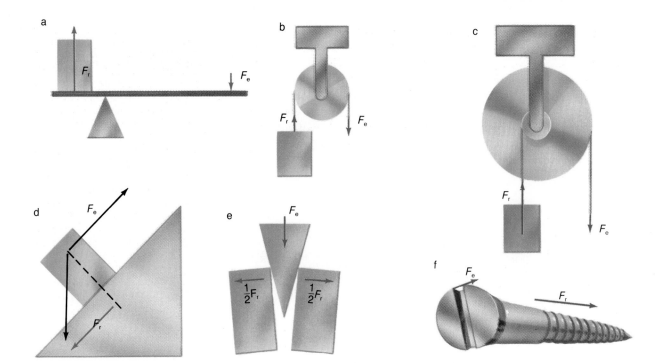

FIGURE 10–10. The simple machines pictured are the lever (a); pulley (b); wheel-and-axle (c); inclined plane (d); wedge (e); and screw (f).

the mechanical advantage is called the **ideal mechanical advantage**, *IMA*,

$$IMA = \frac{d_e}{d_r}.$$

Note that you measure distances moved to calculate the ideal mechanical advantage, *IMA*, but you measure the forces exerted to find the actual mechanical advantage, *MA*.

In a real machine, not all of the input work is available as output work. The **efficiency** of a machine is defined as the ratio of output work to input work. That is,

$$efficiency = \frac{W_o}{W_i} \times 100\%.$$

An ideal machine has equal output and input work, $W_o/W_i = 1$, and the efficiency is 100%. All real machines have efficiencies less than 100%. We can express the efficiency in terms of the mechanical advantage and ideal mechanical advantage.

$$efficiency = \frac{F_r/F_e}{d_r/d_e} \times 100\%$$

$$efficiency = \frac{MA}{IMA} \times 100\%$$

The *IMA* of most machines is fixed by the machine's design. An efficient machine has an *MA* almost equal to its *IMA*. A less efficient machine has a smaller *MA*. Lower efficiency means that a greater effort force is needed to exert the same resistance force.

The mechanical advantage of a machine is the ratio of the force exerted by the machine to the force applied to the machine.

Efficiency is the ratio of the work done by the machine to the work put into the machine.

All machines, no matter how complex, are combinations of up to six simple machines shown in Figure 10–10. They are the lever, pulley, wheel-and-axle, inclined plane, wedge, and screw. Gears, one of the simple machines used in a bicycle, are really a form of the wheel-and-axle. The *IMA* of all machines is the ratio of distances moved. Figure 10–11 shows that for levers and wheel-and-axles this ratio can be replaced by the ratio of the distances between the places where the forces are applied and the pivot point. A common version of the wheel-and-axle is a pair of gears on a rotating shaft. The *IMA* is the ratio of the radii of the two gears.

## Compound Machines

A **compound machine** consists of two or more simple machines linked so that the resistance force of one machine becomes the effort force of the second. For example, in the bicycle, the pedal and sprocket (or gear) act like a wheel-and-axle. The effort force is the force you exert on the pedal, $F_{on\ pedal}$. The resistance is the force the sprocket exerts on the chain, $F_{on\ chain}$.

The chain exerts an effort force on the rear wheel sprocket, $F_{by\ chain}$, equal to the force exerted on the chain. This sprocket and the rear wheel act like another wheel-and-axle. The resistance force is the force the wheel exerts on the road, $F_{on\ road}$. By Newton's third law, the ground exerts an equal forward force on the wheel. This force accelerates the bicycle forward.

The mechanical advantage of a complex machine is the product of the mechanical advantages of the simple machines it is made up of. For example, in the case of the bicycle,

$$MA = \frac{F_{on\ chain}}{F_{on\ pedal}} \cdot \frac{F_{on\ road}}{F_{by\ chain}}$$

$$= \frac{F_{on\ road}}{F_{on\ pedal}}.$$

**Figure 10–11. For levers and wheel and axles, the IMA is $\dfrac{r_e}{r_r}$**

The *IMA* of each wheel-and-axle machine is the ratio of the distances moved. For the pedal sprocket,

$$IMA = \frac{pedal\ radius}{front\ sprocket\ radius}.$$

For the rear wheel, we have

$$IMA = \frac{rear\ sprocket\ radius}{wheel\ radius}.$$

For the bicycle, then

$$IMA = \frac{pedal\ radius}{front\ sprocket\ radius} \cdot \frac{rear\ sprocket\ radius}{wheel\ radius}$$

$$= \frac{rear\ sprocket\ radius}{front\ sprocket\ radius} \cdot \frac{pedal\ radius}{wheel\ radius}.$$

Since both sprockets use the same chain and have teeth of the same size, you can simply count the number of teeth on the gears and find that

$$IMA = \frac{teeth\ on\ rear\ sprocket}{teeth\ on\ front\ sprocket} \cdot \frac{pedal\ arm\ length}{wheel\ radius}.$$

▶ **A-Not-So-Simple Machine**

On a multi-gear bike, the rider can change the mechanical advantage of the machine by choosing the size of one or both sprockets. When accelerating or climbing a hill, the rider increases the mechanical advantage to increase the force the wheel exerts on the road. On the other hand, when going at high speed on a level road, less force is needed, and the rider decreases the mechanical advantage to reduce the distance the pedals must move for each revolution of the wheel.

You know that if the pedal is at the top or bottom of its circle, no matter how much force downward you exert, the pedals will not turn. The force of your foot is most effective when the force is exerted perpendicular to the arm of the pedal. Whenever a force on a pedal is specified, you should assume that it is applied perpendicular to the arm.

**FIGURE 10–12.** Some of the most ingenious compound machines ever conceived came from the imagination of cartoonist Rube Goldberg, who was famous for devising complex ways for doing simple tasks.

# Example Problem

## The Bicycle Wheel

A student uses the bicycle wheel with gear radius 4.00 cm and wheel radius 35.6 cm. When a force of 155 N is exerted on the chain, the wheel rim moves 14.0 cm. Due to friction, its efficiency is 95.0%. **a.** What is the *IMA* of the wheel and gear? **b.** What is the *MA* of the wheel and gear? **c.** What force does the scale attached to the wheel read? **d.** How far did the student pull the chain?

**Given:** effort force, $F_e$ = 155 N   **Unknowns: a.** *IMA*
gear radius = 4.00 cm     **b.** *MA*
wheel radius = 35.6 cm    **c.** resistance force, $F_r$
efficiency = 95.0%        **d.** effort displacement, $d_e$
resistance displacement,
$d_r$ = 14.0 cm

**Solution:**

**a.** $IMA = \dfrac{d_e}{d_r} = \dfrac{gear\ radius}{wheel\ radius}$

$= \dfrac{4.00\ cm}{35.6\ cm}$

$= 0.112$

**b.** Since $efficiency = \dfrac{MA}{IMA} \times 100\%$

$MA = eff \cdot \dfrac{IMA}{100\%}$

$= \dfrac{(95.0\%)(0.112)}{100\%}$

$= 0.107$

**c.** $MA = \dfrac{F_r}{F_e}$

$F_r = (MA)(F_e)$

$= (0.107)(155\ N) = 16.6\ N$

**d.** $IMA = \dfrac{d_e}{d_r}$

$d_e = (IMA)(d_r)$

$= (0.112)(14.0\ cm) = 1.57\ cm$

# Practice Problems

13. A sledge hammer is used to drive a wedge into a log to split it. When the wedge is driven 20 cm into the log, the log is separated a distance of 5.0 cm. A force of $1.9 \times 10^4$ N is needed to split the log, and the sledge exerts a force of $9.8 \times 10^3$ N.
    a. What is the *IMA* of the wedge?
    b. Find the *MA* of the wedge.
    c. Calculate the efficiency of the wedge as a machine.
14. A worker uses a pulley system to raise a 225-N carton 16.5 m. A force of 129 N is exerted and the rope is pulled 33.0 m.
    a. What is the mechanical advantage of the pulley system?
    b. What is the efficiency of the system?
15. A boy exerts a force of 225 N on a lever to raise a $1.25 \times 10^3$-N rock a distance of 0.13 m. If the efficiency of the lever is 88.7%, how far did the boy move his end of the lever?
▶ 16. If the gear radius is doubled in the example above, while the force exerted on the chain and the distance the wheel rim moves remain the same, what quantities change, and by how much?

## The Human Walking Machine

Movement of the human body is explained by the same principles of force and work that describe all motion. Simple machines, in the form of levers, give us the ability to walk and run. Lever systems of the body are complex, but each system has four basic parts: 1) a rigid bar (bone), 2) a source of force (muscle contraction), 3) a fulcrum or pivot (movable joints between bones), and 4) a resistance (the weight of the body or an object being lifted or moved), Figure 10–14. Lever systems of the body are not very efficient, and mechanical advantages are low. This is why walking and jogging require energy (burn calories) and help individuals lose weight.

When a person walks, the hip acts as a fulcrum and moves through the arc of a circle centred on the foot. The centre of mass of the body moves as a resistance around the fulcrum in the same arc. The length of the radius of the circle is the length of the lever formed by the bones of the leg. Athletes in walking races increase their velocity by swinging their hips upward to increase this radius.

A tall person has a lever with a lower *MA* than a short person. Although tall people can usually walk faster than short people, a tall person must apply a greater force to move the longer lever formed by the leg bones. Walking races are usually 20 or 50 km long. Because of the inefficiency of their lever systems and the length of a walking race, very tall people rarely have the stamina to win.

**FIGURE 10–14. The human walking machine.**

## CONCEPT REVIEW

2.1 Many hand tools are simple machines. Classify the tools below as levers, wheel-and-axles, inclined planes, wedges, or pulleys.
    a. screwdriver, b. pliers, c. chisel, d. nail puller, e. wrench

# Physics and technology

## ARTIFICIAL JOINTS

Great progress has been made in designing and substituting artificial joints for damaged or missing joints. Because of the tremendous stresses in the bones and joints of the arms and legs, the materials from which artificial parts are made and the means of attachment must be extremely strong.

Titanium is a common material used to make artificial joints. However, lightweight plastics and materials similar to bone are being developed and tested for strength.

Permanent attachment of artificial joints is usually done by using special cement, by biologic fixation, or with "press-fit" systems. In biologic fixation, a porous material is used that allows bone growth into the artificial part. "Press-fit" bones are made so precisely that they snap into place around natural bones. Whatever method is used, the artificial joint must be able to withstand fairly normal stress loads.

The hip and elbow joints are the most stressed areas. The ball and socket joint in the hip carries most of the body weight and is essential for walking. Though the elbow is not a weight-bearing joint, it is the fulcrum of the forearm lever and must endure significant stress. For example, holding a 10-N weight in the palm of the hand with the elbow at 90° places a force of about 90 N on the elbow.

· What is another major consideration in the design and use of artificial limb and joint materials?

**2.2** If you increase the efficiency of a simple machine, does the
  **a.** MA increase, decrease, or remain the same?
  **b.** IMA increase, decrease, or remain the same?
**2.3** A worker exerts a force of 20 N on a machine with $IMA = 2.0$, moving it 10 cm.
  **a.** Draw a graph of the force as a function of distance. Shade in the area representing the work done by this force and calculate the amount of work.
  **b.** On the same graph, draw the force supplied by the machine as a function of resistance distance. Shade in the area representing the work done by the machine. Calculate this work and compare to your answer above.
**2.4** **Critical Thinking:** The mechanical advantage of a multi-gear bike is changed by moving the chain so that it moves to the correct back sprocket.
  **a.** To start out, you must accelerate the bike, so you want to have the bike exert the largest possible force. Do you choose a small or large sprocket?
  **b.** As you reach your traveling speed, you want to rotate the pedals as few times as possible. Do you choose a small or large sprocket?
  **c.** Many bikes also let you choose the size of the front sprocket. If you want even more force to accelerate while climbing a hill, would you move to a larger or smaller front sprocket?

## SUMMARY

### 10.1 Work and Energy

· Work is the product of the force exerted on an object and the distance the object moves in the direction of the force.
· Work is the transfer of energy by mechanical means.
· Power is the rate of doing work. That is, power is the rate at which energy is transferred. It is measured in watts.

### 10.2 Machines

· Machines, whether powered by engines or humans, make work easier. A machine eases the load either by changing the magnitude or the direction of the force exerted to do work.
· The mechanical advantage, MA, is the ratio of resistance force to effort force.
· The ideal mechanical advantage, IMA, is the ratio of the displacements. In all real machines, MA is less than IMA.

## KEY TERMS

| | |
|---|---|
| work | effort force |
| joule | resistance force |
| energy | mechanical advantage |
| power | ideal mechanical advantage |
| watt | efficiency |
| machine | compound machine |

## REVIEWING CONCEPTS

1. In what units is work measured?
2. A satellite orbits Earth in a circular orbit. Does Earth's gravity do any work on the satellite?
3. An object slides at constant speed on a frictionless surface. What forces act on the object? What work is done?

4. Define work and power.
5. What is a watt equivalent to in terms of kg, m, and s?
6. Is it possible to get more work out of a machine than you put in?
7. How are the pedals of a bicycle a simple machine?

## APPLYING CONCEPTS

1. Which requires more work, carrying a 420-N knapsack up a 200 m high hill or carrying a 210-N knapsack up a 400 m high hill? Why?
2. You slowly lift a box of books from the floor and put it on a table. Earth's gravity exerts a force, magnitude $mg$, downward, and you exert a force, magnitude $mg$, upward. The two forces have equal magnitude and opposite direction. It appears no work is done, but you know you did work. Explain what work is done.
3. Guy has to get a piano onto a 2.0 m high platform. He can use a 3.0 m long, frictionless ramp or a 4.0 m long, frictionless ramp. Which ramp will Guy use if he wants to do the least amount of work?
4. Grace has an after-school job carrying cartons of new copy paper up a flight of stairs, and then carrying used paper back down the stairs. The mass of the paper does not change. Grace's physics teacher suggests that Grace does no work all day, so she should not be paid. In what sense is the physics teacher correct? What arrangement of payments might Grace make to ensure compensation?

**FIGURE 10–15.**

5. Grace now carries the copy paper boxes down a level, 15.0 m long hall. Is Grace working now? Explain.
6. Two people of the same mass climb the same flight of stairs. The first person climbs the stairs in 25 s; the second person takes 35 s.
   a. Which person does more work? Explain your answer.
   b. Which person produces more power? Explain your answer.
7. How can one increase the ideal mechanical advantage of a machine?
8. A claw hammer is used to pull a nail from a piece of wood. How can you place your hand on the handle and locate the nail in the claw to make the effort force as small as possible?
9. How could you increase the mechanical advantage of a wedge without changing the ideal mechanical advantage?

## PROBLEMS

### 10.1 Work and Energy
1. Lee pushes horizontally with a 80-N force on a 20-kg mass 10 m across a floor. Calculate the amount of work Lee did.
2. The third floor of a house is 8.0 m above street level. How much work is needed to move a 150-kg refrigerator to the third floor?
3. Stan does 176 J of work lifting himself 0.300 m. What is Stan's mass?
▶ 4. A crane lifts a $2.25 \times 10^3$-N bucket containing 1.15 m$^3$ of soil (density = $2.00 \times 10^3$ kg/m$^3$) to a height of 7.50 m. Calculate the work the crane performs.
5. The graph in Figure 10–16 shows the force needed to stretch a spring. Find the work needed to stretch it from 0.12 m to 0.28 m.

FIGURE 10–16. Use with Problems 5 and 6.

▶ 6. In Figure 10–16, the magnitude of the force necessary to stretch a spring is plotted against the distance the spring is stretched.
   a. Calculate the slope of the graph and show that
$$F = kd,$$
where $k = 25$ N/m.
   b. Find the amount of work done in stretching the spring from 0.00 m to 0.20 m by calculating the area under the curve from 0.00 m to 0.20 m in Figure 10–16.
   c. Show that the answer to part b can be calculated using the formula
$$W = \tfrac{1}{2}kd^2,$$
where $W$ is the work, $k = 25$ N/m (the slope of the graph), and $d$ is the distance the spring is stretched (0.20 m).

▶ 7. John pushes a crate across the floor of a factory with a horizontal force. The roughness of the floor changes, and John must exert a force of 20 N for 5 m, then 35 N for 12 m, then 10 N for 8 m.
   a. Draw a graph of force as a function of distance.
   b. Find the work John does pushing the crate.

8. Sally applies a horizontal force of 462 N with a rope to drag a wooden crate across a floor with a constant speed. The rope tied to the crate is pulled at an angle of 56.0°.
   a. How much force is exerted by the rope on the crate?
   b. What work is done by Sally if the crate is moved 24.5 m?
   c. What work is done by the floor through force of friction between the floor and the crate?

9. Mike pulls a sled across level snow with a force of 225 N along a rope that is 35.0° above the horizontal. If the sled moved a distance of 65.3 m, how much work did Mike do?

10. An 845-N sled is pulled a distance of 185 m. The task requires $1.20 \times 10^4$ J of work and is done by pulling on a rope with a force of 125 N. At what angle is the rope held?

11. Karen has a mass of 57.0 kg and she rides up the escalator. Karen rode a distance of 65 m. How much work did the escalator do on Karen if it has an inclination of 30°?

**12.** Chris carried a carton of milk, weight 10.0 N, along a level hall to the kitchen, a distance of 3.50 m. How much work did Chris do?

**13.** A student librarian picks up a 22-N book from the floor to a height of 1.25 m. He carries the book 8.0 m to the stacks and places the book on a shelf that is 0.35 m high. How much work does he do on the book?

▶ **14.** Pete slides a crate up a ramp at an angle of 30.0° by exerting a 225-N force parallel to the ramp. The crate moves at constant speed. The coefficient of friction is 0.28. How much work has been done when the crate is raised a vertical distance of 1.15 m?

▶ **15.** A 4200-N piano is to be slid up a 3.5-m frictionless plank that makes an angle of 30.0° with the horizontal. Calculate the work done in sliding the piano up the plank.

▶ **16.** A 60-kg crate is slid up an inclined ramp 2.0 m long onto a platform 1.0 m above floor level. A 400-N force, parallel to the ramp, is needed to slide the crate up the ramp at a constant speed.
  **a.** How much work is done in sliding the crate up the ramp?
  **b.** How much work would be done if the crate were simply lifted straight up from the floor to the platform?

**17.** Brutus, a champion weightlifter, raises 240 kg a distance of 2.35 m.
  **a.** How much work is done by Brutus lifting the weights?
  **b.** How much work is done holding the weights above his head?
  **c.** How much work is done lowering them back to the ground?
  **d.** Does Brutus do work if the weights are let go and fall back to the ground?
  **e.** If Brutus completes the lift in 2.5 s, how much power is developed?

**18.** A force of 300 N is used to push a 145-kg mass 30.0 m horizontally in 3.00 s.
  **a.** Calculate the work done on the mass.
  **b.** Calculate the power.

**19.** Robin pushes a wheelbarrow by exerting a 145-N force horizontally. Robin moves it 60.0 m at a constant speed for 25.0 s.
  **a.** What power does Robin develop?
  **b.** If Robin moves the wheelbarrow twice as fast, how much power is developed?

▶ **20.** Use the graph in Figure 10–17.
  **a.** Calculate the work done to pull the object 7.0 m.
  **b.** Calculate the power if the work were done in 2.0 s.

**FIGURE 10–17. Use with Problem 20.**

▶ **21.** In 35.0 s, a pump delivers 0.550 dm³ of oil into barrels on a platform 25.0 m above the pump intake pipe. The density of the oil is 0.820 g/cm³.
  **a.** Calculate the work done by the pump.
  **b.** Calculate the power produced by the pump.

**22.** A horizontal force of 805 N is needed to drag a crate across a horizontal floor with a constant speed. Pete drags the crate using a rope held at an angle of 32°.
  **a.** What force does Pete exert on the rope?
  **b.** How much work does Pete do on the crate when moving it 22 m?
  **c.** If Pete completes the job in 8.0 s, what power is developed?

**23.** Wayne pulls a 305-N sled along a snowy path using a rope that makes a 45.0° angle with the ground. Wayne pulls with a force of 42.3 N. The sled moves 16 m in 3.0 s. What is Wayne's power?

**24.** A lawn roller is rolled across a lawn by a force of 115 N along the direction of the handle, which is 22.5° above the horizontal. If George develops 64.6 W of power for 90.0 s, what distance is the roller pushed?

▶ **25.** A 12.0 m long conveyor belt, inclined at 30.0°, is used to transport bundles of newspapers from the mail room up to the cargo bay to be loaded on delivery trucks. Each newspaper has a mass of 1.00 kg and there are 25 newspapers per bundle. Determine the useful power of the conveyor if it delivers 15 bundles per minute.

**26.** An engine moves a boat through the water at a constant speed of 15 m/s. The engine must exert a force of $6.0 \times 10^3$ N to balance the force that water exerts against the hull. What power does the engine develop?

**▶ 27.** A 188-W motor will lift a load at the rate (speed) of 6.50 cm/s. How great a load can the motor lift at this speed?

**28.** A car is driven at a constant speed of 21 m/s (76 km/h) down a road. The car's engine delivers 48 kW of power. Calculate the average force of friction that is resisting the motion of the car.

## 10.2 Machines

**29.** Stan raises a 1000-N piano a distance of 5.00 m using a set of pulleys. Stan pulls in 20.0 m of rope.
 **a.** How much effort force did Stan apply if this was an ideal machine?
 **b.** What force is used to overcome friction if the actual effort is 300 N?
 **c.** What is the work output?
 **d.** What is the work input?
 **e.** What is the mechanical advantage?

**30.** A mover's dolly is used to deliver a refrigerator up a ramp into a house. The refrigerator has a mass of 115 kg. The ramp is 2.10 m long and rises 0.850 m. The mover pulls the dolly with a force of 496 N up the ramp. The dolly and ramp constitute a machine.
 **a.** What work does the mover do?
 **b.** What is the work done on the refrigerator by the machine?
 **c.** What is the efficiency of the machine?

**31.** A pulley system lifts a 1345-N weight a distance of 0.975 m. Paul pulls the rope a distance of 3.90 m, exerting a force of 375 N.
 **a.** What is the ideal mechanical advantage of the system?
 **b.** What is the mechanical advantage?
 **c.** How efficient is the system?

**▶ 32.** The ramp in Figure 10–18 is 18 m long and 4.5 m high.
 **a.** What force parallel to the ramp ($F_\parallel$) is required to slide a 25-kg box to the top of the ramp if friction is neglected?

 **b.** What is the *IMA* of the ramp?
 **c.** What are the real *MA* and the efficiency of the ramp if a parallel force of 75 N is actually required?

FIGURE 10–18. Use with Problem 32.

**33.** Because there is very little friction, the lever is an extremely efficient simple machine. Using a 90.0% efficient lever, what input work is required to lift an 18.0-kg mass through a distance of 0.50 m?

**34.** What work is required to lift a 215-kg mass a distance of 5.65 m using a machine that is 72.5% efficient?

**▶ 35.** A motor having an efficiency of 88% operates a crane having an efficiency of 42%. With what constant speed does the crane lift a 410-kg crate of machine parts if the power supplied to the motor is 5.5 kW?

**▶ 36.** A complex machine is constructed by attaching the lever to the pulley system. Consider an ideal complex machine consisting of a lever with an *IMA* of 3.0 and a pulley system with an *IMA* of 2.0.
 **a.** Show that the *IMA* of this complex machine is 6.0.
 **b.** If the complex machine is 60.0% efficient, how much effort must be applied to the lever to lift a 540-N box?
 **c.** If you move the effort side of the lever 12.0 cm, how far is the box lifted?

## THINKING PHYSIC-LY

A powerful rifle is one that propels a bullet with a high muzzle velocity. Does this use of the word "powerful" agree with the physics definition of power? Support your answers.

# 11 Energy

◀ **Who-o-o-o-sh**

Must the first hill of the roller coaster be the highest one?

In everyday speech, we use the term "energy" in many ways. A child who runs and plays long after adults are tired is said to be full of energy. We call the depletion of our oil and natural gas resources an "energy crisis."

In this chapter, you will investigate various forms of energy and ways of converting energy from one form to another.

## ✓ Concept Check

The following terms or concepts from earlier chapters are important for a good understanding of this chapter. If you are not familiar with them, you should review them before studying this chapter.
· Newton's laws of motion, Chapter 5
· conservation of momentum, Chapter 9
· work and energy, Chapter 10

## Objectives

- be able to define kinetic and potential energy.
- be able to calculate kinetic energy and apply the work-energy theorem.
- demonstrate an ability to solve problems involving gravitational potential energy.

Kinetic energy is energy due to the motion of an object.

Potential energy is energy stored in an object because of its state or position.

# 11.1 ENERGY IN ITS MANY FORMS

In Chapter 10, we defined energy as the ability to change an object or its environment. Change can occur in several ways. A speeding automobile can change itself, people, and objects in its path. The energy that causes the car's motion is normally stored in the chemical bonds of gasoline. Energy is stored in many other forms. A heavy object placed high on a shelf has a potential to change almost anything on which it might fall. A stretched spring or rubber band has the ability to give an object a high velocity.

## Forms of Energy

Anything moving, from a roller coaster car to a falling leaf, is capable of causing some kind of change in an object it touches. Moving objects have a form of energy called **kinetic energy**.

Where did the roller coaster car get its kinetic energy? The work done by the electric motor was saved or stored by raising the cars to the top of the hill. The cars were said to have **potential energy**. In the roller coaster example, potential energy is stored in the cars as a result of their height, because work was done on the cars against gravity. When they go downhill, the potential energy is changed into kinetic energy.

Figure 11–1 shows another means of storing energy. The photo shows a football just as it is kicked. The kicker's foot has done work compressing the ball. Energy is transferred from the kicker into the ball in the form of potential energy. In an instant, that potential energy will be converted into kinetic energy, and the ball will move with great velocity off the foot and into the air.

Work is the transfer of energy by mechanical means. In the examples above, work was done, transferring energy into potential energy of an object. From where did this energy come? In the case of the place-kicker, the body obtains energy from food and stores it in certain chemical compounds until needed. The compounds can produce motion in

**FIGURE 11–1. The work done on the football by the kicker's foot is temporarily stored as potential energy.**

FIGURE 11–2. There are a great number of energy transfers in this photograph. See how many you can identify.

muscles, transferring their stored energy to kinetic energy. Energy in both food and the body is stored in chemical bonds, and so is called chemical energy. In the case of the roller coaster, the energy came from electricity, which was probably generated by burning coal. Coal and gasoline also store chemical energy, which is released when they burn.

There are many forms of potential energy. No matter what the form, the amount of potential energy depends on the position, shape, or form of an object. Potential energy can be converted into kinetic energy, the energy of motion, Figure 11–2.

Kinetic energy depends on an object's mass and velocity.

## Doing Work to Change Kinetic Energy

A pitcher winds up and throws the baseball. During the throw, a force is exerted on the ball. As a result, the ball leaves the pitcher's hand with a high velocity and considerable kinetic energy. How can you find the amount of energy? How is the kinetic energy related to the work done on the ball?

The kinetic energy of an object is given by the equation

$$E_k = \frac{1}{2}mv^2,$$

where $m$ is the mass of the object and $v$ is its velocity. The kinetic energy is proportional to the mass of the object. Thus a 7.26-kg shot has much more kinetic energy than a 148-g baseball with the same velocity. Kinetic energy is also proportional to the square of the velocity. A car speeding at 30 m/s has four times the kinetic energy of the same car traveling at 15 m/s. Kinetic energy, like any form of energy, is measured in joules.

Imagine you are the pitcher. How can you give the ball more kinetic energy? You can either pitch the ball with greater force or exert that force over a larger distance. In other words, you can do more work on the ball. Newton's second law shows the connection between work and kinetic energy. According to Newton's second law, $F = ma$, an object

FIGURE 11–3. This device is used to determine the horizontal velocity of such objects as a tennis ball or baseball.

is accelerated with a constant acceleration if a constant net force is exerted on it. The work done on an object is given by $W = Fd$. Thus the work done is $W = (ma)d$. Assume the object was originally at rest, $v_i = 0$. As it accelerates,

$$v^2 = 2ad, \text{ or } d = \frac{v^2}{2a}, \text{ since } a \text{ is a constant.}$$

Therefore, $W = mad$

$$= ma\left(\frac{v^2}{2a}\right)$$

$$= \tfrac{1}{2}mv^2.$$

That is, $W = E_k$; the work done equals the kinetic energy gained by the ball.

Doing work on an object can increase its kinetic energy.

Not all objects start at rest. They may already have kinetic energy when additional work is done on them. If we define initial kinetic energy, $E_{ki}$, and final kinetic energy, $E_{kf}$, as the energies the object has before and after the work is done, we can write

$$W_{net} = E_{kf} - E_{ki} = \Delta E_k.$$

That is, the change in the kinetic energy of an object is equal to the net work done on it, Figure 11–4. This equation represents the **work-energy theorem**. It can be stated: *The net work done on an object is equal to its change in kinetic energy.* Note that the work in the work-energy theorem is the work done on an object by a net force. It is the algebraic sum of work done by all forces.

The work-energy theorem states that the change in the kinetic energy of an object is equal to the net work done on it.

The work-energy theorem indicates that if the net work is positive, the kinetic energy increases. Net work is positive when the net force acts in the same direction as the motion. For example, consider a ball pitched in a baseball game. The net force on the pitched ball is in the same direction as the motion of the ball. The net work is positive and the kinetic energy of the ball increases.

If the net work is negative, the kinetic energy decreases. When the catcher catches the ball, the net force acting on it is in the direction opposite its motion. The kinetic energy decreases to zero as the ball stops in the catcher's mitt. The catcher does negative work on the ball.

The kinetic energy of several common moving objects is shown in Table 11–1.

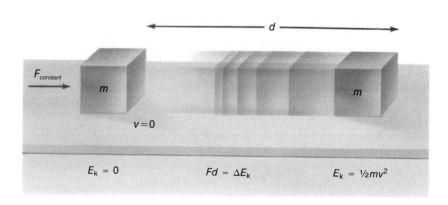

**FIGURE 11–4. The increase in kinetic energy of an object is equal to the work done on it.**

**Table 11-1**

| Typical Kinetic Energies | | |
|---|---|---|
| Item | Remarks | Kinetic Energy (J) |
| Aircraft carrier | 82 920 t at 30 kn | $9.9 \times 10^9$ |
| Orbiting satellite | 100 kg at 7.8 km/s | $3.0 \times 10^9$ |
| Trailer truck | 5700 kg at 100 km/h | $2.2 \times 10^6$ |
| Compact car | 750 kg at 100 km/h | $2.9 \times 10^5$ |
| Football linebacker | 110 kg at 9.0 m/s | $4.5 \times 10^3$ |
| Pitched baseball | 148 g at 45 m/s | $1.5 \times 10^2$ |
| Falling nickel | 5 g from 50-m height | 2.5 |
| Bumblebee | 2 g at 2 m/s | $4 \times 10^{-3}$ |
| Snail | 5 g at 0.05 km/h | $4.5 \times 10^{-7}$ |

## Example Problem

### Kinetic Energy and Work

A shotputter heaves a 7.26-kg shot with a final speed of 7.50 m/s.
**a.** What is the kinetic energy of the shot? **b.** The shot was initially at rest. How much work was done on it to give it this kinetic energy?

**Given:** $m = 7.26 \, \text{kg}$
$v_i = 0 \, \text{m/s}$
$v_f = 7.50 \, \text{m/s}$

**Unknowns: a.** kinetic energy, $E_k$
**b.** work, $W$
**Basic equations: a.** $E_k = \frac{1}{2}mv^2$
**b.** $W = \Delta E_k$

**Solution: a.** $E_k = \frac{1}{2}mv^2 = \frac{1}{2}(7.26 \, \text{kg})(7.50 \, \text{m/s})^2$
$= 204 \, \text{kg} \cdot \text{m}^2/\text{s}^2$
$E_k = 204 \, \text{J}$
**b.** Work done is equal to change in kinetic energy.
$W = \Delta E_k = E_{kf} - E_{ki}$
$= 204 \, \text{J} - 0 \, \text{J}$
$W = 204 \, \text{J}$

## Practice Problems

1. **a.** Using the data in Table 11–1, calculate the kinetic energy of a compact car moving at 50 km/h.
   **b.** How much work must be done on the car to slow it from 100 km/h to 50 km/h?
   **c.** How much work must be done on the car to bring it to rest?
   **d.** The force that does the work slowing the car is constant. Find the ratio of the distance needed to slow the car from 100 km/h to 50 km/h to the distance needed to slow it from 50 km/h to rest. State your conclusion in a sentence.

The total energy of an object is the sum of its potential and kinetic energies.

# F.Y.I.

Try bending a paper clip back and forth rapidly. Then quickly put the clip against your wrist. You will notice the clip is warm. This energy came from the work you did bending the clip.

**2.** A rifle can shoot a 4.20-g bullet at a speed of 965 m/s.
   **a.** Find the kinetic energy of the bullet.
   **b.** What work is done on the bullet if it starts from rest?
   **c.** If the work is done over a distance of 0.75 m, what is the average force on the bullet?
   **d.** If the bullet comes to rest by pushing 1.5 cm into metal, what is the magnitude and direction of the average force it exerts?
**3.** A comet with mass $7.85 \times 10^{11}$ kg strikes Earth at a speed, relative to Earth, of 25 km/s.
   **a.** Find the kinetic energy of the comet in joules.
   **b.** Compare the work done on Earth with the energy released in exploding the largest nuclear weapon ever built, equivalent to $4.2 \times 10^{15}$ J of energy. Such a comet collision has been suggested as having caused the extinction of the dinosaurs.
▶ **4.** Table 11–1 shows that $2.2 \times 10^{6}$ J of work are needed to accelerate a 5700-kg trailer truck to 100 km/h.
   **a.** How fast would it go if just half as much work were done on it?
   **b.** What if twice as much work was done?

## Potential Energy

If you throw a ball up into the air, Figure 11–5, you do work on it. As it leaves your hand, it has kinetic energy. As the ball rises, its speed is reduced because of the downward force of Earth's gravity. The ball moves up, but the force is down, so the work done on the ball is negative, and the kinetic energy of the ball becomes smaller. At the top of its flight, its speed is instantaneously zero and it has no kinetic energy. By the time it returns to your hand, however, gravity has done an equal amount of positive work, and the ball has regained its original speed. Thus its kinetic energy is the same as it was when it left your hand.

The kinetic energy you give the ball is transferred to potential energy and then back into kinetic energy. It makes sense, then, to describe the total energy, E, as the sum of the kinetic energy and potential energy.

$$E = E_k + E_p$$

During the flight of the ball, the sum of kinetic and potential energy is constant. At the start and end of the flight, the energy is totally kinetic. Potential energy is zero. At the top, the energy is fully potential, and the kinetic energy is zero. In between, the energy is partially kinetic and partially potential.

How does potential energy depend on height? As long as the ball is close to Earth, the gravitational acceleration, g, is constant, where g = 9.80 m/s². Using the equation for motion with constant acceleration, we find the velocity of the ball at any height, $v_f$, is given by

$$v_f^2 = v_i^2 + 2gh.$$

**FIGURE 11–5. Kinetic and potential energy are constantly being interchanged in a juggling act.**

In this equation, $h$ is the vertical distance measured from the launching height of the ball. Multiplying each term in this equation by $\frac{1}{2}m$ gives the kinetic energy, $\frac{1}{2}mv_f^2$, at any height, $h$,

$$\frac{1}{2}mv_f^2 = \frac{1}{2}mv_i^2 + mgh.$$

At the start of the flight, $h = 0$. The energy is all kinetic, $E = \frac{1}{2}mv_i^2$. Because the total energy of the ball does not change,

$$\begin{aligned} E &= \frac{1}{2}mv_i^2 \\ &= \frac{1}{2}mv_f^2 + mgh. \end{aligned}$$

But $E = E_k + E_p$, so the gravitational potential energy is given by

$$\boxed{E_p = mgh.}$$

Only changes in potential energy can be measured; thus the total amount of energy cannot be determined. This means that gravitational potential energy can be set equal to zero at any height you choose. Often potential energy is conveniently measured from the surface of Earth or from the floor of a room. That is, $h$ is set equal to zero at the ground or floor level. In fact, any height, called the **reference level**, can be used. It is important, however, that the reference level not be changed in the middle of a problem.

The formula for gravitational potential energy, $E_p = mgh$, is valid only if the gravitational force, and thus the acceleration, is constant. When the distance is far above Earth, the gravitational force, $mg$, is reduced, and the potential energy no longer increases linearly with the height.

Energy also can be stored in the bending or stretching of an object. The stretching, squeezing, or bending of objects such as metal springs, slingshots, and trampolines stores potential energy. The modern fibreglass pole used in the pole vault has led to greatly increased records in

Gravitational potential energy depends on an object's position above Earth's surface.

Only changes in energy can be measured.

Energy can be stored by bending, stretching, or deforming an object.

**FIGURE 11–6. The kinetic energy of a pole vaulter is first stored in the bending of the pole (a). As the pole straightens, it is converted into gravitational potential energy as the vaulter is lifted above the ground (b).**

a

b

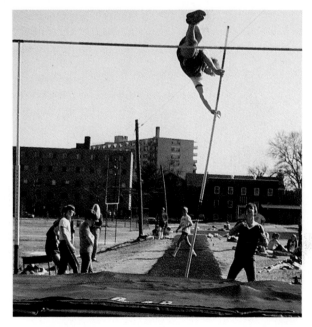

competition. The pole vaulter runs with the pole, then plants the end of it into a socket in the ground. The kinetic energy of the runner is first stored in the bending of the pole. Then, as the pole straightens, the stored energy is converted into gravitational potential energy and kinetic energy as the vaulter is lifted up to 6 m above the ground.

## Example Problem

### Gravitational Potential Energy

A 2.00-kg textbook is lifted from the floor to a shelf 2.10 m above the floor. **a.** What is its gravitational potential energy relative to the floor? **b.** What is its gravitational potential energy relative to the head of a 1.65 m tall person?

**Given:** $m$ = 2.00 kg
change in heights
   **a.** $h$ = 2.10 m − 0.00 m
      = 2.10 m
   **b.** $h$ = 2.10 m − 1.65 m
      = 0.45 m

**Unknown:** potential energy, $E_p$
**Basic equation:** $E_p = mgh$

**Solution:**
**a.** $E_p = mgh = (2.00 \text{ kg})(9.80 \text{ m/s}^2)(2.10 \text{ m}) = 41.2 \text{ J}$
**b.** $E_p = mgh = (2.00 \text{ kg})(9.80 \text{ m/s}^2)(0.45 \text{ m}) = 8.8 \text{ J}$

## Practice Problems

**5.** A 90-kg rock climber first climbs 45 m upward to the top edge of a quarry, then, from the top, descends 85 m to the bottom. Find the potential energy of the climber at the edge and at the bottom, using the initial height as the reference level.

**6.** A 50.0-kg shell is shot from a cannon at Earth's surface to a height of $4.00 \times 10^2$ m.
  **a.** What is the gravitational potential energy with respect to Earth's surface of the Earth-shell system when the shell is at this height?
  **b.** What is the change in potential energy of the system when the shell falls to a height of $2.00 \times 10^2$ m?

**7.** A person weighing 630 N climbs up a ladder to a height of 5.0 m.
  **a.** What work does the person do?
  **b.** What is the increase in the gravitational potential energy of the person from the ground to this height?
  **c.** Where does the energy come from to cause this increase in the gravitational potential energy?

▶ **8.** A pendulum is constructed from a 7.26-kg bowling ball hanging on a 2.5-m long rope. The ball is pulled back until the rope makes a 45° angle with the vertical.
  **a.** What is the potential energy of the ball?
  **b.** What reference level did you use in your calculation?

**FIGURE 11–7.**

# PHYSICS LAB : Down the Hill

## Purpose

To investigate and compare the potential energy, kinetic energy, and speed of a cart on a hill.

## Materials

· 20-N spring scale
· metre stick
· stopwatch
· cart
· 0.5-m to 1.0-m ramp (board, cardboard, and so on)
· 1.0-kg mass
· masking tape
· several textbooks

## Procedure

1. Use the tape to securely attach the 1.0-kg mass to the cart.
2. On the floor, set up the ramp with several books as shown in the diagram. Measure the height to the front of the cart. (See sketch.)
3. Allow the cart to roll down the ramp and measure the time needed to travel 1.0 m along the floor.

4. Repeat step 3 until you have a consistent value for the times.

## Observations and Data

1. Observe the moving cart and write a sentence describing the motion of the cart on the ramp.
2. Write a sentence describing the motion of the cart along the floor.

## Analysis

1. Explain your observations in terms of $E_p$ and $E_k$.
2. Calculate the cart's $E_p$ at the starting point and the $E_k$ along the floor. Compare the values.
3. Suppose that the 1.0-kg mass is removed from the cart and the activity repeated. Would the cart have a different speed? Would it have a different $E_k$? Try it. What happened? Why?

## Applications

1. The soap box derby is a race between two carts as they roll down a hill. Does the weight of the cart make much difference?

**FIGURE 11–8.** The potential energy of the water above the wheel is converted to kinetic energy as the water falls.

......................
## CONCEPT REVIEW

**1.1** Describe the work done and the energy changes taking place when
  **a.** you climb a rope.
  **b.** you throw a ball horizontally.
  **c.** a horizontally thrown ball is caught in a mitt.
  **d.** a horizontally thrown ball falls, gaining vertical velocity.
**1.2** A student is doing a problem involving a ball falling down a well. If the top of the well is chosen as the reference level for potential energy, then what is the sign of the potential energy at the bottom of the well?
**1.3** Describe the work done and energy changes taking place when, using a toy dart gun,
  **a.** you push the dart into the gun barrel, squeezing a spring.
  **b.** after you pull the trigger, the spring expands and the dart leaves the gun.
  **c.** the dart sticks on a wall.
**1.4** In an experiment, a student uses an air hose to exert a constant horizontal force on a block on a frictionless table. The student is told to keep the air aimed at the block during the time the block moves a fixed distance.
  **a.** In terms of work and energy, explain what happens.
  **b.** The experiment is now repeated. Everything is the same except the mass of the block is less. What results will be the same? What will be different? in what way?
**1.5** **Critical Thinking:** The experiment above is modified slightly. The student now exerts the constant force for a fixed amount of time.
  **a.** Explain what happens in terms of impulse and momentum.
  **b.** Compare the results of the new experiment on the two blocks.
  **c.** How do the kinetic energies of the blocks compare? (**Hint:** Assume that during the time the force is exerted on the more massive block, it moves the distance used in the first set of experiments. Now, when the times the force is exerted are equal, will the distance over which the force is exerted on the less massive block be larger or smaller?)

# 11.2 CONSERVATION OF ENERGY

W e found the equation for gravitational potential energy by assuming that the total energy of a ball in flight was constant. Although the energy changed from kinetic to potential and back again, the total amount of energy stayed the same. Unlike the conservation of momentum, the constancy of energy is not predicted by Newton's laws. It is a separate fact of nature. The total amount of this thing we call energy does not change.

## Systems

In your experience, you have probably seen few examples of energy remaining constant. The kinetic energy of a ball rolling on the grass is soon lost. Even on smooth ice, a hockey puck eventually stops. The key to understanding and using the constancy of energy is in selecting the system, the collection of objects we want to study. Just as in the case of conservation of momentum, we need a special kind of a system, a closed, isolated one.

Objects do not enter or leave a closed, isolated system. It is isolated from external forces, and so no work can be done on it. The **law of conservation of energy** states that *within a closed, isolated system, energy can change form, but the total amount of energy is constant.* That is, energy can be neither created nor destroyed.

A ball alone, acted on by gravity, is not an isolated system. A ball and Earth, however, is an example of a closed, isolated system, Figure 11–9. The kinetic energy of the ball can change, but the sum of gravitational potential and kinetic energy is constant. The sum of potential and kinetic energy is often called the **mechanical energy**. Suppose the ball has a weight of 10.0 N. If it is at rest on a shelf 2.00 m above Earth's surface, it has no kinetic energy, but a potential energy related to Earth's surface given by

$$E_p = mgh$$
$$= (10.0\,\text{N})(2.00\,\text{m}) = 20.0\,\text{J}.$$

If the ball rolls from the shelf, there are no forces on the ball other than the gravitational force of Earth, so the ball falls. When it is 1.00 m above Earth's surface, its potential energy is

$$E_p = mgh$$
$$= (10.0\,\text{N})(1.00\,\text{m}) = 10.0\,\text{J}.$$

The ball has lost half its potential energy falling 1.00 m. The ball is moving, however, and has gained kinetic energy. The change in kinetic energy can be found from the work-energy theorem:

$$W = \Delta E_k$$
$$= E_{kf} - E_{ki}$$
$$= E_{kf}.$$

The work done on the falling ball by the gravitational force, $mg$, is given by

$$W = Fd$$
$$= (10.0\,\text{N})(1.00\,\text{m}) = 10.0\,\text{J}.$$

- state the law of conservation of energy.
- demonstrate the ability to solve problems using the law of conservation of energy.
- understand the difference between elastic and inelastic collisions including which quantities are conserved in each kind.

In a closed, isolated system, the total amount of energy does not change.

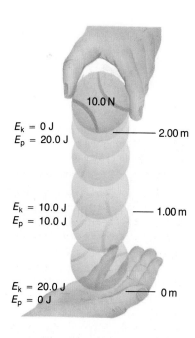

$E_k = 0\,\text{J}$
$E_p = 20.0\,\text{J}$ ———— 10.0 N — 2.00 m

$E_k = 10.0\,\text{J}$
$E_p = 10.0\,\text{J}$ ———— 1.00 m

$E_k = 20.0\,\text{J}$
$E_p = 0\,\text{J}$ ———— 0 m

**FIGURE 11–9. The decrease in potential energy is equal to the increase in kinetic energy.**

The work is positive because the force and motion are in the same direction. Thus the kinetic energy of the ball is

$$E_{kf} = 10.0 \text{ J}.$$

A decrease in potential energy is accompanied by an increase in kinetic energy.

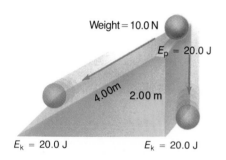

Weight = 10.0 N

$E_p$ = 20.0 J

4.00 m    2.00 m

$E_k$ = 20.0 J          $E_k$ = 20.0 J

FIGURE 11–11. The path an object follows in reaching the ground does not affect the final kinetic energy.

• • • • • • • • • • • • • • • • • •
Who-o-o-o-sh ▶

The decrease in the potential energy of the ball is equal to the increase in its kinetic energy. Thus the sum of potential and kinetic energies is not changed. The mechanical energy is constant. When the ball reaches Earth's surface, its potential energy will be zero. All its energy will be kinetic. The final kinetic energy will equal the initial potential energy. The equation describing the conservation of energy is

$$E_{ki} + E_{pi} = E_{kf} + E_{pf}.$$

Changing the path an object follows as it falls does not change its potential energy. As shown in Figure 11–11, the 10.00-N ball might be on a frictionless inclined plane. As it slides down the plane, it moves horizontally as well as vertically, but its change in height above Earth is still 2.00 m. Its potential energy depends only on its height above Earth's surface. The kinetic energy of the ball at the bottom of the plane is the same whether the ball falls vertically or slides down without friction.

Thus, in the case of a roller coaster that is almost at rest at the top of the first hill, if any hill were higher than the first, the potential energy needed to reach the top of that hill would be larger than the mechanical energy stored in the car at the top of the first hill.

The simple harmonic motion of a pendulum also demonstrates the conservation of energy. Usually the gravitational potential energy is chosen to be zero at the equilibrium position of the bob. The initial gravitational potential energy of a raised pendulum bob is transferred to kinetic energy as the bob moves along its path. At the equilibrium point, the gravitational potential energy is at a minimum (zero) and kinetic energy is at a maximum. Figure 11–12 is a graph of the changing potential and kinetic energy of a pendulum bob during one-half period of its oscillation. The sum of potential and kinetic energies is constant.

FIGURE 11–12. For the simple harmonic motion of a pendulum bob (a), the sum of the potential and kinetic energies is a constant (b).

As you know, the oscillations of a pendulum bob eventually die away, and a bouncing ball finally comes to rest. Where did the mechanical energy go? Work was done against friction, and in the case of the ball, to change its shape when it bounces. The system was not isolated so its mechanical energy was not conserved.

If total energy is conserved, the potential and kinetic energies must have changed into other forms. When a heavy crate is dropped on the floor, you feel the floor tremble. Some energy has changed into the motion of the floor. If you measure the temperature of the dropped crate or of the stopped pendulum bob very accurately, you will find that they are slightly warmer. The energy has changed into a different form, the increased motion of the particles that make up the object. This form of energy, thermal energy, will be discussed in Chapter 12.

Albert Einstein recognized another form of potential energy, mass itself. This equivalence is expressed in his famous equation $E_0 = mc^2$. Mass, by its very nature, has energy, $E_0$, called its rest energy. Further, energy has mass. Stretching a spring or bending a bow causes them to gain mass. In these cases, the mass change is too small to be easily detected. When the strong nuclear forces are involved, however, the energy released by changes in mass can be very large indeed.

## PROBLEM SOLVING STRATEGY

When solving conservation of energy problems:
1. Carefully identify the system. Make sure it is closed; no objects can leave or enter it. It must also be isolated; no external forces can act on any object in the system. Thus, no work can be done on or by objects outside the system.
2. Is friction present? If it is, then the sum of kinetic and potential energies will not be constant. But, the sum of the kinetic energy, potential energy, and the work done against friction will be constant.
3. Finally, if there is no friction, find the initial and final total energies and set them equal.

## Example Problem

### Conservation of Energy

A large chunk of ice with mass 15.0 kg falls from a roof 8.00 m above the ground. **a.** Find the kinetic energy of the ice when it reaches the ground. **b.** What is the speed of the ice when it reaches the ground? **c.** Is the answer the same as you would determine by solving as a constant acceleration problem?

**Given:** $m = 15.0\,\text{kg}$
$g = 9.80\,\text{m/s}^2$
$h = 8.00\,\text{m}$
$E_{ki} = 0$
$E_{pf} = 0$

**Unknowns: a.** $E_{kf}$  **b.** $v_f$
**Basic equation:** $E_{ki} + E_{pi} = E_{kf} + E_{pf}$

**Solution:**

**a.** $E_{ki} + E_{pi} = E_{kf} - E_{pf}$
$0 + mgh = E_{kf} + 0$
$E_{kf} = mgh = (15.0\,\text{kg})(9.80\,\text{m/s}^2)(8.00\,\text{m}) = 1.18 \times 10^3\,\text{J}$

**b.** $E_{kf} = \tfrac{1}{2}mv_f^2$
$v_f^2 = 2\dfrac{E_{kf}}{m} = \dfrac{2(1.18 \times 10^3\,\text{J})}{15.0\,\text{kg}} = 157\,\text{m}^2/\text{s}^2$
$v_f = 12.5\,\text{m/s}$

**c.** yes

> The change in the gravitational potential energy of an object does not depend on the path it takes.

## Practice Problems

**9.** A bike rider approaches a hill with a speed of 8.5 m/s. The total mass of the bike and rider is 85 kg.
   **a.** Find the kinetic energy of the bike and rider.
   **b.** The rider coasts up the hill. Assuming there is no friction, at what height will the bike come to a stop?
   **c.** Does your answer depend on the mass of the bike and rider? Explain.

**10.** Tarzan, mass 85 kg, swings down from a tree limb on the end of a 20-m vine. His feet touch the ground 4.0 m below the limb.
   **a.** How fast is Tarzan moving when he reaches the ground?
   **b.** Does your answer depend on Tarzan's mass?
   **c.** Does your answer depend on the length of the vine?

**11.** A skier starts from rest at the top of a 45-m hill, skis down a 30° incline into a valley, and continues up a 40-m hill. Both hill heights are measured from the valley floor. Assume you can neglect friction and the effect of ski poles.
   **a.** How fast is the skier moving at the bottom of the valley?
   **b.** What is the skier's speed at the top of the next hill?

▶ **12.** Suppose, in the case of Practice Problem 9, the bike rider pedaled up the hill and never came to a stop.
   **a.** How could you define a system in which energy is conserved?
   **b.** From what form of energy did the bike gain kinetic energy?

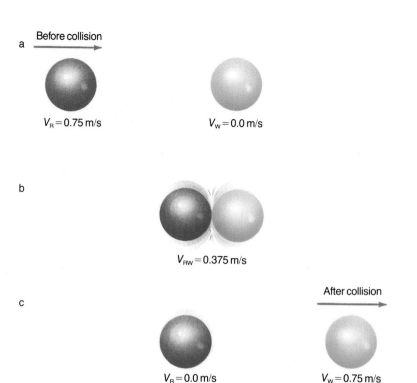

a Before collision →

$V_R = 0.75$ m/s      $V_W = 0.0$ m/s

b

$V_{RW} = 0.375$ m/s

c          After collision →

$V_R = 0.0$ m/s      $V_W = 0.75$ m/s

**FIGURE 11–13.** In an elastic collision between two billiard balls, kinetic energy, as well as momentum, is conserved.

## Analyzing Collisions

During a collision between two objects, forces act that slightly change the shape of the colliding bodies. The kinetic energy of motion is changed into potential energy. If the potential energy is completely converted back into kinetic energy after the collision, the collision is called an **elastic collision**. For this special case, the kinetic energy of the bodies before the collision is equal to their kinetic energy after the collision. The collision between two billiard balls or glass marbles is very nearly elastic.

*Kinetic energy is conserved in elastic collisions.*

What conservation laws can be used to analyse collisions? Momentum is conserved whenever bodies collide with no external forces present. Suppose a red billiard ball of mass m = 95 g moves with a speed $v$ = +0.75 m/s. It collides head-on with a white billiard ball of equal mass that is at rest. The total momentum before the collision is $mv$ = (0.095 kg)(+0.75 m/s) = +0.071 kg · m/s. What are the speeds of the two balls after the collision? Using only the momentum equation, the two speeds cannot be determined—with two unknowns, two equations are needed. If kinetic energy is also conserved, we have a second equation and can solve the two equations simultaneously to find the final speeds. The results show that the moving red ball must come to rest and the white ball must move with the final speed $v_f$ = +0.75 m/s, the initial speed of the red ball.

*Momentum is conserved in all collisions that occur in closed, isolated systems.*

If, during a collision, some kinetic energy is changed into other forms, the collision is called an **inelastic collision**. In the case of real billiard balls, some energy is usually needed to do work against the surface of the table. The red ball will not stop, and the white ball will have a smaller final speed. If, instead of billiard balls, two balls of soft

# Physics and society

## Tidal Energy: Too Costly?

Twice each day the Atlantic Ocean pours into Nova Scotia's Bay of Fundy, producing the highest tides in the world, ranging from 12 m to an extreme of 17 m. Because of the huge amount of kinetic energy available in these tides — each tidal flow through the bay could generate the electrical energy output of 250 large nuclear power plants — the federal government has studied the possibility of building a dam and a hydroelectric power plant at the entrance to the bay.

Such a dam would obstruct the natural movement of the tides to capture their energy. Every twelve hours, the incoming tide would rush through the open floodgates in the dam and be impounded behind the dam. As the tide recedes, the water would exit through turbines, generating electricity.

A dam would be an attractive prospect for several reasons. It would make huge amounts of electricity available to eastern Canada and to the northeastern part of the United States. The construction of a dam would also create jobs and promote general economic development in the area during the ten years required to construct a dam. Finally, a hydroelectric power plant is generally the least expensive way to generate electricity, and it does not create the pollution problems of coal and oil-fired power plants.

Opponents of a dam have pointed out several disadvantages. It has been estimated that the difference between high and low tides in the Gulf of Maine to the south would increase by 10%, raising the high tide level by 10 to 20 cm. This could flood coastal roads and bridges and waterfront homes along the Maine coast. Tidal currents would be altered, resulting in a change of surface water temperature and recreational use of the area. Millions of fish — shad, salmon, and others — could be killed by passage through the turbines. This could affect sport and commercial fishing far away. Numerous migrating birds stop to feed in the mudflats of the Bay of Fundy on their way from South America to the Arctic Circle. They would have to find new feeding grounds because the mudflats behind the dam would be flooded.

## DEVELOPING A VIEWPOINT

Find and read references concerning the potential positive and negative effects of building a dam to harness tidal energy. Come to class prepared to discuss the following questions.

1. What are some advantages and disadvantages if a country were to depend on a source of electricity outside its borders?
2. Consider all the factors involved and be prepared to discuss why you would or would not vote for the construction of such a dam.
3. Would you be willing to share the electrical power with the United States? Why or why not?

## SUGGESTED READINGS

Greenberg, David A. "Modeling Tidal Power." *Scientific American* 257(5), November 1987, pp. 128—131.
Ross, David. "The Potential of Tidal Power . . . Still All at Sea." *New Scientist* 126(1717), May 19, 1990, p. 52.

clay, each with a mass of 0.095 kg, collide and stick together, the collision is said to be completely inelastic. The two clay balls will have the same final speed. As was shown in Chapter 9, because of conservation of momentum, the final speed is half the initial speed. The momentum of the balls is not changed.

$$2m(v/2) = (0.190 \text{ kg})((0.75 \text{ m/s})/2) = 0.07125 \text{ kg} \cdot \text{m/s}$$

The energy after the collision is

$$\frac{1}{2}(2m)(v/2)^2 = \frac{1}{2}(0.190 \text{ kg})(0.375 \text{ m/s})^2 = 0.01336 \text{ J}.$$

This result indicates that half the initial kinetic energy has changed into other forms of energy.

Many collisions are neither completely elastic nor completely inelastic. The velocities can then be calculated only if the amount of energy loss is known.

Many collisions are neither completely elastic nor completely inelastic.

# Example Problem

## Elastic Collision

Block A with mass 12 kg moving at +2.4 m/s makes a perfectly elastic head-on collision with a block B, mass 36 kg, at rest. Find the velocities of the two blocks after the collision. Assume all motion is in one dimension.

**Given:** before collision,  **Unknowns:** after collision,
    block A, $m$ = 12 kg           block A, $\vec{v}'$
          $v$ = +2.4 m/s       block B, $\vec{V}'$
    block B, $M$ = 36 kg
          $V$ = 0 m/s

**Basic equations:**
    conservation of momentum, $m\vec{v} + M\vec{V} = m\vec{v}' + M\vec{V}'$
    conservation of energy, $\frac{1}{2}m\vec{v}^2 + \frac{1}{2}M\vec{V}^2 = \frac{1}{2}m\vec{v}'^2 + \frac{1}{2}M\vec{V}'^2$

**Solution:**

Use the fact that $\vec{V} = 0$ to simplify the basic equations $m\vec{v} = m\vec{v}' + M\vec{V}'$ and $\frac{1}{2}m\vec{v}^2 = \frac{1}{2}m\vec{v}'^2 + \frac{1}{2}M\vec{V}'^2$. Now solve the momentum equation for

$$\vec{V}' = m\left(\frac{\vec{v} - \vec{v}'}{M}\right) \text{ and substitute into the energy equation}$$

$$\frac{1}{2}m\vec{v}^2 = \frac{1}{2}m\vec{v}'^2 + \frac{1}{2}M\left(\frac{m(\vec{v} - \vec{v}')}{M}\right)^2.$$

By solving this quadratic equation for $\vec{v}'$, we obtain

$$\vec{v}' = \frac{m - M}{m + M}\vec{v} \text{ and } \vec{V}' = \frac{2m\vec{v}}{m + M}$$

In this particular case,

$$\vec{v}' = \frac{(12 \text{ kg} - 36 \text{ kg})(+2.4 \text{ m/s})}{12 \text{ kg} + 36 \text{ kg}}$$

$$= -1.2 \text{ m/s (backward), and}$$

$$\vec{V}' = \frac{2(12 \text{ kg})(+2.4 \text{ m/s})}{12 \text{ kg} + 36 \text{ kg}} = +1.2 \text{ m/s (forward)}$$

# POCKET LAB

## ENERGY EXCHANGE

Wear goggles for this activity. Select several different size steel balls and mass them. Stand a spring-loaded laboratory cart on end with the spring mechanism pointing upward. Place a ball on top of the spring mechanism. Press down on the ball to compress the spring until the ball is touching the cart. Quickly release the ball so that the spring shoots it upward. Repeat several times and measure the average height. Predict how high the other sizes of steel balls should go. Try it. Record the values in a data table. Classify the balls in order of height attained.

**FIGURE 11–14. The conservation of momentum sometimes becomes very obvious on a slippery road.**

# Example Problem

## Energy Loss in a Collision

In an accident due to slippery roads, a compact car, mass 575 kg, moving at +15 m/s, smashes head-on into the rear end of a car with a mass of 1575 kg, originally moving at +5.0 m/s. They lock together and slide forward.

**a.** What is the final velocity of the wrecked cars?
**b.** How much kinetic energy was lost in the collision?
**c.** What fraction of the original energy was lost?
**d.** Into what forms did this energy most likely go?

**Given:** $m_A = 575\,kg$
$v_A = +15\,m/s$
$m_B = 1575\,kg$
$v_B = +5.0\,m/s$

**Unknowns:** final velocity, $\vec{V}$
lost kinetic energy,
$\Delta E_k = E_{k\,final} - E_{k\,initial}$
**Basic equations:** conservation of
momentum, $m_A\vec{V}_A + m_B\vec{V}_B = (m_A + m_B)\vec{V}$
kinetic energy,
$E_k = \frac{1}{2}m\vec{V}^2$

**Solution:**

**a.** From conservation of momentum,

$$\vec{V} = \frac{m_A\vec{V}_a + m_B\vec{V}_B}{m_A + m_B}$$
$$= \frac{(575\,kg)(+15\,m/s) + (1575\,kg)(+5.0\,m/s)}{575\,kg + 1575\,kg}$$
$$= +7.7\,m/s$$

**b.** $\Delta E_k = E_{k\,final} - E_{k\,initial}$
$= \frac{1}{2}(m_A + m_B)\vec{V}^2 - \frac{1}{2}m_A\vec{V}_A^2 - \frac{1}{2}m_B\vec{V}_B^2$
$= \frac{1}{2}(2150\,kg)(7.7\,m/s)^2 -$
$\quad \frac{1}{2}(575\,kg)(15\,m/s)^2 - \frac{1}{2}(1575\,kg)(5.0\,m/s)^2$
$= -2.1 \times 10^4\,J$

**c.** Fraction lost is $\Delta E_k/E_{k\,initial} =$
$$\frac{\Delta E_k}{E_{k\,initial}} = \frac{-2.1 \times 10^4\,J}{8.4 \times 10^4\,J} = -\frac{1}{4}\,(25\%\ lost)$$

**d.** Energy went into bent metal, warmed car parts, and so on.

# Practice Problems

**13.** A 2.00-g bullet, moving at 538 m/s, strikes a 0.250-kg piece of wood at rest on a frictionless table. The bullet sticks in the wood, and the combined mass moves slowly down the table.
  **a.** Find the speed of the combination after the collision.
  **b.** Find the kinetic energy of the bullet before the collision.
  **c.** Find the kinetic energy of the combination after the collision.
  **d.** How much kinetic energy did the bullet lose?
  **e.** What percent of the bullet's original kinetic energy is lost?

**14.** An 8.00-g bullet is fired horizontally into a 9.00-kg block of wood on an air table and is embedded in it. After the collision, the block and the bullet slide along a frictionless surface together with a speed of 10 cm/s. What was the initial speed of the bullet?

**15.** As everyone knows, bullets bounce from Superman's chest. Suppose Superman, mass 104 kg, while not moving, is struck by a 4.2-g bullet moving with a speed of 835 m/s. If the collision is elastic, find the speed that Superman had after the collision. (Assume the bottoms of his superfeet are frictionless.)

▶ **16.** A 0.73-kg magnetic target is suspended on a string. A 0.025-kg magnetic dart, shot horizontally, strikes it head on. The dart and the target together swing up 12 cm above the initial level. What was the initial velocity of the dart? (**Hint:** Since your equation will have two unknowns, you will need an additional equation to solve for $v_i$. Consider the fact that the target had zero potential energy before the collision, but the dart and target no longer had zero potential energy after the collision.)

···············

# CONCEPT REVIEW

**2.1** Is "spaceship Earth" a closed, isolated system? Give examples to support your answer.

**2.2** A surfboarder crouches down and moves high up into the "curl" of a wave. How does this person use conservation of energy?

**2.3** A child jumps on a trampoline. What are the forms of energy when
  **a.** the child is as high as he goes in the air?
  **b.** the child's feet are just touching the trampoline?
  **c.** the child is momentarily at rest as low as he goes into the trampoline?

**2.4** Critical Thinking: A ball drops 20 m. When it has fallen half the distance, 10 m, half of its energy is potential, half kinetic. When it has fallen instead for half the amount of time it takes to fall, will more, less, or exactly half of its energy be potential energy?

Copyright © 1982 DC Comics Inc.

**FIGURE 11–15.**

# CHAPTER
## 11 REVIEW

## SUMMARY

### 11.1 Energy in Its Many Forms

· Kinetic energy is the energy an object has because of its motion.

· Potential energy is the energy an object has because of its position, shape, or form.

· According to the work-energy theorem, the work done on an object by the net force acting on it is equal to the change in kinetic energy of the body.

· Gravitational potential energy depends on the weight of the body and its separation from Earth: $E_p = mgh$.

### 11.2 Conservation of Energy

· The sum of kinetic and potential energies of a system is called the mechanical energy.

· According to the law of conservation of energy, the total energy of a closed, isolated system is constant. Within the system, energy can change form, but the total energy does not change.

· In an elastic collision, the total momentum and kinetic energy of the system is the same before and after the collision.

· In an inelastic collision, momentum is conserved; total kinetic energy is decreased.

## KEY TERMS

| | |
|---|---|
| kinetic energy | law of conservation |
| potential energy | of energy |
| work-energy theorem | mechanical energy |
| reference level | elastic collision |
| | inelastic collision |

## REVIEWING CONCEPTS

1. Explain how energy and work are related.
2. What type of energy does a wound watch spring have? What form of energy does a running mechanical watch use? When a watch runs down, what has happened to the energy?
3. Name the types of mechanical energy in the Earth-sun system.
4. Explain how energy and force are related.
5. Can the kinetic energy of a baseball ever have a negative value? Explain.
6. Does the work-energy theorem apply when a speeding car puts on its brakes and comes to a stop? Explain.
7. Can a baseball have potential energy and kinetic energy at the same time?
8. Describe the energy transformations that occur when an athlete is pole vaulting.
9. Pole vaulting was transformed when the wooden pole was replaced by the fiberglass pole. Explain why.
10. Can the gravitational potential energy of a baseball ever have a negative value? Explain.
11. An earthquake can release energy to devastate a city. Where does this energy reside an instant before the earthquake takes place?
12. Work is required to lift a barbell. How many times as much work is required to lift the barbell three times as high?
13. A ball is dropped by Sam from the top of a building, while Sue at the bottom of the building observes the motion. Will these two people agree on the value of the ball's potential energy for reference level? on the change in potential energy of the ball? on the kinetic energy of the ball?
14. A rubber ball is dropped from a height of 8 m. After striking the floor, the ball bounces to a height of 5 m.
    a. If the ball had bounced to a height of 8 m, how would you describe the collision between the ball and the floor?
    b. If the ball had not bounced at all, how would you describe the collision between the ball and the floor?
    c. What happened to the energy lost by the ball during the collision?
15. Does the work–energy theorem hold if friction acts on an object? Explain your answer.
16. Air bags greatly reduce the chance of injury in a car accident. Explain how they do so, in terms of energy transfers.
17. The cue ball hits the eight ball.

**a.** What is an elastic collision?

**b.** What quantities are conserved in an elastic collision?

**c.** Which of the laws does not apply to inelastic collision?

18. A child throws a ball of clay against a wall and it sticks. Has energy been conserved?

## APPLYING CONCEPTS

1. A compact car and a semi-truck are both travelling at the same velocity. Which has more kinetic energy?

2. Sally and Lisa have identical compact cars. Sally drives on the freeway with a greater speed than Lisa. Which car has more kinetic energy?

3. Sally and Lisa have identical compact cars. Sally is northbound on the freeway and Lisa is southbound with the same speed. Which car has more kinetic energy?

4. Is it possible to exert a force and yet not cause a change in kinetic energy?

5. Two bodies of unequal mass each have the same kinetic energy and are moving in the same direction. If the same retarding force is applied to each, how will the stopping distances of the bodies compare?

6. If you drop a tennis ball onto a concrete floor, it will bounce back farther than if you drop it on a rug. Where does the lost energy go when it strikes the rug?

7. Most earth satellites follow an elliptical path rather than a circular path around Earth. The $E_p$ increases when the satellite moves farther from Earth. According to energy conservation, does a satellite have its greatest speed when it is closest to or farthest from Earth?

8. In mountainous areas, road designers build escape ramps to help trucks with failed brakes stop. These escape ramps are usually roads made of loose gravel that go uphill. Describe changes in forms of energy when a fast-moving truck uses one of these escape ramps.

9. If two identical bowling balls are raised to the same height, one on Earth and the other on the moon, which has the larger potential energy relative to the surface of the bodies?

10. Roads seldom go straight up a mountain but wind around and go up gradually. Explain.

11. What will be the kinetic energy of an arrow shot from a bow having a potential energy of 50 J?

12. Two pendulums are swinging side by side. At the bottom of the swing, the speed of one pendulum bob is twice the speed of the other. Compare the heights to which the two bobs rise at the ends of their swings.

13. In a baseball game, two pop-ups are hit in succession. The second rises twice as high as the first. Compare the speeds of the two balls when they leave the bat.

14. Two identical balls are thrown from the top of a cliff, each with the same speed. One is thrown straight down, the other straight up. How do the speeds and the kinetic energies of the balls compare as they strike the ground?

15. A ball is dropped from the top of a tall building and reaches terminal velocity as it falls. Will the potential energy of the ball upon release equal the kinetic energy it has when striking the ground? Explain.

16. According to Einstein's equation $E_0 = mc^2$, does the rock-Earth system have more or less mass when the rock is lifted high above Earth than when the same rock is on Earth's surface?

## PROBLEMS

### 11.1 Energy in Its Many Forms

*Unless otherwise directed, assume air resistance is negligible.*

1. A 1600-kg car travels at a speed of 12.5 m/s. What is its kinetic energy?

2. A racing car has a mass of 1500 kg. What is its kinetic energy if it has a speed of 108 km/h?

3. Sally has a mass of 45 kg and is moving with a speed of 10.0 m/s.

   **a.** Find Sally's kinetic energy.

   **b.** Sally's speed changes to 5.0 m/s. Now what is her kinetic energy?

   **c.** What is the ratio of the kinetic energies in **a** and **b**? Explain the ratio.

4. Shawn and his bike have a total mass of 45.0 kg. Shawn rides his bike 1.80 km in 10.0 min at a constant velocity. What is Shawn's kinetic energy?

**5.** It is not uncommon during the service of a professional tennis player for the racquet to exert an average force of 150.0 N on the ball. If the ball has a mass of 0.060 kg and is in contact with the strings of the racquet for 0.030 s, what is the kinetic energy of the ball as it leaves the racquet? Assume the ball starts from rest.

**6.** Pam has a mass of 40.0 kg and she is at rest on smooth, level, frictionless ice. Pam straps on a rocket pack. The rocket supplies a constant force for 22.0 m and Pam acquires a speed of 62.0 m/s.

  **a.** What is the magnitude of the force?

  **b.** What is Pam's final kinetic energy?

**7.** Sally and Lisa have a mass of 45 kg and they are moving together with a speed of 10.0 m/s.

  **a.** What is their combined kinetic energy?

  **b.** What is the ratio of their combined mass to Sally's mass?

  **c.** What is the ratio of their combined kinetic energy to Sally's kinetic energy. Explain.

**8.** In the 1950s, an experimental train that had a mass of $2.50 \times 10^4$ kg was powered across level track by a jet engine that produced a thrust of $5.00 \times 10^5$ N for a distance of 500 m.

  **a.** Find the work done on the train.

  **b.** Find the change in kinetic energy.

  **c.** Find the final kinetic energy of the train if it started from rest.

  **d.** Find the final speed of the train if there was no friction.

**9.** A 14 700-N car is traveling at 25 m/s. The brakes are suddenly applied and the car slides to a stop. The average braking force between the tires and the road is 7100 N. How far will the car slide once the brakes are applied?

**10.** A 15.0-kg cart is moving with a velocity of 7.50 m/s down a level hallway. A constant force of $-10.0$ N acts on the cart and its velocity becomes 3.20 m/s.

  **a.** What is the change in kinetic energy of the cart?

  **b.** How much work was done on the cart?

  **c.** How far did the cart move while the force acted?

**11.** A $2.00 \times 10^3$-kg car has a speed of 12.0 m/s. The car then hits a tree. The tree doesn't move and the car comes to rest.

  **a.** Find the change in kinetic energy of the car.

  **b.** Find the amount of work done in pushing in the front of the car.

  **c.** Find the size of the force that pushed the front of the car in 50.0 cm.

**12.** How much potential energy does Tim, mass 60.0 kg, gain when he climbs a gymnasium rope a distance of 3.5 m?

**13.** A 6.4-kg bowling ball is lifted 2.1 m into a storage rack. Calculate the increase in the ball's potential energy.

**14.** Mary weighs 500 N and she walks down a flight of stairs to a level 5.50 m below her starting point. What is the change in Mary's potential energy?

**15.** A weightlifter raises a 180-kg barbell to a height of 1.95 m. What is the increase in the barbell's potential energy?

**16.** A 10.0-kg test rocket is fired vertically. Its fuel gives it a kinetic energy of 1960 J by the time the rocket motor burns all of the fuel. What additional height will the rocket rise?

**17.** Ace raised a 12.0-N physics book from a table 75 cm above the floor to a shelf, 2.15 m above the floor. What was the change in potential energy?

**18.** A hallway display of energy is constructed. People are told that to do 1.00 J of work, they should pull on a rope that lifts a block 1.00 m. What should be the mass of the block?

**19.** A constant net force of 410 N, up, is applied to a stone that weighs 32 N. The upward force is applied through a distance of 2.0 m, and the stone is then released. To what height, from the point of release, will the stone rise?

## 11.2 Conservation of Energy

**20.** A 98-N sack of grain is hoisted to a storage room 50 m above the ground floor of a grain elevator.

  **a.** How much work was required?

  **b.** What is the potential energy of the sack of grain at this height?

  **c.** The rope being used to lift the sack of grain breaks just as the sack reaches the storage room. What kinetic energy does the sack have just before it strikes the ground floor?

21. A 20-kg rock is on the edge of a 100-m cliff.
    a. What potential energy does the rock possess relative to the base of the cliff?
    b. The rock falls from the cliff. What is its kinetic energy just before it strikes the ground?
    c. What speed does the rock have as it strikes the ground?
22. An archer puts a 0.30-kg arrow to the bowstring. An average force of 201 N is exerted to draw the string back 1.3 m.
    a. Assuming no frictional loss, with what speed does the arrow leave the bow?
    b. If the arrow is shot straight up, how high does it rise?
23. A 2.0-kg rock initially at rest loses 400 J of potential energy while falling to the ground.
    a. Calculate the kinetic energy that the rock gains while falling.
    b. What is the rock's speed just before it strikes the ground?
▶ 24. Betty weighs 420 N and she is sitting on a playground swing seat that hangs 0.40 m above the ground. Tom pulls the swing back and releases it when the seat is 1.00 m above the ground.
    a. How fast is Betty moving when the swing passes through its lowest position?
    b. If Betty moves through the lowest point at 2.0 m/s, how much work was done on the swing by friction?
▶ 25. Bill throws a 10.0-g ball straight down from a height of 2.0 m. The ball strikes the floor at a speed of 7.5 m/s. What was the initial speed of the ball?
▶ 26. Magen's mass is 28 kg. She climbs the 4.8-m ladder of a slide, and reaches a velocity of 3.2 m/s at the bottom of the slide. How much work was done by friction on Magen?
27. A physics book, mass unknown, is dropped 4.50 m. What speed does the book have just before it hits the ground?
28. A 30.0-kg gun is standing on a frictionless surface. The gun fires a 50.0-g bullet with a muzzle velocity of 310 m/s.
    a. Calculate the momenta of the bullet and the gun after the gun was fired.
    b. Calculate the kinetic energy of both the bullet and the gun just after firing.
29. A railroad car with a mass of $5.0 \times 10^5$ kg collides with a stationary railroad car of equal mass. After the collision, the two cars lock together and move off at 4.0 m/s.
    a. Before the collision, the first railroad car was moving at 8.0 m/s. What was its momentum?
    b. What is the total momentum of the two cars after the collision?
    c. Find the kinetic energies of the two cars before and after the collision.
    d. Account for the loss of kinetic energy.
30. From what height would a compact car have to be dropped to have the same kinetic energy that it has when being driven at 100 km/h?
▶ 31. A golf ball, mass 0.046 kg, rests on a tee. It is struck by a golf club with an effective mass of 0.220 kg and a speed of 44 m/s. Assuming the collision is elastic, find the speed of the ball when it leaves the tee.
32. A steel ball has a mass of 4.0 kg and rolls along a smooth, level surface at 62 m/s.
    a. Find its kinetic energy.
    b. At first, the ball was at rest on the surface. A constant force acted on it through a distance of 22 m to give it the speed of 62 m/s. What was the magnitude of the force?
33. Show that $W = E_{kf} - E_{ki}$ if an object is not originally at rest. Use the equation relating initial and final velocity with constant acceleration and distance.

## THINKING PHYSIC-LY

One of the important concepts in golf, tennis, baseball, and other sports is follow-through! How can applying a force to a ball for the longest possible time affect the speed of the ball?

# CHAPTER
# 12 Thermal Energy

◀ **Perpetual Motion?**

The engine converts the chemical energy stored in the fuel and oxygen into kinetic energy. Could we ever invent an engine that converts all the energy into useful energy of motion?

What invention has changed our lives more than the internal combustion engine? In the 1700s, the steam engine changed our society from a nation of farms to one of factories. The steam engine burned fuel to change water to steam in a boiler outside the engine. The gasoline engine, invented in Germany by Otto in 1876, burns the fuel inside the engine, and thus is an internal combustion engine. These engines and their descendants, the diesel engines and the turbines used in jet aircraft, change the chemical energy in fuel to thermal energy in hot gases. The thermal energy, in turn, is converted into kinetic energy of motion. Internal combustion engines vary in size from the small engines in lawnmowers and motorbikes, to larger ones in cars, buses, and airplanes, to the giant engines that produce electricity for millions of people. Consider how often we make use of this invention in our everyday lives.

## √ Concept Check

The following terms or concepts from earlier chapters are important for a good understanding of this chapter. If you are not familiar with them, you should review them before studying this chapter.
· work and energy, Chapter 10
· energy conservation, Chapter 11

- understand the nature of thermal energy as explained by the kinetic theory.
- define temperature and distinguish it from thermal energy.
- understand the process of reaching equilibrium and its application to the measurement of temperature.
- describe and use the Celsius and Kelvin temperature scales; demonstrate the ability to convert between Celsius and Kelvin.
- distinguish heat from thermal energy.
- define and display an understanding of specific heat; be able to calculate heat transfer.
- display an understanding of the application of conservation of energy to heat transfers; be able to calculate temperature changes due to heat transfer.

# 12.1 TEMPERATURE AND THERMAL ENERGY

In the 1600s and 1700s, Europe went through a "Little Ice Age" when temperatures were lower than any other period in the last one thousand years. Keeping warm was vitally important. As a result, many people devoted themselves to the study of heat. One result was the invention of machines that used the energy produced by burning fuel to produce useful work. Although not as convenient as the internal combustion engine, these machines freed society from its dependence on the energy of people and animals. As inventors tried to make these machines more powerful and more efficient, they developed the science of thermodynamics, the study of heat.

## What Makes a Hot Body Hot?

To operate, internal combustion engines require very high temperatures—usually produced by burning fuel. Although the effects of fire have been known since ancient times, only in the eighteenth century did scientists begin to understand how a hot body differs from a cold body. They proposed that when a body was heated, an invisible fluid called "caloric" was added to the body. Hot bodies contained more caloric than cold bodies. The caloric theory could explain observations such as the expansion of objects when heated, but it could not explain why hands get warm when they are rubbed together.

In the mid-nineteenth century, scientists developed a new theory to replace caloric theory. This theory is based on the assumption that matter is made up of many tiny particles that are always in motion. In a hot body, the particles move faster, and thus have a higher energy than particles in a cooler body. The theory is called the **kinetic-molecular theory**.

The kinetic theory is difficult to visualize because the individual particles are too tiny to be seen. A thrown baseball, Figure 12–1, has a kinetic energy that depends on its velocity and a potential energy that is proportional to its height above the ground. These external properties can be seen. The tiny particles that make up the baseball, however, are

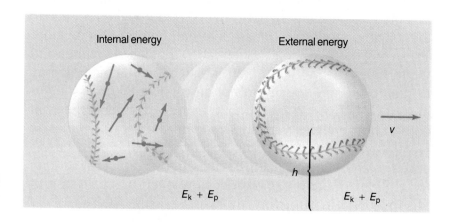

**FIGURE 12–1.** A baseball in flight has both internal and external energy. The internal energy is the result of the kinetic and potential energies of its particles. The external energy is the result of the position and motion of the baseball in flight.

in constant motion within the ball. This internal motion is invisible under most circumstances.

The model of a solid, Figure 12–2, can help you understand the kinetic theory. This model pictures a solid made up of tiny spherical particles held together by massless springs. The springs represent the electromagnetic forces that bind the solid together. The particles vibrate back and forth and thus have kinetic energy. The vibrations compress and extend the springs, so the solid has potential energy as well. The sum of the kinetic and potential energies of the internal motion of particles that make up an object is called the internal energy or **thermal energy** of that object.

FIGURE 12–2. Molecules of a solid behave in some ways as if they were held together by springs.

## Thermal Energy Transfer

Thermal energy is transferred in three ways. **Conduction,** most common in solids, involves transfer of kinetic energy when the particles of an object collide. It is the principle on which the common household thermometer operates. The movement of fluids caused by their different densities at different temperatures transfers heat by **convection.** Convection currents in the atmosphere are responsible for much of Earth's weather. Both conduction and convection depend on the presence of matter. The third method of transfer, **radiation,** does not. Thermal energy can be transferred through space in the form of electromagnetic waves. Solar energy is transmitted to Earth by radiation.

## Thermal Energy and Temperature

According to the kinetic-molecular theory, a hot body has more thermal energy than a similar cold body, Figure 12–3. This means that, as a whole, the particles in a hot body have larger kinetic and potential energies than the particles in a cold body. It does not mean that all the particles in a body have exactly the same energy. The particles have a range of energies, some high, others low. It is the *average* energy of particles in a hot body that is higher than that of particles in a cold body. To help you understand this, consider the heights of students in a sixth-grade class. The heights vary, but you can calculate the average height. This average is likely to be larger than the average height of students in a fourth-grade class, even though some fourth-graders might be taller than some sixth-graders.

Hot body      Cold body

$E_{k \text{ Hot}} > E_{k \text{ Cold}}$

FIGURE 12–3. Particles in a hot body have larger kinetic and potential energies than particles in a cold body.

$5 \times 10^{-3}\,\text{m}^3$    $1 \times 10^{-2}\,\text{m}^3$

**FIGURE 12–4. Temperature does not depend on the number of particles in a body.**

Temperature is hotness measured on some definite scale.

The temperature of a gas is the average kinetic energy of the particles.

Temperature does not depend on the mass of the object; thermal energy does.

How can we measure the "hotness" of an object? Hotness, measured on some definite scale, is a property of an object called its **temperature.** In a hotter object, the particles are moving faster; they have a larger average kinetic energy. For gases, the temperature is proportional to the average kinetic energy of the particles. For solids and liquids, this is only approximately true. For any form of matter, the temperature does not depend on the number of particles in the body. If a one-kilogram mass of steel is at the same temperature as a two-kilogram mass, the average kinetic energy of the particles in both masses is the same. The total amount of kinetic energy of particles in the two-kilogram mass, however, is twice the amount in the one-kilogram mass. The thermal energy in an object is proportional to the number of particles in it, but its temperature is not, Figure 12–4.

## Equilibrium and Thermometry

You are familiar with the idea of measuring temperature. If you suspect that you have a fever, you may place a thermometer in your mouth and wait two or three minutes. The thermometer then provides a measure of the temperature of your body.

You are probably less familiar with the microscopic process involved in measuring temperature. Your body is hot compared to the thermometer, which means the particles in your body have higher thermal energy. The thermometer is made of a glass tube. When the cold glass touches your hotter body, the particles in your body hit the particles in the glass. These collisions transfer energy to the glass particles by conduction. The thermal energy of the particles that make up the thermometer increases. As the particles in the glass become more energetic, they begin to transfer energy back to the particles in your body. At some point, the rate of transfer of energy back and forth between the glass and your body is equal. Your body and the thermometer are in **thermal equilibrium**. That is, the rate at which energy that flows from your body to the glass is equal to the rate of flow from the glass to your body. The thermometer and your body are at the same temperature. Objects that are in thermal equilibrium are at the same temperature, Figure 12–5. Note, however, that if the masses of the objects are different, they may not have the same thermal energy.

**FIGURE 12–5. Thermal energy is transferred from a hot body to a cold body. When thermal equilibrium is reached, the transfer of energy between bodies is equal.**

Before thermal equilibrium

Hot body          Cold body

$E_k \longrightarrow$

After thermal equilibrium

$E_k = E_k$

a

b

FIGURE 12–6. Thermometers use a change in physical properties to measure temperature. A liquid crystal thermometer changes colour with temperature change (a). Some modern thermometers determine temperature electronically (b).

A **thermometer** is a device to measure temperature. It is placed in contact with an object and allowed to come to thermal equilibrium with that object. The operation of a thermometer depends on some property, such as volume, that changes with temperature. Many household thermometers contain coloured alcohol that expands when heated and rises in a narrow tube. The hotter the thermometer, the larger the volume of the alcohol in it and the higher it rises. Mercury is another liquid commonly used in thermometers.

Other properties of materials change with temperature, allowing them to be used as thermometers. In liquid crystal thermometers, Figure 12–6, the arrangement of the molecules changes at a specific temperature, changing the colour of the crystal. As a result, the colour depends on temperature. A set of different kinds of liquid crystals is used. Each changes colour at a different temperature, creating an instrument that can indicate the temperature by colour.

## Temperature Scales: Celsius and Kelvin

Temperature scales were developed by scientists to allow them to compare their temperature measurements with those of other scientists. A scale based on the properties of water was devised in 1741 by the Swedish astronomer and physicist Anders Celsius (1704–1744). On this scale, now called the Celsius scale, Figure 12–7, the freezing point of pure water is 0 degrees (0°C). The boiling point of pure water at sea level is 100 degrees (100°C). On the Celsius scale, the temperature of the human body is 37°C. Figure 12–7 shows representative temperatures on the Celsius and Kelvin scales.

A thermometer measures the temperature of an object with which it is in thermal equilibrium.

### Temperature Scales
Celsius to Kelvin °C + 273

|  | Water Freezes | Body Temperature | Water Boils |
|---|---|---|---|
| Celsius | | | |
| −273° | 0° | 37° | 100° |
| Kelvin | | | |
| 0 | 273 | 310 | 373 |

FIGURE 12–7. Some familiar reference temperatures.

Interstellar space  Human body  Surface of sun  Nuclear bomb
                              Flames  Centre of sun  Supernova explosions

$10^{-8}$ $10^{-6}$ $10^{-4}$ $10^{-2}$ 1   10   100   $10^2$  $10^3$ $10^4$ $10^5$  $10^6$ $10^7$  $10^8$  $10^9$ $10^{10}$

Lowest temperature    Helium liquifies    Superconductivity  Life exists    Uncharged atoms exist         Nuclei exist
in laboratory

**Temperature (K)**

**FIGURE 12–8. There is an extremely wide range of temperatures throughout the universe.**

The wide range of temperatures in the universe is shown in Figure 12–8. Temperatures do not appear to have an upper limit. The interior of the sun is at least $1.5 \times 10^7$°C. Other stars are even hotter. Temperatures do, however, have a lower limit. Generally, materials contract as they cool. If you cooled an "ideal" gas, one in which the particles have no volume and don't interact, it would contract in such a way that it would have zero volume at $-273.15$°C. At this temperature, all the thermal energy would be removed from the gas. It would be impossible to reduce the thermal energy any further. Therefore, there can be no lower temperature than $-273.15$°C. This is called **absolute zero**.

The Kelvin temperature scale is based on absolute zero. Absolute zero is the zero point of the Kelvin scale. On the Kelvin scale, the freezing point of water (0°C) is 273.15 K and the boiling point of water is 373.15 K. Each interval on this scale, called a **kelvin**, is equal to one Celsius degree. Thus, °C + 273.15 = K.

Very cold temperatures are reached by liquefying gases. Helium liquefies at 4.2 K, or $-269.0$°C. Even colder temperatures can be reached by using the properties of special substances placed in the fields of large magnets. By using these techniques, physicists have reached temperatures of only $2.0 \times 10^{-9}$ K.

No temperature can be colder than absolute zero, $-273.15$°C or 0 K.

## Example Problem

### Converting Celsius to Kelvin Temperature

Convert 25°C to kelvins.

**Solution:** K = °C + 273.15 = 25° + 273.15 = 298 K

## Example Problem

### Converting Kelvin to Celsius Temperature

Convert the boiling point of helium, 4.22 K, to degrees Celsius.

**Solution:** °C = K − 273.15 = 4.22 − 273.15 = −268.93°C

# F.Y.I.

For many years, heat was measured in calories. One calorie is equal to 4.18 J.

# Practice Problems

1. Make the following conversions.
   a. 0°C to kelvins
   c. 273°C to kelvins
   b. 0 K to degrees Celsius
   d. 273 K to degrees Celsius
2. Convert these Celsius temperatures to Kelvin temperatures.
   a. 27°C
   b. 560°C
   c. −184°C
   d. −300°C
3. Convert these Kelvin temperatures to Celsius temperatures.
   a. 110 K
   b. 22 K
   c. 402 K
   d. 323 K
▶ 4. Find the Celsius and Kelvin temperatures for the following.
   a. room temperature
   c. typical hot summer day
   b. refrigerator temperature
   d. typical winter night

Water

Thermal
insulator

**FIGURE 12–9. James Joule's
experiment for measuring the
mechanical equivalent of heat. The
falling weights rotate the paddles,
causing the temperature of the water
to rise.**

## Heat and Thermal Energy

One way to increase the temperature of an object is to place it in contact with a hotter object. The thermal energy of the hotter object is decreased, and the thermal energy of the cooler object is increased. Energy flows from the hotter object to the cooler object. **Heat** *is the energy that flows as a result of a difference in temperature.* We will use the symbol $Q$ for heat. Heat, like any other form of energy, is measured in joules.

Note that this definition of heat is different from the one in everyday use. We commonly speak of a body containing "heat". This description is left over from the caloric theory. As we now know, a hot body contains a larger amount of thermal energy than a colder body of the same size. Heat is the energy transferred because of a difference in temperature.

When heat flows into an object, its thermal energy increases, and so does its temperature. The amount of increase depends on the size of the object. It also depends on the material from which the object is made. The **specific heat** of a material is the amount of energy that must be added to raise the temperature of a unit mass one temperature unit. In SI units, specific heat, $c$, is measured in J/kg · K. For example, 903 J must be added to 1 kg of aluminum to raise the temperature 1 K. The specific heat of aluminum is 903 J/kg · K.

Note that water has a high specific heat compared to other substances, even ice and steam. One kilogram of water requires the addition of 4180 J of energy to increase its temperature one kelvin. By comparison, the same mass of copper requires only 385 J. The energy needed to raise the temperature of 1 kg of water 1 K would increase the temperature of the same mass of copper 11 K. The high specific heat of water is the reason water is used in car radiators to remove waste heat.

Specific heat can be used to find the amount of heat that must be transferred to change the temperature of a given mass by any amount. The specific heat of water is 4180 J/kg · K. When the temperature of 1 kg of water is increased by one kelvin, the heat absorbed by the water is 4180 J. When the temperature of 10 kg of water is increased by 5.0 K, the heat absorbed, $Q$, is

$$Q = (10 \text{ kg})(4180 \text{ J/kg} \cdot \text{K})(5.0 \text{ K}) = 2.1 \times 10^5 \text{ J}.$$

Heat is thermal energy transferred because of a difference in temperature. Heat flows spontaneously from a warmer to a cooler body.

Specific heat is the increase in thermal energy that raises one kilogram of a substance one kelvin.

**Table 12–1**

| Specific Heat of Common Substances | |
| --- | --- |
| Material | Specific heat J/kg · K |
| aluminum | 903 |
| brass | 376 |
| carbon | 710 |
| copper | 385 |
| glass | 664 |
| ice | 2060 |
| iron | 450 |
| lead | 130 |
| methanol | 2450 |
| silver | 235 |
| steam | 2020 |
| water | 4180 |
| zinc | 388 |

The heat gained or lost by an object as its temperature changes depends on the mass, change in temperature, and specific heat of the substance. The relationship can be written

$$Q = mc\Delta T,$$

where $Q$ is the heat gained or lost, $m$ is the mass of the object, $c$ is the specific heat of the substance, and $\Delta T$ is the change in temperature. Since one Celsius degree is equal to one kelvin, temperature changes can be measured in either kelvins or Celsius degrees.

## Example Problem

### Heat Transfer

A 0.400-kg block of iron is heated from 295 K to 325 K. How much heat is absorbed by the iron?

**Given:** mass, $m = 0.400$ kg
 specific heat,
 $C = 450$ J/kg · K
 $T_i = 295$ K
 $T_f = 325$ K

**Unknown:** $Q$
**Basic equations:** $\Delta T = T_f - T_i$
 $Q = mc\Delta T$

**Solution:** $Q = mc\Delta T$
 $= (0.400$ kg$)(450$ J/kg · K$)(325$ K $- 295$ K$)$
 $= 5.40 \times 10^3$ J

FIGURE 12–10. Brine solutions are evaporated in solar ponds to obtain potassium compounds. The blue dye added to the brine solutions absorbs solar radiation faster and speeds up evaporation.

## Practice Problems

5. How much heat is absorbed by 60.0 g of copper when it is heated from 20.0°C to 80.0°C?
6. A 38-kg block of lead is heated from −26°C to 180°C. How much heat does it absorb during the heating?
7. The cooling system of a car engine contains 20.0 L of water. (1 L of water has a mass of 1 kg.)
   a. What is the change in the temperature of the water if the engine operates until 836.0 kJ of heat are added?
   b. Suppose it is winter and the system is filled with methanol. The density of methanol is 0.80 g/cm³. What would be the increase in temperature of the methanol if it absorbed 836.0 kJ of heat?
   c. Which is the better coolant, water or methanol? Explain.
▶ 8. A 565-g cube of iron is cooled from the temperature of boiling water to room temperature (20°C).
   a. How much heat must be absorbed from the cube?
   b. If the iron is cooled by dunking it into water at 0°C that rises in temperature to 20°C, how much water is needed?

# PHYSICS LAB

## Heating Up

## Purpose

To discover how the temperature increases with a constant supply of thermal energy.

## Materials

- hot plate (or bunsen burner)
- 250-mL pyrex beaker
- water
- thermometer
- stopwatch
- goggles

## Procedure

1. Turn your hot plate to a medium setting (or as recommended by your teacher). Allow a few minutes for the plate to heat up. While heating water wear goggles.
2. Pour 150 mL of room temperature water into the 250-mL beaker.
3. Measure the initial temperature of the water. Keep the thermometer in the water.
4. Place the beaker on the hot plate and record the temperature every 1.0 min. Carefully stir the water before taking temperature reading.
5. Record the time when the water starts to boil. Continue recording the temperature for an additional 4.0 min.
6. Carefully remove the beaker from the hot plate. Record the remaining water.

## Observations and Data

1. Make a graph of temperature (vertical axis) vs time (horizontal axis).
2. Make a generalization about the graph during the first few minutes of the experiment.

## Analysis

1. What is the slope of the graph for the first 3.0 min? Be sure to include units.
2. What is the thermal energy given to the water in the first 3.0 min? **Hint:** $Q = mc\Delta T$.
3. Use a dotted line on the same graph to predict what the graph would look like if the same procedure was made with only half as much water.

## Applications

1. Would you expect that the hot plate transferred energy to the water at a steady rate? Explain.
2. Where is the energy going when the water is boiling?

**FIGURE 12–11. A calorimeter provides a closed, isolated system in which to measure energy transfer.**

# Calorimetry: Measuring Specific Heat

A **calorimeter,** Figure 12–11, is a device used to measure changes in thermal energy. A measured mass of a substance is heated to a known temperature and placed in the calorimeter. The calorimeter contains a known mass of cold water at a measured temperature. From the resulting increase in water temperature, the change in thermal energy of the substance is calculated.

The calorimeter depends on the conservation of energy in isolated, closed systems. Energy can neither enter nor leave an isolated system. A calorimeter is carefully insulated so that heat transfer in or out is very small. Often a covered Styrofoam cup is used. As a result of the isolation, if the energy of one part of the system increases, the energy of another part must decrease by the same amount. Consider a system composed of two blocks of metal, block A and block B, Figure 12–12. The total energy of the system is constant;

$$E_A + E_B = \text{constant.}$$

Suppose that the two blocks are initially separated but can be placed in contact. If the thermal energy of block A changes by an amount $\Delta E_A$, then the change in thermal energy of block B, $\Delta E_B$, must be related by the equation

$$\Delta E_A + \Delta E_B = 0.$$

The change in energy of one block is positive, while the change in energy of the other block is negative. If the thermal energy change is positive, the temperature of that block rises. If the change is negative, the temperature falls.

The total energy of an isolated, closed system is constant. Energy lost by one part is gained by another.

Assume that the initial temperatures of the two blocks are different. When the blocks are brought together, heat flows from the hotter to the colder block, Figure 12–12. The flow continues until the blocks are in thermal equilibrium. The blocks then have the same temperature.

Heat flows until all parts of the system are at the same temperature.

The change in thermal energy is equal to the heat transferred:

$$\Delta E = Q = mc\Delta T.$$

The increase in thermal energy of block A is equal to the decrease in thermal energy of block B. Thus,

$$m_A c_A \Delta T_A + m_B c_B \Delta T_B = 0.$$

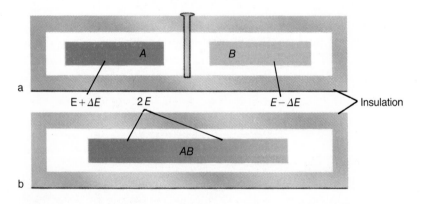

**FIGURE 12–12. The total energy for this system is constant.**

The change in temperature is the difference between the final and initial temperatures, $\Delta T = T_f - T_i$. If the temperature of a block increases, $T_f > T_i$, and $\Delta T$ is positive. If the temperature of the block decreases, $T_f < T_i$, and $\Delta T$ is negative.

The final temperatures of the two blocks are equal. The equation for the transfer of energy is

$$m_A c_A (T_f - T_{A,i}) + m_B c_B (T_f - T_{B,i}) = 0.$$

To solve for $T_f$, expand the equation:

$$m_A c_A T_f - m_A c_A T_{A,i} + m_B c_B T_f - m_B T_{B,i} = 0.$$

Isolate $T_f$ and solve,

$$T_f (m_A c_A + m_B c_B) = m_A c_A T_{A,i} + m_B c_B T_{B,i}.$$

$$T_f = \frac{m_A c_A T_{A,i} + m_B c_B t_{B,i}}{m_A c_A + m_B c_B}$$

Note that either the Celsius or Kelvin temperature scale may be used with this equation.

# POCKET LAB

## COOL TIMES

Place a 100-mL beaker in a 250-mL beaker. Put a thermometer into each beaker. Fill the small beaker with hot, coloured water. Determine the temperature of the coloured water. Slowly pour tap water into the large beaker until the water is at the same height in both beakers. Record the temperature in the large beaker. Record the temperature in both beakers every minute for 5 min. Plot your data for both beakers on the same graph of temperature vs time. Measure and record the mass of water in each beaker. Predict the final temperature. Describe each curve.

# Example Problem

## Conservation in Energy Transfer

A 0.500-kg sample of water is at 15.0°C in a calorimeter. A 0.0400-kg block of zinc at 115°C is placed in the water. Find the final temperature of the system. The specific heat of zinc is 388 J/kg · K.

**Given:** zinc

$m_A = 0.0400$ kg
$T_{A,i} = 115°C$
$c_A = 388$ J/kg · K

water

$m_B = 0.500$ kg
$T_{B,i} = 15.0°C$
$c_B = 4180$ J/kg · K
1 J/kg · K = 1 J/kg · °C

**Unknown:** $T_f$
**Basic equations:** $\Delta E_A + \Delta E_B = 0$
$m_A c_A \Delta T_A + m_B c_B \Delta T_B = 0$

**Solution:** $m_A c_A (T_f - T_{A,i}) + m_B c_B (T_f - T_{B,i}) = 0$

$$T_f = \frac{m_A c_A T_{A,i} + m_B c_B T_{B,i}}{m_A c_A + m_B c_B} =$$

$$\frac{(0.0400 \text{ kg})(388 \text{ J/kg} \cdot °C)(115°C) + (0.500 \text{ kg})(4180 \text{ J/kg} \cdot °C)(15.0°C)}{(0.0400 \text{ kg})(388 \text{ J/kg} \cdot °C) + (0.500 \text{ kg})(4180 \text{ J/kg} \cdot °C)}$$

$$T_f = \frac{(1.78 \times 10^3 \text{ J}) + (3.14 \times 10^4 \text{ J})}{15.5 \text{ J/°C} + 2.09 \times 10^3 \text{ J/°C}}$$

$$T_f = \frac{3.32 \times 10^4 \text{ J}}{2.11 \times 10^3 \text{ J/°C}}$$

$$= 15.7°C$$

## Using Your CALCULATOR

Use the parentheses ( ) function on your calculator to evaluate complex equations. Note the use of two levels of parentheses in the denominator.

$$T_f = \frac{m_A c_A T_{A,i} + m_B c_B T_{B,i}}{m_A c_A + m_B c_B}$$

( (.0400 × 388 × 115 ) )    1784. 8

+ ( (.500 × 4180 × 15 ) )    31 350

= ÷    33 134. 8

( ( (.0400 × 388 ) ) + 15. 52

( (.500 × 4180 ) )    2090

)    2105. 52

=    15. 73711

$T_f = 15.7°C$

Thermodynamics is the study of the properties of thermal energy and its changes.

# Objectives

· **define heats of fusion and vaporization; understand the microscopic basis of changes of state; calculate heat transfers needed to effect changes of state.**
· **distinguish heat from work.**
· **state the first law of thermodynamics.**
· **define a heat engine, refrigerator, and heat pump.**
· **state the second law of thermodynamics; define entropy.**

# Practice Problems

9. A $2.00 \times 10^2$-g sample of water at 80.0°C is mixed with $2.00 \times 10^2$ g of water at 10.0°C. Assume no heat loss to the surroundings. What is the final temperature of the mixture?

10. A $4.00 \times 10^2$-g sample of methanol at 16.0°C is mixed with $4.00 \times 10^2$ g of water at 85.0°C. Assume no heat loss to the surroundings. What is the final temperature of the mixture?

11. A $1.00 \times 10^2$-g brass block at 90.0°C is placed in a styrofoam cup containing $2.00 \times 10^2$ g of water at 20.0°C. No heat is lost to the cup or the surroundings. Find the final temperature of the mixture.

▶ 12. A $1.0 \times 10^2$-g aluminum block at 100.0°C is placed in $1.00 \times 10^2$ g of water at 10.0°C. The final temperature of the mixture is 25°C. What is the specific heat of the aluminum?

# CONCEPT REVIEW

**1.1** Could the thermal energy of a bowl of hot water equal that of a bowl of cold water? Explain.

**1.2** On cold winter nights before central heating, people often placed hot water bottles in their beds. Why would this be better than, say, warmed bricks?

**1.3** If you take a spoon out of a cup of hot coffee and put it in your mouth, you won't burn your tongue. But, you could very easily burn your tongue if you put the liquid in your mouth. Why?

**1.4** **Critical Thinking:** You use an aluminum cup instead of a styrofoam cup as a calorimeter, allowing heat to flow between the water and the environment. You measure the specific heat of a sample by putting the hot object into room-temperature water. How might your experiment be affected? Would your result be too large or too small?

# 12.2 CHANGE OF STATE AND LAWS OF THERMODYNAMICS

If you rub your hands together, you exert a force and move your hands over a distance. You do work against friction. Your hands start and end at rest, so there is no net change in kinetic energy. They remain the same distance above Earth so there is no change in potential energy. Yet, if conservation of energy is true, then the energy transferred by the work you did must have gone somewhere. You notice that your hands feel warm; their temperature is increased. The energy is now in the form of thermal energy. The branch of physics called **thermodynamics** explores the properties of thermal energy.

## Change of State

The three most common states of matter are solids, liquids, and gases, Figure 12–13. As the temperature of a solid is raised, it first changes to a liquid. At even higher temperatures, it will become a gas. How can we explain these changes? Our simplified model of a solid consists of

FIGURE 12–13. The three states of water are represented in this photograph. The gaseous state, water vapour, is dispersed in the air and is invisible until it condenses.

tiny particles bonded together by springs. The springs represent the electromagnetic forces between the particles. When the thermal energy of a solid is increased, both the potential and kinetic energies of the particles increase.

At sufficiently high temperatures, the forces between the particles are no longer strong enough to hold them in fixed locations. The particles are still touching, but they have more freedom of movement. Eventually, the particles become free enough to slide past each other. At this point, the substance has changed from a solid to a liquid. The temperature at which this change occurs is called the **melting point.**

When a substance is melting, added thermal energy increases the potential energy of particles, breaking the bonds holding them together. The added thermal energy does not increase the temperature.

The amount of energy needed to melt one kilogram of a substance is called the **heat of fusion** of that substance. For example, the heat of fusion of ice is $3.34 \times 10^5$ J/kg. If 1 kg of ice at its melting point, 273 K, absorbs $3.34 \times 10^5$ J, the ice becomes 1 kg of water at the same temperature, 273 K. The added energy causes a change in state but not in temperature.

After the substance is totally melted, a further increase in thermal energy once again increases the temperature. Added thermal energy increases the kinetic and potential energies. As the temperature increases, some particles in the liquid acquire enough energy to break free from other particles. At a specific temperature, known as the **boiling point**, further addition of energy causes another change of state. It does not raise the temperature; it converts particles in the liquid state to particles in the vapour or gaseous state. At normal atmospheric pressure, water boils at 373 K. The amount of thermal energy needed to vaporize one kilogram of a liquid is called the **heat of vaporization**. For water, the heat of vaporization is $2.26 \times 10^6$ J/kg. Each substance has a characteristic heat of vaporization.

The heat, $Q$, required to melt a solid of mass $m$ is given by

$$Q = mH_f.$$

The value of some heats of fusion, $H_f$, can be found in Table 12–2.

While a substance is melting, added energy does not increase the temperature.

The heat of fusion is the energy needed to melt one kilogram of a substance.

The heat of vaporization is the energy needed to vaporize one kilogram of a substance.

## POCKET LAB

### MELTING

Label two foam cups A and B. Measure 75 mL of room temperature water into the two cups. Add an ice cube to cup A. Add ice water to cup B until the water levels are equal. Measure the temperature of each cup at 1 min intervals until the ice has melted. Do the samples reach the same final temperature? Why?

Table 12–2

## Heats of Fusion and Vaporization of Common Substances

| Material | Heat of fusion $H_f$ (J/kg) | Heat of vaporization $H_v$ (J/kg) | Material | Heat of fusion $H_f$ (J/kg) | Heat of vaporization $H_v$ (J/kg) |
|---|---|---|---|---|---|
| copper | $2.05 \times 10^5$ | $5.07 \times 10^6$ | mercury | $1.15 \times 10^4$ | $2.72 \times 10^5$ |
| gold | $6.30 \times 10^4$ | $1.64 \times 10^6$ | methanol | $1.09 \times 10^5$ | $8.78 \times 10^5$ |
| iron | $2.66 \times 10^5$ | $6.29 \times 10^6$ | silver | $1.04 \times 10^4$ | $2.36 \times 10^6$ |
| lead | $2.04 \times 10^4$ | $8.64 \times 10^5$ | water (ice) | $3.34 \times 10^5$ | $2.26 \times 10^6$ |

Similarly, the heat, $Q$, required to vaporize a mass, $m$, of liquid is given by

$$Q = mH_v.$$

Heats of vaporization, $H_v$, can also be found in Table 12–2.

When a liquid freezes, an amount of heat $Q = -mH_f$ must be removed from the liquid to turn it into a solid. The negative sign indicates the heat is transferred from the sample to the environment. In the same way, when a vapour condenses to a liquid, an amount of heat, $Q = -mH_v$, must be removed.

## Example Problem

### Heat of Fusion—1

If $5.00 \times 10^3$ J is added to ice at 273 K, how much ice is melted?

**Given:** heat added,
$Q = 5.00 \times 10^3$ J
heat of fusion,
$H_f = 3.34 \times 10^5$ J/kg

**Unknown:** mass, $m$
**Basic equation:** $Q = mH_f$

**Solution:** $m = \dfrac{5.00 \times 10^3 \text{ J}}{3.34 \times 10^5 \text{ J/kg}} = 0.0150$ kg

Figure 12–14 shows the changes in temperature as thermal energy is added to 1.0 g of $H_2O$ at 243 K. Between points **A** and **B,** the ice is warmed to 273 K. Between points **B** and **C,** the added thermal energy melts the ice at a constant 273 K. The horizontal distance from point **B** to point **C** represents the heat of fusion. Between points **C** and **D,** the

**FIGURE 12–14.** A plot of temperature versus heat added when 1 g of ice is initially converted to steam.

water temperature rises. The slope is smaller here than between points **A** and **B**, showing that the specific heat of water is higher than that of ice. Between points **D** and **E**, the water boils, becoming water vapour. The distance from point **D** to point **E** represents the heat of vaporization. Between points **E** and **F**, the steam is heated to 473 K. The slope is larger than that from point **C** to point **D**, indicating that the specific heat of steam is less than that of water.

# Example Problem

## Heat of Fusion—2

How much heat must be transferred to 100.0 g of ice at 0.0°C until the ice melts and the temperature of the resulting water rises to 20.0°C?

**Given:** $m$ = 100.0 g            **Unknown:** $Q_{total}$
$\quad\quad\quad$ $T_i$ = 0.0°C            **Basic equations:** $Q = mH_f$
$\quad\quad\quad$ $T_f$ = 20.0°C $\quad\quad\quad\quad\quad\quad\quad$ $Q = mc\Delta T$
$\quad\quad\quad$ $H_f$ = 3.34 × 10$^5$ J/kg
$\quad\quad\quad$ $c$ = 4180 J/kg · °C

**Solution:**
First, find the amount of heat the ice absorbs as it changes from solid to liquid.

$$Q = mH_f = (0.100 \text{ kg})(3.34 \times 10^5 \text{ J/kg}) = 33\,400 \text{ J}$$

Second, calculate the amount of heat the water absorbs as its temperature rises from 0.0°C to 20.0°C.

$$Q = mc\Delta T = (0.100 \text{ kg})(4180 \text{ J/kg} \cdot °C)(20.0°C - 0.0°C)$$
$$= 8400 \text{ J}$$

Finally, add the two quantities of heat.

$$Q_{total} = 33\,400 \text{ J} + 8400 \text{ J}$$
$$= 41\,800 \text{ J}$$

Thus, 41.8 kJ of heat is transferred from the water to the ice.

# Practice Problems

**13.** How much heat is absorbed by $1.00 \times 10^2$ g of ice at −20.0°C to become water at 0.0°C?

**14.** A $2.00 \times 10^2$-g sample of water at 60.0°C is heated to steam at 140.0°C. How much heat is absorbed?

**15.** How much heat is needed to change $3.00 \times 10^2$ g of ice at −30.0°C to steam at 130.0°C?

▶ **16.** A 175-g lump of molten lead at its melting point, 327°C, is dropped into 55 g of water at 20.0°C.
$\quad$ **a.** What is the temperature of the water when the lead becomes solid?
$\quad$ **b.** When the lead and water are in thermal equilibrium, what is the temperature?

**F.Y.I.**

Blessings on Science, and her handmaid Steam
They make Utopia only half a dream.

$\quad\quad\quad\quad$ Railways 1846
$\quad\quad\quad\quad$ Charles Mackey

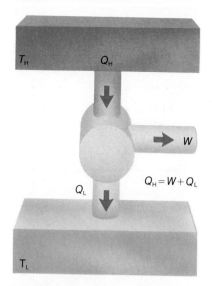

**FIGURE 12–15.** The flow chart diagram represents heat at high temperature transformed into mechanical energy and low temperature waste heat.

Thermal energy is increased by both work done and heat added to a system.

A heat engine accepts heat from a high temperature source, performs work, and transfers heat out at a low temperature.

# The First Law of Thermodynamics

You don't have to transfer heat to increase the thermal energy of a body. If you rub your hands together, they are warmed, yet they were not brought into contact with a hotter body. Instead, work was done on your hands by means of friction. The mechanical energy of your moving hands was changed into thermal energy.

There are other means of converting mechanical energy into thermal energy. If you use a hand pump to inflate a bicycle tire, the air and pump become warm. The mechanical energy in the moving piston is converted into thermal energy of the gas. Other forms of energy—light, sound, electrical, as well as mechanical—can be changed into thermal energy.

Thermal energy can be increased either by adding heat or by doing work on a system. Thus, *the total increase in the thermal energy of a system is the sum of the work done on it and the heat added to it.* This fact is called the **first law of thermodynamics.** Thermodynamics is the study of the changes in thermal properties of matter. The first law is merely a restatement of the law of conservation of energy.

All forms of energy are measured in joules. Work, energy transferred by mechanical means, and heat, energy transferred because of a difference in temperature, are also measured in joules.

The conversion of mechanical energy to thermal energy, as when you rub your hands together, is easy. The reverse process, conversion of thermal to mechanical energy, is more difficult. A device able to convert thermal energy to mechanical energy continuously is called a **heat engine.**

Heat engines require a high temperature source from which thermal energy can be removed, and a low temperature sink into which thermal energy can be delivered, Figure 12–15. An automobile engine is an example of a heat engine, Figure 12–16. A mixture of air and gasoline vapor is ignited, producing a very high temperature flame. Heat flows from the flame to the air in the cylinder. The hot air expands and pushes on a piston, changing thermal energy into mechanical energy. In order to obtain continuous mechanical energy, the engine must be returned to its starting condition. The heated air is expelled and replaced by new

**FIGURE 12–16.** The heat produced by burning gasoline causes the gases produced to expand and exert force on the cylinder.

air, and the piston is returned to the top of the cylinder. The entire cycle is repeated many times each minute. The heat from the burning gasoline is converted into mechanical energy that eventually results in the movement of the car.

Not all the thermal energy from the very high temperature flame is converted into mechanical energy. The exhaust gases and the engine parts become hot. The exhaust comes in contact with outside air, transferring heat to it. Heat from the hot engine is transferred to a radiator. Outside air passes through the radiator and the air temperature is raised. This heat transferred out of the engine is called waste heat, heat that cannot be converted into work. All heat engines generate waste heat. In a car engine, the waste heat is at a lower temperature than the heat of the gasoline flame. The overall change in total energy of the car-air system is zero. Thus, according to the first law of thermodynamics, the thermal energy in the flame is equal to the sum of the mechanical energy produced and the waste heat expelled.

Heat flows spontaneously from a warm body to a cold body. It is possible to remove thermal energy from a colder body and add it to a warmer body. An external source of energy, usually mechanical energy, however, is required to accomplish this transfer. A refrigerator is a common example of a device that accomplishes this transfer. Electrical energy runs a motor that does work on a gas such as Freon. Heat is transferred from the contents of the refrigerator to the Freon. Food is cooled, usually to 4.0°C, and the Freon is warmed. Outside the refrigerator, heat is transferred from the Freon to room air, cooling the Freon again. The overall change in the thermal energy of the Freon is zero. Thus, according to the first law of thermodynamics, the sum of the heat removed from the food and the work done by the motor is equal to the heat expelled to the outside at a higher temperature, Figure 12–17.

A heat pump is a refrigerator that can be run in two directions. In summer, heat is removed from the house, cooling the house. The heat is expelled into the warmer air outside. In winter, heat is removed from the cold outside air and transferred into the warmer house, Figure 12–18. In either case, mechanical energy is required to transfer heat from a cold object to a warmer one.

## Perpetual Motion?

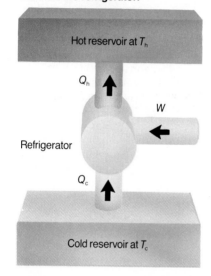

**FIGURE 12–17.** Diagram for a refrigerator. It absorbs heat $Q_c$ from the cold reservoir and gives off heat $Q_h$ to the hot reservoir. Work, $W$, is done *on* the refrigerator.

**FIGURE 12–18.** A heat pump runs in either direction depending on whether it is used in heating or cooling. In cooling, heat is extracted from the air in the house and pumped outside (a). In heating, heat is extracted from the outside and pumped inside (b).

POCKET
LAB

### DRIP, DRIP, DRIP

Measure equal amounts of very hot and very cold water into 2 clear glasses (or beakers). Predict what will happen if you simultaneously put 1 drop of food colouring into each glass. Try it. What happened? Why? Was the mixing symmetric?

Freon is the name of a family of chemical compounds invented for use in refrigerators and air conditioners. Each Freon compound was designed by chemists to have a specific boiling point. They were also designed to be very stable, and not to react with materials used in refrigerators. They work very well in a variety of important applications. Unfortunately, these properties also mean that when these gases escape into the atmosphere, they also do not decompose at low altitudes. In the past few years, however, scientists have found that these chemicals do react when they move into the upper atmosphere, miles above Earth. The products of the reaction can destroy Earth's protective ozone layer, increasing ultraviolet radiation that reaches Earth, and increasing incidence of skin cancer. They may also increase the "greenhouse effect" and raise Earth's temperature. Scientists are now trying to create new molecules to replace the Freons that are safe for the ozone and are not greenhouse gases.

## The Second Law of Thermodynamics

Many processes that do not violate the first law of thermodynamics have never been observed to occur spontaneously. For example, the first law does not prohibit heat flowing from a cold body to a hot body, Figure 12–19a. Still, when a hot body is placed in contact with a cold body, the hot body has never been observed to become hotter and the cold body colder. Heat flows spontaneously from hot to cold bodies. As another example, heat engines could convert thermal energy completely into mechanical energy with no waste heat and still obey the first law, Figure 12–19b. Yet waste heat is always generated.

In the nineteenth century, the French engineer Sadi Carnot (1796–1832) studied the ability of engines to convert heat into mechanical energy. He developed a logical proof that even an ideal engine would generate some waste heat. Real engines generate even more waste heat. Carnot's result is best described in terms of a quantity called **entropy** (EN truh pee). Entropy, like thermal energy, is contained in an object. If heat is added to a body, entropy is increased. If heat is removed from a body, entropy is decreased. If an object does work with no change in temperature, however, the entropy does not change, as long as friction is ignored.

On a microscopic level, entropy is described as the disorder in a system. When heat is added to an object, the particles move in a random way. Some move very quickly, others move slowly, many move at intermediate speeds. The greater the range of speeds exhibited by the particles, the greater the disorder. The greater the disorder, the larger the entropy. While it is theoretically possible that all the particles could have the same speed, the random collisions and energy exchanges of the particles make the probability of this extremely unlikely.

The **second law of thermodynamics** states: *natural processes go in a direction that increases the total entropy of the universe.* Entropy and the second law can be thought of as statements of the probability of events happening. Figure 12–20 illustrates an increase in entropy as food colour molecules, originally separate from clear water, are thoroughly mixed with the water molecules after a time.

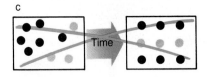

**FIGURE 12–19. A representation of three processes forbidden by the second law of thermodynamics, but not the first law.**

FIGURE 12–20. An example of the second law of thermodynamics.

The second law predicts that heat flows spontaneously only from a hot body to a cold body. Consider a hot iron bar and a cold cup of water. On the average, the particles in the iron will be moving very fast, whereas the particles in the water move more slowly. The bar is plunged into the water. When thermal equilibrium is reached, the average kinetic energy of the particles in the iron and the water will be the same. This final state is less ordered than the first situation. No longer are the fast particles confined mainly in the iron and the slow particles in the water. All speeds are evenly distributed. The entropy of the final state is larger than that of the initial state.

We take for granted many daily events that occur spontaneously, or naturally, in one direction, but that would really shock us if they happened in reverse. You are not surprised when a metal spoon, heated at one end, soon becomes uniformly hot, or when smoke from a too-hot frying pan diffuses throughout the kitchen. Consider your reaction, however, if a spoon lying on a table suddenly, on its own, became red hot at one end and icy cold at the other, or if all the smoke from the skillet collected in a 9-cm³ cube in the exact centre of the kitchen. Neither of the reverse processes violates the first law of thermodynamics. The events are simply examples of the countless events that are not spontaneously reversible because the reverse process would violate the second law of thermodynamics.

The second law and entropy also give new meaning to what is commonly called the "energy crisis." When you use a resource such as natural gas to heat your home, you do not use up the energy in the gas. The potential energy contained in the molecules of the gas is converted into thermal energy of the flame, which is then transferred to thermal energy in the air of your home. Even if this warm air leaks to the outside, the energy is not lost. Energy has not been used up. The entropy, however, has been increased. The chemical structure of natural gas is very ordered. In contrast, the thermal motion of the warmed air is very disordered. While it is mathematically possible for the original order to be reestablished, the probability of this occurring is essentially zero. For this reason, entropy is often used as a measure of the unavailability of energy. The energy in the warmed air in a house is not as available to do mechanical work or to transfer heat to other bodies as the original gas molecules. The lack of usable energy is really a surplus of entropy.

When fuel is burned, energy is not lost; entropy is increased.

a

b

FIGURE 12–21. A familiar example of the second law of thermodynamics. If no work is done on a system, entropy spontaneously reaches a maximum.

# Physics and technology

## RANGE-TOP COOKING

Top-of-the-range cooking is bringing new technology into the kitchen. In addition to the electric coil and gas burner, consumers can select solid disk heating elements, glass-ceramic cooktops, and sealed gas burners, among others.

The familiar electric coil cooks food with radiant heat and conduction. It heats up and cools down quickly. A disadvantage is that the heating elements and drip bowls can be hard to clean.

Solid disk heating elements were introduced in the 1980s and have grown in popularity. The disks consist of cast iron which has electric heating wires embedded in the underside. Solid disks are easier to clean but take longer to heat up and cool down than coil-type elements. They also require cookware with extra-flat bottoms in order to maximize heat transfer from the disk to the utensil.

Glass-ceramic cooktops, or smoothtops, contain their heating elements under a sheet of ceramic glass. They may use electric resistance heating, a halogen gas "bulb", or magnetic induction heating.

· Why would the solid disk heating elements take longer to heat up and cool down than the coil-type elements?

# CONCEPT REVIEW

**2.1** Old-fashioned heating systems sent steam into radiators in each room. In the radiator, the steam condensed back to water. How did this heat the room?

**2.2** James Joule carefully measured the difference in temperature of water at the top and bottom of a waterfall. Why would he have expected a difference?

**2.3** In 1861, the French scientist Hirn used a 320-kg hammer moving at 5 m/s to smash a 3-kg block of lead against a 450-kg rock. He found that the temperature of the lead increased 5°C. Explain.

**2.4** **Critical Thinking:** A new deck of cards has all the suits (clubs, diamonds, hearts, and spades) in order, and the cards ordered by number within the suits. If you shuffle the cards many times, are you likely to return the cards to the original order? Of what physical law is this an example?

# CHAPTER
## 12 REVIEW · · · · · · · · · · · · · · · · · · · · · · · ·

## SUMMARY

### 12.1 Temperature and Thermal Energy

· The thermal energy of an object is the sum of the kinetic and potential energies of the internal motion of the particles.
· The temperature of a gas is proportional to the average kinetic energy of the particles.
· Thermometers use some property of a substance, such as thermal expansion, that depends on temperature.
· Thermometers reach thermal equilibrium with the objects they contact, and then some temperature-dependent property of the thermometer is measured.
· The Celsius and Kelvin temperature scales are widely used in scientific work. One kelvin is equal to one degree Celsius.
· At absolute zero, 0 K or $-273.15°C$, matter has no thermal energy.
· Heat is the energy transferred because of a difference in temperature. Heat flows naturally from a hot to a cold body.
· Specific heat is the quantity of heat required to raise the temperature of one kilogram of a substance one kelvin.
· In an isolated system, the thermal energy of one part may change but the total energy of the system is constant.

### 12.2 Change of State and Laws of Thermodynamics

· The heat of fusion is the quantity of heat required to change 1 kg of a substance from its solid state to its liquid state at its melting point.
· The heat of vaporization is the quantity of heat required to change 1 kg of a substance from the liquid state to the vapour state at its boiling point.
· The heat transferred during a change of state does not produce a change in temperature.
· The first law of thermodynamics states that the total increase in thermal energy of a system is equal to the sum of the heat added to it and the work done on it.
· A heat engine continuously converts thermal energy to mechanical energy.
· A heat pump or refrigerator uses mechanical energy to transfer heat from an area of lower temperature to an area of higher temperature.
· Entropy, a measure of disorder, never decreases in natural processes.

## KEY TERMS

| | |
|---|---|
| kinetic-molecular theory | calorimeter |
| thermal energy | thermodynamics |
| conduction | melting point |
| convection | heat of fusion |
| radiation | boiling point |
| temperature | heat of vaporization |
| thermal equilibrium | first law of |
| thermometer | thermodynamics |
| absolute zero | entropy |
| kelvin | second law of |
| heat | thermodynamics |
| specific heat | |

## REVIEWING CONCEPTS

1. Explain the difference between a ball's external energy and its thermal energy. Give an example.
2. Explain the difference between a ball's thermal energy and temperature.
3. Can temperature be assigned to a vacuum? Explain.
4. Do all of the molecules or atoms in a liquid have about the same speed?
5. Your teacher just told your class that the temperature of the sun is $1.5 \times 10^7$ degrees. Sally asks whether this is the Kelvin or Celsius scale. What is the teacher's answer?
6. Is your body a good judge of temperature? On a cold winter day, a metal door knob feels

much colder to your hand than the wooden door. Is this true? Explain.

7. A hot steel ball is dropped into a cup of cool water. Explain the difference between heat and the ball's thermal energy.

8. Do we ever measure heat transfer directly? Explain.

9. When a warmer object is in contact with a colder object, does temperature flow from one to the other? Do the two have the same temperature changes?

10. Can you add thermal energy to an object without increasing its temperature? Explain.

11. When wax freezes, is energy absorbed or released by the wax?

12. Why does water in a canteen stay cooler if it has a canvas cover that is kept wet?

13. Are the coils of an air conditioner that are inside the house the location of vaporization or condensation of the Freon? Explain.

14. Which situation has more entropy, an unbroken egg or a scrambled egg?

## APPLYING CONCEPTS

1. Sally is cooking pasta in a pot of boiling water. Will the pasta cook faster if the water is boiling vigorously than if it is boiling gently?

2. What temperatures on the following pairs of scales are the same? ($T_F = 9/5\ T_C + 32$)
   a. Celsius and Fahrenheit
   b. Kelvin and Fahrenheit
   c. Celsius and Kelvin

3. Which liquid would an ice cube cool faster, water or methanol? Explain.

4. Explain why the high specific heat of water makes it desirable for use in hot water heating systems.

5. Equal masses of aluminum and lead are heated to the same temperature. The pieces of metal are placed on a block of ice. Which metal melts more ice? Explain.

6. Two blocks of lead are heated to the same temperature. Block A has twice the mass of block B. They are dropped into identical cups of water and both systems come to thermal equilibrium. If the cups started with water at the same temperature, will the water have the same temperature after the blocks are added? Explain.

7. Why do easily vaporized liquids, such as acetone or methanol, feel cool to the skin?

8. Explain why fruit growers spray their trees with water, when frost is expected, to protect the fruit from freezing.

9. Would opening the refrigerator door on a warm day help cool the kitchen? Explain.

## PROBLEMS

### 12.1 Temperature and Thermal Energy

1. Liquid nitrogen boils at 77 K. Find this temperature in degrees Celsius.

2. The melting point of hydrogen is $-259.14°C$. Find this temperature in kelvin.

3. Sadi Carnot showed that no real heat engine can have an efficiency greater than

$$efficiency = \frac{work\ output}{heat\ input} = \frac{T_{hot} - T_{cold}}{T_{hot}}$$

where $T_{hot}$ and $T_{cold}$ are the temperatures of the input and waste thermal energy reservoirs. Note: Kelvin temperatures must be used in this equation.
   a. What is the efficiency of an ideal steam engine that uses superheated steam at 685 K to drive the engine and ejects waste steam at 298 K?
   b. If the steam generator produces $1.00 \times 10^8$ J each second, how much work can the ideal engine do each second?

4. How much heat is needed to raise the temperature of 50.0 g of water from 4.5°C to 83.0°C?

5. How much heat must be added to 50.0 g of aluminum at 25°C to raise its temperature to 125°C?

6. A $5.00 \times 10^2$-g block of metal absorbs 5016 J of heat when its temperature changes from 20.0°C to 30.0°C. Calculate the specific heat of the metal.

7. A $4.00 \times 10^2$-g glass coffee cup is at room temperature, 20.0°C. It is then plunged into hot dishwater, 80.0°C. If the temperature of the cup reaches that of the dishwater, how much heat does the cup absorb? Assume the mass of the dishwater is large enough so its temperature doesn't change appreciably.

8. A copper wire has a mass of 165 g. An electric current runs through the wire for a short

time and its temperature rises from 21°C to 39°C. What minimum quantity of energy is converted by the electric current?

9. A $1.00 \times 10^2$-g mass of tungsten at 100.0°C is placed in $2.00 \times 10^2$ g of water at 20.0°C. The mixture reaches equilibrium at 21.6°C. Calculate the specific heat of tungsten.

10. A $6.0 \times 10^2$-g sample of water at 90.0°C is mixed with $4.00 \times 10^2$ g of water at 22°C. Assume no heat loss to the surroundings. What is the final temperature of the mixture?

11. To get a feeling for the amount of energy needed to heat water, recall from Table 11–1 that the kinetic energy of a compact car moving at 100 km/h is $2.9 \times 10^5$ J. What volume of water (in litres) would $2.9 \times 10^5$ J of energy warm from room temperature (20°C) to boiling (100°C)?

12. A 10.0-kg piece of zinc at 71°C is placed in a container of water. The water has a mass of 20.0 kg and has a temperature of 10.0°C before the zinc is added. What is the final temperature of the water and zinc?

13. A $2.00 \times 10^2$-g sample of brass at 100.0°C is placed in a calorimeter cup that contains 261 g of water at 20.0°C. Disregard the absorption of heat by the cup and calculate the final temperature of the brass and water.

▶ 14. A $3.00 \times 10^2$-W electric immersion heater is used to heat a cup of water. The cup is made of glass and its mass is $3.00 \times 10^2$ g. It contains 250 g of water at 15° C. How much time is needed for the heater to bring the water to the boiling point? Assume the temperature of the cup to be the same as the temperature of the water at all times and no heat is lost to the air.

15. A $2.50 \times 10^2$-kg cast-iron car engine contains water as a coolant. Suppose the engine's temperature is 35°C when it is shut off. The air temperature is 10°C. The heat given off by the engine and water in it as they cool to air temperature is $4.4 \times 10^6$ J. What mass of water is used to cool the engine?

## 12.2 Change of State and Laws of Thermodynamics

16. Years ago, a block of ice with a mass of about 20.0 kg was used daily in a home icebox. The temperature of the ice was 0.0°C when deliv-

ered. As it melted, how much heat did a block of ice that size absorb?

17. A person consumes $1.0 \times 10^7$ J of energy in a day. How much water at 100°C could that much energy vaporize?

18. A 40.0-g sample of chloroform is condensed from a vapour at 61.6°C to a liquid at 61.6°C. It liberates 9870 J of heat. What is the heat of vaporization of chloroform?

▶ 19. How much heat is removed from 60.0 g of steam at 100.0°C to change it to 60.0 g of water at 20.0°C?

20. A 750-kg car moving at 23 m/s brakes to a stop. The brakes contain about 15 kg of iron that absorb the energy. What is the increase in temperature of the brakes?

▶ 21. How much heat is added to 10.0 g of ice at −20.0°C to convert it to steam at 120.0°C?

▶ 22. A 50.0-g sample of ice at 0.00°C is placed in a glass beaker containing $4.00 \times 10^2$ g of water at 50.0°C. All the ice melts. What is the final temperature of the mixture? Disregard any heat loss to the glass.

23. A 4.2-g lead bullet moving at 275 m/s strikes a steel plate and stops. If all its kinetic energy is converted to thermal energy and none leaves the bullet, what is its temperature change?

24. A soft drink from Australia is labeled "Low Joule Cola." The label says "100 mL yields 1.7 kJ." The can contains 375 mL. Sally drinks the cola and then offsets this input of food energy by climbing stairs. How high would she have to climb if Sally has a mass of 65.0 kg?

25. When air is compressed in a bicycle pump, an average force of 45 N is exerted as the pump handle moves 0.24 m. During this time, 2.0 J of heat leave the cylinder through the walls. What is the net change in thermal energy of the air in the cylinder?

## THINKING PHYSIC-LY

1. Picture a cup of hot tea and an iceberg.
   a. Which has a greater amount of internal energy?
   b. Which has a higher temperature?
2. Why can't you tell if you have a fever by touching your own forehead?

# CHAPTER

# 13 States of Matter

◀ **Bottled Cloud**

Janet was helping her parents prepare for a dinner party. As she popped the cork on a bottle of sparkling grape juice, a small cloud formed around the bottle's mouth. The cloud surprised Janet's mother. What explanation did Janet give her mother?

## Chapter Outline

**13.1 THE FLUID STATES**
· Pressure
· Fluids at Rest—Hydrostatics
· Fluids in Motion—Hydrodynamics
· Liquids vs Gases
· Surface Tension
· Evaporation and Condensation
· Plasma

**13.2 THE SOLID STATE**
· Solid Bodies
· Elasticity in Solids
· Thermal Expansion of Matter

You have lived with the three common states of matter all your life. You breathe air, drink and swim in water, and build with solid objects. In general, you are familiar with most of their properties. Yet, there can be some surprises. The photo shows a bottle that contained cold, sparkling grape juice. Carbon dioxide gas is dissolved in the liquid. When the cork is removed, the pressure in the bottle suddenly drops. The result is a beautiful display of the states of matter.

## ✓ Concept Check

The following terms or concepts from earlier chapters are important for a good understanding of this chapter. If you are not familiar with them, you should review them before studying this chapter.
· force, Chapter 5
· work, kinetic energy, potential energy, Chapter 11
· temperature, thermal energy, heat, Chapter 12

# Objectives

- demonstrate an understanding of the concept of pressure, the definition of the pascal, and the ability to calculate pressure and total force.
- understand the origin of Pascal's and Archimedes' principles and their applications.
- explain Bernoulli's principle and its applications in producing lift.
- describe how cohesive and adhesive forces cause surface tension and capillary action, respectively.
- understand the origin of evaporation and condensation from the viewpoint of kinetic energy.
- define a plasma and give examples of plasmas in nature.

Pressure is the force on each unit area of a surface.

FIGURE 13–1. Pressure-measuring instruments.

# 13.1 THE FLUID STATES

What is a fluid? A **fluid** is any material that flows and offers little resistance to a change in its shape when under pressure. Both liquids and gases are fluids.

Much of our life is spent in these two fluid states of matter. We live and breathe in the gaseous atmosphere. The large amounts of liquid water on Earth makes it unique in the solar system and is probably the reason Earth supports life. The properties of fluids allow airplanes to fly, boats to float, and submarines either to float or submerge. They also allow paper towels to absorb spilled milk, and insects to walk on the surface of water. The final fluid state, plasma, provides us with the beautiful northern lights.

## Pressure

The kinetic-molecular theory that we discussed in the last chapter helps to explain the properties of gases. The theory is based on three simplified assumptions.

- Gases are made up of a large number of very small particles.
- The particles are in constant, random motion. They are widely separated and make only elastic collisions with one another.
- The particles make perfectly elastic collisions with the walls of the container that holds them.

The kinetic theory is a microscopic theory. It pictures a volume of gas as a box filled with a large number of very small moving particles. According to the theory, the pressure exerted on the walls of the box is the result of the collisions of the particles with the walls of the box.

What do we mean by the pressure exerted by a gas? **Pressure** is defined as the force on a unit surface area. That is,

$$p = \frac{F}{A}.$$

**Table 13–1**

| Some Typical Pressures | |
|---|---|
| Location | Pressure (Pa) |
| Centre of sun | $2 \times 10^{16}$ |
| Centre of Earth | $4 \times 10^{11}$ |
| Deepest ocean trench | $1.1 \times 10^{8}$ |
| High heels on floor | $1 \times 10^{6}$ |
| Auto tire | $2 \times 10^{5}$ |
| Standard atmosphere | $1 \times 10^{5}$ |
| Blood pressure | $1.6 \times 10^{4}$ |
| Loudest sound | 30 |
| Faintest sound | $3 \times 10^{-5}$ |
| Best vacuum | $1 \times 10^{-12}$ |

In the SI, the unit of pressure is the **pascal**, Pa, one newton per square metre. Because the pascal is a small unit of pressure, the kilopascal, kPa, equal to 1000 Pa, is more commonly used. Earth's atmosphere at sea level is about 100 000 Pa.

The pressure of Earth's gaseous atmosphere is so well balanced by our bodies that we hardly ever notice it. You become aware of the pressure only when your ears "pop" as a result of pressure changes. This might occur when riding the elevator in a tall building, driving on a high mountain road, or flying in an airplane. Yet, on every square centimetre of Earth's surface at sea level, the atmosphere exerts a force of approximately 10 N, about the weight of a 1-kg object. This is equal to about $1.0 \times 10^{5}$ Pa or 100 kPa.

The unit of pressure is the pascal, Pa.

## Example Problem

### Calculating Pressure

A typical high school student weighs 725 N and wears shoes that touch the ground over an area of 412 cm². **a.** What is the average pressure his shoes exert on the ground? **b.** How does the answer change when he stands on only one foot?

**Given:** force, $F = 725$ N  
       area, $A = 412$ cm²  
            $= 0.0412$ m²

**Unknown:** pressure, $p$  
**Basic equation:** $p = F/A$

**Solution:**

**a.** $p = \dfrac{F}{A} = \dfrac{725\,\text{N}}{0.0412\,\text{m}^2} = 1.76 \times 10^{4}$ N/m² $= 17.6$ kPa

**b.** $p = \dfrac{F}{A} = \dfrac{725\,\text{N}}{0.0206\,\text{m}^2} = 3.52 \times 10^{4}$ N/m² $= 35.2$ kPa

The same amount of force can create even larger pressures. If a woman puts her whole weight on the heel of one high-heeled shoe, Figure 13–2, the pressure can exceed 1 000 000 Pa.

**FIGURE 13–2.** Pressure is the force exerted on a unit area of a surface. Similar forces may produce vastly different pressures—the pressure on the ground under a woman's high heel is far greater than that under an elephant's foot.

## Practice Problems

1. The atmospheric pressure at sea level is about $1.0 \times 10^5$ Pa. What is the force exerted on the top of a typical office desk, 152 cm long and 76 cm wide?

2. A car's tire makes contact with the ground on a rectangular "footprint" 12 cm by 18 cm. The car's mass is 925 kg. What pressure does the car exert on the ground?

3. A lead brick, $5.0 \times 10 \times 20$ cm, rests on the ground on its smallest face. What pressure does it exert? (Lead has a density 11.8 g/cm$^3$.)

▶ 4. In a tornado, the pressure can be 15% below normal atmospheric pressure. Further, a tornado can move so quickly that this pressure drop can occur in one second. Suppose a tornado suddenly occurred outside your front door (182 cm high, 91 cm wide). What force would be exerted on the door? in what direction?

## Fluids At Rest—Hydrostatics

The fluid that is most familiar to you is probably liquid water. But honey, oil, tar, and air are also fluids. How are they the same — how different? To simplify our study of fluids, we will examine the behaviour of an ideal fluid, one in which there is no internal friction among the particles.

If you have ever dived deep into a swimming pool or lake, you know that fluids exert pressure. Your body is sensitive to water pressure. You probably noticed that the pressure you felt on your ears did not depend on whether your head was upright or tilted. If your body is horizontal, the pressure is nearly the same on all parts of your body.

Blaise Pascal (1623–1662), a French physician, noted that the shape of a container had no affect on the pressure at any given depth. He was the first to discover that any change in pressure applied to a confined fluid at any point is transmitted undiminished throughout the fluid. This discovery became known as **Pascal's principle**. Every time you squeeze a tube of toothpaste, you use Pascal's principle.

Pascal's principle is applied in the operation of machines that use fluids to multiply forces, as in hydraulic lifts. In a hydraulic system, a fluid is confined in two connecting chambers, Figure 13–4. Each cham-

FIGURE 13–4. Pascal's principle is the basis of a hydraulic lift and other machines that use fluids to multiply forces.

ber has a piston that is free to move. A force, $F_1$, is exerted on piston 1 with surface area $A_1$. The pressure exerted on the fluid is

$$p_1 = \frac{F_1}{A_1}.$$

By Pascal's principle, pressure is transmitted throughout the fluid without change. The pressure exerted by the fluid on piston 2, with surface area $A_2$, is given by

$$p_2 = \frac{F_2}{A_2}.$$

Thus, $p_2$ is the same as $p_1$. Therefore,

$$F_1/A_1 = F_2/A_2.$$

The force that piston 2 can exert is given by

$$F_2 = F_1 A_2/A_1.$$

## F.Y.I.

The Heimlich manoeuver is a sharp pressure applied to the abdomen of a person to dislodge a foreign object caught in the throat. It is an application of Pascal's principle.

A hydraulic machine can increase force exerted, but cannot increase the work done.

## Example Problem

### Hydraulic System

A 20.0-N force is exerted on the small piston of a hydraulic system. The cross-sectional area of the small piston is 0.0500 m². What is the magnitude of the weight that can be lifted by the large piston, which has a surface area of 0.100 m²?

**Given:** $F_1 = 20.0$ N    **Unknown:** $F_2$
 $A_1 = 0.0500$ m²
 $A_2 = 0.100$ m²    **Basic equation:** $\dfrac{F_1}{A_1} = \dfrac{F_2}{A_2}$

**Solution:** $\dfrac{F_1}{A_1} = \dfrac{F_2}{A_2}$    $F_2 = \dfrac{F_1 A_2}{A_1}$

$$F_2 = \frac{(20.0 \text{ N})(0.100 \text{ m}^2)}{0.0500 \text{ m}^2} = 40.0 \text{ N}$$

You can observe another characteristic of fluids while swimming. The deeper you swim, the greater the pressure you feel. The pressure of a fluid on a horizontal surface is the weight per unit area, $A$, of the fluid above the surface. The weight, $\vec{W}$, of the water above you is

$$\vec{W} = mg.$$

Recall that $\rho$ (density) $= m/V$ and $V = Ah$. Therefore, $\vec{W} = \rho Vg = \rho Ahg$. Substituting this value for $\vec{W}$ will give

$$P = \frac{\vec{W}}{A} = \rho \frac{Ahg}{A} \qquad P = \rho hg.$$

Therefore, the pressure is proportional only to the depth of the fluid and its density. The shape of the container has no effect, as shown in Figure 13–5.

When an object of height $l$ is placed in a fluid, force is exerted on all sides, Figure 13–6a. The forces on the four sides are balanced. The forces on the top and bottom, however, are given by

$$F_{\text{top}} = p_{\text{top}} A = \rho h A g$$
$$F_{\text{bottom}} = p_{\text{bottom}} A = \rho (h + l) A g.$$

Pressure depends on the weight of the fluid above you.

**FIGURE 13–5. Pascal's vases show that a container's shape has no effect on pressure.**

FIGURE 13–6. Archimedes' principle can be derived from considering a volume of fluid as shown (a). If the density of an object is less than that of the fluid, the object will sink only until it displaces a volume of water with a weight equal to the weight of the object (b).

The buoyant force is equal to the weight of the fluid displaced.

FIGURE 13–7. FLIP is a research vessel used to study waves in deep water. It is towed into position floating horizontally. Then water is pumped into its stern tanks and it flips to a vertical position, as shown.

The force on the bottom is larger than that on the top. The difference is

$$F_{bottom} - F_{top} = \rho(h + l)Ag - \rho Ahg$$
$$= \rho Alg = \rho Vg.$$

Thus, there is an upward force of the fluid on the object. This force is called the **buoyant force.** Note that the volume of the immersed object is the same as the volume of the fluid displaced. Therefore, the buoyant force, $\rho Vg$, has a magnitude equal to the weight of the fluid displaced by the immersed object. This relationship was discovered by the Greek scientist Archimedes in 212 B.C. and is called **Archimedes' principle**. *An object immersed in a fluid is buoyed up by a force equal to the weight of the fluid displaced by the object.* It is important to note that the buoyant force *does not* depend on the weight of the submerged object, only the weight of the displaced fluid. A solid cube of aluminum, a solid cube of iron, and a hollow cube of iron, all of the same volume, would experience the same buoyant force.

Archimedes' principle applies to objects of all densities. If the density of the object is greater than that of the fluid, the upward buoyant force will be less than the weight of the object, $\vec{W}_{object}$, and the object will sink. If the density of the object is equal to the density of the fluid, the buoyant force and $\vec{W}_{object}$ will be equal. The net force will be zero and the object will neither sink nor float. If the density of the object is less than that of the fluid, the object will float. The portion of the object submerged will just displace a volume of fluid with a weight equal to the weight of the object. Wearing a life jacket filled with material of very low density has the effect of decreasing the body's average density.

Shipbuilders can build ships of steel (density $9.0 \times 10^3$ kg/m³) by designing them with large hollow hulls so that the average density of the ship is less than that of water. You will notice that a ship loaded with cargo rides much lower in the water than a ship with an empty cargo hold. Submarines take advantage of Archimedes' principle by pumping water into or out of special chambers to regulate the vertical force, causing the sub to rise or sink. Fish have air sacs that allow them to adjust their density so they can rise or sink.

# PHYSICS LAB

## Float or Sink

## Purpose

To investigate the buoyancy of objects.

## Materials

- beaker
- water
- film can with top
- 25 pennies
- 250-g spring scale
- pan balance

## Procedure

1. Measure and calculate the volume of a film can. Record the volume in your data table.
2. Fill the can with water. Carefully find the mass of the filled can on the pan balance. Record the value in your data table.
3. Empty the can of water.
4. Place a few pennies in the can and put the top on tightly. Find its mass and record the value in your data table.
5. Put the capped film can into the water to see if it floats.
6. If it floats, estimate the percentage that it is underwater. Record this amount in the data table.
7. If it sinks, use the spring scale to measure the mass while it is underwater (but not touching the bottom). Record this value in the data table.
8. Calculate the density of each trial in g/cm³.

## Observations and Data

Set up a data table similar to the following:
volume of can  =  _____ cm³
mass of can with water  =  _____ g

| FLOATERS | | |
|---|---|---|
| mass with pennies | % below water | density |
|  |  |  |
|  |  |  |
|  |  |  |
|  |  |  |

| SINKERS | | |
|---|---|---|
| mass with pennies | apparent mass | density |
|  |  |  |
|  |  |  |
|  |  |  |
|  |  |  |

## Analysis

1. Look closely at the mass of the floaters and the percentages below the water. What seems to be the rule?
2. Look closely at the sinkers. How much lighter are the cans when massed underwater?

## Applications

1. Explain why a steel-hulled boat can float, even though it is quite massive.

# Example Problem

## Archimedes' Principle

A cubic decimetre ($1 \times 10^{-3}$ m³) of steel is submerged in water.
**a.** What is the magnitude of the buoyant force acting on the steel?
**b.** What is the apparent weight of the body? (The density of steel is $9.0 \times 10^3$ kg/m³.)

**Given:** $V = 1.00 \times 10^{-3}$ m³  **Unknowns: a.** $F_{buoyant}$
$\rho_{steel} = 9.0 \times 10^3$ kg/m³  **b.** $W_{apparent}$
$\rho_{water} = 1.00 \times 10^3$ kg/m³  **Basic equations:**
**a.** $F_{buoyant} = \rho_{water}Vg$
**b.** $W_{apparent} = mg - F_{buoyant}$

**Solution:**

**a.** $F_{buoyant} = \rho_{water}Vg$
$= (1.00 \times 10^3 \text{ kg/m}^3)(1.00 \times 10^{-1} \text{ m})^3(9.8 \text{ m/s}^2)$
$= 9.8$ N

**b.** $\vec{W}_{apparent} = mg - F_{buoyant}$
$= [1.00 \times 10^{-1} \text{ m})^3(9.0 \times 10^3 \text{ kg/m}^3)(9.8 \text{ m/s}^2)] - 9.8$ N
$= 88.2$ N $- 9.8$ N $= 78.4$ N

# Practice Problems

**5.** If the diameter of the larger piston in Figure 13–4 were doubled, what force would be lifted if 20.0 N were applied to the smaller piston?

**6.** Dentists' chairs are examples of hydraulic lift systems. If the chair weighs 1600 N and rests on a piston with a cross-sectional area of 1440 cm², what force must be applied to the small piston with a cross-sectional area of 72 cm² to lift the chair?

**7.** A teenager is floating in a freshwater lake with her head just above the water. If she weighs 600 N, what is the volume of the submerged part of her body?

▶ **8.** What is the tension in a wire supporting a 1250-N camera submerged in water? The volume of the camera is $8.3 \times 10^{-2}$ m³.

# Fluids in Motion–Hydrodynamics

To see the effect of moving fluids, try the experiment in Figure 13–8. Hold a strip of notebook paper just under your lower lip. Now blow hard across the top surface. The strip will rise. The pressure on top of the paper where air is flowing fast is lower than the pressure beneath where air is not in motion. This is an example of Bernoulli's principle, named for the Swiss scientist Daniel Bernoulli (1700–1782).

Imagine a horizontal pipe completely filled with a smoothly flowing ideal fluid. If a certain mass of the fluid enters one end of the pipe, then an equal mass must come out the other end. Now consider a section of pipe where the cross section becomes narrower, as shown in Figure 13–9. To keep the same mass of fluid moving through the narrow section in a fixed amount of time, the velocity of the fluid must increase. If the

**FIGURE 13–8. Blowing across the surface of a sheet of paper demonstrates Bernoulli's principle.**

velocity increases, then so must the kinetic energy. This means that net work must be done on the fluid. The net work is the difference between the work done *on* the mass of fluid to move it into the pipe and the work done *by* the fluid pushing the same mass out of the pipe. The work is proportional to the force on the fluid, which, in turn, depends on the pressure. If the net work is positive, the pressure at the input end of the section, where the velocity is lower, must be larger than the pressure at the output end, where the velocity is higher. The relationship between the velocity and pressure exerted by a moving fluid is described by **Bernoulli's principle**: *As the velocity of a fluid increases, the pressure exerted by that fluid decreases.*

Most aircraft get part of their lift by taking advantage of Bernoulli's principle. Airplane wings are airfoils, devices designed to produce lift when moving through a fluid. The curvature of the top surface of a wing is greater than that of the bottom. As the wing travels through the air, the air moving over the top surface travels farther, and therefore must go faster than air moving past the bottom surface. The decreased air pressure created on the top surface results in a net upward pressure producing an upward force on the wings, or lift, that helps to hold the airplane aloft. Race cars use airfoils with a greater curvature on the bottom surface. The airfoils, called spoilers, produce a net downward pressure that helps to hold the rear wheels of the cars on the road at high speeds.

Did you ever notice that boat docks are designed so that water can flow freely through them? Consider what would happen at a solid-walled pier as a boat approached. As the space between the boat and the pier narrowed, the velocity of the water flowing through the space would increase, and the pressure exerted by the water on the pier side of the boat would decrease. The boat could be pushed against the pier by the greater pressure of the water against the other side.

Figure 13–10 shows that the flow of a fluid can be represented by streamlines. Streamlines can best be illustrated by a simple demonstration. Imagine carefully dropping tiny drops of food colouring into a smoothly flowing fluid. If the coloured lines that form stay thin and well

**FIGURE 13–9. The pressure, $P_1$, is greater than $P_2$ because $v_1$ is less than $v_2$.**

**FIGURE 13–10. Smooth streamlines in a computer simulation of airflow around a space shuttle indicate smooth air flow (a). A turbulent air flow appears around a rotating blade heated in a flame (b).**

a

b

a                                                           b

**FIGURE 13–11. The water strider can stand on water because of surface tension (a). The dewdrops on a spider web are spherical because of surface tension (b).**

defined, the flow is said to be streamlined. Notice that if the flow narrows, the streamlines move closer together. Closely-spaced streamlines indicate greater velocity, and therefore reduced pressure.

If streamlines swirl and become diffused, the flow of a fluid is said to be turbulent. Bernoulli's principle does not apply to turbulent flow. Since objects require less energy to move through a streamline flow, automobile and aircraft manufacturers spend a great deal of time and money testing new designs in wind tunnels to ensure a streamlined flow of air around vehicles.

## Liquids vs Gases

Although liquids and gases are grouped together as fluids, liquids are different from gases in several ways.
- A liquid has a definite volume; a gas takes the volume of any container that holds it.
- A liquid is practically incompressible; a gas is easily compressed.
- The particles of a liquid are very close together—the volume of the particles makes up almost all the volume of a liquid; the particles of a gas take up relatively little space—a container of gas is mostly empty space.

Furthermore, although the particles of an ideal liquid are totally free to slide over and around one another, in real liquids the particles do exert electromagnetic forces of attraction on each other. These forces are called **cohesive forces**, and they directly affect the behavior of the liquid.

Surface tension makes liquids form spherical drops. It results from cohesive forces.

## Surface Tension

Have you ever noticed that dewdrops on spiderwebs and falling drops of milk or oil are nearly spherical? What happens when it rains just after you have washed and waxed your car? The water drops bead up into rounded shapes. But a drop of alcohol on the same surface will flatten out. All of these phenomena are examples of surface tension. **Surface tension** is a result of the cohesive forces among the particles of a liquid. It is the tendency of the surface of a liquid to contract to the smallest area.

Beneath the surface of the liquid in Figure 13–12, each particle of the liquid is attracted equally in all directions by neighboring particles. As a result, there is no net force acting on any of the particles beneath the surface. At the surface, however, the particles are attracted to the sides and downward, but not upward. Thus, there is a net downward force acting on the top layers. This net force causes the surface layer to be slightly compressed. The layer acts like a tightly stretched rubber sheet or a film. The film is strong enough to support the weight of light objects. Water bugs can stand on the surface of quiet pools of water because of surface tension. The surface tension of water also supports an object such as a steel razor blade, even though the density of steel is nine times greater than that of water.

Why does surface tension produce the spherical drops? The force pulling the surface particles into the liquid causes the surface to become as small as possible. The shape that has the least surface for a given volume is a sphere. Liquid mercury has a much stronger cohesive force among its particles than water. This allows small amounts of mercury to form spherical drops, even when placed on a smooth surface. On the other hand, liquids such as alcohol or ether have weaker cohesive forces between their particles. A drop of either of these liquids flattens out when placed on a smooth surface.

A force similar to cohesion is adhesion. **Adhesion** is the attractive force that acts between particles of different substances. Like cohesive forces, adhesive forces are electromagnetic in nature.

If a piece of glass tubing with a small inside diameter is placed in water, the water rises inside the tube. The water rises because the adhesive force between glass and water molecules is stronger than the cohesive force between water molecules. This phenomenon is called **capillary action.** The water continues to rise until the weight of the water lifted balances the adhesive force between the glass and water molecules. If the radius of the tube increases, the volume, and therefore the weight, of the water increases proportionally faster than the surface area of the tube. For this reason, water is lifted higher in a narrow tube than in one that is wider.

As shown in Figure 13–13a, the surface of the water dips in the centre of the tube. This is because the adhesive force between the glass molecules and water molecules is greater than the cohesive force between the water molecules. If the liquid in the tube were mercury, it

FIGURE 13–12. Molecules in the interior of a liquid are attracted in all directions. Molecules at the surface have a net inward attraction that results in surface tension.

· · · · · · · · · · · · · · ·
# BIOLOGY CONNECTION

Botanists use paper chromatography to identify the chemical make-up of plants. Leaves from a plant are ground up and mixed with a solvent to make a mobile phase. Medical technologists use paper chromatography to test the urine of diabetic patients to determine if a patient's pancreas is functioning properly.

a

b

FIGURE 13–13. Water climbs the wall of this capillary tube (a), while the mercury is depressed in the tube (b). The force of attraction between mercury atoms is stronger than any adhesive force between the mercury and the glass.

**FIGURE 13–14. Convection currents carry warm surface air aloft until it reaches the temperature layer at which the water vapour condenses.**

Evaporation cools the remaining liquid.

Bottled Cloud ▶

would not rise in the tube. Furthermore, the centre of the surface would bulge upward, as shown in Figure 13–13b. Both of these phenomena occur because the cohesive forces between the mercury molecules are greater than the adhesive forces between the mercury and glass.

Molten wax rises in the wick of a candle because of capillary action. Paint moves up through the bristles of a brush for the same reason. It is also capillary action that causes water to move up through the soil to the roots of plants.

## Evaporation and Condensation

What happens to a puddle of water on a hot, dry day? After a few hours the water is gone. Why? The particles in a liquid move at random speeds. Some are moving rapidly; others are moving slowly. The temperature of a liquid is dependent on the average $E_k$ of its particles. Suppose a fast-moving particle is near the surface of the liquid. If it can break through the surface layers, it will escape from the liquid. Since there is a net downward cohesive force at the surface, only the more energetic particles escape. The escape of particles is called **evaporation**.

Evaporation cools the remaining liquid. Why? Each time a particle with higher than average kinetic energy escapes from the liquid, the average kinetic energy of the remaining particles decreases. A decrease in kinetic energy is a decrease in temperature. The cooling can be demonstrated by pouring some rubbing alcohol into the palm of your hand. Alcohol molecules have weak cohesive forces (low surface tension). Alcohol molecules, therefore, evaporate easily. The cooling effect is quite noticeable. Liquids such as alcohol and ether evaporate quickly because the forces between their molecules are weak. A liquid that evaporates quickly is called a **volatile** (VAHL uht uhl) liquid.

The opposite process also exists. What happens if you bring a cold glass into a hot, humid area? The outside of the glass soon becomes coated with water. Water molecules moving randomly in the air surrounding the glass may strike the cold surface. If a molecule loses enough energy, the cohesive force will be strong enough to prevent the particle's escape. This process is called **condensation**.

The air above water contains evaporated water vapour, water in the form of a gas. If the temperature is reduced, the water vapour condenses around tiny dust particles in the air, producing droplets only 0.01 mm in diameter. A cloud of these droplets is called a fog. Fogs often form when moist air is chilled by cold ground. Fogs can also be formed in your home. When a carbonated drink is opened, the sudden decrease in pressure causes the temperature to drop, condensing the water vapour and forming the fog seen when Janet opened the bottle of sparkling grape juice.

## Plasma

If you heat a solid, it melts to form a liquid. Further heating results in a gas. What happens if you increase the temperature still further? Collisions between the particles become violent enough to tear the particles apart. Electrons are pulled off the atoms, producing positively-charged ions. The gaslike state of negatively-charged electrons and positively-charged ions is called a **plasma**. Plasma is another fluid state of matter.

A lightning bolt is in the plasma state. So is most of the sun and other stars. In addition, much of the matter between the stars is in the form of plasma. The primary difference between a gas and a plasma is that a plasma can conduct electricity, and gas cannot. Neon signs and mercury and sodium vapour street lights contain glowing plasmas.

**FIGURE 13–15. The spectacular lighting effects in "neon" signs are caused by luminous plasmas formed in the glass tubing.**

. . . . . . . . . . . . . . . . . . . . . . .

# CONCEPT REVIEW

**1.1** You have two boxes. One is 20 cm by 20 cm by 20 cm. The other is 20 cm by 20 cm by 40 cm. **a.** How does the pressure of the air on the outside of the boxes compare on the two boxes? **b.** How does the total force of the air compare on the two boxes?

**1.2** Does a full, soft-drink can float or sink in water? Try it. Does it matter whether the drink is diet or not? All drink cans contain the same volume of liquid, 354 mL, and displace the same volume. What is the difference between a can that sinks and one that floats?

**1.3** When a baby has a high fever, doctors may suggest gently sponging off the baby with "rubbing alcohol." Why would this help?

**1.4 Critical Thinking:** It was a hot, humid day. Nicole had a glass of cold water on her desk. The outside of the glass was coated with water. Dan said that the water had leaked through the glass from the inside to the outside. Suggest an experiment Nicole could do to show Dan where the water came from.

A plasma is a gas of charged particles.

---

# **P**hysics and technology

## AERODYNAMIC HELMETS

**I**n the 74th Indy 500, Arie Luyendyk drove an average speed of 297.5 km/h to win. His maximum speed was greater than 352 km/h. At these speeds, drivers complain that their heads are buffeted severely; their helmets lift up, impairing their vision.

Airflow over the curved top of a racing helmet produces lift in the same way as over an airplane wing. The air speeds up as it passes over the helmet, creating an area of low pressure; the higher pressure below the helmet pushes it upward. Simpson Race Products Company found a way to break up the airflow over the helmet through the use of pressure-relief ducts and stall strips. The Simpson helmet has two gill-like outlet ducts and two ripple strips on each side of the top of the helmet. The ducts allow low-energy airflow out of the helmet to mix with the faster moving air over the top, thus reducing the lift. The ripple-strips enhance the mixing process.

Twenty-one of the thirty-three drivers in the 74th Indy 500, including the winner, wore a Simpson helmet. The helmet won the 1990 Schwitzer Award given by the Society of Automotive Engineers for innovation and excellence in race car design. Besides its improved aerodynamic qualities, the helmet has a new liner that provides better protection and it improves airflow to cool the driver's head.

· What other applications might this improved helmet have?

· display an understanding of the difference between solids and liquids on a microscopic level.
· discuss properties of solids such as elasticity.
· display an understanding of the origin of thermal expansion; be able to solve problems using linear thermal expansion; state some examples of applications and difficulties caused by thermal expansion.

# 13.2 THE SOLID STATE

What is the difference between a liquid and a solid? Solids are stiff. You can push them. Liquids are soft. Can you rest your finger on water? No, it goes right in. Of course, if you "bellyflop" into a swimming pool, you recognize that a liquid can seem rather solid. Scientists have recently found that, under certain laboratory conditions, solids and liquids are not so easily distinguished. The researchers have made clusters containing only a few dozen atoms, suggested by the computer images in Figure 13–16. These clusters can be both liquid and solid at the same temperature. Study of this strange state of matter may help scientists to invent new, useful materials in the future.

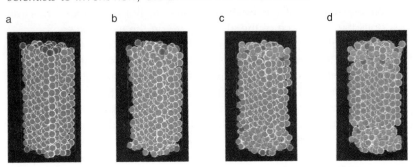

a          b          c          d

FIGURE 13–16. The difference in crystal structure between a solid and a liquid is not great. Solids have a long-range order, while the order in liquids is short range.

## Solid Bodies

When the temperature of a liquid is lowered, the average kinetic energy of the particles is lowered. As the particles slow down, the cohesive forces become more effective, and the particles are no longer able to slide over one another. The particles become frozen into a fixed pattern called a **crystal lattice**, Figure 13–17. Despite the forces that hold the particles in place, the particles do not stop moving completely. Rather, they vibrate around their fixed positions in the crystal lattice. In some solid materials, the particles do not form a fixed crystalline pattern. Their positions are fixed, but the pattern is variable. These substances have no regular crystal structure but have definite volume and shape, so they are called **amorphous solids**. Butter, paraffin, and glass are examples. They are often classified as very viscous (slow-flowing) liquids.

The particles in a true solid are fixed in a crystal lattice.

FIGURE 13–17. The solid form of water, ice, has a larger volume than an equal mass of its liquid form (a). The crystalline structure of ice (b).

a

b

oxygen — hydrogen

As a liquid freezes, its particles usually fit more closely together than in the liquid state. Solids usually are more dense than liquids. Water is an exception. Water is most dense at 4°C. Thus, water expands as it freezes, causing ice to have a lower density than liquid water at 0°C and to float on the surface.

An increase in the pressure on the surface of a liquid forces the particles closer together. The cohesive force becomes more important. For most liquids, the freezing point increases as the pressure on the liquid increases. Water is the exception. Since water expands as it freezes, an increase in pressure opposes this expansion. The freezing point of water is lowered as pressure on its surface is increased. For example, increased pressure from ice skate blades causes ice under the blades to melt. The thin film of water formed acts as a lubricant and allows the skates to move across the ice with almost no friction.

## Elasticity of Solids

External forces applied to a solid object may twist or bend it out of shape. The ability of an object to return to its original form when the external forces are removed is called the **elasticity** of the solid. If too much deformation occurs, the object will not return to its original shape—its elastic limit has been exceeded. Elasticity depends on the electromagnetic forces that hold the particles of a substance together. Malleability and ductility, the ability to be rolled into a thin sheet and drawn into a wire, respectively, are two properties that depend on the structure and elasticity of a substance. Gold is malleable; glass is not.

## Thermal Expansion of Matter

Most materials expand when heated and contract when cooled. This property, known as **thermal expansion,** has many useful applications. For example, when a gas such as air is heated, it becomes less dense. When the air near the floor of a room is warmed, gravity pulls the denser, colder ceiling air down, pushing the warmer air upward. This motion results in the circulation of air, called a convection current.

**FIGURE 13–18. The pressure of the skate blade on the ice melts a thin film of water which acts as a lubricant to reduce friction.**

Elasticity is the ability of an object to return to its original form after external forces are removed.

Table 13–2

| Coefficients of Thermal Expansion at 20°C | | |
|---|---|---|
| Material | Coefficient of linear expansion, $\alpha$(°C)$^{-1}$ | Coefficient of volume expansion, $\beta$(°C)$^{-1}$ |
| *Solids* | | |
| Aluminum | $25 \times 10^{-6}$ | $75 \times 10^{-6}$ |
| Iron, steel | $12 \times 10^{-6}$ | $35 \times 10^{-6}$ |
| Glass (soft) | $9 \times 10^{-6}$ | $27 \times 10^{-6}$ |
| Glass (Pyrex) | $3 \times 10^{-6}$ | $9 \times 10^{-6}$ |
| Concrete | $12 \times 10^{-6}$ | $36 \times 10^{-6}$ |
| Platinum | $9 \times 10^{-6}$ | |
| Copper | $16 \times 10^{-6}$ | $48 \times 10^{-6}$ |
| *Liquids* | | |
| Methanol | | $1100 \times 10^{-6}$ |
| Gasoline | | $950 \times 10^{-6}$ |
| Mercury | | $180 \times 10^{-6}$ |
| Water | | $210 \times 10^{-6}$ |
| *Gases* | | |
| Air (and most other gases) | | $3400 \times 10^{-6}$ |

## POCKET LAB

### JUMPERS

Put on a pair of safety goggles. Examine the jumping disk. Notice that it is slightly curved. Now rub the disk for several seconds until it becomes curved in the other direction. Place the disk on a flat level surface and stand back. Suggest a hypothesis that might explain the jumping. Suggest a method to test your hypothesis.

FIGURE 13–19. The extreme heat of a July day caused these railroad tracks to buckle.

FIGURE 13–20. Computer-calculated paths of particles appear as bright lines on the face of a cathode-ray tube coupled to the computer. Motion of atoms in an atomic crystal (note that the atoms move only about fixed positions) (a). A crystal in the process of melting (note the breakdown of the ordered array but no great increase in distance) (b). A liquid and its vapour (the dark area represents a gas bubble surrounded by particles whose motions are characteristic of a liquid) (c).

The expansion of liquids is useful in thermometers. Expansion also allows a liquid to be heated rapidly. When a container of liquid is heated from the bottom, convection currents form, just as in a gas. Cold, more dense liquid sinks to the bottom where it is warmed and then pushed up by the continuous flow of cooler liquid from the top. Thus, all the liquid is able to come in contact with the hot surface.

The expansion of concrete and steel in highway bridges means that the structures are longer in the summer than in the winter. Temperature extremes must be considered when bridges are designed. Gaps, called expansion joints, are built in to allow for seasonal changes in length.

Some materials have been specifically designed to have the smallest possible thermal expansion. Blocks used as standard lengths in machine shops are often made of Invar, a metal alloy. Pyrex glass is used for laboratory and cooking containers and in large telescope mirrors.

We can explain the expansion of heated solids in terms of the kinetic theory. Our model for a solid is a collection of particles connected by springs. The springs represent the forces that attract the particles to each other. When the particles get too close, the springs push them apart. If a solid did not have these forces of repulsion, it would collapse into a tiny sphere.

When a solid is heated, the kinetic energy of the particles increases; they vibrate more violently. The attractive force between particles in a solid is not exactly like the force exerted by a stretched spring. In the case of a solid, when the particles move farther apart, the force is weaker. As a result, when the particles vibrate more violently, their average separation increases. Thus, the solid expands when its temperature increases.

Most liquids also expand when heated. A good model for a liquid does not exist, but it is useful to think of a liquid as a ground-up solid. Groups of two, three, or more particles move together as if they were a tiny piece of a solid. When heated, particle motion causes these groups to expand just as a solid does. The spaces between groups also increase. As a result, the whole liquid expands. For an equal change in temperature, liquids expand considerably more than solids.

Liquid water expands only when its temperature is raised above 4°C. As water is heated from 0°C to 4°C, it contracts. The solid form of water, ice, has a larger volume than an equal mass of its liquid form. The forces between water molecules are strong. The crystals that make up

a

b

c

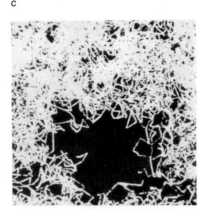

ice have a very open structure. Even when ice melts, tiny crystals remain. Between melting and 4°C, these remaining crystals melt, and the volume decreases. It is found that water is denser at 4°C than at any other temperature. The practical result is that ice floats, and that lakes, rivers, and other bodies of water freeze from the top down.

The change in length of a solid is proportional to the change in temperature. A solid will expand twice as much if the temperature is increased by 20°C than if it is increased by 10°C. The change is also proportional to its length. A two-metre bar will expand twice as much as a one-metre bar. Thus, the length, $L$, of a solid at temperature $T$ is given by

$$L = L_i + \alpha L_i(T - T_i),$$

where $L_i$ is the length at temperature $T_i$ and the proportionality constant, $\alpha$, is called the **coefficient of linear expansion**. The equation can also be written

$$L - L_i = \alpha L_i(T - T_i) \quad \text{or} \quad \Delta L = \alpha L_i \Delta T.$$

Then,

$$\frac{\Delta L}{L_i} = \alpha \Delta T \text{ and } \alpha = \frac{\Delta L}{L_i \Delta T}.$$

The dimensions of $\alpha$ are

$$\frac{\text{(length unit)}}{\text{(length unit)(temperature unit)}}.$$

Therefore, the unit for the coefficient of linear expansion is 1/°C or (°C)$^{-1}$. Volume expansion is three dimensional. The coefficient of volume expansion is approximately three times the coefficient of linear expansion.

Different materials expand at different rates. The expansion rates of gases and liquids are larger than those of solids. Engineers must consider these different expansion rates when designing structures. Steel bars are often used to reinforce concrete. The steel and concrete must have the same expansion coefficient. Otherwise, the structure may crack on a hot day. For a similar reason, a dentist must use filling materials that expand and contract at the same rate as tooth enamel.

Sometimes different rates of expansion are useful. Engineers have taken advantage of these differences to construct a useful device called a bimetallic strip. A bimetallic strip consists of two strips of different metals. These two metals are either welded or riveted together. Usually one strip is brass and the other is iron. When heated, brass expands more than iron. Thus, when the bimetallic strip of brass and iron is heated, the brass strip becomes longer than the iron strip. The bimetallic strip bends with the brass on the outside of the curve. If the bimetallic strip is cooled, it bends in the opposite direction. The brass is now on the inside of the curve.

Thermostats used in homes usually contain a bimetallic strip. The bimetallic strip is installed so that it bends toward an electric contact as the room cools. When the room cools below the setting on the thermostat, the bimetallic strip bends enough to make electric contact with the switch, which turns on the heater. As the room warms, the bimetallic strip bends in the other direction. The electric circuit is broken, and the heater is switched off.

Temperature
Lower  Higher

$L$

$\Delta L$

**FIGURE 13–21. The change in length is proportional to the original length and the change in temperature.**

a

b

**FIGURE 13–22. The properties of a bimetallic strip cause it to bend when heated (b). In this thermostat, a coiled bimetallic strip controls the opening and closing electrical switches (a).**

## Example Problem

### Linear Expansion

A metal bar is 2.60 m long at 21°C. The bar is heated uniformly to a temperature of 93°C and the change in length is measured to be 3.4 mm. What is the coefficient of linear expansion of this bar?

**Given:** $L_i = 2.60$ m
$\Delta L = 3.4 \times 10^{-3}$ m
$T_i = 21$°C
$T = 93$°C

**Unknown:** $\alpha$

**Basic equation:** $\dfrac{\Delta L}{L_i} = \alpha \Delta T$,

where $\Delta T = T - T_i$

**Solution:** $\Delta T = T - T_i = 72$°C

$$\alpha = \frac{\Delta L}{L_i \Delta T} = \frac{3.4 \times 10^{-3} \text{ m}}{(2.60 \text{ m})(72 \text{C}°)} = 1.8 \times 10^{-5} (°\text{C})^{-1}$$

## Practice Problems

**9.** A piece of aluminum house siding is 3.66 m long on a cold winter day ($-28$°C). How much longer is it on a very hot summer day (39°C)?

**10.** A piece of steel is 11.5 m long at 22°C. It is heated to 1221°C, close to its melting temperature. How long is it?

**11.** An aluminum soft-drink can, 354 mL, is filled to the brim with water in the refrigerator (4.4°C). **a.** What will be the volume of the liquid on a warm day (34.5°C)? **b.** What will be the volume of the can? (**Hint:** The can will expand as much as a block of metal the same size.) **c.** How much liquid will spill? ($\Delta V = \beta V \Delta T$)

▶ **12.** A tank truck takes on a load of 45 725 L of gasoline in one city at 32.0°C. The coefficient of volume expansion, $\beta$, for gasoline is $950 \times 10^{-6} (°\text{C})^{-1}$. The truck delivers its load in another city at $-18.0$°C.

**a.** How many litres of gasoline does the truck deliver?

**b.** What happened to the gasoline?

. . . . . . . . . . . . . . . . . . . . . . .

## CONCEPT REVIEW

**2.1** Starting at 0°C, how will the density of water change if it is heated to 4°C? 8°C?

**2.2** You are installing a new aluminum screen door on a hot day. The door frame is concrete. You want the door to fit well on a cold winter day. Should you make the door fit tightly in the frame or leave extra room?

**2.3** Why could candle wax be considered a solid? a viscous liquid?

**2.4** Critical Thinking: If you heat an iron ring with a small gap in it, Figure 13–23, will the gap become wider or narrower?

**FIGURE 13–23. Use with Concept Review 2.4.**

# CHAPTER
## 13 REVIEW

## SUMMARY

### 13.1 The Fluid States

- A gas fills any container in which it is placed. A liquid has a fixed volume but takes the shape of its container. A solid has a fixed volume and fixed shape. A plasma is like a gas but electrically charged.
- Pressure is the force exerted per unit of area. In SI, pressure is measured in pascals, Pa.
- According to Pascal's principle, a change in pressure is transmitted undiminished throughout a fluid.
- An object immersed in a fluid has an upward force exerted on it called the buoyant force.
- According to Archimedes' principle, the buoyant force on an object is equal to the weight of the fluid displaced by that object.
- Bernoulli's principle states that the pressure exerted by a fluid decreases as the velocity of the fluid increases.
- Cohesive forces are the attractive forces that like particles exert on one another.
- Adhesive forces are the attractive forces that particles of different substances exert on one another.
- Evaporation occurs when the most energetic particles in a liquid have enough energy to escape into the gas phase.
- Volatile liquids are those with weak cohesive forces that evaporate quickly.
- Plasma is an energetic state of matter made up of a mixture of positive and negative particles.

### 13.2 The Solid State

- As a liquid solidifies, its particles become frozen into a fixed pattern. If the pattern is regular, the solid is a crystalline solid. If the pattern is irregular, the solid is an amorphous solid.
- The ability of an object to return to its original form when stressed is elasticity.
- The increase of length of a material as the temperature increases varies directly with the temperature change and the original length. It also depends on the type of material.

## KEY TERMS

| | |
|---|---|
| fluid | capillary action |
| pressure | evaporation |
| pascal | volatile |
| Pascal's principle | condensation |
| buoyant force | plasma |
| Archimedes' principle | crystal lattice |
| Bernoulli's principle | amorphous solids |
| cohesive forces | elasticity |
| surface tension | thermal expansion |
| adhesion | coefficient of linear expansion |

## REVIEWING CONCEPTS

1. How are force and pressure different?
2. According to Pascal's principle, what happens to the pressure at the top of a container if the pressure at the bottom is increased?
3. How does the water pressure 1 m below the surface of a small pond compare to the water pressure the same distance below the surface of a lake?
4. Does Archimedes' principle apply inside a spaceship in orbit?
5. A river narrows as it enters a gorge. As the water speeds up, what happens to the water pressure?
6. A gas is placed in a sealed container and some liquid is placed in a same-sized container. They both have definite volume. How do the gas and the liquid differ?
7. A razor blade, which has a density greater than that of water, can be made to float on water. What procedures must you follow for this to happen? Explain.
8. In terms of adhesion and cohesion, explain why alcohol clings to a glass rod and mercury does not.
9. A frozen lake melts in the spring. What effect does it have on the temperature of the air above it?
10. Canteens are often covered with a canvas bag. If you wet the bag, the water in the canteen will be cooled. Explain.

11. Why does high humidity make a hot day even more uncomfortable?
12. In what way are gases and plasmas similar? In what way are they different?
13. Some of the mercury atoms in a fluorescent lamp are in the gaseous form; others are in the form of plasma. How can you distinguish between the two?
14. How does the arrangement of atoms differ in a crystalline and an amorphous substance?
15. Can a spring be considered to be elastic?
16. Does the coefficient of linear expansion depend on the unit of length used? Explain.

# APPLYING CONCEPTS

1. A rectangular box on a table is rotated so its smaller end is now on the table. Has the pressure on the table increased, decreased, or remained the same?
2. Show that a pascal is equivalent to $\dfrac{kg}{m \cdot s^2}$.
3. Is there more pressure at the bottom of a bathtub of water 30 cm deep or at the bottom of a pitcher of water 35 cm deep? Explain.
4. Compared to an identical empty ship, would a ship filled with ping pong balls sink deeper into the water or rise in the water? Explain.
5. Drops of mercury, water, and acetone are placed on a smooth, flat surface. The mercury drop is almost a perfect sphere. The water drop is a flattened sphere. The acetone, however, spreads out over the surface. What do these observations tell you about the cohesive forces in mercury, water, and acetone?
6. Alcohol evaporates more quickly than water at the same temperature. What does this observation allow you to conclude about the properties of the particles in the two liquids?

**FIGURE 13–24.**

7. Based on the observations in the previous question, which liquid would vaporize easier? Which would have the lower boiling point? Explain.
8. Which has a greater weight, 1 L of ice or 1 L of water?
9. Suppose you use a punch to make a circular hole in aluminum foil. If you heat the foil, will the size of the hole decrease or increase? Explain. (**Hint:** Pretend you put the circle you punched out back into the hole. What happens when you heat the foil now?)
10. Equal volumes of water were heated in two narrow almost identical tubes, identical except that tube A was made of soft glass and tube B was made of Pyrex glass. As the temperature increased, the water level rose higher in tube B than in tube A. Give a possible explanation for this observation. Why are many cooking utensils made from Pyrex glass?
11. A platinum wire can be easily sealed into a glass tube, but a copper wire does not form a tight seal with the glass. Explain.
12. Often, before a thunderstorm, when the humidity is high, someone will say, "The air is very heavy today." Is this statement correct? Describe a possible origin for the statement.

# PROBLEMS

## 13.1 The Fluid States

▶ 1. A hydraulic jack is used to lift cars. The large piston is 22 mm in diameter, the small one 6.3 mm. Assume that the jack exerts a force of $3.0 \times 10^4$ N.
   a. What force must be exerted on the small piston to lift the weight?
   b. Most jacks use a lever to reduce the force needed on the small piston. If the resistance arm is 3.0 cm, how long is the effort arm of an ideal lever to reduce the force to 100 N?
▶ 2. In a machine shop, a hydraulic lift is used to raise heavy equipment for repairs. The system has a small piston with a cross-sectional area of $7.0 \times 10^{-2}$ m$^2$ and a large piston with a cross-sectional area of $2.1 \times 10^{-1}$ m$^2$. An engine weighing $2.7 \times 10^3$ N rests on the large piston.

**a.** What force must be applied to the small piston in order to lift the engine?

**b.** If the engine rises 0.20 m, how far does the smaller piston move?

**3.** A 0.75-kg physics book with dimensions of 24 cm by 20 cm is on a table.

**a.** What force does the book apply to the table?

**b.** What pressure does the book apply?

**4.** The pressure exerted by the atmosphere is about $1.0 \times 10^5$ Pa. Convert this to kPa.

**5.** A 75-kg solid cylinder, 2.5 m long and with an end radius of 5.0 cm, stands on one end. How much pressure does it exert?

**6.** A reservoir behind a dam is 15 m deep. What is the pressure

**a.** at the base of the dam?

**b.** 5.0 m from the top of the dam?

**7.** A test tube standing vertically in a test tube rack contains 2.5 cm of oil ($\rho = 0.81$ g/cm$^3$) and 6.5 cm of water. What is the pressure on the bottom of the tube?

**8.** A metal object is suspended from a spring scale. The scale reads 920 N when the object is suspended in air, and 750 N when the object is completely submerged in water.

**a.** Draw a diagram showing the three forces acting on the submerged object.

**b.** Find the volume of the object.

**c.** Find the density of the metal.

**9.** During an ecology experiment, an aquarium filled with water is placed on a scale. The scale reads 195 N.

**a.** A rock weighing 8 N is added to the aquarium. If the rock sinks to the bottom of the aquarium, what will the scale read?

**b.** The rock is removed from the aquarium, and the amount of water is adjusted until the scale again reads 195 N. A small fish weighing 2 N is added to the aquarium. What is the scale reading while the fish is swimming in the aquarium?

**10.** What is the size of the buoyant force that acts on a floating ball that normally weighs 5.0 N?

**11.** What is the apparent weight of a rock submerged in water if the rock weighs 54 N in air and has a volume of $2.3 \times 10^{-3}$ m$^3$?

**12.** If the rock in the previous problem is submerged in a liquid with a density exactly twice that of water, what will be its new apparent weight reading in the liquid?

**13.** A 1.0-L container completely filled with mercury has a weight of 133.3 N. If the container is submerged in water, what is the buoyant force acting on it? Explain.

▶ **14.** What is the acceleration of a small metal sphere as it falls through water? The sphere weighs $2.8 \times 10^{-1}$ N in air and has a volume of 13 cm$^3$.

**15.** What is the maximum weight that a "massless" balloon filled with 1.00 m$^3$ of helium can lift in air? Assume the density of air is 1.20 kg/m$^3$ and that of helium is 0.177 kg/m$^3$.

## 13.2 The Solid State

**16.** What is the change in length of a 2.00-m length of copper pipe if its temperature is raised from 23°C to 978°C?

**17.** Bridge builders often use rivets that are larger than the rivet hole to make the joint tighter. The rivet is cooled before it is put into the hole. A builder drills a hole 1.2230 cm in diameter for a steel rivet 1.2250 cm in diameter. To what temperature must the rivet be cooled if it is to fit into the rivet hole that is at 20°C?

▶ **18.** A steel tank is built to hold alcohol. The tank is 2.000 m in diameter and 5.000 m high. It is completely filled with alcohol at 10°C. If the temperature rises to 40°C, how much alcohol (in litres) will flow out of the tank? Remember that both the tank and the alcohol expand as the temperature rises.

▶ **19.** An aluminum sphere is heated from 11°C to 580°C. If the volume of the sphere were 1.78 cm$^3$ at 11°C, what is the increase in volume of the sphere at 580°C?

▶ **20.** The volume of a copper sphere is 2.56 cm$^3$ after being heated from 12°C to 984°C. What was the volume of the copper sphere at 12°C?

# THINKING PHYSIC-LY

**1.** Why are sharp ice skates important to an ice skater?

**2.** Persons confined to bed are less likely to develop bedsores if they use a water bed rather than an ordinary mattress. Explain.

# CHAPTER 14

# Waves and Energy Transfer

◀ Surf's Up

Where does the surfer's kinetic energy come from? Try to trace the energy source back as far as you can.

Have you ever ridden a wave on a surf board, boogie board, or merely body surfed? Whether in ocean surf or in a wave pool, when you "catch the wave" you gain speed and stay just ahead of the breaking surf. Your body's kinetic energy increases. If you can, you do as this surfer does, and ride almost parallel to the wave at a very high speed. Surfing can be dangerous, however. Unless you are skilled, you can "wipe out" and be thrown down into the water or sand.

Does the water move with the wave? Leonardo da Vinci (1452–1519) answered this question five centuries ago.

*The impetus is much quicker than the water, for it often happens that the wave flees the place of its creation, while the water does not...*

In other words, the wave moves on, the water does not. In this way, water waves are typical of the waves we will study in the next few chapters, those of sound and light.

## ✓ Concept Check

The following terms or concepts from earlier chapters are important for a good understanding of this chapter. If you are not familiar with them, you should review them before studying this chapter.
· velocity, Chapter 3
· period and frequency, Chapter 7
· potential energy and kinetic energy, Chapter 11

· recognize that waves transfer energy without transferring matter.
· distinguish between longitudinal and transverse waves; between a wave pulse and a continuous wave.
· define wavelength, frequency, and period; state the relationship between speed, wavelength, and frequency; solve problems using these quantities.

# 14.1 WAVE PROPERTIES

Both particles and waves transmit energy, but there is an important difference. If you throw a ball at a target, the target may gain some kinetic energy, but the ball will have moved from you to the target. If you tie a rope on the target and shake the rope, the target may also gain some kinetic energy. The rope, however, will remain in position, between you and the target. How do we describe waves, and how fast do they transmit the energy?

## Types of Waves

Water waves, sound waves, and the waves that travel along a spring or rope are mechanical waves. Mechanical wave motion requires a material medium. Water, air, and springs or ropes are the materials that carry the energy of these mechanical waves. Newton's laws govern the motion of mechanical waves.

Light waves, radio waves, and X rays are examples of electromagnetic waves. No medium is needed for the motion of electromagnetic waves. They all travel through space at the speed of light, 299 792 458 m/s. The details of electromagnetic waves cannot be observed directly. Thus, we will use the easily observed mechanical waves as models for the behavior of electromagnetic waves that will be studied in later chapters.

There is a third type of wave, the matter wave. Electrons and other particles show wave-like behavior under certain conditions. Quantum mechanics is needed to describe the properties of matter waves. We will delay our study of matter waves until Chapter 27.

We can divide mechanical waves into three different types. Each type disturbs the medium in a different way. A **transverse wave** causes the particles of the medium to vibrate perpendicularly to the direction of motion of the wave. Figure 14–1a shows a transverse wave. The wave moves along the spring from left to right, but the spring is displaced up and down, at right angles to the motion of the wave. Waves in piano and guitar strings are examples of transverse waves.

A **longitudinal wave** causes the particles of a medium to move parallel to the direction of the wave. Figure 14–1b shows a longitudinal wave. The displacement of the spring is in the same direction as the motion of the wave. A sound wave is an example of a longitudinal

*Energy can be transferred by particles or by waves.*

*Mechanical waves need a medium.*

*In a transverse wave, particles vibrate at right angles to the direction of the wave's velocity.*

**FIGURE 14–1. Two general types of waves are the transverse wave (a) and the longitudinal wave (b).**

a

b

a

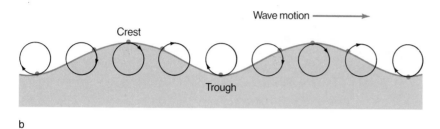

FIGURE 14–2. Surface waves show characteristics of both longitudinal and transverse waves. The paths of the particles are almost perfect circles.

Wave motion ⟶

Crest

Trough

b

A pulse is a single disturbance of a medium.

wave. Fluids, liquids, gases, or plasmas usually transmit only longitudinal waves.

Although waves deep in a lake or ocean are longitudinal, at the surface of the water, Figure 14–2, the particles move both parallel and perpendicular to the direction of the wave. These are **surface waves**, a mixture of transverse and longitudinal waves. The energy of water waves usually comes from storms far away. The energy of the storms initially came from the heating of Earth by solar energy. This energy, in turn, was carried to Earth by transverse electromagnetic waves.

How are waves produced? Suppose you hold one end of a rope. If you suddenly jerk the rope to one side and quickly return it to the centre, Figure 14–3, a wave pulse will travel down the rope. A **wave pulse** is a single disturbance that travels through a medium. A given point on the rope was at rest before the pulse reached it; it returned to rest after the pulse passed. If instead you move the rope from side to side in a regular manner, a **travelling wave** will move along the rope. A source that is vibrating with simple harmonic motion will produce a continuous travelling wave. Each point on the rope will vibrate regularly in response to the travelling wave.

Surf's Up

A wave train, or travelling wave, is a series of pulses at regular intervals.

FIGURE 14–3. The two photographs were taken 1 s apart. During that time, the crest moved 0.8 m. The velocity of the wave is 0.8 m/s.

a

b

14.1 Wave Properties  **289**

**FIGURE 14–4. The left end of the string is attached to a vibrating blade. Note the change in position of the tape, P, over time.**

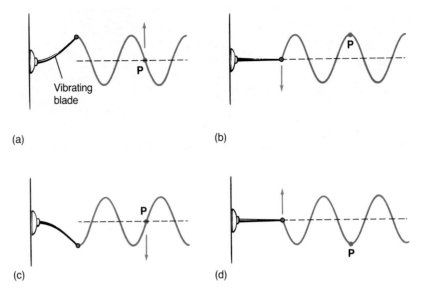

(a)                                        (b)

(c)                                        (d)

## The Measures of a Wave: Frequency, Wavelength, and Velocity

The period of a wave is the time needed for the motion to repeat itself.

Imagine putting a piece of tape at point **P** on the rope. How does that piece of tape move in time? Figure 14–4 shows that the **P** moves back and forth. The shortest time interval during which the motion repeats itself is called the **period**, $T$.

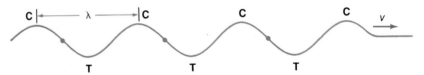

**FIGURE 14–5. Points labeled C represent wave crests; points labeled T represent wave troughs.**

The **frequency** of a wave, $f$, is the number of complete vibrations per second measured at a fixed location. Frequency is measured in hertz. One hertz (Hz) is one vibration per second. The frequency and period of a wave are related by the equation

$$f = \frac{1}{T} .$$

Wavelength is the shortest distance between points where the wave pattern repeats itself.

That is, they are reciprocals of each other.

Rather than focusing on one spot on the wave, think of taking a snapshot of a wave, so you can see the whole wave at one instant of time. From Figure 14–5, you can see that the form of the wave repeats itself at regular distances. The shortest distance between points where the wave pattern repeats itself is called the **wavelength**. The **crests**, C, are the high points of each wave motion; the **troughs**, T, are the low points. Each crest is one wavelength from the next crest. Troughs are also spaced by one wavelength. The Greek letter lambda, $\lambda$, represents the wavelength.

# F.Y.I.

The letter "M" may have originated as a hieroglyphic symbol representing the crests of waves and meaning "water."

## Example Problem

### Period of a Wave

A sound wave has a frequency of 262 Hz. What is the time between successive wave crests?

**Given:** $f = 262$ Hz

**Unknown:** period, $T$

**Basic equation:** $f = \dfrac{1}{T}$

**Solution:** $f = \dfrac{1}{T}$, so $T = \dfrac{1}{f}$

$$T = \frac{1}{262 \text{ Hz}} = \frac{1}{262 \text{ s}^{-1}} = 3.82 \times 10^{-3} \text{ s}$$

How fast does a travelling wave move? You could run alongside the wave just fast enough so that the wave appears to stand still. An easier way is to take two photographs at a known time interval apart. Figure 14–6 shows two photographs taken one second apart. During the one-second time interval, the crests moved 0.8 m to the right. The velocity of any object is the distance moved divided by the time interval. Thus, the wave velocity is 0.8 m/s to the right.

In the special case that the time interval is exactly one period, the wave would move a distance of one wavelength. Thus, the velocity can be calculated from the equation

$$v = \frac{\lambda}{T}.$$

This is more conveniently written as

$$\boxed{v = \lambda f.}$$

Wave velocity is the product of the frequency and the wavelength.

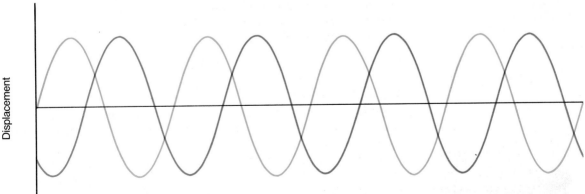

**FIGURE 14–6. The figure shows what the same wave would look like if photographed from the same place at two different times.**

Displacement

Time

# PHYSICS LAB : Waves on a Snakey

## Purpose

To investigate properties of waves using a snakey as a model.

## Materials

· a long coil spring (snakey)
· stopwatch
· metre stick

## Procedure

1. You will need a clear path of about 6 m for this activity.
2. Slowly stretch the snakey to the length suggested by your instructor.
3. Grip the snakey firmly with one hand for the entire activity.
4. It is easier to see the motion of the snakey if you are near one end. Don't watch from the side.
5. As the pulses die out, they can still be felt. Trust your feelings!
6. This activity is a sensual experience. Each student in the group should take some time on the end of the snakey.
7. Make a quick sideways snap with your wrist to produce a transverse pulse in the snakey.
8. Notice how many times the pulse will move back and forth on the snakey.
9. Look closely at the questions in the observation section. Try to design and conduct an experiment to answer each question.

## Observations and Data

1. What happens to
   a. the amplitude of a wave as it travels?
   b. the speed of a wave as it travels?
2. Does the speed depend on the amplitude?
3. Put 2 quick pulses into the snakey. The distance between pulses is called λ. Does λ change as the pulses move?
4. What can you do to decrease the value of λ?
5. Do pulses bounce off each other or pass through?

## Analysis

1. You probably used transverse waves for this activity. Should your answers be accurate for pressure (longitudinal) waves? Why?
2. Check your answers for steps 1-3 with *pressure* waves.
3. Use the snakey to find out if pressure waves go through each other. Describe your results.

## Applications

Sound waves are pressure waves. Make your predictions consistent with your snakey results.
1. Does the speed of the sound depend on the loudness? (Do louder sounds travel *faster* than quiet sounds?)
2. Compare the speed of high frequency (short wavelength) sounds to low frequency (long wavelength) sounds.

* NOTE * Snakeys are *NOT SOCIAL*. Do not allow the snakeys to get tangled together! Each snakey should be stored in its own personal container!

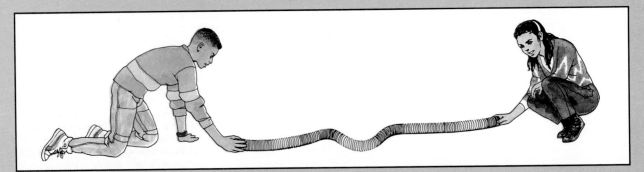

## Example Problem

### Speed of a Travelling Wave

A sound wave with frequency 262 Hz has a wavelength of 1.29 m. What is the speed of the sound wave?

**Given:** frequency, $f$ = 262 Hz
wavelength, $\lambda$ = 1.29 m

**Unknown:** speed, $v$
**Basic equation:** $v = \lambda f$

**Solution:** $v = \lambda f = (1.29 \text{ m})(262 \text{ Hz}) = 338 \text{ m/s}$

## Practice Problems

1. A sound wave produced by a clock chime 515 m away is heard 1.50 s later.
   a. What is the speed of sound in air?
   b. The sound wave has a frequency of 436 Hz. What is its period?
   c. What is its wavelength?
2. A hiker shouts toward a vertical cliff 685 m away. The echo is heard 4.00 s later.
   a. What is the speed of sound in air?
   b. The wavelength of the sound is 0.750 m. What is the frequency?
   c. What is the period of the wave?
3. A radio wave, a form of electromagnetic wave, has a frequency of 99.5 MHz ($99.5 \times 10^6$ Hz). What is its wavelength?
▶ 4. A typical light wave has a wavelength of 580 nm.
   a. What is the wavelength of the light in metres?
   b. What is the frequency of the wave?

## Amplitude of a Wave

Two waves with the same frequency can have different wavelengths. Waves can differ from one another in another way. A rope can be shaken violently or gently; a sound can be loud or soft. A water wave can be a giant tidal wave or a gentle ripple. The **amplitude** of a wave is its maximum displacement from the rest or equilibrium position. The two waves in Figure 14–7 have the same frequency, velocity, and wavelength, but their amplitudes differ.

In order to produce a wave with larger amplitude, more work has to be done. For example, strong winds produce larger water waves than

The speed of sound in air depends on temperature; it may not be the same in all problems.

The amplitude of a wave is its maximum displacement from the rest position.

Wave A

Amplitude

$\lambda$

m

$h_A$

Wave B

Amplitude

m

$h_B$

FIGURE 14–7. The relationship of the amplitude of a wave to the work it can perform is shown here. The greater the work done to create the wave, the greater the amplitude of the wave. The greater the amplitude of the wave, the more work it can do.

The energy transferred by a wave depends on the square of its amplitude.

# Objectives

· understand that wave speed depends on the medium.
· understand what occurs when a wave crosses the boundary between two media with different wave speeds.
· be able to solve problems involving waves crossing boundaries.
· state the principle of superposition and understand how constructive and destructive interference result.
· state the law of reflection.
· describe refraction in terms of behavior of a transmitted wave.
· define diffraction of a wave around a barrier.

gentle breezes. A wave with larger amplitude transfers more energy. A small wave might move sand on a beach back and forth. When a giant wave crashes on a beach, however, it can uproot trees or move heavy boulders. The larger the amplitude, the greater the energy transferred. In fact, for waves that travel at the same velocity, the rate at which energy is carried is proportional to the square of the amplitude of the wave. Thus, if you double the amplitude of the wave, you increase the energy it transfers every second by a factor of four.

## CONCEPT REVIEW

**1.1** Suppose you and your lab partner were asked to measure the speed of a transverse wave in a giant Slinky. How could you do it? List the equipment you would need.
**1.2** You are creating waves in a rope by shaking your hand back and forth. Without changing the distance your hand moves, you begin to shake it faster and faster. What happens to the amplitude, frequency, period, and velocity of the wave?
**1.3** If you pull on one end of a Slinky, does the pulse reach the other end instantaneously? What if you pull on a rope? Hit the end of a metal rod? Discuss any differences.
**1.4** **Critical Thinking:** If a rain drop falls into a pool, small-amplitude waves result. If a swimmer jumps into a pool, a very large-amplitude wave is produced. Why doesn't the heavy rain in a thunderstorm produce large waves?

# 14.2 WAVE INTERFERENCE

Two particles cannot be in the same place at the same time. Matter, after all, takes up space. This is not true for waves. The properties that are characteristic of wave behavior are the result of two or more waves existing in the same area at the same time.

## Waves at Boundaries Between Media

The speed of a mechanical wave does not depend on the amplitude or the frequency of the wave. It depends only on the properties of the

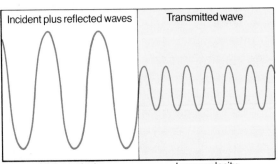

FIGURE 14–8. The speed and wavelength of a wave change when the wave enters a new medium. The left half of the figure shows the sum of the incident and reflected waves. The transmitted wave is on the right.

a

b

FIGURE 14–9. The junction of the two springs is a boundary between two media. A pulse reaching the boundary (a) is partially reflected and partially transmitted.

medium. The speed of water waves depends on the depth of the water. The speed of waves in a rope depends on the force exerted on the rope and its mass per unit length. The speed of sound in air depends on the temperature of the air. Although a wave with larger amplitude transfers more energy, it moves at the same speed as a smaller amplitude wave through a given medium. A wave with a higher frequency has a shorter wavelength, as given by the equation $v = \lambda f$. As long as the material is the same, the speed of high and low frequency waves is the same.

Often a wave moves from one medium to another. Light might move from air into water, Figure 14–8. In Figure 14–9, waves move from large to small springs. The spring can end by being fastened to a rigid wall, as in Figure 14–10, or by being allowed to move freely, Figure 14–11. What happens to a wave when the medium changes?

Suppose a wave, called the incident wave, reaches the boundary of a medium. Part of the energy carried by the incident wave continues on in the new medium as a wave with the same frequency. This wave is called the transmitted wave. In addition, part of the energy moves backward from the boundary as a wave in the old medium. This wave is called the reflected wave.

If the difference in the media is small, then the amplitude of the transmitted wave will be almost as large as that of the incident wave, and the amplitude of the reflected wave will be small. Most of the energy of the incident wave will be transmitted. If the two materials are very different, however, most of the wave energy will be reflected.

Figure 14–10 shows a wave on a spring approaching a rigid wall. The spring and wall are very different, so most of the wave energy is reflected. The figure also shows that the reflected wave is inverted. The incident wave pulse is in the upward direction, the reflected pulse is in the downward direction. Whenever a wave passes from a less dense to a more dense medium, the reflected wave is inverted.

# F.Y.I.

FIGURE 14–10. A pulse is shown as it approaches a rigid wall (a) and as it is reflected from the wall (b). Notice that the amplitude of the reflected pulse is nearly equal to the amplitude of the incident pulse but that the reflected pulse is inverted.

a

b

In Figure 14–11, the spring is supported by light threads. When a pulse reaches the end of the spring, the pulse is transmitted into another medium, air. Because the two media are very different, most of the energy of the wave is reflected. In this case, however, the reflected wave is not inverted. When a wave passes from a more dense to a less dense medium, the reflected pulse is erect, not inverted.

Suppose a wave on a light spring is transmitted to a heavy spring. The wave in the light spring generated the wave in the heavy spring, so the frequencies of the two waves are the same. The speed of the wave in the heavier spring is slower. The speed, frequency, and wavelength of a wave are related by the equation $v = \lambda f$. Because the speed of the transmitted wave is different, but the frequency remains the same, the wavelength of the transmitted wave must also be different. The speed in the heavier spring is less, so the wavelength is smaller. On the other hand, if the speed of a wave increases when it passes into a new medium, then its wavelength also increases.

Although the waves in the examples are transverse waves, longitudinal waves behave in exactly the same way. Whenever a wave reaches a boundary, some of the wave energy is transmitted, some is reflected. The amount of reflected energy is larger if the two media have vastly different properties.

*When the medium changes, wave energy is both reflected and transmitted.*

*Waves passing from one medium to another have the same frequency. The wavelength change depends on velocity change so that $f = v/\lambda$ is constant.*

## Practice Problems

**5.** A pulse is sent along a spring. The spring is attached to a light thread that is tied to the wall, Figure 14–12.
   **a.** What happens when the pulse reaches point **A**?
   **b.** Is the pulse reflected from **A** erect or inverted?
   **c.** What happens when the transmitted pulse reaches **B**?
   **d.** Is the pulse reflected from **B** erect or inverted?

**FIGURE 14–12. Use with Practice Problem 5.**

**6.** A long spring runs across the floor of a room and out the door. A pulse is sent along the spring. After a few seconds, an inverted pulse returns. Is the spring attached to the wall in the next room or is it lying loose on the floor?

**7.** If you want to increase the wavelength of waves in a rope, should you shake it at a higher or lower frequency?

Constructive interference occurs when two waves combine to produce a wave with larger amplitude.

**FIGURE 14–13. Use with Practice Problem 8.**

▶ **8.** A pulse is sent along a thin rope that is attached to a thick rope. The thick rope is itself tied to a wall, Figure 14–13.
   **a.** What happens when the pulse reaches point **A**?
   **b.** Is the pulse reflected from **A** erect or inverted?
   **c.** What happens when the transmitted pulse reaches **B**?
   **d.** Is the pulse reflected from **B** erect or inverted?

Destructive interference occurs when two waves combine to produce a wave with a smaller amplitude.

## Superposition of Waves

What happens when two or more waves travel through a medium at the same time? Each wave affects the medium independently. As a result, we can analyze the effects of these waves using the principle of superposition. The **principle of superposition** states that *the displacement of a medium caused by two or more waves is the algebraic sum of the displacements caused by the individual waves.* The result of the superposition of two or more waves is called **interference.**

Interference can be either constructive or destructive. **Constructive interference** occurs when the wave displacements are in the same direction. The result is a wave with larger amplitude than any of the individual waves. Figure 14–14 shows the constructive interference of two equal pulses. When the two pulses meet, a larger pulse is formed. The amplitude of the larger pulse is the algebraic sum of the amplitudes of the two pulses. After the two pulses have passed through each other, they regain their original shape and size. The pulses are not changed by their interaction.

Figure 14–15 shows the **destructive interference** of two pulses with equal but opposite amplitudes. As the two pulses overlap, the displacement of the medium at each point in the overlap is reduced. When the pulses are at the same location, the displacement is zero. The pulses keep moving and resume their original form. An important characteristic of waves is the ability to pass through one another unchanged.

If the pulses have unequal amplitudes, the destructive interference is not complete. The pulse at overlap is the algebraic sum of the two pulses. Some wave amplitude always remains.

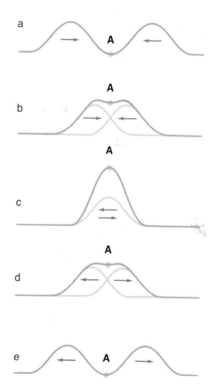

**FIGURE 14–14. Constructive interference of two equal pulses. An antinode is a point of maximum displacement.**

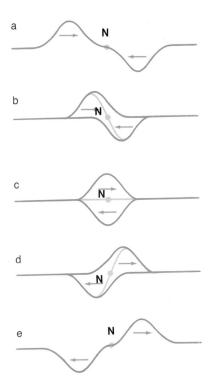

a

b

c

d

e

**FIGURE 14–15. Destructive interference of two equal pulses. A node is a point of the medium that remains undisturbed.**

At a node, the medium is not displaced as the waves pass through each other.

At an antinode, the displacement caused by interfering waves is largest.

A standing wave has stationary nodes and antinodes. It is the result of identical waves traveling in opposite directions.

## Standing Waves

Look again at Figure 14–15. Two pulses with equal but opposite amplitudes meet. You can find one point in the medium that is completely undisturbed at all times. This point is called a **node**. At a node, the medium is never displaced. If you put your finger on the rope at the node, you will feel no motion. A node is produced by the destructive interference of waves.

In Figure 14–14, two pulses with equal amplitudes in the same direction meet. There is one point that undergoes the greatest displacement. Its maximum amplitude is equal to the sum of the amplitudes of the two pulses. This point of maximum displacement is called an **antinode.** Constructive interference of waves produces antinodes.

Imagine one end of a rope attached to a fixed point. You continuously vibrate the other end up and down. A travelling wave will leave your hand, move to the other end, be inverted and reflected, and return toward your hand. At your hand, the wave will be inverted and reflected again. At each reflection, the displacement direction will change. If the original displacement was upward, it will be downward when moving back to your hand, but be upward again after reflection from your hand.

Now, suppose you adjust the motion of your hand so that the period of the rope's vibration equals the time required for the wave to travel to the fixed point and back. The displacement your hand gives to the rope each time will add to the displacement of the reflected wave. The result is a very large amplitude oscillation in the rope, much larger than the motion of your hand. This large amplitude oscillation is an example of resonance. There are nodes at the ends of the rope and an antinode in the middle. The nodes and antinodes are stationary. The wave appears to be standing still. It is called a **standing wave**. If you double the frequency of vibration, you can produce additional nodes in the rope. It appears to vibrate in two segments. Further increases in frequency produce even more nodes, Figure 14–16.

**FIGURE 14–16. Interference produces standing waves in a rope.**

a

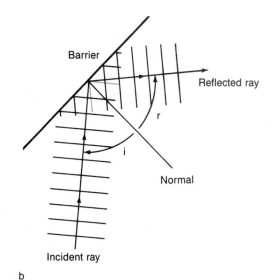

b

## Reflection of Waves

We have studied waves reflecting from a rigid support, where the amplitude of the wave was forced to be zero. These waves move in only one dimension. Waves on the surface of water move in two dimensions, while sound and electromagnetic waves move in three dimensions. A ripple tank can be used to show the properties of two-dimensional waves. A ripple tank contains a thin layer of water. Vibrating boards produce wave pulses or travelling waves with constant frequency. A lamp above the tank produces shadows below the tank that show the locations of the crests of the waves. Figure 14–17 shows a wave pulse travelling toward a straight rigid wall, a barrier that will reflect the wave. The incident pulse moves upward. The reflected pulse moves downward and toward the right.

The direction of waves moving in two or three dimensions is often shown by ray diagrams. A ray is a line drawn at a right angle to the crest of the wave. A ray diagram shows only the direction of the waves, it does not show the actual waves. In Figure 14–17, the ray representing the incident ray is the arrow pointing upward. The ray representing the reflected ray points to the right.

The direction of the barrier is also shown by a line drawn at a right angle to it. This line is called the **normal**. The angle between the incident ray and the normal is called the **angle of incidence**. The angle between the normal and the reflected ray is called the **angle of reflection**. The **law of reflection** states that *the angle of incidence is equal to the angle of reflection*.

## Refraction of Waves

A ripple tank can also be used to study the behaviour of waves as they move from one medium into another. Figure 14–18(a) shows a glass plate placed in a ripple tank. The water above the plate is shallower than in the rest of the tank. The velocity of water waves depends on the water depth, so the water above the plate acts like a different medium.

FIGURE 14–17. Reflection of a plane wave pulse by a barrier (a). In (b), part of the pulse front is shown in time sequence as it approaches, and then is reflected from the barrier.

The angle at which a wave approaches a barrier is equal to the angle at which it is reflected.

a

b

**FIGURE 14–18. Notice the change in wavelength, as the water waves enter a more shallow region (a). When waves enter at an angle they change direction, demonstrating refraction (b).**

Refraction is the change of wave direction at the boundary between two media.

How does the velocity of waves depend on water depth? In Figure 14–18a, a wave train passes over a glass plate, changing the depth of the water. As the waves move from deep to shallow water, their wavelength decreases and the direction of the waves changes. Because the waves in the shallow water are generated by the waves in deep water, their frequency is not changed. From the equation $v = \lambda f$, the decrease in the wavelength of the waves means that the velocity is lower in the shallower water.

In Figure 14–18b, the waves approach the shore at an angle. The ray direction is not parallel to the normal. Not only does the wavelength decrease over the shallower bottom, but the direction of the waves changes. The change in the direction of waves at the boundary between two different media is known as **refraction**.

## Diffraction and Interference of Waves

If particles are thrown at a barrier with holes in it, the particles will either reflect off the barrier or pass straight through the holes. When waves encounter a small hole in a barrier, however, they do not pass straight through. Rather, they bend around the edges of the barrier, forming circular waves that spread out, Figure 14–19. The spreading of

**FIGURE 14–19. Waves bending around barriers demonstrate diffraction.**

a

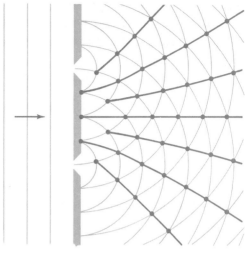

b

waves around the edge of a barrier is called **diffraction**. Diffraction also occurs when waves meet a small obstacle. They can bend around the obstacle, producing waves behind it. The smaller the wavelength in comparison to the size of the obstacle, the less the diffraction.

Figure 14–20a shows the result of waves striking a barrier having two closely-spaced holes. The waves are diffracted by each hole, forming circular waves. But the circular waves interfere with each other. There are regions of constructive interference where the resulting waves are large, and bands of destructive interference where the water remains almost undisturbed. Constructive interference occurs where two crests or two troughs from the two circular waves meet. The antinodes lie on lines called antinodal lines. These lines radiate from the barrier, Figure 14–20b. Between the antinodal lines are areas where a crest from one circular wave and a trough from the other meet. Destructive interference produces nodes where the water is undisturbed. The lines of nodes, or nodal lines, lie between adjacent antinodal lines.

**FIGURE 14–20. Waves are diffracted at two openings in the barrier. At each opening, circular waves are formed. The circular waves interfere with each other, with points of constructive interference appearing as bright spots in the photograph (a). Lines of constructive interference (antinodal lines) occur where crest meets crest (b).**

Diffraction is the spreading of waves around the edge of a barrier.

## CONCEPT REVIEW

**2.1** If a wave moves from a medium with a high wave velocity to one with a low wave velocity, which of the following CANNOT change: frequency, amplitude, wavelength, velocity, direction?

**2.2** A rope vibrates with the two waves at once, Figure 14–21. Sketch the resulting wave.

**2.3** Would you expect high frequency or low frequency sound waves to be more diffracted when they pass through an open door?

**2.4** Critical Thinking: For another way to understand wave reflection, return to Figure 14–15. Cover the right-hand side of each drawing with a piece of paper. The edge of the paper should be at the point **N,** the node. Now, concentrate on the sum wave, shown in blue. Note that it acts like a wave reflected from a boundary. Is the boundary a rigid wall or open ended? Repeat for Figure 14–14.

**FIGURE 14–21. Use with Concept Review 2.2.**

# Physics and technology

## MICROWAVE-POWERED AIRCRAFT

Imagine an aircraft that does not carry on-board fuel and can stay in flight for half a year. Or imagine a spacecraft whose orbits could be adjusted using engines powered by microwave-energy beams transmitted from Earth. With less rocket fuel to carry, larger payloads could be lifted into space. Advances in microwave technology could bring both of these dreams to life.

Microwave-energy beaming is much like radio-wave transmission, except that it works with higher power levels. A transmitter sends out microwave energy, and a distant antenna and receiver pick it up and convert it to another form of energy, usually electricity. The waves transfer energy without moving matter.

Research on the potential of microwave power is underway at NASA's Lewis Research Center in Cleveland, Ohio. Scientists are working on a Mars mission in which a mother ship orbiting the planet would transmit microwave beams to power a remote-controlled drone. The drone would fly down, land, and unload a rover vehicle that would explore the planet's surface and collect samples. It is estimated that the drone could cover about 40% of Mars' surface without refueling.

· What advantages could microwave power have when compared to other power sources such as jet propulsion, chemical, rocket power, and nuclear power?

# CHAPTER
# 14 REVIEW

## SUMMARY

### 14.1 Wave Properties

· Waves transfer energy without the transfer of matter.
· Mechanical waves, such as sound waves and the waves on a rope, require a medium. Electromagnetic waves, such as light and radio waves, do not need a medium.
· In transverse waves, the particles of the medium move perpendicularly to the direction of the wave. In longitudinal waves, the particles move parallel to the wave direction. In surface waves, the particles move both perpendicularly and parallel to the direction of the wave's motion.
· The frequency of a wave, $f$, is the number of vibrations per second of any one point on a wave. The period of a wave is the time interval between successive wave crests or troughs.

· The shortest distance between points where the wave pattern repeats itself is called the wavelength, $\lambda$.
· The velocity of a wave, the distance a point on the wave moves in a unit time interval, can be calculated from the equation $v = \lambda f$.
· The amplitude of a wave is its maximum displacement from the rest or equilibrium position. Energy transferred by a wave is proportional to the square of the amplitude.

### 14.2 Wave Interference

· The speed of a wave depends on the properties of the medium through which the wave moves.
· When waves reach the boundary between two media, they are partially transmitted and partially reflected. The amount reflected depends on how much the two media differ.

- When a wave moves from a less dense to a more dense medium, the reflected wave is inverted. When it moves from a more dense to a less dense medium, the reflected wave is erect.
- The principle of superposition states that the displacement of a medium due to two or more waves is the algebraic sum of the displacements caused by the individual waves.
- The result of the superposition of two or more waves on a medium is called interference. Interference does not affect the individual waves.
- Maximum destructive interference produces a node where there is no displacement. Maximum constructive interference results in an antinode, a location of the largest displacement.
- The nodes and antinodes of a standing wave are stationary.
- The law of reflection states that the angle of incidence is equal to the angle of reflection. Waves are reflected from a barrier at the same angle at which they approach it.
- The change in the direction of waves at the boundary between two different media is known as refraction.
- The spreading of waves around the edge of a barrier is called diffraction.

## KEY TERMS

| | |
|---|---|
| transverse wave | constructive |
| longitudinal wave | interference |
| surface waves | destructive |
| wave pulse | interference |
| travelling wave | node |
| period | antinode |
| frequency | standing wave |
| wavelength | normal |
| crests | angle of incidence |
| troughs | angle of reflection |
| amplitude | law of reflection |
| principle of superposition | refraction |
| interference | diffraction |

## REVIEWING CONCEPTS

1. How many general methods of energy transfer are there? Give two examples of each.
2. What is the primary difference between a mechanical wave and an electromagnetic wave?
3. What is the difference among transverse, longitudinal, and surface waves?
4. Rhonda sends a pulse along a rope. How does the position of a point on the rope, before the pulse comes, compare to the position after the pulse has passed?
5. What is the difference between a pulse and a wave?
6. What is the difference between wave frequency and wave velocity?
7. Suppose you produce a transverse wave by shaking one end of a spring back and forth. How does the frequency of your hand compare with the frequency of the wave?
8. Waves are sent along a spring of fixed length.
   a. Can the speed of the waves in the spring be changed? Explain.
   b. Can the frequency of a wave in the spring be changed? Explain.
9. What is the difference between the speed of a transverse wave pulse down a spring and the motion of a point on the spring?
10. Sharon is lying on a raft in the wave pool. Describe to Sharon, in terms of the waves she is riding, each of the following: amplitude, period, wavelength, speed, frequency.
11. What is the amplitude of a wave and what does it represent?
12. What is the relationship between the amplitude of a wave and the energy carried?
13. When a wave reaches the boundary of a new medium, part of the wave is reflected and part is transmitted. What determines the amount of reflection?
14. A pulse reaches the boundary of a medium more dense than the one from which it came. Is the reflected pulse erect or inverted?
15. A pulse reaches the boundary of a medium less dense than the one from which it came. Is the reflected pulse erect or inverted?
16. When a wave crosses a boundary between thin and thick rope, its wavelength and velocity change, but its frequency does not. Explain why the frequency is constant.
17. When two waves interfere, is there a loss of energy in the system? Explain.
18. What happens to the spring at nodes of a standing wave?
19. A metal plate is held fixed in the centre and sprinkled with sugar. Using a violin bow, the plate is stroked along one edge and made to vibrate. The sugar begins to collect in certain areas and move away from others. Describe these regions in terms of standing waves.

**20.** If a string is vibrating in four parts, there are points it can be touched without disturbing its motion. Explain. How many points exist?

**21.** How does the pulse reflected from a rigid wall differ from the incident pulse?

**22.** Is interference a property of only some types of waves or all types of waves?

## APPLYING CONCEPTS

**1.** George holds a 1-m metal bar in his hand and hits its end with a hammer; first, in a direction parallel to its length; second, in a direction at right angles to its length. Describe the waves George produces in the two cases.

**2.** You repeatedly dip your finger into a sink full of water to make circular waves. What happens to the wavelength as you move your finger faster?

**3.** What happens to the period of a wave as the frequency increases?

**4.** What happens to the wavelength of a wave as the frequency increases?

**5.** Joe makes a single pulse on a stretched spring. How much energy is required to make a pulse with twice the amplitude?

**6.** In each of the four waves in Figure 14–22, the pulse on the left is the original pulse moving toward the right. The center pulse is a reflected pulse; the pulse on the right is a transmitted pulse. Describe the boundaries at **A, B, C,** and **D.**

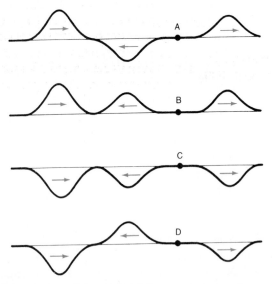

**FIGURE 14-22. Use with Applying Concepts 6.**

**7.** Sonar is the detection of sound waves reflected off boundaries in water. A region of warm water in a cold lake can produce a reflection, as can the bottom of the lake. Which would you expect to produce the stronger echo? Explain.

**8.** You can make water slosh back and forth in a shallow pan only if you shake the pan with the correct frequency. Explain.

**9.** AM radio signals have wavelengths between 600 m and 200 m, while FM signals have wavelengths about 3 m. Explain why AM signals can often be heard behind hills while FM signals cannot.

## PROBLEMS

### 14.1 Wave Properties

**1.** A tall office tower sways back and forth with a frequency of about 0.10 Hz. What is its period of vibration?

**2.** An ocean wave has a length of 10.0 m. A wave passes a fixed location every 2.0 s. What is the speed of the wave?

**3.** Water waves in a shallow dish are 6.0 cm long. At one point, the water oscillates up and down at a rate of 4.8 oscillations per second.
   **a.** What is the speed of the water waves?
   **b.** What is the period of the water waves?

**4.** Water waves in a lake travel 4.4 m in 1.8 s. The period of oscillation is 1.2 s.
   **a.** What is the speed of the water waves?
   **b.** What is their wavelength?

**5.** The frequency of yellow light is $5.0 \times 10^{14}$ Hz. Find its wavelength.

▶ **6.** A group of swimmers is resting in the sun on an off-shore raft. They estimate that 3.0 m separates a trough and an adjacent crest of surface waves on the lake. They count 14 crests that pass by the raft in 20 s. How fast are the waves moving?

**7.** AM radio signals are broadcast at frequencies between 550 kHz and 1600 kHz (kilohertz) and travel $3.0 \times 10^8$ m/s.
   **a.** What is the range of wavelengths for these signals?
   **b.** FM frequencies range between 88 MHz and 108 MHz (megahertz) and travel at the same speed. What is the range of FM wavelengths?

8. A sonar signal of frequency $1.00 \times 10^6$ Hz has a wavelength of 1.50 mm in water.
   a. What is the speed of the signal in water?
   b. What is its period in water?
   c. What is its period in air?
9. A sound wave of wavelength 0.70 m and velocity 330 m/s is produced for 0.50 s.
   a. What is the frequency of the wave?
   b. How many complete waves are emitted in this time interval?
   c. After 0.50 s, how far is the front wave from the source of the sound?
10. The speed of sound in water is 1498 m/s. A sonar signal is sent from a ship at a point just below the water surface and 1.80 s later the reflected signal is detected. How deep is the ocean beneath the ship?
▶ 11. The velocity of the transverse waves produced by an earthquake is 8.9 km/s, while that of the longitudinal waves is 5.1 km/s. A seismograph records the arrival of the transverse waves 73 s before that of the longitudinal waves. How far away was the earthquake?
▶ 12. The speed of a wave on a string depends on how hard the string is stretched, and on the mass per unit length of the string. If $T$ is the force exerted on the string, and $\mu$ is the mass/unit length, then the velocity, $v$, is

$$v = \sqrt{\frac{T}{\mu}}.$$

   A piece of string 5.30 m long has a mass of 15.0 g. What must the force on the string be to make the wavelength of a 125 Hz wave 120.0 cm?
13. The time needed for a water wave to change from the equilibrium level to the crest is 0.18 s.
   a. What fraction of a wavelength is this?
   b. What is the period of the wave?
   c. What is the frequency of the wave?

### 14.2 Wave Interference

▶ 14. The wave speed in a guitar string is 265 m/s. The length of the string is 63 cm. You pluck the centre of the string by pulling it up and letting go. Pulses move in both directions and are reflected off the ends of the string.

   a. How long does it take for the pulse to move to the string end and return to the centre?
   b. When the pulses return, is the string above or below its resting location?
   c. If you plucked the string 15 cm from one end of the string, where would the two pulses meet?

**FIGURE 14-23. Use with Problem 15.**

15. Sketch what happens, for each of the three cases shown in Figure 14–23, when centres of the two wave pulses lie on the dashed line so the pulses exactly overlap.
16. If you slosh the water back and forth in a bathtub at the correct frequency, the water rises first at one end and then at the other. Suppose you can make a standing wave in a 150-cm long tub with a frequency of 0.30 Hz. What is the velocity of the water wave?

## THINKING PHYSIC-LY

1. Why can animals such as bats, that have tiny, light-weight ear parts, hear sounds with much higher frequencies than humans can hear?
2. If you put one ear under water in a bath tub, you can hear sounds from other parts of the house or apartment building where you live. Why is this true?

# CHAPTER
# 15 Sound

## ◀ Bat Music

How can a bat determine how far away an insect is? How can it tell whether it is getting closer to the insect?

Sound and music are important components of the human experience. People make sounds not only with their voices, but also with drums, rattles, and whistles. Some animals use for survival sound with frequencies too high for humans to hear. Bats, in particular, hunt flying insects by emitting pulses of very high-frequency sound. They learn how far away the insect is, how large it is, where it is, and what its relative velocity is. Further, bats that hunt in forests must distinguish the insect from the vegetation. In addition, since bats live in large colonies, they must separate the echoes of their sounds from the sounds of hundreds of other bats. The methods they use are truly amazing, and are based on a few physical principles of sound.

## √ Concept Check

The following terms or concepts from earlier chapters are important for a good understanding of this chapter. If you are not familiar with them, you should review them before studying this chapter.
· velocity, Chapter 3
· pressure, Chapter 13
· frequency, wavelength, amplitude, superposition, diffraction, interference, resonance, Chapter 14

## Objectives

· demonstrate knowledge of the nature of sound waves and the properties sound shares with other waves.
· solve problems relating the frequency, wavelength, and velocity of sound.
· define the Doppler shift and identify some applications.
· relate physical properties of sound waves to perceived pitch and loudness; describe the meaning of the octave; use the decibel scale.

S ound is a longitudinal wave. A longitudinal wave consists of alternate areas of high pressure, compressions, and low pressure, rarefactions. It can be characterized by velocity, frequency, wavelength, and amplitude just as any other periodic wave. It shares with other waves the properties of reflection, refraction, and interference. Living things use sound to obtain information about the surroundings and to communicate with others by means of speech and music.

## Sound Waves

Sound is produced by the compression and rarefaction of matter. Sound waves move through air because a vibrating source produces regular variations in air pressure. The air molecules collide, transmitting the pressure oscillations away from the source of the sound. The pressure of the air varies or oscillates about an average value, the mean air pressure, Figure 15–1. The frequency of the wave is the number of oscillations in pressure each second. Sound is a longitudinal wave because the motion of the air molecules is parallel to the direction of motion of the wave.

Sound waves are longitudinal waves.

**FIGURE 15–1. Graphic representation of the change in pressure over time in a sound wave.**

The velocity of the sound wave in air depends on the temperature of the air. Sound waves move through air at sea level at a velocity of 343 m/s at room temperature (20°C). Sound can also travel through liquids and solids. In general, the velocity of sound is greater in solids and liquids than in gases. Sound cannot travel through a vacuum because there are no particles to move and collide.

The speed in air increases 0.6 m/s for each °C increase.

**FIGURE 15–2. In an anechoic chamber, used for acoustical research, sound is almost completely absorbed by the soft materials covering all the surfaces.**

Sound waves share the general properties of other waves. They can be reflected by hard objects, such as the walls of a room. Reflected sound waves are called echoes. The time required for an echo to return to the source of the sound can be used to find the distance between the source and reflector. This principle is used by bats, by some cameras, and by ships employing *sonar*. Sound waves can also be diffracted, spreading outward after passing through narrow openings. Two sound waves can interfere, causing "dead spots" at nodes where little sound can be heard.

The wavelength of a sound wave is the distance between adjacent regions of maximum pressure. The frequency and wavelength of a wave are related to the velocity of the wave by the equation

$$v = \lambda f.$$

## Example Problem

### Determining the Wavelength of Sound

A sound wave has a frequency of 261.6 Hz. What is the wavelength of this sound traveling in air at 343 m/s?

**Given:** frequency,
$f = 261.6$ Hz
velocity, $v = 343$ m/s

**Unknown:** wavelength, $\lambda$
**Basic equation:** $v = \lambda f$

**Solution:** $v = \lambda f$, so $\lambda = v/f = \dfrac{(343 \text{ m/s})}{(261.6 \text{ Hz})} = 1.31$ m

The speed of sound is higher in liquids and solids than it is in gases.

## Practice Problems

1. Sound with a frequency of 261.6 Hz travels through water at a speed of 1435 m/s. Find its wavelength in water.
2. Find the frequency of a sound wave moving in air at room temperature with a wavelength of 0.667 m.
3. The human ear can detect sounds with frequencies between 20 Hz and 16 kHz. Find the largest and smallest wavelengths the ear can detect, assuming the sound travels through air with a speed of 343 m/s at 20°C.
▶ 4. What is the frequency of sound in air at 20°C having a wavelength equal to the diameter of a 38-cm "woofer" loudspeaker? of a 7.6-cm diameter "tweeter"?

Sound has properties of all other waves: reflection, refraction, interference, diffraction.

## The Doppler Shift

Have you ever noticed the pitch of an ambulance, fire, or police siren as the vehicle sped past you? The frequency is higher when the vehicle is moving toward you, then suddenly drops to a lower pitch as the source moves away. This effect is called the **Doppler shift**, and is shown in Figure 15–3. The sound source is moving to the right with velocity $v_s$. The waves it emits spread in circles centred on the location of the source at the time it produced the wave. The frequency of the

When a sound source moves toward the observer, the detected frequency is higher.

a

b

**FIGURE 15–3.** A point source moving across a ripple tank (a) can be used to show the Doppler shift (b).

The Doppler shift occurs in all waves.

sound source does not change, but when the source is moving toward the sound detector, $O_1$ on Figure 15–3b, more waves are crowded into the space between them. The wavelength is shortened to $\lambda_1$. Because the velocity is not changed, the frequency of the detected sound increases.

When the source is moving away from the detector, $O_2$ on Figure 15–3b, the wavelength is lengthened to $\lambda_2$ and the detected frequency is lower. A Doppler shift also occurs if the detector is moving and the source is stationary.

The Doppler shift occurs in all wave motion, both mechanical and electromagnetic. It has many applications. Radar detectors use the Doppler shift to measure the speed of baseballs and automobiles. Astronomers use the Doppler shift of light from distant galaxies to measure their speed and infer their distance. Physicians can detect the velocity of the moving heart wall in a fetus by means of the Doppler shift in ultrasound. A bat uses the Doppler shift to detect and catch flying insects. When an insect is flying faster than the bat, the reflected frequency is lower, but when the bat is catching up to the insect, the reflected frequency is higher.

## Pitch and Loudness

The physical characteristics of sound waves are measured by frequency, wavelength, and amplitude. In humans, sound is detected by the ear and interpreted by the brain. Sound characteristics are defined in terms describing what we perceive. **Pitch** is essentially the frequency of the wave. **Loudness** depends on the amplitude of the pressure variation wave.

Marin Mersenne (1588–1648) and Robert Hooke (1635–1703) first connected pitch with the frequency of vibration. Pitch can also be given the name of a note on a musical scale. Musical scales are based on the work of Pythagoras, a Greek mathematician who lived in the sixth century B.C. He noted that when two strings had lengths in the ratio of small whole numbers, for example 2:1, 3:2, or 4:3, pleasing sounds resulted when the strings were plucked together. Two notes with frequencies related by the ratio 2:1 are said to differ by an **octave.** For example, if a note has a frequency of 440 Hz, a note an octave higher has a frequency of 880 Hz. A note one octave lower has a frequency of 220 Hz. It is important to recognize that it is the ratio of two frequencies, not the size of the interval between them, that determines the musical interval.

In other common musical intervals, the frequencies have ratios of small whole numbers. For example, the notes in an interval called a "major third" have a ratio of frequencies of 5:4. A typical major third is the notes C and E. The note C has a frequency of 262 Hz, so E has a frequency (5/4)(262 Hz) = 327 Hz. In the same way, notes in a "fourth" (C and F) have a frequency ratio of 4:3 and those in a "fifth" (C and G) have a ratio of 3:2.

The human ear is extremely sensitive to the variations in air pressure in sound. It can detect wave amplitudes of less than one billionth of an atmosphere (or $2 \times 10^{-5}$ N/m$^2$). At the other end of the audible range, the pressure variations that cause pain are one million times greater, (20 N/m$^2$). Notice that this is still less than one one-thousandths of an atmosphere.

Because of this wide range in pressure variation, sound pressures are measured by a quantity called sound level. **Sound level** is measured in **decibels** (dB). The level depends on the ratio of the pressure of a given sound wave to the pressure in the most faintly heard sound, $2 \times 10^{-5}$ N/m$^2$. Such an amplitude has a sound level of zero decibels (0 dB). A sound with 10 times larger pressure amplitude ($2 \times 10^{-4}$ N/m$^2$) is 20 dB. A pressure amplitude 10 times larger than this is 40 dB. Figure 15–5 shows the sound level in decibels for a variety of sounds.

Loudness, as perceived by the human ear, is not directly proportional to the pressure variations in a sound wave. Further, the ear's sensitivity depends on both sound frequency and sound level. Perception is also different for pure tones than it is for mixtures of tones. Most people find that a 10-dB increase in sound level is heard as being about twice as loud.

A note one octave above another has twice the frequency.

The ear can detect very tiny pressure variations.

**FIGURE 15–4. The loudness heard at a concert depends on the sensitivity of our ears to sound in different frequency ranges.**

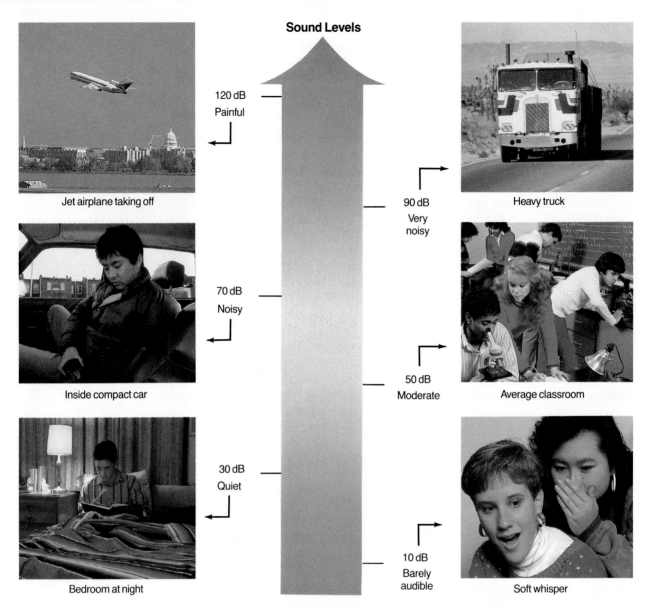

Sound Levels

120 dB
Painful

Jet airplane taking off

90 dB
Very
noisy

Heavy truck

70 dB
Noisy

Inside compact car

50 dB
Moderate

Average classroom

30 dB
Quiet

Bedroom at night

10 dB
Barely
audible

Soft whisper

FIGURE 15–5. Decibel scale showing
the sound level of some familiar
sounds.

## CONCEPT REVIEW

**1.1** The eardrum moves back and forth in response to the pressure variations of a sound wave. Sketch the displacement of the eardrum versus time for a 1-kHz tone and for a 2-kHz tone.

**1.2** If you hear a train whistle pitch drop as the train passes you, can you tell from which direction the train was coming?

**1.3** What physical characteristic of a wave would you change to increase the loudness of a sound? to change the pitch?

**1.4** Critical Thinking: To a person who is hard of hearing, normal conversation sounds like a soft whisper. What increase in sound levels (in dB) must a hearing aid provide? How many times must the sound wave pressure be increased? (Use Figure 15–5.)

# PHYSICS LAB: Speed of Sound

## Purpose

To measure the speed of sound.

## Materials

- tuning fork
- hollow glass tube
- 1000-mL graduated cylinder
- hot water
- ice water
- thermometer
- tuning fork hammer
- goggles

## Procedure

1. Place cylinders with hot water on one side of the classroom and ice water on the other side of the classroom.
2. Record the value of the frequency that is stamped on the tuning fork.
3. Wear goggles while using tuning forks next to the glass tubes. Strike the tuning fork with the rubber hammer.
4. Hold the tuning fork above the glass tube while you slowly raise the tube until the sound is amplified, and is loudest by the tube.
5. Measure $l$, the distance from the water to the top of the tube, to the nearest 0.01 m.
6. Repeat steps 3-5 with the same fork but struck so that the tuning fork sound is quiet.
7. Hold a thermometer in the middle of the glass tube and measure the air temperature.
8. Trade places with another group on the other side of the room and repeat steps 3-7 using the same tuning fork.

## Observations and Data

1. Set up a data table like the one below:
   Ice Water $f$ = ___ Hz; Temperature = ___ °C
   Loud Sound: $l$ = ___ m; $\lambda$ = ___ m
   $v$ = ___ m/s
   Quiet Sound: $l$ = ___ m; $\lambda$ = ___ m
   $v$ = ___ m/s

$\ell = \lambda/4$

$v = f\lambda$

coloured water

Hot Water $f$ = ___ Hz; Temperature = ___ °C
Loud Sound: $l$ = ___ m; $\lambda$ = ___ m
$v$ = ___ m/s
Quiet Sound: $l$ = ___ m; $\lambda$ = ___ m
$v$ = ___ m/s

2. Were the values of "$l$" different for loud and soft sounds?
3. Were the values of "$l$" different for cold and hot air?

## Analysis

1. Calculate the values for $\lambda$ and $v$.
2. Write a general statement describing how the speed of sound depends on loudness.
3. Does the speed seem to depend on the air temperature?

## Applications

1. What would an orchestra sound like if the higher frequencies traveled faster than the lower frequencies?

- describe the origin of sound in general and in various musical instruments in particular.
- show an understanding of resonance, especially applied to an air column; describe or sketch a standing wave; solve problems involving standing waves in resonating air columns.
- identify the parts of the ear and the function of each in detecting sound.
- define timbre; recognize the origin of and solve problems involving beats; define harmonics and their origins.

# 15.2 THE SOUND OF MUSIC

In the middle of the nineteenth century, a German physicist and an English physicist, Hermann Helmholtz and Lord Rayleigh, studied how the human voice as well as musical instruments produce sounds, and how the human ear detects these sounds. In the twentieth century, scientists and engineers have developed electronics that permit not only detailed study of sound, but the creation of electronic musical instruments and recording devices that allow us to have music whenever and wherever we wish.

## Sources of Sound

Sound is produced by a vibrating object. The vibrations of the object create molecular motions and pressure oscillations in the air. A loudspeaker has a diaphragm, or cone, that is made to vibrate by electrical currents. The cone creates the sound waves. Musical instruments such as gongs or cymbals and the surface of a drum are other examples of vibrating sources of sound.

The human voice is the result of vibrations of the vocal cords, two membranes located in the throat. Air from the lungs rushing through the throat starts the vocal cords vibrating. The frequency of vibration is controlled by the muscular tension placed on the cords.

In brass instruments, such as the trumpet, trombone, and tuba, the lips of the performer vibrate, Figure 15–6a. Reed instruments, like the clarinet, saxophone, and oboe, have a thin wooden strip, or reed, that vibrates as a result of air blown across it, Figure 15–6b. In a flute, recorder, organ pipe, or whistle, air is blown across an opening in a pipe. Air moving past the mouthpiece edge sets the column of air in the instrument into vibration.

In stringed instruments, such as the piano, guitar, and violin, a wire or string is set into vibration. In the piano, the wire is struck; in the guitar, it is plucked. In the violin, the friction of the bow pulls the string

*Sound is produced by vibrating objects.*

*Vibrating vocal cords produce the human voice.*

a   Brass instrument

Mouthpiece

b   Woodwind instrument

Mouthpiece

Reed

**FIGURE 15–6.** The shapes of the mouthpieces of a brass instrument (a) and a reed instrument (b) help determine the characteristics of the sound each instrument produces.

aside. The string is attached to a sounding board that vibrates with the string. The vibrations of the sounding board cause the pressure oscillations in the air that we hear as sound. Electric guitars use electronic devices to detect and amplify the vibrations of the strings.

Vibrating air columns determine the sound produced by wind instruments.

## Resonance

If you have ever used just the mouthpiece of a brass or reed instrument, you know that the vibration of your lips or the reed alone does not make a sound with any particular pitch. The long tube that makes up the instrument must be attached if music is to result. When the instrument is played, the air within this tube vibrates at the same frequency, or in resonance, with a particular vibration of the lips or reed. Remember that resonance increases the amplitude of a vibration by repeatedly applying a small external force at the same natural frequency. The pitch of an instrument is varied by changing the length of the resonating column of vibrating air. The length of the air column determines the resonant frequencies of the vibrating air. The mouthpiece creates a mixture of different frequencies. The resonating air column acting on the vibrating lips or reed amplifies a single note.

A tuning fork above a hollow tube, Figure 15–8, can provide resonance in an air column. The tube is placed in water so that the bottom end of the tube is below the water surface. A resonating tube with one end closed is called a **closed-pipe resonator.** The length of the air column is adjusted by changing the height of the tube above the water. The tuning fork is struck with a rubber hammer. When the length of the air column is varied, the sound heard will alternately become louder and softer. The sound is loud when the air column is in resonance with the tuning fork. The air column has intensified the sound of the tuning fork.

Hammer

Tuning fork

Air column

Water

FIGURE 15–8. Resonance of an air column.

**FIGURE 15–9. Reflections of pressure waves in pipes.**

"Normal *p* except at pulse of higher pressure"

High pressure reflects off open end as a region of low pressure

A closed pipe resonates when its length is an odd number of quarter wavelengths.

# POCKET
## LAB

### PLUNK, PLUNK

If possible, look closely at a grand piano. Describe the differences in the strings. Gently push on the different strings. Do the strings seem to have the same tightness?

The vibrating tuning fork produces alternate high and low pressure variations. This sound wave moves down the air column. When the wave hits the water surface, it is reflected back up to the tuning fork, Figure 15–9. If the high pressure reflected wave reaches the tuning fork when the fork has produced high pressure, then the leaving and returning waves reinforce each other. A **standing wave** is produced.

A standing wave has pressure nodes and antinodes, Figure 15–10. At the nodes, the pressure is the mean atmospheric pressure. At the antinodes, the pressure is at its maximum or minimum value. Two antinodes (or two nodes) are separated by one-half wavelength. A pressure wave is reflected from a hard surface without inversion, like a rope wave is reflected from an open end. Thus, there is a pressure antinode at the water surface. A pressure wave is reflected inverted from the open end. That is, if a region of high pressure reaches the open end, a region of low pressure will be reflected. This is similar to the reflection of a rope wave off a fixed end. Thus, the open end of the pipe has a pressure node.

The shortest column of air that can have an antinode at the bottom and a node at the top is one-fourth wavelength long. As the air column is lengthened, additional resonances are found. Thus columns $\lambda/4$, $3\lambda/4$, $5\lambda/4$, $7\lambda/4$, and so on, will all be in resonance with the tuning fork.

In practice, the first resonance length is slightly longer than one-fourth wavelength. This is because the pressure variations do not drop to zero exactly at the end of the pipe. Actually, the node is approximately 1.2 pipe diameters beyond the end. Each additional resonance length, how-

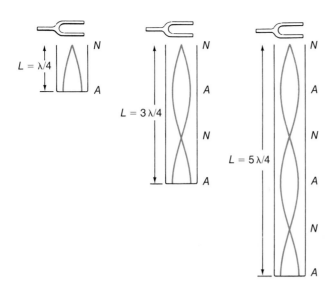

ever, is spaced by exactly one-half wavelength. Measurement of the spacings between resonances can be used to find the velocity of sound in air.

Have you ever put your ear to a large seashell and heard a low frequency sound? The shell acts like a closed-pipe resonator. The source of the sound is the soft background noise that occurs almost everywhere. This sound contains almost all frequencies the ear can hear. The shell increases the intensity of sounds with frequency equal to the resonant frequency of the shell. The result is the almost pure tone you hear.

The small size of the vibrating string of a guitar or other stringed instrument cannot cause much vibration in the air. The instrument uses resonance to increase the sound wave amplitude. Vibration of the string causes the sounding box to vibrate. The large size of the box produces a sound of greater intensity in the air around it.

## BIOLOGY CONNECTION

The human auditory canal acts as a closed-pipe resonator that increases the ear's sensitivity for frequencies between 2000 and 5000 Hz. In the middle ear, the three bones, or ossicles, act as a lever, a simple machine with a mechanical advantage of 1.5. By a feedback mechanism, the bones also help to protect the inner ear from loud sounds. Muscles, triggered by a loud noise, pull the third bone away from the oval window. The pressure variations of sound are also increased by Pascal's principle.

## Example Problem

### Measuring Sound Velocity

A tuning fork with a frequency of 392 Hz is found to cause resonances in an air column at 21.0 cm and 65.3 cm. The air temperature is 27°C. Find the velocity of sound in air at that temperature.

**Given:** $f = 392$ Hz  
$\quad l_2 = 65.3$ cm  
$\quad l_1 = 21.0$ cm

**Unknown:** $v$  
**Basic equation:** $v = \lambda f$

**Solution:** Spacing of resonances, $\Delta l = l_2 - l_1 = (65.3 - 21.0)$ cm $= 44.3$ cm.

Thus, $\frac{1}{2}\lambda = \Delta l$, or $\lambda = 2\Delta l = 2(44.3 \text{ cm}) = 88.6$ cm.

Now, $v = \lambda f = (0.886 \text{ m})(392 \text{ Hz}) = 347$ m/s.

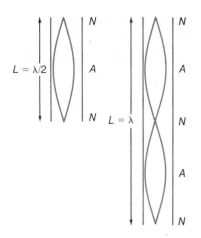

$L = \lambda/2$

$L = \lambda$

**FIGURE 15–11. Standing pressure waves resonating in open pipes. The fundamental and second harmonics are shown.**

An open pipe resonates when its length is an even number of quarter wavelengths.

# Practice Problems

**5.** A 440-Hz tuning fork is held above a closed pipe. Find the spacings between the resonances when the air temperature is 20°C.

**6.** The 440-Hz tuning fork is used with a resonating column to determine the velocity of sound in helium gas. If the spacings between resonances are 110 cm, what is the velocity of sound in He?

**7.** The frequency of a tuning fork is unknown. A student uses an air column at 27°C and finds resonances spaced by 39.2 cm. What is the frequency of the tuning fork?

▶ **8.** The auditory canal, leading to the eardrum, is a closed pipe 3.0 cm long. Find the approximate value (ignoring end correction) of the lowest resonant frequency.

An **open-pipe resonator,** a resonating tube with both ends open, Figure 15–11, will also resonate with a sound source. There are pressure nodes near each of the ends, and at least one antinode between. There is also some sound transmission at the open ends of the tube. We hear the transmitted sound. The remainder is reflected to form a standing wave. The minimum length of a resonating open pipe is one-half wavelength. If open and closed pipes of the same length are used as resonators, the wavelength of the resonant sound for the open pipe will be half as long. Therefore, the frequency will be twice as high for the open pipe as for the closed pipe. The resonances in the open pipe are spaced by half wavelengths just as in closed pipes. Have you ever shouted into a long tunnel or underpass? The booming sound you hear is the tube acting as a resonator. Many musical instruments are also open-pipe resonators. Some examples are the saxophone and the flute.

# Practice Problems

**9.** A bugle can be thought of as an open pipe. If a bugle were straightened out, it would be 2.65 m long.
 **a.** If the speed of sound is 343 m/s, find the lowest frequency that is resonant in a bugle (ignoring end corrections).
 **b.** Find the next two higher resonant frequencies in the bugle.

▶ **10.** A soprano saxophone is an open pipe. If all keys are closed, it is approximately 65 cm long. Using 343 m/s as the speed of sound, find the lowest frequency that can be played on this instrument (ignoring end corrections).

## Detection of Sound

Sound detectors convert sound energy—kinetic energy of the air molecules—into another form of energy. In a sound detector, a diaphragm vibrates at the frequency of the sound wave. The vibration of the diaphragm is then converted into another form of energy. A microphone is an electronic device that converts sound energy into electrical energy. It is discussed in Chapter 25.

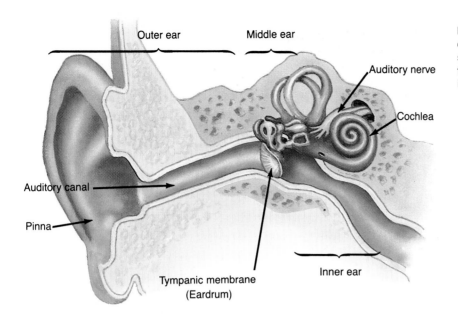

Outer ear
Middle ear
Auditory nerve
Cochlea
Auditory canal
Pinna
Tympanic membrane
(Eardrum)
Inner ear

**FIGURE 15–12. The human ear is a complex sense organ that translates sound vibrations into nerve impulses that are then sent to the brain for interpretation.**

The ear is an amazing sound detector. Not only can it detect sound waves over a very wide range of frequencies, it is also sensitive to an enormous range of wave amplitudes. In addition, human hearing can distinguish many different qualities of sound. The ear is a complex detector that requires knowledge of both physics and biology to understand. The interpretation of sounds by the brain is even more complex and not totally understood.

The ear, Figure 15–12, is divided into three parts: the outer, middle, and inner ear. The outer ear consists of the fleshy, visible part of the ear called the pinna, which collects sound; the auditory canal; and the eardrum. Sound waves cause vibrations in the eardrum. The middle ear consists of three tiny bones in an air-filled space in the skull. The bones transmit the vibrations of the eardrum to the oval window on the inner ear. The inner ear is filled with a watery liquid. Sound vibrations are transmitted through the liquid into sensitive portions of the spiral-shaped cochlea. In the cochlea, tiny hair cells are vibrated by the waves. Vibrations of these cells stimulate nerve cells that lead to the brain, producing the sensation of sound.

The ear is not equally sensitive to all frequencies. Most people cannot hear sounds with frequencies below 20 Hz or above 16 000 Hz. In general, people are most sensitive to sounds with frequencies between 1000 Hz and 5000 Hz. Older people are less sensitive to frequencies above 10 000 Hz than are young people. By age 70, most people can hear nothing above 8000 Hz. This loss affects the ability to understand speech.

Exposure to loud sounds, either noise or music, has been shown to cause the ear to lose its sensitivity, especially to high frequencies. The longer a person is exposed to loud sounds, the greater the effect. A person can recover from a short-term exposure in a period of hours, but the effects of long-term exposure can last for days or weeks. Long exposure to 100 dB or greater sound levels can produce permanent damage. Many rock performers have suffered serious hearing loss, some as

The ear is most sensitive to sounds with frequencies between 1000 and 5000 Hz.

Loud sounds can permanently damage the ears.

**FIGURE 15–13. Continuous exposure to loud sounds can cause serious hearing loss. In many occupations, workers such as aircraft line personnel and rock musicians wear ear protection.**

15.2 The Sound of Music **319**

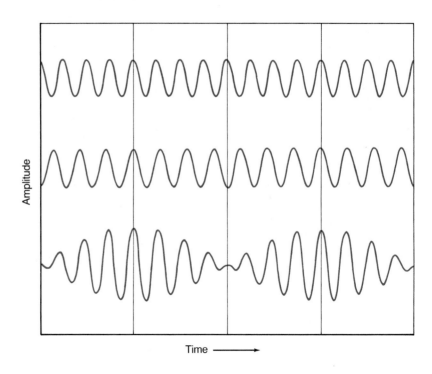

Time ⟶

much as 40%. Cotton ear plugs reduce the sound level only by about 10 dB. Special ear inserts can provide a 25-dB reduction. Specifically designed ear muffs and inserts can reduce the level by up to 45 dB. Another source of hearing loss is the result of loud music from stereo headphones on personal radios and tape players. The wearer may be unaware just how high the sound level is. Some doctors have said that an earphone is "like the nozzle of a fire hose stuck down the ear canal."

*Complex sounds are composed of many frequencies.*

## The Quality of Sound

Musical instruments sound very different from one another, even when playing the same note. This is true because most sounds are made up of a number of frequencies. The quality of a sound depends on the relative intensities of these frequencies. In physical terms, it depends on the spectrum of the sound. In musical terms, sound quality is called **timbre** (TOM bur) or sometimes "tone colour."

When two waves of the same frequency arrive at the ear or another sound detector, the detector senses the sum of the amplitudes of the waves. If the waves are of slightly different frequencies, the sum of the two waves has an amplitude that oscillates in intensity. A listener hears a pulsing variation in loudness. This oscillation of wave amplitude is called a **beat**, Figure 15–14. The frequency of the beat is the difference in the frequencies of the two waves. Musical instruments in an orchestra are often tuned by sounding them against a standard note, and then adjusting them until the beat disappears. This technique is also used by piano tuners.

# F. Y. I.

"Music has charms to
  sooth a savage breast,
To soften rocks, or
  bend a knotted oak."
                    -Congreve

## Example Problem

### Beats

A 442-Hz tuning fork and a 444-Hz tuning fork are struck simultaneously. What beat frequency will be produced?

**Given:** $f_1 = 442$ Hz  
$\qquad\quad f_2 = 444$ Hz

**Unknown:** beat frequency  
**Basic equation:** beat frequency,  
$$\Delta f = |f_2 - f_1|$$

**Solution:** $\Delta f = |f_2 - f_1| = |444\text{ Hz} - 442\text{ Hz}| = 2$ Hz

## Practice Problems

**11.** A 330-Hz and a 333-Hz tuning fork are struck simultaneously. What will the beat frequency be?

▶ **12.** A student has two tuning forks, one with a frequency of 349 Hz and the other with frequency unknown. When struck together, the tuning forks produce three beats per second. What are possible frequencies of the unknown tuning fork?

The human ear can detect beat frequencies as high as 7 Hz. When two waves differ by more than 7 Hz, the ear detects a complex wave. If the resulting sound is unpleasant, the result is called a **dissonance**. If the sound is pleasant, the result is a **consonance**, or a chord. As discovered by Pythagoras, consonances occur when the wave frequencies have ratios that are small whole numbers. Figure 15–15 shows the waves that result when sound waves have frequencies with ratios of 2:1 (octave), 3:2 (fifth), 4:3 (fourth), and 5:4 (major third).

As discussed earlier, open and closed pipes resonate at more than one frequency. As a result, musical instruments using pipe resonators produce sounds that contain more than one resonant frequency. The lowest frequency making up the sound is called the **fundamental**. Waves of frequencies that are whole-number multiples of the fundamental are called **harmonics**. The fundamental is also called the first harmonic. Usually the intensity of the higher harmonics is less than the intensity of the fundamental.

Two sound waves of slightly different frequencies produce beat notes.

**FIGURE 15–15.** Time graphs showing the superposition of two waves having the ratios of 2:1, 3:2, 4:3, and 5:4.

1:2 — Octave

3:4 — Perfect fourth

2:3 — Perfect fifth

4:5 — Major third

**FIGURE 15–16. A violin, clarinet, and piano produce characteristic sound spectra.**

An open pipe resonates when the length is an integral number of half wavelengths, $\lambda/2$, $2\lambda/2$, $3\lambda/2$,.... Thus, the frequencies produced by an open-pipe instrument with fundamental frequency $f$ are $f$, $2f$, $3f$, .... The second harmonic, $2f$, is one octave above the fundamental. The third harmonic, $3f$, is an octave and a fifth (a musical twelfth) above the fundamental. Many familiar musical instruments are open-pipe resonators. Brass instruments, flutes, oboes, and saxophones are some examples. Closed-pipe resonators, like the clarinet, have only the odd harmonics. Notice that in Figure 15–16 the second harmonic in the clarinet spectrum is missing.

Sound can be transmitted through the air or changed into electrical energy and back into sound by a public address system. The air transmits different frequencies with varying efficiencies that can lead to distortion of the original sound. An electrical system can also distort the sound quality. A high-fidelity system is carefully designed to transmit all frequencies with equal efficiency. A system that has a response within 3 dB between 20 and 20 000 Hz is considered to be very good.

On the other hand, it is sometimes useful to transmit only certain frequencies. Telephone systems transmit only frequencies between 300 and 3000 Hz, where most information in spoken language exists. Words can be understood even when the high and low frequencies are missing. The distortion of musical sounds can also produce effects that are interesting and even desired by musicians.

Noise consists of a large number of frequencies with no particular relationship. If all frequencies are present in equal amplitudes, the result is white noise. White noise has been found to have a relaxing effect, and as a result has been used by dentists to help their patients relax.

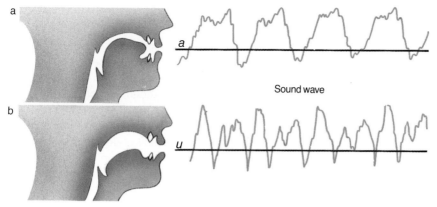

Sound wave

*a*

*u*

The human voice uses the throat and mouth cavity as a resonator. The number of harmonics present, and thus the quality of the tone, depends on the shape of the resonator. Closing the throat, moving the tongue, and closing the teeth change the shape of the resonant cavity. Even nasal cavities, or sinuses, can affect the sound quality. The complex sound waves produced when the vowels *a* (as in sat) and *u* (as in suit) are spoken are shown in Figure 15–17.

# Physics and technology

## SYNTHETIC MUSIC

When Robert Moog introduced his electronic synthesizer in 1964, he could not have known the impact he was to make on the music industry. Musicians could not only mimic a wide variety of instruments, but also create new sounds for the first time.

The original synthesizers were monophonic, meaning that they could play only one musical note at a time. The timbre, or colour, of the tone could be changed to imitate a standard instrument or to make an eerie, unearthly sound. These synthesizers were used to produce background music for low-budget, science fiction films in the 1960s and 1970s. The development of polyphonic synthesizers that could play musical chords made electronic music more commercially acceptable. When synthesizers were coupled with computers and tape recorders, a composer or arranger could sit at a keyboard and orchestrate an entire horn or string section. Now, many personal computers can be used instead of specially designed synthesizer computers.

Synthesizers can produce electronic music that is indistinguishable from music played on traditional instruments. Now, composers need be limited only by their imaginations.

· What are some of the possible future effects of synthesizers on the music industry?

# CONCEPT REVIEW

**2.1** What is the vibrating object that produces sounds in
    **a.** the human voice?    **b.** a clarinet?    **c.** a tuba?

**2.2** Hold one end of a ruler against your desk top, with one-quarter of it extending over the desk. Pluck the extended end of the ruler.
    **a.** Where does the noise you hear come from?
    **b.** Test your answer by placing a towel between the ruler and desk. What do you hear and what does the towel do?
    **c.** How does part **a** demonstrate sound production by a guitar?

**2.3** The speech of a person with a head cold often sounds different from that person's normal speech. Explain.

**2.4 Critical Thinking:** The end correction to a closed organ pipe increases the effective length by about 1.2 pipe diameters.
    **a.** Are the frequencies of the fundamental and higher harmonics still related by the numbers 1, 3, 5, and so on?
    **b.** Actually, the end correction depends slightly on wavelength. Does that change your answer to part **a**? Explain.

# CHAPTER 15 REVIEW

## SUMMARY

### 15.1 Properties of Sound

· Sound is a longitudinal wave transmitted through a gas, liquid, or solid.
· A sound wave is an oscillation in the pressure of the medium.
· The velocity of sound in air at sea level at room temperature (20°C) is 343 m/s.
· The Doppler shift is the change in frequency of sound caused by the motion of either the source or detector.
· The frequency of a sound wave is called its pitch.
· Two notes that differ by one octave have pitches in the ratio of two to one.
· The amplitude of a sound pressure wave is measured on a scale of decibels (dB). The ear and brain perceive the amplitude as loudness.

### 15.2 The Sound of Music

· Sound is produced by vibrating objects.
· An air column can resonate with a sound source, increasing the loudness of the source.
· A closed pipe resonates when its length is $\lambda/4$, $3\lambda/4$, $5\lambda/4$, and so on.
· An open pipe resonates when its length is $\lambda/2$, $2\lambda/2$, $3\lambda/2$, and so on.
· Sound detectors convert sound energy into a different form of energy.
· Two waves with almost the same frequency interfere to produce a beat note.
· Most sounds consist of waves with more than one frequency. The quality of the wave is called its timbre.
· The timbre of a musical instrument depends on the number and intensity of the harmonics it produces.
· The shape of the throat and mouth cavity determine the vowel sounds produced by the human voice.

## KEY TERMS

| | |
|---|---|
| Doppler shift | open-pipe resonator |
| pitch | timbre |
| loudness | beat |
| octave | dissonance |
| decibel | consonance |
| sound level | fundamental |
| closed-pipe resonator | harmonics |
| standing wave | |

# REVIEWING CONCEPTS

1. A firecracker is set off at the same level as a set of hanging ribbons. Describe how they might vibrate.
2. When a ringing bell is placed inside a jar connected to a vacuum pump and the air is removed, no sound is heard. Explain.
3. In the last century, people put their ears to a railroad track to get an early warning of an approaching train. Why did this work?
4. When timing the 100-m run, officials at the finish line are instructed to start their stopwatches at the sight of smoke from the starter's pistol and not on the sound of its firing. Explain. What would happen to the times for the runners if the timing started when sound was heard?
5. Does the Doppler shift occur for only some types of waves or all types of waves?
6. Sound waves with frequencies higher than can be heard by humans, called ultrasound, can be transmitted through the human body. How could ultrasound be used to measure the speed of blood flowing in veins or arteries?
7. How can a certain note sung by an opera singer cause a crystal glass to shatter?
8. In the military, as marching soldiers approach a bridge, the command "route step" is given. The soldiers then walk out-of-step with each other as they cross the bridge. Explain.
9. How must the length of an open tube compare to the wavelength of the sound to produce the strongest resonance?
10. Explain how the slide of a trombone changes the pitch of the sound using the idea of a trombone as a resonance tube.
11. What property distinguishes notes played on both a trumpet and a clarinet if they have the same pitch and loudness?

# APPLYING CONCEPTS

1. A common method of estimating how far a lightning flash is from you is to count the seconds between the flash and the thunder, and divide by three. The result is the distance in kilometres. Explain how this rule works.

2. The speed of sound increases when the air temperature increases. For a given sound, as the temperature rises, what happens to
   a. the frequency?
   b. the wavelength?
3. In a science fiction movie, when a spaceship explodes, the vibrations from the sound nearly destroy a nearby spaceship. If you were the science consultant for the movie, what would your advice be for the producer?
4. Suppose the horns of all cars emitted sound to the same pitch or frequency. What would be the change in the frequency of the horn of a car moving
   a. toward you?
   b. away from you?
5. A bat emits short pulses of high-frequency sound and detects the echoes.
   a. In what way would the echoes from large and small insects compare if they were the same distance from the bat?
   b. In what way would the echo from an insect flying toward the bat differ from that of an insect flying away from the bat?
6. If the pitch of sound is increased, what are the changes in
   a. the frequency?
   b. the wavelength?
   c. the wave velocity?
   d. the amplitude of the wave?
7. Does a sound of 40 dB have a factor of 100 ($10^2$) times greater pressure variations than the threshold of hearing, or a factor of 40 times greater?
8. Simon lit a firecracker, and the firecracker produced a sound level of 90 dB. How many identical firecrackers would have to be exploded simultaneously at the same location to produce a 100-dB sound level?
9. The speed of sound increases with temperature. Would the pitch of a closed pipe increase or decrease when the temperature rises? Assume the length of the pipe does not change.
10. Two flutes are tuning up. If the conductor hears the beat frequency increasing, are the two flute frequencies getting closer together or farther apart?
11. A covered organ pipe plays a certain note. If the cover is removed to make it an open pipe, is the pitch increased or decreased?

# PROBLEMS

## 15.1 Properties of Sound

1. Andrew hears the sound of the firing of a distant cannon 6.00 s after seeing the flash. How far is Andrew from the cannon?
2. A rifle is fired in a valley with parallel vertical walls. The echo from one wall is heard 2.0 s after the rifle was fired. The echo from the other wall is heard 2.0 s after the first echo. How wide is the valley?
3. If Karen claps her hands and hears the echo from a distant wall 0.20 s later, how far away is the wall?
4. If Karen shouts across a canyon and hears an echo 4.00 s later, how wide is the canyon?
5. A certain instant camera determines the distance to the subject by sending out a sound wave and measuring the time needed for the echo to return to the camera. How long would it take the sound wave to return to the camera if the subject were 3.00 m away?
▶ 6. Carol drops a stone into a mine shaft 122.5 m deep. How soon after she drops the stone does she hear it hit the bottom of the shaft?
7. If the wavelength of a $4.40 \times 10^2$ Hz sound in fresh water is 3.30 m, what is the speed of sound in water?
8. Sound with a frequency of 442 Hz travels through steel. A wavelength of 11.66 m is measured. Find the speed of the sound in steel.
9. The sound emitted by bats has a wavelength of 3.5 mm. What is its frequency in air?
10. Ultrasound with a frequency of 4.25 MHz can be used to produce images of the human body. If the speed of sound in the body is the same as in salt water, 1.50 km/s, what is the wavelength in the body?
11. The equation for the Doppler shift of a sound wave of speed $v$, reaching a moving detector, is

$$f' = f\left(\frac{v + v_d}{v - v_s}\right),$$

where $v_d$ is the speed of the detector; $v_s$ is the speed of the source; $f$ is the frequency of the source; $f'$ is the frequency at the detector. If the detector moves toward the source, $v_d$ is positive; if the source moves toward the detector, $v_s$ is positive. A train moving toward a

detector at 31 m/s blows a 305-Hz horn. What frequency is detected by a
   a. stationary train?
   b. train moving toward the first train at a speed of 21 m/s?
12. The train in the previous problem is moving away from the detector. Now what frequency is detected by a
   a. stationary train?
   b. train moving away from the first train at a speed of 21 m/s?
13. A slide whistle has a length of 27 cm. If you want to play a note one octave higher, the whistle should be how long?
14. Adam, an airport worker, working near a jet plane taking off, experiences a sound level of 150 dB.
   a. If Adam wore ear protectors that reduce the sound level to that of a chain saw (110 dB), what decrease in dB would be required?
   b. If Adam now heard something that sounds like a whisper, what would a person not wearing the protectors hear?
15. A rock band plays at a 80-dB sound level. How many times greater is the sound pressure from another rock band playing at
   a. 100 dB?
   b. 120 dB?

## 15.2 The Sound of Music

16. An open vertical tube is filled with water and a tuning fork vibrates over its mouth. As the water level is lowered in the tube, resonance is heard when the water level has dropped 17 cm, and again after 49 cm of distance exists from the water to the top of the tube. What is the frequency of the tuning fork?
17. If you hold a 1.0-m metal rod in the centre and hit one end with a hammer, it will oscillate like an open pipe. Antinodes of air pressure correspond to nodes of molecular motion, so there is a pressure antinode in the centre of the bar. The speed of sound in aluminum is 5150 m/s. What would be the lowest frequency of oscillation?
18. The lowest note on an organ is 16.4 Hz.
   a. What is the shortest open organ pipe that will resonate at this frequency?
   b. What would be the pitch if the same organ pipe were closed?

19. During normal conversation, the amplitude of the pressure wave is 0.020 N/m².
    a. If the area of the eardrum is 0.52 cm², what is the force on the eardrum?
    b. The mechanical advantage of the bones in the inner ear is 1.5. What force is exerted on the oval window?
    c. The area of the oval window is 0.026 cm². What is the pressure increase transmitted to the liquid in the cochlea?

20. One tuning fork has a 445-Hz pitch. When a second fork is struck, beat notes occur with a frequency of 3 Hz. What are the two possible frequencies of the second fork?

21. A flute acts like an open pipe and sounds a note with a 370-Hz pitch. What are the frequencies of the second, third, and fourth harmonics of this pitch?

22. A clarinet sounds the same note as in the previous problem, 370 Hz. It, however, produces harmonics that are only odd multiples of the fundamental frequency. What are the frequencies of the lowest three harmonics produced by the clarinet?

23. One closed organ pipe has a length of 2.40 m.
    a. What is the frequency of the note played by this pipe?
    b. When a second pipe is played at the same time, a 1.40 Hz beat note is heard. By how much is the second pipe too long?

▶ 24. One organ pipe has a length of 836 mm. A second pipe should have a pitch one major third higher. The pipe should be how long?

▶ 25. The Doppler shift was first tested in 1845 by the French scientist B. Ballot. He had a trumpet player sound an A, 440 Hz, while riding on a flatcar pulled by a locomotive. At the same time, a stationary trumpeter played the same note. Ballot heard 3.0 beats per second. How fast was the train moving toward him?

▶ 26. A student wants to repeat Ballot's experiment. She plans to have a trumpet played in a rapidly moving car. Rather than listening for beat notes, she wants to have the car move fast enough so the moving trumpet sounds a major third above a stationary trumpet.
    a. How fast would the car have to move?
    b. Should she try the experiment?

## USING A GRAPHING CALCULATOR

Graph the equation $y = \sin x$ on a graphing calculator, using $-360$ to $360$ as the range for $x$ and 2 to $-2$ as the range for $y$. Now graph $y = 2 \sin x$ and notice if the wavelength or amplitude changed. Also graph $y = \sin 2x$ and notice how the wave changes. Next clear the graphics area and graph $y = \sin x$. Next graph $y = \cos x$. Finally graph $y = \sin x + \cos x$. What is the amplitude of this wave? the wavelength? Trace along the graph to find out.

## THINKING PHYSIC-LY

1. Light coming from a point on the left edge of the sun is found by astronomers to have a slightly higher frequency than light from the right side. What do these measurements tell you about the sun's motion?

2. When you blow across the top of a soda bottle, a puff of air (compression) travels downward, bounces from the bottom, and travels back to the opening. When it arrives (in less than a thousandth of a second), it disturbs the flow of air that you are still producing across the top. This causes a slightly bigger puff of air to start again on its way down the bottle. This happens repeatedly until a very large and loud vibration is built up that you hear as sound. The pitch depends on the time taken for the back and forth trip. What happens to the pitch as liquid is added to the bottle?

# CHAPTER

# 16 Light

◀ Colours to Mix and Match

Explain how each of the colours in the shadows are formed.

L ight and sound are the two major ways that we receive
information about the world. Of the two, light provides
the greater variety of information. The eye can detect tiny
changes in the size, brightness, and colour of an object.
Examine, for example, the photo of the hand illuminated by
adjacent red, blue, and green lights. Notice the variety of
colours, both on the hand and in the multicoloured shadows
on the wall.

## Chapter Outline

**16.1 LIGHT FUNDAMENTALS**
· The Facts of Light
· The Speed of Light
· Sources of Light

**16.2 LIGHT AND MATTER**
· Colour
· Formation of Colour in Thin
  Films
· Polarization of Light

## ✓ Concept Check

The following terms or
concepts from earlier chapters
are important for a good
understanding of this chapter. If
you are not familiar with them,
you should review them before
studying this chapter.
· $v = d/t$ for constant velocity,
  Chapter 3
· wave characteristics,
  Chapter 14
· $v = \lambda f$, Chapter 14

# 16.1 LIGHT FUNDAMENTALS

Objectives

· recognize that light is an electromagnetic wave, and know its wavelength range.
· define a ray and give examples of evidence that light in a uniform medium travels in straight lines.
· state the speed of light to 1 or 3 significant digits; solve problems involving the speed of light.
· define luminous intensity, luminous flux, and illuminance; solve illumination problems.

We see objects because light is either reflected or emitted by them. Light is emitted by incandescent and fluorescent lamps, by television screens and tiny LEDs (light-emitting diodes), by flames, sparks, and even fireflies. Our major source of emitted light is the sun. Light is reflected not only by mirrors and white paper, but by the moon, trees, and even dark, black cloth. In fact, it is very difficult to find an object that does not reflect some light. Although light is only a small portion of the entire range of electromagnetic waves, the study of light is, in many ways, a study of all electromagnetic radiation.

## The Facts of Light

Light is an electromagnetic wave that the human eye can detect.

**Light** is the range of frequencies of electromagnetic waves that stimulates the retina of the eye. Light waves have wavelengths from about 400 nm ($4.00 \times 10^{-7}$ m) to 700 nm ($7.00 \times 10^{-7}$ m). The shortest wavelengths are seen as violet light. As the wavelength increases, the colours change to blue, green, yellow, orange, and finally, red, Figure 16-1.

Different light wavelengths are seen as different colours.

Light travels in a straight line in a vacuum or uniform medium. When your body blocks sunlight, you see a sharp shadow. If light from the sun or a flashlight is made visible by dust particles in the air, the path of the light is seen to be a straight line. We locate objects by assuming that light travels from them to our eyes in straight lines.

A ray is a straight line that represents the path of a light beam.

The straight-line path of light has led to the **ray model** of light. A **ray** is a straight line that represents the path of a very narrow beam of light. Using ray diagrams to study the travel of light is called **ray optics**. Even though ray optics ignores the wave nature of light, it is very useful in describing how light is reflected and refracted.

**FIGURE 16–1. The visible spectrum is only a very small portion of the whole electromagnetic spectrum.**

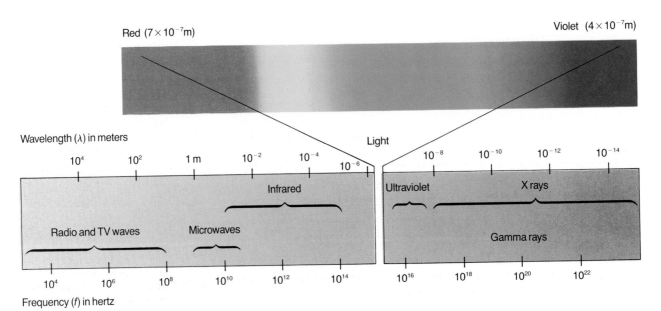

Red ($7 \times 10^{-7}$m)   Violet ($4 \times 10^{-7}$m)

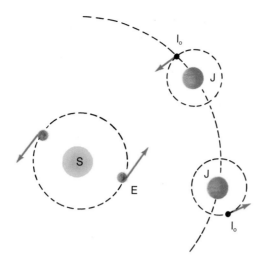

# The Speed of Light

Before the seventeenth century, most people believed that light travelled instantaneously. Galileo was the first to hypothesize that light had a finite speed and to suggest a method of determining it. His method, however, was not sensitive enough, and he was forced to conclude that the speed of light was too fast to be measured at all over a distance of a few kilometres. The Danish astronomer Ole Roemer (1644–1710) was the first to determine that light did travel with a measurable speed. Between 1668 and 1674, Roemer made 70 careful measurements of the 42.5-hour orbital period of Io, one of the moons of Jupiter, Figure 16–2. He recorded the times when Io emerged from behind Jupiter and found that the period varied slightly. The variation was as much as 14 s longer when Earth was moving away from Jupiter and 14 s shorter when Earth was approaching Jupiter. He concluded that as Earth moved away from Jupiter, the light from each new appearance of Io took longer to travel the increasing distance to Earth. Thus the measured period was increased. Based on these data, in 1676 Roemer calculated that light took 22 min to cross a diameter of Earth's orbit. The speed of light was finite, but so fast that light took less than one second to cross the entire Earth!

Roemer was more interested in proving that light did move at a finite speed than calculating exactly what that speed was. If we use the correct value of the diameter of Earth's orbit, $3.0 \times 10^{11}$ m, Roemer's value of 22 min gives a speed of $2.2 \times 10^8$ m/s. Today we know that light takes 16 min, not 22, to cross Earth's orbit.

Although many laboratory measurements have been made, the most notable was a series performed by the American physicist Albert A. Michelson (1852–1931), Figure 16–3. Between 1880 and the 1920s, he developed Earth-based techniques of measuring the speed of light. In 1926, Michelson measured the time light required to make a round trip through a pipe from which all air had been removed. The pipe was constructed between two California mountains 35 km apart. Michelson's best result was $2.997996 \pm 0.00004 \times 10^8$ m/s. For this work, he became the first American scientist to receive the Nobel prize.

Ole Roemer was the first to take data from which the speed of light could be measured.

A. A. Michelson won the Nobel prize for his measurements of the speed of light.

FIGURE 16–3. For his investigations of the speed of light, Albert A. Michelson became the first American to win the Nobel prize.

The development of the laser in the 1960s provided new methods of measuring the speed of light. As with other electromagnetic waves, the speed of light is equal to the product of its frequency and wavelength. The speed of light in a vacuum is such an important and universal value that it has its own special symbol, $c$. Thus $c = \lambda f$. The frequency of light can be counted with extreme precision using the time standard provided by atomic clocks. Measurements of its wavelength, however, are much less precise. As a result, in 1983 the International Committee on Weights and Measurements decided to make the speed of light a defined quantity. In principle, an object's length is now measured in terms of the time required by light to travel from one end of the object to the other. The committee defined the speed of light in a vacuum to be exactly $c = 299\ 792\ 458$ m/s. For most calculations you should use $c = 3.00 \times 10^8$ m/s.

## Practice Problems

1. What is the frequency of yellow light, $\lambda = 556$ nm?
2. One nanosecond (ns) is $10^{-9}$ s. How far, in metres, does light actually travel in 1.0 ns?
3. Modern lasers can create a pulse of light that lasts only a few femtoseconds (1 fs $= 1 \times 10^{-15}$ s).
   a. What is the length of a pulse of light that lasts 6.0 fs?
   b. How many wavelengths of violet light ($\lambda = 400$ nm) are included in such a pulse?
4. The distance to the moon can be found with the help of mirrors left on the moon by astronauts. A pulse of light is sent to the moon and returns to Earth in 2.562 s. Using the defined speed of light, calculate the distance to the moon.
▶ 5. Use the correct time taken for light to cross Earth's orbit, 16 min, and the diameter of the orbit, $3.0 \times 10^{11}$ m, to calculate the speed of light using Roemer's method.

The speed of light is now a defined quantity.

Officially, one metre is the distance light travels in 1/(299 792 458) s.

a

b

**FIGURE 16–4. Objects that emit light waves are luminous (a). Objects that reflect light waves are illuminated (b).**

## Sources of Light

A **luminous** body emits light waves; an **illuminated** body reflects light waves. The sun is a luminous body and the moon is an illuminated body. An incandescent lamp, such as a common light bulb, is luminous because electrical energy heats a thin tungsten wire in the bulb and causes it to glow. An incandescent object emits light as a result of its being extremely hot.

We register the sensation of light when rays from either a luminous or an illuminated body reach our eyes. Our eyes have different sensitivities for different wavelengths. For that reason, measurements of light are made in units based on comparisons with standard luminous bodies.

The rate at which light is emitted from a source is called the **luminous flux**, $P$. The unit of luminous flux is the **lumen**, lm. A typical 100-W incandescent light bulb emits 1750 lm. A bulb emits light in almost all directions. Imagine placing the bulb at the centre of a sphere one metre in radius. The 1750 lm of luminous flux refers to all of the light that strikes the surface of the sphere.

Often we are not interested in the total amount of light emitted. We are more interested in the amount of illumination the bulb provides on a book, sheet of paper, or highway. The illumination of a surface is called the **illuminance**, $E$. Illuminance is measured in lumens per square metre, $lm/m^2$, or lux, lx.

Suppose a bulb is in the middle of a sphere. What is the illumination of the sphere's surface? The area of the surface of a sphere is $4\pi r^2$. Thus the area of a sphere of 1-m radius is $4\pi$ m$^2$. Figure 16–5 shows that the luminous flux striking each square metre of the sphere is

$$\frac{1750}{4\pi}\ lm/m^2.$$

That is, the illumination provided by the bulb on the surface of the 1-m radius sphere is $1750/4\pi$ lux.

What happens if the sphere surrounding the lamp is larger? If the sphere had a radius of 2 m, the luminous flux would still total 1750 lm, but the area of the sphere would now be $4\pi(2\ m)^2 = 16\pi$ m$^2$, four times larger. The illumination on the surface would be reduced by a factor of four to $1750/16\pi$ lx. Thus, if the distance from a point source of light is doubled, the illumination provided by the source is one fourth as great. In the same way, if the distance is increased to 3 m, the illumination would be $(\frac{1}{3})^2$ or one ninth as large as it was when the light source was 1 m away.

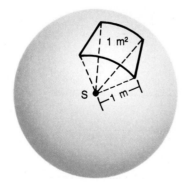

An object that emits light is luminous; one that reflects light is illuminated.

Measurements of light depend on the sensitivity of the human eye.

**FIGURE 16–5.** The lumen is the unit of luminous flux and is a measure of the rate of flow of light energy from a source.

# PHYSICS LAB : Pinhole Camera

## Purpose

To discover how light rays travel.

## Materials

· large coffee can with translucent cover
· 5 cm masking tape
· 40-W light bulb (non-frosted) in fixture
· small nail (#2 finishing)
· large nail (#8 common)

## Procedure

1. Select a coffee can and punch two holes in the bottom—one with the small nail and one with the large nail.
2. Place the masking tape over the larger hole.
3. Place the translucent top on the coffee can.
4. Turn on the 40-W light bulb. Turn off the room lights.
5. Point the hole at the light and notice the pattern (image) formed on the cover of the can. (See sketch below.)
6. Draw the path of the light to show the orientation of the image.

## Observations and Data

1. Is the image reversed right to left? Design an activity to find out. Record your results.
2. Move the can farther away from the bulb. Notice how the image changes. Record your observations.
3. Measure for three values of $d_o$, $d_i$, $h_o$, and $h_i$.

## Analysis

1. Make a drawing to show why the image gets smaller as the can is moved away from the light.
2. Predict how the image formed by the nail hole would compare to the image formed by the pinhole. List the similarities and differences.
3. Check your predictions. Record your results.
4. Try to determine a mathematical rule between $h_i$, $h_o$, $d_i$, and $d_o$. Show your results.

## Applications

1. Your eye is a form of pinhole camera. Would you expect the images to be upside down? Explain.

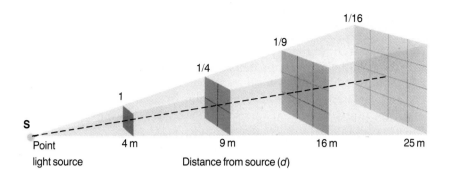

**FIGURE 16-6.** The illuminance on a surface varies inversely as the square of its distance from a light source.

1/16

1/9

1/4

1

S

Point light source

4 m    9 m    16 m    25 m

Distance from source (d)

Some light sources are specified in candela, cd, or candle power. A **candela** is not a measure of luminous flux, but of luminous intensity. The luminous intensity of a point source is the luminous flux that falls on one square metre of a sphere one metre in radius. Thus luminous intensity is luminous flux divided by $4\pi$. A bulb with 1750 lm flux has an intensity (1750 lm)/$4\pi$ = 139 cd. A flashlight bulb labelled 1.5 cd emits a flux of $4\pi$ (1.5 cd) = 19 lm. The candela (cd) is the official SI unit from which all light intensity units are calculated.

There are two ways to increase the illumination on a surface. The luminous flux of a light source can be increased, or the distance between the source and surface can be decreased. Thus illuminance varies directly with the flux of the light source and inversely with the square of the distance from the source, Figure 16-6. The illuminance, $E$, directly under a small light source, is given by

$$E = \frac{P}{4\pi d^2},$$

where $P$ represents the luminous flux of the source and $d$ its distance from the surface. This equation is valid only if a line perpendicular to the surface points toward the bulb. It is also valid only for sources that are small enough or far enough away to be considered point sources. Thus the equation does not give accurate values with long fluorescent lamps, or with incandescent bulbs in large reflectors that are close to the illuminated surface.

## Example Problem

### Illumination of a Surface

A student's desktop is 2.5 m below a 1750-lm incandescent lamp. What is the illumination on the desktop?

**Given:** luminous flux,
  $P$ = 1750 lm
  distance,
  $d$ = 2.50 m

**Unknown:** illuminance, $E$

**Basic equation:** $E = \dfrac{P}{4\pi d^2}$

**Solution:**

$$E = \frac{P}{4\pi d^2} = \frac{1750 \, lm}{4\pi (2.5 \, m)^2} = 22.3 \, lm/m^2 = 22.3 \, lx$$

**POCKET LAB**

**AN ILLUMINATING MATTER**
This is an at-home lab. Which is more efficient, has the highest lm/W, a lower or higher power light bulb? Look through your light bulbs and record the power (W) and lumens for at least three different bulbs. Make a graph of power (horizontal axis) vs lumens (vertical axis). Summarize your results.

## Practice Problems

6. A lamp is moved from 30 cm to 90 cm above the pages of a book. Compare the illumination before and after the lamp is moved.
7. What is the illumination on a surface 3.0 m below a 150-W incandescent lamp that emits a luminous flux of 2275 lm?
8. Draw a graph of the illuminance from a 150-W incandescent lamp between 0.50 m and 5.0 m.
9. A 64-cd point source of light is 3.0 m above the surface of a desk. What is the illumination on the desk's surface in lux?
▶ 10. The illumination on a tabletop is $2.0 \times 10^1$ lx. The lamp providing the illumination is 4.0 m above the table. What is the intensity of the lamp?

## CONCEPT REVIEW

1.1 How far does light travel in the time it takes sound to go 1 cm (at 20°C)?
1.2 The speed of light is slower in air or water than in a vacuum. The frequency does not change when light enters water. Does the wavelength change? in which direction?
1.3 What provides greater illumination of a surface, putting in two equal bulbs instead of one or bringing the bulb twice as close?
1.4 Critical Thinking: A bulb illuminating your desk provides only half the illumination it should. If it is 1.0 m away, how far should it be to provide the correct illumination?

## Objectives

- define transparent, translucent, and opaque.
- understand the formation of colour by addition of light and by subtraction by pigments or dyes.
- explain the cause and give examples of interference in thin films.
- describe methods of producing polarized light.

# 16.2 LIGHT AND MATTER

Objects can be seen clearly through air, glass, some plastics, and other materials. These materials transmit light waves and are called **transparent** materials. Other materials, such as frosted glass, transmit light but do not permit objects to be seen clearly through them. These materials are called **translucent**. Lampshades and frosted light bulbs are translucent. Materials such as brick transmit no light. They absorb or reflect all the light waves that fall on them. These materials are called **opaque**. All three types are illustrated in Figure 16–7.

FIGURE 16–7. The figurine and its stand illustrate transparent, translucent, and opaque objects.

## Colour

One of the most beautiful phenomena in nature is a rainbow. People have long wondered about the source of the colours. Artificial rainbows can be produced by prisms. In 1666, the 24-year-old Isaac Newton did his first scientific experiments on the colours produced when a narrow beam of sunlight passed through a prism. Newton called the ordered arrangement of colours from violet to red a **spectrum**, Figure 16–8. He thought that some unevenness in the glass might be producing the spectrum. To test this assumption, he allowed the spectrum from one prism to fall on a second, reversed prism. If the spectrum were caused by irregularities in the glass, the second prism should have increased the

Colours of the spectrum are associated with specific light wavelengths.

# Physics and technology

## COMPACT DISCS

The audio compact disc (CD) represents a technology that is made for no other purpose than to enhance listening pleasure. The invention of many new industrial processes involved in mass producing CDs has been a major accomplishment. Music can now be reproduced with a clarity and accuracy never before possible.

The CD is essentially a sandwich of three layers of different materials: the plastic substrate, the reflective coating, and the sealing layer. The musical in-formation in a digital recording consists of binary numbers, strings of 1s or 0s. These digits are represented by approximately five billion tiny pits in the substrate. The reflective coating covers the surface of these tiny pits. The laser beam from the CD player reflects off these coated pits and is translated into a digital code. This code is converted into an analog signal (continuously changing voltage) that is amplified to make music.

Since the microscopic pits are smaller than most dirt particles, the manufacturing process must take place under strict clean-room conditions. The "dirty" areas of a CD plant are usually cleaner than the "clean" areas of other factories. · Why won't a compact disc wear out the way a phonograph record does?

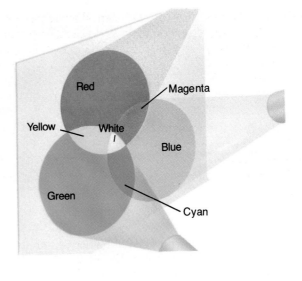

**FIGURE 16–9. The additive mixture of blue, green, and red light produces white light.**

spread in colours. Instead, a spot of white light was formed. After more experiments, Newton convinced himself that white light is composed of colours. We now know that each colour in the spectrum is associated with a specific wavelength of light, Figure 16–1.

White light can be formed from coloured light in a variety of ways. For example, if correct intensities of red, green, and blue light are projected onto a white screen, as in Figure 16–9, the screen will appear white. Thus red, green, and blue light added together form white light. This is called the additive colour process. A colour television tube uses the additive process. It has tiny dot-like sources of red, blue, and green light. When all have the correct intensities, the screen appears white. For this reason red light, green light, and blue light are called the **primary colours** of light. The primary colours can be mixed by pairs to form three different colours. Red and green light together produce yellow light. Blue and green light produce cyan, and red and blue light produce magenta. These three colours, yellow, cyan, and magenta, are called the **secondary light colours**.

Red, green, and blue are the primary light colours.

**FIGURE 16–10. A tomato absorbs the blue and green wavelengths of white light and reflects red light (a). In red light, the tomato still appears red (b). In blue light, the tomato appears black since the blue light is absorbed (c).**

a

b

c

In the chapter-opening photograph, each shadow occurs when the hand blocks one colour of light, leaving the secondary colours. Thus, in order from the left, the yellow shadow is illuminated by red and green lights, the cyan shadow by blue and green, and the magenta shadow by red and blue. Smaller shadows showing the primary light colours appear where two lights are blocked. In the central, black shadow, all three are blocked.

Yellow light consists of red light and green light. If yellow light and blue light are projected onto a white screen with the correct intensities, the surface will appear white. Thus yellow and blue light add to form white light. Yellow light is called the **complementary colour** to blue light. Yellow light is made up of the two other primary colours. In the same way, cyan and red are complementary colours, as are magenta and green.

A **dye** is a molecule that absorbs certain wavelengths of light and transmits or reflects others. A tomato is red because it reflects red light to our eyes. When white light falls on the tomato, dye molecules in the tomato skin absorb the blue and green light and reflect the red. When only blue light falls on the tomato, no light is reflected. The tomato appears black, Figure 16–10. Black is the absence of reflected light.

Like a dye, a **pigment** is a coloured material that absorbs certain colours and transmits or reflects others. A pigment particle is larger than a molecule and can be seen with a microscope. Often a pigment is a finely ground inorganic compound such as titanium(IV) oxide (white), chromium(III) oxide (green), or cadmium sulfide (yellow). Pigments mix to form suspensions rather than solutions.

The absorption of light forms colours by the subtractive process. Molecules in pigments and dyes absorb certain colours from white light. A pigment that absorbs only one colour from white light is called a **primary pigment**. Yellow pigment absorbs blue light and reflects red and green light. Yellow, cyan, and magenta are the primary pigments. A pigment that absorbs two primary colours and reflects one is a **secondary pigment**. The secondary pigments are red (absorbs green and blue light), green (absorbs red and blue light), and blue (absorbs red and green light). Note that the primary pigment colours are the secondary light colours. In the same way, the secondary pigment colours are the primary light colours.

········· ·
**Colours to Mix and Match**

Light of a colour and its complementary colour add to produce white light.

········· ·
**CHEMISTRY CONNECTION**

**FIGURE 16–11.** The primary pigment colours are yellow, cyan, and magenta. In each case the pigment absorbs one of the primary light colours and reflects the other two.

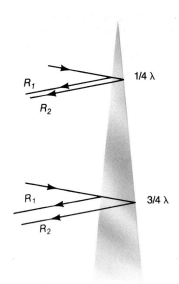

FIGURE 16–12. Each colour is reinforced where the soap film is 1/4, 3/4, 5/4,... of the wavelength for that colour. Since each colour has a different wavelength, a series of colour bands is seen reflected from the soap films.

The colours of thin films are the result of interference of light reflected from the front and back surfaces of the film.

The primary pigment yellow absorbs blue light. If it is mixed with the secondary pigment blue that absorbs green and red light, all light will be absorbed. No light will be reflected, so the result will be black. Yellow and blue are called complementary pigments. Cyan and red, as well as magenta and green, are also complementary pigments.

## Formation of Colours in Thin Films

Have you ever seen a spectrum of colours produced by a soap bubble or by the oil film on a water puddle in a parking lot? These colours are not the result of separation of white light by a prism or absorption of colours in a pigment. They are a result of the constructive and destructive interference of light waves or thin-film interference.

If a soap film is held vertically, Figure 16–12, its weight makes it thicker at the bottom than at the top. The thickness varies gradually from top to bottom. When a light wave strikes the film, part of it is reflected, as shown by $R_1$, and part is transmitted. The transmitted wave travels through the film to the back surface where again part is reflected, $R_2$. If the thickness of the film is one-quarter of the wavelength of the wave in the film ($\lambda/4$), the "round trip" path length in the film is $\lambda/2$. It would appear that the wave returning from the back surface would reach the front surface one-half wavelength behind the first reflected wave and the two waves would cancel. But, as we learned in Chapter 14, when a wave is reflected from a more optically dense medium, it is inverted. As a result, the first reflected wave, $R_1$, is inverted on reflection. The second reflected wave, $R_2$, is reflected from a less dense medium and is not inverted. Thus, when the film has a thickness of $\lambda/4$, the wave reflected from the back surface returns to the front surface in step with the first reflected wave. The two waves reinforce each other as they leave the film. Light with other wavelengths suffers partial or complete destructive interference. At any point on the film, the light most strongly reflected has a wavelength satisfying the requirement that the film thickness equals $\lambda/4$.

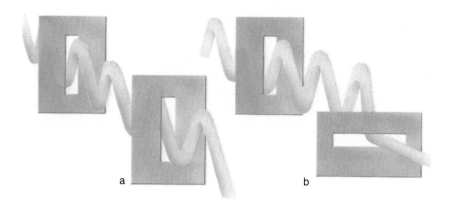

**FIGURE 16–13. Waves are polarized with respect to the vertical plane (a). Vertically polarized waves can't pass through a horizontal polarizer (b).**

a                    b

Different colours of light have different wavelengths. As the thickness of the film changes, the $\lambda/4$ requirement will be met at different locations for different colours. As the thickness increases, first light with the shortest wavelength, blue, will be most strongly reflected, then green, yellow, orange, and finally red, which has the longest wavelength. A rainbow of colour results. Notice in Figure 16–12 that the spectrum repeats. When the thickness is $3\lambda/4$, the round trip distance is $3\lambda/2$, and constructive interference occurs again. Any thickness equal to an odd multiple of quarter wavelengths, $\lambda/4$, $3\lambda/4$, $5\lambda/4$, $7\lambda/4$, and so on satisfies the conditions for reinforcement for a given colour. At the top of the right-hand film there is no colour; the film appears black. Here the film is too thin to produce constructive interference for any colour. Shortly after the top of the film becomes thin enough to appear black, it breaks.

Light, being a transverse wave, can be polarized.

## Polarization of Light

Have you ever looked at light reflected off a road through Polaroid sunglasses? As you rotate the glasses, the road first appears dark, then light, then dark again. Light from a lamp, however, changes very little as the glasses are rotated. The light reflected from the road is partially polarized. Only transverse waves can be polarized.

Polarization can be understood by considering the rope model of light waves, Figure 16–13. The transverse mechanical waves in the rope represent the transverse electromagnetic waves of light. The slots represent the polarizing axis of the Polaroid material. When the rope waves are parallel to the slots, they pass through. When they are perpendicular to the slots, the waves are blocked. Polaroid material contains long molecules that allow electromagnetic waves of one direction to pass while absorbing the waves vibrating in the other direction. One direction of the Polaroid material is called the polarizing axis. Only waves vibrating parallel to that axis can pass through.

Ordinary light contains electromagnetic waves vibrating in every direction perpendicular to its direction of travel. Each wave can be resolved into two perpendicular components. On the average, therefore, half the waves vibrate in one plane, the other half in a plane perpendic-

FIGURE 16–14. The arrows show that unpolarized light vibrates in many planes (a). Plane polarized light vibrates in only one plane. Polarized light from the first polarizer (b) is absorbed by the analyser (c).

A polarizer produces polarized light.

A polarizer will permit only light of one polarization to be transmitted.

Light can be polarized by reflection and by scattering.

ular to the first. If polarizing material is placed in a beam of ordinary light, only those waves vibrating in one plane pass through. Half the light passes through and the intensity of the light is reduced by half. The polarizing material produces light that is **polarized** in a particular plane of vibration. The material is said to be a "polarizer" of light and is called a polarizing filter.

Suppose a second polarizing filter is placed in the path of the polarized light. If the direction of the plane of vibration that passes through the filter is perpendicular to the plane of the polarized light, no light will pass through, Figure 16–14c. If it is parallel, most light will be transmitted, Figure 16–14b. Thus a polarizing filter can also analyse the polarization of light, and is often called an "analyser."

Light can also be polarized by reflection. If you look through a polarizing filter at the light reflected by a sheet of glass and rotate the filter, you will see the light brighten and dim. The light was partially polarized when it was reflected. The polarization of light reflected by roads is the reason polarizing sunglasses reduce glare. The fact that the intensity of light reflected off a road varies as Polaroid sunglasses are rotated suggests that the reflected light must contain a great deal of light vibrating in only one direction. Light is also polarized when it is scattered by molecules in the air. If you look through Polaroid glasses along the horizon when the sun is overhead and rotate the glasses, you will see the brightness change, showing the light is polarized.

# POCKET LAB

## LIGHT POLARIZATION

This is an at-home lab. Check out a polarizing filter to take home. Look through the filter at various objects as you rotate the filter. Make a record of those objects that seem to change in brightness as the filter is rotated. What seems to be the pattern?

## CONCEPT REVIEW

**2.1** Why might you choose a window shade that is translucent? opaque?

**2.2** What light colour do you add to blue light to obtain white?

**2.3** What primary pigment colours must be mixed to get red?

**2.4** Critical Thinking: Colours in butterfly wings are caused by the constructive interference of light reflected from closely-spaced spine-like structures. Assume that the light wave is inverted when reflected from all these structures. At what fraction of a wavelength are they spaced?

# CHAPTER
# 16 REVIEW

## SUMMARY

### 16.1 Light Fundamentals

· Light is electromagnetic radiation capable of stimulating the retina of the eye.
· Light in a uniform medium travels in a straight line at a speed of $3.00 \times 10^8$ m/s in a vacuum.
· The rate at which light energy is emitted by a source is called luminous flux. The unit of luminous flux is the lumen.
· The rate at which light energy falls on a unit area is illuminance, measured in lux.

### 16.2 Light and Matter

· Materials may be characterized as either transparent, translucent, or opaque depending on the amount of light they reflect, transmit, or absorb.
· White light is a combination of the spectrum of colours, each having a different wavelength.
· White light can be formed by adding together the primary light colours, red, blue, and green.
· The subtractive primary colours, cyan, magenta, and yellow, are used in pigments and dyes to produce a wide variety of colours.
· Colours in soap and oil films are caused by the interference of specific colours of light reflected from the front and back surfaces of the thin film.
· Light is polarized if only waves vibrating in a particular plane are present.

## KEY TERMS

| | |
|---|---|
| light | opaque |
| ray model | spectrum |
| ray | primary colours |
| ray optics | secondary light |
| luminous | colours |
| illuminated | complementary colour |
| luminous flux | dye |
| lumen | pigment |
| illuminance | primary pigment |
| candela | secondary pigment |
| transparent | polarized |
| translucent | |

## REVIEWING CONCEPT

1. Sound doesn't travel through a vacuum; how do we know light does?
2. What is the range of wavelength, from shortest to longest, the human eye can detect?
3. What colour of visible light has the shortest wavelength?
4. What was changed in the equation $v = \lambda f$ in this chapter?
5. Distinguish between a luminous body and an illuminated body.
6. Look carefully at an ordinary frosted incandescent bulb. Is it a luminous or an illuminated body?
7. Explain how we can see ordinary nonluminous classroom objects.
8. State the units for each of the following.
   a. luminous intensity
   b. illuminance
   c. luminous flux
9. State the symbol that represents each of the following.
   a. luminous intensity.
   b. illuminance
   c. luminous flux
10. Distinguish among transparent, translucent, and opaque objects.
11. Of what colours does white light consist?
12. Is black a colour? Why does an object appear black?
13. Name each primary colour and its secondary light colour.
14. Name each primary pigment and its secondary pigment.
15. Why can sound waves not be polarized?
16. Why would a perfect polarizing filter transmit half the nonpolarized light incident on it?

## APPLYING CONCEPTS

1. What happens to the wavelength of light as the frequency increases?
2. To what is the illumination of a surface by a light source directly proportional? To what is it inversely proportional?

3. A point source of light is 2.0 m from screen A and 4.0 from screen B. How does the illumination of screen B compare with the illumination of screen A?

4. You have a small reading lamp 35 cm from the pages of a book. You decide to double the distance. Is the illumination on the book the same? If not, how much more or less is it?

5. Why are the insides of binoculars and cameras painted black?

6. The eye is most sensitive to 550-nm wavelength light. Its sensitivity to red and blue light is less than 10% as great. Based on this knowledge, what colour would you recommend fire trucks and ambulances be painted? Why?

7. Some very efficient streetlights contain sodium vapour under high pressure. They produce light that is mainly yellow with some red. Should a community having these lights buy dark blue police cars? Why or why not?

8. Suppose astronauts made a soap film in the space shuttle. Would you expect an orderly set of coloured lines, such as in Figure 16—12? Explain.

9. Photographers often put polarizing filters over the camera lens to make clouds more visible in the sky. The clouds remain white while the sky looks darker. Explain this based on your knowledge of polarized light.

10. An apple is red because it reflects red light and either absorbs or transmits blue and green. Follow these steps to decide if a piece of transparent red cellophane absorbs or transmits blue and green.
    a. Explain why it looks red in reflected light.
    b. When you hold it between your eye and a white light, it looks red. Explain.
    c. Now, what happens to the blue and green?

11. What colour will a yellow banana appear when illuminated by
    a. white light?
    b. green plus red light?
    c. blue light?

12. A soap film is too thin to absorb any colour. If such a film reflects blue light, what kind of light does it transmit?

13. You put a piece of red cellophane over one flashlight and a piece of green cellophane over another. You shine the light beams on a white wall. What colour will you see where the two flashlight beams overlap?

14. You now put both the red and green cellophane pieces over one of the flashlights in the previous problem. If you shine the flashlight beam on a white wall, what colour will you see? Explain.

15. If you have yellow, cyan, and magenta pigments, how can you make a blue pigment? Explain.

16. Consider a thin film of gasoline floating on water. The speed of light is slower in gasoline than in air, and slower in water than in gasoline. Would you expect the $\lambda/4$ rule to hold in this case? Explain.

## PROBLEMS

### 16.1 Light Fundamentals

1. Convert 700 nm, the wavelength of red light, to metres.

2. Light takes 1.28 s to travel from the moon to Earth. What is the distance between them?

3. The sun is $1.5 \times 10^8$ km from Earth. How long does it take for its light to reach us?

4. Ole Roemer found that the maximum increased delay in the appearance of Io from one orbit to the next was 14 s.
   a. How far does light travel in 14 s?
   b. Each orbit of Io is 42.5 h. Earth traveled the distance calculated above in 42.5 h. Find the speed of Earth in km/s.
   c. See if your answer for part b is reasonable. Calculate Earth's speed in orbit using the orbital radius, $1.5 \times 10^8$ km, and the period, one year.

5. Radio stations are usually identified by their frequency. One radio station in the middle of the FM band has a frequency of 99.0 MHz. What is its wavelength?

6. Suppose you wanted to measure the speed of light by putting a mirror on a distant mountain, setting off a camera flash, and measuring the time it takes the flash to reflect off the mirror

and return to you. Without instruments, a person can detect a time interval of about 0.1 s. How many kilometers away would the mirror have to be? Compare this size with that of some known objects.

7. What is the frequency of a microwave that has a wavelength of 3.0 cm?

8. Find the illumination 4.0 m below a 405-lm lamp.

9. A public school law requires a minimum illumination of 160 lx on the surface of each student's desk. An architect's specifications call for classroom lights to be located 2.0 m above the desks. What is the minimum luminous flux the lights must deliver?

10. A 3-way bulb uses 50-100-150 W of electrical power to deliver 665, 1620, or 2285 lm in its three settings. The bulb is placed 80 cm above a sheet of paper. If an illumination of at least 175 lx is needed on the paper, what is the minimum setting that should be used?

▶ 11. A streetlight contains two identical bulbs 3.3 m above the ground. If the community wants to save electrical energy by removing one bulb, how far from the ground should the streetlight be positioned to have the same illumination on the ground under the lamp?

12. A student wants to compare the luminous flux from a bulb with that of a 1750-lm lamp. The two bulbs illuminate a sheet of paper equally. The 1750-lm lamp is 1.25 m away; the unknown bulb is 1.08 m away. What is its luminous flux?

13. A screen is placed between two lamps so that they illuminate the screen equally. The first lamp emits a luminous flux of 1445 lm and is 2.5 m from the screen. What is the distance of the second lamp from the screen if the luminous flux is 2375 lm?

14. Two lamps illuminate a screen equally. The first lamp has an intensity of 101 cd and is 5.0 m from the screen. The second lamp is 3.0 m from the screen. What is the intensity of the second lamp?

▶ 15. A 10-cd point source lamp and a 60-cd point source lamp cast equal intensities on a wall. If the 10-cd lamp is 6.0 m from the wall, how far is the 60-cd lamp?

## THINKING PHYSIC-LY

In a dress shop that has only fluorescent lighting, Jill insists on taking a sweater and scarf to the front door to check them together in daylight. Is she being reasonable?

# CHAPTER 17

# Reflection and Refraction

◀ ## A Smile in the Sky

Rainbows are created by a combination of refraction and reflection in raindrops. As the rainbow is viewed, violet always appears on the bottom and red on the top. Explain the origin of the rainbow in this photograph.

A rainbow! Has anything seen in the sky captured the human imagination more than a rainbow? All you need to produce a rainbow is simultaneous sunshine and rain. Even the drops from a hose or lawn sprinkler will do. Stand with the sun low and behind you and look into the water drops. Each drop of water separates sunlight into a spectrum. Violet at the inside of the arc, then blue, green, yellow, and, at the outside, red. Look carefully at the photo, and you will see more. The sky is brighter inside the bow than outside. There is also a secondary rainbow, with the order of colours reversed. The fact that we can use our knowledge of the behaviour of light to explain the rainbow makes it no less beautiful.

✔ ## Concept Check

The following terms or concepts from earlier chapters are important for a good understanding of this chapter. If you are not familiar with them, you should review them before studying this chapter.
· wave properties, behavior at boundaries, reflection, Chapter 14
· light wavelengths, Chapter 16

347

- state the law of reflection.
- distinguish between diffuse and regular reflection and give examples.
- define refraction; predict whether a ray will be bent toward or away from normal when light moves from one medium to another.
- state Snell's law; be able to solve refraction problems.
- relate index of refraction to speed of light in medium; solve problems relating these two quantities.

## POCKET LAB

### REFLECTIONS

Toss a tennis ball or a hand-ball against a wall so that it will bounce to a lab partner. Can you predict where the ball must hit on the wall to bounce in the right direction? If your partner is closer (or farther) from the wall, does your rule still work? Write a general rule that seems to work. Does your rule for the bouncing ball work for predicting the path of light? How is it similar?

**FIGURE 17–1.** A light ray reflecting from a mirror shows that the angle of incidence equals the angle of reflection.

# 17.1 HOW LIGHT BEHAVES AT A BOUNDARY

Light, as we know, travels in straight lines and at a very high velocity. But, its velocity depends on the medium through which it moves. So, it acts just like any other wave moving from one medium to another. What happens to light striking such a surface?

## The Law of Reflection

When a light ray strikes a reflecting surface, the angle of reflection is equal to the angle of incidence. Both of these angles are measured from a normal (perpendicular) to the surface at the point of incidence. The incident ray, the reflected ray, and the normal all lie in the same plane, Figure 17–1.

When a beam of light strikes most surfaces, it reflects in many directions. A painted wall or a page in a book may appear to be very smooth. On the scale of the wavelength of light, these surfaces are rough and have many small projections. Rays of light strike different parts of these projections. Each ray reflects according to the law of reflection. The rays are reflected in many different directions, producing a **diffuse reflection,** in Figure 17–2b, d.

If a beam of light falls on a very smooth surface, the rays undergo **regular reflection**. Figure 17–2a and c shows a beam of parallel rays reflecting from a smooth, flat surface. Since each ray follows the law of reflection, the reflected rays are also parallel. The rays are arranged in the same order after they leave a smooth surface as they were before they approached the surface.

## Refraction of Light

Light travels at different speeds in different media. When the speed of light in one medium is slower than that in another, the medium is said to be more **optically dense**. Light also changes direction, or bends, as it moves from one medium to another if the angle of incidence is not zero. The change in direction or bending of light at the boundary between two media is called **refraction**.

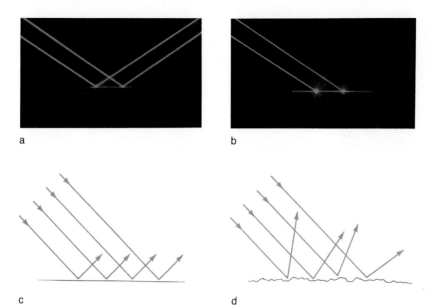

a

b

c

d

FIGURE 17–2. When parallel light rays strike a mirror surface, they reflect as parallel rays (a) (c). When parallel light rays strike a rough surface, they are randomly reflected (b) (d).

Consider an incident ray that falls on the boundary between two media. Once the ray enters a new medium, it is a refracted ray. The angle between the incident ray and a normal to the surface at the point of incidence is the angle of incidence, $i$. The angle between the refracted ray and the same normal is the angle of refraction, $r$. The incident ray, the refracted ray, and the normal lie in the same plane. Refraction occurs only when the incident ray strikes the boundary between the two media at a non-zero angle. When the angle of incidence is zero (the ray is perpendicular to the surface), the angle of refraction is also zero. The ray changes speed but passes straight into the new medium.

Figure 17–3 shows two rays of light as they pass from air into glass. Part of the rays are reflected and part are transmitted (refracted). Note that as the rays enter a more optically dense medium where they travel more slowly, the refracted rays bend toward the normal. The angle of refraction is smaller than the angle of incidence.

Refraction is the change in angle of light when moving from one medium into another.

FIGURE 17–3. Light is refracted toward the normal as it enters a more dense medium. Compare the deflection of a set of wheels as it crosses a pavement-mud boundary.

Light ray

Air

Glass

Pavement

Mud

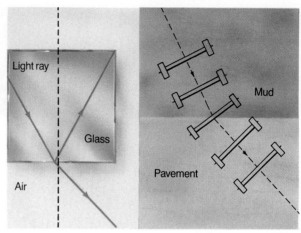

FIGURE 17–4. Light is refracted away from the normal as it enters a less dense medium. Compare the deflection of a set of wheels as it crosses a mud-pavement boundary.

In Figure 17–4, a light ray passes from glass into air. Rays that strike the surface at an angle are refracted away from the normal. When a light ray passes into a medium in which it travels faster, the light ray bends or refracts away from the normal. In other words, the angle of refraction is larger than the angle of incidence.

Figures 17–3 and 17–4 compare the refraction of light to a car entering or leaving a patch of mud. When the wheels enter the mud at an angle, Figure 17–3, the right wheel enters the mud before the left wheel. The right wheel slows before the left wheel. As a result, the car swings to the right or toward the normal. Figure 17–4 shows the car as it leaves the mud at an angle. The right wheel leaves the mud first and speeds up. The left wheel is still held back. Therefore, the car swings to the left or away from the normal. Keep this car analogy in mind until the behavior of light at various surfaces becomes more familiar to you.

## Snell's Law

Rays of light that travel from air into glass, or any other medium more optically dense than air, are refracted toward the normal. As the angle of incidence increases, the angle of refraction increases, Figure 17–5. The relationship between the angle of incidence and the angle of refraction was discovered by the Dutch scientist Willebrord Snell (1591–1626) and is called **Snell's law**. This law states: *a ray of light bends in such a way that the ratio of the sine of the angle of incidence to the sine of the angle of refraction is a constant.* For a light ray passing from a vacuum into a given medium, this constant (the ratio of the sines) is called the **index of refraction**, $n$, for that medium. Snell's law can be written

$$n = \frac{\sin \theta_i}{\sin \theta_r}.$$

In this equation, $\theta_i$ is the angle of incidence, $\theta_r$ is the angle of refraction, and $n$ is the index of refraction of the medium. Note that this equation applies *only* to a ray traveling from a vacuum into another medium.

In general, for a ray traveling from one medium into another medium, Snell's law can be written

$$n_i \sin \theta_i = n_r \sin \theta_r.$$

In this equation, $n_i$ is the index of refraction of the incident medium, and $n_r$ is the index of refraction of the second medium. Angles $\theta_i$ and $\theta_r$ are the angles of incidence and refraction, respectively. Figure 17–6 shows the path of light rays into and out of glass and water.

A ray diagram is very useful in solving problems involving the reflection and refraction of light. Some problems can be solved, at least approximately, using a diagram. You should sketch a ray diagram for all problems involving reflection or refraction to check the answer you get using a calculator.

The index of refraction of many transparent substances, such as water or glass, can be found by measurement. Direct a ray of light on the substance at a measured angle of incidence and measure the angle of refraction. The sine of the angle of incidence divided by the sine of the angle of refraction gives the index of refraction of the substance.

The refractive index can be determined by measuring angles of incidence and refraction.

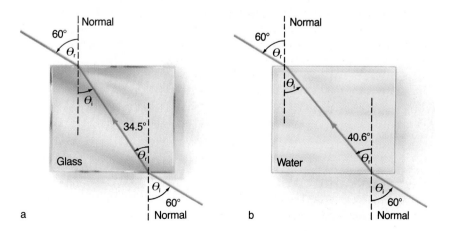

FIGURE 17–6. The index of refraction for glass is greater than that for water. If light enters both media at the same angle, the angle of refraction is greater for water. This result agrees with Snell's law.

# PHYSICS LAB : Bending of Light

## Purpose

To observe when light bends and determine the index of refraction of water (or glycerine).

## Materials

· graph paper
· felt-tip pen
· ruler
· semicircular plastic dish
· water (or glycerine)

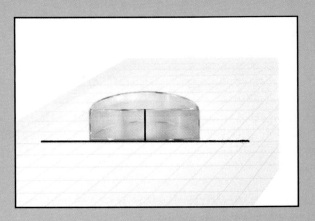

## Procedure

### Part 1

**1.** Draw a line on the graph paper dividing the paper in half.
**2.** Use the felt-tip pen to draw a vertical line at the center of the straight edge of the plastic dish. This line will be your object.
**3.** Place the edge of the dish along the straight line so that the dish is on the bottom half of the paper and trace the outline of the dish on the paper.
**4.** Mark the position of the object on your paper.
**5.** Fill the dish three-quarters full of water (or glycerine) as your teacher indicates.
**6.** Lay a ruler on the bottom half of the paper. Adjust the position until the edge of the ruler seems to point at the object when you look through the water.
**7.** Have a lab partner look to verify that the ruler position is accurate.
**8.** Draw the line along the ruler edge to the edge of the dish.
**9.** Repeat steps 5-7 for a different position of the ruler.

### Part 2

**1.** Wipe the vertical line from the dish and draw a vertical line at the centre of the curved edge. This is your new object.

**2.** Repeat all steps above except this time the sighting of the ruler will be placed on the top half of the paper.
**3.** Carefully remove the dish from the graph paper.

## Observations and Data

**1.** Look at the sight lines drawn in Part 1. Did the light bend when moving from water to air?
**2.** For Part 2, do the sight lines point directly toward the object?

## Analysis

**1.** Explain why the light did not bend in Part 1. **Hint:** Draw the normal to the surface.
**2.** For Part 2, draw a line from the object position to where each sight line touched the dish.
**3.** Draw the normal at each point where the sight line touched the dish.
**4.** Measure the angles from the normal for the angles in air and water.
**5.** Calculate $n$, using Snell's law.
**6.** Write the values of the angles and the ratio of the sines on the chalkboard.

## Applications

**1.** Could a flat piece of material be used for focusing light? Make a drawing to support your answer.

**Table 17–1**

| Indices of Refraction | | | |
|---|---|---|---|
| Medium | *n* | Medium | *n* |
| vacuum | 1.00 | crown glass | 1.52 |
| air | 1.0003 | quartz | 1.54 |
| water | 1.33 | flint glass | 1.61 |
| ethanol | 1.36 | diamond | 2.42 |

# PROBLEM SOLVING STRATEGY

1. Draw a diagram showing the two media. Label them, indicating the two indices of refraction, $n_1$ and $n_2$.
2. Draw the incoming ray to the point where it hits the surface. Draw a normal to the surface at that point.
3. Use a protractor to measure the angle of incidence.
4. Use Snell's law to calculate the angle of refraction.
5. Draw the refracted ray, using a protractor to find the correct angle.
6. Always make sure your answer obeys the qualitative statement of Snell's law: "Light moving from smaller *n* to larger *n* is bent toward the normal. Light moving from larger *n* to smaller *n* is bent away from the normal."

# Example Problem

### Snell's Law

A ray of light travelling through air is incident upon a sheet of crown glass at an angle of 30.0°. What is the angle of refraction?

**Given**: incident medium (air)
second medium (crown glass)
incident angle,
$\theta_i = 30.0°$

**Unknown**: refracted angle, $\theta_r$
**Basic equation**: $n_i \sin \theta_i = n_r \sin \theta_r$

**Solution**:
From Table 17–1, the index of refraction of air is 1.00 and that of crown glass is 1.52.

$$n_i \sin \theta_i = n_r \sin \theta_r$$

so, $\sin \theta_r = \dfrac{n_i \sin \theta_i}{n_r}$

$$= \frac{1.00 \sin 30.0°}{1.52} = \frac{0.500}{1.52} = 0.329$$

or $\theta_r = 19.2°$

## Practice Problems

1. Light in air is incident upon a piece of crown glass at an angle of 45.0°. What is the angle of refraction?
2. A ray of light passes from air into water at an angle of 30.0°. Find the angle of refraction.
3. A ray of light is incident upon a diamond at 45.0°.
   a. What is the angle of refraction?
   b. Compare your answer for a to your answer for Practice Problem 1. Does glass or diamond bend light more?
▶ 4. A block of unknown material is submerged in water. Light in the water is incident on the block at an angle of 31°. The angle of refraction in the block is 27°. What is the index of refraction of the unknown material?

## Index of Refraction and the Speed of Light

Refraction occurs because the speed of light depends on the medium through which it travels. The index of refraction is a measure of the amount that light bends when passing into the medium from a vacuum.

Figure 17–7 shows the behavior of two parallel rays of light that are incident upon a glass plate from air. The rays are refracted toward the normal. Consider the wave front CB as it approaches the glass plate. After a time interval, the wave front reaches position DA. Since the speed of the wave is slower in the glass, point C on ray y travels only distance CD. Point B on ray x travels distance BA. This difference causes the wave front to turn.

During a time interval t, point B on ray x travels to A and point C on ray y travels to D. Therefore, the ratio of BA to CD is the same as the ratio of the speed of light in vacuum, c, to the speed of light in glass, $v_g$.

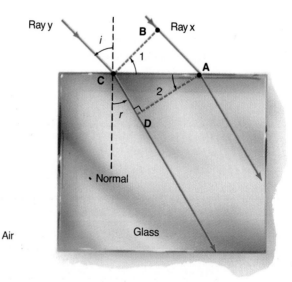

**FIGURE 17–7. A diagram for refraction of two parallel light rays incident on a piece of glass. Dashed red lines represent wave fronts.**

$$\frac{\dfrac{BA}{t}}{\dfrac{CD}{t}} = \frac{BA}{CD} = \frac{c}{v_g}$$

Angle $\theta_i$ in Figure 17–7 is equal to the angle of incidence of the ray. Angle $\theta_r$ is equal to the angle of refraction of the ray (corresponding sides mutually perpendicular). The sine of angle $\theta_i$ is $BA/CA$. The sine of angle $\theta_r$ is $CD/CA$. Since $n_{vacuum} = 1$, using Snell's law, the index of refraction is

$$n_g = \frac{\sin i}{\sin r} = \frac{\sin \theta_i}{\sin \theta_r} = \frac{BA/CA}{CD/CA} = \frac{BA}{CD} = \frac{c}{v_g}.$$

The index of refraction for any substance is then

$$n_s = \frac{c}{v_s},$$

where $v_s$ represents the speed of light in the substance. The speed of light in a vacuum, $3.00 \times 10^8$ m/s, is known. Therefore, it is possible to calculate the speed of light in many substances by using the equation $v_s = c/n_s$.

## Example Problem

### Speed of Light in a Medium

The index of refraction of water is 1.33. Calculate the speed of light in water.

**Given:** $n_{water} = 1.33$
$c = 3.00 \times 10^8$ m/s

**Unknown:** $v_{water}$

**Basic equation:** $n_s = \dfrac{c}{v_s}$

**Solution:** $n_{water} = \dfrac{c}{v_{water}}$

so, $v_{water} = \dfrac{c}{n_{water}} = \dfrac{3.00 \times 10^8 \text{ m/s}}{1.33} = 2.26 \times 10^8$ m/s

The index of refraction is the ratio of the speed of light in a vacuum to the speed in the medium.

## Practice Problems

**5.** Use Table 17–1 to find the speed of light in
   **a.** ethanol.     **b.** quartz.     **c.** flint glass.
**6.** The speed of light in a plastic is $2.00 \times 10^8$ m/s. What is the index of refraction of the plastic?
**7.** What is the speed of light for the substance of Practice Problem 4?
**8.** Suppose you had two pulses of light "racing" each other, one in air, the other in a vacuum. You could tell the winner if the time difference is 10 ns ($10 \times 10^{-9}$ s). How long would the race have to be to determine the winner?

# CONCEPT REVIEW

**1.1** Give examples of diffuse and regular reflectors.
**1.2** If you double the angle of incidence, the angle of reflection also doubles. Does the angle of refraction?
**1.3** You notice that when a light ray enters a certain liquid from water, it is bent toward the normal, but when it enters the same liquid from crown glass, it is bent away from the normal. What can you conclude about its index of refraction?
**1.4** **Critical Thinking:** Could an index of refraction ever be less than 1? What would that imply about the velocity of light in that medium?

## Objectives

· explain total internal reflection; define the critical angle.
· explain effects caused by the refraction of light in a medium with varying refractive indices.
· explain dispersion of light in terms of index of refraction.

# 17.2 APPLICATIONS OF REFLECTED AND REFRACTED LIGHT

**M**odern societies depend on communication systems. The telephone has become necessary for both homes and businesses. But, in many cities, the underground pipes containing telephone wires are so full that no new customers can be added. Now the old wires can be replaced by a bundle of optical fibres that can carry thousands of telephone conversations at once. Moreover, illegal tapping of optical fibres is almost impossible. This application of the reflection of light is revolutionizing our communication systems.

## Total Internal Reflection

When a ray of light passes from a more optically dense medium into air, the light is bent away from the normal. In other words, the angle of refraction is larger than the angle of incidence. The fact that the angle of refraction is larger than the angle of incidence leads to an interesting phenomenon known as total internal reflection. **Total internal reflection** occurs when light passes from a more optically dense medium to a less optically dense medium at an angle so great that there is no refracted ray. Figure 17–8 shows such an occurrence. Ray 1 is incident upon the surface of the water at angle $\theta_i$. Ray 1 produces the angle of refraction, $\theta_r$. Ray 2 is incident at such a large angle, $\theta_i$, that the refracted ray lies along the surface of the water. The angle of refraction is 90°.

For light traveling from one medium into another, Snell's law is

$$n_i \sin \theta_i = n_r \sin \theta_r$$
$$(n_{water})(\sin \theta_i) = (n_{air})(\sin \theta_r)$$
$$(1.33)(\sin \theta_i) = (1.00)(\sin 90°).$$

## POCKET LAB

### NOW YOU SEE IT...

Fill an aquarium with water. Place a hand-held calculator against the back side (outside) of the aquarium. Look at the calculator through the front side of the aquarium. Look at the calculator through the left side and right side of the aquarium. Explain your observations.

**FIGURE 17–8. Ray 1 is refracted. Ray 2 is refracted along the boundary of the medium showing the critical angle. An angle of incidence greater than the critical angle results in the total internal reflection of ray 3.**

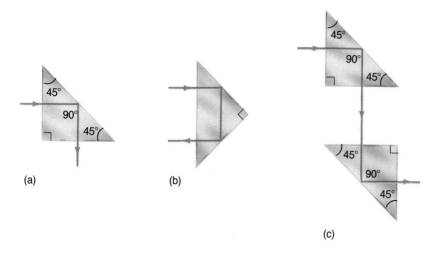

FIGURE 17–9. Internal reflection in a prism.

(a)

(b)

(c)

Solving the equation for sin $\theta_i$,

$$\sin \theta_i = \frac{(1.00)(\sin 90°)}{1.33} = 0.752$$

so, $\theta_i = 48.8°$.

When an incident ray of light passing from water to air makes an angle of 48.8°, the angle of refraction is 90°.

The incident angle that causes the refracted ray to lie right along the boundary of the substance, angle $\theta_c$, is unique to the substance. It is known as the **critical angle** of the substance. The critical angle, $\theta_c$, of any substance may be calculated as follows.

$$n_i \sin \theta_i = n_r \sin \theta_r$$

In this situation, $\theta_i = \theta_c$; $n_r = 1.000$; and $\theta_r = 90.0°$.

$$\sin \theta_c = \frac{(1.00)(\sin 90.0°)}{n_i} = \frac{1}{n_i}$$

For crown glass, the critical angle can be calculated as follows.

$$\sin \theta_c = \frac{1}{1.52} = 0.658$$

$$\theta_c = 41.1°$$

Any ray that reaches the surface of water at an angle greater than the critical angle, Figure 17–8, ray 3 cannot leave the water. All of the light is reflected. Total internal reflection has occurred.

Total internal reflection causes some curious effects. Suppose you look at the surface of a tank from underwater, Figure 17–10. A doll with its legs submerged may appear to be inverted. Likewise, if a swimmer is near the surface of a quiet pool, the swimmer may not be visible to an observer standing near the side of the pool. Total internal reflection has also given rise to the field of fiber optics.

FIGURE 17–10. This underwater photograph shows both the direct and transmitted images.

**FIGURE 17–11.** Fibre optics makes it possible to use light instead of electricity to transmit voices and data.

Optical fibres are used to transmit light signals.

What happens to light that enters a long, thin glass rod? Figure 17–11 shows the path of one ray. Each surface reflection is at an angle larger than the critical angle. The reflection is total, keeping the light within the rod. Light acts the same way in a thin glass fibre coated with a layer of glass with a lower index of refraction. Such a thin, flexible optical fibre can be easily bent around corners or combined with many other fibres into a cable.

Light passing through optical fibres can be used to transmit information. Normally telephone, radio, and television information is transmitted by varying the amplitude of the signal. In fibre optics technology, the amplitude of the electromagnetic signal can be converted into a digital signal, a series of binary bits, "0"'s and "1"'s. For example, a signal with amplitude 13 would be 1,1,0,1, while 3 would be 0,0,1,1. A light that is turned on (for a 1) and off (for a 0) produces a signal made up of a series of light pulses that can be transmitted by a fibre. A solid-state laser at one end of an optical fibre is turned on and off very rapidly. The series of pulses is detected at the other end of the fibre and is converted back into a signal of varying amplitude. Information equivalent to 25 000 telephone conversations can be carried by a fibre the thickness of a human hair. For this reason, optical fibres are being used to transmit telephone, computer, and video signals within buildings, from city to city, and even across oceans.

Optical fibres are used for more than communication. Two bundles of fibres are used to explore the inside of the human body. One bundle transmits light, while the other carries the reflected light back to the doctor. Plants have also been shown to use total internal reflection to "pipe" light to cells that utilize light energy.

## Effects of Refraction

Many interesting effects are caused by the refraction of light. Mirages, the apparent shift in the position of objects immersed in liquids, and the lingering daylight after the sun is below the horizon are a few examples.

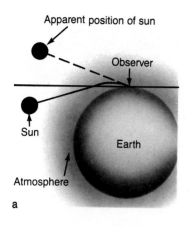

Apparent position of sun

Observer

Sun

Earth

Atmosphere

a

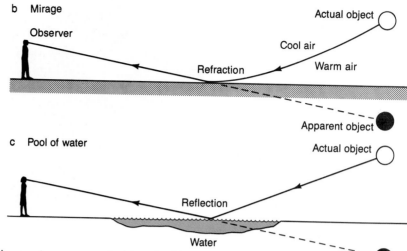

b  Mirage

Observer

Actual object

Cool air

Refraction

Warm air

Apparent object

c  Pool of water

Actual object

Reflection

Water

Apparent object

Mirages can be observed along highways in summer. A driver looking almost parallel to the road sees what looks like a puddle of water. The puddle, however, disappears as the car approaches. The mirage is the result of the sun heating the road. The hot road, in turn, heats the air above it, while the air farther above the road remains cool. The index of refraction of air at 30°C, for example, is 1.00026, while that of air at 15°C is 1.00028. Thus, there is a continuous change in the index of refraction of the air. A ray of light aimed toward the road encounters the smaller index of refraction and is bent away from the normal, that is, more parallel to the road. The ray bends, in Figure 17–12b. The motorist actually sees light from the sky, which looks like light reflected from a puddle.

An object submerged in a liquid is not where it appears to be. As a result of refraction, an object may appear to be much closer to the surface of the liquid than it really is. Refraction also makes a spoon placed in a glass of water appear bent.

Light travels at a slightly slower speed in Earth's atmosphere than it does in outer space. As a result, sunlight is refracted by the atmosphere. In the morning, this refraction causes sunlight to reach us before the sun is actually above the horizon, Figure 17–12a. In the evening, the sunlight is bent above the horizon after the sun has actually set. Thus, daylight is extended in the morning and evening because of the refraction of light.

**FIGURE 17–12.** After the sun has actually set, it is still visible due to refraction of light over the horizon through the atmosphere (a). Refraction of light in air of different densities (b) produces an effect similar to the reflection of light off a pool of water (c).

# F.Y.I.

In 1880, a few years after he invented the telephone, Alexander Graham Bell created a device, called the photophone, that transmitted sound using a beam of light. However, the device was not useful because there were no wires or means of transmitting the light signals from the photophone.

**FIGURE 17–13.** Mirages are caused by the refracting properties of a nonuniform atmosphere. Scientists are unable to explain exactly some complex mirages.

FIGURE 17–14. White light directed
through a prism is dispersed into
bands of different colours.

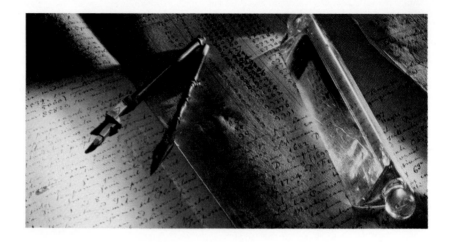

## Dispersion of Light

In most materials, the index of
refraction depends on the wavelength.

Light of all wavelengths travels through the vacuum of space at $3.00 \times 10^8$ m/s. In other media, however, light waves travel more slowly. In addition, waves of different wavelengths travel at different speeds. This fact means that the index of refraction of a material depends on the wavelength of the incident light.

If the angle of refraction depends on
wavelength, the light is dispersed.

In glass and most other materials, red light travels fastest; it has the smallest index of refraction. Violet light, on the other hand, is slowed the most; it has the largest index of refraction. As a result, when white light falls on a prism, red light is bent the least and violet light the most, Figure 17–14. The wavelengths (colours) are separated. The light leaving the prism is dispersed to form a spectrum. **Dispersion** is the separation of light into a spectrum by refraction. Newton investigated dispersion as shown in Figure 17–15. The first prism, ABC, spread the colours into the spectrum p, q, r, s, t. Newton then used a lens to direct all colours on to the second prism, EDG. White light came out of this prism. In this way Newton demonstrated that the prisms did not somehow add the colours to the light.

Glass is not the only substance that disperses light. A diamond not only has one of the highest refractive indices of any material, it also has one of the largest variations in the index. Thus, it disperses light more than most other materials. The intense colours seen when light is dispersed in a diamond is the reason these gems are said to have "fire."

FIGURE 17–15. "And the Colours
generated by the...two Prisms, will
be mingled at Point T, and there
compound white. For if either Prism
be taken away, the colours made by
the other will appear in that Place,
and when the Prism is restored to its
Place again, so that its Colours may
there fall upon the Colours of the
other, the Mixture of them both will
restore the Whiteness."

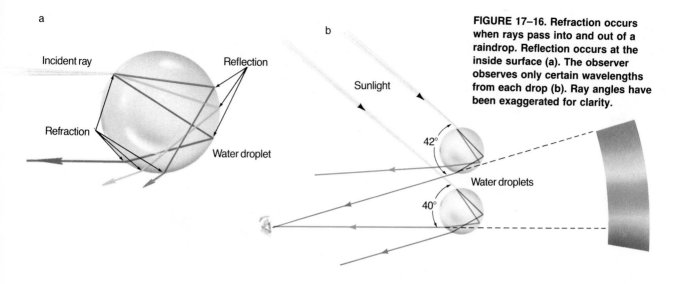

a

Incident ray

Reflection

Refraction

Water droplet

b

Sunlight

42°

Water droplets

40°

**FIGURE 17–16.** Refraction occurs when rays pass into and out of a raindrop. Reflection occurs at the inside surface (a). The observer observes only certain wavelengths from each drop (b). Ray angles have been exaggerated for clarity.

Different light sources have different spectra. A prism can be used to determine the spectrum of a source. Light from an incandescent lamp, for example, contains all visible wavelengths of light. When this light passes through a prism, a continuous band of colour is seen. Light from a flourescent lamp has both a continuous spectrum and light emitted at four individual wavelengths. Thus, its spectrum contains both a continuous band and bright lines at specific colours.

A rainbow is a spectrum formed when sunlight is dispersed by water droplets in the atmosphere. Sunlight that is incident on a water droplet is refracted. Because of dispersion, each colour is refracted at a slightly different angle, Figure 17–16a. At the back surface of the droplet, the light undergoes total internal reflection. On the way out of the droplet, the light is once more refracted and dispersed. Although each droplet produces a complete spectrum, an observer will see only a certain wavelength of light from each droplet. The wavelength depends on the relative positions of sun, droplet, and observer. Because there are millions of droplets in the sky, a complete spectrum is seen. The droplets reflecting red light make an angle of 42° with respect to the direction of the sun's rays; the droplets reflecting blue light make an angle of 40°, Figure 17–16b.

Dispersion in a prism is used to analyse the spectrum of light source.

The separation of colours in a rainbow is the result of dispersion in a raindrop.

. . . . . . . . . . . . . . . . . . .

◀**A Smile in the Sky**

. . . . . . . . . . . . . . . . . . . .

# CONCEPT REVIEW

**2.1** If you were to use quartz and crown glass to make an optical fibre, which would you use for the coating layer? Why?

**2.2** Is there a critical angle for light going from glass to water? How about water to glass?

**2.3** Why can you see the sun just above the horizon when it has already set?

**2.4** Critical Thinking: In what direction can you see a rainbow on a rainy late afternoon?

## FIBRE OPTICS IN MEDICINE

Optical fibres are providing physicians with revolutionary tools for medical imaging, diagnosis, and treatment. The small, flexible fibres can be inserted into many areas of the body that are inaccessible by other means.

By directing a light source through the fibres, physicians can examine light reflected from internal organs and blood vessels in minute detail. Using a variety of sensing techniques, optical fibres can analyse blood chemistry, measure blood flow, compute various body pressures, and monitor levels of toxins, hormones, and therapeutic drugs.

Some of the most important applications of optical fibres are in laser surgery. Laser light transmitted through optical fibres is used to cauterize blood vessels and incisions to stop bleeding, vaporize blockages in coronary arteries, and destroy localized tumors.

Many fibre-optic procedures do not require anesthesia or hospitalization. They thus have the potential to reduce the cost and risk of many types of medical care.

· What would be the desirable characteristics of materials used as optical fibres?

# CHAPTER
## 17 REVIEW

## SUMMARY

### 17.1 How Light Behaves at a Boundary

· The law of reflection states that the angle of reflection is equal to the angle of incidence.
· Refraction is the bending of light rays at the boundary between two media. Refraction occurs only when the incident ray strikes the boundary at an angle.
· Snell's law states that when light goes from a medium with small $n$ to one with large $n$, it is bent toward the normal. Light going from materials with a large $n$ to those with a small $n$ is bent away from the normal.

### 17.2 Applications of Reflected and Refracted Light

· Total internal reflection occurs if light is incident on a boundary from the medium with the larger index of refraction. If the angle of incidence is greater than the critical angle, no light leaves; it is all reflected.
· Light waves of different wavelengths have slightly different refractive indices. Thus they are refracted at different angles. Light falling on a prism is dispersed into a spectrum of colours.

## KEY TERMS

| | |
|---|---|
| diffuse reflection | total internal |
| regular reflection | reflection |
| optically dense | critical angle |
| refraction | dispersion |
| Snell's law | |
| index of refraction | |

# REVIEWING CONCEPTS

1. What is meant by the normal to a surface?
2. How does regular reflection differ from diffuse reflection?
3. Does the law of reflection hold for diffuse reflection? Explain.
4. Copy Figure 17–17 onto your paper. Draw a normal and label the angle of incidence and the angle of refraction if the light went from substance A to substance B.

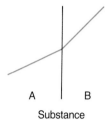

A | B
Substance

**FIGURE 17–17. Use with Reviewing Concepts 4 and Applying Concepts 7.**

5. Compare the angle of incidence with the angle of refraction when a light ray passes from air into glass at a non-zero angle.
6. Compare the angle of incidence with the angle of refraction when a light ray leaves glass and enters air at a non-zero angle.
7. What are the units of the index of refraction?
8. State Snell's law in your own words.
9. Derive $n = \dfrac{\sin \theta_i}{\sin \theta_r}$ from the general form of Snell's law, $n_1 \sin \theta_1 = n_2 \sin \theta_2$. State any assumptions and restrictions.
10. What is the "critical angle" of incidence?
11. What happens to a ray of light with an angle of incidence greater than the critical angle?
12. Explain mirages.
13. List the different colours of light in the order of increasing
    a. wavelength    b. frequency.
14. What evidence is there that diamond has a slightly different index of refraction for each colour of light?

# APPLYING CONCEPTS

1. A dry road is a diffuse reflector, while a wet road is not. Sketch a car with headlights illuminating the road ahead. Show why the wet road would appear darker to the driver than the dry road.

2. Why is it desirable that the pages of a book be rough rather than smooth and glossy?
3. Is it necessary to measure the volume of a glass block to find its optical density? Explain.
4. A light ray strikes the boundary between two transparent media. What is the angle of incidence for which there is no refraction?
5. In the Example Problem on Snell's law, a ray of light is incident upon crown glass at 30.0°. The angle of refraction is 19.2°. Assume the glass is rectangular in shape. Construct a diagram to show the incident ray, the refracted ray, and the normal. Continue the ray through the glass until it reaches the opposite edge.
   a. Construct a normal at this point. What is the angle at which the refracted ray is incident upon the opposite edge of the glass?
   b. Assume the material outside the opposite edge is air. What is the angle at which the ray leaves the glass?
   c. As the ray leaves the glass, is it refracted away from or toward the normal?
   d. How is the orientation of the ray leaving the glass related to the ray entering the glass?
6. Assume the angle of incidence remains the same. What happens to the angle of refraction as the index of refraction increases?
7. Which substance, A or B, in Figure 17–17 has a larger index of refraction? Explain.
8. How does the speed of light change as the index of refraction increases?
9. How does the size of the critical angle change as the index of refraction increases?
10. Which two pairs of media, air and water or air and glass, have the smaller critical angle?
11. Examine Figure 17–5. Why do the two left-hand bottom rays that enter the prism exit vertically while the two top rays exit horizontally? **Hint:** If you look carefully, you will find that the middle ray has both vertical and horizontal intensity and that there is a trace of the other ray moving vertically.
12. If you crack the windshield in your car, you will see a silvery line along the crack. The two pieces of glass have separated at the crack, and there is air between them. The silvery line indicates light is reflecting off the crack. Draw a ray diagram to explain why this occurs. What phenomenon does this illustrate?

**13.** According to legend, Erik the Red sailed from Iceland and discovered Greenland after he had seen the land in a mirage. Draw a sketch of Iceland and Greenland and explain how the mirage might have occurred.

**FIGURE 17–18.**

**14.** A prism bends violet light more than red light. Explain.

**15.** Which colour of light travels fastest in glass: red, green, or blue?

**16.** Why would you never see a rainbow in the southern sky if you were in the northern hemisphere?

# PROBLEMS

## 17.1 How Light Behaves at a Boundary

**1.** A ray of light strikes a mirror at an angle of 53° to the normal.
   **a.** What is the angle of reflection?
   **b.** What is the angle between the incident ray and the reflected ray?

**2.** A ray of light incident upon a mirror makes an angle of 36.0° with the mirror. What is the angle between the incident ray and the reflected ray?

**3.** A ray of light has an angle of incidence of 30.0° on a block of quartz and an angle of refraction of 20.0°. What is the index of refraction for this block of quartz?

**4.** A ray of light travels from air into a liquid. The ray is incident upon the liquid at an angle of 30.0°. The angle of refraction is 22.0°.
   **a.** What is the index of refraction of the liquid?
   **b.** Refer to Table 17–1. What might the liquid be?

**5.** A ray of light is incident at an angle of 60.0° upon the surface of a piece of crown glass. What is the angle of refraction?

**6.** A light ray strikes the surface of a pond at an angle of incidence of 36.0°. At what angle is the ray refracted?

**7.** Light is incident at an angle of 60.0° on the surface of a diamond. Find the angle of refraction.

**8.** A ray of light has an angle of incidence of 33.0° in crown glass. What is the angle of refraction?

**9.** A ray of light passes from water into crown glass at an angle of 23.2°. Find the angle of refraction.

**10.** Light goes from flint glass into ethanol. The angle of refraction in the ethanol is 25°. What is the angle of incidence in the glass?

**11.** A beam of light strikes the flat, glass side of a water-filled aquarium at an angle of 40° to the normal. For glass, $n = 1.50$. At what angle does the beam
   **a.** enter the glass?
   **b.** enter the water?

▶ **12.** A thick sheet of plastic, $n = 1.500$, is used as the side of an aquarium tank. Light reflected from a fish in the water has an angle of incidence of 35.0°. At what angle does the light enter the air?

▶ **13.** A light source, $S$, is located 2.0 m below the surface of a swimming pool and 1.5 m from one edge of the pool. The pool is filled to the top with water.
   **a.** At what angle does the light reaching the edge of the pool leave the water?
   **b.** Does this cause the light viewed from this angle to appear deeper or shallower than it actually is?

▶ **14.** A ray of light is incident upon a 60-60-60-degree glass prism, $n = 1.5$, Figure 17–19.
   **a.** Using Snell's law, determine the angle $\theta_r$ to the nearest degree.
   **b.** Using elementary geometry, determine the values of angles $A$, $B$, and $C$.
   **c.** Determine angle $D$.

**FIGURE 17–19. Use with Problem 14.**

**15.** A sheet of plastic, $n = 1.500$, 25 mm thick is used in a bank teller's window. A ray of light strikes the sheet at an angle of 45°. The ray leaves the sheet at 45° but at a different location. Use a ray diagram to find the distance between the ray that leaves and the one that would have left if the plastic were not there.

**16.** What is the speed of light in diamond?

**17.** The speed of light in chloroform is $1.99 \times 10^8$ m/s. What is its index of refraction?

**18.** The speed of light in a clear plastic is $1.90 \times 10^8$ m/s. A ray of light enters the plastic at an angle of 22°. At what angle is the ray refracted?

**19.** How many more minutes would it take light from the sun to reach Earth if the space between them were filled with water rather than a vacuum? The sun is $1.5 \times 10^8$ km from Earth.

## 17.2 Applications of Reflected and Refracted Light

**20.** Find the critical angle for diamond.

**21.** A block of glass has a critical angle of 45.0°. What is its index of refraction?

**22.** A ray of light in a tank of water has an angle of incidence of 55°. What is the angle of refraction in air?

**23.** A light ray enters a rectangle of crown glass, Figure 17–20. Use a ray diagram to trace the path of the ray until it leaves the glass.

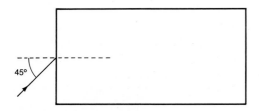

**FIGURE 17–20. Use with Problem 23.**

**24.** The critical angle for special glass in air is 41°. What is the critical angle if the glass is immersed in water?

**25.** The index of refraction for a diamond for red light, 656 nm, is 2.410, while that for blue light, 434 nm, is 2.450. Suppose white light is incident on the diamond at 30.0°. Find the angles of refraction for these two colours.

**26.** The index of refraction for crown glass for red light is 1.514, while that for blue light is 1.528. White light is incident on the glass at 30.0°.
   **a.** Find the angles of refraction for these two colours.
   **b.** Compare the difference in angles to that for diamond found in Problem 25.
   **c.** Use the results to explain why diamonds are said to have "fire."

**27.** The index of refraction of crown glass for violet light is 1.53, while for red light it is 1.51.
   **a.** What is the speed of violet light in crown glass?
   **b.** What is the speed of red light in crown glass?

**28.** Just before sunset, you see a rainbow in the water from a lawn sprinkler. Carefully draw your location and the locations of the sun and the water from the sprinkler that show the rainbow.

## THINKING PHYSIC-LY

Although the light coming from the sun is retracted while passing through Earth's atmosphere, the light is not separated into its spectrum. What does this tell us about the speeds of different colours of light travelling through air?

# CHAPTER 18
# Mirrors and Lenses

◀ Butterfly Butterfly

Wing-Yui produced this image of a butterfly on the screen. Wesley said, "That must be a concave lens since the butterfly image is spread out and larger than the real butterfly. Wing-Yui replied, "Maybe, but I'm not so sure." Who is correct, and what is the source of the two small images that seem to float in the lens?

W e are so accustomed to using mirrors and lenses that we give them little thought. Eyeglasses, magnifying glasses, microscopes, and camcorders use the laws of refraction and reflection. Notice the four butterflies in the photo. Only one is the real butterfly. The other three, small, large, upright or turned upside down, are the result of reflection and refraction in a single piece of glass. Moreover, our entire view of the world is the result of the optical images formed on our retinas by the lenses in our eyes.

## ✓ Concept Check

The following terms or concepts from earlier chapters are important for a good understanding of this chapter. If you are not familiar with them, you should review them before studying this chapter.
· law of reflection, Snell's law, law of refraction, Chapter 17

- describe the image produced by a plane mirror.
- define the focal point; explain the origin of parallel rays.
- explain the rules of ray tracing in concave mirrors.
- define spherical aberration and describe uses of parabolic mirrors.
- distinguish between real and virtual images.
- explain how concave mirrors form real and virtual images; locate the image with ray diagrams; use the mirror equation to calculate location and magnification.
- explain how convex mirrors form virtual images using ray diagrams; locate image; calculate location and magnification with mirror equation.

# 18.1 MIRRORS

**M**irrors are probably the oldest optical instrument. Polished metal was used to reflect the faces of inhabitants of ancient Egypt almost four thousand years ago. It wasn't until 1857, however, that the bright images we see today became possible. In that year, Jean Foucault developed a method of coating glass with silver.

## Objects and Their Images in Plane Mirrors

When you look at yourself in a bathroom mirror, you are seeing your image in a plane mirror. A **plane mirror** is a flat, smooth surface that reflects light in a regular way. You are the object. An **object** is a source of diverging light rays. An object may be luminous, like a candle or lamp. More often an object is illuminated, like the moon or the page you are reading. An illuminated object diffusely reflects light in all directions.

Figure 18–1a shows how some of the rays from point **P** strike the mirror and are reflected with equal angles of incidence and reflection. After reflection, the rays continue to spread. If we extend the rays backward, behind the mirror, as done with the dashed lines in Figure 18–1, we find that they intersect at a point **P'**. Point **P'**, where the extended rays apparently intersect, is called the **image.** Although, to an observer, the rays appear to come from point **P'**, you can see that no source is really there. For that reason, this kind of image is called a **virtual image.**

Where is the image located? Figure 18–2 shows two rays from object **P.** One strikes the mirror at **B,** the other at **M.** Both rays are reflected with equal angles of incidence and reflection. Thus the triangles **BPM**

Light rays spread from each point on an object.

There is one image for each point on the object.

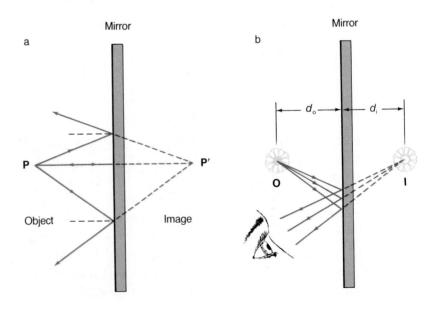

**FIGURE 18–1.** The image formed by a plane mirror appears to be a distance $d_i$ behind the mirror, equal to the object distance, $d_o$.

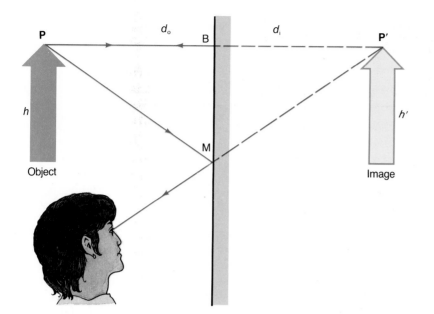

Object

$d_o$    B    $d_i$    P′

$h$

M

$h'$

Image

FIGURE 18–2. Ray diagram for locating an image in a plane mirror. Two rays from the object are traced to the point behind the mirror at which they intersect.

and **BP′M** are congruent. From **P** to **B,** the distance between the object and the mirror, is $d_o$. From **P′** to **B,** the distance between the image and the mirror, is $d_i$; $d_o = d_i$. The image is thus the same distance behind the mirror that the object is in front of it. In a similar way, you can show that the image is the same size as the object and is erect, Figure 18–3a.

In Figure 18–3b, the right and left hands of an image appear to be reversed. You might ask why the top and bottom are not also reversed. If you look at the figure carefully, you will see that the direction that is really reversed is the one perpendicular to the surface of mirror. Left and right are interchanged, in the same manner that a right-hand glove can be worn on the left hand by turning it inside out. Thus, it is more correct to say that the front and back of an image are reversed.

FIGURE 18–3. The image formed in a plane mirror is the same size as the object and is the same distance behind the mirror as the object is in front (a). A mirror seems to reverse right and left. More careful consideration shows that it interchanges front and back (b).

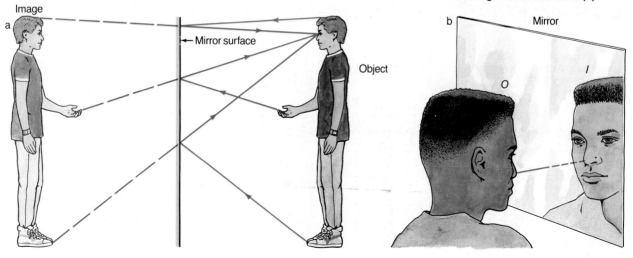

Image

a

← Mirror surface

Object

b    Mirror

O    I

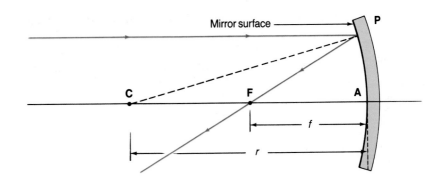

**FIGURE 18–4.** The focus of a concave spherical mirror is located halfway between the centre of curvature and the mirror surface. Rays entering parallel to the principal axis are reflected to converge at the focal point.

A concave mirror is caved in.

Incident rays parallel to the principal axis are reflected to converge at the focal point.

# F.Y.I.

A parabolic mirror can also be used for cooking in areas where fuel is scarce. If a cooking pot is placed at the focal point of a large concave mirror, the energy of the sunlight can be concentrated at one point, producing high temperatures.

**FIGURE 18–5.** The surface of a concave mirror reflects light to a given point (b), much like a group of plane mirrors arranged in a curve (a).

## Concave Mirrors

Examine the inside surface of a spoon. It acts like a concave mirror. A **concave mirror** reflects light from its inner ("caved in") surface. In a spherical concave mirror, the mirror is part of the inner surface of a hollow sphere, Figure 18–4. The sphere of radius $r$ has a geometric centre, **C**. Point **A** is the centre of the mirror, and the line **CA** is the **principal axis**, the straight line perpendicular to the surface of the mirror at its centre.

How does light reflect from a concave mirror? Think of a concave mirror as a large number of small plane mirrors arranged around the surface of a sphere, Figure 18–5. Each mirror is perpendicular to a radius of the sphere. When a ray strikes a mirror, it is reflected with equal angles of incidence and reflection. A ray parallel to the principal axis is reflected at **P** and crosses the principal axis at some point **F**, as in Figure 18–4. A parallel ray an equal distance below the principal axis would, by symmetry, also cross the principal axis at **F**. These parallel rays would meet, or converge, at the **focal point** of the mirror. The two sides **FC** and **FP** of the triangle **CFP** are equal in length. Thus, for very small angles, the focal point, **F**, is half the distance between the mirror and the centre of curvature, **C**.

How can you find the location of the focal point of a concave mirror? A source of nearly parallel rays is the sun. Therefore, if you point the principal axis of a concave mirror at the sun, all the rays will be reflected through a point near the focal point. Hold a piece of paper near the mirror and move the paper toward and away from the mirror until

a

b

the smallest and sharpest spot is formed. The spot must be at the focal point because, as discussed above, the rays striking the mirror were, for all practical purposes, parallel. The distance from the focal point to the mirror along the principal axis is the **focal length,** *f,* of the mirror. The focal length is half the radius of curvature of the mirror.

## Spherical Aberration and Parabolic Mirrors

Parallel rays converge at the focal point of a spherical mirror only if they are close to the principal axis. As seen in Figure 18–6, the two rays farthest from the principal axis converge at a point slightly closer to the mirror than the others. The image formed by parallel rays in a large spherical mirror is a disk, not a point. This effect is called **spherical aberration** (ab uh RAY shuhn).

Parabolic mirrors have no spherical aberration. They are used to focus parallel rays from distant stars to a sharp focus in telescopes. Perfectly parabolic mirrors are very difficult to make. Makers of the mirror in the Hubble Space Telescope made an error in grinding the glass of $2\mu m$, about the thickness of a human hair, resulting in spherical aberration in the mirror. It focuses only 15% of the light into a tiny spot, not the 70% it was designed to.

Parabolic mirrors can also produce the parallel beams of light needed in flashlights, car headlights, and searchlights. The light source is placed at **F** and the reflected rays leave in a parallel beam. This illustrates an important principle of ray optics, the object and the image can be interchanged. Light rays can go in either direction.

## Real vs Virtual Images

Parallel rays of the sun or other distant objects reflected from a concave mirror converge at the focal point of the mirror. The converging rays form a bright spot on a piece of paper at the focal point. An image is a **real image** if rays actually converge and pass through the image. A real image can be seen on a piece of paper or screen.

In contrast, the image produced by a plane mirror is behind the mirror. The rays reflected from a plane mirror never actually converge but appear to diverge from a point behind the mirror. A virtual image cannot be projected on a screen or captured on a piece of paper because light rays do not converge at a virtual image.

The focal length is the distance between the focal point and the mirror.

Because of spherical aberration, parallel rays are not reflected to a point.

Perfectly parabolic mirrors have no spherical aberration.

A real image can be projected on a screen.

a **Spherical mirror**

b **Parabolic mirror**

**FIGURE 18–6. In a concave spherical mirror, some rays converge at points other than the focus (a). A parabolic mirror focuses all parallel rays at a point (b).**

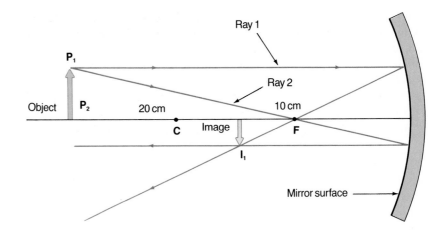

**FIGURE 18–7. Finding the real image formed by a concave spherical mirror when the object is located beyond the centre of curvature, C, of the mirror.**

## Real Images Formed by Concave Mirrors

A virtual image cannot be projected on a screen.

Ray diagrams can be used to find the location and size of images.

Concave mirrors can form both real and virtual images. We will use ray diagrams to show how concave mirrors form real images and how to locate these images. Figure 18–7 shows a concave mirror with an object farther from the mirror than C, the centre of curvature of the mirror. Such an object is said to be "beyond C." Rays leave the object in all directions. A few of these rays fall on the mirror. We will now find the image formed by those rays.

## PROBLEM SOLVING STRATEGIES

Two rules are used to find the images formed by mirrors.
1. Incident light rays parallel to the principal axis of a mirror are reflected through the focal point.
2. Incident rays that pass through the focal point are reflected parallel to the principal axis.

To construct a ray diagram follow these steps:
1. Choose a scale. Your goal is to make the drawing close to the width of your paper, about 20 cm. You will find that if the object is beyond **F**, the image is real and on the object side of the mirror. If the object is beyond **2F**, we will see that the object distance is larger than the image distance. If not, the image distance is equal or larger. Choose the scale such that the larger distance, object or image, is 15 to 20 cm on your paper. To make calculating simpler, let 1 cm on the paper equal 1, 2, 4, 5, or 10 cm.
2. Draw the principal axis and put the mirror at the right-hand side of the paper. Draw a vertical line at the location of the mirror. Place a dot on the axis at the location of the focal point.
3. Draw the object. Usually the object and image height have to be drawn to a larger scale than used in Step 1 to be visible.
4. Select a point, **P₁**, to be the top of the object. Draw Ray 1 parallel to the principal axis. As shown above, Ray 1, called the parallel ray, reflects through the focal point, **F**. Draw Ray 2 so it passes through **F**

on its way to the mirror. Ray 2 is called the focus ray. This ray reflects parallel to the principal axis. The two rays drawn from $P_1$ converge at $I_1$.

5. Draw the image as a vertical line between $I_1$ and the principal axis.

The image formed by an object beyond **C** is found to be between **C** and **F**. It is a real image because the rays actually come together at this point. The image is inverted. That is, point $I_1$, the image of the top of the object, is below the principal axis. The image is also smaller than the object.

As an object is moved inward toward **C**, the image position moves outward toward **C**. When the object is at **C**, the image is also located there. The image is real, inverted, and, in this case, the same size as the object. If the object is moved from **C** toward **F**, the image moves out beyond **C**. This can be seen by reversing the direction of the light rays in Figure 18–7. The roles of image and object are reversed.

An equation can also be used to locate the image and find its size. The focal length, $f$, the distance of the object from the mirror, $d_o$, and the distance of the image from the mirror, $d_i$, are related by the **mirror equation.**

$$\frac{1}{f} = \frac{1}{d_i} + \frac{1}{d_o}$$

The ratio of the size of the image, $h_i$, to the size of the object, $h_o$, is called the **magnification,** $m$. The magnification is related to the distances to the mirror by the equation

$$m = \frac{h_i}{h_o} = \frac{-d_i}{d_o}.$$

If $d_i$ and $d_o$ are both positive, then both $m$ and $h_i$ are negative. This means the image is inverted.

For objects beyond F, as the object is moved closer to a concave mirror, the image moves farther away and grows in size.

# F.Y.I.

In 1857, Jean Foucault developed a technique for silvering glass to make mirrors for reflecting telescopes. Mirrors became lighter and less likely to tarnish than they were with the metal previously used.

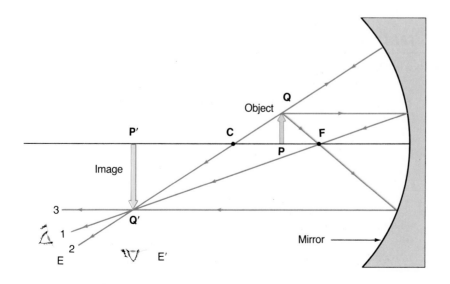

**FIGURE 18–8.** To the eye, **E**, it appears that there is an object at **Q'** blocking the view of the mirror behind. However, if the eye moves to **E'** and looks toward **Q'**, the "object" disappears because there is then no light reflected from **Q'** to **E'**.

# Example Problem

## Real Image from a Concave Mirror

An object 2.0 cm high is 30.0 cm from a concave mirror. The radius of curvature of the mirror is 20.0 cm. **a.** What is the location of the image? **b.** What is the size of the image?

**Given:** object height,
$h_o = 2.0$ cm
object location,
$d_o = 30.0$ cm
radius of curvature,
$r = 20.0$ cm
focal length,
$f = \frac{1}{2}r$

**Unknowns: a.** image location, $d_i$
**b.** image height, $h_i$

**Basic equations:** $\dfrac{1}{f} = \dfrac{1}{d_i} + \dfrac{1}{d_o}$

$m = \dfrac{h_i}{h_o} = \dfrac{-d_i}{d_o}$

**Solution: a.** $f = \frac{1}{2}r = \dfrac{20.0 \text{ cm}}{2} = 10.0$ cm

$$\frac{1}{f} = \frac{1}{d_o} + \frac{1}{d_i}$$

$$\text{so } \frac{1}{d_i} = \frac{1}{f} - \frac{1}{d_o}$$

$$\text{or } d_i = \frac{fd_o}{d_o - f}$$

$$= \frac{(10.0 \text{ cm})(30.0 \text{ cm})}{(30.0 \text{ cm} - 10.0 \text{ cm})} = 15.0 \text{ cm}$$

**b.** $m = \dfrac{h_i}{h_o} = \dfrac{-d_i}{d_o},$

$$\text{so } h_i = \frac{-d_i h_o}{d_o}$$

$$= \frac{-(15.0 \text{ cm})(2.0 \text{ cm})}{30.0 \text{ cm}} = -1.0 \text{ cm}$$

The image size is negative, meaning it is inverted.

## Mirror Equation Conventions

$d_o$ is  positive for real objects.
negative for virtual objects.

$d_i$ is  positive for real images.
negative for virtual images.

$f$ is  positive for concave mirrors.
negative for convex mirrors.

# Practice Problems

1. Solve the Example Problem above using a ray diagram.
2. An object 3.0 mm high is 10.0 cm in front of a concave mirror having a 6.0-cm focal length. Find the image by means of
   **a.** a ray diagram.
   **b.** the mirror equation.
   **c.** Find the magnification of the mirror.
   **d.** What is the height of the image?
3. The image of an object is 30.0 cm from a concave mirror with a 20.0-cm radius of curvature. Locate the object.
▶ 4. An old "magic trick" used a concave mirror to project an image the same size as the object and at the same distance from the mirror. If the object is 25 cm from the mirror, what should be the radius of curvature of the mirror?

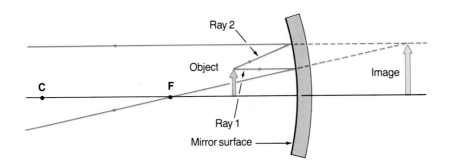

## Virtual Images Formed by Concave Mirrors

We have seen that as the object approaches the focal point, **F**, of a mirror, the image moves farther out. If the object is at the focal point, all reflected rays are parallel. The image is said to be at infinity. What happens if the object is closer to the mirror than **F**? Figure 18–9 shows an object 5.0 cm in front of a mirror of 10.0 cm focal length. The two rays have been drawn to locate the image. Ray 1 approaches the mirror parallel to the principal axis and is reflected through the focal point. Ray 2 moves away from the object as if it has come from the focal point. It is reflected parallel to the principal axis. The two reflected rays spread apart and will never converge. No real image exists. The dashed lines show the rays coming from their apparent origin behind the mirror. This virtual image is located behind the mirror.

An object closer to a concave mirror than the focal point forms a virtual image.

## Example Problem

### Virtual Image from a Concave Mirror

Find the location of the image in Figure 18–9 if an object 2.0 cm in height is 5.0 cm in front of a concave mirror of focal length 10.0 cm. How large is the image?

**Given:** $d_o = 5.0$ cm  
$h_o = 2.0$ cm  
$f = 10.0$ cm

**Unknowns:** image distance, $d_i$  
image height, $h_i$

**Basic equations:** $\dfrac{1}{f} = \dfrac{1}{d_i} + \dfrac{1}{d_o}$

$m = \dfrac{h_i}{h_o} = \dfrac{-d_i}{d_o}$

**Solution:** $\dfrac{1}{f} = \dfrac{1}{d_o} + \dfrac{1}{d_i}$, so $d_i = \dfrac{fd_o}{d_o - f} = \dfrac{(10.0 \text{ cm})(5.0 \text{ cm})}{5.0 \text{ cm} - 10.0 \text{ cm}}$

$= \dfrac{5.0 \times 10^1 \text{ cm}^2}{-5.0 \text{ cm}} = -1.0 \times 10^1 \text{ cm}$

A negative image distance indicates a virtual image, located behind the mirror.

$m = \dfrac{h_i}{h_o} = \dfrac{-d_i}{d_o}$, so $h_i = \dfrac{-h_o d_i}{d_o}$

$= \dfrac{-(2.0 \text{ cm})(-10.0 \text{ cm})}{5.0 \text{ cm}} = +4.0 \text{ cm}$

**FIGURE 18–10.** Objects placed between the focal point and the surface of a concave mirror form enlarged virtual images.

A positive height indicates an upright image. Notice that the image height is larger than the object height; the image is enlarged.

If an object is located between the focal point and a concave mirror, its image will be virtual, erect, and enlarged. Shaving and makeup mirrors are concave. If you hold the mirror close to your face, the image will be virtual, erect, and enlarged.

## Practice Problems

5. An object is 4.0 cm in front of a concave mirror having a 12.0-cm radius. Locate the image using the mirror equation and a ray diagram.
6. A concave mirror has a focal length of 9.0 cm. A 15-mm high object is placed 6.0 cm from the mirror.
   **a.** Find the image using the mirror equation.
   **b.** How large is the image?
7. A 4.0-cm high candle is placed 10.0 cm from a concave mirror having a focal length of 16.0 cm.
   **a.** Where is the image located?
   **b.** What is the height of the candle's image?
► 8. What should be the radius of curvature of a concave mirror that magnifies an object placed 25 cm from the mirror by a factor of $+3.0$?

## Virtual Images Formed by Convex Mirrors

A **convex mirror** is a spherical mirror that reflects light from its outer surface. The outside bottom of a spoon is a convex mirror. Rays reflected from a convex mirror always diverge. Thus, convex mirrors do not form real images. When doing ray diagrams, the focal point, **F**, is placed behind the mirror, half the distance to the centre of curvature. When using the mirror equation, the focal length, $f$, of a convex mirror is a negative number.

The ray diagram, Figure 18–11, shows how an image is formed in a convex mirror. Ray 1 approaches the mirror parallel to the principal

Images formed by convex mirrors are virtual, erect, and reduced in size.

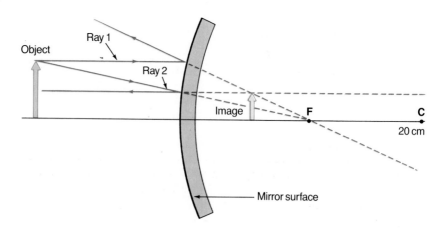

**FIGURE 18–11. Convex spherical mirrors cause reflected light rays to diverge.**

axis. To draw the reflected ray, draw a dashed line from the focal point, **F,** to the point where Ray 1 strikes the mirror. The reflected ray is in the same direction on the dashed line. Ray 2 approaches the mirror on a path that, if extended behind the mirror, would pass through **F.** The reflected part of Ray 2 is parallel to the principal axis. The two reflected rays diverge, as if coming from a point behind the mirror. The image, located at the apparent intersection of the extended rays behind the mirror, is virtual, erect, and reduced in size.

The mirror equation can be used to predict the location and size of images formed by convex lenses. The value of $f$ is negative, and $d_i$ will be negative if the image is behind the mirror.

Convex mirrors are called diverging mirrors because the reflected rays spread apart. Convex mirrors form images reduced in size, but they also reflect an enlarged field of view. Rearview mirrors used in cars are often convex mirrors, as are mirrors used in stores to observe shoppers.

Glass that has not been silvered also reflects light. If that glass is curved outward it will act like a convex mirror. You can frequently see reduced images of yourself if you look into someone's eyeglasses. The photo at the beginning of this chapter has a glass lens that reflects some light off both its front (convex) and rear (concave) surfaces. Both are reduced in size; one is inverted. The upright one comes from the convex surface, the inverted one from the concave surface.

A convex lens is thicker in the centre than at the edges.

A concave lens is thicker at the edges than in the centre.

◀ ·  ·  ·  ·  ·  ·  ·  ·  ·  ·  ·  ·  ·  ·  ·  ·  ·  ·
**Butterfly    ylⅎɹǝʇʇnꓭ**

## Example Problem

### Image from a Convex Mirror

Calculate the position of the image in Figure 18–11. Use the mirror equation.

**Given:** $d_o = 15$ cm
$\quad\quad\quad f = -10.0$ cm

**Unknown:** $d_i$

**Basic equation:** $\dfrac{1}{f} = \dfrac{1}{d_i} + \dfrac{1}{d_o}$

**Solution:** $\dfrac{1}{f} = \dfrac{1}{d_o} + \dfrac{1}{d_i}$,

$\quad$ so $d_i = \dfrac{fd_o}{d_o - f}$

$\quad\quad\quad = \dfrac{(-10.0 \text{ cm})(15 \text{ cm})}{15 \text{ cm} - (-10.0 \text{ cm})}$

$\quad\quad\quad = -6.0$ cm

Since $d_i$ is negative, the image is virtual, located 6.0 cm behind the mirror.

## Practice Problems

9. An object is 20.0 cm in front of a convex mirror with a −15.0-cm focal length. Find the location of the image using
   **a.** a ray diagram.
   **b.** the mirror equation.

**FIGURE 18–12.** Convex mirrors form smaller, virtual images. For this reason they are often used as wide-angle mirrors for safety and security.

10. A convex mirror has a focal length of −12 cm. A light bulb with a diameter of 6.0 cm is placed 60.0 cm in front of the mirror.
    **a.** Where is the image of the light bulb? Use the mirror equation.
    **b.** What is the diameter of the image?
11. In a department store, a mirror used to watch for shoplifters has a focal length of −40.0 cm. A person stands in an aisle 6.0 m from the mirror. Locate the person's image using the mirror equation. Is it erect or inverted? larger or smaller than the object?
▶ 12. A convex mirror is needed to produce an image located 24 cm behind the mirror that is three-quarters the size of the object. What focal length should be specified?

## CONCEPT REVIEW

**1.1** Draw a ray diagram showing your eye placed 12 cm from a plane mirror. Two rays leave a point on an eyelash and enter opposite sides of the pupil of your eye, 1 cm apart. Locate the image of the eyelash.

**1.2** If a beam of parallel light rays is sent into a spherical concave mirror, do all the rays converge at the focal point?

**1.3** If a mirror produces an erect, virtual image, can you immediately say it is a plane mirror? Explain.

**1.4** **Critical Thinking:** A concave mirror is used to produce a real image of a distant object. A small plane mirror is put between the mirror and the image. The mirror is put at a 45° angle to the principal axis of the concave mirror. **a.** Make a ray diagram. Is the image of the plane mirror real or virtual? Explain. **b.** If the small mirror were a convex mirror, would the image be real or virtual? Explain.

# 18.2 LENSES

Eyeglasses were made from lenses as early as the thirteenth century. Around 1610, Galileo combined two lenses into a telescope. With this instrument he discovered the moons of Jupiter. Lenses have since been used in optical instruments such as microscopes and cameras. Lenses are probably the most useful and important of all optical devices.

## Types of Lenses

A **lens** is made of transparent material, such as glass or plastic, with a refractive index larger than that of air. Each of a lens's two faces is part of a sphere and can be convex or concave. One face may also be plane, or flat. A lens is called a **convex lens** if it is thicker at the centre than at the edges, Figure 18–14a. Convex lenses are converging lenses because they refract parallel light rays so that they meet. A **concave lens** is thinner in the middle than at the edges and is called a diverging lens, Figure 18–14b. Rays passing through concave lenses spread out.

# Seeing Is Believing

## Purpose

To draw lines of sight to locate virtual images produced by lenses.

## Materials

· large diameter convex lens
· large diameter concave lens
· 2 small balls of clay
· 2 rulers
· one 2-3 cm long nail

## Procedure

**Part 1**

1. Assemble the equipment as shown in the sketch below using the concave lens.
2. Look through the lens to make sure that you can see both ends of the nail. (Move the nail closer or farther from the lens until both ends are visible.)
3. Mark the paper to show the ends of the nail and also the lens line.
4. Line up your straightedge to point to the head of the nail.
5. Have your lab partner verify that the edge is accurate.
6. Draw the line of sight.
7. Move to position 2 and draw a line of sight to the head of the nail.

8. Repeat steps 4-7 and draw 2 lines of sight to the tip of the nail.

**Part 2**

Use a new sheet of paper and repeat the procedures for the convex lens. Be sure to mark the lens line and the endpoints of the nail.

## Observations and Data

1. The image position can be located by extending lines of sight until they intersect. Extend the two lines of sight that point to the image head. Extend the two lines of sight that point to the image point. Describe the results.
2. Repeat this procedure for the convex lens. Describe the results.

## Analysis

1. Describe the image from the concave lens. What was surprising about the image?
2. Describe the image from the convex lens. What was surprising about the image?

## Applications

1. Describe an application of a similar arrangement for a convex lens.

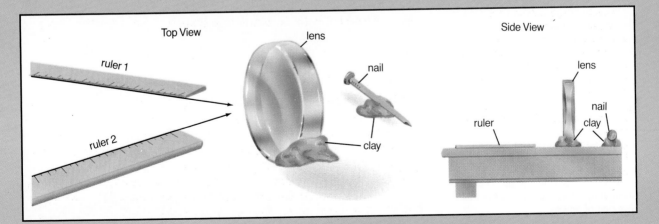

Top View · ruler 1 · ruler 2 · lens · nail · clay · Side View · lens · nail · clay · ruler

a

b

The image of an object that is beyond the focal point of a convex lens is real and inverted.

# Real Images Formed by Convex Lenses

A convex lens can form an image that can be projected on a screen. In Figure 18–15, a convex lens is used to form an image of the sun on a leaf. As in the case of a mirror, the principal axis of a lens is a line perpendicular to the plane of the lens that passes through its midpoint. The rays of the sun are examples of light rays that approach a convex lens parallel to the principal axis. After being refracted, these rays will converge to a tiny spot at a point called the focal point, **F,** of the lens. The distance from the lens to the focal point is the focal length, $f$. The focal length of a lens depends on its shape and on the refractive index of the lens material.

As discussed in Chapter 17, refraction occurs at the two lens surfaces. Snell's law and geometry can be used to predict the paths of rays passing through a lens. To simplify our drawings and calculations, we use the approximation that all refraction occurs on a plane, called the principal plane, passing through the middle of the lens. This approximation is good for the thin lenses we will be discussing.

Let's trace rays from an object far from a convex lens, Figure 18–16. Problem Solving Strategies used for mirrors can also be used for lenses. Ray 1 is parallel to the principal axis. It refracts and passes through **F** on the other side of the lens. Ray 2 passes through **F** on its way to the lens. After refraction, its path is parallel to the principal axis. The two rays intersect at a point beyond **F,** locating the image. Rays selected from other points on the object would converge at corresponding points on the image. Note that the image is real, inverted, and smaller than the object.

To find the image of an object that is closer to the focal point, reverse the path of light through the lens in Figure 18–16. The image and object are reversed. The image is again real and inverted, but it is now larger than the object.

If the object were placed at a distance twice the focal length from the lens, the point **2F** on Figure 18–16, then the image is also found to be at **2F.** By symmetry, the two have the same size. Thus we see that if an object is more than twice the focal length from the lens, the image is reduced in size. If the object is between **F** and **2F,** then the image is enlarged.

As the object comes closer to the focal point of the lens, the image moves farther away and increases in size.

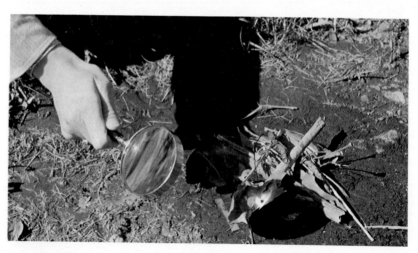

FIGURE 18–15. This camper is using a converging lens to start a fire in this pile of leaves.

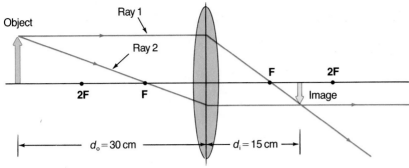

The lens equation can also be used to find the location of the image and the magnification equation can be used to find its size.

$$\frac{1}{f} = \frac{1}{d_i} + \frac{1}{d_o}$$

$$m = \frac{h_i}{h_o} = \frac{-d_i}{d_o}$$

The **lens equation,** as well as the equation for magnification, is the same as that used for mirrors.

**Lens Equation Conventions**

$d_o$ is positive for real objects.
negative for virtual objects.

$d_i$ is positive for real images.
negative for virtual images.

$f$ is positive for convex lenses.
negative for concave lenses.

## Example Problem

### Real Image from a Convex Lens

An object is 32.0 cm to the left of a convex lens of $+8.0$-cm focal length. Use the lens equation to locate the image.

**Given:** $d_o = 32.0$ cm
$f = +8.0$ cm

**Unknown:** image distance, $d_i$

**Basic equation:** $\frac{1}{f} = \frac{1}{d_i} + \frac{1}{d_o}$

**Solution:** $\frac{1}{f} = \frac{1}{d_o} + \frac{1}{d_i}$, so $d_i = \frac{fd_o}{d_o - f}$

$$= \frac{(+8.0 \text{ cm})(32.0 \text{ cm})}{32.0 \text{ cm} - 8.0 \text{ cm}} = +11 \text{ cm}$$

The positive sign indicates the image is on the right side of the lens. It is real.

## Practice Problems

13. Use a ray diagram to find the image position of an object 30 cm to the left of a convex lens with a $+10$-cm focal length. (Let 1 cm on the drawing represent 20 cm.)
14. An object 2.25 mm high is 8.5 cm to the left of a convex lens of 5.5-cm focal length. Find the image location and height.
15. An object is placed to the left of a 25-mm focal length convex lens so that its image is the same size as the object. What are the image and object locations?
▶ 16. A lens is needed to create an inverted image twice as large as the object when the object is 7.0 cm from the lens. What focal length lens is needed?

## POCKET LAB

### BURNED UP

Convex (converging) lenses can be used as magnifying glasses. Borrow someone's eyeglasses and see if they magnify. Are the glasses converging?

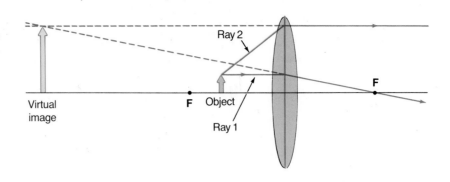

FIGURE 18–17. Finding the virtual image formed by a convex lens when the object is placed between the lens and principal focus, F.

The image of an object closer than the focal point of a convex lens is virtual, upright, and enlarged.

## Virtual Images Formed by Convex Lenses

If an object is placed at the focal point of a convex lens, the refracted rays will emerge in a parallel beam. If the object is brought closer to the lens, the rays do not converge on the opposite side of the lens. We will find that the image appears on the same side of the lens as the object. This image is virtual, erect, and enlarged.

Figure 18–17 shows how a convex lens forms a virtual image. The object is between **F** and the lens. Ray 1, as usual, approaches the lens parallel to the principal axis and is refracted through the focal point, **F.** Ray 2 starts at the tip of the object, in the direction it would have if it had started at **F** on the object side of the lens. It leaves the lens parallel to the principal axis. Rays 1 and 2 diverge as they leave the lens. Thus no real image is possible. Tracing the two rays back to their apparent intersection locates the virtual image. It is on the same side as the object, erect, and larger than the object. A magnifying glass is a convex lens used to produce an enlarged, virtual image.

## Example Problem

### Virtual Image from a Convex Lens

An object is 4.0 cm to the left of a convex lens of 6.0-cm focal length. **a.** Locate its image. **b.** What kind of image is formed?

**Given:** $d_o = 4.0$ cm
$f = 6.0$ cm

**Unknown:** image distance, $d_i$

**Basic equation:** $\dfrac{1}{f} = \dfrac{1}{d_i} + \dfrac{1}{d_o}$

**Solution:**

**a.** $\dfrac{1}{f} = \dfrac{1}{d_i} + \dfrac{1}{d_o}$,

so $d_i = \dfrac{f d_o}{d_o - f} = \dfrac{(6.0 \text{ cm})(4.0 \text{ cm})}{4.0 \text{ cm} - 6.0 \text{ cm}} = -12$ cm

**b.** Since the image distance is negative, the image is virtual. It is on the same side, the left side, of the lens as the object and is erect.

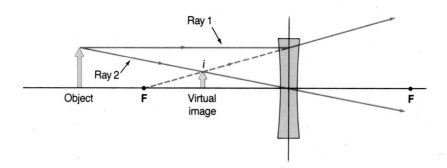

FIGURE 18–18. Formation of a virtual image by a concave lens.

# Practice Problems

17. A newspaper is held 6.0 cm from a convex lens of 20.0-cm focal length. Find the image distance of the newsprint image.
18. A magnifying glass has a focal length of 12.0 cm. A coin, 2.0 cm in diameter, is placed 3.4 cm from the lens.
    **a.** Locate the image of the coin.
    **b.** What is the diameter of the image?
19. A stamp collector wants to magnify images by 4.0 when the object is 3.5 cm from the lens. What focal length lens is needed?
▶ 20. Suppose you are looking at a stamp through a magnifying glass and want to increase the size of the image. Should you move the glass closer to the stamp or farther away? Explain and indicate the maximum distance you should move it.

Concave lenses produce virtual images from real objects.

The dispersion of light in lenses causes different colours to be focused different distances from the lenses.

## Virtual Images Formed by Concave Lenses

Image formation by a concave lens is shown in Figure 18–18. A concave lens causes all rays to diverge. Ray 1 approaches the lens parallel to the principal axis. It leaves the lens in the direction it would have if it had passed through the focal point. Ray 2 passes directly through the centre of the lens. Such a ray is not bent at all. Rays 1 and 2 diverge after passing through the lens. Their apparent intersection is on the same side of the lens as the object. The image is virtual, erect, and reduced in size. This is true no matter how far from the lens the object is located. The focal length of a concave lens is negative. Concave lenses are used in eyeglasses to correct nearsightedness and in combination with convex lenses in cameras and telescopes.

a       Lens

b       Achromatic lens

FIGURE 18–19. In chromatic aberration, rays of different wavelengths focus at different points, causing an object to appear ringed with colour (a). An achromatic lens reduces chromatic aberration (b).

## Chromatic Aberration

The edges of a lens resemble a prism, and different wavelengths of light are bent at slightly different angles, Figure 18–19a. Thus, the light that passes through a lens, especially near the edges, is slightly dispersed. An object viewed through a lens appears ringed with colour. This effect is called **chromatic aberration**. The term chromatic comes from the Greek *chromo*, related to colour.

18.2 Lenses    **383**

Chromatic aberration is always present when a single lens is used. By joining a convex lens with a concave lens that has a different index of refraction, chromatic aberration can be greatly reduced, Figure 18–19b. Both lenses disperse the light. The dispersion caused by the converging lens, however, is almost cancelled by that caused by the diverging lens. The index of refraction of the diverging lens is chosen so that the combination lens still converges the light. A lens constructed in this way is called an **achromatic lens**. All precision optical instruments use achromatic lenses.

## Optical Instruments

Although the eye itself is a remarkable optical device, its abilities can be greatly extended by a wide variety of instruments based on lenses and mirrors. The eye is a fluid-filled, almost spherical object that focuses the image of an object on the retina, Figure 18–20. Most of the refraction occurs at the curved surface of the cornea. The eye lens is made of flexible material with a refractive index different from that of the fluid. Muscles can change the shape of the lens, thereby changing its focal length. When the muscles are relaxed, the image of distant objects is focused on the retina. When the muscles contract, the focal length is shortened, permitting images of objects 25 cm or closer to be focused on the retina.

The eyes of many people do not focus sharp images on the retina. External lenses, eyeglasses or contact lenses, are needed to adjust the focal length and move the image to the retina, Figure 18–21. The nearsighted, or myopic, eye has too short a focal length. Images of distant

Most of the eye's refraction occurs at the surface of the cornea.

BIOLOGY CONNECTION

The eye lens changes shape to allow the eye to focus at objects different distances away.

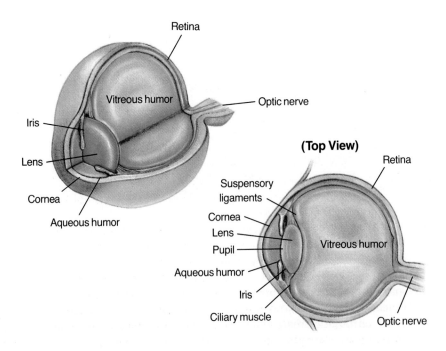

**FIGURE 18–20. Structure of the eye.**

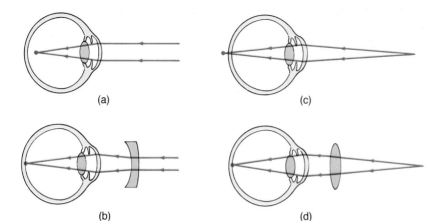

objects are formed in front of the retina. Concave lenses correct this defect by diverging the light rays, increasing the image distance, and placing the image on the retina. Farsightedness, or hyperopia, is the result of too long a focal length, resulting in the image falling behind the retina. A similar result is caused by the increasing rigidity of the lens in people more than about 45 years old. Their muscles cannot shorten the focal length enough to focus images of close objects on the retina. For either defect, convex lenses produce a virtual image farther from the eye than the object. This image then becomes the object for the eye lens and can be focused on the retina, correcting the defect. Some people have lenses or eye shapes that are not spherical. This defect is called astigmatism, and the result is that vertical lines of images can be in focus while horizontal lines are not. Eyeglasses having a non-spherical shape can correct astigmatism.

Contact lenses have the same result, Figure 18–22. They are very thin lenses placed directly on the cornea. A thin layer of tears between the cornea and lens keeps the lens in place. Most of the refraction occurs at the air-lens surface where the change in refractive index is greatest.

Microscopes allow the eye to see extremely small objects. They use at least two convex lenses. An object is placed very close to a lens with a very short focal length, the objective lens. This lens produces a real image located between the second lens, the eyepiece lens, and its focal point. The eyepiece produces a greatly magnified virtual image of the image formed by the objective lens.

An astronomical refracting telescope uses two convex lenses. The objective lens of a telescope has a long focal length. The parallel rays from a star or other distant object come to focus in a plane at the focal point of this lens. The eyepiece lens, with a short focal length, then refracts the rays into another parallel beam. The viewer sees a virtual, enlarged, inverted image. The primary purpose of a telescope is not to magnify the image. It is to increase the angle between the rays from two different stars and to collect more light than would strike the unaided eye.

A microscope produces a very enlarged virtual image by means of at least two lenses.

A telescope collects more light and separates the images of stars.

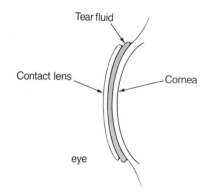

**FIGURE 18–22. A contact lens rests on a layer of tears between it and the surface of the cornea.**

FIGURE 18–23. Use with Concept
Review 2.1.

a     b     c     d

FIGURE 18–24. Use with Concept
Review 2.4.

## CONCEPT REVIEW

**2.1** Which of the lenses whose cross-sections are shown in Figure 18–23 are convex or converging lenses? Which are concave or diverging lenses?

**2.2** Suppose your camera has focused the image of a person 2 m away on the film. You now want it to focus the image of a tree farther away. Should the lens be moved closer to the film or farther away? Explain.

**2.3** You first focus white light through a single lens so that red is focused to the smallest point on a sheet of paper. Which direction should you move the paper to best focus the blue?

**2.4 Critical Thinking:** An "air lens" constructed of two watch glasses, Figure 18–24, is placed in a tank of water. Draw the effect of this lens on parallel light rays incident on the lens.

## Physics and technology

### STARGAZING

Astronomers have known for decades that to push the observational horizon farther back in space and time would require radically different telescopes. To see farther, more light must be collected, and this requires larger mirrors. But massive mirrors bend under their own weight, distorting the images being observed. Atmospheric distortions, temperature effects, and light pollution from nearby cities also limit the performance of existing telescopes.

Scientists are using two approaches to overcome these limitations—active optics and the space telescope. Earth-bound telescopes using active optics have flexible mirrors whose shape is changed under computer control to keep a sharp focus despite the effects of gravity and temperature changes. The giant Keck telescope now under construction in Hawaii will use active optics to control a mosaic-type mirror made of 36 separate hexagonal glass segments. It will be the largest optical telescope in the world when completed.

A second approach is to put a telescope into Earth orbit. The Hubble Space Telescope was launched into orbit in 1990. Spherical aberration in one of the telescope's mirrors, however, has reduced its capabilities.

· What do you see as the advantages and disadvantages of the solid-mirror vs. segmented-mirror telescope technology?

# 18 REVIEW

## SUMMARY

### 18.1 Mirrors

· The image in a plane mirror is the same size as the object. It is as far behind the mirror as the object is in front of the mirror. The image is virtual and erect.
· The focal point of a spherical mirror, concave or convex, is halfway between the centre of curvature of the mirror and the mirror.
· The distance from the focal point to the centre of the mirror is the focal length of the mirror.
· An imaginary line that passes from the centre of the mirror through the centre of curvature and beyond is called the principal axis of the mirror.
· Parallel light rays that fall far from the centre of the spherical mirror do not pass through its focal point. This defect is called spherical aberration.
· A real image is located where light rays actually converge and can be displayed on a screen. Light rays only appear to converge at a virtual image. A virtual image thus cannot be displayed on a screen.
· Concave mirrors produce real, inverted images if the object is farther from the mirror than the focal point and virtual, upright images if the object is between the mirror and the focal point.
· Convex mirrors always produce virtual, upright, reduced images.

### 18.2 Lenses

· Lenses that are thinner at their outer edges than at their centres are called converging or convex lenses. Lenses that are thicker at their outer edges are diverging or concave lenses.
· The location of an image can be found either by ray tracing or by using the lens or mirror equation, as fits the situation.
· Convex lenses produce real, inverted images if the object is farther from the lens than the focal point. A virtual image is formed if the object is closer than the focal point.
· Concave lenses are seldom used alone. When they are, they produce virtual, upright, reduced images.

· Chromatic aberration is a lens defect caused by the dispersion of different wavelengths of light as they pass through the lens.

## KEY TERMS

| | |
|---|---|
| plane mirror | mirror equation |
| object | magnification |
| image | convex mirror |
| virtual image | lens |
| concave mirror | convex lens |
| principal axis | concave lens |
| converging mirror | lens equation |
| focal length | chromatic aberration |
| spherical aberration | achromatic lens |
| real image | |

## REVIEWING CONCEPTS

1. Describe the physical properties of the image of a person seen in a plane mirror.
2. Where is the image of an object in a plane mirror?
3. What causes the defect that all concave spherical mirrors have?
4. Describe the physical properties of a virtual image.
5. How does a virtual image differ from a real image?
6. A student believes that very sensitive photographic film can detect a virtual image. The student puts photographic film at the location of the image. Does this attempt succeed? Explain.
7. How can you prove to someone that an image is a real image?
8. Consider a plane mirror.
   a. What is its focal length?
   b. Does the mirror equation work for plane mirrors? Explain.
9. An object produces a virtual image in a concave mirror. Where is the object located?
10. Locate and describe the physical properties of the image produced by a convex lens if an object is placed some distance beyond 2F.

11. Convex mirrors are used as rearview mirrors on school buses. Why are convex mirrors used?

12. What factor, other than the curvature of the surfaces of a lens, determines the location of the focal point of a lens?

13. To project an image from a movie projector onto a screen, the film is placed between $F$ and $2F$ of a converging lens. This arrangement produces an inverted image. Why do the actors appear to be erect when the film is viewed?

## APPLYING CONCEPTS

1. If you use a shaving or makeup mirror underwater in a swimming pool, will its focal length change? Explain.

2. You have to order a large concave mirror for a piece of high quality equipment. Should you order a spherical mirror or a parabolic mirror? Explain.

3. Locate and describe the physical properties of the image produced by a concave mirror when the object is located at the centre of curvature.

4. An object is located beyond the centre of curvature of a spherical concave mirror. Locate and describe the physical properties of the image of the object.

5. An object is located between the centre of curvature and the focus of a concave mirror. Locate and describe the physical properties of the image of the object.

6. Describe the physical properties of the image seen in a convex mirror.

7. List all the possible arrangements in which you can use a spherical mirror, either concave or convex, to form a real image.

8. List all the possible arrangements in which you can use a spherical mirror, either concave or convex, to form an image reduced in size.

9. What physical characteristic of a lens distinguishes a converging lens from a diverging lens?

10. The outside rearview mirrors of cars often carry the warning "Objects in the mirror are closer than they appear."

a. What kind of mirror would have such a warning?

b. What advantage does this type of mirror have?

11. If you try to use a magnifying glass underwater, will its properties change? Explain.

12. Suppose Figure 18–16 was redrawn with a lens of the same focal length but a larger diameter. How would the location of the image change?

13. Why is there chromatic aberration for light that goes through a lens but there is no chromatic aberration for light that reflects from a mirror?

## PROBLEMS

### 18.1 Mirrors

1. Find the image of the object in Figure 18–25.

FIGURE 18–25. Use with Problem 1.

2. Penny wishes to take a picture of her image in a plane mirror. If the camera is 1.2 m in front of the mirror, at what distance should the camera lens be focused?

▶ 3. Draw a ray diagram of a plane mirror to show that if you want to see yourself from your feet to the top of your head, the mirror must be at least half your height.

4. A concave mirror has a focal length of 10.0 cm. What is its radius of curvature?

5. Light from a distant star is collected by a concave mirror. How far from the mirror is the image of the star if the radius of curvature is 150 cm?

▶ 6. The sun falls on a concave mirror and forms an image 3.0 cm from the mirror. If an object 24 mm high is placed 12.0 cm from the mirror, where will its image be formed?

a. Use a ray diagram.
b. Use the mirror equation.
c. How high is the image?

7. An object is 30.0 cm from a concave mirror of 15-cm focal length. The object is 1.8 cm high.
   a. Find the image with the mirror equation.
   b. How high is the image?

8. A jeweller inspects a watch with a diameter of 3.0 cm by placing it 8.0 cm in front of a concave mirror of 12.0 cm focal length.
   a. Where will the image of the watch appear?
   b. What will be the diameter of the image?

9. A dentist uses a small mirror of radius 40 mm to locate a cavity in a patient's tooth. If the mirror is concave and is held 16 mm from the tooth, what is the magnification of the resulting image?

10. A production line inspector wants a mirror that produces an upright image with magnification of 7.5 when it is located 14.0 mm from a machine part.
    a. What kind of mirror would do this job?
    b. What is its radius of curvature?

▶ 11. Shiny lawn spheres placed on pedestals are convex mirrors. One such sphere has a diameter of 40 cm. A 12 cm robin sits in a tree 1.5 m from the sphere.
    a. Where is the image of the robin?
    b. How long is the robin's image?

## 18.2 Lenses

12. The focal length of a convex lens is 17 cm. A candle is placed 34 cm in front of the lens. Make a ray diagram to find the location of the image.

13. The convex lens of a copy machine has a focal length of 25.0 cm. A letter to be copied is placed 40.0 cm from the lens.
    a. How far from the lens is the copy paper located?
    b. The machine was adjusted to give an enlarged copy of the letter. How much larger will the copy be?

14. Camera lenses are described in terms of their focal length. A 50.0-mm lens has a focal length of 50.0 mm.
    a. A camera is focused on an object 3.0 m away using a 50.0 mm lens. Locate the position of the image.

b. A $1.00 \times 10^3$ mm lens is focused on an object 125 m away. Locate the position of the image.

15. Solve Problem 10 using a lens rather than a mirror.

16. A convex lens is needed to produce an image located 24 cm behind the lens that is 0.75 the size of the object. What focal length should be specified?

▶ 17. A slide of an onion cell is placed 12 mm from the objective lens of a microscope. The focal length of the objective lens is 10.0 mm.
    a. How far from the lens is the image formed?
    b. What is the magnification of this image?
    c. The real image formed is located 10.0 mm beneath the eyepiece lens. If the focal length of the eyepiece is 20.0 mm, where does the final image appear?
    d. What is the final magnification of this compound system?

18. In order to clearly read a book at 25 cm away, a farsighted person needs an image distance of −45 cm. What focal length lens is needed?

 USING A GRAPHING CALCULATOR

Mary has just captured a beautiful butterfly and is proudly examining it under a magnifying glass. The focal length of the magnifying glass is 15cm and the butterfly is 5cm across. As you have learned, the equation for calculating how large the butterfly appears is $h_1 = (-h_0 f)/(d - f)$. Graph this equation on a graphing calculator with $h_1$ on the y axis (with a range of −50cm to 50cm) and $d_0$ on the x axis (with a range of 0cm to 50cm). How large does the butterfly appear at 5cm? At 10cm? 13cm? 17cm? 20cm? 30cm? 50cm? For what distances is the image upright?

## THINKING PHYSIC-LY

1. What is responsible for the rainbow-coloured fringe commonly seen at the edges of a spot of white light from a slide projector or overhead projector?

2. Maps of the moon are actually upside down. Explain.

# CHAPTER 19
# Diffraction and Interference of Light

## In the Eyes of the Beholder

The South American Morpho butterfly has a unique and beautiful colouration. In daylight its wings appear a brilliant, metallic, iridescent blue. What characteristic of light could explain this unusual colouration?

You have seen that dyes and pigments produce colours when they absorb some wavelengths of light while transmitting or reflecting others. In prisms and raindrops, different wavelengths are bent through different angles. The colours in peacock tails, mother-of-pearl shells, and soap films are due to interference in thin films discussed in Chapter 16. None of these methods produces the colours in beetles and the wings of butterflies, which are some of the most beautiful in nature.

## ✓ Concept Check

The following terms or concepts from earlier chapters are important for a good understanding of this chapter. If you are not familiar with them, you should review them before studying this chapter.
· superposition of waves, wavelength, Chapters 14, 16

391

## Objectives

· define diffraction of light.
· display an understanding of how light falling on two slits produces a pattern of dark and bright bands on a screen.
· understand the geometrical interpretation of two-slit interference.
· demonstrate an ability to calculate the wavelength of light from measurements of the two-slit interference pattern.
· explain geometrically how single-slit diffraction patterns occur; use the derived equation to relate the pattern width to slit width and light wavelength.

Diffraction is the bending of light around the edges of barriers.

# 19.1 WHEN LIGHT WAVES INTERFERE

An English physician, Thomas Young (1773–1829), became interested in optics when he studied the human eye. Young's early medical studies of the human voice led him to investigate waves. The insights he gained he applied to the understanding of wave interference in oceans and lakes. He read Newton's book on optics and became convinced that Newton's results could be explained if light were a wave of almost unimaginably small wavelength. In 1801, he developed an experiment that would allow him to make a precise measurement of that wavelength.

## The Two-Slit Interference Pattern

The Italian, Francesco Maria Grimaldi (1618–1663) first noted that the edges of shadows are not perfectly sharp. He named the slight spreading of light waves diffraction. **Diffraction** is the bending of waves around the edges of barriers. The Dutch scientist Christiaan Huygens (1629–1695) proposed a model to explain diffraction. According to Huygens, you can replace the crest of any wave by series of equally-spaced wave sources, each producing new waves in step with one another. Figure 19–1 shows how Huygens' wavelets explain diffraction.

Huygens' model may explain diffraction, but does that mean light has to be a wave? Young's experiment gave additional evidence of the wave nature of light. Young allowed light to fall on two closely-spaced narrow slits. The light passing through each slit was spread out, or diffracted. The spreading light from the two slits overlapped. When the light fell on an observing screen, the overlap did not produce extra light, but a pattern of bright and dark bands called **interference fringes.** Young explained that these bands were the result of constructive and destructive interference of the light waves from the two slits.

Young used a **monochromatic** (mahn uh croh MAT ik) light source, one that emits light of only one wavelength. He placed a narrow slit in front of the source. This slit allowed light from only a small part of the source to pass through. As a result, the waves were not only the same wavelength, but all were in step. That is, they were **coherent.** The

**FIGURE 19–1. According to Huygens, the crest of each wave could be thought of as a series of point sources.**

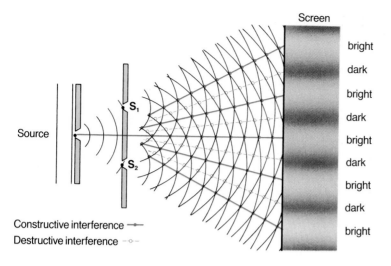

**FIGURE 19–2. The diffraction of monochromatic light through a double slit produces bright and dark bands on a screen.**

Screen

bright
dark
bright
dark
bright
dark
bright
dark
bright

Source

S₁

S₂

Constructive interference ——•——
Destructive interference ——○——

waves spread after passing through the single slit and fell on the double slit. The double slit acted as two sources of new circular waves. In Figure 19–2, the semicircles represent wave crests moving outward from the slits. Midway between the crests are the troughs. The waves from the two sources interfere constructively at points where two crests overlap. They interfere destructively where a crest and a trough meet.

When monochromatic light is used, Figure 19–3a, b, bright bands of light appear at points where the constructive interference occurs on the screen. One bright band appears at the centre of the screen. On either side of the central band are bright bands corresponding to the other points of constructive interference. Between the bright bands are dark areas located where destructive interference occurs on the screen.

When white light is used in a double-slit experiment, Figure 19–3c, coloured spectra are seen instead of bright and dark bands. The positions of the constructive and destructive interference bands depend on the wavelength of the light. All wavelengths interfere constructively in the central bright band, so that band is white. The positions of the other bands depend on the wavelength, so the light is separated by diffraction into a spectrum of colour at each band.

a

b

c

**FIGURE 19–3. The diffraction of a monochromatic light source produces an interference pattern on the screen resulting in a pattern, such as the one shown for blue light (a), and for red light (b). The diffraction of white light produces bands of colours (c).**

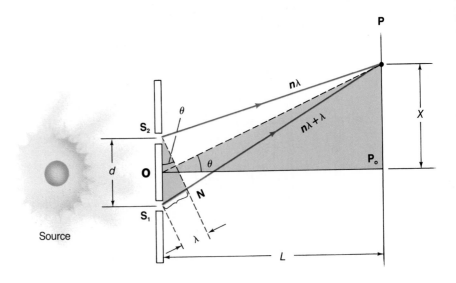

**FIGURE 19–4. Schematic diagram for analysis of double-slit interference. The diagram is not to scale. Typically, $L$ is about $10^5$ times the slit separation, $d$.**

## Measuring the Wavelength of a Light Wave

Young used the double-slit experiment to make the first precise measurement of the wavelength of light. The central bright band that falls on the screen at point $P_0$ in Figure 19–4 does not depend on the wavelength, so another bright band is used. The first bright band on either side of the central band is called the first-order line. It falls on the screen at point **P.** The band is bright because light from the two slits interferes constructively. The two path lengths differ by one wavelength. That is, the distance **PS$_1$** is one wavelength longer than **PS$_2$**.

To follow Young's experiment using Figure 19–4, you must understand that the drawing is not to scale. The length **PO** ($L$) is really very much greater than **S$_1$S$_2$** ($d$). It is necessary to distort the diagram so the details close to the slit can be shown. To measure the wavelength, Young first measured the distance between **P$_0$** and **P,** labeled $x$ in the diagram. The distance between the screen and the slits is $L$, and the separation of the two slits is $d$. In the right triangle **NS$_1$S$_2$**, the side **S$_1$N** is the length difference of the two paths. **S$_1$N** is one wavelength, $\lambda$, long. The lines from the slits to the screen are almost parallel because length $L$ is so much larger than $d$. Thus the lines **NS$_2$** and **OP** are perpendicular. The triangle **NS$_1$S$_2$** is similar to triangle **PP$_0$O**. Therefore, the ratio of the corresponding sides of these similar triangles is the same. That is,

$$\frac{x}{L} = \frac{\lambda}{d}.$$

Solving this equation for $\lambda$ gives

$$\lambda = \frac{xd}{L}.$$

The wavelengths of light waves can be measured with considerable precision using double-slit interference patterns. It is not unusual for wavelength measurements to be precise to four digits.

## Example Problem

### Wavelength of Light

Red light falls on two narrow slits 0.0190 mm apart. A first-order bright line is 21.1 mm from the central bright line on a screen 0.600 m from the slits. What is the wavelength of the red light?

**Given:** $d = 1.90 \times 10^{-5}$ m  **Unknown:** $\lambda$
  $x = 21.1 \times 10^{-3}$ m  **Basic equation:** $\lambda = xd/L$
  $L = 0.600$ m

**Solution:** $\lambda = xd/L = \dfrac{(21.1 \times 10^{-3}\text{ m})(1.90 \times 10^{-5}\text{ m})}{(0.600\text{ m})}$

$= 6.68 \times 10^{-7}$ m $= 668$ nm

## Practice Problems

1. Violet light falls on two slits separated by $1.90 \times 10^{-5}$ m. A first-order line appears 13.2 mm from the central bright line on a screen 0.600 m from the slits. What is the wavelength of the violet light?
2. Yellow-orange light from a sodium lamp of wavelength 596 nm is used instead of the violet light of Problem 1. The slit separation and distance to the screen are not changed. What is the distance from the central line to the first-order yellow line?
3. A physics class uses a laser with a known wavelength of 632.8 nm in a double-slit experiment. The slit separation is unknown. A student places the screen 1.000 m from the slits and finds the first-order line 65.5 mm from the central line. What is the slit separation?
▶ 4. Using the double-slit apparatus of Problem 3, the student measures the wavelength of an unknown green light. The first-order line is 55.8 mm from the central line. What is the wavelength of the light?

## Single-Slit Diffraction

As you are leaving school, you walk by the open door of the band rehearsal room. You hear the music, however, long before you can see the players through the door. Sound seems to have bent around the edge of the door, while light has traveled only in a straight line. They are both waves—why don't they act the same? Actually, they do. As Grimaldi first noted, the spreading, or diffraction, is there in both cases, but, because of light's much smaller wavelengths, the effect is tiny.

When light passes through a small single opening, a series of bright and dark interference bands appears. Instead of the equally-spaced, bright bands produced by two slits, the pattern from a single slit has a wide, bright central band with dimmer bright bands on either side.

To observe single-slit diffraction, fold a small piece of paper and cut a narrow slit along its folded edge. Unfold the paper and look through the slit at a light source. You will see an interference pattern. You can vary the width of the slit by pulling on the opposite edges of the paper. Observe the effect the change in slit width has on the pattern.

### POCKET LAB

**LASER SPOTS**

Turn on the laser so that it makes a spot on the centre of the movie screen. What do you expect should happen to the spot if you were to put a piece of screen door screen in the centre of the beam? Explain your prediction. Try it. What really happened? Use the wave theory to explain your results.

What causes the diffraction pattern? Figure 19–6 shows monochromatic light from a distant source falling on a slit of width $w$. Because the light is so far away, a crest in the wave strikes all points of the slit at the same time. Light coming through the slit falls on a screen placed a distance $L$ from the slit. There is a wide central band, $\mathbf{P_0}$. What waves contribute to the central band? For this discussion we have divided the width of the slit into twelve parts. Because $L$ is so much larger than $w$, all rays falling on the slit are, in effect, the same distance from $\mathbf{P_0}$. The distances $\mathbf{AP_0}$, $\mathbf{BP_0}$, $\mathbf{CP_0}$, and $L$ are equal, and the crests of all waves arrive at $\mathbf{P_0}$ at the same time. Thus, the central band is bright. $\mathbf{P_p}$ is any point on the screen.

As you move away from the centre, the distance $\mathbf{CP}$ becomes larger than $\mathbf{AP}$. When you reach point $\mathbf{P_d}$, $\mathbf{CD} = \lambda$, so the distance $\mathbf{CP_d}$ is exactly one wavelength longer than $\mathbf{AP_d}$. Therefore, waves from point $\mathbf{1'}$ travel one-half wavelength longer than those from point $\mathbf{1}$. They destructively interfere. The same is true for points $\mathbf{2'}$ and $\mathbf{2}$, $\mathbf{3'}$ and $\mathbf{3}$, and so on down the slit. A wave from one point of the slit is cancelled by a wave from another. The result is darkness.

If you go either closer to or farther away from the centre, the distance $\mathbf{CP}$ is not exactly one wavelength longer and some waves no longer cancel. Thus the darkness is not complete. Consider going out far enough to make $\mathbf{CP_p}$ two wavelengths ($2\lambda$) larger than $\mathbf{AP_p}$. Then there is a second dark band. Third, fourth, and higher bands are reached when the difference in path length is $3\lambda$, $4\lambda$, and so forth.

What is the distance from $\mathbf{P_0}$ to the first dark band, $\mathbf{P_d}$? If angle $\theta$ is very small, triangles $\mathbf{CDA}$ and $\mathbf{BP_dP_0}$ are similar. From triangle $\mathbf{CDA}$,

$$\sin \theta = \frac{\lambda}{w} \, .$$

In the same way, consider triangle $\mathbf{BP_dP_0}$. Because $\mathbf{BP_d}$ and $L$ are nearly equal, we can say

$$\sin \theta = \frac{x}{BP_d} = \frac{x}{L} \, .$$

Light passing through a single slit produces a series of bright and dark bands equally spaced around a bright central band.

a

b

**FIGURE 19–5. The beautiful colours of this opal (a) are produced by diffraction from ridges on the surface of the gem (b).**

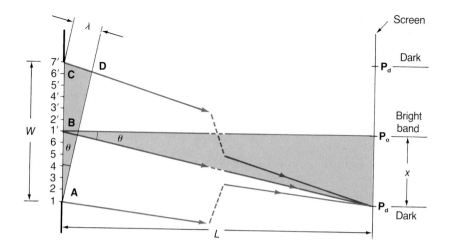

**FIGURE 19–6. Schematic diagram for analysis of single-slit diffraction. The diagram is not to scale. Typically $L$ is $10^5$ times the slit width.**

Therefore,

$$\frac{\lambda}{w} = \frac{x}{L}, \text{ or } x = \frac{\lambda L}{w}.$$

Notice that the smaller the slit width, $w$, the larger the distance, $x$. That is, the smaller the slit, the wider the central band. As a model, imagine a beam of light shining through an open door. The beam has sharp edges because the interference fringes are very close together and almost unnoticeable. As you close the door, the beam becomes smaller. If the opening is reduced to a few wavelengths wide, the edges of the beam become less well defined. The interference fringes become more widely spaced and more visible, making the edges appear fuzzy. Thus, sharp shadows are cast only by large openings. The pattern width also depends on wavelength. For a fixed slit width, the shorter the wavelength, the narrower the pattern, Figure 19–7.

*Diffraction is at a maximum when the width of the opening is equal to the wavelength of light.*

## Example Problem

### Single-Slit Diffraction

Monochromatic orange light of wavelength 605 nm falls on a single slit of width 0.095 mm. The slit is located 85 cm from a screen. How far from the centre of the central band is the first dark band?

**Given:** slit width,
$w = 0.095$ mm
distance to screen,
$L = 85$ cm
light wavelength,
$\lambda = 605$ nm $= 6.05 \times 10^{-7}$ m

**Unknown:** separation between central band and dark band, $x$

**Basic equation:** $x = \dfrac{\lambda L}{w}$

**Solution:** $x = \dfrac{\lambda L}{w} = \dfrac{(6.05 \times 10^{-7} \text{ m})(0.85 \text{ m})}{9.5 \times 10^{-5} \text{ m}} = 5.4$ mm

# Practice Problems

5. Monochromatic green light of wavelength 546 nm falls on a single slit of width 0.095 mm. The slit is located 75 cm from a screen. How far from the centre of the central band is the first dark band?

6. Light from a He-Ne laser ($\lambda$ = 632.8 nm) falls on a slit of unknown width. A pattern is formed on a screen 1.15 m away where the first dark band is 7.5 mm from the centre of the central bright band. How wide is the slit?

7. Yellow light falls on a single slit 0.0295 mm wide. On a screen 60.0 cm away, there is a dark band 12.0 mm from the centre of the bright central band. What is the wavelength of the light?

▶ 8. White light falls on a single slit 0.050 mm wide. A screen is placed 1.00 m away. A student first puts a blue-violet filter ($\lambda$ = 441 nm) over the slit, then a red filter ($\lambda$ = 622 nm). The student measures the width of the central peak, that is, the distance between the two dark bands.
   a. Will the band be wider with the blue-violet or the red filter?
   b. Find the width for the two filters.

## CONCEPT REVIEW

1.1 Two very narrow slits are cut close to each other in a large piece of cardboard. They are illuminated by monochromatic red light. A sheet of white paper is placed far from the slits, and a pattern of bright and dark bands is seen on the paper. Explain why some regions are bright while others are dark.

1.2 Sketch a graph that shows the pattern seen.

1.3 Sketch what happens to the pattern if the red light is replaced by blue light.

1.4 **Critical Thinking:** One of the slits is covered so no light can get through. What happens to the pattern?

**FIGURE 19–7. These diffraction patterns for red light (a), blue light (b), and white light (c) were produced with a slit of width 0.02 cm. Red light has a longer wavelength than blue light.**

# Wavelengths of Colors

## Purpose

To measure accurately the wavelength of four colours of light.

## Materials

- metre stick
- index card
- 40-W straight filament light
- ball of clay
- tape
- diffraction grating

## Procedure

1. Cut the index card (lengthwise) into four equal strips.
2. Write the letters "O" (orange), "Y" (yellow), "G" (green), and "B" (blue) on the strips of index card.
3. Place the ball of clay 1.0 m in front of the lamp. Use the ball of clay to support the diffraction grating.
4. Plug in the lamp and turn off the room lights.
5. When you look through the diffraction grating, you should see the colours to the sides of the bulb. If you do not see the colours to the sides, then rotate the diffraction grating (90°) until you do.

6. Have a lab partner move the "O" orange index card strip until it seems to be in the middle of its colour. Tape the strip to the table.
7. Repeat for each of the other coloured index card strips.

## Observations and Data

1. What colour is closest to the lamp? Suggest a reason.
2. List the order that colours occur, beginning from red.
3. Set up a data table to record x, d, and L for each of the four colours. Measure x for each index card strip (to the nearest 0.1 cm).
4. Record the value of d from the chalkboard.

## Analysis

Use the following equation to estimate the wavelength for each colour. Convert your answers for the wavelength to nm.

$$\lambda = xd/L$$

5. Record the value of L.

## Applications

1. How could diffraction gratings be used in conjunction with telescopes?

diffraction grating

index card strip

90°

clay

1.0 m

## Objectives

- explain the interference pattern formed by the diffraction grating.
- understand the operation of a grating spectrometer.
- explain how diffraction effects limit the resolution of a lens.

In the Eyes of the Beholder ▶

# 19.2 APPLICATIONS OF DIFFRACTION

Many beetles and butterflies, including the *morpho* butterfly shown in the chapter-opening photo, produce their iridescent colors by means of diffraction. The butterfly's wings are covered with tiny ridges only a few hundred nanometers apart. They each diffract the light hitting them, producing interference effects. Because of the orientation of the ridges, blue is the predominant color. Some dragonfly wings have dark veins spaced in such a way that sunlight is diffracted into spectra. Such a series of slits makes the interference pattern of two slits even stronger. It is called a **diffraction grating.**

## Diffraction Gratings

Although single- or double-slit diffraction can be used to measure the wavelength of light, in practice a diffraction grating, Figure 19–8, is used. Diffraction gratings are made by scratching very fine lines with a diamond point on glass. The clear spaces between the lines serve as slits. Gratings can have as many as 10 000 lines per centimetre. That is, the spacing between the lines is $10^{-6}$ m, or 1000 nm. Inexpensive *replica gratings* are made by pressing a thin plastic sheet onto a glass grating. When the plastic is pulled away, it contains an accurate imprint of the scratches. Jewellery can be made from replica gratings.

Gratings form interference patterns in the same way a double slit does. The bright bands are in the same location, but they are narrower, and the dark regions are broader. As a result, individual colours are not smeared out and can be distinguished more easily. This means that wavelengths can be measured more precisely than with double slits.

In Section 19.1 the equation used to calculate the wavelength of light using double-slit interference was given as

$$\frac{x}{L} = \frac{\lambda}{d}.$$

The same equation holds for a diffraction grating where $d$ is the distance between the lines. Instead of measuring the distance from the central band to the first bright band, $x$, most laboratory instruments mea-

**FIGURE 19–8. Diffraction gratings are used to create interference patterns to analyse light sources.**

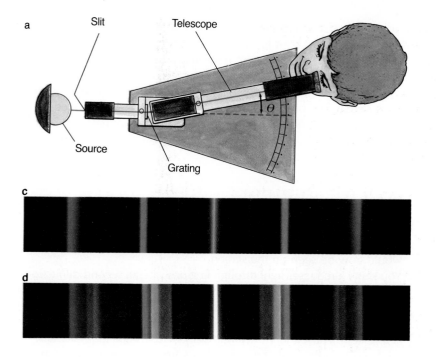

a

Slit  Telescope

θ

Source

Grating

c

d

b

**FIGURE 19–9. A spectrometer is used to measure the wavelengths of light emitted by a light source (a, b). A grating was used to produce interference patterns for red light (c) and white light (d).**

sure the angle $\theta$ shown in Figure 19–4. Because $x$ is so small with light, $\sin \theta \approx x/L$. Therefore, the wavelength can be found by measuring the angle between the central bright band and the first-order line, and using the equation

$$\lambda = \frac{xd}{L} = d \sin \theta.$$

The instrument used to measure light wavelengths with a diffraction grating is called a grating spectrometer, Figure 19–9. The source emits light that falls on a slit and then passes through a diffraction grating. When monochromatic red light is used, Figure 19–9c, a series of bright bands appears to the left and right of the central bright line. When white light falls on the instrument, each red band is replaced by a spectrum. The red band in the spectrum is at the same location as when monochromatic light is used. The telescope is moved until the desired line appears in the middle of the viewer. The angle $\theta$ is then read directly from the calibrated base of the spectrometer. Because $d$ is known, $\lambda$ can be calculated.

## Resolving Power of Lenses

When light passes through the lens of a telescope, it passes through a circular hole. The lens diffracts the light just as a slit does. The smaller the lens, the wider the diffraction pattern. If the light comes from a star, the star will appear spread out. If two stars are close enough together, the images will be so blurred that a viewer cannot tell whether there are two stars or only one. The telescope can no longer resolve the images of the two stars. Lord Rayleigh set the **Rayleigh criterion** for resolution. If the central bright band of one star falls on the first dark band of the

# F.Y.I.

The Hubble Space Telescope was designed to resolve stars. It can resolve objects whose spacing is the equivalent to the spacing of car headlights 4000 km away.

## ASTRONOMY CONNECTION

a

b

c

**FIGURE 19–10. The diffraction patterns of two point sources (a). As the sources move closer together, the images become fuzzy (b) and eventually merge into one image (c).**

second, the two stars are just resolved. That is, a viewer can tell that there are two stars and not just one.

The effects of diffraction on the resolving power of the telescope can be reduced by increasing the size of the lens. Diffraction also limits the resolving power of microscopes. The objective lens of a microscope cannot be enlarged, but the wavelength of light can be reduced. The diffraction pattern formed by blue light is narrower than that of red light. Thus biologists often use blue or violet light to illuminate microscopes.

## CONCEPT REVIEW

**2.1** The two slits of Concept Review Question 1.1 are replaced by very many narrow slits with the same spacing. Sketch the pattern that would now be seen on the screen.

**2.2** You shine a red laser light through first one, then a second diffraction grating. Patterns of red dots are seen on a screen. The dots from one grating are spread more than those from the other. Which grating has more lines per millimetre?

**2.3** A telescope is used to view a number of closely-spaced stars. Filters are used to select only certain colours from the starlight. In which colour, red or blue, would the stars be more easily counted? Explain.

**2.4** **Critical Thinking:** You are shown a spectrometer, but do not know whether it produces its spectrum with a prism or a grating. By looking at a white light spectrum, how could you tell?

# Physics and technology

## HOLOGRAMS

Interference properties of light are used to produce three-dimensional images called holograms. Developed by Dennis Gabor, who won the 1971 Nobel Prize in physics for his work, holograms record both the intensity and phase of light.

To make a hologram, laser light is split by a mirror into two parts. One part is directed to the object and then reflected off the object onto film. The other part goes directly to the film. The result is complex interference patterns. When the film is illuminated by laser light, the emerging light is an exact duplicate of the light reflected originally by the object. The image appears three-dimensional; you can observe it from all sides.

Because holograms are very difficult to counterfeit, holography is being used in security identification and credit cards. Research is being conducted to apply holograms in microscopic work, medicine, and information storage and display. Holograms may find uses in video games and displays, and motion pictures.

· What property of light, sound, and electrons enables them all to be used in making holograms?

# CHAPTER
## 19 REVIEW
................................

## SUMMARY

### 19.1 When Light Waves Interfere

· Light passing through a narrow hole or slit is diffracted, or bent from a straight-line path.
· Interference between light diffracted from two closely-spaced narrow slits causes an interference pattern to appear on a distant screen.
· The wavelength of light can be measured by analysing the double-slit interference pattern.
· When light passes through a narrow opening, diffraction causes a pattern of light and dark bands to form.
· Single slits produce diffraction patterns that are less well defined than those formed by double slits.

### 19.2 Applications of Diffraction

· Diffraction gratings with large numbers of evenly-spaced slits produce interference patterns that are used to measure the wavelength of light precisely.
· Diffraction limits the resolving power of lenses.

## KEY TERMS

| | |
|---|---|
| diffraction | coherent |
| interference fringes | diffraction grating |
| monochromatic | Rayleigh criterion |

## REVIEWING CONCEPTS

1. Why is it important that monochromatic light be used to make the interference pattern in Young's interference experiment?
2. Explain why the central bright line produced when light is diffracted by a double slit cannot be used to measure the wavelength of the light waves.
3. Describe how you could use light of a known wavelength to find the distance between two slits.
4. Why is blue light used for illumination in an optical microscope?

5. Why is the diffraction of sound waves more familiar in everyday experience than the diffraction of light waves?
6. In each of the following examples, state whether the colour is produced by diffraction, refraction, or the presence of pigments: (a) soap bubbles (b) peacock tails (c) rose petals (d) mother of pearl (e) oil films (f) blue jeans (g) the halo around the moon on a night when there is a high, thin cloud cover.
7. As monochromatic light passes through a diffraction grating, what is the difference in path length between two adjacent slits and a dark area on the screen?
8. When white light is passed through a grating, what is seen on the screen? Why are no dark areas seen?
9. Why do diffraction gratings have a large number of slits? Why are the slits so close together?
10. Why would a small diameter telescope not be able to resolve the images of two closely-spaced stars?

## APPLYING CONCEPTS

1. Suppose you are using a double slit to measure light wavelength precisely. It is easier to measure a larger than a smaller distance precisely. How can the value of $x$ be increased?
2. Two loudspeakers are placed 1.0 m apart on the edge of a stage. They emit sound of two wavelengths, 1.0 m long and 2.0 m long.
   a. If you are sitting 3.0 m from the stage, equidistant from the speakers, do you hear loud or quiet sounds for each of the wavelengths? Explain.
   b. If you sit 0.50 m from one speaker and 1.5 m from the other, what do you hear for each wavelength? Explain.
3. How can you tell whether an interference pattern is from a single slit or a double slit?
4. Describe the changes in a single-slit pattern as slit width is decreased.
5. Does interference aid or hinder radio reception? Explain.

6. Does diffraction aid or hinder the viewing of images in a microscope? Explain.
7. For a given grating, which color of light produces a bright line closest to the central bright line?
8. What changes occur in the characteristics of the interference patterns formed by a diffraction grating containing $10^4$ lines/cm and one having $10^5$ lines/cm?
9. Using Figure 16–1 or Figure 26–8, decide for which part of the electromagnetic spectrum a picket fence could possibly be used as a diffraction grating.

# PROBLEMS

## 19.1 When Light Waves Interfere

1. Using a compass and ruler, construct a scale diagram of the interference pattern that results when waves 1 cm in length fall on two slits 2 cm apart. The slits may be represented by two dots spaced 2 cm apart and kept to one side of the paper. Draw a line through all points of reinforcement. Draw dotted lines through all nodal lines.
2. A radio station uses two antennas and broadcasts at 600 kHz. Radio waves travel at the speed of light. The waves from the two antennas are kept in step.
   a. What is the wavelength of the signals emitted by the station?
   b. The occupants of a home located 17 500 m from one antenna and 19 500 m from the other antenna have their receiver tuned to the station. Is the reception good or poor? Explain.
3. Light falls on a pair of slits $1.90 \times 10^{-3}$ cm apart. The slits are 80.0 cm from the screen. The first-order bright line is 1.90 cm from the central bright line. What is the wavelength of the light?
4. Light of wavelength 542 nm falls on a double slit. First-order bright bands appear 4.00 cm from the central bright line. The screen is 1.20 m from the slits. How far apart are the slits?
5. A lecturer is demonstrating two-slit interference with sound waves. Two speakers are used, 4.0 m apart. The sound frequency is 325 Hz and the speed of sound is 343 m/s. Students sit in seats 4.5 m away. What is the

spacing between the locations where no sound is heard because of destructive interference?
6. Monochromatic light passes through a single slit with a width of 0.010 cm and falls on a screen 100 cm away. If the distance from the centre of the pattern to the first band is 0.60 cm, what is the wavelength of the light?
7. Light with a wavelength of $4.5 \times 10^{-5}$ cm passes through a single slit and falls on a screen 100 cm away. If the slit is 0.015 cm wide, what is the distance from the centre of the pattern to the first dark band?
8. Monochromatic light with a wavelength of 400 nm passes through a single slit and falls on a screen 90 cm away. If the distance of the first-order dark band is 0.30 cm from the centre of the pattern, what is the width of the slit?
▶ 9. Sound waves of frequency 550 Hz enter a window 1.2 m wide. The window is in the exact centre of one wall of a theater 24 m × 12 m. The window is 12 m from the opposite wall, along which is a row of seats occupied by people. The theater is acoustically prepared to prevent the reflection of sound waves, and the speed of sound is 330 m/s. Two people in the row along the wall hear no sound. Where are they sitting?

## 19.2 Applications of Diffraction

10. A good diffraction grating has $2.50 \times 10^3$ lines/cm. What is the distance between two lines in the grating?
11. Using grating with a spacing of $4.00 \times 10^{-4}$ cm, a red line appears 16.5 cm from the central line on a screen. The screen is 1.00 m from the grating. What is the wavelength of the red light?
12. A spectrometer uses a grating with 12 000 lines per centimetre. Find the angles at which red light, 632 nm, and blue light, 421 nm, have the first-order bright bands.
▶ 13. The ridges in the *Morpho* butterfly wing in the chapter-opening photograph are spaced about $2.2 \times 10^{-7}$ m apart. Explain how they could cause the wing to appear iridescent blue.
▶ 14. Janet uses a 33-1/3 phonograph record as a diffraction grating. She shines a laser, $\lambda = $ 632.8 nm, on the record. On a screen 4.0 m from the record, a series of red dots 21 mm apart are seen.

**a.** How many ridges are there in 1 cm along the radius of the record?

**b.** She checks her results by noting that the ridges came from a song that lasted 4.01 min and took up 16 mm on the record. How many ridges should there be in 1 cm?

15. A camera with a 50-mm lens set at *f*/8 aperture has an opening 6.25 mm in diameter. Suppose this lens acts like a slit 6.25 mm wide. For light with $\lambda = 550$ nm, what is the resolution of the lens, the distance from the middle of the central bright band to the first-order dark band? The film is 50 mm from the lens.

16. The owner of the camera in Problem 15 tries to decide which film to buy for it. The expensive one, called fine-grain film, has 200 grains/mm. The less costly, coarse-grain film has only 50 grains/mm. If the owner wants a grain to be no smaller than the width of the central bright band calculated above, which film should be purchased?

17. Suppose the Hubble Space Telescope, 2.4 m in diameter, is in orbit 100 km above Earth and is turned to look at Earth. If you ignore the effect of the atmosphere, what is the resolution of this telescope? Use $\lambda = 500$ nm.

**FIGURE 19–11. Hubble Telescope**

18. The image formed on the retina of the eye shows the effect of diffraction. The diameter of the iris opening in bright light is 3.0 mm. For green light, 545 nm wavelength, find the resolution of the eye. That is, find the distance from the centre of the central band to the dark band. Assume the distance from iris to retina is 2.5 cm.

▶ 19. Cone cells in the retina are about 1.5 μm apart. On how many cone cells does the image found in Problem 18 fall? Would the eye's resolution be better if the iris were much larger, like the 10 mm diameter of an eagle's eye? Explain.

## THINKING PHYSIC-LY

Why are TV broadcasts in the VHF, Very High Frequency, range more easily received in areas of marginal reception than broadcasts in the UHF, Ultra High Frequency, range?

# CHAPTER
# 20

# Static Electricity

◀ **Sky Light**

During a thunderstorm, Molly and Paresh were watching lightning bolts as they lit up the sky. Paresh was impressed by the patterns of the bolts. Molly asked Paresh, "Why do you suppose lightning jumps between a cloud and Earth?" What explanation might Paresh give?

Nature provides few more awesome displays than lightning. Starting in 1740, Benjamin Franklin studied electricity produced by friction, charges that result from rubbing two surfaces together. Franklin proposed his famous kite experiment in 1750, and two years later showed that "electrical fire" could be drawn from a cloud. Franklin became famous as a scientist throughout Europe. This fame probably helped assure his diplomatic successes in France during the American Revolution.

## √ Concept Check

The following terms or concepts from earlier chapters are important for a good understanding of this chapter. If you are not familiar with them, you should review them before studying this chapter.
· forces and force addition, Chapter 5
· gravitation, Chapter 8

## Objectives

- recognize the basic properties of the electrical interaction.
- know how to charge an object.
- know that charging is the separation, not the creation, of charges.
- state the differences between conductors and insulators.

### Charge and Field Conventions

- *Positive charges are red.*
- *Negative charges are blue.*

A charged object shows electrical effects.

# 20.1 ELECTRICAL CHARGES

You may have rubbed your shoes on the carpet hard enough to create a lightning-like spark when you touched someone. Franklin's kite experiment showed that lightning is similar to frictional electricity. We now call electrical effects produced this way static electricity. In this chapter we will investigate **electrostatics,** the study of electrical charges that can be collected and held in one place. Current electricity, produced by batteries and generators, will be explored in later chapters.

## Charged Objects

Have you ever noticed the way your hair is attracted to the comb when you comb your hair on a dry day? Perhaps you have also found socks stuck together in a clothes dryer. Then you will recognize the attraction of bits of paper to a comb shown in Figure 20–1. If the weather is dry, you should try it now. Rub a plastic comb or ball-point pen on your clothing. Wool clothing is best. Then hold the pen or comb close to a pile of paper bits. Notice the way the paper pieces jump up toward the comb. There must be a new, relatively strong force causing this upward acceleration, because it is larger than the downward acceleration caused by the gravitational force of the entire Earth.

There are other differences between this new force and gravity. Paper is attracted to a comb only after the comb has been rubbed. If you wait awhile, the attractive property of the comb disappears. Gravity, on the other hand, does not require rubbing and does not leak away. The ancient Greeks noticed these effects when they rubbed amber. We now call the interaction "electrical" after the Greek word for amber, *elektron.* An object that exhibits this electrical interaction after rubbing is said to be "charged."

You can explore the electrical interaction with very simple equipment. You will need some Scotch Brand "Magic"™ tape. Fold over about 5 mm on the end of the tape for a handle and then stick an 8 to

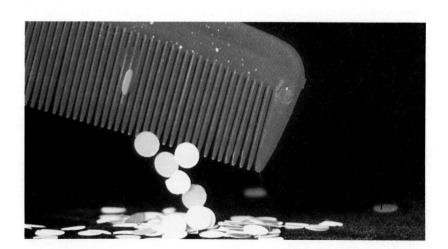

**FIGURE 20–1. Running a comb through your hair transfers electrons to the comb, giving it a negative charge. When the charged comb is brought close to bits of paper, a charge separation is induced on the paper bits. The attractive electric force accelerates the paper bits upward against the force of gravity.**

a

b

# F.Y.I.

12-cm long piece on a dry, smooth surface like your desk top. Stick a second, similar, piece on top of the first, Figure 20–2a. Now quickly pull both pieces off together, then pull them apart. Finally stick one end of each piece to the edge of a table, bottom of a lamp shade, and so on. The two should hang down a short distance apart, Figure 20–2b. Now rub the comb or pen on your clothing and bring it near first one tape and then the other. You will find that one tape will be attracted to the comb, the other repelled from it. You can now explore the interactions of charged objects with the tapes.

Now charge two strips of tape by pressing the strips side by side on the desk and then pulling them off. Notice that these two tapes repel when they are suspended near each other. You will find that any tape pulled directly off the desk will repel another similarly prepared tape. On the other hand, two tapes attract when they are unlike in the way they were charged. A tape pulled off the back of another tape will attract a tape pulled off the desk. Try other objects like plates, glasses, or plastic bags. Rub them with different materials like silk, fur, wool, or plastic wrap. If the air is dry, scuff your shoes on the carpet and bring your finger near the tapes. You should find that most charged objects attract one tape and repel the other. To test silk, fur, or wool, you should slip a plastic bag over your hand before holding the cloth. After rubbing, take your hand out of the bag and bring both bag and cloth near the tapes.

You will never find an object that repels both tapes, although you might find some that attract both tapes. Bring your finger near first one tape, then the other. You will find it attracts both tapes. We will explore this effect in Section 20.2.

From your experiments you can make a list of objects that are charged like the tape stuck on the desk and a list of other objects that are charged like the tape stuck on the back of the other tape. There are only two lists; thus there are only two states of charge. We could give these states the names "yellow" and "green." Benjamin Franklin called them *positive* and *negative*. The choice of which list to call positive and which negative was also made by Franklin. We still follow his convention and call the charge states for materials like vinyl and hard rubber negative, while materials like fur, glass, and wool we call positive.

*Identical objects charged the same way repel each other.*

*Objects charged differently attract.*

**FIGURE 20–3. A piece of plastic 0.02 mm wide was given a net positive charge. Areas of negative charge show as dark regions. Areas of positive charge show as yellow regions.**

Charges are not created but separated.

Electrons can be removed from or added to atoms.

You were probably able to show that if you rubbed plastic with wool, the plastic was charged negatively, the wool positively. The two kinds of charges were not created alone, but in pairs. This experiment suggests that normal matter contains both charges, positive and negative. Rubbing in some way separates the two. To explore this further, we have to consider the microscopic picture of matter.

## A Microscopic View of Charge

Electric charges exist in the atom itself. In 1890, J. J. Thomson discovered that all materials contain light, negatively-charged particles he called electrons. Between 1909 and 1911, Ernest Rutherford, a New Zealander, discovered that atoms have a massive, positively-charged nucleus, or centre. The electrons surround the nucleus. The positive charge of the nucleus is exactly balanced by the negative charge of the electrons. That is, the atom is uncharged; it is **neutral**.

With the addition of energy, electrons can be removed from atoms. The positively-charged particle that results is called a positive ion. The freed electrons can remain unattached or become attached to other atoms, resulting in negatively-charged particles, or negative ions.

If two objects are rubbed together, each can become charged. Scientists do not yet understand all the details of this process. They do know that when two different objects, like rubber and fur, are rubbed together, electrons from atoms on the fur are transferred to the rubber, Figure 20–4. Positive ions remain in the fur. Additional electrons give the atoms in the rubber a net negative charge. The total charge of the two objects remains the same, it is conserved. Individual charges are never created or destroyed. The separation of positive and negative charges means that electrons have been transferred.

Friction between the tires of a moving car or truck and the road can cause the tires to become charged. Violent winds cause friction in thunderclouds that separate charges. Usually the tops of the clouds become positive, the bottoms negative.

**FIGURE 20–4. A rubber object can be charged when rubbed with fur.**

Hard rubber rod

Fur

## Conductors and Insulators

Hold a plastic rod or comb in its middle and rub only one end. You will find that only the rubbed end becomes charged. The charges you added to the plastic stayed where they were put, they did not move. Materials through which charges will not move easily are called electrical **insulators.** Charges removed from one area on an insulator are not replaced by charges from another area. Glass, dry wood, most plastics, cloth, and dry air are good insulators.

Suppose you support a metal rod on an insulator so that it is isolated, or completely surrounded by insulators. If you now touch the charged comb to one end of the metal rod, you will find that the charge spreads very quickly over the entire piece. Materials such as metals that allow charges to move about easily are called electrical **conductors.** Electrons carry, or conduct, electric charge through the metal. Metals are good conductors because at least one electron on each atom can be removed easily. These electrons act as if they no longer belong to any one atom, but to the metal as a whole. They are free to move throughout the metal in the same way atoms in a gas move about a container. They are said to form an electron gas. Copper and aluminum are both excellent conductors and are used commercially to carry electricity. Graphite, the form of carbon used in pencils, also is a good conductor.

Air is an insulator, but under certain conditions sparks or lightning occurs, allowing charge to move as through a conductor. The spark that jumps between your finger and a doorknob after you have rubbed your feet on the carpet discharges you. That is, the charges separating during charging have recombined. Similarly, lightning discharges the charges in thunderclouds. How can air become a conductor? The forces exerted by the charges must have ripped electrons off of molecules in the air. The electrons and positively- or negatively-charged atoms, or ions, become free to move. They form a conductor called a plasma.

Charges stay in one place on an insulator.

Charges move easily on a conductor.

···················

# CONCEPT REVIEW

**1.1** How could you find out which strip of tape, the one pulled off the desk or the one pulled off the back of the other tape, is positively charged?

**1.2** Suppose you attach a long metal rod to a plastic handle so the rod is isolated. You touch a charged glass rod to one end of the metal rod. Describe the charges on the metal rod.

**1.3** In the 1730s, Stephan Gray tried to see how far electrical charge could be conducted by metal rods. He hung metal rods by thin silk cords from the ceiling. When the rods were longer than 89.3 m the silk broke. Gray replaced the silk with stronger wires made of brass, but now the experiments failed. The metal rod would no longer transmit charge from one end to the other. Why?

**1.4 Critical Thinking:** Suppose there was a third type of charge. What experiments could you suggest to explore its properties?

# F.Y.I.

Benjamin Franklin was cautious while performing his famous kite experiment, in which he charged a Leyden jar with electricity drawn from the clouds. The first two men who tried to repeat the experiment were electrocuted.

—*Isaac Asimov's Book of Facts*

# PHYSICS LAB : What's the Charge?

## Purpose

To see and feel the effects of electrostatic charging.

## Materials

· 30 cm x 30 cm block of plastic foam insulation material
· 22-cm aluminum pie pan
· plastic drinking glass
· drinking straw
· fur
· transparent tape
· thread
· pith ball (or small piece of plastic foam packing material)
· liquid graphite

## Procedure

1. Paint the small pith (or plastic foam) ball with graphite and allow it to dry.
2. Securely tape the inverted glass to the centre (inside) of the aluminum pie pan.
3. Tape the drinking straw to the top of the plastic glass as shown below. Use the thread to attach the ball as shown.
4. Rub the foam with the fur, then remove the fur.
5. Move the pie pan by holding onto the plastic glass.
6. Slowly lower the pie pan until it is about 3 cm above the charged plastic foam block and then slowly lift it away.
7. Place the pie pan directly on the charged foam block and lift it away.

8. Bring your finger near the ball until it touches.
9. Remove the straw, thread, and ball from the glass.
10. Place the pie pan on the foam block and touch the edge of the pie pan with your finger. Now remove the pie pan from the foam block and touch the ball again with your finger.
11. Repeat step 10 several times without recharging the foam block.

## Observations and Data

1. As the pie pan was brought near the charged block, could you feel a force between the neutral pie pan and the charged foam? Describe it.
2. Describe what happened to the ball in step 6.
3. Describe what happened to the ball in step 7.

## Analysis

1. Make a drawing to show the distribution of charges on the neutral pie pan as it is lowered toward the charged foam block.
2. What was the reason for using the ball on a thread?
3. State a hypothesis that explains the back and forth motion of the ball in step 8.
4. Does the plastic foam block seem to "run out of charges" in step 11?

## Applications

1. Clear plastic wrap is sold to seal up containers of food. Suggest a reason why it clings to itself.

plastic drinking straw

plastic foam

plastic drinking glass

pith ball

aluminum pie pan

# 20.2 ELECTRICAL FORCES

Electrical forces must be strong, as they can easily produce accelerations larger than the acceleration caused by gravity. We have also seen that they can be either repulsive or attractive, while gravitational forces are always attractive. Many scientists made attempts to measure the electrical force. Daniel Bernoulli, otherwise known for his work on fluids, made some crude measurements in 1760. In 1770, Henry Cavendish showed electric forces must obey an inverse square force law, but, being extremely shy, he did not publish his work. His manuscripts were discovered over a century later, after all his work had been duplicated by others.

## Forces on Charged Bodies

The forces you observed on tape strips can also be demonstrated by suspending a negatively-charged hard rubber rod so that it turns easily, Figure 20–5. If you bring another negatively-charged rod near the suspended rod, it will turn away. The negative charges on the rods repel each other. It is not necessary to bring the rods very close; the force, called the electric force, acts over a distance. If a positively-charged glass rod is suspended and a similarly-charged glass rod is brought close, the two positively-charged rods will also repel. If a negatively-charged rod is brought near the positively-charged rod, however, the two will attract each other, and the suspended rod will turn toward the oppositely-charged rod. The results of your tape experiments and these observations with charged rods can be summarized in this way:
· There are two kinds of electrical charges, positive and negative.
· Charges exert force on other charges over a distance.
· Like charges repel; opposite charges attract.
Neither a strip of tape nor a large rod hanging in open air is a very sensitive or convenient way of determining charge. Instead, a device

## Objectives

· be able to summarize the observed forces between charged objects; know how an electroscope detects the presence of charge and how an object is charged by conduction.
· explain separation of charge and charging by induction.
· state Coulomb's law and how the force depends on charges and their separation.
· state the SI unit of charge; understand the vector nature of the electric force; solve problems using Coulomb's law.
· understand the cause of the attractive force on neutral objects; list examples of this force.

Like-charged objects repel.
Unlike-charged objects attract.

An electroscope can measure the quantity of charge.

FIGURE 20–5. A charged rod, when brought close to another suspended rod, will attract or repel the suspended rod.

a                    b                    c

FIGURE 20–6. Electroscope.

Charges can be transferred directly by conduction.

FIGURE 20–7. A negatively-charged rod repels electrons from the electroscope down to the leaves; a positively-charged rod attracts electrons from the leaves to the top of the electroscope.

Sky Light ▶

EARTH SCIENCE CONNECTION ▶

An uncharged object can attract objects of either charge.

called an **electroscope** is used. An electroscope consists of a metal knob connected by a metal stem to two thin, lightweight pieces of metal foil called leaves, Figure 20–6. Note that the leaves are enclosed to eliminate stray air currents.

When a negatively-charged rod is touched to the knob, negative charges (electrons) are added to the knob. The charges spread over all the metal surfaces. The two leaves are charged negatively and repel each other, causing them to spread apart. The electroscope has been given a net charge. Charging a neutral body this way, by touching it with a charged body, is called **charging by conduction**.

The leaves will also spread if the electroscope is charged positively. How then can you find out whether the electroscope is charged positively or negatively? The type of charge can be determined by observing what happens to the spread leaves if a rod of known charge is brought close to the knob. The leaves will spread farther apart if the electroscope has the same charge as that of the rod. The leaves will fall slightly if the electroscope has a charge opposite to that of the rod, Figure 20–7.

## Separation of Charge and Charging by Induction

When you brought your finger near either charged tape, the tape was attracted toward your finger. Your finger was not charged; it was neutral and had equal amounts of positive and negative charge. We know that in materials that are conductors, charges can move easily; and that in the case of sparks, electric forces can change insulators into conductors. Given this information, we can suggest a plausible model for the force your finger exerted on the charged objects.

Suppose you move your finger, or any other uncharged object, close to a positively-charged object. The negative charges in your finger will be attracted to the positively-charged object, and the positive charges will be repelled. Your finger will remain neutral, but the positive and negative charges will be separated. The separation results in an attractive force between the neutral object and the charged object. The force of a charged comb on your hair or neutral pieces of paper can be seen easily. The equal and opposite force of your hair on the comb is much harder to observe.

The negative charges at the bottom of thunderclouds can also cause charge separation in Earth. Positive charges are attracted to Earth's surface under the cloud. The forces of the charges in the cloud and on Earth's surface on the neutral air molecules can rip the molecules apart. The charges from the cloud and Earth then pass through the conducting path, called the lightning bolt.

Charge separation can be used to charge an object without touching it. Suppose a negatively-charged rod is brought close to one of two identical insulated metal spheres that are touching, as in Figure 20–8. Electrons from the first sphere will be pushed onto the sphere farther from the rod making it negatively charged. The closer sphere is now positively charged. If the spheres are separated while the rod is nearby, each sphere will have a charge, and the charges will be equal but opposite. This process is called **charging by induction**.

## Coulomb's Law

How does the electric force depend on the size of the charges and their separation? Your tape experiments demonstrated some basic properties. You found that the force depends on distance. The closer you brought the charged rod to the tape, the stronger the force. You also found that the more you charged the rod, the stronger the force. But how can you vary the quantity of charge in a controlled way? This problem was solved in 1785 by a French physicist Charles Coulomb (1736–1806). The type of apparatus used by Coulomb is shown in Figure 20–9. An insulating rod with small conducting spheres, **A, A'** at each end was suspended by a thin wire. A similar sphere, **B,** was placed in contact with sphere **A.** When they were touched with a charged object, the charge spread evenly over the two spheres. Because they were the same size, they received equal amounts of charge.

Coulomb found how the force between the two charged spheres, **A** and **B,** depended on the distance. First, he carefully measured the amount of force needed to twist the suspending wire through a given angle. He then placed equal charges on spheres **A** and **B** and varied the distance, *d*, between them. The electric force moved **A** from its rest position, twisting the suspending wire. By measuring the deflection of **A,** Coulomb could calculate the force of repulsion. He made many

**FIGURE 20–8. The negative rod is brought near the touching spheres and the electrons are repelled to the right-hand sphere. The spheres are separated and their charge is determined with an electroscope.**

# F.Y.I.

Victor Hess won the Nobel Prize for physics in 1936 for his discovery of cosmic radiation. He performed research by sending up balloons carrying electroscopes into the atmosphere.

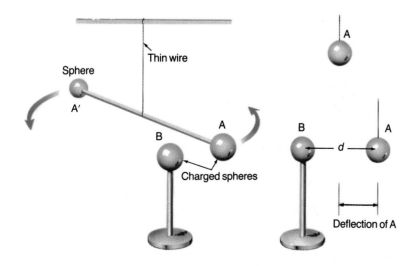

**FIGURE 20–9. Coulomb used this type of apparatus to measure the force between two spheres, A and B. He observed the deflection of A while varying the distance between A and B.**

**FIGURE 20–10.** Static electric precipitators are used to reduce the fly ash released into the environment. An electric field exerts a force on charged particles, deflecting them sideways. In (a) the device is off, in (b) it is on.

a

b

The electric force varies inversely with the square of the distance between the two charged objects.

The electric force between two charged objects varies directly with the product of their charges.

Coulomb's law describes the force between two charged objects.

# POCKET
# LAB

### REACH OUT

Start with the leaves of an electroscope down. Predict what should happen if you bring a charged balloon near (but not touching) the top of an electroscope. Explain your prediction. Try it. Describe and explain your results. **Hint:** Electrons move within the metal.

measurements with spheres charged both positively and negatively. He showed that the magnitude of the force, $F$, varied inversely with the square of the distance between the centres of the spheres.

$$F \propto \frac{1}{d^2}$$

To investigate the way the force depended on the amount of charge, Coulomb had to change the charges on the spheres in a measured way. Coulomb first charged spheres **A** and **B** equally as before. Then he selected an extra uncharged sphere, **C**, the same size as sphere **B**. When **C** was placed in contact with **B**, the spheres shared the charge that had been on **B** alone. Because the two were the same size, **B** now had only half its original charge. Therefore, the charge on **B** was only one half the charge on **A**. The extra sphere was then removed. After Coulomb adjusted the position of **B** so that the distance, $d$, between **A** and **B** was the same as before, he found that the force between **A** and **B** was half of its former value. That is, he found that the magnitude of the electric force varied directly with the charge of the bodies.

$$F \propto qq'$$

After many similar measurements, Coulomb summarized the results in a law now known as **Coulomb's law**. *The magnitude of the force that a tiny sphere with charge q exerts on a second sphere with charge q', separated a distance d, is*

$$F = \frac{kqq'}{d^2}.$$

This equation gives the strength of the force that charge $q$ exerts on $q'$ and also the force that $q'$ exerts on $q$. These two forces are equal in magnitude but opposite in direction. You can observe this example of Newton's third law in action when you bring two tapes with like charge together. Each exerts forces on the other. If you bring a charged comb near the tape, the tape, with its small mass, moves readily. The acceleration of the comb and you is, of course, much less because of the much greater mass.

In the Coulomb's law equation, $k$ is a constant that depends on the units used to measure charge, force, and distance. Experimental tests show that Coulomb's law works at all distances. It has even been found to be true for individual electrons separated by less than $10^{-18}$ m. This is a separation one ten-millionth as large as the size of the atom.

Each charged object exerts an equal but opposite force on the other charged object.

## The Unit of Charge: The Coulomb

Coulomb showed that the quantity of charge could be related to force. Thus he could define a standard quantity of charge in terms of the amount of force it produces. The SI standard unit of charge is thus called the **coulomb**, C. One coulomb is the charge of $6.25 \times 10^{18}$

# Physics and technology

## THE PHOTOCOPIER

Forces on charged and uncharged bodies are important in photocopiers. A typical copier has a drum made of a conductor, aluminum, which is coated with a thin layer of the semiconductor selenium. In operation, the selenium layer is first charged by a spray of charged air molecules. In the dark, selenium is a poor conductor, and the charges remain in place. Light is reflected from the white parts of the page to be copied, passed through a lens, and focused on the drum. Where the light strikes the selenium, the semiconductor becomes a conductor, letting the charges flow away from the sur-

face to the aluminum drum. However, where there was a dark area on the page, there will be a dark area on the drum, and the charge will remain on the selenium layer. The drum is then rotated through a container of toner. The toner consists of tiny charged plastic beads coated with carbon grains. The coated beads are attracted to the charged areas of the selenium

layer on the drum but not to the areas where the charge has flowed away. A sheet of paper is then pressed against the drum and the coated beads are transferred to the paper. The paper is heated and the beads melt, attaching the carbon to the paper to form the image.
· Why does the photocopier drum need to be coated with a semiconductor rather than a conductor?

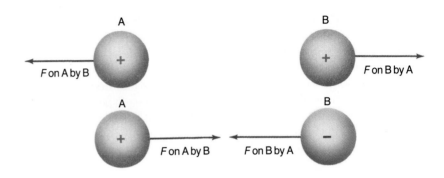

electrons. The charge that produces a large lightning bolt is about 10 coulombs. The charge of an individual electron is only $1.60 \times 10^{-19}$ C. The magnitude of the charge of an electron is called the **elementary charge**. Thus, as we will calculate in Problem 3 in the Chapter Review, even small pieces of matter, such as the coins in your pocket, contain up to 1 000 000 C of negative charge. This enormous amount of charge produces almost no external effects because it is balanced by an equal amount of positive charge. A charge even as small as $10^{-9}$ C can result in large forces.

*The coulomb is the SI unit charge.*

*A repulsive force has a positive sign.*

According to Coulomb's law, the force on a body with charge $q$ caused by a body with charge $q'$ a distance $d$ away can be written

$$F = \frac{kqq'}{d^2}.$$

When charges are measured in coulombs, the distance in metres, and the force in newtons, the constant $k$ is $9.0 \times 10^9$ N · m$^2$/C$^2$.

The electric force, like all other forces, is a vector quantity. Consider the direction of force on a positively-charged object called **A**. If another positively-charged object, **B**, is brought near, the force on **A** is repulsive. It is in the direction *from* **B** *to* **A**, Figure 20–11. The sign of the force is positive.

*An attractive force has a negative sign.*

If, instead, **B** is negatively charged, the force on **A** is attractive. The force is in the opposite direction. The sign of the force is negative. Thus, it is important to include the positive or negative sings for $q$ and $q'$ when using Coulomb's law and to interpret the directions carefully.

## Example Problem

### Coulomb's Law—Two Charges

Object **A** has a positive charge of $6.0 \times 10^{-6}$ C. Object **B**, carrying a positive charge of $3.0 \times 10^{-6}$ C, is 0.030 m away.

  **a.** Calculate the force on **A**.

  **b.** What would be the force if the charge on **B** were negative?

**Given:** $q = +6.0 \times 10^{-6}$ C     **Unknown:** $F_A$
        $q' = +3.0 \times 10^{-6}$ C
        $d = 0.030$ m      **Basic equation:** $F = \dfrac{kqq'}{d^2}$

**Solution:**

**a.** $F_A = \dfrac{kqq'}{d^2}$

$= \dfrac{(9.0 \times 10^9 \, N \cdot m^2/C^2)(+6.0 \times 10^{-6} \, C)(3.0 \times 10^{-6} \, C)}{(0.030 \, m)^2}$

$= \dfrac{(9.0 \times 10^9 \, N \cdot m^2/C^2)(+18 \times 10^{-12} \, C^2)}{9.0 \times 10^{-4} \, m^2}$

$= +1.8 \times 10^2 \, N$

The positive sign of the force indicates repulsion. The force on **A** is in the direction from **B** toward **A**.

**b.** If the second charge were negative, the sign of the force would be negative, in the opposite direction.

# Example Problem

## Coulomb's Law—Three Charges

An object, **A**, with $+6.0 \times 10^{-6}$ C charge, has two other charges nearby. Object **B**, $-3.00 \times 10^{-6}$ C, is 0.040 m to the right. Object **C**, $+1.5 \times 10^{-6}$ C, is 0.030 m below. What is the net force on **A**? Solve the problem graphically.

**Solution:**

Choose a coordinate system, with **A** at the origin, **B** on the positive x axis, **C** on the negative y axis. See Figure 20–12a. First the magnitude of the individual forces are calculated.

$F_B = \dfrac{kqq'}{d^2}$

$= \dfrac{(9.0 \times 10^9 \, N \cdot m^2/C^2)(+6.0 \times 10^{-6} \, C)(-3.0 \times 10^{-6} \, C)}{(4.0 \times 10^{-2} \, m)^2}$

$= -1.0 \times 10^2 \, N$

Force $F_B$, is attractive, toward **B**, in the positive x direction.

$F_C = \dfrac{kqq'}{d^2}$

$= \dfrac{(9.0 \times 10^9 \, N \cdot m^2/C^2)(+6.0 \times 10^{-6} \, C)(+1.5 \times 10^{-6} \, C)}{(3.0 \times 10^{-2} \, m)^2}$

$= +9.0 \times 10^1 \, N$

Force $F_C$ is repulsive, away from **C**, in the positive y direction.

Next, the forces are added vectorially to find the net force. See the drawing.
We obtain

$F_{net} = 1.3 \times 10^2 \, N$ at 42° above the x axis, Figure 20–12b.

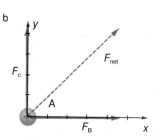

**FIGURE 20–12. Example Problem set up is (a). graphical solution (b).**

# Practice Problems

1. Two positive charges of $6.0 \times 10^{-6}$ C are separated by 0.50 m. What force exists between the charges?
2. A negative charge of $-2.0 \times 10^{-4}$ C and a positive charge of $8.0 \times 10^{-4}$ C are separated by 0.30 m. What is the force between the two charges?
3. A negative charge of $-6.0 \times 10^{-6}$ C exerts an attractive force of 65 N on a second charge 0.050 m away. What is the magnitude of the second charge?
4. An object with charge $+7.5 \times 10^{-7}$ C is placed at the origin. The position of a second object, charge $+1.5 \times 10^{-7}$ C, is varied from 1.0 cm to 5.0 cm. Draw a graph of the force on the object at the origin.
▶ 5. The charge on **B** in the Example Problem is replaced by $+3.00 \times 10^{-6}$ C. Use graphical methods to find the net force on **A.**

## Using Electric Forces on Neutral Bodies

As you have seen, a charged object may either attract or repel another charged object. A charged object, however, is always attracted by a neutral (uncharged) object. By Newton's third law, that neutral object must also be attracted toward the charged object. It doesn't matter whether the charge is positive or negative.

There are many applications of electric forces on neutral particles. These forces can collect soot in smokestacks, reducing air pollution, Figure 20–10. Tiny paint droplets, charged by induction, can be used to paint automobiles and other objects very uniformly.

. . . . . . . . . . . . . . . . . . . .
# CONCEPT REVIEW

2.1 When an electroscope is charged, the leaves rise to a certain angle and remain at that angle. Why don't they rise farther?
2.2 Two charged spheres are on a frictionless horizontal surface. One has $+3 \times 10^{-6}$ C charge, the other $+6 \times 10^{-6}$ C charge. Sketch the two spheres, showing all forces on them. Make the length of your force arrows proportional to the strength of the forces.
2.3 Explain why a balloon that has been rubbed on a wool shirt sticks to the wall.
2.4 **Critical Thinking:** Suppose you are testing Coulomb's law using a small, charged plastic sphere and a large, charged metal sphere. Both are charged positively. According to Coulomb's law, the force depends on $1/d^2$, where $d$ is the distance between the centres of the spheres. As the two spheres get close together, the force is smaller than expected from Coulomb's law. Explain.

# 20 REVIEW

## SUMMARY

### 20.1 Electrical Charges

· There are two kinds of electrical charges, positive and negative. Electrons are a negative.
· Electrical charge is conserved; it cannot be created or destroyed.
· Bodies can be charged negatively or positively by transferring electrons. An object is charged negatively by adding electrons to it. An object is charged positively by removing electrons from it.
· Charges added to one part of an insulator remain on that part.
· Charges added to a conductor very quickly spread over the surface of the body. This is called electrical conduction.
· Charges exert forces on other charges. Like charges repel; unlike charges attract.

### 20.2 Electrical Forces

· An electroscope indicates electrical charge. In an electroscope, forces on charges cause thin metal leaves to spread.
· A charged rod can charge an electroscope by induction by causing a separation of charges.
· Coulomb's law states that *the force between two charged point objects varies directly with the product of the two charges and inversely with the square of the distance between them.*
· The unit of charge is the coulomb. One coulomb, C, is the magnitude of the charge of $6.25 \times 10^{18}$ electrons or protons. The elementary charge, the charge of the proton or electron, is $1.60 \times 10^{-19}$ C.
· A charged body of either sign can produce separation of charge in a neutral body. Thus a charged body attracts a neutral body.

## KEY TERMS

| | |
|---|---|
| electrostatics | charging by conduction |
| neutral | charging by induction |
| insulators | Coulomb's law |
| conductors | coulomb |
| electroscope | elementary charge |

## REVIEWING CONCEPTS

1. If you comb your hair on a dry day, the comb can become positively charged. Can your hair remain neutral? Explain.
2. The combined charge of all electrons in a nickel coin is hundreds of thousands of coulombs, a unit of electrical charge. Does that imply anything about the net charge on the coin? Explain.
3. List some insulators and conductors.
4. What property makes a metal a good conductor and rubber a good insulator?
5. Why does a woolen sock taken from a clothes dryer sometimes cling to other clothes?
6. If you wipe a stereo record with a clean cloth, why does the record now attract dust?
7. Name three methods to charge an object.
8. Explain how to charge a conductor negatively if you have only a positively-charged rod.

## APPLYING CONCEPTS

1. How does the charge of an electron differ from the charge of a proton?
2. If you scuff electrons from your feet while walking across a rug, are you now negatively charged or positively charged?
3. Using a charged rod and an electroscope, how can you find if an object is a conductor?
4. Explain why an insulator that is charged can be discharged by passing it above a flame.
5. A charged rod is brought near a pile of tiny plastic spheres. Some of the spheres are attracted to the rod, but as soon as they touch the rod, they fly away in different directions. Explain.
6. A rod-shaped insulator is suspended so it can rotate. A negatively-charged comb held nearby attracts the rod.
   a. Does this mean the rod is positively charged? Explain.
   b. If the comb repelled the rod, what could you conclude, if anything, about the charge on the rod?

7. Lightning usually occurs when a negative charge in a cloud is transported to Earth. If Earth is neutral, what provides the attractive force that pulls the electrons toward Earth?

8. Explain what happens to the leaves of a positively-charged electroscope when rods with the following charges are nearby but not touching the electroscope.
   a. positive   b. negative

9. Coulomb's law and Newton's law of universal gravitation appear similar. In what ways are the electrical and gravitational forces similar? How are they different?

10. The text describes Coulomb's method for obtaining two charged spheres, **A** and **B**, so that the charge on **B** was exactly half the charge on **A**. Suggest a way Coulomb could have placed a charge on sphere **B** that was exactly one third the charge on sphere **A**.

11. Coulomb measured the deflection of sphere **A** when **A** and **B** had equal charges and were a distance $d$ apart. He then made the charge on **B** one third the charge on **A**. How far apart would the two spheres have to be now for **A** to have the same deflection it had before?

12. Two charged bodies exert a force of 0.145 N on each other. If they are now moved so they are one fourth as far apart, what force is exerted?

13. The constant $K$ in Coulomb's equation is much larger than the constant $G$ in the Universal Gravitation equation. Of what significance is this?

14. Salt water drips slowly from a narrow dropper inside a negatively-charged metal ring, as seen in Figure 20–13.
   a. Will the drops be charged?
   b. If they are charged, are they positive or negative?

FIGURE 20–13. Use with Applying Concepts 14.

15. Benjamin Franklin once wrote that he had "erected an iron rod to draw the lightning down into my house, in order to make some experiment on it, with two bells to give notice when the rod should be electrify'd...." The chime had two small bells mounted side by side. One bell was connected to the iron rod for a charge; the other bell was attached to Earth. Between the two bells, a small metal ball was suspended on a silk thread so it could swing back and forth, striking the two bells. Explain why, when the one bell was charged, the ball would keep swinging, hitting first one bell then the other.

# PROBLEMS

## 20.2 Electrical Forces

1. Two charges, $q_1$ and $q_2$, are separated by a distance, $d$, and exert a force, $F$, on each other. What new force will exist if
   a. $q_1$ is doubled?
   b. $q_1$ and $q_2$ are cut in half?
   c. $d$ is tripled?
   d. $d$ is cut in half?
   e. $q_1$ is tripled and $d$ is doubled?

2. How many excess electrons are on a ball with a charge of $-4.00 \times 10^{-17}$ C?

3. How many coulombs of charge are on the electrons in a nickel coin? Follow this method to find the answer.
   a. Find the number of atoms in a nickel coin. A nickel coin has a mass of about 5 g. Each mole ($6.02 \times 10^{23}$ atoms) has a mass of about 58 g.
   b. Find the number of electrons in the coin. Each nickel atom has 28 electrons.
   c. Find how many coulombs of charge are on the electrons.

4. A strong lightning bolt transfers about 25 C to Earth.
   a. How many electrons are transferred?
   b. If each water molecule donates one electron, what mass of water lost an electron to the lightning? One mole of water has a mass of 18 g.

5. What is the total charge on all of the electrons in 1.0 L (1.0 kg) of water? One mole of water has a mass of 18 g and each molecule of water contains 10 electrons.

6. Two electrons in an atom are separated by $1.5 \times 10^{-10}$ m, the typical size of an atom. What is the force between them?

7. Object **A** has a charge $+1.8 \times 10^{-6}$ C. Object **B** has a charge $-1.0 \times 10^{-6}$ C. They are 0.014 m apart. What is the force on **A**? on **B**?

8. A positive and a negative charge, each of magnitude $1.5 \times 10^{-5}$ C, are separated by a distance of 15 cm. Find the force on each of the particles.

9. Two negatively-charged bodies with $-5.0 \times 10^{-5}$ C are 0.20 m from each other. What force acts on each particle?

10. Two negative charges of $-3.0 \times 10^{-6}$ C exert a repulsive force of 2.0 N on each other. By what distance are they separated?

11. How far apart are two electrons if they exert a force of repulsion of 1.0 N on each other?

12. A force of $-4.4 \times 10^3$ N exists between a positive charge of $8.0 \times 10^{-4}$ C and a negative charge of $-3.0 \times 10^{-4}$ C. What distance separates the charges?

13. Two identical positive charges exert a repulsive force of $6.4 \times 10^{-9}$ N when separated by a distance of $3.8 \times 10^{-10}$ m. Calculate the charge of each.

▶ 14. The hydrogen atom contains a proton, mass $1.67 \times 10^{-27}$ kg, and an electron, mass $9.11 \times 10^{-31}$ kg. The average distance between them is $5.3 \times 10^{-11}$ m. The charge of the proton is the same size, opposite sign of an electron.
   a. What is the magnitude of the average electrostatic attraction between them?
   b. What is the magnitude of the average gravitational attraction between them?
   c. How do the magnitudes of the two forces compare?

▶ 15. A positive charge of $3.0 \times 10^{-6}$ C is pulled on by two negative charges. One, $-2.0 \times 10^{-6}$ C, is 0.050 m to the north and the other, $-4.0 \times 10^{-6}$ C, is 0.030 m to the south. What total force is exerted on the positive charge?

▶ 16. Three particles are placed in a line. The left particle has a charge of $-67 \times 10^{-6}$ C, the middle, $+45 \times 10^{-6}$ C, and the right, $-83 \times$

$10^{-6}$ C. The middle particle is 72 cm from each of the others.
   a. Find the net force on the middle particle.
   b. Find the net force on the right particle.

▶ 17. Charges of $4.5 \times 10^{-6}$ C exist on the three spheres in Figure 20–12. Find the magnitude of the total force on sphere B.

▶ 18. Two charges, $q_1$ and $q_2$, are at rest near a positive test charge, $q$, of $7.2 \times 10^{-6}$ C. The first charge, $q_1$, is a positive charge of $3.6 \times 10^{-6}$ C, located 0.025 m away from $q$ at 35°; $q_2$ is a negative charge of $-6.6 \times 10^{-6}$ C, located 0.068 m away at 125°.
   a. Determine the magnitude of each of the forces acting on $q$.
   b. Sketch a force diagram.
   c. Graphically determine the resultant force acting on $q$.

▶ 19. The two pith balls in Figure 20–14 each have a mass of 1.0 g and equal charges. One pith ball is suspended by an insulating thread. The other is brought to 3.0 cm from the suspended ball. The suspended ball is now hanging with the thread forming an angle of 30.0° with the vertical. The ball is in equilibrium with $\vec{F}_E$, $m\vec{g}$, and $\vec{T}$ adding vectorially to yield zero. Calculate
   a. $m\vec{g}$.  b. $\vec{F}_E$.
   c. the charge on the balls.

**FIGURE 20–14. Use with Problem 19.**

## THINKING PHYSIC-LY

Electric forces between charges are enormous in comparison to gravitational forces. Yet, we normally do not sense electrical forces between us and our surroundings, while we do sense gravitational interreactions with Earth. Explain.

# CHAPTER
# 21 Electric Fields

◀ High Energy Halo

Research into ultra-high-voltage — up to two million volts — transmission of electricity is essential for development of future power technology. At a special test facility, this ultra-high-voltage test line demonstrates a human-made corona effect. Why is the corona visible around this power line when the effect is not seen in the electric wires in our homes?

T he blue glow around the wires in the photo is a modern version of "St. Elmo's Fire." Sailors in the fifteenth century saw these ghostly-coloured streamers issuing from their high ships' masts. They recognized them as warning signs of an approaching lightning storm. The glow is indeed related to lightning. The human-made "fire" in the photo is called a corona discharge. Besides causing the eerie glow, it causes radio interference and can start a spark jumping from the wire to another conductor, so designers of these experimental power lines try to reduce or eliminate it entirely.

## √ Concept Check

The following terms or concepts from earlier chapters are important for a good understanding of this chapter. If you are not familiar with them, you should review them before studying this chapter.
· gravitational field, Chapter 8
· gravitational potential energy, Chapter 11
· electrical interactions, Coulomb's law, Chapter 20

# Objectives

- define an electric field; explain how to measure it.
- distinguish between force and field.
- be able to solve problems relating field, force, and charge.
- distinguish between electric field and field lines.

# 21.1 CREATING AND MEASURING ELECTRIC FIELDS

The electric force, like the gravitational force, varies inversely as the square of the distance between two objects. Both forces can act at a great distance. How can a force be exerted across what seems to be empty space? In trying to understand the electric force, Michael Faraday (1791–1867) developed the concept of an electric field. According to Faraday, a charge creates an electric field about it in all directions. If a second charge is placed at some point in the field, the second charge interacts with the field at that point. The force it feels is the result of a local interaction. Interaction between particles separated by some distance is no longer required.

## Charge and Field Conventions

- *Positive charges are red.*
- *Negative charges are blue.*
- ▶ *Electric fields are red.*

## The Electric Field

It is easy to state that a charge produces an electric field. But how can the field be detected and measured? We will describe a method that can be used to measure the field produced by an electric charge $q$.

You must measure the field at a specific location, for example, point **A**. An electrical field can be observed only because it produces forces on other charges, so a small positive test charge is placed at **A**. The force exerted on the test charge, $q'$, at this location is measured. According to Coulomb's law, the force is proportional to the test charge. If the size of the charge is doubled, the force is doubled. Thus, the ratio of the force to charge is independent of the size of the charge. If we divide the force, $\vec{F}$, on the test charge, measured at point **A**, by the size of the test charge, $q'$, we obtain a vector quantity, $\vec{F}/q'$. This quantity does not depend on the test charge, only on the charge $q$ and the location of point **A**. We call this vector quantity the **electric field**. The electric field at point **A**, the location of $q'$, is

$$\vec{E} = \frac{\vec{F}_{on\ q'}}{q'}.$$

The direction of the electric field is the direction of the force on the positive test charge. The magnitude of the electric field intensity is measured in newtons per coulomb, N/C.

Notice that just as the electric field is the force per unit charge, the gravitational field is the force per unit mass, $\vec{g} = \vec{F}/m$.

We said that an electric field should be measured by a small test charge. Why? The test charge exerts a force on $q$. We want to make sure the force exerted by the test charge doesn't move $q$ to another location, and thus change the force on $q'$ and the electric field we are measuring.

So far we have found the field at a single point. The test charge is now moved to another location. The force on it is measured again and the electric field at that location calculated. This process is repeated again and again until every location in space has a measurement of the vector quantity, the electric field, on the test charge associated with it.

## POCKET LAB

### ELECTRIC FIELDS

Use a 5-cm long thread to hang a pith ball (or small plastic-foam ball) from the end of a dangling straw. Rub a 25-cm square piece of plasticfoam with fur to put a large negative charge on the foam. Stand the foam in a vertical orientation. Give the pith ball a positive test charge (use the fur). Notice that the pith ball hangs straight down until you bring it toward the charged foam. The pith ball is now in an electric field. How does the pith ball indicate the "strength" of the field? Move the test charge (pith ball) to investigate the electric field around the foam. Record your results.

## Example Problem

### Calculating the Magnitude of the Electric Field

A positive test charge of $4.0 \times 10^{-5}$ C is placed in an electric field. The force on it is 0.60 N acting at 10°. What is the magnitude and direction of the electric field at the location of the test charge?

**Given:** size of test charge,
$q' = 4.0 \times 10^{-5}$ C
force on test charge,
$\vec{F} = 0.60$ N at 10°

**Unknown:** electric field, $\vec{E}$

**Basic equation:** $\vec{E} = \dfrac{\vec{F}}{q'}$

**Solution:**
Find the size of the field intensity.

$$\vec{E} = \frac{\vec{F}}{q'} = \frac{0.60\,\text{N}}{4.0 \times 10^{-5}\,\text{C}} = 1.5 \times 10^4 \text{ N/C}$$

The field direction is in the direction of the force since it is a positive test charge, so
$\vec{E} = 1.5 \times 10^4$ N/C at 10°.

If the force were in the opposite direction, the field at the test charge would also be in the opposite direction, that is, $\vec{E} = 1.5 \times 10^4$ N/C at $10° + 180° = 190°$.

# F.Y.I.

Robert Van de Graaff devised the high-voltage electrostatic generator in the 1930s. These generators can build up giant potentials that can accelerate particles to high energies.

## Practice Problems

1. A negative charge of $2.0 \times 10^{-8}$ C experiences a force of 0.060 N to the right in an electric field. What is the field magnitude and direction?

2. A positive test charge of $5.0 \times 10^{-4}$ C is in an electric field that exerts a force of $2.5 \times 10^{-4}$ N on it. What is the magnitude of the electric field at the location of the test charge?

3. Suppose the electric field in Practice Problem 2 were caused by a point charge. The test charge is moved to a distance twice as far from the charge. What is the magnitude of the force that the field exerts on the test charge now?

▶ 4. You are probing the field of a charge of unknown magnitude and sign. You first map the field with a $1.0 \times 10^{-6}$ C test charge, then repeat your work with a $2.0 \times 10^{-6}$ C charge.
   a. Would you measure the same forces with the two test charges? Explain.
   b. Would you find the same fields? Explain.

The collection of all the force vectors on the test charge is called an electric field. Any charge placed in an electric field experiences a force on it due to the electric field at that location. The strength of the force depends on the magnitude of the field, $E$, and the size of the charge, $q$. Thus $F = Eq$. The direction of the force depends on the direction of the field and the sign of the charge.

The total electric field is the vector sum of the fields of individual charges.

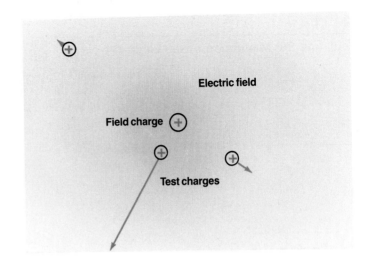

FIGURE 21–1. An electric field can be shown by using arrows to represent the direction of the field at various locations.

A picture of an electric field can be made by using arrows to represent the field vectors at various locations, Figure 21–1. The length of the arrow shows the magnitude of the field; the direction of the arrow shows its direction.

To find the field from two charges, the fields from the individual charges can be added vectorially. Or, a test charge can be used to map out the field due to any collection of charges. Typical electric fields produced by charge collections are shown in Table 21–1.

## Picturing the Electric Field

An alternative picture of an electric field is shown in Figure 21–3. The lines are called **electric field lines**. The direction of the field at any point is the tangent drawn to the field line at that point. The strength of the electric field is indicated by the spacing between the lines. The field is strong where the lines are close together. It is weaker where the lines are spaced farther apart. Remember that electric fields exist in three dimensions. Our drawings are only two-dimensional models.

The direction of the force on the positive test charge near a positive charge is away from the charge. Thus, the field lines extend radially outward like the spokes of a wheel, Figure 21–3a. Near a negative charge the direction of the force on the positive test charge is toward the charge, so the field lines point radially inward, Figure 21–3b.

FIGURE 21–2. Charge is transferred onto a moving belt at A, and from the belt to the metal dome at B. An electric motor does the work needed to increase the electric potential energy.

Table 21–1

| Approximate Values of Typical Electric Fields | |
|---|---|
| Field | Value (N/C) |
| Near charged hard rubber rod | $1 \times 10^3$ |
| In television picture tube | $1 \times 10^5$ |
| Needed to create spark in air | $3 \times 10^6$ |
| At electron orbit in hydrogen atom | $5 \times 10^{11}$ |

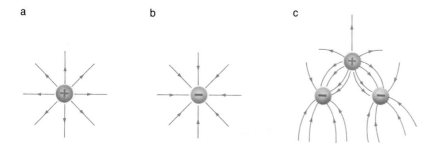

a  b  c

**FIGURE 21–3. Lines of force are drawn perpendicularly away from the positive object (a) and perpendicularly into the negative object (b). Electric field lines between like- and oppositely-charged objects are shown in (c).**

When there are two or more charges, the field is the vector sum of the fields due to the individual charges. The field lines become curved and the pattern complex, Figure 21–3c. Note that field lines always leave a positive charge and enter a negative charge.

The Van de Graaff machine is a device that transfers large amounts of charge from one part of the machine to the top metal terminal Figure 21–2. A person touching the terminal is charged electrically. The charges on the person's hairs repel each other, causing the hairs to follow the field lines. Another method of visualizing field lines is to use grass seed in an insulating liquid such as mineral oil. The electric forces cause a separation of charge in each long, thin grass seed. The seeds then turn so they line up along the direction of the electric field. Therefore, the seeds form a pattern of the electric field lines. The patterns in Figure 21–4 were made this way.

Field lines do not really exist. They are just a means of providing a model of an electric field. Electric fields, on the other hand, do exist. An electric field is produced by one or more charges and is independent of the existence of the test charge that is used to measure it. The field provides a method of calculating the force on a charged body. It does not explain, however, why charged bodies exert forces on each other. That question is still unanswered.

An electric field points away from positive charges and toward negative charges.

Electric fields are real. Electric field lines are imaginary, but help in making a picture of the field.

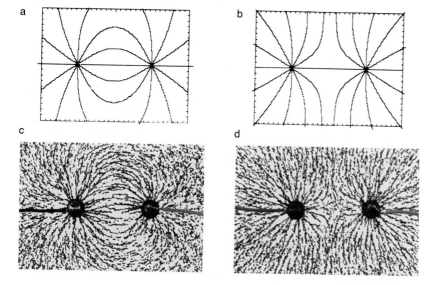

a  b  c  d

**FIGURE 21–4. Lines of force between unlike charges (a, c) and between like charges (b, d) describe the behaviour of a positively-charged object in a field. The top photographs are computer tracings of electric field lines.**

# PHYSICS LAB

# Charges, Energy, Voltage

## Purpose

To make a model that demonstrates the relationship of charge, energy, and voltage.

## Materials

· ball of clay
· ruler
· cellophane tape
· 12 of 3-mm diameter steel balls

## Procedure

1. Use the clay to support the ruler vertically on the tabletop. (The 0 cm end should be at the table.)
2. Cut a 2 cm × 8 cm rectangular piece of paper and write on it "3 V = 3 J/C".
3. Cut three more rectangles and label them: 6 V = 6 J/C, 9 V = 9 J/C, 12 V = 12 J/C.

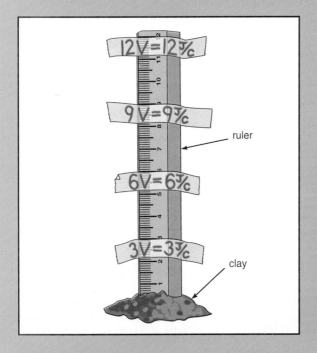

ruler

clay

4. Tape the 3-V rectangle to the 3 cm mark on the ruler, the 6-V to the 6 cm mark, and so on.
5. Let each steel ball represent 1 C of charge.
6. Lift and tape 4 steel balls to the 3-V rectangle, 3 to the 6-V rectangle, and so on.

## Observations and Data

1. The model shows different amounts of charges at different energy levels. Where should steel balls be placed to show a zero energy level? Explain.
2. Make a data table with the columns labeled "charge", "voltage", and "energy".
3. Fill in the data table for your model for each level of the model.

## Analysis

1. How much energy is required to lift each coulomb of charge from the tabletop to the 9-V level?
2. What is the total potential energy stored in the 9-V level?
3. The total energy of the charges in the 6-V level is not 6 J. Explain this.
4. How much energy would be given off if the charges in the 9-V level fell to the 6-V level? Explain.

## Applications

1. A 9-V battery is very small. A 12-V car battery is very big. Use your model to help explain why two 9-V batteries would not start your car.

# CONCEPT REVIEW

**1.1** Suppose you are asked to measure the electric field in space. Answer the questions of this step-by-step procedure.
   **a.** How do you detect the field at a point?
   **b.** How do you determine the magnitude of the field?
   **c.** How do you choose the size of the test charge?
   **d.** What do you do next?
**1.2** Suppose you are given an electric field, but the charges that produce the field are hidden. If all the field lines point into the hidden region, what can you say about the sign of the charge in that region?
**1.3** How does the electric field, *E*, differ from the force, *F*, on the test charge?
**1.4** **Critical Thinking:** Figure 21–4b shows the field from two like charges. The top positive charge in Figure 21–3c could be considered a test charge measuring the field due to the two negative charges. Is this positive charge small enough to produce an accurate measure of the field? Explain.

# 21.2 APPLICATIONS OF THE ELECTRIC FIELD

The concept of energy is extremely useful in mechanics. The law of conservation of energy allows us to solve problems without knowing the forces in detail. The same is true in our study of electrical interactions. The work done moving a charged particle in an electric field can result in the particle gaining either potential or kinetic energy, or both. In this chapter, since we are investigating charges at rest, we will discuss only changes in potential energy.

## Energy and the Electric Potential

Recall the change in potential energy of a ball when you lift it, Figure 21–5. Both the gravitational force, $\vec{F}$, and the gravitational field, $\vec{g} = \vec{F}/m$, point toward Earth. If you lift a ball against the force of gravity, you do work on it, and thus its potential energy is increased.

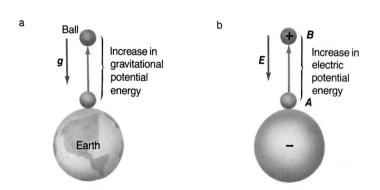

a

Ball

g

Increase in gravitational potential energy

Earth

b

+ B

E

Increase in electric potential energy

A

−

Objectives

· **define the electric potential difference in terms of work done moving a unit test charge; distinguish potential from potential difference.**
· **know the units of potential; solve problems involving potential in uniform electric fields.**
· **understand how Millikan used electric fields to find the charge of the electron.**
· **understand how minimizing energy determines sharing of charge; define grounding and relate to charge sharing.**
· **know where charges reside on solid and hollow conductors; recognize the relationship between conductor shape and field strength.**
· **define capacitance; describe the principle of the capacitor; solve capacitor problems.**

**FIGURE 21–5. Work is needed to move an object against the force of gravity (a) and against the electric force (b). In both cases, the potential energy of the object is increased.**

The electric potential is the potential energy of a unit charge.

The volt is the unit of electric potential.

The reference point of zero level of potential is arbitrary.

Only potential differences are meaningful.

The situation is similar with two unlike charges. These two attract each other, and so you must do work to pull one away from the other. When you do the work, you store it as potential energy. The larger the test charge, the greater the increase in its potential energy, $\Delta E_p$.

The electric field at the location of the test charge does not depend on the size of the test charge. The field is the force per unit charge, or $F/q'$. In the same way, we will define a quantity that is the change in potential energy per unit charge. This quantity is called the **electric potential difference** and is defined by the equation $\Delta V = \Delta E_p/q'$. The unit of electric potential, joule per coulomb, is called a **volt** ($J/C = V$).

Consider the situation shown in Figure 21–5. Work must be done on the test charge to move it from point **A** to point **B**. Therefore, the potential energy of the positive test charge at point **B**, farther from the negative charge, is larger than the potential energy at point **A**. Thus the electric potential at point **B** is larger than the potential at point **A**. The electric potential difference from point **A** to point **B** will then be positive. Conversely, from point **B** to point **A** it is negative.

As the positive test charge is returned to point **A**, its potential decreases. The change in potential when moving from **B** to **A** will be equal and opposite to the change when moving from **A** to **B**. There is no net change in potential in carrying the charge over this closed path. Thus, the potential of point **A** depends only on its location, not on the path taken to get there.

As is the case for any kind of potential energy, only differences in electric potential energy can be measured. The same is true of electric potential. The reference, or zero, level is arbitrary. Thus, only differences in electric potential are important. We define the **potential difference** from point **A** to point **B** to be $V = V_B - V_A$. Potential differences are measured with a voltmeter. Sometimes the potential difference is simply called the *voltage*.

As described in Chapter 11, the potential energy of a system can be defined to be zero at any convenient reference point. In the same way, the electric potential of any point, for example point **A,** can be defined to be zero. If $V_A = 0$, then $V_B = V$. If instead, $V_B = 0$, then $V_A = -V$. No matter what reference point is chosen, the value of the potential difference from point **A** to point **B** will always be the same.

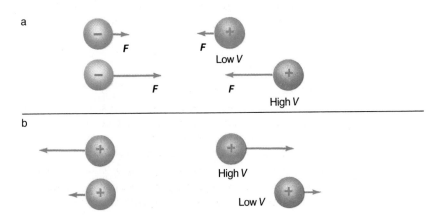

FIGURE 21–6. Electric potential energy is smaller when two unlike charges are closer together (a) and larger when two like charges are closer together (b).

FIGURE 21–7. An electric field between parallel plates.

We have seen that electric potential increases as a positive test charge is separated from a negative charge. What happens when a positive test charge is separated from a positive charge? There is a repulsive force between these two charges. Potential energy decreases as the two charges are moved farther apart. Therefore, the electric potential is smaller at points farther from the positive charge, Figure 21–6.

## The Electric Potential in a Uniform Field

How does the potential difference depend on the electric field? In the case of the gravitational field, near the surface of Earth the gravitational force and field are relatively constant. A constant electric force and field can be made by placing two large flat conducting plates parallel to each other. One is charged positively and the other negatively. The electric field between the plates is constant except at the edges of the plates. Its direction is from the positive to the negative plate. Figure 21–7 shows grass seeds representing the field between parallel plates.

The electric field between two parallel plates is uniform.

In a constant gravitational field, the change in potential energy when a body of mass $m$ is raised a distance $h$ is given by $\Delta E_p = mgh$. Remember that $g$, the gravitational field intensity near Earth, is given by $\vec{g} = \vec{F}/m$. The gravitational potential, or potential energy per unit of mass, is $mgh/m = gh$.

What is the potential difference between two points in a uniform electric field? If a positive test charge is moved a distance $d$, in the direction opposite the electric field direction, the change in potential energy is given by $\Delta E_p = +Fd$. Thus, the potential difference, the change in potential energy per unit charge, is $V = +Fd/q = +(F/q)d$. Now, the electric field intensity is the force per unit charge, $\vec{E} = \vec{F}/q$. Therefore, the potential difference, $V$, between two points a distance $d$ apart in a uniform field, $\vec{E}$, is given by

$$V = Ed.$$

The potential increases in the direction opposite the electric field direction. That is, the potential is higher near the positively-charged plate. By dimensional analysis, the product of the units of $E$ and $d$ is $(N/C) \cdot m$. This is equivalent to a J/C, the definition of a volt.

## Example Problem

### Potential Difference Between Two Parallel Plates

Two large, charged parallel plates are 4.0 cm apart. The magnitude of the electric field between them is 625 N/C. **a.** What is the potential difference between the plates? **b.** What work is done moving a charge equal to that of one electron from one plate to another?

**Given:** $d = 0.040$ m
$E = 625$ N/C

**Unknowns:** $V$, $W$
**Basic equations:** $V = Ed$
$W = qV$

**Solution: a.** $V = Ed$
$= (625 \text{ N/C})(0.040 \text{ m})$
$= 25 \text{ N} \cdot \text{m/C} = 25 \text{ J/C}$
$= 25 \text{ V}$

**b.** $W = qV$
$= (1.6 \times 10^{-19} \text{ C})(25 \text{ V})$
$= 4.0 \times 10^{-18} \text{ CV} = 4.0 \times 10^{-18} \text{ J}$

## Example Problem

### Electric Field Between Two Parallel Plates

A voltmeter measures the potential difference between two large parallel plates to be 60.0 V. The plates are 3.0 cm apart. What is the magnitude of the electric field between them?

**Given:** $V = 60.0$ V
$d = 0.030$ m

**Unknown:** $E$
**Basic equation:** $V = Ed$

**Solution:** $V = Ed$, so $E = \dfrac{V}{d}$

$= \dfrac{60.0 \text{ V}}{0.030 \text{ m}}$

$= \dfrac{60.0 \text{ J/C}}{0.030 \text{ m}}$

$= 2.0 \times 10^3 \text{ N/C}$

## Practice Problems

5. The electric field intensity between two large, charged, parallel metal plates is 8000 N/C. The plates are 0.05 m apart. What is the potential difference between them?
6. A voltmeter reads 500 V when placed across two charged, parallel plates. The plates are 0.020 m apart. What is the electric field between them?
7. What potential difference is applied to two metal plates 0.500 m apart if the electric field between them is $2.50 \times 10^3$ N/C?
▶ 8. What work is done when 5.0 C is raised in potential by 1.5 V?

# Physics and society

## MINIMOTIVE FORCE

Imagine machines so small you could fit hundreds into a space no larger than the diameter of a single strand of hair. Engineers have been imagining machines this small for years. Today, microtechnology has become one of the most exciting branches of engineering. Microengineers are now building micromachines and microbots [microrobots] so small they can only be seen through a microscope. In the auto industry, engineers have suggested using micromachines to replace the switches used to trigger air bags, adjust engine performance, and alert drivers when tire pressure is low.

How do these tiny machines work? Conventional electric motors use electromagnets to spin their rotors. Because of the even tinier wires needed, such magnets are not practical on a micro scale. Instead, micromachine motors employ electrostatic forces between motor elements to propel their rotors. Though these motors do a relatively small amount of work (one typical micromotor would barely run the minute hand on a watch), they are long-lasting. The nearly frictionless wobble motor, for example, has a rotor that spins inside a tube, without gears or bearings. Researchers have run such motors for almost a year at a time with no breakdowns.

Unlike conventional electric motors that depend on electromagnets to activate switches, micromotors use transistors as switches to move negative and positive electical charges around a circle of electrodes. The charges jump around the stator electrodes, causing a statically-charged rotor inside the circle to spin around. As in conventional electric motors, the spinning rotor provides the external mechanical energy.

The type of micromachine with the broadest application today is the microsensor. Some microsensors use a tiny, vibrating part that resonates at a precise frequency, unless disturbed by the slightest change in outside conditions. Other sensors rely on a diaphragm-like component that bends in response to pressure changes. (See also Chapter 23: Robots and Ohm's Law.)

The potential uses for micromachines have only begun to be imagined. Some of the most exciting possibilities are in the field of medicine, including "cell-repair machines" able to identify and destroy bacteria, viruses, blood clots, and cancer cells. Microsensors already in use have the capability of reading minute changes in blood pressure from within the heart.

## DEVELOPING A VIEWPOINT

Read further concerning micromachines and microtechnology (also called nanotechnology). Come to class prepared to discuss the following questions.

1. One micromachine maker has said that the main advantage of these devices is that they can be mass-produced. Why would this be an advantage?

2. Suggest applications for microtechnology in some of the following fields: medicine; consumer electronics; aviation; telecommunications; civil defense; computer electronics; optics; health and nutrition; structural engineering.

## SUGGESTED READINGS

Heppenheimer, T. A. "Microbots." *Discover*, March 1989, pp. 78–84.

Gannon, Robert. "Micromachine Magic." *Popular Science*, March 1989, pp. 88–92.

Stewart, Doug. "New Machines Are Smaller Than a Hair, and Do Real Work." *Smithsonian*, October 1990, pp. 85–95.

Hapgood, Fred. "No Assembly Required." *Omni*, May 1990, pp. 66–70.

Millikan measured the charge of an electron.

A drop is suspended if the electric and gravitational forces are balanced.

## POCKET LAB

### UNIT CHARGE

Place a small container on a balance and determine the mass of the empty container. (On an electronic balance, push the tare bar.) Place a small handful of 3-mm diameter steel balls in the container. Don't count them! Record the mass. Dump the balls out of the container and repeat the procedure with a different number of balls. Don't count! Record the mass. Repeat this loading and massing process a third time. Look closely at your mass values. Suggest a possible unit mass of each ball. Could your unit mass be too large? Could it be too small? Explain.

## Millikan's Oil Drop Experiment

One important application of the uniform electric field between two parallel plates was the measurement of the charge of an electron. This was made by American physicist Robert A. Millikan (1868–1953) in 1909.

Figure 21–8 shows the method used by Millikan to measure the charge carried by a single electron. Fine oil drops were sprayed from an atomizer into the air. These drops were often charged by friction with the atomizer as they were sprayed. Gravity acting on the drops caused them to fall. A few entered the hole in the top plate of the apparatus. A potential difference was placed across the two plates. The resulting electric field between the plates exerted a force on the charged drops. When the top plate was made positive enough, the electric force caused negatively-charged drops to rise. The potential difference between the plates was adjusted to suspend a charged drop between the plates. At this point, the downward force of the weight and the upward force of the electric field were equal in magnitude.

The magnitude of the electric field, $E$, was determined from the potential difference between the plates. A second measurement had to be made to find the weight of the drop, $mg$, which was too tiny to measure by ordinary methods. To make this measurement, a drop was first suspended. Then the electric field was turned off and the rate of the fall of the drop measured. Because of friction with the air molecules, the oil drop quickly reached terminal velocity. This velocity was related to the mass of the drop by a complex equation. Using the measured terminal velocity to calculate $mg$, and knowing $E$, the charge $q$ could be calculated. Millikan found that the drops had a large variety of charges. When he used X rays to ionize the air and add or remove electrons from the drops, he noted, however, that the *changes* in the charge were always a multiple of $-1.6 \times 10^{-19}$ C. The changes were caused by one or more electrons being added to or removed from the drops. He concluded that the smallest change in charge that could occur was the amount of charge of one electron. Therefore, Millikan said that each electron always carried the same charge, $-1.6 \times 10^{-19}$ C. Millikan's experiment showed that charge is quantized. This means that an object can have only a charge with a magnitude that is some integral multiple of the charge of the electron.

The presently accepted theory of matter says that protons are made up of fundamental particles called quarks. The charge on a quark is either $+1/3$ or $-2/3$ the charge on an electron. A theory of quarks that agrees with other experiments states that quarks can never be isolated. Many experimenters have used an updated Millikan apparatus to look for fractional charges on drops or tiny metal spheres. There have been no reproducible discoveries of fractional charges. Thus, no isolated quark has been discovered; the quark theory remains consistent with experiments.

## Example Problem

### Finding the Charge on an Oil Drop

An oil drop weighs $1.9 \times 10^{-14}$ N. It is suspended in an electric field of intensity $4.0 \times 10^4$ N/C. **a.** What is the charge on the oil drop? **b.** If the upper plate is positive, how many excess electrons does it have?

**Given:** $\vec{W} = m\vec{g}$
$\qquad = 1.9 \times 10^{-14}$ N
$\qquad \vec{E} = 4.0 \times 10^4$ N/C

**Unknown:** excess charge, $q$
**Basic equation:** $\vec{E}q = m\vec{g}$

**Solution: a.** Electronic and gravitational forces balance, so $\vec{E}q = m\vec{g}$.

$$\text{Thus, } q = \frac{m\vec{g}}{\vec{E}} = \frac{1.9 \times 10^{-14}\,\text{N}}{4.0 \times 10^4\,\text{N/C}}$$
$$= 4.8 \times 10^{-19}\,\text{C}$$

**b.** number of electrons $= \dfrac{\text{(total charge on drop)}}{\text{(charge per electron)}}$
$$= \frac{4.8 \times 10^{-19}\,\text{C}}{1.6 \times 10^{-19}\,\text{C/e}}$$
$$= 3 \text{ electrons}$$

There are three extra electrons because a negatively-charged drop is attracted toward a positively-charged plate.

The drop's mass was found from its terminal velocity.

The charge of an electron is $-1.6 \times 10^{-19}$ C.

## Practice Problems

**9.** A drop is falling in a Millikan oil drop apparatus when the electric field is off.
   **a.** What are the forces on it, regardless of its acceleration?
   **b.** If it is falling at constant velocity, what can be said about the forces on it?

**10.** An oil drop weighs $1.9 \times 10^{-15}$ N. It is suspended in an electric field of $6.0 \times 10^3$ N/C.
   **a.** What is the charge on the drop?
   **b.** How many excess electrons does it carry?

**11.** A positively-charged oil drop weighs $6.4 \times 10^{-13}$ N. An electric field of $4.0 \times 10^6$ N/C suspends the drop.
  **a.** What is the charge on the drop?
  **b.** How many electrons is the drop missing?
▶ **12.** If three more electrons were removed from the drop in Practice Problem 11, what field would be needed to balance the drop?

## Sharing of Charge

All systems, mechanical and electrical, come to equilibrium when the energy of the system is at a minimum. For example, if a ball is put on a hill, it will finally come to rest in a valley where its gravitational potential energy is least. This same principle explains what happens when an insulated, negatively-charged metal sphere, Figure 21–9, touches a second, uncharged sphere.

The excess negative charges on sphere A repel each other. Thus the potential of sphere A is high. We can choose the potential of the neutral sphere, B to be zero. When one charge is transferred from sphere A to sphere B, the potential of sphere A is reduced because it has fewer excess charges. The potential of sphere B does not change because no work is done adding the first extra charge to this neutral sphere. As more charges are transferred, however, work must be done on the charge to overcome the growing repulsive force between it and the other charges on sphere B. Therefore, the potential of sphere B increases as the potential of sphere A decreases. Negative charges continue to flow from sphere A to sphere B until the work done adding a charge to sphere B is equal to the work gained in removing a charge from sphere A. The potential of sphere A now equals the potential of sphere B. Thus charges flow until all parts of a conducting body, the two touching spheres in this case, are at the same potential.

Consider a large sphere and a small sphere that have the same charge, Figure 21–10. The larger sphere has a larger surface area, so charges can spread farther apart than they can on the smaller sphere. With the charges farther apart, the repulsive force between them is reduced. Therefore, as long as the spheres have the same charge, the

> Charges move until all parts of a conductor are at the same potential.

> If a large and a small sphere have the same charge, the large sphere will have a lower potential.

Charged sphere

Metal spheres of equal size

a   b

Neutral sphere

**FIGURE 21–9. A charged sphere shares charge equally with a neutral sphere of equal size.**

Metal spheres of unequal size

Low V

High V

Same q

High q

Low q

Same V

potential on the larger sphere is lower than the potential on the smaller sphere. If the two spheres are now touched together, charges will move to the sphere with the lower potential; that is, from the smaller to the larger sphere. The result is a greater charge on the larger sphere when two different-sized spheres are at the same potential.

Earth is a very large sphere. If a charged body is touched to Earth, almost any amount of charge can flow without changing Earth's potential. When all the excess charge on the body flows to Earth, the body becomes neutral. Touching an object to Earth to eliminate excess charge is called **grounding**. Moving gasoline trucks can become charged by friction. If that charge were to jump to Earth through gasoline vapour, it could cause an explosion. Instead, a metal wire safely conducts the charge to ground, Figure 21–11. If a computer or other sensitive instrument were not grounded, static charges could accumulate, raising the potential of the computer. A person touching the computer could suddenly lower the potential of the computer. The charges flowing through the computer to the person could damage the equipment or hurt the person.

The charges are closer together at sharp points of a conductor. Therefore, the field lines are closer together; the field is stronger, Figure 21–10.

If the two spheres are at the same potential, the large one will have greater charge.

FIGURE 21–11. Ground wire on a fuel truck.

## Electric Fields Near Conductors

The charges on a conductor are spread as far apart as they can be to make the energy of the system as low as possible. The result is that all charges are on the surface of a solid conductor. If the conductor is hollow, excess charges will move to the outer surface. If a closed metal container is charged, there will be no charges on the inside surfaces of the container. In this way, a closed metal container shields the inside from electric fields. For example, people inside a car are protected from the electric fields generated by lightning. On an open coffee can there will be very few charges inside, and none near the bottom.

Even though the electric potential is the same at every point of a conductor, the electric field around the outside of it depends on the shape of the body as well as its potential. The charges are closer together at sharp points of a conductor. Therefore, the field lines are closer together; the field is stronger, Figure 21–12. The field there can become so strong that nearby air molecules are separated into electrons and positive ions. As the electrons and ions recombine, energy is released and light is produced. The result is the blue glow of a corona. The electrons and ions are accelerated by the field. If the field is strong enough, when the particles hit other molecules they will produce more ions and electrons. The stream of ions and electrons that results is a plasma, a conductor. The result is a spark, or, in extreme cases, lightning. To reduce corona and sparking, conductors that are highly charged or operate at high potentials are made smooth in shape to reduce the electric fields.

On the other hand, lightning rods, Figure 21–13, are pointed so that the electric field will be strong near the end of the rod. Air molecules are pulled apart near the rod, forming the start of a conducting path from the rod to the clouds. As a result of the sharply-pointed shape, charges in the clouds spark to the rod rather than to a chimney or other high point on a house. From the rod, a conductor takes the charges safely to the ground.

## Storing Charges—The Capacitor

When you lift a book, you increase its potential energy. This can be interpreted as "storing" energy in a gravitational field. In a similar way, you can store energy in an electric field. In 1746, the Dutch physician and physicist Pieter Van Musschenbroek invented a device that could

**FIGURE 21–12. The electric field around a conducting body depends on the structure and shape (b is hollow) of the body.**

Negatively charged cloud

Positive ions in atmosphere

FIGURE 21–13. A lightning rod allows charges from the clouds to be grounded, rather than conducted through a barn.

store electric charge. In honour of the city in which he worked, it was called a Leyden jar. The Leyden jar was used by Benjamin Franklin to store the charge from lightning and in many other experiments.

As described previously, as charge is added to an object, the potential between that object and Earth increases. For a given shape and size of the object, the ratio of charge to potential difference, $q/V$, is a constant. The constant is called the **capacitance**, $C$, of the object. For a small sphere far from the ground, even a small amount of added charge will increase the potential difference. Thus, $C$ is small. The larger the sphere, the greater the charge that can be added for the same increase in potential difference, thus the larger the capacitance. Van Musschenbroek found a way of producing a large capacitance in a small device. A device that is designed to have a specific capacitance is called a **capacitor**. All capacitors are made up of two conductors, separated by an insulator. The two conductors have equal and opposite charges. Capacitors are used today in electrical circuits to store charge.

Capacitors often are made of parallel conducting sheets, or plates, separated by air or another insulator. Commercial capacitors, Figure 21–14, contain strips of aluminum foil separated by thin plastic and are tightly rolled up to save room.

The capacitance is independent of the charge on it. Capacitance can be measured by placing charge $q$ on one plate and $-q$ on the other, and measuring the potential difference, $V$, that results. The capacitance is then found by using the equation

$$C = \frac{q}{V}.$$

Capacitance is measured in farads, F, named after Michael Faraday. One farad is one coulomb per volt (C/V). Just as one coulomb is a large amount of charge, one farad is an enormous capacitance. Capacitors are usually between 10 pF ($10 \times 10^{-12}$ F) and 500 μF ($500 \times 10^{-6}$ F).

Capacitors store charge.

Capacitance is the ratio of charge stored to potential difference.

FIGURE 21–14. Various types of capacitors.

## Example Problem

### Finding the Capacitance from Charge and Potential Difference

A sphere has a potential difference between it and Earth of 60.0 V when charged with $3.0 \times 10^{-6}$ C. What is its capacitance?

**Given:** potential difference,
$V = 60.0$ V
$q = 3.0 \times 10^{-6}$ C

**Unknown:** capacitance, $C$

**Basic equation:** $C = \dfrac{q}{V}$

**Solution:** $C = \dfrac{q}{V} = \dfrac{3.0 \times 10^{-6} \text{ C}}{60.0 \text{ V}} = 5.0 \times 10^{-8}$ C/V
$= 5.0 \times 10^{-8}$ F $= 0.050\ \mu$F

## Practice Problems

**13.** A 27-$\mu$F capacitor has a potential difference of 25 V across it. What is the charge on the capacitor?

**14.** Both a 3.3-$\mu$F and a 6.8-$\mu$F capacitor are connected across a 15-V potential difference. Which capacitor has a greater charge? What is it?

**15.** The same two capacitors are each charged to $2.5 \times 10^{-4}$ C. Across which is the potential difference larger? What is it?

▶ **16.** A 2.2-$\mu$F capacitor is first charged so that the potential difference is 6.0 V. How much *additional* charge is needed to increase the potential difference to 15.0 V?

## CONCEPT REVIEW

**2.1** If an oil drop with too few electrons is motionless in a Millikan oil drop apparatus,
  **a.** what is the direction of the electric field?
  **b.** which plate, upper or lower, is positively charged?

**2.2** If the charge on a capacitor is changed, what is the effect on
  **a.** the capacitance, $C$?
  **b.** the potential difference, $V$?

**2.3** If a large, charged sphere is touched by a smaller, uncharged sphere, as in Figure 21–9, what can be said about
  **a.** the potentials of the two spheres?
  **b.** the charges on the two spheres?

**2.4** **Critical Thinking:** Suppose we have a large, hollow sphere that has been charged. Through a small hole in the sphere, we insert a small, uncharged sphere into the hollow interior. The two touch. What is the charge on the small sphere?

# 21 REVIEW

## SUMMARY

### 21.1 Creating and Measuring Electric Fields

· An electric field exists around any charged object. The field produces forces on other charged bodies.
· The electric field intensity is the force per unit charge. The direction of the electric field is the direction of the force on a tiny, positive test charge.
· Electric field lines provide a picture of the electric field. They are directed away from positive charges and toward negative charges.

### 21.2 Applications of Electric Fields

· Electric potential difference is the change in potential energy per unit charge in an electric field. Potential differences are measured in volts.
· The electric field between two parallel plates is uniform between the plates except near the edges.
· Robert Millikan's experiments showed that electric charge is quantized and that the charge carried by an electron is $-1.6 \times 10^{-19}$ C.
· Charges will move in conductors until the electric potential is the same everywhere on the conductor.
· A charged object can have its excess charge removed by touching it to Earth or to an object touching Earth. This is called grounding.
· Electric fields are strongest near sharply-pointed conductors.
· Capacitance is the ratio of the charge on a body to its potential. The capacitance of a body is independent of the charge on the body and the potential difference across it.

## KEY TERMS

| | |
|---|---|
| electric field | potential difference |
| electric field lines | grounding |
| electric potential difference | capacitance |
| volt | capacitor |

## REVIEWING CONCEPTS

1. Draw the electric field lines between
   a. two like charges.
   b. two unlike charges.
2. What are the two properties a test charge must have?
3. How is the direction of an electric field defined?
4. What are electric field lines?
5. How is the strength of an electric field indicated with electric field lines?
6. What SI unit is used to measure electrical potential energy? electric potential?
7. What will happen to the electric potential energy of a charged particle in an electric field when the particle is released and free to move?
8. Define the volt in terms of the change in potential energy of a charge moving in an electric field.
9. Draw the electric field lines between two parallel plates of opposite charge.
10. Why does a charged object lose its charge when it is touched to the ground?
11. A charged rubber rod placed on a table maintains its charge for some time. Why is the charged rod not grounded immediately?
12. A metal box is charged. Compare the concentration of charge at the corners of the box to the charge concentration on the sides.
13. In your own words, describe a capacitor.

## APPLYING CONCEPTS

1. What happens to the size of the electric field if the charge on the test charge is halved?
2. Does it require more energy or less energy to move a fixed positive charge through an increased electric field?
3. Figure 21–15 shows three spheres with charges of equal magnitude, but with signs as shown. Spheres y and z are held in place but sphere x is free to move. Initially sphere x is equidistant from spheres y and z. Choose the

path that sphere *x* will follow, assuming no other forces are acting.

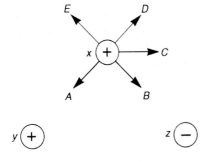

**FIGURE 21–15. Use with Applying Concepts 3.**

4. What is the unit of potential difference in terms of m, kg, s, and C?
5. What do the electric field lines look like when the electric field has the same strength at all points in a region?
6. When doing a Millikan oil drop experiment, it is best to work with drops that have small charges. Therefore, when the electric field is turned on, should you try to find drops that are moving fast or slow? Explain.
7. If two oil drops can be held motionless in a Millikan oil drop experiment,
    a. can you be sure that the charges are the same?
    b. the ratios of what two properties of the drops would have to be equal?
8. Tim and Sue are holding hands when they are given a charge while they are standing on an insulating platform. Tim is larger than Sue. Who has the larger amount of charge or do they both have the same amount?
9. Which has a larger capacitance, a 1-cm diameter or a 10-cm diameter aluminum sphere?
10. How can you store a different amount of charge in a capacitor?

## PROBLEMS

### 21.1 Creating and Measuring Electric Fields

*The charge on an electron is* $-1.60 \times 10^{-19}$ C.
1. A positive charge of $1.0 \times 10^{-5}$ C experiences a force of 0.20 N when located at a certain point. What is the electric field intensity at that point?

2. What charge exists on a test charge that experiences a force of $1.4 \times 10^{-8}$ N at a point where the electric field intensity is $2.0 \times 10^{-4}$ N/C?
3. A test charge has a force of 0.20 N on it when it is placed in an electric field intensity of $4.5 \times 10^{5}$ N/C. What is the magnitude of the charge?
4. The electric field in the atmosphere is about 150 N/C, downward.
    a. What is the direction of the force on a positively-charged particle?
    b. Find the electric force on a proton with charge $+1.6 \times 10^{-19}$ C.
    c. Compare the force in **b** with the force of gravity on the same proton (mass $1.7 \times 10^{-27}$ kg).
▶ 5. Electrons are accelerated by the electric field in a television picture tube, Table 21–1.
    a. Find the force on an electron.
    b. If the field is constant, find the acceleration of the electron (mass $= 9.11 \times 10^{-31}$ kg).
▶ 6. A lead nucleus has the charge of 82 protons.
    a. What is the direction and magnitude of the electric field at $1.0 \times 10^{-10}$ m from the nucleus?
    b. Use Coulomb's law to find the direction and magnitude of the force exerted on an electron located at this distance.
7. Carefully sketch
    a. the electric field produced by a $+1.0$ μC charge.
    b. the electric field due to a $+2.0$ μC charge. Make the number of field lines proportional to the change in charge.
8. Charges X, Y, and Z are all equidistant from each other. X has a $+1.0$ μC charge, Y a $+2.0$ μC charge, and Z a small negative charge.
    a. Draw an arrow showing the force on charge Z.
    b. Charge Z now has a small positive charge on it. Draw an arrow showing the force on it.
9. A positive test charge of $8.0 \times 10^{-5}$ C is placed in an electric field of 50.0-N/C intensity. What is the strength of the force exerted on the test charge?

### 21.2 Applications of Electric Fields

10. If 120 J of work are done to move 1 C of charge from a positive plate to a negative

plate, what voltage difference exists between the plates?

**11.** How much work is done to transfer 0.15 C of charge through a potential difference of 9.0 V?

**12.** An electron is moved through a potential difference of 500 V. How much work is done on the electron?

**13.** A 12-V battery does 1200 J of work transferring charge. How much charge is transferred?

▶ **14.** A force 0.053 N is required to move a charge of 37 $\mu$C a distance of 25 cm in an electric field. What is the size of the potential difference between the two points?

**15.** The electric field intensity between two charged plates is $1.5 \times 10^3$ N/C. The plates are 0.080 m apart. What is the potential difference, in volts, between the plates?

**16.** A voltmeter indicates that the difference in potential between two plates is 50.0 V. The plates are 0.020 m apart. What electric field intensity exists between them?

**17.** A negatively-charged oil drop weighs $8.5 \times 10^{-15}$ N. The drop is suspended in an electric field intensity of $5.3 \times 10^3$ N/C.
   **a.** What is the charge on the drop?
   **b.** How many electrons does it carry?

▶ **18.** In an early set of experiments (1911), Millikan observed that the following measured charges, among others, appeared at different times on a single oil drop. What value of elementary charge can be deduced from these data?
   **a.** $6.563 \times 10^{-19}$ C    **f.** $18.08 \times 10^{-19}$ C
   **b.** $8.204 \times 10^{-19}$ C    **g.** $19.71 \times 10^{-19}$ C
   **c.** $11.50 \times 10^{-19}$ C    **h.** $22.89 \times 10^{-19}$ C
   **d.** $13.13 \times 10^{-19}$ C    **i.** $26.13 \times 10^{-19}$ C
   **e.** $16.48 \times 10^{-19}$ C

**19.** A capacitor that is connected to a 45.0-V source contains 90.0 $\mu$C of charge. What is the capacitor's capacitance?

**20.** A 5.4-$\mu$F capacitor is charged with $2.7 \times 10^{-3}$ C. What potential difference exists across it?

**21.** What is the charge in a 15.0-pf capacitor when it is connected across a 75.0-V source?

▶ **22.** The energy stored in a capacitor with capacitance $C$, having a potential difference $V$, is given by $W = \frac{1}{2}CV^2$. One application is in the electronic photoflash or strobe light. In such a unit, a capacitor of 10.0 $\mu$F is charged to $3.00 \times 10^2$ V. Find the energy stored.

▶ **23.** Suppose it took 30 s to charge the capacitor in the previous problem.
   **a.** Find the power required to charge it in this time.
   **b.** When this capacitor is discharged through the strobe lamp, it transfers all its energy in $1.0 \times 10^{-4}$ s. Find the power delivered to the lamp.
   **c.** How is such a large amount of power possible?

▶ **24.** Lasers are used to try to produce controlled fusion reactions that might supply large amounts of electrical energy. The lasers require brief pulses of energy that are stored in large rooms filled with capacitors. One such room has a capacitance of $61 \times 10^{-3}$ F charged to a potential difference of 10 kV.
   **a.** Find the energy stored in the capacitors, given $W = \frac{1}{2}CV^2$.
   **b.** The capacitors are discharged in 10 ns ($1.0 \times 10^{-8}$ s). What power is produced?
   **c.** If the capacitors are charged by a generator with a power capacity of 1.0 kW, how many seconds will be required to charge the capacitors?

## THINKING PHYSIC-LY

Why are many parts of stereo components covered with metal boxes or containers?

# CHAPTER
# 22

# Current Electricity

## ◀ More for Less?

High-voltage power transmission lines, such as these 765-kV lines, crisscross our country. It would seem to be cheaper to eliminate all transformers and simply transmit electrical energy at the voltage used in the home. Why is this not true?

The most important aspects of electrical energy are its ability to be transferred efficiently over long distances and its ability to be changed into other forms of energy. The large amounts of natural potential and kinetic energy possessed by resources such as Niagara Falls are of little use to an industrial complex 100 km away unless that energy can be transferred efficiently. Electrical energy provides the means to transfer large quantities of energy great distances with little loss. This transfer is usually done at very high potentials, such as the 765 000 V in the power line pictured.

## ✓ Concept Check

The following terms or concepts from earlier chapters are important for a good understanding of this chapter. If you are not familiar with them, you should review them before studying this chapter.
· power, forms of energy, Chapters 10,11
· electric charge and potentials, Chapters 20, 21

# Objectives

- define an electric current and the ampere; describe conditions that permit current flow.
- be able to draw circuits; recognize they are closed loops; understand energy transfer in circuits.
- explain definition of power in electric circuits; solve problems involving current, potential difference, and power.
- define resistance; solve problems involving current, potential difference, and resistance.
- describe Ohm's law; be able to tell whether a device obeys Ohm's law.
- explain how current can be controlled in a circuit.
- diagram simple electric circuits; recognize the correct use of ammeters and voltmeters.

Charged particles flow around a closed loop called a circuit.

# 22.1 CURRENT AND CIRCUITS

You have had many experiences with electric circuits. Every time you turn on a light, radio, or television, or turn the ignition key to start a car, or turn on a flashlight, you complete an electric circuit. Electric current flows and energy is transferred. In this section you will learn how these events came about.

## Producing Electric Current

In Chapter 21 we discussed what happened when two conducting spheres at different potentials touched. When they touched, charges flowed from the object at a higher potential to the one at a lower potential. The flow continued until the potentials were equal.

A flow of charged particles is called an **electric current**. In some conductors, negatively-charged electrons move; in others, positively charged particles move. In this text, we will always assume that positive charges move as the result of a potential difference. In Figure 22–1a, two conductors, A and B, are at different potentials and connected by a wire conductor, C. Charges flow from B to A through C. The flow stops when the potentials of A, B, and C are equal. How could you keep the flow going? You would have to maintain a potential difference between B and A. This could be done by pumping charged particles from conductor A back to conductor B. The electrical potential energy of the charges would have to be increased by this pump, so it would require external energy to run. The electric energy could come from one of several other forms of energy. A familiar source, a voltaic or galvanic cell (a common dry cell) converts chemical energy to electric energy. Several cells connected together are called a **battery**. A **photovoltaic cell**, or solar cell, changes light energy into electric energy. A generator, driven by moving water, rushing steam, or the wind, converts kinetic energy into electric energy.

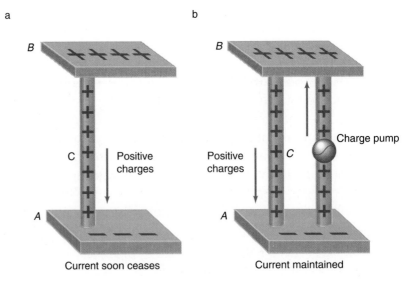

**FIGURE 22–1.** Positive charges flow from the positive to the negative plate (a). A generator (b) pumps the positive charges back to the positive plate, allowing current to continue to flow.

# Electric Circuits

The charges in Figure 22–1b move around a closed loop from the pump through $B$ to $C$ to $A$, and back to the pump. Such a closed loop is called an **electric circuit**. A circuit consists of a charge pump that increases the potential energy of the charges connected to a device that reduces the potential energy of the charges. The change in potential energy of the charge ($qV$) can be converted into some other form of energy. A motor converts electric energy to kinetic energy. A lamp changes electric energy into light. A heater converts electric energy into thermal energy.

Charged particles flowing through any of these energy conversion devices lose electric potential energy. Any device that reduces the potential energy of charges flowing through it is said to have resistance.

The charge pump creates the flow of charged particles, or current. Consider a generator driven by a waterwheel, Figure 22–2a. The water falls as it rotates the waterwheel and generator. Thus its potential energy is converted to electric energy by the generator. The generator increases the electric potential difference, $V$, between $B$ and $A$ as it removes charges from wire $B$ and adds them to wire $A$. Energy in the amount $qV$ is needed to increase the potential of the charges. This energy comes from the loss of potential energy of the water. No generator, however, is 100% efficient. Only 98% of the kinetic energy put into most generators is converted into electric energy. The remainder becomes thermal energy; the temperature of the generator increases, Figure 22–2b.

If wires $A$ and $B$ are connected to a motor, the charges in wire $A$ flow through the wires in the motor. The flow continues through wire $B$ back to the generator. A motor converts electric energy to kinetic energy. Like generators, motors are not 100% efficient. Typically, 90% of the electric energy is changed into kinetic energy.

A charge pump increases the potential energy of the charges. Batteries, generators, and photovoltaic cells are charge pumps.

### Charge and Field Conventions

- *Positive charges are red.*
- *Negative charges are blue.*
- *Electric field lines are red.*
- **Ammeters are blue.**
- ▶ *Voltmeters are red.*

a

b

c

**FIGURE 22–3. Sources of electric energy include chemical, solar, hydrodynamic, wind, and nuclear energies.**

One watt of power is the transfer of one joule of energy each second.

One ampere of current is the flow of a coulomb of charge each second.

You know that charges can't be created or destroyed, only separated. Thus, the total amount of charge (number of negative electrons and positive ions) in the circuit does not change. If 1 C flows through the generator in 1 s, 1 C will also flow through the motor in 1 s. Thus, charge is a conserved quantity. Energy is also conserved. The change in electric energy, $E$, equals $qV$. Since $q$ is conserved, the net change in potential energy of the charges going completely around the circuit must be zero. The potential increase produced by the generator equals the potential drop across the motor.

If the difference in potential between the two wires is 120 V, the generator must do 120 J of work on each coulomb of positive charge that it transfers from the more negative wire to the more positive wire. Every coulomb of positive charge that moves from the more positive wire through the motor and back to the more negative wire delivers 120 J of energy to the motor. Thus electric energy serves as a way to transfer the initial potential energy of falling water to the kinetic energy of a turning motor.

## Rates of Charge Flow and Energy Transfer

Power measures the rate at which energy is transferred. If a generator transfers 1 J of kinetic energy to electric energy each second, it is transferring energy at the rate of 1 J/s, or 1 W.

The energy carried by an electric current depends on the charge transferred and the potential difference across which it moves, $E = qV$. The unit used for quantity of electric charge is the coulomb. Thus the rate of flow of electric charge, or electric current, $I$, is measured in coulombs per second. A flow of one coulomb per second is called an **ampere**, A.

$$1 \text{ C/s} = 1 \text{ A}$$

The ampere is named for the French scientist Andre Marie Ampere (1775–1836). A device that measures current is called an ammeter. The flow of positive charge is called **conventional current.**

Suppose that the current through the motor shown in Figure 22–2 is 3.0 C/s (3.0 A). Since the potential difference is 120 V, each coulomb of charge supplies the motor with 120 J of energy. The power, or energy delivered to the motor per second, is

$$(120 \text{ J/C})(3.0 \text{ C/s}) = 360 \text{ J/s} = 360 \text{ W}.$$

The power of an electric device is found by multiplying the potential difference, $V$, by the current, $I$, or $P = VI$.

## Example Problem

### Electric Power

A 6-V battery delivers a 0.5-A current to an electric motor that is connected across its terminals. **a.** What power is consumed by the motor? **b.** How much electric energy is delivered in 5.0 min?

Given: $V = 6$ V      Unknowns: **a.** $P$ **b.** $E$
     $I = 0.5$ A      Basic equations: **a.** $P = VI$
     $t = 5.0$ min (300 s)          **b.** $P = E/t$

Solution:
**a.** $P = VI = (6 \text{ V})(0.5 \text{ A}) = (6 \text{ J/C})(0.5 \text{ C/s}) = 3 \text{ J/s} = 3 \text{ W}$
**b.** $P = E/t$, so $E = Pt = (3 \text{ W})(300 \text{ s}) = 9 \times 10^2 \text{ J}$

*Power is the product of potential difference and current, $P = VI$.*

## Practice Problems

1. The current through a light bulb connected across the terminals of a 120-V outlet is 0.5 A. At what rate does the bulb convert electric energy to light?
2. A car battery causes a current of 2.0 A to flow through a lamp while 12 V is across it. What is the power used by the lamp?
3. What current flows through a 75-W light bulb connected to a 120-V outlet?
▶ 4. The current through the starter motor of a car is 210 A. If the battery keeps 12 V across the motor, what electric energy is delivered to the starter in 10.0 s?

*Resistance is the ratio of potential drop to current flow, $R = V/I$.*

## Resistance and Ohm's Law

Suppose two conductors have a potential difference between them. If you connect them with a copper rod, a large current will flow. If, on the other hand, you put a glass rod between them, there will be almost no current. The property that determines how much current will flow is called the **resistance**. Resistance is measured by placing a potential difference across two points on a conductor and measuring the current that flows. The resistance, $R$, is defined to be the ratio of the potential difference, $V$, to the current, $I$,

$$R = \frac{V}{I}.$$

**FIGURE 22–4. The current flow through a simple circuit (a) can be regulated by removing some of the dry cells (b) or increasing the resistance of the circuit (c).**

The electric current, $I$, is in amperes. The potential difference, $V$, is in volts. The resistance of the conductor, $R$, is measured in ohms. One ohm, $1\ \Omega$, is the resistance that permits a current of 1 A to flow when a potential difference of 1 V is applied across the resistance.

The German scientist Georg Simon Ohm (1787–1854) measured the resistance of many conductors. He found that *the resistance for most conductors does not depend on size or direction of the potential difference across it.* A device that has a constant resistance that is independent of the potential difference is said to obey Ohm's law.

Most metallic conductors obey Ohm's law, at least over a limited range of voltages. Many important devices, however, do not. A transistor radio or pocket calculator contains many devices, such as transistors and diodes, that do not obey Ohm's law. Even a light bulb has a resistance that depends on the voltage and does not obey Ohm's law.

Wires used to connect electric devices have very small resistances. One metre of a typical wire used in physics labs has a resistance of about $0.03\ \Omega$. Wires used in house wiring offer as little as $0.004\ \Omega$ resistance for each metre of length. **Resistors** are devices designed to have a specific resistance. They may be made of long, thin wires, graphite, or semiconductors.

Superconductors are materials that have zero resistance. There is no potential drop, $V$, across a superconductor. Since the power dissipated in a conductor is given by the product $IV$, a superconductor can conduct electricity without loss of energy. The development of superconductors that can be cooled by relatively inexpensive liquid nitrogen may lead to more efficient transfer of energy by electricity.

For a device that obeys Ohm's law, resistance is independent of voltage.

**FIGURE 22–5. A variable resistor can be used to regulate current in an electric circuit.**

There are two ways to control the current in a circuit. Since $I = V/R$, $I$ can be changed by varying either $V$ or $R$, or both. Figure 22–4a shows a simple circuit. When $V$ is 6 V and $R$ is 30 $\Omega$, the current flow is 0.2 A. How could the current be reduced to 0.1 A?

The larger the potential difference, or voltage, placed across a resistor, the larger the current that passes through it. If the current through a resistor is to be cut in half, the drop in potential is cut in half. In Figure 22–4b, the voltage applied across the resistor has been reduced from 6 V to 3 V to reduce the current to 0.1 A. This may be an easy solution, since a 6-V battery is often made of two 3-V batteries connected in series.

A second way to reduce the current to 0.1 A is to increase the resistance to 60 $\Omega$ by adding a 30-$\Omega$ resistor to the circuit, Figure 22–4c. Both of these methods will reduce the current to 0.1 A. Resistors are often used to control the current in circuits or parts of circuits.

Sometimes a smooth, continuous variation of the current is desired. A lamp dimmer allows continuous rather than step-by-step change of light intensity. To achieve this kind of control, a variable resistor, called a rheostat or **potentiometer,** is used, Figure 22–5. A variable resistor consists of a coil of resistance wire and a sliding contact point. By moving the contact point to various positions along the coil, the amount of wire added to the circuit is varied. As more wire is placed in the circuit, the resistance of the circuit increases; thus the current decreases in accordance with the equation $I = V/R$. In this way the light output of a lamp can be adjusted. This same type of device controls the speed of electric fans, electric mixers, and other appliances. To save space, the coil of wire is often bent into a circular shape and a sliding contact is moved by a knob, Figure 22–6.

Your body is a moderately good electrical conductor. If enough current flows through your body, your breathing or heart can be stopped. In addition, the power dissipated can burn you. If your skin is dry, its resistance is high enough to keep currents produced by small and moderate voltages low. If the skin becomes wet, however, its resistance is lower, and the currents can rise to dangerous levels, to tens of milliamps.

**FIGURE 22–6. An inside view of a potentiometer.**

Current can be changed by varying either voltage or resistance.

A variable resistor is called a potentiometer or rheostat.

# Example Problem

### Current Flow Through a Resistor

A 30-V battery maintains current through a 10-$\Omega$ resistance, Figure 22–7. What is the current?

**Given:** potential difference,
$\qquad V = 30$ V
$\qquad$ resistance, $R = 10$ $\Omega$

**Unknown:** current, $I$
**Basic equation:** $R = V/I$

**Solution:** $R = \dfrac{V}{I}$, so $I = \dfrac{V}{R}$

$\qquad = \dfrac{30 \text{ V}}{10 \text{ }\Omega}$

$\qquad = 3.0$ A

Current flow

$I = \dfrac{V}{R}$

$\quad = \dfrac{30 \text{ V}}{10 \text{ }\Omega}$

$\quad = 3.0$ A

**FIGURE 22–7. In a circuit having a 10-$\Omega$ resistance and 30-V battery, there is a 3-A current.**

# Practice Problems

*In all problems you should assume that the battery voltage is constant, no matter what current flows.*

5. An automobile headlight with a resistance of 30 Ω is placed across a 12-V battery. What is the current through the circuit?
6. A motor with an operating resistance of 32 Ω is connected to a voltage source. The current in the circuit is 3.8 A. What is the voltage of the source?
7. A transistor radio uses $2 \times 10^{-4}$ A of current when it is operated by a 3-V battery. What is the resistance of the radio circuit?
8. A lamp draws a current of 0.5 A when it is connected to a 120-V source.
   a. What is the resistance of the lamp?
   b. What is the power consumption of the lamp?
9. A 75-W lamp is connected to 120 V.
   a. How much current flows through the lamp?
   b. What is the resistance of the lamp?
▶ 10. A resistor is now added in series with the lamp to reduce the current to half its original value.
   a. What is the potential difference across the lamp? Assume the lamp resistance is constant.
   b. How much resistance was added to the circuit?
   c. How much power is now dissipated in the lamp?

# Diagramming Circuits

*A schematic diagram uses symbols rather than pictures for components.*

A simple circuit can be described in words. You can also use photographs or an artist's drawings of the parts. More frequently, a diagram of an electric circuit is drawn using standard symbols for the circuit elements. Such a diagram is called a circuit **schematic**. Some of the symbols are shown in Figure 22–8. Both an artist's drawing and a schematic of the same circuit are shown in Figure 22–9.

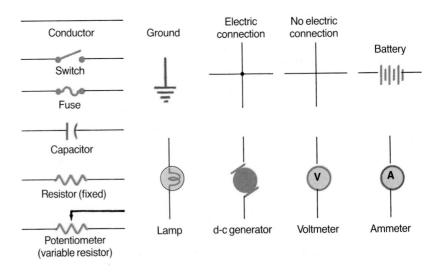

**FIGURE 22–8. Electric circuit symbols.**

Notice that in both the artist's drawing and the schematic, current is shown flowing out of the positive terminal of the battery. In metals, electrons are the mobile charged particles, but in other conductors the current can be carried by either positively- or negatively-charged particles. In diagramming electric circuits, we will draw current arrows in the direction that positive charge carriers would move. Often this is called a conventional current. The convention works because the effect of a negative charge moving from left to right is the same as that of a positive charge moving from right to left.

Ammeters measure current. They must be connected in series.

Voltmeters measure potential difference. They must be connected in parallel.

# PROBLEM SOLVING STRATEGY

## Drawing Schematic Diagrams

When drawing schematic diagrams, follow these steps.
1. Draw the symbol for the battery or other source of electric energy at the left side of the page. Put the positive terminal at the top.
2. Draw a wire following the conventional current out of the positive terminal. When you reach a resistor or other device, draw the symbol for it.
3. If you reach a point where there are two current paths, such as at a voltmeter, draw a + the diagram and follow one path until the two paths join again. Then draw the second path.
4. Follow the path until you reach the negative terminal of the battery.
5. Check your work to see that you have included all parts and that there are complete paths for current to follow.

Often instruments that measure current and voltage are connected into circuits. They must be connected in specific ways. An ammeter, which measures current, must be connected so there is only one current path. Such a connection is called a **series connection**, Figure 22–9. A voltmeter measures the potential difference across a circuit element. One voltmeter terminal is connected to one side of the element. The other terminal is connected to the other side. This connection is called a **parallel connection**. The potential difference across the element is equal to the potential difference across the voltmeter.

# POCKET LAB

## RUNNING OUT

Use the proper symbols and design a drawing that shows a power supply in a continuous circuit with two miniature lamps. Next draw the circuit with an ammeter included to measure the electrical flow between the power supply and the bulbs. Make a third drawing to show the ammeter at a position to measure the electrical flow between the bulbs. Would you predict the current between the lamps to be more or less than the current before the lamps? Why? Build the circuits to find out. Record your results.

# PHYSICS LAB : Mystery Cans

## Purpose

To design and construct a circuit to measure the resistance of mystery film cans.

## Materials

· film cans (with a resistor inside)
· 0 - 6 V variable power supply
· wires
· ammeter
· voltmeter

## Procedure

1. Use the proper symbols to make a drawing of the set-up that would allow you to calculate the resistance of each can.
2. Show your diagram to your teacher before proceeding to step 3. Turn the power supply all the way down usually by rotating the knob in a counterclockwise direction.
3. Build the circuit that you designed and slowly turn up the power supply as you watch the needles on the meters. Do not exceed one amp or the current limitation set by your teacher.
4. If the needle(s) move in a negative direction, reverse the connections of the positive and negative on that meter.
5. Record the voltage and current readings for two different settings on your power supply.
6. Repeat steps 4-5 with two more film cans.

## Observations and Data

1. Set up a data table with space for two voltage and current readings for each of the three film cans to be tested.
2. Describe what happened to the current as you increased the setting on the power supply.
3. Look inside each film can to determine the actual value of each resistor. Record these values.

## Analysis

1. Calculate the value of each film can resistance. Compare your value to the known values.
2. Look closely at your data table. Did the resistors change resistance as they heated up? Use your values to support your answer.

## Applications

1. Most light bulbs "burn out" when they are first switched on. Write a hypothesis suggesting why this happens.

35 mm film can

Voltmeter

Ammeter

# Practice Problems

11. Draw a circuit diagram to include a 60-V battery, an ammeter, and a resistance of 12.5 Ω in series. Indicate the ammeter reading and the direction of current flow.
12. Draw a series circuit diagram showing a 4.5-V battery, a resistor, and an ammeter reading 90 mA. Label the size of the resistor. Choose a direction for the conventional current and indicate the positive terminal of the battery.
▶ 13. Add a voltmeter that measures the potential difference across the resistors in each of the Practice Problems above.

# F.Y.I.

$V = IR$ is often taken as a statement of Ohm's law, but this is not true. The equation simply defines resistance and applies to all resistances whether they obey Ohm's law or not.

## CONCEPT REVIEW

**1.1** Draw a schematic diagram of a circuit containing a battery and bulb that will make the bulb light.
**1.2** Joe argues that, since $R = V/I$, if he increases the voltage, the resistance will increase. Is Joe correct? Explain.
**1.3** You are asked to measure the resistance of a long piece of wire. Show how you would construct a circuit containing a battery, voltmeter, ammeter, and the wire to be tested to make the measurement. Specify what you would measure and how you would compute the resistance.
**1.4** **Critical Thinking:** We have said that power is "dissipated" in a resistor. To dissipate is to use, or to waste, or to squander. What is "used" when charge flows through a resistor?

# 22.2 USING ELECTRICAL ENERGY

At an industrial site, electrical energy can be converted into other forms of energy, such as kinetic, sound, light, and thermal energy. Devices that make these conversions are very important in our everyday lives. Motors, loudspeakers, lamps, television sets, heaters, and air conditioners are examples of common devices that convert electric energy into other forms of energy.

## Objectives

· **explain how heaters convert electrical energy to thermal energy.**
· **describe the use of capacitors for energy storage in circuits.**
· **describe the reason for the use of high-voltage lines for transmitting electrical energy.**
· **define the kilowatt hour; solve problems involving the use and cost of electrical energy.**

## Energy Transfer in Electric Circuits

The motors, resistors, and lamps that we have discussed convert electrical energy into other forms. The capacitor, introduced in Chapter 21, stores electrical energy. If a capacitor is initially uncharged, then the voltage across it, $V = q/C$, will be zero. Suppose the capacitor is now

When a capacitor is charged or discharged through a resistor, the current is high initially and falls to zero.

Power dissipated in a resistor is proportional to the resistance.

Power dissipated in a resistor is proportional to the square of the current.

connected to a battery, voltage $V_o$, through a resistor, $R$, Figure 22–10a. Charges will flow from the battery through the resistor to the capacitor. Initially, with a large potential difference across the resistor, the current, $I$, will be large. The voltage across the capacitor will increase and current will become smaller until the voltage across the capacitor reaches the battery voltage. With no potential difference across the resistor, no more current will flow. The capacitor will be fully charged. Some energy from the battery is now stored in the electric field of the capacitor.

The capacitor is discharged as in Figure 22–10b by connecting it across a resistor or other device. Because there is a potential difference, $V$, across the resistor, there will be current, $I$. As the charge in the capacitor decreases, so does the voltage across it. Thus the current, the rate at which the capacitor is discharging, also drops. Eventually the capacitor will be completely discharged; both $q$ and $V$ will be zero. All the energy will have been transferred to thermal energy at the resistor.

Electric power is the energy per unit time converted by an electric circuit into another form of energy. Power is equal to the voltage multiplied by the current, $P = VI$. For a resistor that obeys Ohm's law, by definition $V = IR$. Substituting this expression into the equation for electric power, we obtain

$$P = I^2R.$$

The power dissipated in a resistor is thus proportional to the square of the current that passes through it and to the resistance. The energy is changed from electrical to thermal energy; the resistor gets hot.

The energy supplied to a circuit can be used in different ways. A motor converts electric energy into mechanical energy. An electric lamp changes electric energy into light. Unfortunately, not all of the electric energy delivered to a motor or to an electric light ends up in a useful form. Some energy is always converted into excess thermal energy. Certain devices, such as space heaters, are designed to convert most of the electric energy into thermal energy. Some electric energy is also converted into light.

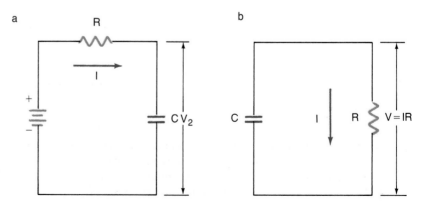

**FIGURE 22–10. A capacitor is charged by connecting it to a battery (a). It is discharged by connecting it across some resistance (b).**

The electric energy transferred to a resistor in a time interval, $t$, is equal to $I^2Rt$. If all the electric energy is converted into thermal energy of the resistor, the increase in thermal energy is

$$E = I^2Rt.$$

The temperature of the resistor increases, allowing heat to flow into its colder surroundings. For example, in an immersion heater, a resistor placed in a cup of water can bring the water to the boiling point in a few minutes.

The energy transferred is the product of the power and the time.

## Example Problem

### Thermal Energy Produced by an Electric Current

A heater has a resistance of 10.0 $\Omega$. It operates on 120.0 V.
**a.** What is the current through the resistance? **b.** What thermal energy in joules is supplied by the heater in 10.0 s?

**Given:** resistance, $R$ = 10.0 $\Omega$    **Unknowns: a.** $I$ **b.** $E$
      potential difference,     **Basic equations: a.** $R = V/I$
      $V$ = 120.0 V                  **b.** $E = I^2Rt$
      time, $t$ = 10.0 s

**Solution: a.** $R = V/I$, so $I = V/R$ = (120.0 V)/(10.0 $\Omega$ ) = 12.0 A
      **b.** $E = I^2Rt$
           = (12.0 A)$^2$(10.0 $\Omega$ )(10.0 s) = 14 400 J or 14.4 kJ

## Practice Problems

**14.** A 15-$\Omega$ electric heater operates on a 120-V outlet.
     **a.** What is the current through the heater?
     **b.** How much energy is used by the heater in 30.0 s?
     **c.** How much thermal energy is liberated by the heater in this time?
**15.** A 30-$\Omega$ resistor is connected across a 60-V battery.
     **a.** What is the current in the circuit?
     **b.** How much energy is used by the resistor in 5 min?

16. A 100.0-W light bulb is 20.0% efficient. That means 20.0% of the electric energy is converted to light energy.
    a. How many joules does the light bulb convert into light each minute it is in operation?
    b. How many joules of thermal energy does the light bulb produce each minute?

▶ 17. The resistance of an electric stove element at operating temperature is 11 Ω.
    a. 220 V are applied across it. What is the current through the stove element?
    b. How much energy does the element convert to thermal energy in 30.0 s?
    c. The element is being used to heat a kettle containing 1.20 kg of water. Assume that 70% of the heat is absorbed by the water. What is its increase in temperature during the 30.0 s?

## Transmission of Electric Energy

Hydroelectric generating stations can produce electric energy with little pollution. The energy, however, must often be transmitted long distances to reach homes and industries. How can the transmission take place with as little loss to thermal energy as possible? Thermal energy is produced at a rate given by $P = I^2R$. Electrical engineers call this unwanted thermal energy the "Joule heating" or "$I^2R$" loss. To reduce this loss, either the current, $I$, or the resistance, $R$, must be reduced.

All wires have some resistance, even though it is small. For example, 1 km of the large wire used to carry electric current into a home has a resistance of 0.2 Ω. Suppose a farmhouse were connected directly to a power plant 3.5 km away, Figure 22–12. The resistance in the wires needed to carry a current to the home and back to the plant is

**FIGURE 22–12. Electrical energy is transferred over long distances at high voltages to minimize $I^2R$ losses.**

Power Plant

Current flow

House

3.5 km

2(3.5 km) (0.2 Ω /km) = 1.4 Ω. An electric stove might cause a 41-A current through the wires. The power dissipated in the wires is given by $P = I^2R = (41 \text{ A})^2 \times 1.4 \ \Omega = 2400 \text{ W}$. All this power is wasted.

This loss could be reduced by reducing the resistance. Cables of high conductivity and large diameter are used, but such cables are expensive and heavy. Since the loss is also proportional to the square of the current in the conductors, it is even more important to keep the current in the transmission lines low.

The electrical energy per second (power) transferred over a long-distance transmission line is determined by the relationship $P = VI$. The current can be reduced without reducing the power by increasing the voltage. Some long-distance lines use voltages over one-half million volts. The resulting lower current reduces the $I^2R$ loss in the lines by keeping the $I^2$ factor low. Long-distance transmission lines always operate at high voltage to reduce $I^2R$ loss.

High voltage transmission lines carry electrical energy over long distances with minimal loss.

More for Less?

FIGURE 22–14. Computerization of modern power grids makes it possible to draw electrical energy from distant sources in emergency situations.

FIGURE 22–15. Watthour meters (a) measure the amount of electrical energy used by a consumer. The more current being used at a given time, the faster the horizontal disk in the centre of the meter turns. Meter readings are then used in calculating the cost of energy (b).

a

b

## The Kilowatt Hour

While electric companies often are called "power" companies, they really provide energy. When you pay your home electric bill, Figure 22–15, you pay for electric energy, not power.

The electric energy used by any device is its rate of energy consumption, in joules per second (watts), times the number of seconds it is operated. Joules per second times seconds, J/s · s, equals total joules of energy.

The joule, a watt-second, is a relatively small amount of energy. For that reason, electric companies measure their energy sales in a large number of joules called a kilowatt hour, kW·h. A **kilowatt hour** is equal to 1000 W delivered continuously for 3600 s (1 h). It is

$$1 \text{ KW·h} = (1000 \text{ J/s})(3600 \text{ s}) = 3.6 \times 10^6 \text{ J}.$$

Not many devices in the home other than hot-water heaters, stoves, heaters, curling irons, and hair dryers require more than 1000 W. Ten 100-W light bulbs operating all at once would use 1 kW·h of energy if left on for a full hour.

The kilowatt hour (kWh) is a unit of energy, the product of power (kW) and time (h).

## Example Problem

### The Cost of Operating an Electric Device

A modern colour television set draws 2.0 A when operated on 120 V. **a.** How much power does the set use? **b.** If the set is operated for an average of 7.0 h/d, what energy in KW·h does it consume per month (30 d)? **c.** At \$0.11 per KW·h, what is the cost of operating the set per month?

**Given:** $I = 2.0$ A
$V = 120$ V
$t = 7.0$ h/d $\times$ 30 d
$= 2.1 \times 10^2$ h

**Unknowns: a.** $P$  **b.** $E$
**Basic equations:** $P = VI$
$P = E/t$

**Solution:**
**a.** $P = VI$
$= (120 \text{ V})(2.0 \text{ A})$
$= 2.4 \times 10^2$ W

**b.** $E = Pt$
$= (2.4 \times 10^2 \text{ W})(2.1 \times 10^2 \text{ h})$
$= 5.0 \times 10^4 \text{ W·h} = 5.0 \times 10^1 \text{ kW·h}$

**c.** cost $= (5.0 \times 10^1 \text{ kW·h})(\$0.11/\text{kW·h}) = \$5.50$

# Practice Problems

18. An electric space heater draws 15.0 A from a 120-V source. It is operated, on the average, for 5.0 h each day.
    a. How much power does the heater use?
    b. How much energy in kW·h does it consume in 30 d?
    c. At $0.11 per kW·h, what does it cost to operate it for 30 d?

▶ 19. A digital clock has an operating resistance of 12 000 Ω and is plugged into a 115-V outlet. Assume the clock obeys Ohm's law.
    a. How much current does it draw?
    b. How much power does it use?
    c. If the owner of the clock pays $0.09 per kW·h, what does it cost to operate the clock for 30 d?

······················

# CONCEPT REVIEW

2.1 A battery charges a capacitor. The capacitor is discharged through a photo flashlamp. List the forms of energy in these two operations.

2.2 A hair dryer operating from 120 V has two settings, hot and warm. In which setting is the resistance likely to be smaller? Why?

2.3 Why would a home using an electric range and hot water heater connect these appliances to 240 V rather than 120 V?

2.4 **Critical Thinking:** When demand for electrical power is high, power companies sometimes reduce the voltage, producing a "brown out." What is being saved?

# **P**hysics and *technology*

## ULTRA-HIGH VOLTAGE ELECTRIC POWER TRANSMISSION

Long-term projections continue to indicate a growing demand for electric energy. This means that electricity generation and transmission capacity must increase to keep pace with the need.

To deliver electric energy with less waste, transmission levels greater than the present extra-high voltage (EHV) levels of 345 and 765 kV will be needed in the years ahead. The new levels of transmission capacity being studied are called ultra-high voltage (UHV). UHV transmission levels of more than 2000 kV are being tested.

Research on environmental effects of high voltage electricity transmission is becoming increasingly important. Research generally falls into three areas: possible ozone emission by transmission lines, audible noise and radio- and television-frequency interference, and the biological effects of electrostatic and electromagnetic fields on organisms.

· If electric power lines could be shown to cause specific health problems, how might this affect electric utilities and homeowners?

# 22 REVIEW

## SUMMARY

### 22.1 Current and Circuits

- Batteries, generators, and solar cells convert various forms of energy to electric energy.
- In an electric circuit, electric energy is transmitted from a device that produces electric energy to a resistor or other device that converts electric energy into the form needed.
- As a charge moves through resistors in a circuit, its potential energy is reduced. The energy released when the charge moves around the remainder of the circuit equals the work done to give the charge its initial potential energy.
- One ampere is one coulomb per second.
- Electric power is found by multiplying voltage by current.
- The resistance of a device is the ratio of the voltage across it divided by the current through it.
- In a device that obeys Ohm's law, the resistance does not depend on the current through it.
- The current in a circuit can be varied by changing either the voltage or the resistance, or both.
- In a circuit diagram we use conventional current, the direction in which a positive current carrier would move.

### 22.2 Using Electrical Energy

- A capacitor can store electrical energy.
- The thermal energy produced in a circuit from electric energy is equal to $I^2Rt$.
- In long-distance transmission, current is reduced without reducing power by increasing the voltage.
- A kilowatt hour, KW·h, is an energy unit. It is equal to $3.6 \times 10^6$ J.

## KEY TERMS

| | |
|---|---|
| electric current | resistors |
| battery | potentiometer |
| photovoltaic cell | schematic |
| electric circuit | series connection |
| ampere | parallel connection |
| conventional current | kilowatt hour |
| resistance | |

## REVIEWING CONCEPTS

1. Describe the energy conversions that occur in each of these devices.
   a. incandescent light bulb
   b. clothes dryer
   c. digital clock radio
2. Define the unit of electric charge in terms of fundamental MKS units.
3. Which wire conducts electricity with the least resistance: one with a large cross-sectional diameter or one with a small cross-sectional diameter?

**FIGURE 22–16.**

4. How many electrons flow past a point in a wire each second if the wire has a current of 1 A?
5. Why do light bulbs burn out more frequently just as they are switched on rather than while the bulbs are operating?
6. Explain, in terms of the average kinetic energy of the atoms in the wire, why the resistance of a wire increases as the temperature of the wire increases.
7. A simple circuit consists of a battery, a resistor, and some connecting wires. Draw a circuit schematic of this simple circuit. Show the polarity of the battery and the direction of the current.
8. A simple circuit consists of a resistor, a battery, and connecting wires.
   a. How must an ammeter be connected in a circuit to correctly read the current?
   b. How must a voltmeter be connected to a resistor in order to read the potential difference across it?

9. If a battery is short-circuited by connecting a heavy copper wire from one terminal to the other, the temperature of the copper wire rises. Explain.
10. Why does a wire become warmer as current flows through it?
11. What electrical quantities must be kept small to transmit electric energy economically over long distances?

# APPLYING CONCEPTS

1. When a battery is connected to a complete circuit, charges flow in the circuit almost instantaneously. Explain.
2. Explain why a cow that touches an electric fence experiences a mild shock.
3. Why can birds perch on high-voltage lines without being injured?
4. Describe two ways of increasing a circuit's current in a device that obeys Ohm's law.
5. You have two light bulbs that work on a 120-V circuit. One is 50 W, the other 100 W. Which bulb has a higher resistance? Explain.
6. If the voltage across a circuit is kept constant and the resistance is doubled, what effect does this have on the circuit's current?
7. What is the effect on the current in a circuit if both the voltage and the resistance are doubled? Explain.
8. Sue finds a device that looks like a resistor. When she connects it to a 1.5-V battery, only $45 \times 10^{-6}$ A flows, but when a 3.0-V battery is used, $25 \times 10^{-3}$ A flows. Does the device obey Ohm's law?
9. If the ammeter in Figure 22–4 were moved to the bottom of the diagram, would the ammeter have the same reading?
10. Two wires can be placed across the terminals of a 6.0-V battery. One has a high resistance, one low. Which wire will produce thermal energy at the faster rate? Explain.

# PROBLEMS

## 22.1 Current and Circuits

1. The current through a toaster connected to a 120-V source is 8.0 A. What power is dissipated by the toaster?

2. A current of 1.2 A flows through a light bulb when it is connected across a 120-V source. What power is dissipated by the bulb?
3. A lamp draws 0.50 A from a 120-V generator.
   a. How much power does the generator deliver?
   b. How much energy does the lamp convert in 5.0 min?
4. A 12-V automobile battery is connected to an electric starter motor. The current through the motor is 210 A.
   a. How many joules of energy does the battery deliver to the motor each second?
   b. What power, in watts, does the motor use?
5. A 4000-W clothes dryer is connected to a 220-V circuit. How much current does the dryer draw?
6. A flashlight bulb is connected across a 3.0-V difference in potential. The current through the lamp is 1.5 A.
   a. What is the power rating of the lamp?
   b. How much electric energy does the lamp convert in 11 min?
▶ 7. How much energy does a 60.0-W light bulb use in 30 min? If the light bulb is 12% efficient, how much thermal energy does it generate during that time?
8. A resistance of 60 Ω has a current of 0.40 A through it when it is connected to the terminals of a battery. What is the voltage of the battery?
9. What voltage is applied to a 4.0-Ω resistor if the current is 1.5 A?
10. What voltage is placed across a motor of 15 Ω operating resistance if the current is 8.0 A of current?
11. A voltage of 75 V is placed across a 15-Ω resistor. What is the current through the resistor?
12. A 20.0-Ω resistor is connected to a 30.0-V battery. What is the current in the resistor?
13. A 12-V battery is connected to a device and 24 mA, $24 \times 10^{-3}$ A, of current flows through it. If the device obeys Ohm's law, how much current will flow when a 24-V battery is used?
14. The damage caused by electric shock depends on the current flowing through the body—1 mA can be felt; 5 mA is painful. Above 15 mA, a person loses muscle control, and 70 mA can be fatal. A person with dry skin has a resistance from one arm to the other of about $1 \times 10^5$ Ω. When skin is wet,

the resistance drops to about $5 \times 10^3$ $\Omega$.
  a. What is the minimum voltage placed across the arms that would produce a current that could be felt by a person with dry skin?
  b. What effect would the same voltage have if the person had wet skin?
  c. What would be the minimum voltage that would produce a current that could be felt when the skin is wet?
15. A lamp draws a 66-mA current when connected to a 6.0-V battery. When a 9.0-V battery is used, the lamp draws 75 mA.
  a. Does the lamp obey Ohm's law?
  b. How much power does the lamp dissipate at 6.0 V?
  c. How much power does it dissipate at 9.0 V?
▶ 16. Table 22–1 shows data taken by students. They connected a length of nichrome wire to a variable power supply that could produce from 0 V to 10 V across the wire. They then measured the current through the wire for several voltages. The data table shows the voltages used and currents measured.
  a. For each measurement, calculate the resistance.
  b. Graph I versus V.
  c. Does the nichrome wire obey Ohm's law? If not for all the voltages, specify the voltage range for which Ohm's law holds.

Table 22–1

| Voltage V (volts) | Current I (amps) | Resistance $R = V/I$ (ohms) |
|---|---|---|
| 2.00 | 0.014 | |
| 4.00 | 0.027 | |
| 6.00 | 0.040 | |
| 8.00 | 0.052 | |
| 10.00 | 0.065 | |
| −2.00 | −0.014 | |
| −4.00 | −0.028 | |
| −6.00 | −0.039 | |
| −8.00 | −0.051 | |
| −10.00 | −0.064 | |

17. The current through a lamp connected across 120 V is 0.40 A when the lamp is on.
  a. What is its resistance when it is on?
  b. When the lamp is cold, its resistance is one fifth as large as when the lamp is hot. What is its cold resistance?

  c. What is the current through the lamp as it is turned on if it is connected to a potential difference of 120 V?
▶ 18. The graph in Figure 22–17 shows the current that flows through a device called a silicon diode.
  a. A potential difference of +0.70 V is placed across the diode. What resistance would be calculated?
  b. What resistance would be calculated if a +0.60-V potential difference was used?
  c. Does the diode obey Ohm's law?

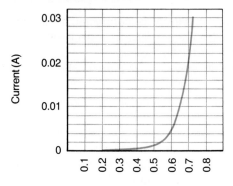

FIGURE 22–17. Use with Problem 18.

▶ 19. Draw a schematic diagram to show a circuit that includes a 90-V battery, an ammeter, and a resistance of 45 $\Omega$ connected in series. What is the ammeter reading? Draw arrows showing the direction of conventional current flow.
▶ 20. Draw a series circuit diagram to include a 16-$\Omega$ resistor, a battery, and an ammeter that reads 1.75 A. Current flows through the meter from left to right. Indicate the positive terminal and the voltage of the battery.

## 22.2 Using Electrical Energy

21. What is the maximum current that should be allowed in a 5.0-W, 220-$\Omega$ resistor?
22. The wire in a house circuit is rated at 15.0 A that has a resistance of 0.15 $\Omega$.
  a. What is its power rating?
  b. How much heat does the wire give off in 10.0 min?
23. A current of 1.2 A flows through a 50-$\Omega$ resistor for 5.0 min. How much heat was generated by the resistor?
24. A 6.0-$\Omega$ resistor is connected to a 15 V battery.

a. What is the current in the circuit?

b. How much thermal energy is produced in 10 min?

25. A 110-V electric iron draws 3.0 A of current. How much heat is developed per hour?

▶ 26. An electric motor operates a pump that irrigates a farmer's crop by pumping 10 000 L of water a vertical distance of 8.0 m into a field each hour. The motor has an operating resistance of 22.0 Ω and is connected across a 110-V source.

a. What current does it draw?

b. How efficient is the motor?

27. A transistor radio operates by means of a 9.0-V battery that supplies it with a 50-mA current.

a. If the cost of the battery is $0.90 and it lasts for 300 h, what is the cost per kW·h to operate the radio in this manner?

b. The same radio, by means of a converter, is plugged into a household circuit by a homeowner who pays $0.08 per kW·h. What does it now cost to operate the radio for 300 h?

**FIGURE 22–18.**

▶ 28. A heating coil has a resistance of 4.0 Ω and operates on 120 V.

a. What is the current in the coil while it is operating?

b. What energy is supplied to the coil in 5.0 min?

c. If the coil is immersed in an insulated container holding 20.0 kg of water, what will be the increase in the temperature of the water? Assume that 100% of the heat is absorbed by the water.

d. At $0.08/kW·h, what does it cost to operate the heating coil 30 min/d for 30 d?

▶ 29. An electric heater is rated at 500 W.

a. How much energy is delivered to the heater in half an hour?

b. The heater is being used to heat a room containing 50.0 kg of air. If the specific heat of air is 1.10 kJ/kg·°C, 1100 J/kg·°C, and 50% of the thermal energy heats the air in the room, what is the change in air temperature?

c. At $0.08/kW·h, what does it cost to run the heater 6.0 h/d for 30 d?

## THINKING PHYSIC-LY

1. What causes electric shock, current or voltage?

2. Some people say that an electrical appliance "uses up" electricity. What does the appliance "use up" and what becomes of it?

# 23
# Series and Parallel Circuits

◀ **Which Light Lights Lighter?**

A 60-W light bulb and a 100-W light bulb are connected in series with a 120-V source. If the circuit is closed, which bulb will glow brighter?

The electric circuits introduced in Chapter 22 had one source of electric energy and one device that used energy. Often many devices must be connected to one source. In this chapter, you will explore the ways in which devices can be connected in electric circuits. The photograph on the opposite page shows two light bulbs connected in series. Do you think the results would be the same if the two bulbs were connected in parallel?

If devices are connected in series, all the current travels through each device. A parallel connection allows the current to split and travel through several devices at once. A closer look will show how these connections work and how they can be used.

## ✓ Concept Check

The following terms or concepts from earlier chapters are important for a good understanding of this chapter. If you are not familiar with them, you should review them before studying this chapter.
· potential difference, Chapter 21
· electric circuits, resistance, Chapter 22

# 23.1 SIMPLE CIRCUITS

## Objectives

- describe a series connection; state its important characteristics.
- calculate current, voltage drops, and equivalent resistance when devices are connected in series.
- describe a voltage generator and solve problems involving one.
- describe a parallel connection; state its important characteristics.
- calculate the voltage drop, currents, and equivalent resistance when devices are connected in parallel.

In a series circuit there is only one current path.

The current in a series circuit is the same in each element.

The total potential drop in a series circuit is the sum of the individual drops.

Have you ever driven along a single-lane road with no turn-offs? If there is an accident or if the road is being repaired, all traffic stops. There is only one path over which cars can move. This is like the path of electric charges in a series connection. In the case where there is a second road, however, cars can use either path and avoid road blocks. A parallel connection has the same characteristics as this second case.

## Series Circuits

When resistors or other electrical devices are connected in a **series circuit**, all current travels through each resistor. It moves through one resistor after the other. Consider the flow of water in a river as a model of an electric current. At the river's source, the gravitational potential of the water is highest. Rapids are like resistors. A river having one rapid after another is like a series connection. All the water in the river passes through each of the rapids but loses some potential energy at each one. In Figure 23–1, current passes through the generator, the ammeter, and each lamp in succession. The current is the same in each device and in the generator. To find the current, we first find the potential drops around the circuit. If a charge is carried completely around the circuit, its potential returns to the original value. Thus the increase in potential across the generator is equal to the sum of the potential drops around the remainder of the circuit. The total distance the river drops is the sum of the vertical drops through each of the rapids. In the electrical circuit, there is almost no drop across the ammeter or the wires. The potential difference across the three lamps in series, $V$, is equal to the sum of the potential drops across the individual lamps,

$$V = V_1 + V_2 + V_3.$$

FIGURE 23–1. A series circuit can be represented both pictorially and schematically. The total resistance of a series circuit is equal to the sum of the individual resistances.

470   Series and Parallel Circuits

The resistance of each lamp is defined as $R = V/I$. Thus, the potential drop across the first lamp is $V_1 = IR_1$. Therefore,

$$V = IR_1 + IR_2 + IR_3, \text{ or } V = I(R_1 + R_2 + R_3).$$

The current is given by

$$I = \frac{V}{R_1 + R_2 + R_3}.$$

The same current would exist in a circuit with a single resistor, $R$, that has a resistance equal to the sum of the three lamp resistances. Such a resistance is called the **equivalent resistance** of the circuit. For resistors in series, the equivalent resistance is the sum of all the resistances,

$$\boxed{R = R_1 + R_2 + R_3.}$$

Notice that the equivalent resistance is larger than any single resistance.

The current through a series circuit is most easily found by first calculating the equivalent resistance, $R$, and then using the equation

$$I = \frac{V}{R}.$$

An equivalent resistance is the value of a single resistor that could replace all resistors in a circuit and not change the current. The equivalent resistance in a series circuit is the sum of the individual resistances.

## Example Problem

### Current in a Series Circuit

Four 15-$\Omega$ resistors are connected in series with a 45-V battery, Figure 23–2. What is the current in the circuit?

$$R = R_1 + R_2 + R_3 + R_4$$
$$= 15\ \Omega + 15\ \Omega + 15\ \Omega + 15\ \Omega = 60\ \Omega$$

Using the definition of resistance in the form $I = V/R$ gives

$$I = \frac{V}{R} = \frac{45\ \text{V}}{60\ \Omega} = 0.75\ \text{A}$$

## Practice Problems

*Assume batteries and generators provide the stated potential difference for any current that flows.*

1. There are three 20-$\Omega$ resistors connected in series across a 120-V generator.
   **a.** What is the effective resistance of the circuit?
   **b.** What is the current in the circuit?
2. A 10-$\Omega$ resistor, a 15-$\Omega$ resistor, and a 5-$\Omega$ resistor are connected in series across a 90-V battery.
   **a.** What is the equivalent resistance of the circuit?
   **b.** What is the current in the circuit?

**FIGURE 23–2. Use with the Example Problem.**

Hook up a power supply, a resistor, and an ammeter in a series circuit. Predict what will happen to the current in the circuit when a second, identical resistor is added in series to the circuit. Predict the new currents when the circuit contains three and four resistors in series. Explain your prediction. Try it. Make a data table to show your results. Write a sentence that explains your results. (**Hint:** Include the idea of resistance.)

3. Consider a 9-V battery in a circuit with three resistors connected in series.
   a. If the resistance of one of the devices increases, how will the series resistance change?
   b. What will happen to the current?
   c. Will there be any change in the battery voltage?

▶ 4. Ten Christmas tree bulbs connected in series have equal resistances. When connected to a 120-V outlet, the current through the bulbs is 0.06 A.
   a. What is the equivalent resistance of the circuit?
   b. What is the resistance of each bulb?

The total change in potential around a closed circuit is zero.

A voltage divider is a simple series circuit.

## Voltage Drops in a Series Circuit

The net change in potential going around a circuit must be zero. A battery or generator raises the potential. While passing through the resistors, the potential drops an amount equal to the increase. The net change is zero.

The potential drop across each device in a series circuit can be calculated by rewriting the equation that defines resistance, $R = V/I$, as $V = IR$. First find the equivalent resistance, $R$, in the circuit. Then use the equivalent resistance to find the current. Find $I = V/R$, where $V$ is the potential drop. Once the current in the circuit has been determined, multiply $I$ by the resistance of the individual device to find the potential drop across that device.

An important application of series resistors is the **voltage divider**. Suppose you have a 9-V battery but need a 5-V potential source. A voltage divider can supply this voltage. Consider the circuit in Figure 23–3. Two resistors, $R_1$ and $R_2$, are connected in series across a battery of magnitude $V$. The equivalent resistance of the circuit is $R = R_1 + R_2$. The current $I$ is given by $I = V/R = V/(R_1 + R_2)$. The desired voltage, 5 V, is the voltage drop, $V_2$, across resistor $R_2$.

$$V_2 = IR_2$$

Replacing $I$ by the equation above gives

$$V_2 = IR_2 = \left(\frac{V}{R_1 + R_2}\right) \cdot R_2$$

$$= \frac{VR_2}{R_1 + R_2}.$$

Voltage dividers are often used with sensors like photoresistors. The resistance of a photoresistor depends on the amount of light that strikes it. Photoresistors are made of semiconductors like selenium or cadmium sulfide. A typical photoresistor can have a resistance of 400 Ω when light strikes it, but 400 000 Ω when in the dark. The output voltage of a voltage divider that uses a photoresistor depends on the amount

**FIGURE 23–3.**

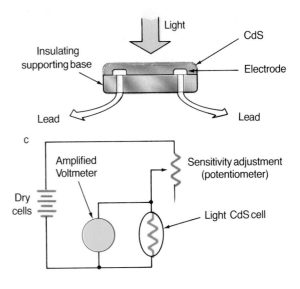

Light
CdS
Insulating
supporting base
Electrode
Lead
Lead

c

Amplified
Voltmeter
Sensitivity adjustment
(potentiometer)

Dry
cells

Light CdS cell

a

b

**FIGURE 23–4. A light meter (a) and schematic diagram (b).**

of light striking the photoresistor sensor. This circuit can be used as a light meter, Figure 23–4. In this device, an electronic circuit detects the potential difference and converts it to a measurement of illuminance that can be read on the digital display.

## Example Problem

### Voltage Drops in a Series Circuit

A 45.0-V potential difference is placed across a 5.0-$\Omega$ resistor and a 10.0-$\Omega$ resistor connected in series, Figure 23–5. **a.** What is the equivalent resistance of the circuit? **b.** What is the current through the circuit? **c.** What is the voltage drop across each resistor? **d.** What is the total voltage drop across the circuit?

**Given:** $R_1 = 5.0 \ \Omega$  
$R_2 = 10.0 \ \Omega$  
$V = 45.0 \ V$

**Unknowns:** $R, I, V_1, V_2$  
**Basic equation:** $V = IR$

**Solution:**

**a.** $R = R_1 + R_2$  
$\quad = 5.0 \ \Omega + 10.0 \ \Omega = 15.0 \ \Omega$  
**b.** $I = V/R = (45.0 \ V)/(15.0 \ \Omega) = 3.00 \ A$  
**c.** The voltage drop across $R_1$ is  
$\quad V_1 = IR_1 = (3.00 \ A)(5.0 \ \Omega) = 15 \ V.$  
$\quad$ The voltage drop across $R_2$ is  
$\quad V_2 = IR_2 = (3.00 \ A)(10.0 \ \Omega) = 30.0 \ V.$  
**d.** $V = V_1 + V_2$  
$\quad = 15 \ V + 30.0 \ V = 45 \ V$

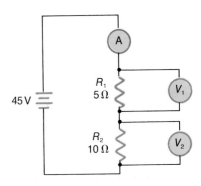

**FIGURE 23–5. Use with the Example Problem.**

**FIGURE 23–6. Use with the Example Problem.**

## Example Problem

### Voltage Divider

A 9.0-V battery and two resistors, $R_1 = 400\ \Omega$ and $R_2 = 500\ \Omega$, are connected as a voltage divider, Figure 23–6. What is the voltage across $R_2$?

**Given:** $V = 9.0$ V
$\qquad R_1 = 400\ \Omega$
$\qquad R_2 = 500\ \Omega$

**Unknown:** $V_2$

**Basic equation:** $V_2 = \dfrac{VR_2}{R_1 + R_2}$

**Solution:** $V_2 = \dfrac{VR_2}{R_1 + R_2} = \dfrac{(9.0\ \text{V})(500\ \Omega)}{400\ \Omega + 500\ \Omega} = 5.0$ V

### Using Your CALCULATOR

Since multiplication is the inverse of division, you can use the inverse key, 1/x, to perform calculation without having to reenter numbers.

$$\frac{(9\ V)\ (500\ \Omega)}{400\ \Omega + 500\ \Omega}$$

| Keys | Answer |
|------|--------|
| [4][0][0][+][5][0][0][=] | 900 |
| [1/x][=] | 1.11... -03 |
| [×][9][×][5][0][0][=] | 5 |

**FIGURE 23–7. A typical parallel circuit is shown using both its pictorial and schematic representations. The total resistance of a parallel circuit is smaller than any of its individual resistances.**

## Practice Problems

5. A 20.0-$\Omega$ resistor and a 30.0-$\Omega$ resistor are connected in series and placed across a 120-V potential difference.
   a. What is the equivalent resistance of the circuit?
   b. What is the current in the circuit?
   c. What is the voltage drop across each resistor?
   d. What is the voltage drop across the two resistors together?
6. Three resistors of 3.0 k$\Omega$ ($3.0 \times 10^3\ \Omega$), 5.0 k$\Omega$, and 4.0 k$\Omega$ are connected in series across a 12-V battery.
   a. What is the equivalent resistance?
   b. What is the current through the resistors?
   c. What is the voltage drop across each resistor?
   d. Find the total voltage drop across the three resistors.
7. A student makes a voltage divider from a 45-V battery, a 475-k$\Omega$ ($475 \times 10^3\ \Omega$) resistor, and a 235-k$\Omega$ resistor. The output voltage is measured across the smaller resistor. What is the voltage?

Generator    Lamps

Generator

$R_1$

$R_2$

$R_3$

FIGURE 23–8. In a parallel circuit, the reciprocal of the total resistance is equal to the sum of the reciprocals of the individual resistances. Here you see three 6.0-Ω resistors connected in parallel. For each resistor, the voltage drop is 120 V and the current is 2 A.

▶ **8.** A photoresistor is used in a voltage divider as $R_2$. $V = 9.0$ V and $R_1 = 500$ Ω.
   **a.** What is the output voltage, $V_2$, across $R_2$, when a bright light strikes the photoresistor and $R_2 = 475$ Ω?
   **b.** When the light is dim, $R_2 = 4.0$ kΩ. What is $V_2$?
   **c.** When the photoresistor is in total darkness, $R_2 = 0.40$ MΩ $(0.40 \times 10^6$ Ω$)$. What is $V_2$?

## Parallel Circuits

In a **parallel circuit** there are several current paths. A typical parallel circuit is shown in Figure 23–7. The circuit contains a voltage source and three resistors. The three resistors are connected in parallel; their left-hand ends are connected together and their right-hand ends are connected together. The current flows through three paths in this parallel circuit. Rapids in a wide river can illustrate a parallel circuit. The water going through rapids often divides into several channels. Some channels may have a large flow of water, others a small flow. The sum of the flows, however, is equal to the total flow of water in the river. In addition, no matter which channel the water follows, the loss in gravitational potential will be the same. All the water starts at the same level and comes together again at the same level below the rapids. In the same way, in a parallel electrical circuit, the total current is the sum of the currents through each current path, and the potential difference across each path is the same.

A schematic diagram of three identical resistors connected in parallel is shown in Figure 23–8. The 120-V generator provides the source of potential difference for the circuit. Each current path is part of a closed circuit including the generator, resistors, and ammeters. Each path acts as if the other paths were not present. What is the current through one resistor? There is a 120-V potential difference across each resistor. The current through a 6-Ω resistor across a 120-V potential difference is

$$I = \frac{V}{R} = \frac{120\,\text{V}}{6.0\,\Omega} = 20 \text{ A}.$$

There is more than one current path in a parallel circuit.

## POCKET LAB

### PARALLEL RESISTANCE

Hook up a power supply, a resistor, and an ammeter in a series circuit. Predict what will happen to the current in the circuit when a second, identical resistor is added in parallel to the first. Predict the new currents when the circuit contains three and four resistors in parallel. Explain your prediction. Try it. Make a data table to show your results. Write a sentence that explains your results. (**Hint:** Include the idea of resistance.)

The current flow through each path from **A** to **B** is 20 A. The total current between the two points is 60 A. The potential difference across the two points is 120 V. A single resistor that would permit 60-A current with 120-V potential difference has a resistance given by

$$R = \frac{V}{I} = \frac{120 \text{ V}}{60 \text{ A}} = 2 \ \Omega.$$

The equivalent resistance can be replaced by this single resistor. Placing a resistor in parallel with an existing resistor always decreases the equivalent resistance of the circuit. The resistance decreases because each new resistor provides an additional path for current to flow between points **A** and **B.** Notice that the equivalent resistance of the circuit is less than the resistance of any resistor in the circuit.

To find the equivalent resistance of a parallel circuit, start by noting that the total current in the circuit is the sum of the currents through the branches of the circuit. Recall also that the potential across each is the same. If $I$ is the total current, and $I_1$, $I_2$, and $I_3$ are the currents through each of the branches, then

$$I = I_1 + I_2 + I_3.$$

The current through each resistor, for example $R_1$, can be found from $I_1 = V/R_1$. The total current through the equivalent resistance, $R$, of the circuit is given by $I = V/R$, but all potential drops in a parallel circuit are the same.

$$\frac{V}{R} = \frac{V}{R_1} + \frac{V}{R_2} + \frac{V}{R_3}$$

Dividing both sides of the equation by $V$ then gives an equation for the equivalent resistance of three parallel resistors,

$$\boxed{\frac{1}{R} = \frac{1}{R_1} + \frac{1}{R_2} + \frac{1}{R_3}.}$$

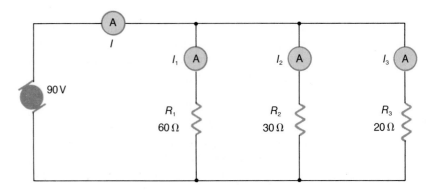

**FIGURE 23–9. Use with the Example Problem.**

# Example Problem

## Total Resistance and Current in a Parallel Circuit

Three resistors of 60.0 $\Omega$, 30.0 $\Omega$, and 20.0 $\Omega$ are connected in parallel across a 90.0-V difference in potential, Figure 23–9.
**a.** Find the equivalent resistance of the circuit.
**b.** Find the current in the entire circuit.
**c.** Find the current through each branch of the circuit.

**Given:** $R_1 = 60.0\ \Omega$
$\phantom{Given:}\ R_2 = 30.0\ \Omega$
$\phantom{Given:}\ R_3 = 20.0\ \Omega$
$\phantom{Given:}\ V = 90.0\ V$

**Unknowns:** $R, I, I_1, I_2, I_3$
**Basic equations:** $V = IR$
$$\frac{1}{R} = \frac{1}{R_1} + \frac{1}{R_2} + \frac{1}{R_3}$$

**Solution:**

**a.** $\dfrac{1}{R} = \dfrac{1}{60.0\ \Omega} + \dfrac{1}{30.0\ \Omega} + \dfrac{1}{20.0\ \Omega}$

$\dfrac{1}{R} = \dfrac{6}{60.0\ \Omega}$

$R = 10.0\ \Omega$

**b.** $I = \dfrac{V}{R} = \dfrac{90.0\ V}{10.0\ \Omega} = 9.00\ A$

**c.** The voltage drop across each resistor is 90.0 V. The currents are:

$(\text{for } R_1)\ I_1 = \dfrac{V}{R_1} = \dfrac{90.0\ V}{60.0\ \Omega}$

$= 1.50\ A$

$(\text{for } R_2)\ I_2 = \dfrac{V}{R_2} = \dfrac{90.0\ V}{30.0\ \Omega}$

$= 3.00\ A$

$(\text{for } R_3)\ I_3 = \dfrac{V}{R_3} = \dfrac{90.0\ V}{20.0\ \Omega}$

$= 4.50\ A$

# Practice Problems

9. Three 15-$\Omega$ resistors are connected in parallel and placed across a 30-V potential difference.
   **a.** What is the equivalent resistance of the parallel circuit?
   **b.** What is the current through the entire circuit?
   **c.** What is the current through each branch of the parallel circuit?
10. A 12.0-$\Omega$ resistor and a 15.0-$\Omega$ resistor are connected in parallel and placed across the terminals of a 15.0-V battery.
    **a.** What is the equivalent resistance of the parallel circuit?
    **b.** What is the current through the entire circuit?
    **c.** What is the current through each branch of the parallel circuit?

**11.** A 120.0-$\Omega$ resistor, a 60.0-$\Omega$ resistor, and a 40.0-$\Omega$ resistor are connected in parallel and placed across a potential difference of 12.0 V.

   **a.** What is the equivalent resistance of the parallel circuit?

   **b.** What is the current through the entire circuit?

   **c.** What is the current through each of the branches of the parallel circuit?

▶ **12.** Suppose the 12.0-$\Omega$ resistor in Practice Problem 10 is replaced by a 10.0-$\Omega$ resistor.

   **a.** Does the equivalent resistance become smaller, larger, or remain the same?

   **b.** Does the amount of current through the entire circuit change? in what way?

   **c.** Does the amount of current through the 15.0-$\Omega$ resistor change? in what way?

---

## Which Light Lights Lighter? ▶

You learned in Chapter 22 that the resistance of a 60-W bulb is greater than the resistance of a 100-W bulb. The brightness of a bulb is directly proportional to the power dissipated by the filament of the bulb. In a series circuit, the same current flows through all elements in the circuit. Therefore, according to $P = I^2R$, the 60-W bulb has a higher resistance, and for this reason, will dissipate more power and glow more brightly.

## CONCEPT REVIEW

**1.1** Are car headlights connected in series or parallel? Draw on your experience.

**1.2** Lamp dimmers often consist of rheostats.

   **a.** Would a dimmer be hooked in series or in parallel with the lamp to be controlled? Why?

   **b.** Should the resistance of the dimmer be increased or decreased to dim the lamp?

**1.3** Some Christmas tree light sets that have lamps in series have a device that allows the other lamps to light in case one burns out. It is a small wire placed in parallel with the glowing wire in the lamp. Should the wire resistance be smaller or larger than the glowing wire resistance? Explain.

**1.4 Critical Thinking:** The circuit in Figure 23–10 has four identical resistors. Suppose a wire is connected between points **A** and **B**. Answer each question, explaining your reasoning.

   **a.** What current flows through the wire?

   **b.** What happens to the current through each resistor?

   **c.** What happens to the current drawn from the battery?

   **d.** What happens to the potential difference across each resistor?

**FIGURE 23–10. Use with Concept Review 1.4.**

# PHYSICS LAB : Circuits

## Purpose

To construct series, parallel, and combination circuits.

## Materials

· 0 - 12 V power supply
· 4 small lamps with sockets and connecting wires

## Procedure

1. Turn the dial on the power supply to the off position. Use caution while working with line current electricity to prevent shocks.
2. Build a circuit with 2 lamps. Turn the power supply on so that both bulbs glow brightly. Record the setting on the power supply. This will be called the original setting.
3. Loosen one bulb from its socket and observe what happens to the other bulb. Turn the power supply off. If the other bulb goes out, you have made a series circuit. Go to the section marked SERIES CIRCUITS. If the other bulb stayed on you have made a parallel circuit. Go to the section marked PARALLEL CIRCUITS.

## Series Circuits

1. Make a series circuit with three bulbs. Turn the power supply dial to the original setting and notice the brightness of the bulbs. Turn the power supply off.
2. Make a series circuit with four bulbs. Turn the power supply dial to the original setting and notice the brightness of the bulbs.
3. Try loosening one of the middle bulbs. What happens to the others? Sketch the circuit.

5. If you have not done the parallel circuits, try to make a circuit with 2 lamps so that when you loosen one bulb the other stays on. Then go to PARALLEL CIRCUITS.

## Parallel Circuits

1. Make a parallel circuit with three bulbs.
2. Loosen one of the bulbs to verify that the other 2 stay on. Relight the bulbs.
3. Compare the brightness of the bulbs to the original brightness. Sketch the circuit.
4. If you have not already done series circuits, try to design a circuit with 2 bulbs so that when one is loosened the other will also go out. Then go to SERIES CIRCUITS.

## Observations and Data

1. Describe what happens to the brightness of the bulbs as more are added in a series circuit and a parallel circuit.

## Analysis

The brightness of each bulb depends on the current passing through the bulb.
1. Write a statement that compares the current through each bulb in the same series circuit.
2. What happens to the current as more lamps are added to the series circuit?

## Applications

1. Design and construct a circuit with three lamps so that 1 is bright and 2 are dim. Draw the circuit.

# Objectives

- describe a combination series-parallel circuit.
- calculate the equivalent resistance in a combination circuit.
- distinguish between voltmeters and ammeters and state the important characteristics of each.
- describe how each is wired into a circuit and explain why such a method is used.

A fuse or circuit breaker protects against dangerously large currents.

A ground-fault interrupter opens the circuit if a shock hazard exists.

**FIGURE 23–11. If too much current flows through the bimetallic strip, it will bend down, releasing the latch. The handle will move to the "off" position, opening the switch contacts. The handle will not stay in the "on" position with the switch contacts closed unless the bimetallic strip is cool and straight.**

# 23.2 APPLICATIONS OF CIRCUITS

Home wiring circuits are examples of the ideas we have examined in the earlier part of this chapter. We need to understand the requirements and limitations of these systems. Above all, it is important that we are aware of the safety measures that must be practiced to prevent accidents.

## Safety Devices

In an electric circuit, fuses and circuit breakers are switches that act as safety devices. They prevent circuit overloads that can occur when too many appliances are turned on at the same time or a short circuit occurs in one appliance. When appliances are connected in parallel, each additional appliance placed in operation reduces the equivalent resistance in the circuit and causes more current to flow through the wires. The additional current may produce enough thermal energy (at the rate $P = I^2R$) to melt insulation on the wires, causing a short circuit in the wires or even a fire.

A **fuse** is a short piece of metal that melts from the heating effect of the current. The thickness of the metal is adjusted to determine the current needed to melt the fuse. A circuit breaker, Figure 23–11, is an automatic switch that opens when the current reaches some set value. If current greater than the set value flows in the circuit, it will be overloaded. The circuit breaker will open stopping all current flow.

A **ground-fault interrupter** is often required by law in electrical outlets in bathrooms. Current flows both through the wire bringing charges from the power source and in the wire returning the charges. If there is no other current path, the magnitude of these two currents is the same. Sometimes, when an appliance, such as a hair dryer, is used, the appliance or user might touch a cold water pipe or a sink full of water. Another current path, through the user, could exist—as little as 5 mA is serious. The ground-fault interrupter contains an electronic circuit that detects small differences in current caused by the extra current path and opens the circuit, preventing dangerous shocks.

FIGURE 23–12. The wiring diagram for this house indicates the parallel nature of the circuit. This wiring arrangement will permit the use of one or more appliances.

Electric wiring in a home uses parallel circuits, Figure 23–12, so that the current in any one circuit does not depend on the current in the other circuits. The current in a device that dissipates power, $P$, when connected to a voltage source, $V$, is given by $I = P/V$. Figure 23–13 shows a schematic diagram of the circuit. Suppose, first, that a 240-W television is plugged into a 120-V outlet. The current that flows is given by $I = (240 \text{ W})/(120 \text{ V}) = 2$ A. Then a 720-W curling iron is plugged in. The current through the iron is $I = (720 \text{ W})/(120 \text{ V}) = 6$ A. Finally, a 1440-W hair dryer is added. The current through the hair dryer is $I = (1440 \text{ W})/(120 \text{ V}) = 12$ A.

The current through these three appliances can be found by considering them as a parallel circuit where the currents are independent of each other. Each resistor represents an appliance. The value of the resistance is found by first calculating the current the appliance draws as above and then using the equation $R = V/I$. The equivalent resistance of the three appliances is

Home wiring uses parallel circuits.

$$\frac{1}{R} = \frac{1}{10 \, \Omega} + \frac{1}{20 \, \Omega} + \frac{1}{60 \, \Omega} = \frac{10}{60 \, \Omega} = \frac{1}{6 \, \Omega}$$
$$R = 6.0 \, \Omega.$$

The 15-A fuse is connected in series with the power source so the entire current flows through it. The current flowing through the fuse is

$$I = \frac{V}{R} = \frac{120 \text{ V}}{6 \, \Omega} = 20 \text{ A}.$$

The 20-A current exceeds the rating of the 15-A fuse, so the fuse will melt, or "blow," cutting off current to the entire circuit.

A **short circuit** occurs when a circuit is formed that has a very low resistance. The low resistance causes the current to be very large. If there were no fuse or circuit breaker, such a large current could easily

FIGURE 23–13. A 60-$\Omega$, a 20-$\Omega$, and a 10-$\Omega$ resistor are connected in parallel across a 120-V source. The current through the circuit will cause the fuse to melt.

start a fire. A short circuit can occur if the insulation on a lamp cord becomes old and brittle. The two wires in the cord could accidently touch. The resistance of the wire might be only 0.010 Ω. When placed across 120 V, this resistance would result in a current of

$$I = \frac{V}{R} = \frac{120\,V}{0.010\,\Omega} = 1.20 \times 10^4 \text{ A.}$$

Such a current would cause a fuse or a circuit breaker to open the circuit immediately, preventing the wires from becoming hot enough to start a fire.

## Combined Series-Parallel Circuits

Circuits often consist of combinations of series and parallel circuits, such as the three resistors in Figure 23–14. The circuits can be understood by analyzing them in steps.

1. If any resistors are connected in parallel, calculate the single equivalent resistance that can replace them.
2. If any equivalent resistances are now connected in series, calculate a single new equivalent resistance that can replace them.
3. By repeating steps 1 and 2, you can reduce the circuit to a single resistance. The total circuit current can now be found. The voltage drops and currents through individual resistors can then be calculated.

A short circuit is a very low resistance in a location where the resistance should be very high.

## F.Y.I.

André Marie Ampère was a physicist, chemist, and mathematician. His experiments with electric currents and the discoveries he made in this field laid the foundation for the science of electrodynamics. Ampère's discovery that magnetic fields are produced by the flow of current through a wire led to the invention of the galvanometer.

## PROBLEM SOLVING STRATEGY

1. How do you figure out which resistors are in parallel? Resistors in parallel have separate current paths. They are in parallel only if they have the same potential differences across them.
2. How do you figure out which resistors are in series? Remember that a simple series circuit has only one current path. Resistors are in series only if there is one and only one current path through them.

# Example Problem

## Series-Parallel Circuit

In Figure 23–14, a 30.0-$\Omega$ resistor is connected in parallel with a 20.0-$\Omega$ resistor. The parallel connection is placed in series with an 8.0-$\Omega$ resistor, and the entire circuit is placed across a 60.0-V difference of potential. **a.** What is the equivalent resistance ($R_{2,3}$) of the parallel portion of the circuit? **b.** What is the equivalent resistance of the entire circuit? **c.** What is the current in the entire circuit? **d.** What is the voltage drop across the 8.0-$\Omega$ resistor? **e.** What is the voltage drop across the parallel portion of the circuit? **f.** What is the current in each line of the parallel portion of the circuit?

**Given:** See Figure 23–14. **Unknowns:** $R_{2,3}$, $R$, $I$, $V_1$, $V_p$, $I_2$, $I_3$
**Basic equations:** $V = IR$
$$R = R_1 + R_2 + \ldots$$
$$1/R = 1/R_1 + 1/R_2 + \ldots$$

**Solution:**

**a.** $R_2$ and $R_3$ are connected in parallel. Their equivalent resistance is
$$\frac{1}{R_{2,3}} = \frac{1}{R_2} + \frac{1}{R_3} = \frac{1}{30.0\ \Omega} + \frac{1}{20.0\ \Omega} = \frac{5}{60.0\ \Omega}$$
$$R_{2,3} = 12.0\ \Omega$$

**b.** The circuit is equivalent to a series circuit with an 8.0-$\Omega$ resistor and a 12.0-$\Omega$ resistor in series, Figure 23–13.
$$R = R_1 + R_{2,3} = 8.0\ \Omega + 12.0\ \Omega = 20.0\ \Omega$$

**c.** The current in the circuit is
$$I = \frac{V}{R} = \frac{60.0\ V}{20.0\ \Omega} = 3.00\ A.$$

**d.** The voltage drop across the 8.0-$\Omega$ resistor is
$$V_1 = IR_1 = (3.00\ A)(8.0\ \Omega) = 24\ V.$$

**e.** The parallel branch ($R_2$ and $R_3$) behaves as a 12.0-$\Omega$ resistor, with the sum of the currents through $R_2$ and $R_3$ flowing through it. Therefore, the voltage drop across it is
$$V_p = IR_{2,3} = (3.00\ A)(12.0\ \Omega) = 36.0\ V.$$

**f.** The 36.0-V drop across the parallel portion of the circuit is the same across all parts of the parallel circuit. Therefore, the current through the 30.0-$\Omega$ resistor is
$$I_2 = \frac{V}{R_2} = \frac{36.0\ V}{30.0\ \Omega} = 1.20\ A.$$

The current through the 20.0-$\Omega$ resistor is
$$I_3 = \frac{V}{R_3} = \frac{36.0\ V}{20.0\ \Omega} = 1.80\ A.$$

The current through the parallel part of the circuit is
$$1.20\ A + 1.80\ A, \text{ or } 3.00\ A.$$

This value agrees with the value for the current calculated in Part **c.**

## ECONOMICS CONNECTION

Thomas Edison did not invent the light bulb, but he did develop the first bulb that could be used in homes, and even more important, a commercially viable distribution system for electricity. Edison started with the basic assumption that each customer should be able to turn on and off light bulbs without affecting the other bulbs connected in the circuit. This meant that bulbs must be connected in parallel. Since only part of the circuit current flowed through each bulb, Edison had to design a high-resistance filament that required only a small current for a large heating effect. His assistants tried over 1600 materials including paper, cloth, thread, fishline, fibre, celluloid, boxwood, coconut shells, spruce, hickory, hay, maple shavings, rosewood, punk, cork, flax, bamboo, and the hair out of a redheaded Scotsman's beard before he developed a high vacuum-sealed bulb with a carbonized cotton.

## Practice Problems

13. Two 60-Ω resistors are connected in parallel. This parallel arrangement is connected in series with a 30-Ω resistor. The combination is then placed across a 120-V potential difference.
    a. Draw a diagram of the circuit.
    b. What is the equivalent resistance of the parallel portion of the circuit?
    c. What single resistance could replace the three original resistors?
    d. What is the current in the circuit?
    e. What is the voltage drop across the 30-Ω resistor?
    f. What is the voltage drop across the parallel portion of the circuit?
    g. What is the current in each branch of the parallel portion of the circuit?

14. Three 15-Ω resistors are connected in parallel. This arrangement is connected in series with a 10-Ω resistor. The entire combination is then placed across a 45-V difference in potential.
    a. Draw a diagram of the circuit.
    b. What is the equivalent resistance of the parallel portion of the circuit?
    c. What is the equivalent resistance of the entire circuit?
    d. What is the current in the entire circuit?
    e. What is the voltage drop across the 10-Ω resistor?

▶ 15. Suppose you are given three 68-Ω resistors. You can use them in a series, parallel, or series-parallel circuit. Find the three different resistances you can produce in the circuit.

**FIGURE 23–15. An ammeter measures current (a), and a standard laboratory voltmeter (b) measure potential differences. Ammeters are always placed in series within a circuit (c) and voltmeters are placed in parallel (d).**

a

b

c

d

## Ammeters and Voltmeters

An **ammeter** is used to measure the current in any branch or part of a circuit. If, for example, we want to measure the current through a resistor, we would place an ammeter in series with the resistance. This requires opening a current path and inserting an ammeter. The use of an ammeter should not change the current in the circuit we are trying to measure. Because current would decrease if the ammeter increased the resistance in the circuit, the resistance of an ammeter should be as low as possible. Figure 23–15c shows a real ammeter as an ideal, zero-resistance meter placed in series with a 0.01-$\Omega$ resistor. The ammeter resistance is much smaller than the values of the resistors. The current decrease would be from 1.0 A to 0.9995 A, too small to notice.

A **voltmeter** is used to measure the voltage drop across some part of a circuit. To measure the potential drop across a resistor, connect the voltmeter in parallel with the resistor. To cause the smallest change in currents or voltages in the circuit, a voltmeter should have a very high resistance. Consider the circuit in Figure 23–15d. A typical real voltmeter consists of an ideal, infinite-resistance meter in parallel with a 10-k$\Omega$ resistor. When it is connected in parallel with $R_2$, the equivalent resistance of the combination is smaller than $R_2$ alone. Thus the total resistance of the circuit decreases, increasing the current. $R_1$ has not changed, but the current through it has increased, increasing the potential drop across it. The battery, however, holds the potential drop across $R_1$ and $R_2$ constant. Thus, the potential drop across $R_2$ must decrease. The result of connecting a voltmeter across a resistor is to lower the potential drop across it. The higher the resistance of the voltmeter, the smaller the voltage change. Using a voltmeter with a 10 000-$\Omega$ resistance changes the voltage across $R_2$ from 10 V to 9.9975 V, too small a change to detect. Modern electronic voltmeters, Figure 23–16, have even higher resistances, $10^7$ $\Omega$, and so produce even smaller changes.

**FIGURE 23–16. A modern digital multimeter can be used to measure a wide range of currents, voltages, and resistances in electrical circuits.**

An ammeter is put in series with the circuit to be measured.

A voltmeter is connected in parallel with the element to be measured.

## CONCEPT REVIEW

**2.1** Home fires were often caused by people who replaced fuses with pennies. Why would this cause a problem?

**2.2** Consider the circuit in Figure 23–17 made with identical bulbs.
   **a.** Compare the brightness of the three bulbs.
   **b.** What happens to the brightness of each bulb when bulb **1** is unscrewed from its socket? What happens to the three currents?
   **c.** Bulb **1** is screwed in again and bulb **3** is unscrewed. What happens to the brightness of each bulb? What happens to the three currents?

**2.3** Consider again the circuit in Figure 23–17.
   **a.** What happens to the brightness of each bulb if a wire is connected between points **B** and **C**?
   **b.** A fourth bulb is connected in parallel with bulb **3** alone. What happens to the brightness of each bulb?

**2.4** **Critical Thinking:** In the same circuit as 2.3, the wire at point **C** is broken and a small resistor is inserted in series with bulbs **2** and **3**. What happens to the brightness of the two bulbs? Explain.

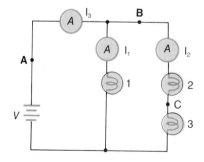

**FIGURE 23–17. Use with Concept Review 2.2, 2.3, and 2.4.**

## ROBOTS AND OHM'S LAW

In 1854, the year that Georg Simon Ohm died, Lord Kelvin discovered that the resistance of a wire changes when it is strained (stretched).

Engineers first used this phenomenon to analyse stresses in structural surfaces. For example, by monitoring the current through a fine metal wire mounted alongside a bridge, machines can indicate strain on the bridge based on the wire's varying resistance. Such a device is called a strain gauge.

Researchers seeking ways to imitate the complex capabilities of the human hand have used a version of a strain gauge to give robots a sense of touch. As recently as 1985, robotic hands, equipped with superhuman strength, had the dexterity to gently crack an egg into a mixing bowl. However, a robot still needs some kind of tactile sensor in order to "see" with its hands.

One of the most promising sensor designs consists of an electronic chip printed with a fine metallic network and covered by a thin sheet of conducting rubber. Pressure on the rubber changes the resistance of the chip, transmitting a "picture" of the strain on the robotic skin.

· What might be some other valuable applications for strain gauge "sensors"?

# CHAPTER
## 23 REVIEW

## SUMMARY

### 23.1 Simple Circuits

· The current is the same everywhere in a simple series circuit.
· The equivalent resistance of a series circuit is the sum of the resistances of its parts.
· The sum of the voltage drops across resistors in series is equal to the potential difference applied across the combination.
· A voltage divider is a series circuit used to produce a voltage source from a higher voltage battery.
· The voltage drops across all branches of a parallel circuit are the same.
· In a parallel circuit, the total current is equal to the sum of the currents in the branches.
· The reciprocal of the equivalent resistance of parallel resistors is equal to the sum of the reciprocals of the individual resistances.

· If any branch of a parallel circuit is opened, there is no current in that branch. The current in the other branches is unchanged.

### 23.2 Circuit Applications

· A fuse or circuit breaker, placed in series with appliances, creates an open circuit when dangerously high currents flow.
· A complex circuit is often a combination of series and parallel branches. Any parallel branch is first reduced to a single equivalent resistance. Then any resistors in series are replaced by a single resistance.
· An ammeter is used to measure the current in a branch or part of a circuit. An ammeter always has a low resistance and is connected in series.
· A voltmeter measures the potential difference (voltage) across any part or combination of parts of a circuit. A voltmeter always has a high resistance and is connected in parallel with the part of the circuit being measured.

# KEY TERMS

series circuit
equivalent resistance
voltage divider
parallel circuit
fuse
ground-fault interrupter

combination series-
   parallel circuits
short circuit
ammeter
voltmeter

# REVIEWING CONCEPTS

1. Why is it frustrating when one bulb burns out on a string of Christmas tree lights connected in series?
2. Why does the equivalent resistance decrease as more resistors are added to a parallel circuit?
3. Several resistors with different values are connected in parallel. The equivalent resistance will be less than which resistor?
4. Compare the amount of current entering a junction in a parallel circuit with that leaving the junction. Note: a junction is a point where three or more conductors are joined.
5. Why is household wiring done in parallel instead of in series?
6. Why is there a difference in total resistance between three 60-$\Omega$ resistors connected in series and three 60-$\Omega$ resistors connected in parallel?
7. Explain the function of a fuse in an electric circuit.
8. What is a short circuit? Why is a short circuit dangerous?
9. Why does an ammeter have a very low resistance?
10. Why does a voltmeter have a very high resistance?

# APPLYING CONCEPTS

1. What happens to the current in the other two lamps if one lamp in a three-lamp series circuit burns out?
2. In the voltage divider in Figure 23–3, the resistor $R_1$ is a variable resistor. What happens

to the voltage output, $V_2$ of the voltage divider if the resistance of the variable resistor is increased?

3. Circuit **A** contains three 60-$\Omega$ resistors in series. Circuit **B** contains three 60-$\Omega$ resistors in parallel. How does the current in the second 60-$\Omega$ resistor change if a switch cuts off the current to the first 60-$\Omega$ resistor in
   **a.** circuit **A**?   **b.** circuit **B**?
4. What happens to the current in the other two lamps if one lamp in a three-lamp parallel circuit burns out?
5. An engineer needs a 10-$\Omega$ resistor and a 15-$\Omega$ resistor. But there are only 30-$\Omega$ resistors in stock. Must new resistors be purchased? Explain.
6. If you have a 6-V battery and many 1.5-V bulbs, how could you connect them so they light but do not have more than 1.5-V across each bulb ?
7. Two lamps have different resistances, one larger than the other.
   **a.** If they are connected in parallel, which is brighter (dissipates more power)?
   **b.** When connected in series, which is brighter?
8. Two 100-W light bulbs are connected in series to a 12-V battery and another two 100-W light bulbs are connected in parallel to a separate 12-V battery. Which battery will run out of energy first? Why?
9. For each part of this question, write the form of circuit that applies: series or parallel.
   **a.** The current is the same throughout.
   **b.** The total resistance is equal to the sum of the individual resistances.
   **c.** The voltage drop is the same across each resistor.
   **d.** The voltage drop is proportional to the resistance.
   **e.** Adding a resistor decreases the total resistance.
   **f.** Adding a resistor increases the total resistance.
   **g.** If the current through one resistor goes to zero there is no current in the entire circuit.
   **h.** If the current through one resistor goes to zero, the current through all other resistors remains the same.
   **i.** This form is suitable for house wiring.
10. Why is it dangerous to replace a 15-A fuse in a circuit with one of 30 A?

# PROBLEMS

## 23.1 Simple Circuits

1. A 20.0-$\Omega$ lamp and a 5.0-$\Omega$ lamp are connected in series and placed across a potential difference of 50 V. What is
   a. the equivalent resistance of the circuit?
   b. the current in the circuit?
   c. the voltage drop across each lamp?
   d. the power dissipated in each lamp?

2. Three identical lamps are connected in series to a 6.0-V battery. What is the voltage drop across each lamp?

3. The load across a 12-V battery consists of a series combination of three resistors of 15 $\Omega$, 21 $\Omega$, and 24 $\Omega$.
   a. What is the total resistance of the load?
   b. What is the current in the circuit?

4. The load across a battery consists of two resistors, with values of 15 $\Omega$ and 45 $\Omega$ connected in series.
   a. What is the total resistance of the load?
   b. What is the voltage of the battery if the current in the circuit is 0.10 A?

5. A lamp having a resistance of 10 $\Omega$ is connected across a 15-V battery.
   a. What is the current through the lamp?
   b. What resistance must be connected in series with the lamp to reduce the current to 0.50 A?

6. A string of eighteen identical Christmas tree lights are connected in series to a 120-V source. The string dissipates 64.0 W.
   a. What is the equivalent resistance of the light string?
   b. What is the resistance of a single light?
   c. What power is dissipated by each lamp?

7. One of the bulbs in the previous problem burns out. The lamp has a wire that shorts out the lamp filament when it burns out. This drops the resistance of the lamp to zero.
   a. What is the resistance of the light string now?
   b. Find the power dissipated by the string.
   c. Did the power go up or down when a bulb burned out?

8. A 75.0-W bulb is connected to a 120-V source.
   a. What is the current through the bulb?
   b. What is the resistance of the bulb?

   c. A lamp dimmer puts a resistance in series with the bulb. What resistance would be needed to reduce the current to 0.300 A?

9. In the previous problem, you found the resistance of a lamp and a dimmer resistor.
   a. Assuming the resistances are constant, find the voltage drops across the lamp and the resistor.
   b. Find the power dissipated by the lamp.
   c. Find the power dissipated by the dimmer resistor.

10. Amy needs 5.0 V for some integrated circuit experiments. She uses a 6.0-V battery and two resistors to make a voltage divider. One resistor is 330 $\Omega$. She decides to make the other resistor smaller. What value should it have?

11. Pete is designing a voltage divider using a 12.0-V battery and a 100.0-$\Omega$ resistor as $R_2$. What resistor should be used as $R_1$ if the output voltage across $R_2$ is to be 4.00 V?

▶ 12. A typical television dissipates 275 W when plugged into a 120-V outlet.
   a. Find the resistance of the television.
   b. The 2.5-$\Omega$ television and wires connecting the outlet to the fuse form a series circuit that works like a voltage divider. Find the voltage drop across the television.
   c. A 12-$\Omega$ hair dryer is now plugged into the same outlet. Find the equivalent resistance of the two appliances.
   d. Find the voltage drop across the television and hair dryer combination. The lower voltage explains why the television picture sometimes shrinks when another appliance is turned on.

13. Three identical lamps are connected in parallel to each other and then connected to a 6.0-V battery. What is the voltage drop across each lamp?

14. A 16.0-$\Omega$ and a 20.0-$\Omega$ resistor are connected in parallel. A difference in potential of 40.0 V is applied to the combination.
   a. Compute the equivalent resistance of the parallel circuit.
   b. What is the current in the circuit?
   c. How large is the current through the 16.0-$\Omega$ resistor?

15. During a laboratory exercise, you are supplied with the following appartus: a battery of potential difference V, two heating elements of low resistance that can be placed in water, an

ammeter of negligible resistance, a voltmeter of extremely high resistance, wires of negligible resistance, a beaker that is well-insulated and has negligible heat capacity, 100.0 g of water at 25° C.

a. By means of a diagram using standard symbols, show how these components should be connected to heat the water as rapidly as possible.

b. If the voltmeter reading holds steady at 50.0 V and the ammeter reading holds steady at 5.0 A, estimate the time in seconds required to completely vaporize the water in the beaker. Use 4200 J/kg·C° as the specific heat of water and $2.3 \times 10^6$ J/kg as the heat of vaporization of water.

## 23.2 Applications of Circuits

16. A circuit contains six 240-$\Omega$ lamps, 60-W bulbs, and a 10.0-$\Omega$ heater connected in parallel. The voltage across the circuit is 120 V. What is the current in the circuit
   a. when four lamps are turned on?
   b. when all lamps are on?
   c. if six lamps and the heater are operating?
   d. If the circuit has a fuse rated at 12 A, will it melt if everything is on?

17. Determine the reading of each ammeter and each voltmeter in Figure 23–18.

FIGURE 23–18. Use with Problem 17 and 18.

18. Determine the power used by each resistance shown in Figure 23–18.

19. A typical home circuit is diagrammed in Figure 23–19. Note that the lead lines to the kitchen lamp each have very low resistances of 0.25 $\Omega$. The lamp has a resistance of 240.0 $\Omega$. Although the circuit is a parallel circuit, the lead lines are in series with each of the components of the circuit.

   a. Compute the equivalent resistance of the circuit consisting of just the light and the lead lines to and from the light.

b. Find the current to the bulb.
c. Find the power rating of the bulb.
d. Since the current in the bulb is 0.50 A, the current in the lead lines must also be 0.50 A. Calculate the voltage drop due to the two leads.

FIGURE 23–19. Use with Problem 19 and 20.

20. A power saw is operated by an electric motor. When electric motors are first turned on, they have a very low resistance. Suppose that a kitchen light discussed in the previous problem is on and a power saw is turned on. The saw, light, and the lead lines have an initial total resistance of 6.0 $\Omega$.
   a. Compute the equivalent resistance of the light–saw parallel circuit.
   b. What current flows to the light?
   c. What is the total voltage drop across the two leads to the light?
   d. What voltage remains to operate the light? Will this cause the light to dim temporarily?

## THINKING PHYSIC-LY

Figure 23–20 is a diagram of a "flashing" Christmas tree light bulb. These bulbs can be used in light sets wired either in series or in parallel.
   a. Describe how the flashing bulb operates.
   b. How would a manufacturer use this type of bulb to produce a flashing series set? Describe the flashing pattern.
   c. How would a flashing parallel string be produced? What would the pattern be?

FIGURE 23–20. Use with Thinking Physic-ly.

# CHAPTER
# 24 Magnetic Fields

## Earth's Halo

The Dynamics Explorer-1 satellite took this photo of Earth and a computer added the outline of the continents. But what is the band that circles the north polar region like a halo? It is the aurora borealis, the northern lights. The satellite detected ultraviolet radiation from oxygen atoms high in Earth's atmosphere and displayed it in yellow. How do charged particles from the sun and Earth's magnetic field combine to produce the flickering lights that thrill people who live in northern latitudes?

The displays of the aurora borealis have fascinated and mystified people for centuries. Story tellers and poets have found inspiration in the luminous streaks and patches of colour in the night sky. According to ancient myths, the lights were caused by ghostly spirits. More recent observers believed the lights could be reflections from arctic ice or even from large schools of fish in arctic waters. Scientific studies tell us that the lights result from interaction between the solar wind and Earth's magnetic field.

Magnets are not new. The properties of naturally occurring magnetic rocks (lodestones) have been known for over 2000 years. The Chinese were using magnets as compasses when the first European explorers reached China in the 1500s. In 1600, the English physician William Gilbert wrote the first European book describing their properties. Today magnets are used in all the generators that supply us with electricity. In addition, motors, television sets, and tape recorders depend on the magnetic effects of electric currents. Thus, the study of magnetism is an important part of our investigation of electricity.

## ✓ Concept Check

The following terms or concepts from earlier chapters are important for a good understanding of this chapter. If you are not familiar with them, you should review them before studying this chapter.
· force, Chapter 5
· circular motion, Chapter 7
· charged particles, charging by induction, Chapter 20
· electric fields, Chapter 21
· electric current, Chapter 22

- summarize the properties of magnets.
- describe magnetic fields around permanent magnets and between like and unlike poles.
- describe the field around a current-carrying wire; explain the use of the right-hand rule in finding the direction of the field lines.
- explain the nature of the field due to both one and many wire loops; apply the right-hand rule to find direction.
- describe the origin of magnetism in materials.

A magnet has polarity. The two ends are called the north and south poles.

Two like poles repel, two unlike poles attract.

Some metals can be polarized by being brought near a magnet. They become temporary magnets.

# 24.1 MAGNETS: PERMANENT AND TEMPORARY

Have you ever played with magnets? Certainly you have picked up tacks or paper clips with a magnet. Perhaps you made an electromagnet by winding wire around a nail and connecting it to a dry cell. But, did you ever play with two magnets? Your study of this chapter will be greatly enhanced if you have two bar magnets or two small ceramic magnets, Figure 24–1, like those that are often sold in hardware stores.

## General Properties of Magnets

Suspend a magnet from a thread, Figure 24–2a. If it is a bar magnet, you may have to tie a yoke to keep it horizontal. What do you observe? When it comes to rest, the magnet will line up in a north-south direction. If you rotate it away from that direction, it will return. Put a mark on the magnet end that points north. Repeat this procedure for other magnets. From this simple experiment, you can conclude that a magnet has polarity. It has two ends, one of which is the north-seeking end, or north pole. The other is the south-seeking end or south pole. A compass is nothing more than a small magnet pivoted so it can turn.

While one magnet is suspended, bring a second magnet nearby, Figure 24–2b. Note that the two ends that pointed north, the north poles, repel each other, as do the two south poles. A north pole, however, will attract the south pole of the other magnet. That is, like poles repel, unlike poles attract.

If you consider these results, it may occur to you that Earth itself must be a giant magnet. The south pole of the Earth-magnet must be near Earth's geographic north pole.

As you probably discovered as a child, a magnet will attract nails, tacks, paper clips, and other metal objects, not only other magnets. Unlike the case of two magnets, however, either end of the magnet will attract either end of the metal. What is happening? You can get a hint by touching the magnet to a nail and then touching the nail to smaller

FIGURE 24–1. Inexpensive ceramic magnets are available in most hardware stores.

a

b

FIGURE 24–2. A magnet suspended by a thread will align itself with Earth's magnetic field (a). When the N-pole of another magnet is brought close to the N-pole of the suspended magnet, the suspended N-pole moves away.

metal pieces. The nail has become a magnet itself, Figure 24–3. The nail has become polarized, and the direction of polarization of the nail depends on the polarization of the magnet. The nail is only temporarily magnetized; if you pull away the magnet, the nail's magnetism disappears. The polarization induced in the nail is similar to the polarization induced in a conductor by a nearby charged object.

You can separate a polarized neutral conductor into a positively-charged conductor and a negatively-charged conductor. Can you do the same with a magnet? It seems not. As far as it is known, poles always come in pairs. Scientists have tried "breaking" magnets, even on the microscopic level, into separated "monopoles," but no one has succeeded.

The magnetism of the permanent magnets you used was produced in the same way you created the magnetism of the nail. But, because of the microscopic structure of the magnet material, the induced magnetism became permanent. Many permanent magnets are made of ALNICO, an alloy of ALuminum, NIckel, and CObalt. A variety of rare-earth elements, such as neodymium, produce permanent magnets that are extremely strong for their size.

FIGURE 24–3. The nail has become a temporary magnet, attracting the tacks. If the bar magnet is removed, the nail will lose its magnetism.

a

b

FIGURE 24–4. Iron filings suspended in glycerol give a 3-D representation of a magnetic field (a). Iron filings on a glass plate over a magnet show a 2-D model.

## Charge and Field Conventions

- *Positive charges are red.*
- *Negative charges are blue.*
- *Electric field lines are red.*
- ▶ **Magnetic field lines are blue.**
- *Ammeters are blue.*
- *Voltmeters are red.*

# Magnetic Fields Around Permanent Magnets

The forces between magnets, both attraction and repulsion, occur not only when the magnets touch each other, but when they are at a distance. In the same way that electric and gravitational forces can be explained by electric and gravitational fields, magnetic forces can be explained by the existence of a **magnetic field** around a magnet.

The presence of a magnetic field around a magnet can be shown with iron filings. Each long, thin iron filing becomes a small magnet by induction. Just like a tiny compass needle, the filing rotates until it is tangent to the magnetic field at that point. Figure 24–4a shows filings in a glycerol solution surrounding a bar magnet. The three-dimensional shape of the field is visible. In Figure 24–4b, filings show a two-dimensional plot of the field. These lines of filings help you to visualize magnetic field lines.

Note that the magnetic field lines, like the electric field lines, are imaginary. They help, not only in visualizing the field, but also in providing a measure of its strength. The number of magnetic field lines passing through a surface is called the **magnetic flux**. The flux per unit area is proportional to the strength of the magnetic field. As you can see in Figure 24–4, the flux lines are most concentrated at the poles, where the flux per unit area, that is, the magnetic field, is the greatest.

The direction of the magnetic field lines is defined as the direction to which the N-pole of a compass points when it is placed in the magnetic field. Outside the magnet, the field lines come out of the magnet at its N-pole and enter the magnet at its S-pole, Figure 24–5. What happens inside the magnet? There are no isolated poles on which field lines can start or stop, so magnetic field lines always form closed loops.

What are the magnetic fields produced by pairs of bar magnets? You can visualize the fields by placing a sheet of paper over the poles of two magnets. Sprinkle the paper with iron filings. Figure 24–6a shows the field lines between two like poles. By contrast, two unlike poles (N and S) placed close together produce the pattern in Figure 24–6b. The filings show that the field lines between two unlike poles run directly from one magnet to the other.

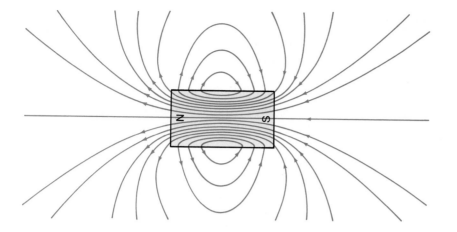

Magnetic fields exert forces on other magnets. The field produced by the N-pole of one magnet pushes the N-pole of a second magnet in the direction of the field line. The force exerted by the same field on the S-pole of the second magnet is in a direction opposite the field lines. The second magnet rotates, like the compass needle, to line up with the field. If the magnet field strength varies, it can also exert a net force, attractive or repulsive, on the second magnet.

When a sample made of iron, cobalt, or nickel is placed in the magnetic field of a permanent magnet, the field lines are concentrated in the sample. Lines leaving the N-pole of the magnet enter one end of the sample, pass through it, and leave the other end. Thus the end of the sample closest to the N-pole magnet becomes the sample's S-pole. The sample is attracted to the magnet.

A superconductor, on the other hand, repels a magnet. Why? Superconductors, act in the opposite way. Magnetic field lines are expelled from a superconductor so there is no magnetic flux inside. The same result would occur if field lines from the permanent magnet not only went through the superconductor, but induced a new field in the opposite direction. Each line from the magnet would be balanced by an induced line in the opposite direction. Thus, there would be no net flux inside the superconductor. But the superconductor would act like a magnet with its N-pole near the N-pole of the permanent magnet. The superconductor and the magnet would repel each other.

# F. Y. I.

Earth's magnetic field has flip-flopped, north and south, at least 171 times in the last 76 million years.

A temporary magnet concentrates magnetic field lines in it. It is attracted to a permanent magnet.

A superconductor repels magnetic field lines from it. It is repelled from a permanent magnet.

a

b

FIGURE 24–6. The field lines for like poles (a) and unlike poles (b).

## Practice Problems

1. A student holds a bar magnet in each hand. If both hands are brought close together, will the force be attractive or repulsive if the magnets are held so that
   **a.** the two N-poles are brought close together?
   **b.** an N-pole and an S-pole are brought together?
2. Figure 24–7 shows five disk magnets floating above each other. The N-pole of the top-most disk faces up. Which poles are on the top side of the other magnets?
3. In the Chapter 1 opening photo, page 2, assume the N-pole is the bottom face of the floating magnet. Which is the direction of the induced field in the superconducting disk?
▶ 4. Figure 24–3 shows a magnet attracting a nail to it which, in turn, has attracted many small tacks to it. If the N-pole of the permanent magnet is the top face, which end of the nail is the N-pole?

**FIGURE 24–7. Use with Practice Problem 2.**

## Electromagnetism

Make a pair of Scotch-tape electrometers, Chapter 21, and bring the magnets near them. You will see no effect. There is no force exerted on the charges on the tapes by the magnets.

In 1820, the Danish physicist Hans Christian Oersted (1777–1851) was experimenting with electric currents in wires. Oersted laid one of his wires across the tip of a small compass, Figure 24–8. He had expected the needle to point toward the wire or along the wire, and was amazed to see that, instead, it rotated until it pointed perpendicular to the wire. The forces on the poles were perpendicular to the direction of current in the wire. Oersted also found that when the charges were stationary no magnetic forces existed, in agreement with the results of the tape-electrometer experiment.

If a compass needle turns, it must be the result of a magnetic field. The magnetic field around a current-carrying wire can easily be shown by placing a wire vertically through a horizontal piece of cardboard on which iron filings are sprinkled. When a current is flowing, tap the cardboard. The filings form a pattern of concentric circles around the wire, Figure 24–9. The centre of each circle is the wire itself.

**FIGURE 24–8. Using apparatus similiar to that shown on the right, Oersted showed a connection between electricity and magnetism.**

FIGURE 24–9. The magnetic field produced by current in a straight wire conductor reverses if the current in the wire is reversed.

The circular lines indicate that magnetic field lines form closed loops in the same way that field lines about permanent magnets form closed loops. The strength of the magnetic field around a long, straight wire is proportional to the current flowing in the wire. The strength also varies inversely with the distance from the wire.

A compass shows the direction of the field lines. If you reverse the direction of current flow, the compass needle also reverses its direction. You can find the direction of the field using the **first right-hand rule**. Grasp the wire with your right hand, Figure 24–10. Keep your thumb pointed in the direction of the conventional (positive) current flow. The fingers of your hand circle the wire and point in the direction of the magnetic field.

## Magnetic Field Near a Coil

When an electric current flows through a single circular loop of wire, a magnetic field appears all around the loop. By applying the right-hand rule as in Figure 24–11 to any part of the wire loop, it can be shown that the direction of the field inside the loop is always the same. In the case shown in the diagram, the field is always up, out of the page. Outside the loop, it is always down, into the page.

Suppose wire is looped several times to form a coil. When a current flows through the coil, the field around all loops will be in the same direction. The field from each loop adds to the fields of the other loops.

FIGURE 24–10. The right-hand rule for a current-carrying straight wire shows the direction of the magnetic field.

FIGURE 24–11. The magnetic field about a circular loop of current-carrying wire is shown.

A current-carrying coil of wire is an electromagnet.

A right-hand rule shows the direction of the field produced by an electromagnet.

The field inside the coil is up, out of the page. The field outside the coil is in the opposite direction, into the page.

When an electric current flows through a coil of wire, the coil has a field like that of a permanent magnet. When this current-carrying coil is brought close to a suspended bar magnet, one end of the coil repels the north pole of the magnet. Thus, the current-carrying coil has a north and a south pole and is itself a magnet. This type of magnet is called an **electromagnet**.

The direction of the field produced by an electromagnet can be found by using a **second right-hand rule**. Grasp the coil with the right hand. Curl your fingers around the loops in the direction of the conventional (positive) current flow, Figure 24–13. Your thumb points toward the N-pole of the electromagnet.

The strength of an electromagnet can be increased by placing an iron rod or core inside the coil. The field inside the coil magnetizes the core by induction. The magnetic strength of the core adds to that of the coil to produce a much stronger magnet.

The strength of the magnetic field around a current-carrying wire is proportional to the current in the wire. The strength of the field of an electromagnet is also proportional to the current flowing through the coil. The magnetic field produced by each loop of a coil is the same as that produced by any other loop. These fields are in the same direction. Thus, increasing the number of loops in an electromagnet increases the strength of the magnetic field. The strength of the field of an electromagnet is proportional to the current and to the number of loops, and depends on the nature of the core.

FIGURE 24–13. The second right-hand rule can be used to determine the polarity of an electromagnet.

# Practice Problems

5. A long, straight, current-carrying wire runs from north to south.
    a. A compass needle is placed above the wire points with its N-pole toward the east. In what direction is the current flowing?
    b. If a compass is put underneath the wire, in which direction will the needle point?
6. Suppose you measure the strength of the magnetic field 1 cm from a current-carrying wire. Compare this value with
    a. the strength of the field 2 cm from the wire.
    b. the strength of the field 3 cm from the wire.
7. The loop in Figure 24–11a has current running in a clockwise direction (from left to right above the cardboard). If a compass is placed on the cardboard beneath the loop, in which direction will the N-pole point?
▶ 8. A student makes a magnet by winding wire around a large nail as in Figure 24–14. The magnet is connected to the battery as shown. Which end of the nail, pointed end or head, will be the N-pole?

**FIGURE 24–14. Use with Practice Problem 8.**

## A Microscopic Picture of Magnetic Materials

If you put a sample containing iron, nickel, or cobalt in a magnetic field, the sample will become magnetic. That is, north and south poles will be created. The polarity created depends on the direction of the external field. When you take away the external field, the sample will lose its magnetism.

Iron, nickel, and cobalt, three ferromagnetic elements, behave in many ways like an electromagnet. Why is this so? In the early 19th century, a theory of magnetism in iron was proposed by André Marie Ampère to explain this behaviour. Ampère knew that the magnetic effects of an electromagnet are the result of electric current flowing through its loops. He reasoned that the effects of a bar magnet must result from tiny "loops" of current within the bar.

Although the details of Ampère's reasoning were wrong, his basic idea was correct. Each electron in an atom acts like a tiny electromagnet. The magnetic fields of the electrons in a group of neighboring atoms can add together. Such a group is called a **domain**. Although domains may contain $10^{20}$ individual atoms, they are still very small. Thus, even a small sample of iron contains a huge number of domains.

When a piece of iron is not in a magnetic field, the domains point in random directions. Their magnetic fields cancel one another. If, however, the iron is placed in a magnetic field, the domains tend to align with the external field, as in Figure 24–15. In the case of a temporary magnet, after the external field is removed, the domains return to their random arrangement. In permanent magnets, the iron has been alloyed with other substances that keep the domains aligned after the external magnetic field is removed.

Sound or video tape recorders create electric signals representing the sounds or pictures being recorded. The electric signals produce currents in an electromagnet called a recording head. Magnetic recording tape passes directly over the recording head. The tape has many very tiny

Magnetism in a permanent magnet is the result of magnetic fields of electrons.

**FIGURE 24–15. A piece of iron becomes a magnet only when its domains align.**

**FIGURE 24–16. A scanning tunnelling micrograph shows a pattern of magnetic fields on a recording tape.**

10 μm

Tape recorders align the magnetic fields of magnetic material on the tape.

. . . . . . . . . . . . . . . . . .

# GEOLOGY CONNECTION

The motion of electrons in superconductors produces magnetic fields that repel other magnets.

bits of magnetic material bonded to thin plastic. When the tape passes over the recording head, the domains of the bits are aligned by the magnetic fields of the head. The direction of the alignment depends on the direction of the current in the head. The directions of the magnetic fields of the tiny bits become a magnetic record of the sounds or pictures being recorded. The material on the tape is chosen so that the domains keep their alignment permanently. In Chapter 25, the method of playing back the recordings will be described. "Floppy disks" are magnetically-coated disks that record computer data in the same way. Figure 24–16 shows a pattern of magnetic fields on such a disk.

Rocks that contain iron have made a "tape recording" of the direction of Earth's magnetic field. Rocks on the seafloor were produced when molten rock poured out of cracks in the bottom of the oceans. As they cooled, they were magnetized in the direction of Earth's field at that time. The seafloor spreads, so rocks farther from the crack are older than those near the crack. When scientists examined these rocks, they were surprised to find that the direction of the magnetization varied. They concluded that the north and south magnetic poles of Earth have exchanged places many times in Earth's history. The origin of Earth's magnetic field is not well understood. How this field might reverse direction periodically is even more of a mystery.

. . . . . . . . . . . . . . . . . . .

# CONCEPT REVIEW

**1.1** Are magnetic field lines real? Is the magnetic field real or just a convenience?

**1.2** A wire is passed through a card on which iron filings are sprinkled. The filings show the magnetic field around the wire. A second wire is close to the first wire and parallel to it. An identical current flows through the second wire. If the two currents are in the same direction, how would the magnetic field be affected? What if the two currents were in opposite directions?

**1.3** Explain the right-hand rule used to determine the direction of a magnetic field around a straight, current-carrying wire.

**1.4** Critical Thinking: Lei has a toy containing two parallel metal rods.
  **a.** The top rod floats above the lower one. If the rod's direction is reversed, however, it falls down on to the lower rod. Explain what the rods could be.
  **b.** Lei once lost the top rod and replaced it with another bar. In this case, the top rod fell down no matter what the orientation. What type of rod must Lei have used?

# PHYSICS LAB : Electric Motor

## Purpose

To construct an electric motor and to modify it for greater speed.

## Materials

- 1.5 V D-cell
- small disk magnet
- 1 m length of #26 or #28 magnet wire
- 2 paper clips
- cellophane tape
- sandpaper

## Procedure

1. Wrap the wire around the disk magnet leaving 2 cm of straight wire at each end. (See sketch.)
2. Remove the wire from the magnet and use thin strips of tape to keep it in a loop. (See sketch.)
3. Tape the disk magnet to the dry cell as shown.
4. Bend the paper clips as shown and tape to the ends of the battery.
5. Place the straight ends of the wire on the paper clips. Adjust the straight ends so that the loop will turn without wobbling.
6. Use sandpaper to remove the coating on the top side only of the straight ends of the wire.
7. Place the loop back on the paper clips and give the coil a small spin. The motor should work.
8. Make fine adjustments on the loop, paper clips, and so on, to reduce friction until the motor works easily and spins quickly on its own.

## Observations and Data

1. Will the loop turn in both directions?
2. Predict what will happen if the coil is reversed. Try reversing the straight ends of the loop on the paper clips. Describe the results.

## Analysis

1. Why does the loop rotate? (**Hint:** Start by describing the electrical path from the battery.)
2. Why might your motor work better in one direction than the other?

## Applications

1. Look closely at the insides of a conventional electric motor. Identify the major components. Explain why it is so heavy for its size.

remove coating of wire from ends of loop

bent paper clip

loop of wire

D-cell battery

Objectives

· define magnetic induction; explain the direction of the force on a current-carrying wire in a magnetic field.
· list the factors that determine the magnitude of the force on a wire; solve problems involving a wire in a magnetic field.
· explain the design, operation, and uses of a galvanometer.
· explain the design and operation of an electric motor.
· list the factors that determine the magnitude of the force on a moving charge in a magnetic field; solve problems involving this force.

A force is exerted on a current-carrying wire in a magnetic field.

The right-hand rule gives the direction of the force on a wire.

FIGURE 24-17. A representation of forces on currents in magnetic fields.

## 24.2 FORCES CAUSED BY MAGNETIC FIELDS

The test with Scotch-tape electrometers showed that a magnetic field exerts no force on an electric charge. Ampère noted that a moving charge, an electric current, produces a magnetic field like that of a permanent magnet. Since a magnetic field exerts forces on permanent magnets, Ampère suggested that there should be a force on a current-carrying wire placed in a magnetic field.

### Forces on Currents in Magnetic Fields

The force on a wire in a magnetic field can be demonstrated using the arrangement shown in Figure 24–17. A battery produces the current that flows from left to right. The magnets have either the N-pole or S-pole facing out, and thus the field is either toward the camera or away from it. As you can see, the force on the wire either pushes it down or pulls it up. As discovered by Michael Faraday (1791–1867), the force on the wire is at right angles to the direction of the magnetic field. The force is also at right angles to the direction of the current.

The direction of the force on a current-carrying wire in a magnetic field can be found by using a **third right-hand rule**, Figure 24–18. The magnetic field is indicated by the symbol B. Its direction is given by an arrow, but when a field is into or out of the page, its direction is indicated by crosses or dots, Figure 24–19. The crosses suggest the feathers at the end of an archery arrow, while the dot suggests the point. To use the right-hand rule, point the fingers of your right hand in the direction of the magnetic field. Point your thumb in the direction of the conventional (positive) current flow in the wire. The palm of your hand then faces in the direction of the force acting on the wire.

A week after the news of Oersted's discovery reached France, Ampère demonstrated the forces that current-carrying wires exert on each other. Figure 24–20a shows that the direction of the magnetic field around each of the current-carrying wires as given by the first right-hand rule. By applying the third right-hand rule to either wire you can show that the wires are forced together, or attract each other. In Figure 24–20b, we see the opposite situation. When currents are in opposite directions, the forces push the wires apart.

### Measuring the Force on a Wire Due to a Magnetic Field

Imagine a current-carrying wire passing through a magnetic field at right angles to the wire. Experiments show that the magnitude of the force on the wire is proportional to three factors: the strength, $B$, of the field; the current, $I$, in the wire; and the length, $L$, of the wire that lies in the magnetic field.

The magnitude of the force is given by the expression

$$F = BIL.$$

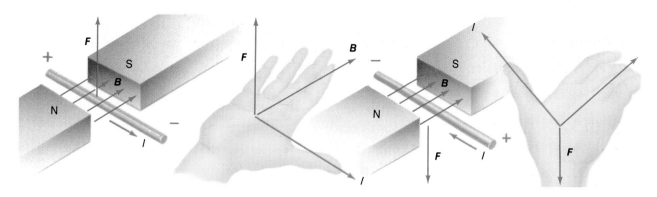

FIGURE 24–18. The third right-hand rule is used to determine the direction of force when the current and magnetic field are known.

We know how to measure force, current, and length, but not $B$. By rewriting the equation above, the strength of the field, $B$, can be calculated using the equation

$$B = \frac{F}{IL}.$$

The strength of a magnetic field is called **magnetic induction**, measured in teslas, represented by the symbol T. One tesla is equivalent to one newton per ampere-meter, N/A · m. Thus, the strength of a magnetic field is defined in terms of the force on a section of straight wire one meter long carrying one ampere of current.

**Table 24-1**

| Typical Magnetic Field | |
| --- | --- |
| Source and location | Strength (T) |
| surface of neutron star (predicted) | $10^8$ |
| strong laboratory electromagnet | 10 |
| small bar magnet | 0.01 |
| Earth's magnetic field | $5 \times 10^{-5}$ |

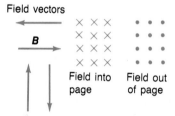

FIGURE 24–19. Directions of magnetic fields are indicated by directional arrows (a) when the field is in the same plane as the page, by crosses (b) when the field is into the page, and by dots (c) when the field is out of the page toward you.

FIGURE 24–20. Two current-bearing conductors (a) are attracted when the currents are in the same direction, and (b) are repelled when the currents are in opposite directions.

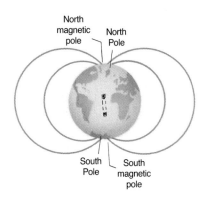

FIGURE 24–21. Earth's magnetic field lines run from the south magnetic pole to the north magnetic pole.

A magnetic field of 1 T (N/A · m) field strength is a very strong field, found only in powerful electromagnets. The magnetic fields of most magnets found in the laboratory are closer to 0.01 T. Earth's magnetic field has a strength of approximately $5 \times 10^{-5}$ T. The direction of Earth's field is toward the north magnetic pole. The field does not point along the surface of Earth, but, in the northern hemisphere, it points down into Earth, Figure 24–21.

## Example Problem

### Calculating the Strength of the Magnetic Field

A wire 0.10 m long carries a current of 5.0 A. The wire is at right angles to a uniform magnetic field. The force on the wire is 0.20 N. What is the magnitude of the magnetic field, $B$?

**Given:** $F = 0.20$ N
$I = 5.0$ A
$L = 0.10$ m

**Unknown:** magnetic field strength, $B$
**Basic equation:** $B = F/IL$

**Solution:**

$$B = \frac{F}{IL} = \frac{0.20 \text{ N}}{(5.0 \text{ A})(0.10 \text{ m})} = 0.40 \frac{\text{N}}{\text{A} \cdot \text{m}} = 0.40 \text{ T}$$

## Example Problem

### Force on a Current-Carrying Wire in a Magnetic Field

A wire 115 m long is at right angles to a uniform magnetic field. The field has a magnetic field strength of $5.0 \times 10^{-5}$ T. The current through the wire is 400 A. Find the magnitude of the force.

**Given:** $L = 115$ m
$B = 5.0 \times 10^{-5}$ T
$I = 4.0 \times 10^2$ A

**Unknown:** $F$
**Basic equation:** $B = F/IL$

**Solution:** $F = BIL$
$= (5.0 \times 10^{-5} \text{ T})(4.0 \times 10^2 \text{ A})(115 \text{ m})$
$= (5.0 \times 10^{-5} \text{ N/A} \cdot \text{m})(4.0 \times 10^2 \text{ A})(115 \text{ m})$
$= 2.3$ N

## Practice Problems

9. A straight wire 0.10 m long carrying a current of 2.0 A is at right angles to a magnetic field. The force on the wire is 0.04 N. What is the strength of the magnetic field?
10. A wire 0.50 m long carrying a current of 8.0 A is at right angles to a 0.40 T magnetic field. How strong a force acts on the wire?

11. A wire 75 cm long carrying a current of 6.0 A is at right angles to a uniform magnetic field. The magnitude of the force acting on the wire is 0.60 N. What is the strength of the magnetic field?

▶ 12. A copper wire 40 cm long carries a current of 6.0 A and weighs 0.35 N. A certain magnetic field is strong enough to balance the force of gravity on the wire. What is the strength of the magnetic field?

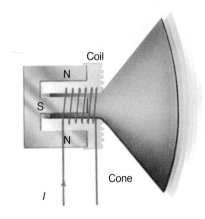

**FIGURE 24–22. A schematic diagram of a loudspeaker.**

One use of the force on a current-carrying wire in a magnetic field is a loudspeaker. A loudspeaker changes electrical energy to sound energy using a coil of fine wire mounted on a paper cone and placed in a magnetic field, Figure 24–22. The amplifier driving the loudspeaker sends a current through the coil. A force is exerted on the coil because it is in a magnetic field. The force pushes the coil either into or out of the magnetic field, depending on the direction of the current. The motion of the coil causes the cone to vibrate, creating sound waves in the air. An electric signal that represents a musical tone consists of a current that changes direction between 20 and 20 000 times each second, depending on the pitch of the tone.

## Galvanometers

The **galvanometer** is a device to measure very small currents. For this reason, it is used in many voltmeters and ammeters. A galvanometer consists of a small coil of wire placed in the strong magnetic field of a permanent magnet. Each turn of wire in the coil is a wire loop. The current passing through such a loop in a magnetic field goes in one side of the loop and out the other side. Applying the third right-hand rule to each side of the loop, we find that one side of the loop is forced down while the other side of the loop is forced up. As a result, the loop has a torque on it and rotates.

The magnitude of the forces acting on the coil is proportional to the magnitude of the current. Figure 24–23 shows how the forces exerted on a loop of wire in a magnetic field can be used to measure current.

Force on a wire in a galvanometer moves the needle, indicating the strength of the current.

**FIGURE 24–23. If a wire loop is placed in a magnetic field when current flows, the loop will rotate because of the torque exerted by the field.**

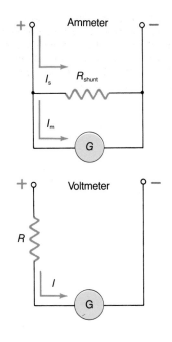

FIGURE 24–24. The components of an electric meter are shown.

The forces due to the current are opposed by a small spring. Thus, the amount of rotation is proportional to the current. The meter is calibrated by finding out how much the coil turns when a known current is sent through it. The galvanometer can then be used to measure unknown currents.

Many galvanometers produce a full-scale deflection with as little as 50 $\mu$A (50 $\times$ 10$^{-6}$ A) current. The resistance of the coil of wire in a sensitive galvanometer is about 1000 $\Omega$. Such a galvanometer can be converted into an ammeter by placing a resistor with resistance smaller than that of the galvanometer in parallel with the meter, Figure 24–24. Most of the current, $I_S$, flows through the resistor, called the shunt, because the current is inversely proportional to resistance, while only a few microamps, $I_M$, flow through the galvanometer.

A galvanometer can also be connected as a voltmeter. To make a voltmeter, a resistor, called the multiplier, is placed in series with the meter. The galvanometer measures the current through the multiplier. The current is given by $I = V/R$, where $V$ is the voltage across the voltmeter and $R$ is the effective resistance of the galvanometer and the multiplier resistor. Suppose you want a meter that reads full scale when 10 V are placed across it. The resistor is chosen so that at 10 V, the meter is deflected full scale by the current flowing through the meter and resistor.

## Electric Motors

The force on a current-carrying wire in a magnetic field causes an electric motor to rotate.

The simple loop of wire used in a galvanometer cannot rotate more than 180°. As shown in Figure 24–23, the forces push the right side of the loop up and the left side of the loop down. The loop turns until it reaches the vertical position. The loop will not continue to turn because the forces are still up and down, now parallel to the loop, and can cause no further rotation.

For the loop to rotate 360° in the field, the current running through the loop must reverse direction just as the loop reaches its vertical position. This reversal allows the loop to continue rotating, Figure 24–25. To reverse current direction, a split-ring commutator is used. Brushes, pieces of graphite that make a rubbing or brushing contact with the commutator, allow current to flow into the loop. The split ring is arranged so that each half of the commutator changes brushes just as the loop reaches the vertical position. Changing brushes reverses the current in the loop. As a result, the direction of the force on each side of the loop is reversed and the loop continues to rotate. This process is repeated each half-turn. Thus, the loop spins in the magnetic field.

In practice, electric motors have several rotating loops of wire. Together they make up the armature of the motor. The total force acting on the armature is proportional to $nBIL$, where $n$ is the total number of loops on the armature and $L$ is the length of wire in each loop that moves through the magnetic field. The magnetic field can be produced either by permanent magnets or by an electromagnet called a field coil. The force on the armature, and as a result the speed of the motor, is controlled by varying the current flowing through the motor.

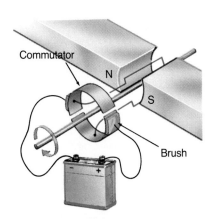

FIGURE 24–25. In an electric motor, split-ring commutators allow the wire loops in the motor to rotate 360°.

Tube base: pins connect to heater, cathode and all anodes except the final anode

Deflecting electromagnets

Final anode

Connection to final anode

Phosphor coating on inside of screen

Electron beam

Bright spot where beam strikes phosphor

Graphite final anode

Cathode

1st and 2nd anode

3rd anode

Steel reinforcing band

Armoured glass front

**FIGURE 24–26. A television uses a cathode-ray tube to form pictures for viewing. The magnets shown deflect the electron beam vertically. There is another pair (not shown) that deflect the beam horizontally.**

## The Force on a Single Charged Particle

The force exerted by a magnetic field on a current-carrying wire is a result of the forces on the individual charges that make up the current flow. The charged particles do not have to be confined to a wire, but can move across any region as long as the air has been removed to prevent collisions with air molecules.

The picture tube, or cathode-ray tube, in a television set uses electrons deflected by magnetic fields to form the pictures on the screen, Figure 24–26. In the tube, electric fields pull electrons off atoms in the negative electrode, or cathode. Other electric fields gather, accelerate, and focus the electrons into a narrow beam. Magnetic fields are used to deflect the beam back and forth and up and down across the screen of the tube. The screen is coated with a phosphor that glows when struck by the electrons, producing the picture.

The force produced by a magnetic field on a single electron depends on the velocity of the electron, the strength of the field, and the angle between directions of the velocity and the field. It can be found by starting with the force on a current-carrying wire in a magnetic field, $F = BIL$. Consider a single electron moving in a wire of length $L$. The electron is moving perpendicular to the magnetic field. The current, $I$, is equal to the charge per unit time entering the wire, $I = q/t$. In this case, $q$ is the charge of the electron and $t$ is the time it takes to move the length of the wire, $L$. The time required for a particle with velocity $v$ to travel a distance $L$ is found by using the equation of motion, $d = vt$, or here, $t = L/v$. As a result, the equation for the current, $I = q/t$, can be replaced by $I = qv/L$. Therefore, the force on a single electron moving perpendicular to a magnetic field of strength $B$ is

$$F = BIL = B\left(\frac{qv}{L}\right)L = Bqv.$$

The particle's charge is measured in coulombs, the velocity in m/s, and the strength of the magnetic field in teslas, T.

The direction of the force is perpendicular to both the velocity of the particle and the magnetic field. It is *opposite* that given by the third

Magnetic fields change the direction of electrons in a television picture tube.

right-hand rule with the thumb pointed along the velocity of the positive particle. The direction of the force is opposite because the electron has a negative charge and "conventional current" has a positive charge.

The path of a charged particle in a uniform magnetic field is circular because, since the force is always perpendicular to the particle's velocity, it is a centripetal force. The radius of the circle can be found by equating the magnetic force to the centripetal force, $Bqv = mv^2/r$. The circular motion allows charged particles to be trapped and held in magnetic fields. High energy nuclear particle accelerators, such as the one at Fermilab and the proposed SSC, use magnets to force the particles to travel in circular paths. Electrons trapped in the magnetic field of Earth, Figure 24–27, form the Van Allen radiation belts. Solar storms send tremendous numbers of high-energy charged particles toward Earth. They disturb Earth's magnetic field, dumping electrons out of the Van Allen belts. These electrons excite atoms of nitrogen and oxygen in Earth's atmosphere and cause them to emit the red, green, and blue called the northern lights. The "halo" circles the north magnetic pole.

Strong magnetic fields will be used in magnetic confinement fusion devices that are under development. The fields confine protons and other nuclei. The nuclei collide at high speed, producing large amounts of energy. The details are discussed in Chapter 31.

· · · · · · · · · · · · · · · · · · · · ·

### Earth's Halo ▶

**FIGURE 24–27. A representation of the Van Allen radiation belts around Earth.**

## Example Problem

### Force on a Charged Particle in a Magnetic Field

A beam of electrons travels at $3.0 \times 10^6$ m/s through a $4.0 \times 10^{-2}$-T uniform magnetic field. **a.** The beam is at right angles to the magnetic field. What is the magnitude of the force acting on each electron? **b.** Compare the force acting on a proton moving at the same speed and in the same direction to the force acting on the electron in part **a.**

**Given:** $v = 3.0 \times 10^6$ m/s          **Unknown:** $F$
$\quad\quad\quad B = 4.0 \times 10^{-2}$ T          **Basic equation:** $F = Bqv$
$\quad\quad\quad q = 1.6 \times 10^{-19}$ C

**Solution:**

**a.** $F = Bqv$
$\quad = (4.0 \times 10^{-2}$ T$)(1.6 \times 10^{-19}$ C$)(3.0 \times 10^6$ m/s$)$
$\quad = (4.0 \times 10^{-2}$ N/A · m$)(1.6 \times 10^{-19}$ C$)(3.0 \times 10^6$ m/s$)$
$\quad = 1.9 \times 10^{-14}$ N

**b.** The magnitude of the force is exactly the same on a proton as it is on an electron, since the proton and the electron have exactly the same charge magnitude. Because the proton's charge is of the opposite sign, however, it is deflected in the opposite direction.

## Practice Problems

**13.** An electron passes through a magnetic field at right angles to the field at a velocity of $4.0 \times 10^6$ m/s. The strength of the magnetic field is 0.50 T. What is the magnitude of the force acting on the electron?

14. A stream of doubly-ionized particles (missing two electrons and thus carrying a net charge of two elementary charges) moves at a velocity of $3.0 \times 10^4$ m/s perpendicular to a magnetic field of $9.0 \times 10^{-2}$ T. What is the magnitude of the force acting on each ion?

15. Triply-ionized particles in a beam carry a net positive charge of three elementary charge units. The beam enters a $4.0 \times 10^{-2}$-T magnetic field. The particles have a velocity of $9.0 \times 10^6$ m/s. What is the magnitude of the force acting on each particle?

▶ 16. Doubly-ionized helium atoms (alpha particles) are traveling at right angles to a magnetic field at a speed of $4.0 \times 10^{-2}$ m/s. The field strength is $5.0 \times 10^{-2}$ T. What force acts on each particle?

## CONCEPT REVIEW

**2.1** A horizontal, current-carrying wire runs north-south through Earth's magnetic field. If the current flows north, in which direction is the force on the wire?

**2.2** A beam of electrons in a cathode ray tube approaches the deflecting magnets. The N-pole is at the top of the tube, the S-pole on the bottom. If you are looking at the tube from the phosphor screen, in which direction are the electrons deflected?

**2.3** When the plane of the coil in a motor is perpendicular to the magnetic field, the forces do not exert a torque on the coil. Does this mean the coil doesn't rotate? Explain.

**2.4** **Critical Thinking:** How do you know that the forces on parallel current-carrying wires aren't due to electrostatics? **Hints:** 1. Consider what the charges would be like when the force is attractive. 2. Consider what the forces are if three wires carry currents in the same direction.

# Physics and technology

## MAGLEV TRAINS

Trains that travel by means of magnets are known as maglev. Maglev is short for magnetic levitation. Maglevs are trains that "fly".

Germany is probably closer to building a high-speed intercity maglev system than its competitor, Japan. The German system utilizes conventional electromagnets that are attracted upwards to a metal rail lifting the maglev cars about 1 cm above the guideways.

The Japanese system uses pairs of electromagnets made of superconducting wire. The Japanese maglevs utilize the repulsion between like magnetic poles. Superconducting wire for the electromagnets has no resistance to current when it is in liquid helium at near-absolute-zero temperatures. Thus, no electric energy is needed to levitate the train.

· What might be a disadvantage of using superconductive magnets over conventional magnets.

# 24 REVIEW

## SUMMARY

### 24.1 Magnets: Permanent and Temporary

· The like magnetic poles of dipoles repel; the unlike magnetic poles attract.
· Magnetic fields run out from the north pole of a magnet and enter its south pole.
· Magnetic field lines always form closed loops.
· A magnetic field exists around any wire that carries current.
· A coil of wire through which a current flows also has a magnetic field. The field about the coil is like the field about a permanent magnet.

### 24.2 Forces Caused by Magnetic Fields

· When a current-carrying wire is placed in a magnetic field, there is a force on the wire that is perpendicular to the field and also to the wire. Galvanometers are based on this principle.
· The strength of a magnetic field is measured in teslas (newton per ampere-metre).
· An electric motor consists of a coil of wire placed in a magnetic field. When current flows in the coil, the coil rotates due to the force on the wire in the magnetic field.
· The force a magnetic field exerts on a charged particle depends on the velocity and charge of the particle and the strength of the field and is in a direction perpendicular to both.

## KEY TERMS

magnetic field
magnetic flux
first right-hand rule
electromagnet
second right-hand rule

domain
third right-hand rule
magnetic induction
galvanometer

## REVIEWING CONCEPTS

1. State the rule for magnetic attraction and repulsion.
2. Describe how a temporary magnet differs from a permanent magnet.
3. Name the three most important common magnetic elements.
4. Draw a small bar magnet and show the magnetic field lines as they appear around the magnet. Use arrows to show the direction of the field lines.
5. Draw the magnetic field between two like magnetic poles and then between two unlike magnetic poles. Show the directions of the fields.
6. If you broke a magnet in two, would you have isolated north and south poles? Explain.
7. Describe how to use the right-hand rule to determine the direction of a magnetic field around a straight current-carrying wire.
8. If a current-carrying wire is bent into a loop, why is the magnetic field inside the loop stronger than the magnetic field outside?
9. Describe how to use the right-hand rule to determine the polarity of an electromagnet.
10. Each electron in a piece of iron is like a tiny magnet. The iron, however, is not a magnet. Explain.
11. Why will dropping or heating a magnet weaken it?
12. Describe how to use the right-hand rule to determine the direction of force on a current-carrying wire placed in a magnetic field.
13. A strong current is suddenly switched on in a wire. No force acts on the wire, however. Can you conclude that there is no magnetic field at the location of the wire? Explain.
14. Adding a shunt to a galvanometer makes the galvanometer what kind of meter?

## APPLYING CONCEPTS

1. A small bar magnet is hidden in a fixed position inside a tennis ball. Describe an experiment you could do to find the location of the N-pole and the S-pole of the magnet.
2. A piece of metal is attracted to one pole of a large magnet. Describe how you could tell whether the metal is a temporary magnet or a permanent magnet.

3. Is the magnetic force Earth exerts on a compass needle less than, equal to, or greater than the force the compass needle exerts on Earth? Explain.

4. Iron, nickel, and cobalt are electrical conductors. So are superconductors. Do they behave the same way in magnetic fields?

5. You are lost in the woods but have a compass with you. Unfortunately, the red paint marking the N-pole has worn off. You do have a flashlight with a battery and a length of wire. How could you identify the N-pole?

6. A magnet can attract a piece of iron that is not a permanent magnet. A charged rubber rod can attract an uncharged insulator. Describe the different microscopic processes that produce these similar phenomena.

7. A bare current-carrying wire runs across a lecture table. Describe at least two ways you could find the direction of the current.

8. In what direction with respect to a magnetic field would you run a wire so that the force on it due to the field is minimized or even made zero?

9. Two wires carry equal currents and run parallel to each other.
   a. If the two currents are in the opposite direction, where will the magnetic field from the two wires be larger than the field from either wire alone?
   b. Where will the magnetic field be exactly twice as large?
   c. If the two currents are in the same direction, where will the magnetic field be exactly zero?

10. How is the range of a voltmeter changed when the resistor is increased?

11. A magnetic field can exert a force on a charged particle. Can it change the particle's kinetic energy? Explain.

12. A beam of protons is moving from the back to the front of a room. It is deflected upward by a magnetic field. What is the direction of the field causing the deflection?

13. As shown by the spacing of the field lines in Figure 24–21, Earth's magnetic field in space is stronger near the poles than over the equator. At what location would the circular paths followed by the charged particles around the magnetic field lines have larger radii? Explain.

# PROBLEMS

## 24.1 Magnets: Permanent and Temporary

1. A wire 1.50 m long carrying a current of 10.0 A is at right angles to a uniform magnetic field. The force acting on the wire is 0.60 N. What is the induction of the magnetic field?

2. The repulsive force between two ceramic magnets was measured and found to depend on distance, as given in the table below.

| Separation, $d$ (mm) | Force, $\vec{F}$ (N) |
|---|---|
| 10 | 3.93 |
| 12 | 0.40 |
| 14 | 0.13 |
| 16 | 0.057 |
| 18 | 0.030 |
| 20 | 0.018 |
| 22 | 0.011 |
| 24 | 0.0076 |
| 26 | 0.0053 |
| 28 | 0.0038 |
| 30 | 0.0028 |

   a. Plot the force as a function of distance.
   b. Does this force follow an inverse square law?

3. A conventional current flows in a wire as shown in Figure 24–28. Copy the wire segment and sketch the magnetic field the current generates.

**FIGURE 24–28. Use with Problem 3.**

4. The current is coming straight out of the page in Figure 24–29. Copy the figure and sketch the magnetic field the current generates.

**FIGURE 24–29. Use with Problem 4.**

**5.** Figure 24–30 shows the end view of an electromagnet with the current as shown.
   **a.** What is the direction of the magnetic field inside the loop?
   **b.** What is the direction of the magnetic field outside the loop?

FIGURE 24–30. Use with Problem 5.

## 24.2 Forces Caused by Magnetic Fields

**6.** A current-carrying wire is placed between the poles of a magnet as shown in Figure 24–31. What is the direction of the force on the wire?

FIGURE 24–31. Use with Problem 6.

▶ **7.** A room contains a strong, uniform magnetic field. A loop of fine wire in the room has current flowing through it. You rotate the loop until there is no tendency for it to rotate as a result of the field. What is the direction of the magnetic field relative to the plane of the coil?

**8.** A wire 0.50 m long carrying a current of 8.0 A is at right angles to a uniform magnetic field. The force on the wire is 0.40 N. What is the strength of the magnetic field?

**9.** The current through a wire 0.80 m long is 5.0 A. The wire is perpendicular to a 0.60-T magnetic field. What is the magnitude of the force on the wire?

**10.** A wire 25 cm long is at right angles to a 0.30-T uniform magnetic field. The current through the wire is 6.0 A. What is the magnitude of the force on the wire?

**11.** A wire 35 cm long is parallel to a 0.53-T uniform magnetic field. The current through the wire is 4.5 A. What force acts on the wire?

**12.** A wire 625 m long is in a 0.40-T magnetic field. A 1.8-N force acts on the wire. What current is in the wire?

**13.** The force on an 0.80-m wire that is perpendicular to Earth's magnetic field is 0.12 N. What current flows through the wire?

**14.** The force acting on a wire at right angles to a 0.80-T magnetic field is 3.6 N. The current flowing through the wire is 7.5 A. How long is the wire?

**15.** A power line carries a 225-A current from east to west parallel to the surface of the Earth.
   **a.** What is the magnitude of the force acting on each metre of the wire due to Earth's magnetic field?
   **b.** What is the direction of the force?
   **c.** In your judgment, would this force be important in designing towers to hold these power lines?

▶ **16.** The magnetic field in a loudspeaker is 0.15 T. The wire consists of 250 turns wound on a 2.5-cm diameter cylindrical form. The resistance of the wire is 8.0 Ω. Find the force exerted on the wire when 15 V is placed across the wire.

▶ **17.** A wire carrying 15 A of current has a length of 25 cm between a magnetic field of 0.85 T. The force on a current carrying wire in a uniform magnetic field can be found by $F = BIL \sin \theta$. Find the force on the wire if it makes an angle with the magnetic field lines of
   **a.** 90°.   **b.** 45°.   **c.** 0°.

**18.** A galvanometer deflects full scale for a 50.0-µA current.
   **a.** What must be the total resistance of the series resistor and the galvanometer to make a voltmeter with 10.0-V full-scale deflection?
   **b.** If the galvanometer has a resistance of 1.0 kΩ, what should be the resistance of the series (multiplier) resistor?

**19.** The galvanometer in the previous problem is used to make an ammeter that deflects full scale for 10 mA.
   **a.** What is the potential difference across the galvanometer (1.0 kΩ resistance) when 50 µA flows through it?
   **b.** What is the equivalent resistance of parallel resistors that have the potential difference calculated in part **a** for a circuit with a total current of 10 mA?

**c.** What resistor should be placed in parallel with the galvanometer to make the resistance calculated in part **b?**

**20.** A beam of electrons moves at right angles to a $6.0 \times 10^{-2}$-T magnetic field. The electrons have a velocity of $2.5 \times 10^6$ m/s. What is the magnitude of the force on each electron?

**21.** A beta particle (high-speed electron) is traveling at right angles to a 0.60-T magnetic field. It has a speed of $2.5 \times 10^7$ m/s. What size force acts on the particle?

**22.** The mass of an electron is $9.11 \times 10^{-31}$ kg. What is the acceleration of the beta particle described in the previous problem?

**23.** A magnetic field of 16 T acts in a direction due west. An electron is traveling due south at $8.1 \times 10^5$ m/s. What is the magnitude and direction of the force acting on the electron?

▶ **24.** In a nuclear research laboratory, a proton moves in a particle accelerator through a magnetic field of intensity 0.10 T at a speed of $3.0 \times 10^7$ m/s.
   **a.** If the proton is moving perpendicular to the field, what force acts on it?
   **b.** If the proton continues to move in a direction that is consistently perpendicular to the field, what is the radius of curvature of its path? (mass of proton = $1.67 \times 10^{-27}$ kg)

▶ **25.** An electron is accelerated from rest through a potential difference of 20 000 V, which exists between the plates $P_1$ and $P_2$, Figure 24–32. The electron then passes through a small opening into a magnetic field of uniform field strength B. As indicated, the magnetic field is directed into the page.
   **a.** State the direction of the electric field between the plates as either $P_1$ to $P_2$ or $P_2$ to $P_1$.

**b.** In terms of the information given, calculate the electron's speed at plate $P_2$.
**c.** Describe the motion of the electron through the magnetic field.

**26.** A muon (a particle with the same charge as an electron) is traveling at $4.21 \times 10^7$ m/s at right angles to a magnetic field. The muon experiences a force of $5.00 \times 10^{-12}$ N. How strong is the field?

**27.** The mass of a muon is $1.88 \times 10^{-28}$ kg. What acceleration does the muon described in the previous problem experience?

**28.** A singly-ionized particle experiences a force of $4.1 \times 10^{-13}$ N when it travels at right angles through a 0.61-T magnetic field. What is the velocity of the particle?

▶ **29.** A force of $5.78 \times 10^{-16}$ N acts on an unknown particle traveling at a $90°$ angle through a magnetic field. If the velocity of the particle is $5.65 \times 10^4$ m/s and the field is $3.20 \times 10^{-2}$ T, how many elementary charges does the particle carry?

## THINKING PHYSIC-LY

A current is sent through a vertical spring as shown in Figure 24–33. The end of the spring is in a cup filled with mercury. What will happen? Why?

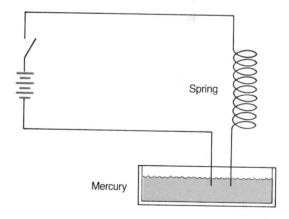

Spring

Mercury

**FIGURE 24–33. Use with Thinking Physic-ly.**

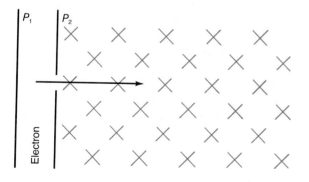

$P_1$  $P_2$

Electron

**FIGURE 24–32.**

# CHAPTER 25

# Electromagnetic Induction

◀ Go With the Flow

Aluminum is classified as a non-magnetic substance. Two aluminum rings, one with a slit and one a continuous ring, are placed over a magnetic field generator that is producing a constantly-changing magnetic field. Why does one ring float but the other one does not?

L evitation? There is no superconductor or permanent magnet in this photograph. The ring is made of aluminum, a non-magnetic conductor. The coil of wire around the central rod produces a continually changing magnetic field. You may never have seen such a floating ring, but the physical principle that explains why it is levitated also explains how the modern electrical distribution system works.

## √ Concept Check

The following terms or concepts from earlier chapters are important for a good understanding of this chapter. If you are not familiar with them, you should review them before studying this chapter.
· potential difference, electron pump, current, resistance, Chapter 22
· right-hand rules, electric motor, Chapter 24

- explain how a changing magnetic field produces an electric current.
- define *EMF*; show an ability to calculate *EMF* of wires moving in a magnetic field and know the limitations of the equation.
- explain how an electric generator works and how it differs from a motor.
- explain the difference between peak and effective voltage and current; use both in solving problems.

To induce current, there must be relative motion of a wire and the magnetic field.

# F. Y. I.

Michael Faraday left school at age 14 to become an apprentice to a bookmaker. He read most of the books in the shop. Joseph Henry left school at age 13 to work for a watch maker. Later in life, Faraday became director of the Royal Institution in London, founded by the American Benjamin Thomson (Count Rumford). Henry became the director of the Smithsonian Institution in Washington DC, founded by the Englishman James Smithson.

# 25.1 CREATING ELECTRIC CURRENT FROM CHANGING MAGNETIC FIELDS

In 1822, Michael Faraday wrote a goal in his notebook: "Convert Magnetism into Electricity." After nearly ten years of unsuccessful experiments, he was able to show that a changing magnetic field could produce electric current. In the same year, Joseph Henry, an American high school teacher, made the same discovery.

## Faraday's Discovery

Oersted had discovered that an electric current produces a magnetic field. Faraday tried all combinations of field and wire without success until he found he could induce current by *moving* the wire in a magnetic field. Figure 25–1 shows one of Faraday's experiments. A wire loop that is part of a closed circuit is placed in a magnetic field. If the wire moves up through the field, the current moves in one direction. When the wire moves down through the field, the current moves in the opposite direction. If the wire is held stationary or is moved parallel to the field, no current flows. An electric current is generated in a wire only when the wire cuts magnetic field lines.

To generate current, either the conductor can move through a magnetic field, or the magnetic field can move past a conductor. It is the relative motion between the wire and the magnetic field that produces the current. The process of generating a current through a circuit in this way is called **electromagnetic induction**.

In what direction does the current move? To find the force on the charges in the wire, use the third right-hand rule described in Chapter 24. Hold your right hand so that your thumb points in the direction in which the wire is moving and your fingers point in the direction of the magnetic field. The palm of your hand will point in the direction of the conventional (positive) current flow, Figure 25–2.

Wire moving up  Wire moving down
Current  Current

**FIGURE 25–1. When a wire is moved in a magnetic field, an electric current flows in the wire, but only while the wire is moving. The direction of the current flow depends on the direction the wire is moving through the field. The arrows indicate the direction of conventional current flow.**

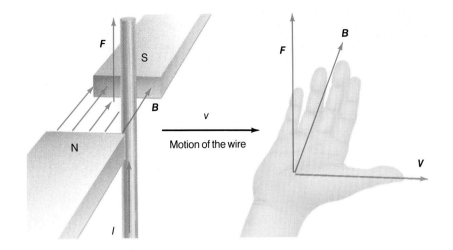

FIGURE 25–2. The right-hand rule can be used to find the direction of the forces on the charges in a conductor that is moving in a magnetic field.

# Electromotive Force

When we studied electric circuits, we learned that a charge pump is needed to produce a continuous current flow. The potential difference, or voltage, given to the charges by the pump is called the **electromotive force**, or *EMF*. *Electromotive force, however, is not a force; it is a potential difference and is measured in volts.* Thus the term *EMF* is misleading. Like many other historical terms still in use, it originated before electricity was well understood.

What creates the potential difference that can cause an induced current to flow? When a wire is moved through a magnetic field, a force acts on the charges and they move in the direction of the force. Work is done on the charges. Their electrical potential energy, and thus their potential, is increased. The difference in potential is called the induced *EMF*. The *EMF*, measured in volts, depends on the magnetic field strength, *B*, the length of the wire in the magnetic field, *L*, and the velocity of the wire in the field, *v*. If *B*, *v*, and the direction of the length of the wire are mutually perpendicular,

$$EMF = BLv.$$

If the moving wire is part of a closed circuit, the *EMF* will cause a current to flow in the circuit in the direction of the *EMF*.

If a wire moves through a magnetic field at an angle to the field, only the component of the wire's velocity that is perpendicular to the direction of the field generates *EMF*.

A microphone is a simple application that depends on an induced *EMF*. The "dynamic" microphone is similar in construction to a loudspeaker. The microphone in Figure 25–3 has a diaphragm attached to a coil of wire that is free to move in a magnetic field. Sound waves vibrate the diaphragm, which moves the coil in the magnetic field. The motion of the coil, in turn, induces an *EMF* across the ends of the coil. The voltage generated is small, typically $10^{-3}$ V, but it can be increased, or amplified, by electronic devices.

Electromotive force is potential difference, measured in volts.

The *EMF* depends on magnetic field strength, the length of the wire, and its velocity perpendicular to the field.

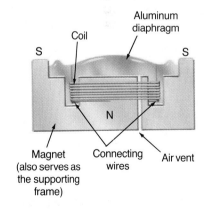

FIGURE 25–3. Schematic of a moving coil microphone. The aluminum diaphragm is connected to a coil in a magnetic field. When sound waves vibrate the diaphragm, the coil moves in the magnetic field, generating a current proportional to the sound wave.

## Example Problem

### Induced *EMF*

A straight wire 0.20 m long moves perpendicularly through a magnetic field of magnetic induction $8.0 \times 10^{-2}$ T at a speed of 7.0 m/s. **a.** What *EMF* is induced in the wire? **b.** The wire is part of a circuit that has a resistance of 0.50 $\Omega$. What current flows in the circuit?

**Given:** $L = 0.20$ m
$B = 8.0 \times 10^{-2}$ T
$v = 7.0$ m/s
$R = 0.50\ \Omega$

**Unknowns: a.** *EMF* **b.** *I*
**Basic equations: a.** $EMF = BLv$
**b.** $I = V/R$

**Solution: a.** $EMF = BLv$
$= (8.0 \times 10^{-2}\ \text{T})(0.20\ \text{m})(7.0\ \text{m/s})$
$= (8.0 \times 10^{-2}\ \text{N/A·m})(0.20\ \text{m})(7.0\ \text{m/s})$
$EMF = 0.11\left(\dfrac{\text{N}}{\text{A·m}}\right)(\text{m})\left(\dfrac{\text{m}}{\text{s}}\right) = 0.11\ \dfrac{\text{W}}{\text{A}} = 0.11$ V

**b.** $I = \dfrac{V}{R} = \dfrac{0.11\ \text{V}}{0.50\ \Omega} = 0.22$ A

## Practice Problems

1. A straight wire, 0.5 m long, is moved straight up through a 0.4-T magnetic field pointed in the horizontal direction at a speed of 20 m/s.
   a. What *EMF* is induced in the wire?
   b. The wire is part of a circuit of total resistance of 6.0 $\Omega$. What is the current in the circuit?
2. A straight wire, 25 m long, is mounted on an airplane flying at 125 m/s. The wire moves perpendicularly through Earth's magnetic field ($B = 5.0 \times 10^{-5}$ T). What *EMF* is induced in the wire?
3. A permanent horseshoe magnet is mounted so that the magnetic field lines are vertical. If a student passes a straight wire between the poles and pulls it toward herself, the current flow through the wire is from right to left. Which is the N-pole of the magnet?
▶ 4. A straight wire, 30.0 m long, moves at 2.0 m/s perpendicularly through a 1.0-T magnetic field.
   a. What *EMF* is induced in the wire?
   b. The total resistance of the circuit of which the wire is a part is 15.0 $\Omega$. What is the current?

## Electric Generators

The **electric generator**, invented by Michael Faraday, converts mechanical energy to electric energy. An electric generator consists of a number of wire loops placed in a strong magnetic field. The wire is wound around an iron form to increase the strength of the field. The iron and wires are called the armature, similar to that of an electric motor.

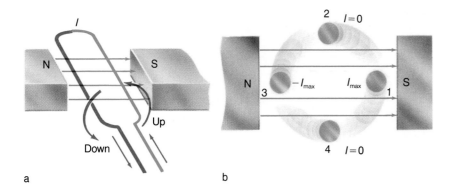

**FIGURE 25–4.** An electric current is generated in a wire loop as the loop rotates (a). The cross-sectional view (b) shows the position of the loop when maximum current is generated. The numbered positions correspond to the numbered points on the graph in Figure 25–5.

The armature is mounted so that it can rotate freely in the field. As the armature turns, the wire loops cut through the magnetic field lines, inducing an *EMF*. The *EMF*, commonly called the voltage, developed by the generator depends on the magnetic induction, *B*, the length of wire rotating in the field, *L*, and *v*, the speed of the loops perpendicular to the magnetic field. Increasing the number of loops in the armature increases the wire length, *L*, increasing the induced *EMF*.

When a generator is connected in a closed circuit, current flows that is proportional to the induced *EMF*. Figure 25–4 shows a single loop generator. The direction of the induced current can be found from the third right-hand rule. As the loop rotates, the strength and direction of the current change. The current is greatest when the component of the loop's velocity perpendicular to the field is largest. This occurs when the motion of the loop is perpendicular to the magnetic field—when the loop is in the horizontal position. As the loop rotates from the horizontal to the vertical position, it moves through the magnetic field lines at an ever-increasing angle. Thus, it cuts through fewer magnetic field lines per unit time, and the current decreases. When the loop is in the vertical position, the wire segments move parallel to the field and the current is zero. As the loop continues to turn, the segment that was moving up begins to move down, reversing the direction of the current in the loop. This change in direction takes place each time the loop turns through 180°. The current changes smoothly from zero to some maximum value and back to zero during each half-turn of the loop. Then it reverses direction. The graph of current versus time is shown in Figure 25–5.

The strength and direction of the induced current change as the armature rotates.

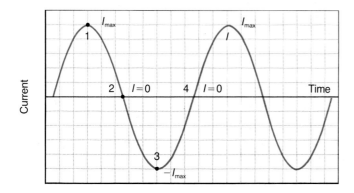

**FIGURE 25–5.** This graph shows the variation of current with time as the loop in Figure 25–4b rotates. The variation of *EMF* with time is given by a similar graph.

**FIGURE 25–6.** Alternating current generators transmit current to an external circuit by way of a brush-slip-ring arrangement (a). The alternating current varies with time (b).

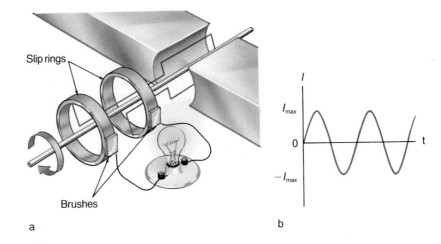

Slip rings

Brushes

a

b

Generators and motors are almost identical in construction but convert energy in opposite directions. A generator converts mechanical energy to electric energy while a motor converts electric energy to mechanical energy. In a generator, mechanical energy turns an armature in a magnetic field. The induced voltage causes current to flow. In a motor, a voltage is placed across an armature coil in a magnetic field. The voltage causes current to flow in the coil and the armature turns, producing mechanical energy from electrical energy.

## Alternating Current Generator

An energy source turns the armature of a generator in a magnetic field at a fixed number of revolutions per second. In North America, electric utilities use a 60-Hz frequency. The current goes from one direction, to the other, and back to the first, 60 times a second.

Figure 25–6 shows how an alternating current in an armature is transmitted to the rest of the circuit. The brush-slip-ring arrangement permits the armature to turn freely while still allowing the current to pass into the external circuit. As the armature turns, the alternating current varies between some maximum value and zero. If the armature is turning rapidly, the light in the circuit does not appear to dim or brighten because the changes are too fast for the eye to detect.

The power produced by a generator is the product of the current and the voltage. Power is always positive because either $I$ and $V$ are both positive or both negative. Because $I$ and $V$ vary, however, the power associated with an alternating current varies and its average value is less than the power supplied by a direct current with the same $I_{max}$ and $V_{max}$. In fact, the average AC power is

$$P_{AC} = \tfrac{1}{2}P_{ACmax} = \tfrac{1}{2}P_{DC}.$$

It is common to describe alternating currents and voltages in terms of effective currents and voltages. Recall that $P = I^2R$. Thus, the average AC power can be written in terms of the effective current,

$$P_{AC} = I^2_{eff}R.$$
$$P_{AC} = \tfrac{1}{2}P_{DC}$$
$$I^2_{eff}R = \tfrac{1}{2}(I^2_{max})R$$

$$I_{eff} = \sqrt{1/2 I^2_{max}}$$
$$\boxed{\begin{array}{l} I_{eff} = 0.707 I_{max} \\ V_{eff} = 0.707 V_{max} \end{array}}$$

The voltage generally available at wall outlets is described as 120 V, where 120 is the magnitude of the effective voltage, not the maximum voltage.

## Example Problem

### Effective Voltage and Effective Current

An AC generator develops a maximum voltage of 34 V and delivers a maximum current of 0.17 A to a circuit. **a.** What is the effective voltage of the generator? **b.** What effective current is delivered to the circuit? **c.** What is the resistance of the circuit?

**Given:** $V_{max} = 34$ V
$I_{max} = 0.17$ A

**Unknowns: a.** $V_{eff}$ **b.** $I_{eff}$ **c.** $R$
**Basic equations: a.** $V_{eff} = 0.707\ V_{max}$
**b.** $I_{eff} = 0.707\ I_{max}$
**c.** $R = \dfrac{V_{eff}}{I_{eff}}$

**Solution: a.** $V_{eff} = 0.707(V_{max})$
$= 0.707(34$ V$) = 24$ V
**b.** $I_{eff} = 0.707(I_{max})$
$= 0.707(0.17$ A$) = 0.12$ A
**c.** $R = \dfrac{V_{eff}}{I_{eff}} = \dfrac{24\ V}{0.12\ A} = 200\ \Omega = 2.0 \times 10^2\ \Omega$

## Practice Problems

**5.** A generator in a power plant develops a maximum voltage of 170 V.
  **a.** What is the effective voltage?
  **b.** A 60-W light bulb is placed across the generator. A maximum current of 0.70 A flows through the bulb. What effective current flows through the bulb?
  **c.** What is the resistance of the light bulb when it is working?
**6.** The effective voltage of a particular AC household outlet is 117 V.
  **a.** What is the maximum voltage across a lamp connected to the outlet?
  **b.** The effective current through the lamp is 5.5 A. What is the maximum current in the lamp?
**7.** An AC generator delivers a peak voltage of 425 V.
  **a.** What is the effective voltage in a circuit placed across the generator?
  **b.** The resistance of the circuit is $5.0 \times 10^2\ \Omega$. What is the effective current?
▶ **8.** If the average power dissipated by an electric light is 100 W, what is the peak power?

## POCKET LAB

### MOTOR AND GENERATOR

Make a series circuit with a Genecon (or efficient DC motor), a miniature lamp, and ammeter. Rotate the handle (or motor shaft) to try to light the lamp. Describe your results. Predict what might happen if you connect your Genecon to the Genecon from another lab group and crank yours. Try it. Describe what happens. Can more than two be connected?

# PHYSICS LAB : The Pick Up

## Purpose

To investigate changing magnetic fields with a telephone pickup coil.

## Materials

- telephone pickup coil (Radio Shack #44-533 or similar)
- mini audio amplifier (Radio Shack #277-1008 or similar)
- strong permanent magnet
- iron or air core solenoid coil
- 9-V battery
- low-voltage AC power supply
- battery-powered car
- 1 m of string
- masking tape

## Procedure

1. Put the 9-V battery into the amplifier and plug in the telephone pickup coil.
2. Place the strong permanent magnet on the table. Slowly bring the pickup coil near the magnet.

Mini audio amplifier

Magnet

Pickup coil

3. Use the suction cup to stick the pickup coil on the table. Attach the magnet to a string so that it hangs just above the pickup coil.
4. Swing the magnet like a pendulum. Twist the string so that as it untwists it will spin the magnet.
5. Attach the low-voltage AC power supply to the solenoid coil. Turn the power supply to about 2–3 V.
6. Hold the pickup coil near the solenoid coil to find where the sound is loudest. Listen to the amplifier as the pickup coil is rotated.

## Observations and Data

1. When does the pickup coil and amplifier make a sound in Procedure 2–4?
2. Describe the sound as the pickup coil and amplifier approaches the solenoid coil.

## Analysis

1. The pickup coil produces no signal when it is held stationary near the permanent magnet. Explain this.
2. Explain why rotating the pickup coil (Procedure 6) changes the loudness of the signal.
3. Predict the sound that you would hear if the solenoid coil was connected to a battery. Explain your prediction.

## Applications

1. Turn the battery-powered car on low speed and bring the pickup coil near to "hear" the changing magnetic fields. Predict how the sound will be different when the battery-powered car is on high speed. Try it. What happened? Why?

# CONCEPT REVIEW

**1.1** Could you make a generator by mounting permanent magnets on the rotating shaft and having the coil stationary? Explain.

**1.2** A bike generator lights the headlamp. What is the source of the energy for the bulb when the rider travels along a flat road?

**1.3** Consider the microphone shown in Figure 25–3. When the diaphragm is pushed in, what is the direction of the current in the coil?

**1.4** **Critical Thinking:** A student asks: "Why doesn't AC dissipate any power? The energy going into the lamp when the current is positive is removed when the current is negative. The net is zero." Explain why this argument is wrong.

# 25.2 EFFECTS OF CHANGING MAGNETIC FIELDS: INDUCED EMF

**O**bjectives

· state Lenz's law; explain back-*EMF* and how it affects the operation of motors and generators.

· explain the nature of self-inductance and its effects in circuits.

· describe the transformer; explain the connection of turns ratio to voltage ratio; solve transformer problems.

In a generator, current flows when the armature turns through a magnetic field. We learned in Chapter 24 that when current flows through a wire in a magnetic field, a force is exerted on the wire. Thus, a force is exerted on the wires in the armature. In a sense, then, a generator is, at the same time, a motor.

## Lenz's Law

In what direction is the force on the wires of the armature? The direction of the force on the wires opposes the original motion of the wires. That is, the force acts to slow down the rotation of the armature. The direction of the force was first determined in 1834 by H. F. E. Lenz and is called Lenz's law.

**Lenz's law** states: *The direction of the induced current is such that the magnetic field resulting from the induced current opposes the change in flux that caused the induced current.* Note that it is the *change* in flux and not the flux itself that is opposed by the induced magnetic effects.

Figure 25–7 is a simple example of how Lenz's law works. The N-pole of a magnet is moved toward the right end of a coil. To oppose the approach of the N-pole, the right end of the coil must also become

According to Lenz's law, the direction of the induced current is such that the current's magnetic effects oppose the changes that produced the current.

**FIGURE 25–7. The magnet approaching the coil causes an induced current to flow. Lenz's law predicts the direction of flow shown.**

Induced current

**FIGURE 25–8. Sensitive balances use eddy current damping to control oscillations of the balance beam (a). As the metal plate on the end of the beam moves through the magnetic field, a current is generated in the metal. This current, in turn, produces a magnetic field that opposes the motion that caused it, and the motion of the beam is dampened (b).**

an N-pole. In other words, the magnetic field lines must emerge from the right end of the coil. Use the second right-hand rule you learned in Chapter 24. You will see that if Lenz's law is correct, the induced current must flow in a counterclockwise direction. Experiments have shown that this is so. If the magnet is turned so an S-pole approaches the coil, the induced current will be in a clockwise direction.

If a generator produces only a small current, then the opposing force on the armature will be small, and the armature will be easy to turn. If the generator produces a larger current, the force on the larger current will be larger, and the armature will be more difficult to turn. A generator supplying a large current is producing a large amount of electrical energy. The opposing force on the armature means that an armature of mechanical energy must be supplied to the generator to produce the electrical energy, consistent with the law of conservation of energy.

Lenz's law also applies to motors. When a current-carrying wire moves in a magnetic field, an *EMF* is generated. This *EMF*, called the back-*EMF*, is in a direction that opposes the current flow. When a motor is first turned on, a large current flows because of the low resistance of the motor. As the motor begins to turn, the motion of the wires across the magnetic field induces the back-*EMF* that opposes the current flow. Therefore, the net current flowing through the motor is reduced. If a mechanical load is placed on the motor, slowing it down, the back-*EMF* is reduced and more current flows. If the load stops the motor, current flow can be so high that wires overheat.

The heavy current required when a motor is started can cause voltage drops across the resistance of the wires that carry current to the motor. The voltage drop across the wires reduces the voltage across the motor. If a second device, such as a light bulb, is near the motor in a parallel circuit with it, the voltage at the bulb will also drop when the motor is started. The bulb will dim. As the motor picks up speed, the voltage will rise again and the bulb will brighten.

When the current to the motor is interrupted by turning off a switch in the circuit or by pulling the motor's plug from a wall outlet, the sudden change in the magnetic field generates a back-*EMF* that can be large enough to cause a spark across the switch or between the plug and the wall outlet.

A sensitive balance, Figure 25–8, such as the kind used in chemistry laboratories, uses Lenz's law to stop its oscillation when an object is placed on the pan. A piece of metal attached to the balance arm is

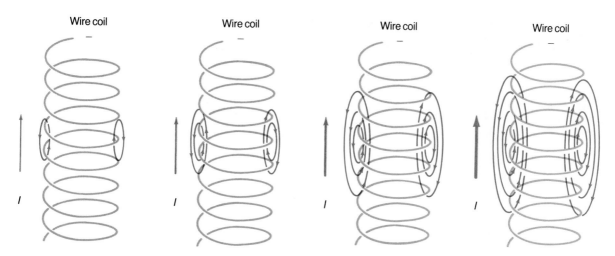

located between the poles of a horseshoe magnet. When the balance arm swings, the metal moves through the magnetic field. Currents, called eddy-currents, are generated in the metal. These currents produce a magnetic field that acts to oppose the motion that caused the currents. Thus the metal piece is slowed down. The force opposes the motion of the metal in either direction, but does not act if the metal is still. Thus it does not change the mass read by the balance. This effect is called "eddy-current damping."

The magnetic field caused by the induced *EMF* causes the ring in the chapter-opening photo to float. The coil is driven by AC, so the magnetic field is constantly changing, and this change induces an *EMF* in the ring. The resulting ring current produces a magnetic field that opposes the change in the generating field, the ring is pushed away. The lower ring has been sawed through. There is an *EMF* generated, but no current flow, and hence no magnetic field is produced by the ring.

## Self-Inductance

Back-*EMF* can be explained another way. As Faraday showed, *EMF* is induced whenever a wire cuts lines of magnetic flux. Consider the coil of wire shown in Figure 25–9. The current through the wire increases as we move from left to right. Current generates a magnetic field, shown by magnetic field lines. As the current and magnetic field increase, new lines are created. As the lines expand, they cut through the coil wires, generating an *EMF* to oppose the current changes. This induction of *EMF* in a wire carrying changing current is called **self-inductance**. The size of the *EMF* is proportional to the rate at which flux lines cut through the wires. The faster you try to change the current, the larger the opposing *EMF*, and the slower the current change. If the current reaches a steady value, the magnetic flux is constant, and the *EMF* is zero. When the current is decreased, an *EMF* is generated that tends to prevent the reduction in magnetic flux and current.

Because of self-inductance, work has to be done to increase the current flowing through the coil. Energy is stored in the magnetic field. This is similar to the way a charged capacitor stores energy in the electric field between its plates.

**FIGURE 25–9. As the current in the coil increases from left to right, the *EMF* generated by the current also increases.**

· · · · · · · · · · · · · · · · · · ·

◀ **Go With The Flow**

# F. Y. I.

Many modern automobiles have an electronic ignition system that varies the magnetic field. An aluminum armature with 4, 6, or 8 protrusions (depending on the number of spark plugs) spins. Each protrusion in turn passes through the magnetic field, causing it to vary.

A transformer uses two coupled coils to increase or decrease the voltage in an AC circuit.

## Transformers

Inductance between coils is the basis for the operation of a transformer. A **transformer** is a device used to increase or decrease AC voltages. Transformers are widely used because they change voltages with essentially no loss of energy.

Self-inductance produces an *EMF* when current changes in a single coil. A transformer has two coils, electrically insulated from each other, but wound around the same iron core. One coil is called the **primary coil**. The other coil is called the **secondary coil**. When the primary coil is connected to a source of AC voltage, the changing current creates a varying magnetic field. The varying magnetic flux is carried through the core to the secondary coil. In the secondary coil, the varying flux induces a varying *EMF*. This effect is called **mutual inductance**.

The *EMF* induced in the secondary coil, called the secondary voltage, is proportional to the primary voltage. The secondary voltage also depends on the ratio of turns on the secondary to turns on the primary.

$$\frac{\text{secondary voltage}}{\text{primary voltage}} = \frac{\text{number of turns on secondary}}{\text{number of turns on primary}}$$

$$\boxed{\frac{V_s}{V_p} = \frac{N_s}{N_p}}$$

$$V_s = \frac{N_s}{N_p}V_p$$

If the secondary voltage is larger than the primary voltage, the transformer is called a **step-up transformer**. If the voltage out of the transformer is smaller than the voltage put in, then it is called a **step-down transformer**.

In an ideal transformer, the electric power delivered to the secondary circuit equals the power supplied to the primary. An ideal transformer dissipates no power itself. Since $P = VI$,

$$V_p I_p = V_s I_s.$$

The current that flows in the primary depends on how much current is required by the secondary circuit.

$$\frac{I_s}{I_p} = \frac{V_p}{V_s} = \frac{N_p}{N_s}$$

**FIGURE 25–10. For a transformer, the ratio of input voltage to output voltage depends upon the ratio of the number of turns on the primary to the number of turns on the secondary.**

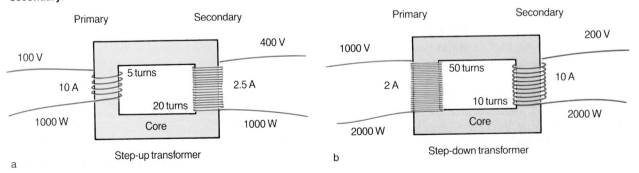

A step-up transformer increases voltage; the current in the primary circuit is greater than that in the secondary. In a step-down transformer, the current is greater in the secondary circuit than it is in the primary.

**FIGURE 25–11.** If the input voltage is connected to the coils on the left, with the larger number of turns, the transformer functions as a step-down transformer. If the input voltage is connected at the right, it is a step-up transformer.

# Example Problem

## Step-Up Transformer

A certain step-up transformer has $2.00 \times 10^2$ turns on its primary coil and $3.00 \times 10^3$ turns on its secondary coil. **a.** The primary coil is supplied with an alternating current at an effective voltage of 90.0 V. What is the voltage in the secondary circuit? **b.** The current flowing in the secondary circuit is 2.00 A. What current flows in the primary circuit? **c.** What is the power in the primary circuit? in the secondary circuit?

**Given:** $N_p = 2.00 \times 10^2$
$N_s = 3.00 \times 10^3$
$V_p = 90.0 \text{ V}$
$I_s = 2.00 \text{ A}$

**Unknowns: a.** $V_s$ **b.** $I_p$ **c.** $P$
**Basic equations:**
**a.** $\dfrac{V_s}{V_p} = \dfrac{N_s}{N_p}$
**b.** $V_p I_p = V_s I_s$

**Solution:**

**a.** $\dfrac{V_p}{V_s} = \dfrac{N_p}{N_s}$ or $V_s = \dfrac{V_p N_s}{N_p}$

$= \dfrac{(90.0 \text{ V})(3.00 \times 10^3)}{2.00 \times 10^2} = 1.35 \times 10^3 \text{ V}$

**b.** $V_p I_p = V_s I_s$ or $I_p = \dfrac{V_s I_s}{V_p} = \dfrac{(1350 \text{ V})(2.00 \text{ A})}{90.0 \text{ V}} = 30.0 \text{ A}$

**c.** $P_p = V_p I_p = (90.0 \text{ V})(30.0 \text{ A}) = 2.70 \times 10^3 \text{ W}$
$P_s = V_s I_s = (1350 \text{ V})(2.00 \text{ A}) = 2.70 \times 10^3 \text{ W}$

# Practice Problems

*In all problems, effective currents and voltages are indicated.*

**9.** A step-down transformer has 7500 turns on its primary and 125 turns on its secondary. The voltage across the primary is 7200 V.
  **a.** What voltage is across the secondary?
  **b.** The current in the secondary is 36 A. What current flows in the primary?
**10.** The secondary of a step-down transformer has 500 turns. The primary has 15 000 turns.
  **a.** The *EMF* of the primary is 3600 V. What is the *EMF* of the secondary?
  **b.** The current in the primary is 3.0 A. What current flows in the secondary?

# F.Y.I.

A transformer is similar to a lever. The voltage is similar to the amount of movement; the current is similar to the force. In an ideal lever, the energy input equals the energy output. The same is true of a transformer.

**FIGURE 25–12. Transformers are used to reduce voltages to consumer levels at the points of use.**

11. An ideal step-up transformer's primary circuit has 500 turns. Its secondary circuit has 15 000 turns. The primary is connected to an AC generator having an *EMF* of 120 V.
   a. Calculate the *EMF* of the secondary.
   b. Find the current in the primary if the current in the secondary is 3.0 A.
   c. What power is drawn by the primary? What power is supplied by the secondary?

▶ 12. A step-up transformer has 300 turns on its primary and 90 000 ($9.000 \times 10^4$) turns on its secondary. The *EMF* of the generator to which the primary is attached is 60.0 V.
   a. What is the *EMF* in the secondary?
   b. The current flowing in the secondary is 0.50 A. What current flows in the primary?

As was discussed in Chapter 23, long-distance transmission of electric energy is economical only if low currents and very high voltages are used. Step-up transformers are used at power sources to develop voltages as high as 480 kV. The high voltage reduces the current flow required in the transmission lines, keeping $I^2R$ losses low. When the energy reaches the consumer, step-down transformers provide appropriately low voltages for consumer use.

There are many other important uses of transformers. Television picture tubes require up to 25 kV, developed by a transformer within the set. The spark or ignition coil in an automobile is a transformer designed to step up the 12 V from the battery to thousands of volts. The "points" interrupt the DC current from the battery to produce the changing magnetic field needed to induce *EMF* in the secondary coil. Some arc welders require currents of $10^4$ A. Large step-down transformers are used to provide these currents, which can heat metals to 3000°C or more.

## CONCEPT REVIEW

2.1 You hang a coil of wire with its ends joined so it can swing easily. If you now plunge a magnet into the coil, the coil will swing. Which way will it swing with respect to the magnet and why?

2.2 If you unplug a running vacuum cleaner from the wall outlet, you are much more likely to see a spark than if you unplug a lighted lamp from the wall. Why?

2.3 Frequently, transformer windings that have only a few turns are made of very thick (low-resistance) wire, while those with many turns are made of thin wire. Why is this true?

2.4 **Critical Thinking:** Would permanent magnets make good transformer cores? Explain.

# Physics and society

## WEAK ELECTROMAGNETIC FIELDS—A HEALTH CONCERN?

Alternating currents, such as those in household wiring, produce electric and magnetic fields. The very low AC frequency is call Extremely Low Frequency, or ELF. The many sources of ELF electric and magnetic fields include power lines, home wiring, electric clocks, electric blankets, televisions and computer terminals. Twenty years ago, most scientists would have claimed that very weak electric and magnetic fields produced by ELFs could not affect living systems. Electric fields do exert forces on the ions in cellular fluids, and changing magnetic fields can induce such electric fields. Fields normally present in cells, however, are much larger than fields induced by ELFs, and, unlike ultraviolet radiation, ELFs can't break chemical bonds.

Recently, however, experiments have shown that cells are sensitive to even very weak ELF fields. They can affect flow of ions across cell membranes, synthesis of DNA, and the response of cells to hormones. Abnormal development of chick embryos has been seen. The experimental results, however, are very complex. Some effects of ELFs occur only at certain frequencies or amplitudes. Others occur only if the fields are turned on or off abruptly. Finally, for most environmental health hazards the larger the exposure, or dose, the larger the effect. For ELFs, there is no clear way to define or measure dose.

Some action has already been taken to reduce ELF fields. Electric blankets producing much lower magnetic fields are now sold. Several computer manufacturers sell terminals that produce smaller fields. Without knowing how to measure dose, however, it is not clear if such changes are enough to solve the problem.

Is there an association between cancer and exposure to ELF? Some studies found small increases in leukemia, breast cancer, and brain cancer. Studies of users of electric blankets have shown no effects on men, but increases in cancers and brain tumors in children whose mothers slept under electric blankets while pregnant. Studies to find the causes will take years and may not have conclusive results. In the meantime, what should be done?

## DEVELOPING A VIEWPOINT

Read articles about ELFs and come to class ready to discuss the following questions.
1. What do you think should be done? Should no action be taken until there is conclusive evidence of health hazards of ELFs? Or, is there enough reason for concern to take measures to limit exposure to ELFs?
2. Suppose a study finds many cancer cases among people who live near power lines. Would this prove that ELF fields from power lines cause cancer?
3. What steps could you take to reduce exposure to ELF?
4. What could utility companies do to reduce ELF fields?

## SUGGESTED READINGS

Noland, David. "Power Play." *Discover* 10 (12), 62–68, December, 1989.
Pool, Robert. "Electromagnetic Fields: The Biological Evidence." *Science* 249, 1378–1381, September 21, 1990.
Raloff, Janet. "EPA Suspects ELF Fields Can Cause Cancer." *Science News* 137, 404–405, June 30, 1990.

## SUMMARY

### 25.1 Creating Electric Current from Changing Magnetic Fields

· Michael Faraday and Joseph Henry discovered that if a wire moves through a magnetic field, an electric current can be induced in the wire.

· The direction that current flows in a wire moving through a magnetic field depends upon the direction of the motion of the wire and the direction of the magnetic field.

· The current produced depends upon the angle between the velocity of the wire and the magnetic field. Maximum current occurs when the wire is moving at right angles to the field.

· Electromotive force, *EMF*, is the increased potential of charges in the moving wire. *EMF* is measured in volts.

· The *EMF* in a straight length of wire moving through a uniform magnetic field is the product of the magnetic induction, *B*, the length of the wire, *L*, and the component of the velocity of the moving wire, *v*, perpendicular to the field.

· An electric generator consists of a number of wire loops placed in a magnetic field. Because each side of the coil moves alternately up and down through the field, the current alternates direction in the loops. The generator develops alternating voltage and current.

· A generator and a motor are similar devices. A generator converts mechanical energy to electric energy; a motor converts electric energy to mechanical energy.

### 25.2 Effects of Changing Magnetic Fields: Induced *EMF*

· Lenz's law states: *An induced current is always produced in a direction such that the magnetic field resulting from the induced current opposes the change in flux that is causing the induced current.*

· A transformer has two coils wound about the same core. An AC current through the primary coil induces an alternating *EMF* in the secondary coil. The voltages in alternating current circuits may be increased or decreased by transformers.

## KEY TERMS

electromagnetic induction
electromotive force
electric generator
Lenz's law
self-inductance
transformer

primary coil
secondary coil
mutual inductance
step-up transformer
step-down
   transformer

## REVIEWING CONCEPTS

1. How are Oersted's and Faraday's results similar? How are they different?
2. Matt has a coil of wire and a bar magnet. Describe how Matt could use them to generate an electric current.
3. What does *EMF* stand for? Why is the name inaccurate?
4. What is the armature of an electric generator?
5. Why is iron used in an armature?
6. What is the difference between a generator and a motor?
7. List the major parts of an AC generator.
8. Why is the effective value of an AC current less than the maximum value?
9. Water trapped behind Hoover Dam turns turbines that rotate generators. List the forms of energy between the stored water and the final electricity produced.
10. State Lenz's law.
11. What produces the back-*EMF* of an electric motor?
12. Why is there no spark when you close a switch, putting current through an inductor, but there is a spark when you open the switch?
13. Why is the self-inductance of a coil a major factor when the coil is in an AC circuit but a minor factor when the coil is in a DC circuit?
14. Explain why the word "change" appears so often in this chapter.
15. Upon what does the ratio of the *EMF* in the primary of a transformer to the *EMF* in the secondary of the transformer depend?

# APPLYING CONCEPTS

1. What is the difference between the current generated in a wire when the wire is moved up through a horizontal magnetic field and the current generated when the wire is moved down through the same field?
2. Substitute units to show that the unit of *BLv* is volts.
3. If the strength of a magnetic field is fixed, in what three ways can you vary the size of the *EMF* you can generate?
4. When a wire is moved through a magnetic field, resistance of the closed circuit affects
   **a.** current only.      **c.** both.
   **b.** *EMF* only.        **d.** neither.
5. As Logan slows his bike, what happens to the *EMF* produced by his bike's generator?
6. A hand-cranked generator is dropped, weakening the permanent magnet. How does this affect the speed at which the generator must be cranked to keep the same *EMF*?
7. The direction of AC voltage changes 120 times each second. Does that mean a device connected to an AC voltage alternately delivers and accepts energy?
8. A wire segment is moved horizontally between the poles of a magnet as shown in Figure 25–13. What is the direction of the induced current?

**FIGURE 25–13. Use with Applying Concepts 8 and 10.**

9. Martha makes an electromagnet by winding wire around a large nail. If she connects the magnet to a battery, is the current larger just after she makes the connection or several tenths of seconds after the connection is made? Or is it always the same? Explain.
10. A wire segment is moving downward through the poles of a magnet as shown in Figure 25–14. What is the direction of the induced current?
11. Thomas Edison proposed distributing electrical energy using constant voltages (DC). George Westinghouse proposed using the present AC system. What are the reasons the Westinghouse system was adopted?

12. A transformer is connected to a battery through a switch. The secondary circuit contains a light bulb. Which of these statements best describes when the lamp will be lighted?
    **a.** as long as the switch is closed
    **b.** only the moment the switch is closed
    **c.** only the moment the switch is opened
    Explain.
13. An inventor claims that a very efficient transformer will step up power as well as voltage. Should we believe this? Explain.
14. Suppose a magnetic field is directed vertically downward. You move a wire at constant speed, first horizontally, then downward at 45°, then directly down.
    **a.** Compare the induced *EMF* for the three motions.
    **b.** Explain the variations in voltage.
15. The direction of Earth's magnetic field in the northern hemisphere is downward and to the north. If an east-west wire moves from north to south, in which direction does the current flow?
16. Steve is moving a loop of copper wire down through a magnetic field *B,* as shown in Figure 25–16.
    **a.** Will the induced current move to the right or left in the wire segment in the diagram?
    **b.** As soon as the wire is moved in the field, a current appears in it. Thus, the wire segment is a current-carrying wire located in a magnetic field. A force must act on the wire. What will be the direction of the force acting on the wire due to the induced current?

Down

**FIGURE 25–14. Use with Applying Concepts 16.**

17. Kathleen, a physics instructor, drops a magnet through a copper pipe, Figure 25–15. The magnet falls very slowly and the class concludes that there must be some force opposing gravity.

**a.** What is the direction of the current induced in the pipe by the falling magnet if the S-pole is toward the bottom?

**b.** The induced current produces a magnetic field. What is the direction of the field?

**c.** How does this field reduce the acceleration of the falling magnet?

**FIGURE 25–15. Use with Applying Concepts 17.**

**18.** Why is a generator more difficult to rotate when it is connected to a circuit and supplying current than it is when it is standing alone?

# PROBLEMS

## 25.1 Creating Electric Current From Changing Magnetic Fields

**1.** A wire segment, 31 m long, moves straight up through a $4.0 \times 10^{-2}$-T magnetic field at a speed of 15.0 m/s. What *EMF* is induced in the wire?

**2.** A wire, 20.0 m long, moves at 4.0 m/s perpendicularly through a 0.50-T magnetic field. What *EMF* is induced in the wire?

**FIGURE 25–16. Use with Problem 2.**

**3.** An airplane traveling at 950 km/h passes over a region where Earth's magnetic field is $4.5 \times 10^{-5}$ T and is nearly vertical. What voltage is induced between the plane's wing tips, which are 75 m apart?

**4.** A straight wire, 0.75 m long, moves upward through a horizontal 0.30-T magnetic field at a speed of 16 m/s.
  **a.** What *EMF* is induced in the wire?
  **b.** The wire is a part of a circuit with a total resistance of 11 $\Omega$. What current flows in the circuit?

▶ **5.** A 40-cm wire is moved perpendicularly through a magnetic field of 0.32 T with a velocity of 1.3 m/s. If this wire is connected into a circuit of 10-$\Omega$ resistance, how much current is flowing?

▶ **6.** Jennifer connects both ends of a copper wire, total resistance 0.10 $\Omega$, to the terminals of a galvanometer. The galvanometer has a resistance of 875 $\Omega$. Jennifer then moves a 10.0-cm segment of the wire upward at 1.0 m/s through a $2.0 \times 10^{-2}$-T magnetic field. What current will the galvanometer indicate?

▶ **7.** The direction of a 0.045-T magnetic field is 60° above the horizontal. A wire, 2.5 m long, moves horizontally at 2.4 m/s.
  **a.** What is the vertical component of the magnetic field?
  **b.** What *EMF* is induced in the wire?

**8.** An *EMF* of 0.0020 V is induced in a 10-cm wire when it is moving perpendicularly across a uniform magnetic field at a speed of 4.0 m/s. What is the size of the magnetic field?

**9.** At what speed would a 0.2-m length of wire have to move across a 2.5-T magnetic field to induce an *EMF* of 10 V?

**10.** An AC generator develops a maximum *EMF* of 565 V. What effective *EMF* does the generator deliver to an external circuit?

**11.** An AC generator develops a maximum voltage of 150 V. It delivers a maximum current of 30.0 A to an external circuit.
  **a.** What is the effective voltage of the generator?
  **b.** What effective current does it deliver to the external circuit?
  **c.** What is the effective power dissipated in the circuit?

**12.** An electric stove is connected to an AC source with effective voltage of 240 V.
  **a.** Find the maximum voltage across one of the stove's elements when it is operating?

**b.** The resistance of the operating element is 11 Ω. What effective current flows through it?

▶ **13.** A generator at a hydroelectric site can supply 375 MW ($375 \times 10^6$ W) of electrical power. Assume that the turbine and generator are 85% efficient.
　**a.** Find the rate which falling water must supply energy to the turbine.
　**b.** The energy of the water comes from a change in potential energy, *mgh*. What is the needed change in potential energy each second?
　**c.** If the water falls 22 m, what is the mass of the water that must pass through the turbine each second to supply this power?

### 25.2 Effects of Changing Magnetic Fields: Induced *EMF*

**14.** The primary of a transformer has 150 turns. It is connected to a 120-V source. Calculate the number of turns on the secondary needed to supply these voltages.
　**a.** 625 V　**b.** 35 V　**c.** 6.0 V

**15.** A step-up transformer has 80 turns on its primary. It has 1200 turns on its secondary. The primary is supplied with an alternating current at 120 V.
　**a.** What voltage is across the secondary?
　**b.** The current in the secondary is 2.0 A. What current flows in the primary circuit?
　**c.** What is the power input and output of the transformer?

**16.** A portable computer requires an effective voltage of 9.0 V from the 120-V line.
　**a.** If the primary of the transformer has 475 turns, how many does the secondary have?
　**b.** A 125-mA current flows through the computer. What current flows through the transformer's primary?

**17.** In a hydroelectric plant, electricity is generated at 1.2 kV. It is transmitted at 240 kV.
　**a.** What is the ratio of the turns on the primary to the turns on the secondary of a transformer connected to one of the generators?
　**b.** One of the plant generators can deliver 40.0 A to the primary of its transformer. What current is flowing in the secondary?

**18.** A hair dryer uses 10 A at 120 V. It is used with a transformer in England, where the line voltage is 240 V.
　**a.** What should be the ratio of the turns of the transformer?
　**b.** What current will it draw from the 240-V line?

**19.** A step-up transformer is connected to a generator that is delivering 125 V and 95 A. The ratio of the turns on the secondary to the turns on the primary is 1000 to 1.
　**a.** What voltage is across the secondary?
　**b.** What current flows in the secondary?

▶ **20.** A 150-W transformer has an input voltage of 9.0 V and an output current of 5.0 A.
　**a.** Is this a step-up or step-down transformer?
　**b.** What is the ratio of output voltage to input voltage?

▶ **21.** A transformer has input voltage and current of 12 V and 3.0 A respectively, and an output current of 0.75 A. If there are 1200 turns on the secondary side of the transformer, how many turns are on the primary side?

▶ **22.** Scott connects a transformer to a 24-V source and measures 8.0 V at the secondary. If the primary and secondary were reversed, what would the new output voltage be?

## THINKING PHYSIC-LY

1. A bike's headlamp is powered by a generator that rubs against a wheel. Why is it harder to pedal when the generator is lighting the lamp?
2. Suppose an "anti-Lenz's law" existed that meant a force was exerted to increase the change in magnetic flux. Thus, when more electrical energy was demanded from a generator, the force needed to turn it would be reduced. What conservation law would be violated by this new "law"? Explain.

# CHAPTER 26

# Electric and Magnetic Fields

◀ Big Ears

These parabolic dish antennas are used to detect radio-frequency radiation having short wavelengths. Why are dish-style antennas used rather than normal television or radio antennas for detecting radio signals from deep space?

## Chapter Outline

**26.1 ACTION OF ELECTRIC AND MAGNETIC FIELDS ON MATTER**
· Mass of the Electron
· The Mass Spectrometer

**26.2 ELECTRIC AND MAGNETIC FIELDS IN SPACE**
· Electromagnetic Waves
· Production of Electromagnetic Waves
· Reception of Electromagnetic Waves
· X Rays

## √ Concept Check

The following terms or concepts from earlier chapters are important for a good understanding of this chapter. If you are not familiar with them, you should review them before studying this chapter.

· transverse waves, Chapter 14
· electric fields, Chapter 21
· magnetic fields, Chapter 24
· magnetic induction, Chapter 25

These huge parabolic dish antennas detect radio waves from space. They are used to receive information sent from space probes and to pick up signals from distant galaxies. They have the same function as television antennas on the roofs of homes, but are very different in form.

The mass of the electron is found indirectly from its charge, $q$, and its charge-to-mass ratio, $q/m$.

# 26.1 ACTION OF ELECTRIC AND MAGNETIC FIELDS ON MATTER

The source of radio and television waves is usually accelerating electrons. It is their charge that results in electric fields, and their motion that produces magnetic fields. Electrons are also part of every atom that makes up the dish antennas. Therefore it is important to understand some of the properties of electrons. The same techniques used to study electrons can be extended to study the properties of positive ions, atoms stripped of one or more electrons.

## Mass of the Electron

The charge of the electron was first measured by Robert Millikan using the force of an electric field on the charge on an oil drop. The mass of an electron is too small to measure on an ordinary balance. It is possible, however, to find the **charge-to-mass ratio**, $q/m$, by balancing the forces of an electric and a magnetic field acting on an electron. From this ratio and the charge, the mass can be found.

The ratio of charge-to-mass of the electron was first measured in 1897 by the British physicist J. J. Thomson (1856–1940). He used a cathode-ray tube similar to the one in Figure 26–1. All air is removed from the glass tube. An electric field pulls electrons out of the negatively-charged cathode and accelerates them toward the positively-charged anode. Some of the electrons pass through a hole in the anode and travel in a narrow beam toward a fluorescent screen. The screen glows at the point where the electrons hit.

a

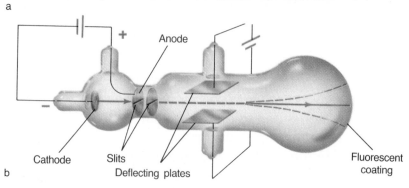

b

**FIGURE 26–1.** The Thomson $q/m$ tube (a) is diagrammed in (b). The electromagnets have been moved forward to show the deflection plates. When the tube is in use, the electromagnets and the deflection plates lie in the same plane.

Electric and magnetic fields in the centre of the tube exert forces on the electrons. Charged parallel plates produce a uniform electric field perpendicular to the beam. The electric field intensity, $\vec{E}$, produces a force, $qE$, on the electrons that deflects them upward. Two coils produce a magnetic field at right angles to both the beam and the electric field. Remember that the force exerted by a magnetic field is perpendicular to the field and to the direction of motion of the particles. The magnitude of the force exerted by the magnetic field is equal to $Bqv$. Here, $B$ is the magnetic field strength, and $v$ is the electron velocity. The magnetic force acts downward.

Crossed electric and magnetic fields exert forces in opposite directions on the electrons.

The electric and magnetic fields are adjusted until the beam of electrons follows a straight, or undeflected, path. Then the forces due to the two fields are equal in magnitude and opposite in direction.

For electrons of a selected velocity, the two forces are exactly balanced.

$$Bqv = Eq$$

Solving this equation for $v$, we obtain the expression

$$v = \frac{Eq}{Bq}$$
$$= \frac{E}{B}.$$

If the electric field is turned off, only the force due to the magnetic field remains. The magnetic force acts perpendicular to the direction of motion of the electrons, causing a centripetal acceleration. The electrons follow a circular path with radius $r$. Newton's second law gives

With only the magnetic force, electrons follow a circular path.

$$Bqv = m\frac{v^2}{r}.$$

Solving for $q/m$ gives

$$\boxed{\frac{q}{m} = \frac{v}{Br}.}$$

Thomson calculated the velocity, $v$, using the measured values of $E$ and $B$. Next, he measured the distance between the undeflected spot and the position of the spot when only the magnetic field acted on the electrons. Using this distance, he calculated the radius of the circular path of the electron, $r$. This allowed Thomson to calculate $q/m$. The average of many experimental trials gave the value $q/m = 1.759 \times 10^{11}$ C/kg. Using the value, $q = 1.602 \times 10^{-19}$ C, gives the mass of the electron, $m$.

$$m = \left(\frac{q}{q/m}\right)$$
$$= \frac{1.602 \times 10^{-19} \text{ C}}{1.759 \times 10^{11} \text{ C/kg}}$$
$$= 9.107 \times 10^{-31} \text{ kg}$$
$$= 9.11 \times 10^{-31} \text{ kg to 3 significant digits.}$$

Positively-charged particles bend the opposite way when in either an electric field or a magnetic field, Figure 26–2. Thomson found $q/m$ for positive ions in the same way he measured the quantity for electrons. A

## POCKET LAB

### ROLLING ALONG

Place a small ball of clay under one end of a grooved ruler to make a ramp. Roll a 6-mm diameter steel ball down the ramp and along the table top. Place a strong magnet near the path of the ball so that the ball will curve, but not hit the magnet. Predict what will happen to the path when the ball is started higher or lower on the ramp. Try it. Is this consistent for a charged particle moving through a magnetic field?

positive ion is produced by removing one or more electrons from an atom. To accelerate positively-charged particles into the deflection region, he reversed the direction of the field between the cathode and anode. A small amount of a gas, such as hydrogen, was put into the tube. The field pulled the electrons off the hydrogen atoms and accelerated the positively-charged protons through a tiny hole in the negatively-charged electrode. The proton beam then passed through the electric and magnetic deflecting fields to the fluorescent screen of the Thomson $q/m$ tube. The mass of the proton was determined in the same manner as was the mass of the electron. The mass of the proton was found to be $1.67 \times 10^{-27}$ kg. Heavier ions produced by stripping an electron from gases such as helium, neon, or argon were measured by a similar method.

**FIGURE 26–2. This photograph shows the circular tracks of two electrons (e⁻) and a positron (e⁺) moving through the magnetic field in a bubble chamber. Note that the electrons and positron curve in opposite directions.**

## Example Problem

### Balancing Electric and Magnetic Fields in a *q/m* Tube

A beam of electrons travels an undeflected path in a $q/m$ tube. $E$ is $7.0 \times 10^3$ N/C. $B$ is $3.5 \times 10^{-2}$ T. What is the speed of the electrons as they travel through the tube?

**Given:** $E = 7.0 \times 10^3$ N/C
$\quad\quad\quad\; B = 3.5 \times 10^{-2}$ T

**Unknown:** $v$

**Basic equation:** $v = \dfrac{E}{B}$

**Solution:** $v = \dfrac{E}{B}$

$\quad\quad\quad = \dfrac{7.0 \times 10^3 \text{ N/C}}{3.5 \times 10^{-2} \text{ N/A} \cdot \text{m}}$

$\quad\quad\quad = 2.0 \times 10^5$ m/s

## Example Problem

### Path of an Electron in a Magnetic Field

An electron of mass $9.11 \times 10^{-31}$ kg moves with a speed $2.0 \times 10^5$ m/s across and perpendicular to a $8.0 \times 10^{-5}$-T magnetic field. What is the predicted radius of the circular path followed by the electrons?

**Given:** $m = 9.11 \times 10^{-31}$ kg
$\quad\quad\quad v = 2.0 \times 10^5$ m/s
$\quad\quad\quad B = 8.0 \times 10^{-5}$ T
$\quad\quad\quad q = 1.6 \times 10^{-19}$ C

**Unknown:** $r$

**Basic equation:** $Bqv = \dfrac{mv^2}{r}$

**Solution:** $Bqv = \dfrac{mv^2}{r}$

$\quad\quad r = \dfrac{mv}{Bq} = \dfrac{(9.11 \times 10^{-31} \text{ kg})(2.0 \times 10^5 \text{ m/s})}{(8.0 \times 10^{-5} \text{ N/A} \cdot \text{m})(1.6 \times 10^{-19} \text{ C})}$

$\quad\quad r = 1.4 \times 10^{-2}$ m

# F.Y.I.

Sir Joseph John Thomson was awarded the Nobel Prize in physics in 1906 for his work on the electron. Eventually, seven of his research assistants won Nobel Prizes. In 1908 he was knighted.

# Practice Problems

*Assume the direction of all moving charged particles is perpendicular to the uniform magnetic field.*

1. Protons passing without deflection through a 0.6-T magnetic field are balanced by a $4.5 \times 10^3$-N/C electric field. What is the speed of the moving protons?
2. A proton moves at a speed of $7.5 \times 10^3$ m/s as it passes through a 0.6-T magnetic field. Find the radius of the circular path. The charge carried by the proton is equal to that of the electron, but it is positive.
3. Electrons move through a $6.0 \times 10^{-2}$-T magnetic field balanced by a $3.0 \times 10^3$-N/C electric field. What is the speed of the electrons?
▶ 4. Calculate the radius of the circular path the electrons in Practice Problem 3 follow in the absence of the electric field.

## The Mass Spectrometer

When Thomson put neon gas into his tube, he found two dots on the screen, and thus two values of $q/m$. This meant that atoms could have the same chemical properties but have different masses. Thus Thomson had shown the existence of **isotopes**, a possibility first proposed by the chemist Frederick Soddy.

The masses of positive ions can be measured precisely using a **mass spectrometer**, an adaptation of the Thomson tube. The type of mass spectrometer used by K. T. Bainbridge is shown in Figure 26–3. It uses either a gas or a material that can be heated to form a gas. In the ion source, accelerated electrons strike the gas atoms, knocking off electrons to form positive gas ions. A potential difference, $V$, between the electrodes produces an electric field that accelerates the ions.

A mass spectrometer can make precision measurements of the mass of ions.

**FIGURE 26–3. The mass spectrometer is used extensively as an analytical tool. Inside the spectrometer, a magnet (a) causes the positive ions to be deflected according to their mass. In the vacuum chamber (b), the process is recorded on a photographic plate or a solid-state detector.**

a

Pole face · To vacuum pump · Vacuum chamber

Magnet

b

Pole face

Positive ions

To vacuum

Photographic plate

To vacuum pump

Electron beam

Gas entry

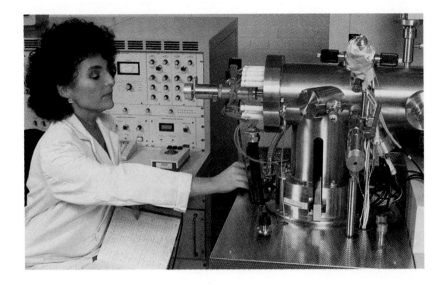

**FIGURE 26–4. The mass spectrometer is widely used to determine relative concentrations of various isotopes of an element. Marks are left on a film by $^{50}$Cr, $^{52}$Cr, $^{53}$Cr, and $^{54}$Cr. Note that the weight of the mark is proportional to the percentage of the isotope.**

The location where ions hit is marked on photographic film.

To select ions with a specific velocity, the ions pass through electric and magnetic deflecting fields as in the Thomson tube. The ions that go through undeflected move into a region with a uniform magnetic field. There they follow a circular path with a radius found from Newton's second law, $Bqv = mv^2/r$. Solving for $r$ yields

$$r = \frac{mv}{qB}.$$

The velocity of the ion can be found from the equation for the kinetic energy of ions accelerated from rest through a known potential difference $V$,

$$E_k = \tfrac{1}{2}mv^2 = qV$$

$$v = \sqrt{\frac{2qV}{m}}.$$

Substituting this expression for $v$ in the previous equation gives the radius of the circular path,

$$r = \frac{1}{B}\sqrt{\frac{2Vm}{q}}.$$

From this equation, the charge-to-mass ratio of the ion is found to be

$$\frac{q}{m} = \frac{2V}{B^2 r^2}.$$

The ions hit a photographic film, where they leave a mark. The radius, $r$, is found by measuring the distance between the mark and the hole in the electrode. This distance is twice the radius of the circular path. Figure 26–4 shows marks on film from the isotopes of the element chromium. The isotope with mass number 52 makes the darkest mark, showing that most chromium atoms have this mass.

All of the chromium ions have the same charge. The charge depends on how many electrons were removed in the ion source. It takes more-energetic electrons to remove a second electron from the gas atoms. For low electron energies, only one electron is removed from an atom. When the energy is increased, however, both singly- and doubly-charged ions are produced. In this way, the operator of the mass spectrometer can choose the charge on the ion.

Mass spectrometers can be used to separate isotopes of atoms such as uranium. Instead of film, cups are used to collect the separated isotopes. A mass spectrometer (often called an MS) is used by chemists as a very sensitive tool to find small amounts of molecules in samples. Amounts as small as one molecule in 10 billion molecules can be identified. Investigators detect the ions using electronic devices and are able to separate ions with mass differences of one ten-thousandth of one percent. Many dangerous contaminants in the environment have been detected with this device.

## Example Problem

### The Mass of a Neon Atom

The operator of a mass spectrometer produces a beam of doubly-ionized neon atoms (charge $q = 2(1.60 \times 10^{-19}$ C)). The accelerating voltage is $V = 34$ V. In a 0.050-T magnetic field, the radius of the path of the ions is $r = 0.053$ m. **a.** Calculate the mass of a neon atom. **b.** How many proton masses are in the neon atom? (The mass of a proton is $1.67 \times 10^{-27}$ kg.)

**Given:** $V = 34$ V
      $B = 0.050$ T
      $r = 0.053$ m
      $q = 3.2 \times 10^{-19}$ C

**Unknown:** $m$
**Basic equation:** $\dfrac{q}{m} = \dfrac{2V}{B^2 r^2}$

**a.** $m = \dfrac{qB^2 r^2}{2V}$

$= \dfrac{(3.2 \times 10^{-19} \text{ C}) (0.050\text{-T})^2 (0.053 \text{ m})^2}{2(34 \text{ V})}$

$= 3.3 \times 10^{-26}$ kg

**b.** number of protons $= \dfrac{3.3 \times 10^{-26} \text{ kg}}{1.67 \times 10^{-27} \text{ kg/proton}}$

$= 20$ protons

## Practice Problems

**5.** A stream of singly-ionized lithium atoms is not deflected as it passes through a $1.5 \times 10^{-3}$-T magnetic field perpendicular to a $6.0 \times 10^2$-V/m electric field.

  **a.** What is the speed of the lithium atoms as they pass through the crossed fields?

  **b.** The lithium atoms move into a 0.18-T magnetic field. They follow a circular path of radius 0.165 m. What is the mass of a lithium atom?

**6.** A mass spectrometer gives data for a beam of doubly-ionized argon atoms. The values are $B = 5.0 \times 10^{-2}$ T, $q = 2(1.6 \times 10^{-19}$ C), $r = 0.106$ m, and $V = 66.0$ V. Find the mass of an argon atom.

**7.** A beam of singly-ionized oxygen atoms is sent through a mass spectrometer. The values are $B = 7.2 \times 10^{-2}$ T, $q = 1.6 \times 10^{-19}$ C, $r = 0.085$ m, and $V = 110$ V. Find the mass of an oxygen atom.

▶ **8.** The Example Problem found the mass of a neon isotope. Another neon isotope has a mass of 22 proton masses. How far on the film from the first isotope would these ions land?

········
# CONCEPT REVIEW

**1.1** Consider what changes Thomson would have to make to change his $q/m$ tube from electrons to protons. **a.** To select particles of the same velocity, would the ratio $E/B$ have to be changed? **b.** To have the deflection caused by the magnetic field alone be the same, would the $B$ field have to be made smaller or larger? Explain.

**1.2** As Thomson raised the energy of the electrons producing the ions, he found ions with two positive elementary charges rather than just one. How would he have recognized this?

**1.3** A modern mass spectrometer can analyse molecules having masses of hundreds of proton masses. If their singly-charged ions are produced using the same accelerating voltage, how would the magnetic field have to be changed for them to hit the film?

**1.4 Critical Thinking:** Thomson did not know the number of electrons in the atoms. He found with most atoms that, as he raised the energy of the electrons that produced ions, he would first get ions with one electron missing, then ions with two missing, and so on. With hydrogen, however, he could never remove more than one electron. What could he then conclude about the positive charge of the hydrogen atom?

· **describe formation of electric and magnetic fields without charges.**
· **describe the generation of electromagnetic waves by accelerated charges; recognize the use of resonance.**
· **know the frequency and wavelength of common electromagnetic waves.**
· **explain how electromagnetic waves can be detected.**

········
# 26.2 ELECTRIC AND MAGNETIC FIELDS IN SPACE

Signals from galaxies, satellites, and television stations are electromagnetic waves. The properties of electric and magnetic fields were studied over most of the last century. In 1820 Oersted did his work on magnetic fields, and eleven years later Faraday discovered induction. In that year James Clerk Maxwell, a Scottish physicist, was born. In the 1860s, Maxwell predicted that even without wires, electric fields changing in time cause magnetic fields, and the magnetic fields changing in time produce electric fields. The result of this coupling is energy transmitted across empty space in the form of electromagnetic waves. Maxwell's theory led to a complete description of electricity and magnetism. It also gave us radio, television, and many other devices important to our lives.

# PHYSICS LAB

## Homemade Mass Spectrometer

## Purpose

To simulate the working parts of a mass spectrometer.

## Materials

· ball of clay
· grooved ruler
· 6-mm steel ball
· glass marble
· 2 permanent magnets
· cafeteria tray or glass wave tank
· graph paper
· masking tape

## Procedure

1. Build the apparatus as shown in the diagram below. Place a ball of clay under one side of the wave tank so that the tank is slightly sloped.
2. Make a test trial allowing the steel ball to roll down the track. The ball should follow a path similar to the one shown in the diagram when started one-half way up the ruler.

3. Starting from the same spot, roll the steel ball down the track three times. Mark the positions where the ball crosses the far side of the graph paper.
4. Place the permanent magnet(s) on the paper so they pull the ball slightly upward. Adjust the magnet(s) so that the ball crosses the far side of the graph paper on the same line as the end of the ramp.

## Observations and Data

1. Describe the path of the ball in step 3.
2. What happens to the path as the magnet is brought closer to the path of the ball? Why?

## Analysis

1. In this model, you used gravity to simulate the electric field of a mass spectrometer. How could the electric field in this model be varied?

## Applications

1. Predict what would happen to a 6-mm ball that had the same mass, but less or no iron content. Explain your prediction. Test it.

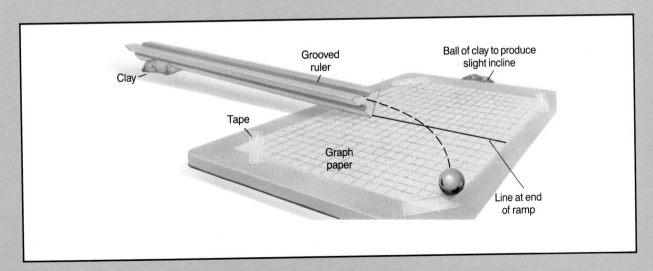

Clay

Grooved ruler

Ball of clay to produce slight incline

Tape

Graph paper

Line at end of ramp

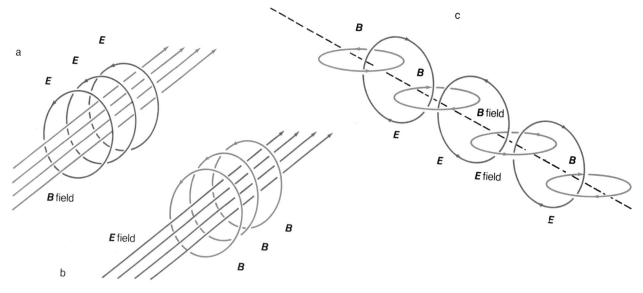

**FIGURE 26–5. Representation of an induced electric field (a), magnetic field (b), and both electric and magnetic fields (c).**

## Electromagnetic Waves

Oersted found that an electric current in a conductor produces a magnetic field. Changing the current changes the magnetic field, and, as Faraday discovered, changing the magnetic field can induce an electric current in a wire. Furthermore, the current-producing electric fields exist even without a wire, Figure 26–5a. Thus a *changing magnetic field produces a changing electric field.* The field lines of the induced electric field will be closed loops because, unlike an electrostatic field, there are no charges on which the lines begin or end.

In 1860 Maxwell postulated that the opposite is also true. *A changing electric field produces a changing magnetic field,* Figure 26–5b. Maxwell suggested that charges were not necessary; the changing electric field alone would produce the magnetic field.

Maxwell then predicted that either accelerating charges or changing magnetic fields would produce electric and magnetic fields that move through space. The combined fields are called an **electromagnetic wave**. The speed at which the wave moves, calculated Maxwell, was the speed of light, $3.00 \times 10^8$ m/s, as measured by Fizeau in 1849. Not only were electricity and magnetism linked, but optics, the study of light, became a branch of the study of electricity and magnetism. Heinrich Hertz (1857–1894), a German physicist, demonstrated in 1887 that Maxwell's theory was correct.

Figure 26–6 shows the formation of an electromagnetic wave. A wire, called an **antenna**, is connected to an alternating current (AC) source. The source produces changing currents in the antenna that alternate at the frequency of the AC source. The changing currents generate a changing electric field that moves outward from the antenna. There is also a magnetic field perpendicular to the page that is not shown. The waves spread out in space, moving at the speed of light.

Changing magnetic fields induce changing electric fields.

Changing electric fields induce changing magnetic fields.

Antenna

Electric field

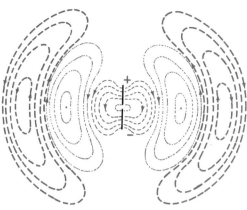

FIGURE 26–6. The changing current in the antenna generates a changing electric field. The electric field generates a changing magnetic field (not shown).

If you stood to the right of the antenna as the waves approached, you could visualize the electric and magnetic fields changing in time, Figure 26–7. The electric field oscillates, first up, then down. The magnetic field also oscillates at right angles to the electric field. The two fields are also at right angles to the direction of the motion of the wave. An electromagnetic wave produced by the antenna in Figure 26–6 is polarized. That is, the electric field is always parallel to the direction of the antenna wires.

The electric and magnetic fields are at right angles to each other and to the direction of motion of the wave.

## Production of Electromagnetic Waves

Electromagnetic waves can be generated over a wide range of frequencies. Figure 26–8 shows the electromagnetic spectrum. One method of creating the oscillating fields in the antenna has already been described, the AC generator. Frequency can be changed by varying the speed at which the generator is rotated. The highest frequency that can be generated in this way is about 1000 Hz.

The most common method of generating higher frequencies is to use a coil and capacitor connected in a series circuit. If the capacitor is charged by a battery, the potential difference across the capacitor creates an electric field. When the battery is removed, the capacitor discharges, and the stored electrons flow through the coil, creating a magnetic field. After the capacitor has discharged, the magnetic field of the coil collapses. A back-*EMF* develops that recharges the capacitor, this

A coil-capacitor combination resonates at frequencies of radio and television waves.

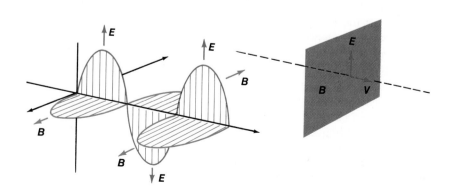

FIGURE 26–7. A look at portions of the electric and magnetic fields at an instant in time.

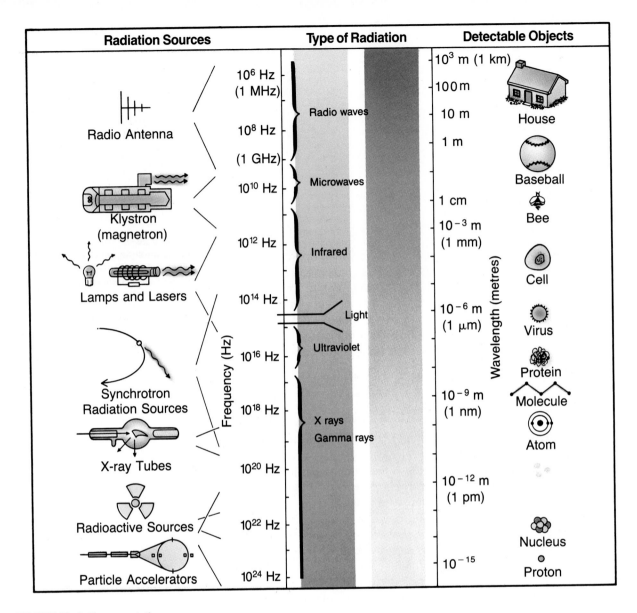

| Radiation Sources | Type of Radiation | Detectable Objects |
|---|---|---|

Radio Antenna

$10^6$ Hz (1 MHz)

Radio waves

$10^3$ m (1 km)

100 m

10 m — House

Klystron (magnetron)

$10^8$ Hz

(1 GHz)

$10^{10}$ Hz

Microwaves

1 m — Baseball

1 cm

Bee

Lamps and Lasers

$10^{12}$ Hz

Infrared

$10^{-3}$ m (1 mm)

Cell

Light

$10^{-6}$ m (1 µm)

Virus

Synchrotron Radiation Sources

$10^{14}$ Hz

$10^{16}$ Hz

Ultraviolet

Protein

Molecule

X-ray Tubes

$10^{18}$ Hz

X rays

Gamma rays

$10^{-9}$ m (1 nm)

Atom

Radioactive Sources

$10^{20}$ Hz

$10^{22}$ Hz

$10^{-12}$ m (1 pm)

Nucleus

Particle Accelerators

$10^{24}$ Hz

$10^{-15}$

Proton

Frequency (Hz)

Wavelength (metres)

**FIGURE 26–8. Representative examples of various types of electromagnetic radiation.**

A pendulum is a good model of resonance in a coil-capacitor circuit.

time in the opposite direction. The capacitor again discharges, and so on. One complete oscillation cycle is seen in Figure 26–9. The number of oscillations each second is called the frequency, which depends on the size of the capacitor and the coil. The antenna, connected across the capacitor, extends the fields of the capacitor into space.

A pendulum analogy, Figure 26–10, is a good model to help you understand the coil and capacitor circuit. The electrons in the coil and capacitor are represented by the pendulum bob. The pendulum bob moves fastest when its displacement from vertical is zero. This is similar to the largest current flowing in the coil when the charge on the capacitor is zero. When the bob is at its greatest angle, its displacement from the vertical is largest, and it has a zero velocity. This position is like the instant when the capacitor holds the largest charge and the current through the coil is zero.

E field strongest

B field strongest

B field strongest

E field strongest

FIGURE 26–9. Production of electromagnetic waves.

The model can be used when considering energy. The potential energy of the pendulum is largest when its displacement is greatest. The kinetic energy is largest when the velocity is greatest. The sum of the potential and kinetic energies, the total energy, is constant. Both the magnetic field produced by the coil and the electric field in the capacitor contain energy. When the current is largest, the energy stored in the magnetic field is greatest. When the current is zero, the electric field of the capacitor is largest and all the energy is in the electric field. The total energy, the sum of magnetic field energy and electric field energy, is constant. The electromagnetic waves carry this energy through space in the form of electric and magnetic fields. Energy carried, or radiated, this way is frequently called **electromagnetic radiation**.

Just as the pendulum will eventually stop swinging if left alone, due to resistance in the circuit, the oscillations in a coil and capacitor will also die out if energy is not added to the circuit. Gentle pushes, applied at the correct times, will keep a pendulum moving. The largest amplitude swing occurs when the frequency of pushing is the same as the frequency of swinging. This is the condition of resonance discussed in

Energy must be added periodically to keep the oscillation going.

$E_p = 0$
$E_k = $ max

$E_p = $ max
$E_k = 0$

Energy stored in magnetic field

Energy stored in electric field

FIGURE 26–10. A pendulum is analogous to the action of electrons in a coil and capacitor combination.

# Physics and society

## THE GREENHOUSE EFFECT

For many people, the phrase "greenhouse effect" brings fears of polar ice caps melting and of coastal cities being flooded. For others, the words describe a simple, useful process that florists use to grow plants. Just what is the greenhouse effect?

The sun emits radiations of short wavelengths, most of which are transmitted through Earth's atmosphere. Earth radiates energy of longer wavelengths back into the atmosphere. This longer-wavelength radiation, infrared, is absorbed by atmospheric components such as carbon dioxide, water vapour, methane, chlorofluorocarbons, and nitrogen oxides. These molecules reemit this radiation in all directions, some of the radiation going into space, some going back toward Earth's surface. The radiation that goes into space provides cooling that is necessary to maintain the thermal energy balance of Earth and its atmosphere.

This process is known as the greenhouse effect because a greenhouse that florists use also traps Earth's radiation. Glass is transparent to short-wavelength radiation but not to the longer wavelengths emitted by Earth; this warms a greenhouse. This analogy is only partly correct, because most of the warming inside a greenhouse occurs because air circulation is restricted.

The concern in recent years over the greenhouse effect has focused on carbon dioxide, ($CO_2$), because its concentration in the atmosphere is increasing. Since the beginning of the industrial revolution, $CO_2$ concentration has risen from 280 to 350 parts per million. More $CO_2$ molecules means that more of the surface-emitted radiation will be absorbed and less will escape into space, with the result that the thermal energy balance may be upset and the average temperature of Earth may increase.

Although the past few years have been warmer than normal, this might not be the result of the greenhouse effect. Scientists do not yet fully understand Earth's atmosphere. Predicting the future is also difficult.

## DEVELOPING A VIEWPOINT

More research is needed to predict the effects of increased amounts of greenhouse gases on global temperature. Read as much as you can on the subject and come to class prepared to discuss the following questions.

1. Assume that the temperature increase caused by increased $CO_2$ in the atmosphere is balanced by the temperature decrease brought about by polluting particles reflecting infrared radiation into space. Do you see this situation as acceptable?

2. Probably one of the major effects of a warmer Earth would be shifts in rainfall patterns and in crop-growing regions. How might this be a problem?

3. What are your recommendations for dealing with the possibility that increasing levels of $CO_2$ may warm the planet several degrees over the next century?

## SUGGESTED READINGS

Gushee, David E. "Global Climate Change." CHEMTECH 19 (8), August 1989, pp. 470–479.

Levi, Barbara Goss. "Climate Modelers Struggle to Understand Global Warming." *Physics Today* 43 (2), February 1990, pp. 17–19: "Scientific Perspectives on the Greenhouse Effect." *Consumers' Research* 73 (4), April 1990, pp. 22–24, 36.

Chapter 7. Voltage pulses applied to the coil-capacitor circuit at the right frequency keep the oscillations going. One way of doing this is to add a second coil to form a transformer, Figure 26–11. The AC induced in the secondary coil is increased by an amplifier and added back to the coil and capacitor. This type of circuit can produce frequencies up to approximately 100 MHz.

Coils and capacitors are not the only method of generating oscillation voltages. Quartz crystals have a property called **piezoelectricity**. They bend or deform when a voltage is applied across them. Just as a piece of metal will vibrate at a specific frequency when it is bent and released, so will a quartz crystal. A crystal can be cut so that it will vibrate at a specific desired frequency. An applied voltage bends it to start it vibrating. The piezoelectric property also generates an *EMF* when the crystal is bent. Since this *EMF* is produced at the vibrating frequency of the crystal, it can be amplified and returned to the crystal to keep it vibrating. Quartz crystals are used in wristwatches because the frequency of vibration is so constant. Frequencies in the range from 1 kHz to 10 MHz can be generated in this way.

To increase the oscillation frequency, the size of the coil and capacitor must be made smaller. Above 1000 MHz, individual coils and capacitors will not work. For these electromagnetic waves, called microwaves, a rectangular box, called a resonant cavity, acts as both a coil and a capacitor. The size of the box determines the frequency of oscillation. Such a cavity is in every microwave oven.

At frequencies of infrared waves, the size of resonant cavities would have to be reduced to the size of molecules. The oscillating electrons that produce infrared waves are in fact within the molecules. Visible and ultraviolet waves are generated by electrons within atoms.

**X rays** can be generated by electrons in heavy atoms. **Gamma rays** are the result of accelerating charges in the nucleus of an atom. Most electromagnetic waves arise from accelerated charges and travel at the speed of light.

## Reception of Electromagnetic Waves

Electromagnetic waves are caused by the acceleration of electrons in an antenna. When the electric fields in these electromagnetic waves strike another antenna, Figure 26–12, they accelerate the electrons in it. The acceleration is largest when the antenna is turned in the direction

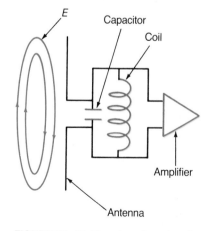

FIGURE 26–12. The changing electric fields from a radio station cause electrons in the antenna to accelerate.

of the polarization of the wave. That is, when it is parallel to the direction of the electric fields in the wave. An *EMF* across the terminals of the antenna oscillates at the frequency of the electromagnetic wave. The *EMF* is largest if the length of the antenna is one half the wavelength of the wave. The antenna then resonates in the same way an open pipe one-half wavelength long resonates with sound waves. For that reason, an antenna designed to receive radio waves is much longer than one designed to receive microwaves.

While a simple wire antenna can detect electromagnetic waves, several wires can be used to increase the detected *EMF*. A television antenna often consists of two or more wires spaced about one-quarter wavelength apart. Electric fields generated in the individual wires form constructive interference patterns that increase the strength of the signal. At very short wavelengths, parabolic dishes reflect the waves just as parabolic mirrors reflect light waves. Giant parabolic dishes focus waves with wavelengths of 2 to 6-cm on the antennas held by the tripod above the dish.

Radio and television waves are used to transmit information across space. There are many different radio and television stations producing electromagnetic waves at the same time. If the information being broadcast is to be understood, it must be possible to select the waves of a particular station. To select waves of a particular frequency and reject the others, a coil and capacitor circuit is connected to the antenna. The capacitance is adjusted until the oscillation frequency of the circuit equals the frequency of the desired wave. Only this frequency can cause significant oscillations of the electrons in the circuit. The information carried by the oscillations is then amplified and ultimately drives a loudspeaker. The combination of antenna, coil and capacitor circuit, and amplifier is called a **receiver**.

Waves carry energy as well as information. At microwave and infrared frequencies, the electromagnetic waves accelerate electrons in molecules. The energy of the electromagnetic waves is converted to thermal energy in the molecules. Microwaves cook foods in this way. Infrared waves from the sun produce the warmth we feel.

Light waves can transfer energy to electrons in atoms. In photographic film, this energy causes a chemical reaction. The result is a permanent record of the light reaching the camera from the subject. In the eye, the energy produces a chemical reaction that stimulates a nerve, resulting in a response in our brain that we call vision. At higher frequencies, UV radiation causes many chemical reactions to occur, including those that produce sunburn and tanning.

## X Rays

In 1895 in Germany, Wilhelm Roentgen (1845–1923) sent electrons through an evacuated glass tube. Roentgen used a very high voltage across the tube to give the electrons a large kinetic energy. The electrons struck the metal anode of the tube. When this happened, Roentgen noted a glow on a phosphorescent screen a short distance away. The glow continued even if a piece of wood was placed between the tube and the screen. He concluded that some kind of highly-penetrating rays were coming from the tube.

Electromagnetic waves induce changing electric fields in a receiving antenna.

. . . . . . . . . . . . . . . . . . . . ▶
**Big Ears**

A coil-capacitor circuit allows only the signal with the selected frequency to be amplified.

**FIGURE 26–13. This tube is similar to the one used by Moseley in studying X rays. The metal target in the X-ray tube can be changed to produce X rays of different wavelengths.**

Because Roentgen did not know what these strange rays were, he called them X rays. A few weeks later, Roentgen found that photographic plates were darkened by X rays. He also discovered that soft body tissue was transparent to the rays, but that bone blocked them. He produced an X-ray picture of his wife's hand. Within months, doctors recognized the medical uses of this phenomenon.

It is now known that X rays are high frequency electromagnetic waves. They are produced when electrons are accelerated to high speeds by means of potential differences of 20 kV or more, Figure 26–13. When the electrons crash into matter, their kinetic energies are converted into very-high-frequency electromagnetic waves, or X rays.

Electrons are accelerated to these speeds in cathode-ray tubes, such as the picture tube in a television. When the electrons hit the faceplate, they cause the coloured phosphors to glow. The sudden stopping of the electrons can also produce X rays. The faceplate glass contains lead to stop the X rays and protect viewers.

◀ · · · · · · · · · · · · · · · · · · ·
# BIOLOGY CONNECTION

## CONCEPT REVIEW

**2.1** What was Maxwell's contribution to electromagnetism?

**2.2** Television antennas normally have the metal rod elements horizontal. From that, what can you deduce about the directions of the electric fields in television signals?

**2.3** Television Channels 2-6 have frequencies just below the FM radio band, while Channels 7-13 have much higher frequencies. Which signals would require a longer antenna, Channel 7 or Channel 6?

**2.4** Critical Thinking: Most of the UV radiation from the sun is blocked by the ozone layer in Earth's atmosphere. Recently scientists have found "holes" in the ozone layer over both Antarctica and the Arctic Ocean. Why should we be concerned about this?

# CHAPTER
# 26 REVIEW · · · · · · · · · · · · · · · · · ·

## SUMMARY

### 26.1 Action of Electric and Magnetic Fields on Matter

· The ratio of charge to mass of the electron was measured by J. J. Thomson using balanced electric and magnetic fields.
· The mass of the electron can be found by combining Thomson's result with Millikan's measurement of the electron charge.
· The mass spectrometer uses both electric and magnetic fields to measure the masses of atoms and molecules.

### 26.2 Electric and Magnetic Fields in Space

· An electric field changing in time generates a changing magnetic field.
· A changing magnetic field generates a changing electric field in space.
· Electromagnetic waves are coupled changing electric and magnetic fields that move through space.
· Changing currents in an antenna generate electromagnetic waves.
· The frequency of oscillating currents can be selected by a resonating coil and capacitor circuit.

- Electromagnetic waves can be detected by the *EMF* they produce in an antenna. The length of the most efficient antenna is one-half wavelength.
- Microwave and infrared waves can accelerate electrons in molecules, producing thermal energy.
- When high-energy electrons strike an anode in an evacuated tube, their kinetic energies are converted to electromagnetic waves of very high energy called X rays.

## KEY TERMS

charge-to-mass ratio
isotopes
mass spectrometer
electromagnetic wave
antenna

electromagnetic
  radiation
piezoelectricity
X rays
gamma rays
receiver

## REVIEWING CONCEPTS

1. What is the mass of an electron and what is the charge of an electron?
2. What are isotopes?
3. The direction of an induced magnetic field is always at what angle to the changing electric field?
4. Like all waves, microwaves can be transmitted, reflected, and absorbed. Why can soup be warmed in a ceramic mug in a microwave but not in a metal pan? Why does the handle of the mug not get as hot as the soup?
5. Why must an AC generator be used to propagate electromagnetic waves? If a DC generator were used, when would it create electromagnetic waves?
6. A vertical antenna wire transmits radio waves. Sketch the antenna and the electric and magnetic fields it produces.
7. What happens to quartz crystals when a voltage is placed across them?
8. Many car radio antennas are vertical. What is the direction of the electric fields they detect?
9. How does an antenna receiving circuit select electromagnetic radio waves of a certain frequency and reject all others?

## APPLYING CONCEPTS

1. The electrons in a Thomson tube, like the one in Figure 26–1, travel from left to right. Which deflection plate should be charged positively to bend the electron beam up?
2. The electron beam in the previous question has a magnetic field to make the beam path straight. What would be the direction of the magnetic field needed to bend the beam down?
3. Show that the units of $E/B$ are the same as the units for velocity.
4. A mass spectrometer operates on neon ions. What is the direction of the magnetic field needed to bend the beam in a clockwise semicircle?
5. Charged particles are moving through an electric field and a magnetic field that are perpendicular to each other. Suppose you adjust the fields so that a certain ion, with the correct velocity, passes without deflection. Now another ion with the same velocity, but a different mass, enters the fields. Describe the path of the second ion.
6. If the sign of the charge on the particle in the previous question is changed from positive to negative, do the directions of either or both of the two fields have to be changed to keep the particle undeflected? Explain.
7. Of radio waves, light, or X rays, which has the largest
   a. wavelength?  b. frequency?  c. velocity?
8. The frequency of television waves broadcast on channel 2 is about 58 MHz. The waves on channel 7 are about 180 MHz. Which channel requires a longer antenna?
9. Suppose the eyes of an alien being are sensitive to microwaves. Would you expect such a being to have larger or smaller eyes than ours? Explain.

## PROBLEMS

### 26.1 Action of Electric and Magnetic Fields on Matter

1. A beam of ions passes through a pair of crossed electric and magnetic fields. *E* is $6.0 \times 10^5$ N/C and *B* is $3.0 \times 10^{-3}$ T. What is the speed of the ions?

2. Electrons moving at $3.6 \times 10^4$ m/s pass through an electric field of intensity $5.8 \times 10^3$ N/C. How large a magnetic field must the electrons also experience for their path to be undeflected?

3. The electrons in a beam are moving at $2.8 \times 10^8$ m/s in an electric field of $1.4 \times 10^4$ N/C. What value must the magnetic field have if the electrons pass through the crossed fields undeflected?

4. A proton moves across a 0.36-T magnetic field in a circular path of radius 0.2 m. What is the speed of the proton?

5. Electrons move across a 4.0-mT magnetic field. They follow a circular path, radius 2.0 cm.
   a. What is their speed?
   b. An electric field is applied perpendicularly to the magnetic field. The electrons then follow a straight-line path. Find the magnitude of the electric field.

▶ 6. What energy must be given to an electron to transfer it across a potential difference of $4.0 \times 10^5$ V?

7. A proton enters a $6.0 \times 10^{-2}$-T magnetic field with a speed of $5.4 \times 10^4$ m/s. What is the radius of the circular path it follows?

8. A proton enters a magnetic field of $6.4 \times 10^{-2}$T with a speed of $4.5 \times 10^4$ m/s. What is the circumference of the circular path that it follows?

▶ 9. An alpha particle has a mass of approximately $6.6 \times 10^{-27}$ kg and bears a double elementary positive charge. Such a particle is observed to move through a 2.0-T magnetic field along a path of radius 0.15 m.
   a. What speed does it have?
   b. What is its kinetic energy?
   c. What potential difference would be required to give it this kinetic energy?

10. A $3.0 \times 10^{-2}$-T magnetic field in a mass spectrometer causes an isotope of sodium to move in a circular path with a radius of 0.081 m. If the ions have a single positive charge and are moving with a speed of $1.0 \times 10^4$ m/s, what is the isotope's mass?

11. An alpha particle, a doubly-ionized helium atom, has a mass of $6.7 \times 10^{-27}$ kg and is accelerated by a voltage of 1.0 kV. If a uniform magnetic field of $6.5 \times 10^{-2}$ T is maintained on the alpha particle, what will be the particle's radius of curvature?

12. An electron is accelerated by a 4.5-kV potential difference. How strong a magnetic field must be experienced by the electron if its path is a circle of radius 5.0 cm?

13. A mass spectrometer yields the following data for a beam of doubly-ionized sodium atoms: $B = 8.0 \times 10^{-2}$ T; $q = 2(1.60 \times 10^{-19}$ C); $r = 0.077$ m; and $V = 156$ V. Calculate the mass of a sodium atom.

▶ 14. In a mass spectrometer, ionized silicon atoms have radii with curvatures of 16.23 cm and 17.97 cm. If the smaller radius corresponds to an atomic mass of 28 units, what is the atomic mass of the other silicon isotope?

▶ 15. A mass spectrometer is used to analyse a molecule with a mass of $175 \times 10^3$ proton masses. The operator wants to know whether the carbon in the molecule has mass 12 or 13 proton masses. What percent differentiation is needed?

## 26.2 Electric and Magnetic Fields in Space

▶ 16. The difference in potential between the cathode and anode of a spark plug is $1.0 \times 10^4$ V.
   a. What energy does an electron give up as it passes between the electrodes?
   b. One fourth of the energy given up by the electron is converted to electromagnetic radiation. The frequency of the wave is related to the energy by the equation $E = hf$, where $h$ is Planck's constant, $6.6 \times 10^{-34}$ J/Hz. What is the frequency of the waves?

▶ 17. Television Channel 6 broadcasts on a frequency of 85 MHz.
   a. What is the wavelength of the electromagnetic wave broadcast on Channel 6?
   b. What is the length of an antenna that will detect Channel 6 most easily?

18. The radio waves reflected by a parabolic dish are 2.0 cm long. How long is the antenna that detects the waves?

# THINKING PHYSIC-LY

H.G. Wells wrote a science fiction book called *The Invisible Man,* in which a man drinks a potion and becomes invisible, although he retains all of his other faculties. If this could actually be accomplished, however, the subject would be blind. Explain.

# CHAPTER
# 27 Quantum Theory

## ◀ Red Hot or Not

Jann's class, visiting a steel plant, was watching a vat of molten steel being poured into moulds. Jann commented that the molten red steel was very hot, but not as hot as the yellowish-white steel. Her friend disagreed, saying, "Everyone knows that red hot is supposed to be the hottest." How did Jann defend her statement?

In 1889, the experiments of Heinrich Hertz confirmed the predictions of Maxwell's theory. All of optics seemed to be explainable by electromagnetic theory. Only two small problems remained. Wave theory could not describe the spectrum of light emitted by a hot body, such as the hot steel in the photo. Also, as discovered by Hertz himself, ultraviolet light discharged electrically-charged metal plates. This effect, called the photoelectric effect, could not be explained by Maxwell's wave theory.

The solution of these two problems required a total change in our understanding of the structure of matter, and of electromagnetic radiation as well. It required development of the quantum theory and its experimental confirmation, one of the highlights of the history of the twentieth century.

## √ Concept Check

The following terms or concepts from earlier chapters are important for a good understanding of this chapter. If you are not familiar with them, you should review them before studying this chapter.
· momentum, Chapter 9
· conservation of energy, elastic scattering, Chapter 11
· wavelength, frequency, wave speed, Chapter 14
· diffraction, interference, diffraction gratings, Chapter 19
· electric potential and potential energy, Chapter 21
· electromagnetic waves, Chapter 26

· understand the spectrum emitted
  by a hot body and the basics of the
  theory that explains this spectrum.
· define the photoelectric effect;
  recognize that the quantum theory
  can explain it while the wave
  theory can't; solve problems
  involving the photoelectric
  equation.
· define the Compton effect and
  explain in terms of the momentum
  and energy of the photon.
· describe experiments that
  demonstrate the particle-like
  properties of electromagnetic
  radiation.

The hotter the temperature, the more radiation at shorter wavelengths.

## Red Hot or Not ▶

Planck explained the spectrum of an incandescent object by assuming atoms could vibrate only at specific frequencies.

**FIGURE 27–1. This graph shows spectra of incandescent bodies at various temperatures.**

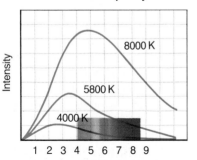

Intensity of Blackbody Radiation versus Frequency

# 27.1 WAVES BEHAVE LIKE PARTICLES

The radiation from hot bodies was a puzzle. Hot bodies contain vibrating particles, which radiate electromagnetic waves. Maxwell's theory should have no trouble with this, but it gave the wrong prediction. Why? What radiation do hot bodies emit?

## Radiation From Incandescent Bodies

If you look through a prism at the light coming from an incandescent light bulb, you will see all the colours of the rainbow. The bulb also emits infrared radiation, which you cannot see. Figure 27–1 shows the spectrum of an incandescent body. A spectrum is a plot of the intensity of radiation emitted at various frequencies. Light and infrared radiation are produced by the vibration of the charged particles within the atoms of a body that is so hot it glows, or is incandescent.

Suppose you put the light bulb on a dimmer control. You gradually turn up the voltage, increasing the temperature of the glowing filament. The colour changes from deep red through orange to yellow and finally to white. The higher the temperature, the more radiation at frequencies of yellow, green, blue, and violet is produced, and the "whiter" the body appears. The colour you see depends on the relative amounts of emission at various frequencies and the sensitivity of your eyes to those colours. Spectra of incandescent bodies at various temperatures are shown in Figure 27–1. The frequency at which the maximum amount of light is emitted is proportional to the Kelvin temperature.

The total power emitted also increases with temperature. The amount of energy emitted every second in electromagnetic waves is proportional to the absolute temperature raised to the fourth power, $T^4$. Thus, as the figure shows, hotter sources radiate considerably more power than cooler bodies. The sun, for example, is a dense ball of gasses heated to incandescence by the energy produced within it. It has a surface temperature of 5800 K and a yellow colour. The sun radiates $4 \times 10^{26}$ W, a truly enormous amount of power. Each square metre on Earth receives about one thousand joules of energy each second.

Why does the spectrum have the shape shown in Figure 27–1? Maxwell's theory could not account for it. Between 1887 and 1900, many physicists tried to predict the shape of this spectrum using existing physical theories, but all failed. In 1900, the German physicist Max Planck (1858–1947) found that he could calculate the spectrum only if he introduced a revolutionary hypothesis. Planck assumed that the energy of vibration of the atoms in a solid could have only the specific frequencies given by the equation

$$E = nhf.$$

Here $f$ is the frequency of vibration of the atom, $h$ is a constant, and $n$ is an integer like 0, 1, 2, or 3. The energy, $E$, could have the values $hf$, $2hf$, $3hf$, and so on, but never, for example, $\frac{2}{3}hf$. This behaviour is described by saying that energy is quantized. Energy only comes in packages of specific sizes.

Further, Planck proposed that atoms did not radiate electromagnetic waves all the time they were vibrating, as predicted by Maxwell. Instead, they could emit radiation *only when their vibration energy changed*. For example, when the energy changed from $3hf$ to $2hf$, the atom emitted radiation. The energy radiated was equal to the change in energy of the atom, $hf$.

Planck found that the constant $h$ was extremely small, about $7 \times 10^{-34}$ J/Hz. This meant that the energy-changing steps were too small to be noticeable in ordinary bodies. Still, the introduction of quantized energy was extremely troubling to physicists, especially Planck himself. It was the first hint that the physics of Newton and Maxwell might be valid only under certain conditions.

## Photoelectric Effect

There was a second troubling experimental result unexplained by Maxwell. A negatively-charged zinc plate was discharged when ultraviolet radiation fell on it, but it remained charged when ordinary light fell on it. Furthermore, a positively-charged plate was never discharged. Further study showed that the zinc plate was discharged by emitting electrons. The emission of electrons when electromagnetic radiation falls on an object is called the **photoelectric effect**.

The photoelectric effect can be studied in a photocell like that in Figure 27–3. The cell contains two metal electrodes sealed in an evacuated tube. The air has been removed to keep the metal surface clean and to keep electrons from being stopped by air molecules. The large electrode, the cathode, is usually coated with cesium or another alkali metal. The second electrode, the anode, is made of a thin wire so it does not block any radiation. The tube is often made of quartz to permit ultraviolet wavelengths to pass through. A potential difference that attracts electrons to the anode is placed across the electrodes.

When no radiation falls on the cathode, current does not flow in the circuit. When radiation does fall on the cathode, however, a current, shown by the meter, flows in the circuit. Current is the result of electrons, called photoelectrons, being ejected from the cathode by the radiation. The electrons travel to the positive electrode, the anode.

**FIGURE 27–2. Max Planck, 1858-1947. Planck was awarded the Nobel Prize in 1918 for his discovery of the quantized nature of energy.**

The emission of electrons from metal as a result of electromagnetic radiation is the photoelectric effect.

**FIGURE 27–3. A diagram of a photocell circuit shows the ejection of electrons from a metal. Photocells are used to turn lights on automatically at dusk.**

**FIGURE 27–4. The kinetic energy of the ejected electrons can be measured with this device. An ammeter is used to measure the current flowing through the circuit.**

Light source

Cathode

Anode

Photocell

Variable rheostat

Only high frequency (short wavelength) radiation ejects electrons. The threshold frequency depends on the cathode material.

Not all radiation results in current flow. Electrons are ejected only if the frequency of the radiation is above a certain minimum value, called the **threshold frequency**, $f_0$. The threshold frequency varies with the metal. All wavelengths of light except red, for example, will eject electrons from cesium, while ultraviolet is needed with zinc. Radiation of a frequency below $f_0$ does not eject any electrons from the metal, no matter how bright it is. Even if it is very dim, radiation at or above the threshold frequency causes electrons to leave the metal immediately—the greater the intensity of radiation, the larger the flow of photoelectrons.

The electromagnetic wave theory cannot explain these facts. In the wave theory, a more intense radiation, regardless of frequency, has stronger electric and magnetic fields. According to wave theory, the electric field accelerates and ejects the electrons from the metal. With very faint light shining on the metal, electrons would require a very long time before they gained enough energy to be ejected.

Maxwell's theory cannot explain the photoelectric effect.

In 1905, Albert Einstein published a revolutionary theory that explained the photoelectric effect. According to Einstein, light and other forms of radiation consist of discrete bundles of energy, which were later called **photons**. The energy of each photon depends on the frequency of the light. The energy is given by the equation $E = hf$, where $h$ is Planck's constant, $6.626 \times 10^{-34}$ J/Hz.

According to Einstein's photon theory, light and other forms of electromagnetic radiation consists of particles.

It is important to note that Einstein's theory of the photon goes further than Planck's theory of hot bodies. While Planck had proposed that vibrating atoms emitted radiation with energy equal to $hf$, he did not suggest that light and other forms of radiation acted like particles. Einstein's theory of the photon reinterpreted and extended Planck's theory of hot bodies.

Einstein's photoelectric-effect theory explains the existence of a threshold frequency. A photon with a minimum energy, $hf_0$, is needed to eject an electron from the metal. If the photon has a frequency below $f_0$, it does not have the energy needed to eject an electron. Light with a frequency greater than $f_0$ has more energy than needed to eject an electron. The excess energy, $hf - hf_0$, becomes the kinetic energy of the electron. Thus,

$$E_k = hf - hf_0.$$

# F.Y.I.

Einstein's equation is really little more than conservation of energy. The incoming photon has energy $hf$. An amount of energy, $hf_0$, is needed to free the electron from the metal. The remainder becomes the kinetic energy of the electron. Notice that an electron cannot simply accumulate photons until it has enough energy; only one photon interacts with one electron. In addition, $hf_0$ is actually the minimum energy needed to free an electron. Not all electrons in a solid have the same energy, so most need more than this minimum to escape. Thus, when we speak of the kinetic energy of the ejected electrons, we mean the maximum kinetic energy an ejected electron could have. Other electrons will have less kinetic energy.

How can Einstein's theory be tested? The kinetic energy of the ejected electrons can be measured indirectly by a device like the one pictured in Figure 27–4. A variable electric potential difference across the tube makes the anode negative. By analogy to gravity, the electrons must climb a hill to reach the anode. Only if they have enough kinetic energy at the cathode will they reach the anode before turning back. Light of the chosen frequency illuminates the cathode. An ammeter measures the current flowing through the circuit. The experimenter increases the opposing potential difference, making the anode more negative. Electrons must be ejected from the cathode with higher and higher kinetic energies to reach the anode. At some voltage, called the stopping potential, no electrons have enough energy to reach the anode, and the current falls to zero. The maximum kinetic energy of the electrons at the cathode equals their potential energy at the anode, $E_k = -qV_0$. Here, $V_0$ is the magnitude of the stopping potential in volts (J/C) and $q$ is the charge of the electron ($-1.60 \times 10^{-19}$ C).

The joule is too large a unit of energy to use with atomic systems. A more convenient energy unit is the electron volt (eV). One electron volt is the energy of an electron accelerated across a potential difference of one volt. That is,

$$1 \text{ eV} = (1.60 \times 10^{-19} \text{ C})(1 \text{ V}) = 1.60 \times 10^{-19} \text{ C} \cdot \text{V}$$
$$1 \text{ eV} = 1.60 \times 10^{-19} \text{ J}$$

## POCKET LAB

### SEE THE LIGHT

Close the shades and turn off all the room lights. Look at a 120-W lamp as you slowly increase and decrease the voltage across the lamp with a dimmer switch. Describe your results. What would you expect to see if you repeat the experiment as you look through a diffraction grating? Why? Try it. Describe your results.

Part of the photon's energy frees the electron from the metal. The remainder becomes the kinetic energy of the electron.

The $E_k$ of the electrons can be determined by measuring the potential difference needed to stop them.

## Example Problem

### Kinetic Energy of a Photoelectron

The stopping potential that prevents electrons from flowing across a certain photocell is 4.0 V. What is the kinetic energy given to the electrons by the incident light? Give the answer in both J and eV.

**Given:** stopping potential, $V_0 = 4.0$ V

**Unknown:** $E_k$

**Basic equation:** $E_k = -qV_0$

**Solution:** $E_k = -qV_0$

$$= -(-1.60 \times 10^{-19} \text{ C})(4.0 \text{ J/C})$$
$$= +6.4 \times 10^{-19} \text{ J}$$
$$= (6.4 \times 10^{-19} \text{ J}) \left( \frac{1 \text{ eV}}{1.6 \times 10^{-19} \text{ J}} \right)$$
$$= 4.0 \text{ eV}$$

**FIGURE 27–5.** This graph shows the kinetic energy of ejected electrons versus frequency of incident radiation.

Planck's constant, $h$, is the slope of the graph of maximum $E_k$ of ejected electrons versus light frequency.

The work function is the energy needed to free an electron from a metal.

A graph of the kinetic energies of the electrons ejected from a metal versus the frequencies of the incident photons is a straight line, Figure 27–5. All metals have similar graphs with the same slope. The slope of all of the lines is Planck's constant, $h$.

$$h = \frac{\Delta E_k}{\Delta f} = \frac{\text{change in maximum } E_K \text{ of ejected electrons}}{\text{change in frequency of incident radiation}}$$

The graphs differ only in the threshold frequency that is needed to free electrons. The threshold frequency is related to the energy needed to free the most weakly-bound electron from a metal, called the **work function** of the metal. The work function is thus measured by $hf_0$.

Robert A. Millikan did the experiments that proved Einstein's photoelectric theory to be correct. Einstein won the Nobel Prize in 1921 for his work on the photoelectric effect. Millikan won the prize two years later.

## Example Problem

### Photoelectric Equation

The threshold frequency of sodium is $5.6 \times 10^{14}$ Hz. **a.** What is the work function of sodium in J and eV? **b.** Sodium is illuminated by light of frequency $8.6 \times 10^{14}$ Hz. What is the kinetic energy of the ejected electrons in eV?

**Given:** threshold frequency,
$f_0 = 5.6 \times 10^{14}$ Hz
illumination frequency,
$f = 8.6 \times 10^{14}$ Hz

**Unknown:** $E_k$
**Basic equation:** $E_k = hf - hf_0$

**Solution:**
**a.** work function $= hf_0$
$= (6.6 \times 10^{-34} \text{ J/Hz})(5.6 \times 10^{14} \text{ Hz})$
$= 3.7 \times 10^{-19} \text{ J}$

$\dfrac{3.7 \times 10^{-19} \text{ J}}{1.6 \times 10^{-19} \text{ J/eV}} = 2.3 \text{ eV}$

**b.** $hf = (6.6 \times 10^{-34} \text{ J/Hz})(8.6 \times 10^{14} \text{ Hz})(1 \text{ eV}/1.6 \times 10^{-19} \text{ J})$
$= 3.5 \text{ eV}$

$E_k = hf - hf_0$
$= 3.5 \text{ eV} - 2.3 \text{ eV}$
$= 1.2 \text{ eV}$

The wavelength of light is more easily measured than its frequency. If the wavelength is given in a problem, the frequency may be found using the equation $\lambda = c/f$, as discussed in Chapter 14. The energy (in eV) of the photon with wavelength $\lambda$ is given by the formula

$$E = hf = \frac{hc}{\lambda}$$

$$= \frac{(6.6 \times 10^{-34} \text{ J/Hz})(3.00 \times 10^8 \text{ m/s})(1 \text{ eV}/1.6 \times 10^{-19} \text{ J})}{\lambda(10^{-9} \text{ m/nm})}$$

$$E = \frac{1.2 \times 10^2}{\lambda} \text{ eV} \cdot \text{nm}.$$

> SOCIOLOGY
> CONNECTION
>
> Many public buildings have doors that open automatically as people approach. These doors are often operated by so-called "electric eyes". A light beam shines across the door opening onto a photovoltaic cell, causing electrons to be given off and a current to flow in a circuit. When the beam is broken, the current stops, and a mechanism is triggered that opens the door. These devices have allowed easier access to many people who would otherwise find door-opening mechanisms difficult to use.

## Practice Problems

1. The stopping potential to prevent current through a photocell is 3.2 V. Calculate the kinetic energy in joules of the photoelectrons as they are emitted.
2. The stopping potential for a photoelectric cell is 5.7 V. Calculate the kinetic energy in electron volts of the photoelectrons as they are emitted.
3. The threshold wavelength of zinc is 310 nm ($310 \times 10^{-9}$ m).
   **a.** Find the threshold frequency of zinc.
   **b.** What is the work function in eV of zinc?
   **c.** Zinc in a photocell is irradiated by ultraviolet light of 240 nm wavelength. What is the kinetic energy of the photoelectrons in eV?
▶ **4.** The work function for cesium is 1.96 eV.
   **a.** Find the threshold wavelength for cesium.
   **b.** What is the kinetic energy in eV of photoelectrons ejected when 425-nm violet light falls on the cesium?

## The Compton Effect

The photoelectric effect demonstrates that, even though it has no mass, a photon has kinetic energy just as a particle does. In 1916, Einstein predicted that the photon should have another particle property, momentum. He showed that the momentum of a photon should be $hf/c$. Since $f/c = 1/\lambda$, the photon's momentum is

$$p = \frac{hf}{c} = \frac{h}{\lambda}.$$

# PHYSICS LAB

## Photoelectric Steel Balls

## Purpose

To simulate the photoelectric effect.

## Materials

· 4 2-cm steel balls
· grooved channel (U channel or shelf bracket)
· red, orange, yellow, green, blue, violet coloured marking pens or coloured stickers

## Procedure

1. Shape the grooved channel as shown in the diagram. Mark a point 4 cm above the table, on the channel, as "R" for red.
2. Mark a point 14 cm above the table, on the channel, with a "V" for violet. Place marks for B, G, Y, and O uniformly between them.
3. Place two steel balls at the lowest point on the channel. These steel balls represent valence electrons in the atom.
4. Place a steel ball on the channel at the red mark. This represents a photon of red light.
5. Release the photon and see if the electrons are removed from the atom. See if either steel ball escapes from the channel.

6. Remove the steel ball that represents the photon from the lower part of the channel.
7. Repeat steps 4-6 for each color mark on the channel. Note: Always start with two electrons at the low point in the channel.

## Observations and Data

1. Which colour photons were able to remove the electrons?
2. Did one photon ever remove more than one electron?

## Analysis

1. Predict what would happen if two red photons could hit the electrons at the same time.
2. Start two steel balls (photons) at the red mark on the channel and see what happens. Describe the results.

## Applications

1. Photographers often have a red light in their darkrooms. Explain why a red light is safe, but a blue light is not safe.

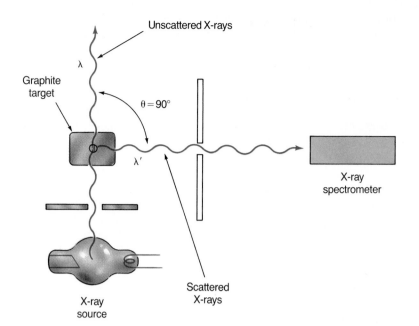

Unscattered X-rays

λ

Graphite
target

θ = 90°

λ'

X-ray
spectrometer

Scattered
X-rays

X-ray
source

**FIGURE 27–6.** Diagram of apparatus used by Compton to study the nature of photons (a). An increased wavelength denotes that the X-ray photons have lost energy (b).

b

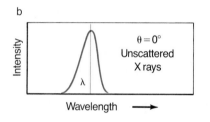

θ = 0°
Unscattered
X rays

λ

Intensity

Wavelength ⟶

θ = 90°
Scattered
X rays

λ   λ'

Intensity

Wavelength ⟶

The American Arthur Holly Compton tested Einstein's theory in 1922. Compton directed X rays of known wavelength at a graphite target, Figure 27–6a, and measured the wavelengths of the X rays scattered by the target. He found that some of the X rays were scattered without change in wavelength. Other scattered X rays, however, had a longer wavelength than the original, as shown in Figure 27–6b. The energy of a photon is *hf*, given by

$$E = \frac{hc}{\lambda}.$$

Thus, an increased wavelength meant that the X-ray photons had lost both energy and momentum. The shift in energy of scattered photons is called the **Compton effect**. It is a tiny shift, about $10^{-3}$ nm, and so is measurable only when X rays, having wavelengths of $10^{-2}$ nm or smaller, are used. In later experiments, Compton observed that electrons were ejected from the graphite block during the experiment. He suggested that the X-ray photons collided with electrons in the graphite target and transferred energy and momentum. These collisions were similar to the elastic collisions experienced by two billiard balls, Figure 27–7. Compton tested this suggestion by measuring the energy of the ejected electrons. He found that the energy and momentum gained by the electrons equaled the energy and momentum lost by the photons. Photons obeyed the laws of conservation of momentum and energy.

The Compton effect is the increase in wavelength when X rays are scattered off of electrons.

Some X rays lose energy when they strike matter and are scattered with longer wavelengths.

**FIGURE 27–7. The energy and momentum gained by electrons equal the energy and momentum lost by photons.**

In the Compton effect, the incoming photon suffers an elastic collision with an atomic electron. Energy and momentum are transferred to the electron.

Compton's experiments further verified Einstein's theory of photons. A photon is a particle that has energy and momentum. Unlike matter, however, a photon has no mass and travels at the speed of light.

## CONCEPT REVIEW

**1.1** Describe, in general, how the intensity of a hot body at a fixed temperature varies with frequency of the radiation.

**1.2** As the temperature of a body is increased, how does the frequency of peak intensity change? How does the total energy radiated change?

**1.3** An experimenter sends an X ray into a target. An electron, but no other radiation, comes out. Was the event the photoelectric or Compton effect?

**1.4 Critical Thinking:** The photon and electron are treated as "billiard balls" in the Compton effect. Suppose the electron were replaced by the much more massive proton. Would the proton gain as much energy from the collision as the electron? Would the photon lose as much energy as it would colliding with the electron?

## Objectives

· describe evidence of the wave nature of matter; solve problems relating wavelength to particle momentum.

· recognize the dual nature of both waves and particles and the impact of the Heisenberg uncertainty principle.

# 27.2 PARTICLES BEHAVE LIKE WAVES

The photoelectric effect and Compton scattering showed that electromagnetic waves had particle properties. The French physicist Louis-Victor de Broglie (di-BROY-lee) (1892–1987) suggested in 1923 that material particles have wave properties. His suggestions were ignored by other scientists until Einstein read his papers and supported his ideas.

## Matter Waves

By analogy with the momentum of the photon, $p = h/\lambda$, de Broglie said that the momentum of a particle is given by the equation

$$p = mv = \frac{h}{\lambda}.$$

# Physics and society

## LIGHT POLLUTION AND OBSERVATORIES

Depending upon where you live, you're probably only able to see a small percentage of the stars and planets at night. That's because in most industrially-developed countries, the sky is rarely completely dark at night. For years, scientists have been alerting us to a form of pollution that threatens our ability to learn about the rest of our universe: it's called light pollution.

Light pollution is a general glow in the night sky caused by thousands of unshielded lights along highways and in cities to make them safer for travellers. Most of these lights emit light over virtually the entire visible spectrum. "Skyglow" from large metropolitan areas can be seen for more than 160 km. Scientists estimate that lighting has increased 40-fold in the past 20 years. As more light is generated on Earth, less light from the stars is visible to us with the naked eye.

Observatories must attempt to filter out skyglow from starlight. In recent years, new observatories have had to be located in remote locations to avoid light pollution from nearby communities. For example, the Canada-France-Hawaii Telescope sits 4600 m above sea level at the top of an extinct volcano. Today, there is almost no observatory on Earth where illumination from distant cities has not or will not become a problem. For example, a telescope on Mt. Wilson in California was recently put out of use partly because of the severe skyglow from the Los Angeles area.

Earth's atmosphere causes problems of its own for astronomers: thick and dusty, it either blocks or smears much of the light from stars before the light can reach telescopes on Earth. The atmosphere also blocks almost all ultraviolet light, which due to its shorter wavelength, could be focused into much sharper images than visible light. The Hubble Space Telescope, orbiting above Earth's surface, is designed to receive light of all wavelengths. The goal is for astronomers to be able to see five to ten times farther and more clearly than ever before.

## DEVELOPING A VIEWPOINT

Read more about light pollution and observatories, and come to class to discuss the following questions.
1. When do you think is the best time for observing the stars and planets?
2. Can you suggest a solution to the growing problem of light pollution?

## SUGGESTED READINGS

John Bortle, "A Bright Future? Perhaps Too Bright!" *Sky & Telescope*, Nov. 1988, p. 578.
Terry Dunkle, "The Big Glass," *Discover*, July '89, pp. 69–81.
David L. Crawford and Tim B. Hunter, "The Battle Against Light Pollution," *Sky & Telescope*, July 1990, pp. 23–29.

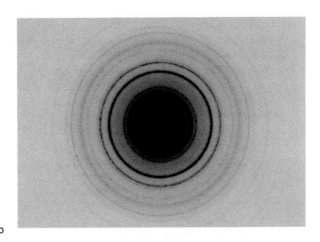

FIGURE 27–8. In the apparatus of Davisson and Germer, a beam of electrons from a hot cathode is directed at a crystal, and angles of the scattered electrons are detected (a). Electron diffraction patterns of aluminum demonstrate the wave characteristics of particles (b).

According to de Broglie, particles should have wavelike properties.

The de Broglie wavelength of ordinary matter is far too small to produce observable effects.

Thus, the **de Broglie wavelength** of the particle is given by

$$\lambda = \frac{h}{p} = \frac{h}{mv}.$$

According to de Broglie, particles such as electrons or protons should show wavelike properties. Effects like diffraction and interference had never been observed, so de Broglie's work was greeted with considerable doubt. In 1927, the results of two different experiments showed the diffraction of electrons. One experiment was conducted by the Englishman G. P. Thomson, the son of J. J. Thomson, and the other by two Americans, C. J. Davisson and L. H. Germer. The experiments used a beam of electrons with a small crystal as a target. The atoms in the crystal formed a mesh-like pattern that acted as a diffraction grating. Electrons diffracted from the crystal formed the same patterns that X rays of a similar wavelength formed, Figure 27–8. The two experiments proved that material particles have wave properties.

The wave nature of ordinary matter is not obvious because the wavelengths are so extremely short that wavelike behaviors such as diffraction and interference are not observed. Consider the de Broglie wavelength of a 0.25-kg baseball when it leaves a bat with a speed of 20 m/s.

$$\lambda = \frac{h}{mv} = \frac{6.6 \times 10^{-34} \text{ J} \cdot \text{s}}{(0.25 \text{ kg})(20 \text{ m/s})} = 1.3 \times 10^{-34} \text{ m}$$

The wavelength is far too small to have effects that can be observed.

## Example Problem

### de Broglie Wavelength of an Electron

An electron is accelerated by a potential difference of 150 V. What is the de Broglie wavelength of this electron?

**Given:** potential difference, $V = 150$ V

**Unknown:** de Broglie wavelength, $\lambda$
**Basic equations:** $qV = \frac{1}{2}mv^2$, $\lambda = h/mv$

**Solution:** $qV = \frac{1}{2}mv^2$, so

$$v = \sqrt{\frac{2qV}{m}}$$

$$= \sqrt{\frac{2(1.6 \times 10^{-19}\,\text{C})(150\,\text{V})}{9.11 \times 10^{-31}\,\text{kg}}}$$

$$= 7.3 \times 10^6\,\text{m/s}$$

Thus, $\lambda = \dfrac{h}{mv} = \dfrac{6.6 \times 10^{-34}\,\text{J}\cdot\text{s}}{(9.11 \times 10^{-31}\,\text{kg})(7.3 \times 10^6\,\text{m/s})}$

$$= 9.9 \times 10^{-11}\,\text{m}$$

This wavelength is approximately the distance between the atoms in a crystal. For this reason, a crystal used as a grating produces diffraction and interference effects, making the wave properties of very small particles of matter observable.

## Practice Problems

**5. a.** Find the speed of an electron accelerated by a potential difference of 25 V.
   **b.** What is the de Broglie wavelength of this electron?
**6.** A 7.0-kg bowling ball rolls down the alley with a velocity of 8.5 m/s.
   **a.** What is the de Broglie wavelength of the bowling ball?
   **b.** Why does the bowling ball show little wave behaviour?
**7.** An X ray of wavelength $5.0 \times 10^{-12}$ m is travelling in a vacuum.
   **a.** Calculate the momentum associated with this X ray.
   **b.** Why does the X ray show little particle behaviour?
▶ **8. a.** In what ways are electrons and photons the same?
   **b.** In what ways are they different?

## Particles and Waves

When you think of a particle, you think of properties like mass, size, kinetic energy, and momentum. You can locate a particle at one point in space. You do not think of particles showing diffraction and interference effects.

The measures of a wave, on the other hand, are frequency, wavelength, and amplitude. A wave travels with a given velocity. A wave cannot be located at one point in space because it must be at least one wavelength long. Thus a wave must be spread out in space. It produces effects like diffraction and interference.

In this chapter, however, we have shown, as another example of the symmetry of the natural world, that light and other electromagnetic waves also have particle-like properties. We have also shown that matter, which is normally considered to be made of particles, can behave like a wave.

Is light a particle or a wave? In the years since the work of Einstein, de Broglie, and others, many physicists and philosophers have tried to work out a satisfactory answer to this question. Some have suggested

Electromagnetic waves show particle-like properties.

Particles show wavelike properties.

The particle and wave properties complement each other to produce a more complete picture of both particles and waves.

Properties of an object cannot be defined in the abstract. A means of measuring them must be described.

The Heisenberg uncertainty principle states that a particle's momentum and position cannot both be known precisely at the same time.

that the nature of light depends on the experiment. In the Compton effect, for example, the X ray acts like a particle when it is scattered from the graphite target. It is being treated like a wave when its wavelength is measured using a crystal like a diffraction grating. Most physicists share a belief that the particle and wave aspects of light show complementary views of the true nature of light. They must be taken together. Either picture alone, particle or wave, is incomplete.

Most physicists hold that the properties of an object can only be defined by thinking of an experiment that can measure them. One cannot simply say that a particle is at a certain location moving with a specific speed. Rather, an experiment must be described that will locate the particle and measure its speed.

How can you find the location of a particle? You must touch it or reflect light from it, Figure 27–9. The reflected light then must be collected by an instrument or the human eye. Because of diffraction effects, light spreads out, making it impossible to locate the particle exactly. You can reduce the spreading by decreasing the wavelength of the light. Thus the shorter the wavelength, the more precisely you can measure the location.

The Compton effect, however, proves that when light of short wavelengths strikes a particle, the momentum of the particle is changed. Therefore, the act of precisely measuring the location of an object changes its momentum, and the more precisely we try to measure its location, the larger the likely change in its momentum.

In the same way, if the momentum of the particle is measured, the position of the particle will be changed. *The position and momentum of a particle cannot both be precisely known at the same time.* This fact is called the **Heisenberg uncertainty principle** after the German physicist Werner Heisenberg. It is the result of the dual wave and particle description of light and matter.

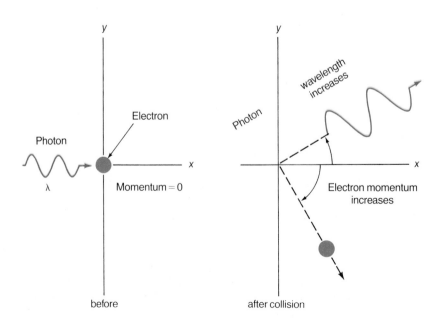

**FIGURE 27–9. A particle can be seen only by scattering light off of it. The scattering changes the electron momentum.**

# CONCEPT REVIEW

**2.1** If Davisson and Germer had wanted to increase the wavelength of the electrons they used, should they have decreased or increased their energy?

**2.2** If you want to increase the wavelength of a proton, you slow it down. If you want to increase the wavelength of a photon, what could you do?

**2.3** If you try to find the location of a beam of light by having it pass through a narrow hole, why can you not tell much about the direction of the beam?

**2.4** **Critical Thinking:** Physicists recently made a "diffraction grating" of standing waves of light. They sent atoms through this grating and observed interference. If the spacing of the "slits" in the grating was half a wavelength, 250 nm, roughly what would you expect that the de Broglie wavelength of the atoms should be?

# C H A P T E R
# 27  REVIEW

. . . . . . . . . . . . . . . . . . . .

## SUMMARY

### 27.1 Waves Behave Like Particles

· Objects hot enough to be incandescent emit light because of the vibrations of the charged particles inside their atoms.
· The spectrum of incandescent objects covers a wide range of wavelengths. The spectrum depends on their temperature.
· Planck explained the spectrum of an incandescent object by supposing that a particle can have only certain energies that are multiples of a small constant now called Planck's constant.
· The photoelectric effect is the emission of electrons when certain metals are exposed to light.
· Einstein explained the photoelectric effect by postulating that light came in bundles of energy called photons.
· The photoelectric effect allows the measurement of Planck's constant, $h$.
· The work function, the energy with which electrons are held inside metals, is measured by the threshold frequency in the photoelectric effect.
· The Compton effect demonstrates the momentum of photons, first predicted by Einstein.

· Photons, or light quanta, are massless and travel at the speed of light. Yet they have energy, $hf$, and momentum, $p = h/\lambda$.

### 27.2 Particles Behave Like Waves

· The wave nature of material particles was suggested by de Broglie and verified experimentally by diffracting electrons off crystals.
· The particle and wave aspects are complementary parts of the complete nature of both matter and light.
· The Heisenberg uncertainty principle states that the position and momentum of a particle (light or matter) cannot both be known precisely at the same time.

## KEY TERMS

| | |
|---|---|
| photoelectric effect | Compton effect |
| threshold frequency | de Broglie wave- |
| photons | length |
| work function | Heisenberg uncer- |
| | tainty principle |

# REVIEWING CONCEPTS

1. Define the word *quantized*.
2. What is quantized in Planck's blackbody radiation theory?
3. What is a quantum of light called?
4. Light above the threshold frequency shines on the metal cathode in a photocell. How does Einstein's theory explain that, as the light intensity is increased, the current of photoelectrons increases?
5. Explain how Einstein's theory accounts for the fact that light below the threshold frequency of a metal produces no photoelectrons, no matter how intense it is.
6. Certain types of black-and-white film are not sensitive to red light. They can be developed with a red "safelight" on. Explain this on the basis of the photon theory of light.
7. How does the Compton effect demonstrate that photons have momentum as well as energy?
8. The momentum of a material particle is *mv*. Can you calculate the momentum of a photon using *mv*? Explain.
9. Describe how the following properties of the electron could be measured. Explain in each case what is to be done.
   **a.** charge   **b.** mass   **c.** wavelength
10. Describe how the following properties of a photon could be measured. Explain in each case what is to be done.
   **a.** energy   **b.** momentum   **c.** wavelength

# APPLYING CONCEPTS

1. What is the change in the intensity of red light given off by blackbody radiation if the temperature increases from 4000 K to 8000 K?
2. Two iron rods are held in a fire. One glows dark red while the other is glowing bright orange.
   **a.** Which rod is hotter?
   **b.** Which rod is radiating more energy?
3. Will high frequency light eject a greater number of electrons from a photo-sensitive surface than low frequency light, assuming both frequencies are above the threshold frequency?

4. Potassium in a photocell emits photoelectrons when struck by blue light. Tungsten emits them only when ultraviolet light is used.
   **a.** Which metal has a higher threshold frequency?
   **b.** Which metal has a larger work function?
5. Electrons in one electron beam have a greater speed than those in another. Which electrons have the longer de Broglie wavelength?
6. As the speed of a particle increases, does its associated wavelength increase or decrease?
7. Compare the de Broglie wavelength of a baseball moving 20 m/s with the size of the baseball.

# PROBLEMS

## 27.1 Waves Behave Like Particles

▶ 1. A home uses about $4 \times 10^{11}$ J of energy each year. In many parts of North America, there are about 3000 h of sunlight each year.
   **a.** How much energy from the sun falls on 1 m² each year?
   **b.** If the solar energy can be converted to useful energy with an efficiency of 20%, how large an area of converters would produce the energy needed by the home?
2. The stopping potential of a certain metal is 5.0 V. What is the maximum kinetic energy of the photoelectrons in
   **a.** electron volts?   **b.** joules?
3. To block the current in a photocell, a stopping potential of 3.8 V is used. Find the kinetic energy of the photoelectrons in J.
4. What potential difference is needed to stop electrons having a maximum kinetic energy of $4.8 \times 10^{-19}$ J?
5. The threshold frequency of sodium is $4.4 \times 10^{14}$ Hz. How much work must be done to free an electron from the surface of the sodium?
6. If light with a frequency of $1.00 \times 10^{15}$ Hz falls on the sodium in the previous problem, what is the maximum kinetic energy of the photoelectrons?
7. Barium has a work function of 2.48 eV. What is the longest wavelength of light that will cause electrons to be emitted from barium?

8. A photocell is used by a photographer to measure the light falling on the subject to be photographed. What should be the work function of the cathode if the photocell is to be sensitive to red light ($\lambda = 680$ nm) as well as the other colours?

9. The threshold frequency of tin is $1.2 \times 10^{15}$ Hz.
   a. What is the threshold wavelength?
   b. What is the work function of tin?
   c. Electromagnetic radiation of 167 nm wavelength falls on tin. What is the kinetic energy of the ejected electrons in eV?

10. The threshold frequency of a given metal is $6.7 \times 10^{14}$ Hz. Calculate the kinetic energy in eV of the electrons ejected when the surface is illuminated with light of wavelength
    a. 350 nm.  b. 550 nm.

▶ 11. The work function of iron is 4.7 eV.
   a. What is the threshold wavelength of iron?
   b. Iron is exposed to radiation of wavelength 150 nm. What is the maximum kinetic energy of the ejected electrons in eV?

▶ 12. Suppose a 5.0-g object, such as a nickel, vibrates while connected to a spring. Its maximum velocity is 1.0 cm/s.
   a. Find a maximum kinetic energy of the vibrating object.
   b. The object emits energy in the form of light of frequency $5.0 \times 10^{14}$ Hz and its energy is reduced by one step. Find the energy lost by the object.
   c. How many step reductions would this object have to make to lose all its energy?

13. What is the momentum of a photon of yellow light whose wavelength is 600 nm?

**27.2 Particles Behave Like Waves**

14. Find the de Broglie wavelength of a deuteron of mass $3.3 \times 10^{-27}$ kg that moves with a speed of $2.5 \times 10^4$ m/s.

15. What is the de Broglie wavelength of a proton moving with a speed of $1.00 \times 10^6$ m/s? The mass of a proton is $1.67 \times 10^{-27}$ kg.

16. An electron is accelerated across a potential difference of 54 V.
   a. Find the maximum velocity of the electron.
   b. Calculate the de Broglie wavelength of the electron.

17. A neutron is held in a trap with a kinetic energy of only 0.025 eV.
   a. What is the velocity of the neutron?
   b. Find the de Broglie wavelength of the neutron.

18. The kinetic energy of the hydrogen atom electron is 13.65 eV.
   a. Find the velocity of the electron.
   b. Calculate the de Broglie wavelength of this electron.
   c. Compare your answer with the radius of the hydrogen atom, 5.19 nm.

▶ 19. An electron has a de Broglie wavelength of 400 nm, the shortest wavelength of visible light.
   a. Find its velocity.
   b. Calculate the energy of this electron in eV.

▶ 20. An electron microscope is useful because the de Broglie wavelength of electrons can be made smaller than the wavelength of visible light. What energy in eV has to be given to an electron for it to have a de Broglie wavelength of 20 nm?

▶ 21. An electron has a de Broglie wavelength of 0.18 nm.
   a. How large a potential difference did it experience if it started from rest?
   b. If a proton has a de Broglie wavelength of 0.18 nm, how large of a potential difference did it experience if it started from rest?

## THINKING PHYSIC-LY

Sun tanning produces cell damage in the skin. Why is ultraviolet light capable of producing this damage while infrared radiation is not?

# CHAPTER
# 28 : The Atom

### ◀ Atomic Secrets

The neon and sodium street lamps and the car headlights in this photograph were photographed with a diffraction grating over the camera lens. Why are the images of the lights different, and how could these differences be used to identify the types of lights?

## √ Concept Check

The following terms or concepts from earlier chapters are important for a good understanding of this chapter. If you are not familiar with them, you should review them before studying this chapter.
· Newton's laws of motion, Chapter 5
· centripetal acceleration, Chapter 7
· energy, Chapter 11
· light spectrum, Chapter 16
· Coulomb's law, Chapter 20
· quantization, photons, Chapter 27

As you have learned, a diffraction grating separates white light into its component colours. Different sources of light look very different through diffraction gratings. While some sources emit continuous spectra, others give off only certain colours. Why is this so? How can the light emitted by atoms be used to help unravel their structure? Today the answers are known, but at the end of the last century these important questions were unsolved.

- explain the method Rutherford and co-workers used to determine the structure of the atom; describe the nuclear model.
- distinguish continuous from line spectra; contrast emission and absorption spectra.
- list Bohr's assumptions; define energy levels, ground and excited states; understand the connection between photon energy and energy level differences.
- referring to the text, use the orbital radius and energy level equations to solve problems using the Bohr model.

# 28.1 THE BOHR MODEL

By the end of the nineteenth century, most scientists agreed that atoms exist. Furthermore, as a result of the discovery of the electron by J. J. Thomson (1856 – 1940), the atom could not be an indivisible particle. All the atoms Thomson tested contained electrons. Yet atoms were known to be electrically neutral and much more massive than electrons. Therefore, atoms must contain not only electrons, but a massive, positively-charged part as well. It took three decades to work out how the parts of the atom are arranged.

## The Nuclear Model

Discovering the nature of the massive part of the atom and the arrangement of the electrons was a major challenge. Physicists and chemists from many countries both cooperated and competed in searching for the solution to this puzzle. The result provided not only knowledge of the structure of the atom, but a totally new approach to both physics and chemistry. The story of this work is one of the most exciting stories of the twentieth century.

J. J. Thomson believed that a massive, positively-charged substance filled the atom. He pictured the electrons arranged within this substance like raisins in a muffin. Ernest Rutherford, who was working in England at the time, performed a series of brilliant experiments that showed that the atom was very different.

Rutherford probed atoms with high speed particles emitted by uranium. In 1896 the French physicist Henri Becquerel (1852–1908) found that compounds containing the element uranium emitted penetrating rays. Some of the emissions were found to be massive, positively-charged particles moving at high speed. These were later named **alpha (α) particles**. The α particles could be detected by a screen coated with zinc sulfide that emitted a small flash of light, or scintillation (sint uhl AY shuhn), each time an α particle hit it, Figure 28–1.

Rutherford's group studied atomic structure by bombarding metal foils with alpha particles.

**FIGURE 28–1. After bombarding metal foil with alpha particles, Rutherford's team concluded that most of the mass of the atom was concentrated in the nucleus.**

Source of α particles

Beam of α particles

Deflected particles

Circular fluorescent screen

Gold foil

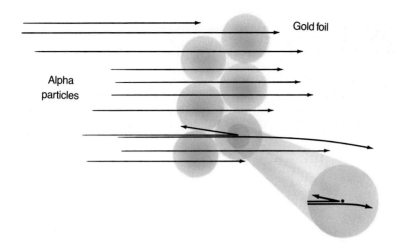

Alpha particles

Gold foil

**FIGURE 28–2.** Most of the alpha particles went through the foil without deflection. A few, however, were deflected at large angles.

# F.Y.I.

Born and raised in New Zealand, Ernest Rutherford later spend much of his time in Canada and England. Between 1898 and 1907, he conducted experiments involving alpha, beta, and gamma particles at Montréal's McGill University.

Rutherford directed a beam of α particles at a thin sheet of metal only a few atoms thick. He noticed that while most of the α particles passed through the sheet, the beam was spread slightly by the metal. Two members of Rutherford's team, Hans Geiger and Ernest Marsden, made detailed studies of the deflection of α particles by metal sheets. In 1910, they found that a few of the particles were deflected at large angles, even larger than 90°, Figure 28–2. Rutherford was amazed because he had assumed that the mass was spread throughout the atom. He commented that it was as surprising as if you had fired a 38.1-cm cannon shell at tissue paper and the shell had bounced back and hit you.

Rutherford, using Coulomb's force law and Newton's laws of motion, found that the results could be explained only if all the positive charge of the atom were concentrated in a tiny, massive central core, now called the nucleus. Rutherford's model is, therefore, called a **nuclear model** of the atom. All the positive charge and essentially all the mass of the atom are in its nucleus. Electrons are outside the nucleus and do not contribute a significant amount of mass. The electrons are far away from the nucleus; the atom is 10 000 times larger than the nucleus. So the atom is mostly empty space.

> The nucleus contains all the positive charge and almost all the mass of the atom.

## Atomic Spectra

How are the electrons arranged around the nucleus of the atom? One of the clues to answering this question came from studying the light emitted by atoms. The set of light wavelengths emitted by an atom is called the atom's **emission spectrum**.

You know that the continuous spectrum of an incandescent blackbody does not depend on the type of atom that makes up the body. The properties of individual atoms become apparent only when they are not packed together. Many substances can be vaporized by heating them in a flame. Then they can emit light that is characteristic of the atoms of the elements that make up the substance. For example, if sodium chloride is put on a wire and held in a flame, the sodium atoms will emit a bright yellow light. Similarly, lithium salts emit red light, and barium salts, green light.

## POCKET LAB

### NUCLEAR BOUNCING

What will happen when an alpha particle "hits" a proton? Place an aluminum pie pan on the table. Gently press four glass marbles (protons) into the pie pan so that they make small indentations near the centre of the pan. Roll a 12-mm steel ball (alpha particle) down a grooved ruler to see if you can hit the marbles. Does the steel ball change its path? Does the steel ball ever bounce "back"? Now put the steel marbles into the indentations (each steel ball represents a nucleus) in the pie pan and roll a marble (alpha particle) down the grooved ruler. How are the results different? Why are the results different?

a      b       c      d

**FIGURE 28–3. A gas discharge tube apparatus (a). Neon (b), argon (c), mercury (d) gases glow when high voltage is applied.**

Gas atoms can be made to emit their characteristic colours by a method shown in Figure 28–3. A glass tube containing neon gas at low pressure has metal electrodes at each end. When a high voltage is applied across the tube, electrons pass through the gas. The electrons collide with the neon atoms, transferring energy to them. The atoms then give up this extra energy, emitting it in the form of light. The light emitted by neon is red. Nitrogen and argon emit a bluish colour, and mercury a greenish blue.

The emission spectrum of an atom can be seen by looking at the light through a replica diffraction grating or by putting such a grating in front of a camera lens, as was done in the opening photo. The spectrum can be studied in greater detail using the instrument shown in Figure 28–4b. In this **spectroscope,** the light passes through a slit and is then dis-

**FIGURE 28–4. A prism spectroscope can be used to observe emission spectra (a, b). The emission spectra of neon (c) and molecular hydrogen (d) show characteristic lines.**

High voltage

Aligning slits

Prism

Detector

b

Gas discharge tube containing gas

a

c

d

persed, passing through a prism or diffraction grating. A lens system collects the dispersed light for viewing through a telescope or for recording on a photographic plate. Each wavelength of light forms an image of the slit. The spectrum of an incandescent solid is a continuous band of colours from red through violet. The spectrum of a gas, however, is a series of lines of different colours. Each line corresponds to a particular wavelength of light emitted by the atoms of the gas. Suppose an unidentified gas, perhaps mercury, argon, or nitrogen, is contained in a tube. When excited, the gas will emit light at wavelengths characteristic of the atoms of that gas. Thus, the gas can be identified by comparing its wavelengths with the lines present in the spectrum of a known sample. Some emission spectra are shown in Figure 28–4c, d.

When the emission spectrum of a combination of elements is photographed, analysis of the lines on the photograph can indicate both the elements present and their relative amounts. If the substance being examined contains a large amount of any particular element, the lines for that element are more intense on the photograph. By comparing the intensities of the lines, the percentage composition of the substance can be determined. An emission spectrum is a useful analytic tool.

A gas that is cool and does not emit light will absorb light at characteristic wavelengths. This set of wavelengths is called an **absorption spectrum**. To obtain an absorption spectrum, white light is sent through a sample of gas and then through a spectroscope, Figure 28–5. The normally continuous spectrum of the white light now has dark lines in it. These lines show that light of some wavelengths has been absorbed. It has been found that often the bright lines of the emission spectrum of a gas and the dark lines of the absorption spectrum occur at the same wavelengths. Thus, cool gaseous elements absorb the same wavelengths that they emit when excited, Figure 28–6. Suppose white light shines through a cool gas. The spectrum will be continuous, but there will be a few dark lines in it. Analysis of the wavelengths of the missing lines can indicate the composition of the gas.

A spectroscope is used to study the wavelength of light emitted by atoms.

. . . . . . . . . . . . . . . . .
◄ **Atomic Secrets**

# F.Y.I.

It was absolutely marvellous working for Wolfgang Pauli. You could ask him anything. There was no worry that he would think a particular question was stupid, since he thought all questions were stupid.

—Victor Weisskopf

Gaseous atoms can also absorb light. The wavelength absorbed is the same as that emitted by excited, hot atoms.

a

b

FIGURE 28–6. The emission spectrum (a) and the absorption spectrum (b) of sodium.

In 1814, while examining the spectrum of sunlight, Josef von Fraunhofer (1787–1826) noticed some dark lines. The dark lines he found in the sun's spectrum are now called Fraunhofer lines, Figure 28–7. To account for these lines, he assumed that the sun has a relatively cool atmosphere of gaseous elements. As light leaves the sun, it passes through these gases. The gases absorb light at their characteristic wavelengths. As a result, these wavelengths are missing from the sun's absorption spectrum. By comparing the missing lines with the known lines of the various elements, the composition of the atmosphere of the sun was determined. In this manner, the element helium was discovered in the sun before it was found on Earth. Spectrographic analysis has made it possible to determine the composition of stars.

Both emission and absorption spectra are valuable scientific tools. As a result of the characteristic spectrum emitted by each element, chemists are able to analyze unknown materials by observing the spectra they emit. Not only is this an important research tool, it is important in industry as well. For example, steel mills reprocess large quantities of scrap iron of varying compositions. The exact composition of a sample of scrap can be determined in minutes by spectrographic analysis. The composition of the steel can then be adjusted to suit commercial specifications. Aluminum, zinc, and other metal processing plants employ the same method.

The study of spectra is a branch of science known as spectroscopy. Spectroscopists are employed throughout the research and industrial communities.

## The Bohr Model of the Atom

In the nineteenth century many physicists tried to use atomic spectra to determine the structure of the atom. Hydrogen was studied extensively because it is the lightest element and has the simplest spectrum. The visible spectrum of hydrogen consists of four lines: red, green, blue, and violet, Figure 28–8. The Swedish scientist A. J. Ångstrom (1814–1874) made very careful measurements of the wavelengths of these lines. Any theory that explained the structure of the atom would have to account for these wavelengths.

410 nm  434 nm  486 nm  656 nm

**FIGURE 28–8. The emission spectrum of hydrogen in the visible range has four lines.**

# PHYSICS LAB : Shots in the Dark

## Purpose

To study atomic scattering by investigating the "size" of a target through use of a model.

## Materials

- 3 dozen # 0 rubber stoppers
- bed sheet (or blanket)
- goggles
- atomic model (see diagram)
- blindfold (or darkened goggles)

## Procedure

Each student must wear goggles while using the model.

1. Construct the model according to the diagram. Set up a data table with columns for student, number of shots, and number of hits.
2. Each student will be blindfolded and led to a position 3 m directly in front of the target area.
3. Each student will be allowed to toss 10 rubber stoppers (1 at a time) into the target area. If a rubber stopper does not strike within the target area, the shooter should be told "too high", "too low", etc. and given an extra rubber stopper.
4. Students will be able to hear the a nuclear "hit". After a hit, the guide should instruct the shooter that another hit cannot be counted on the same target and the shots should be moved around.
5. After a student finishes her throws, she will be the guide for the next student "shooter".
6. After serving as guide, each student should record her initials and the number of hits on the chalkboard.

## Observations and Data

1. Record each student, the number of shots, and the number of hits.
2. Did the students with more hits have better data?

## Analysis

There are six circular targets within the target area. The ratio of hits/shots is given by the following:

$$\frac{\text{hits}}{\text{shots}} = \frac{\text{target area}}{\text{total model area}} = \frac{6\pi r^2}{\text{width} \times \text{height}}$$

1. Find the class total for the number of shots and hits. Use the totals to calculate the total area for the six targets. Divide the total area by 6 to estimate the area for each target. Then calculate the radius for each target.
2. The uncertainty for this type of experiment decreases with more shots. The percent uncertainty is given by the following:

$$\% \text{ uncertainty} = \frac{(\text{shots})^{\frac{1}{2}}}{\text{shots}} \times 100\%$$

Find the uncertainty for your class.

## Applications

1. A recent phone poll sampled 800 people. What is the estimate of uncertainty in the poll?

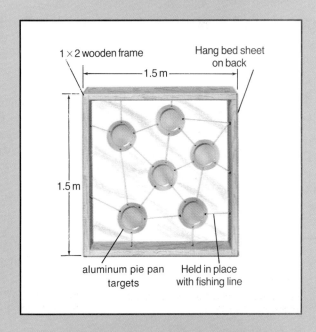

1 × 2 wooden frame

Hang bed sheet on back

1.5 m

1.5 m

aluminum pie pan targets

Held in place with fishing line

**FIGURE 28–9. Bohr's planetary model of the atom postulated that electrons moved in fixed orbits around the nucleus.**

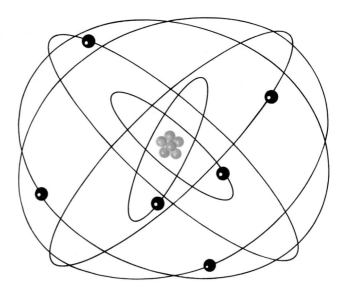

Rutherford's model did not account for (1) the lack of emission of radiation as electrons move about the nucleus, and (2) the emission of light at only certain wavelengths.

Bohr assumed that electrons in a stable orbit around the nucleus did not radiate energy.

**FIGURE 28–10. The energy of the emitted photon is equal to $E_f - E_i$.**

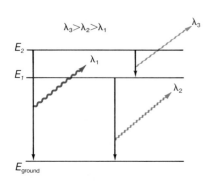

Any valid theory of the structure of the atom would also have to fit Rutherford's nuclear model. Rutherford had suggested that electrons orbited the nucleus much as the planets orbit the sun. There was, however, a serious problem with this planetary model. An electron in an orbit is constantly accelerated toward the nucleus. As discussed in Chapter 27, accelerated electrons radiate energy by emitting electromagnetic waves. At the rate an electron would lose energy, it would spiral into the nucleus in only $10^{-9}$ s. Atoms are known to be stable, however, and to last for long times. Thus, the planetary model was not consistent with the laws of electromagnetism. In addition, if the planetary theory were true, the accelerated electron should radiate energy at all wavelengths. But, as we have seen, the light emitted by atoms is radiated only at specific wavelengths.

The Danish physicist Niels Bohr (1885–1962) went to England in 1911 and soon joined Rutherford's group to work on the problem of the atom. He tried to unite the nuclear model with Einstein's quantum theory of light. This was a courageous idea because in 1911 Einstein's revolutionary theory of the photoelectric effect had not yet been confirmed by experiment and was not widely accepted.

Bohr started with the planetary arrangement of electrons, Figure 28–9, but made the bold hypothesis that the laws of electromagnetism do not operate inside atoms. He postulated that an electron in a stable orbit does not radiate energy, even though it is accelerating.

If energy was not radiated when electrons were in stable orbits, when was it radiated? Bohr suggested light was emitted when the electron's energy *changed*, Figure 28–10. According to Einstein, the energy of a photon of light is given by the equation $E = hf = hc/\lambda$. Thus, said Bohr, if the emission spectrum contains only certain wavelengths, then an electron can emit or absorb only specific amounts of energy. Therefore, the atomic electrons can have only certain amounts of energy. That is, the energy of an electron in an atom is **quantized**.

The quantization of energy in atoms is unlike everyday experience. For example, if the energy of a pendulum were quantized, it could oscillate only with certain amplitudes, such as 10 cm or 20 cm, but not, for example, 11.3 cm.

The atomic electron is allowed to have different amounts of energy called **energy levels**. When an electron has the smallest allowable amount of energy, it is in the lowest energy level, called the **ground state**. If an electron absorbs energy, it can make a transition to a higher energy level, called an **excited state**. Atomic electrons usually remain in excited states only a very small fraction of a second before returning to the ground state and emitting energy.

The energy of an orbiting electron in an atom is the sum of the kinetic energy of the electron and the potential energy resulting from the attractive force between the electron and the nucleus. The energy of an electron in an orbit near the nucleus is less than that of an electron in an orbit farther away because work must be done to move an electron to orbits farther away from the nucleus. The electrons in excited states have larger orbits and correspondingly higher energies.

Einstein's theory says the light photon has an energy $hf$. Bohr postulated that the change in the energy of an atomic electron when a photon is absorbed is equal to the energy of the photon. That is:

$$hf = E_{excited} - E_{ground}.$$

When the electron makes the return transition to the ground state, a photon is emitted. The energy of the photon is equal to the energy difference between the excited and ground states. Molecules have additional discrete energy levels. For example, they can rotate and vibrate, which individual atoms cannot do. As a result, molecules can emit a much wider variety of light frequencies than can atoms, Figure 28–4d.

**FIGURE 28–11. Ernest Rutherford and Niels Bohr devised the planetary model of the atom.**

## Predictions of the Bohr Model

A scientific theory must do more than present postulates; it must allow predictions to be made that can be checked against experimental data. A good theory can also be applied to many different problems, and ultimately provides a simple, unified explanation of some part of the physical world.

Bohr was able to show that his two postulates could be used with the known laws of physics to calculate the wavelengths of light emitted by hydrogen. The calculations were in excellent agreement with the values measured by Ångstrom. As a result, Bohr's model was widely accepted. Unfortunately, the model could not predict the spectrum of the next simplest element, helium. In addition, there was no reason to suggest that the laws of electromagnetism should work everywhere *but* inside the atom. Not even Bohr believed that his model was a complete theory of the structure of the atom.

Despite its shortcomings, the Bohr model describes the energy levels and wavelengths of light emitted and absorbed by hydrogen atoms remarkably well. We will outline the method used by Bohr to calculate the wavelengths of light emitted by an atom. Bohr's calculations start with Newton's law, $F = ma$, applied to an electron of mass $m$ and charge $-q$, in a circular orbit of radius $r$ about a massive particle, a proton, of charge $q$.

$$F_c = ma_c$$
$$Kq^2/r^2 = mv^2/r$$

K is the constant $9.0 \times 10^9$ N · m$^2$/C$^2$ from Coulomb's law.

Bohr's theory correctly predicts the emission wavelengths of hydrogen.

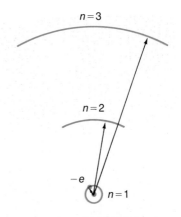

FIGURE 28–12. Radii of electron orbits for the first three energy levels of hydrogen according to the Bohr model.

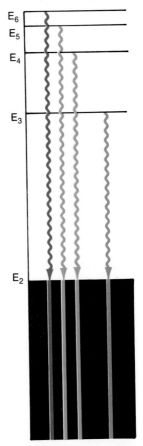

FIGURE 28–13. Bohr's model of the hydrogen atom showed that a definite amount of energy is released when an electron moves from a higher to a lower energy level. The energy released in each transition corresponds to a definite line in the hydrogen spectrum.

Bohr proposed a third postulate. The angular momentum, the product of the momentum of the electron and the radius of its circular orbit, $mvr$, can have only certain values. These values are given by the equation $mvr = nh/2\pi$, where $h$ is Planck's constant and $n$ is an integer. Because the quantity $mvr$ can have only certain values, the angular momentum is said to be quantized.

The result of combining Newton's law with the quantization of angular momentum gives the predicted radii of the orbits of the electrons in the hydrogen atom.

$$r_n = \frac{h^2}{4\pi^2kmq^2} n^2$$

If we substitute SI values for the quantities into the equation, we can calculate the radius of the innermost orbit of the hydrogen atom, where $n = 1$.

$$r_n = \frac{(6.626 \times 10^{-34} \text{J} \cdot \text{s})^2}{4\pi^2(9.00 \times 10^9 \text{N} \cdot \text{m}^2/\text{C}^2)(9.11 \times 10^{-31} \text{kg})(1.60 \times 10^{-19} \text{C})^2}$$

$$= 5.30 \times 10^{-11} \frac{\text{J}^2 \cdot \text{s}^2}{\text{N} \cdot \text{m}^2 \cdot \text{kg}}$$

$$= 5.30 \times 10^{-11} \text{ m, or } 0.053 \text{ nm}$$

A little more algebra shows that the total energy of the electron in its orbit, the sum of the potential and kinetic energy of the electron, is given by

$$E_n = \frac{-2\pi^2k^2mq^4}{h^2} \times \frac{1}{n^2}$$

By substituting numerical values for the constants, we can calculate the energy of the electron.

$$E_n = -2.17 \times 10^{-18} \text{ J}(1/n^2)$$

or, using the electron volt as the unit of energy,

$$E_n = -13.6 \text{ eV}(1/n^2).$$

Both the radius of an orbit and the energy of the electron can have only certain values. That is, both are quantized. The integer $n$ is called the principal **quantum number**. The number $n$ determines the values of $r$ and $E$. The radius increases as the square of $n$, as shown in Figure 28–12. The energy depends on $1/n^2$. The energy is negative because the energy has to be added to the electron to free it from the attractive force of the nucleus, that is, to ionize the atom. The energy levels of hydrogen are shown in Figure 28–13.

## Example Problem

### Orbital Energy of Electrons in the Hydrogen Atom

For the hydrogen atom, determine **a.** the energy of the innermost energy level ($n = 1$), **b.** the energy of the second energy level, **c.** the energy difference between the first and second energy levels.

**Given:** $n = 1, n = 2$  **Unknowns:** $E_1, E_2, \Delta E$

**Basic equation:** $E_n = -13.6 \text{ eV}(1/n^2)$

**Solution:**

**a.** $E_1 = \dfrac{-13.6\,\text{eV}}{(1)^2} = 13.6\,\text{eV}$

**b.** $E_2 = \dfrac{-13.6\,\text{eV}}{(2)^2} = -3.4\,\text{eV}$

**c.** $\Delta E = E_f - E_i = E_2 - E_1$
$= -3.40\,\text{eV} - (-13.6\,\text{eV}) = 10.2\,\text{eV}$

This is the energy that must be added to the atom to raise the electron from its ground state to its first energized state.

**FIGURE 28–14.** Wolfgang Pauli and Niels Bohr, both Nobel laureates for their contributions to the understanding of atomic structure, watch the motions of a spinning top.

# Example Problem

### Frequency and Wavelength of Emitted Photons

An electron in an excited hydrogen atom drops from the second energy level to the first energy level. **a.** Determine the energy of the photon emitted. **b.** Calculate the frequency of the photon emitted. **c.** Calculate the wavelength of the photon emitted.

**Given:** initial quantum number,
$n = 2$
final quantum number,
$n = 1$

**Unknowns:** $hf, f, \lambda$
**Basic equations:** $hf = E_i - E_f,$
$\lambda = c/f$

**a.** $hf = E_i - E_f = E_2 - E_1$
$= -3.4\,\text{eV} - (-13.6\,\text{eV}) = 10.2\,\text{eV}$

**b.** $f = \dfrac{(10.2\,\text{eV})(1.60 \times 10^{-19}\,\text{J/eV})}{6.63 \times 10^{-34}\,\text{J/Hz}} = 2.46 \times 10^{15}\,\text{Hz}$

**c.** $\lambda = \dfrac{c}{f} = \dfrac{3.00 \times 10^8\,\text{m/s}}{2.46 \times 10^{15}\,\text{Hz}} = 1.22 \times 10^{-7}\,\text{m}$

# Practice Problems

**1.** According to the Bohr model, how many times larger is the orbit of hydrogen in the second level than in the first?

**2.** The discussion on page 582 shows how to calculate the radius of the innermost orbit of the hydrogen atom. Note that all factors in the equation are constants with the exception of $n^2$. Use the solution to the Example Problem to find the radius of the orbit of the second, third, and fourth allowable energy levels in the hydrogen atom.

**3.** Calculate the energies of the second, third, and fourth energy levels in the hydrogen atom.

▶ **4.** Calculate the energy difference between $E_3$ and $E_2$ in the hydrogen atom. Do the same for $E_4$ and $E_3$.

**1.1** Which of these quantities are quantized: your height, number of siblings, mass of a sample of gas?

**1.2** Why can't the electrons in Rutherford's nuclear model fly away from the nucleus?

**1.3** Explain how energy is conserved when an atom absorbs a photon of light.

**1.4** How does the Bohr model differ from the Rutherford nuclear model?

**1.5** **Critical Thinking:** An emission spectrum can contain wavelengths produced when an electron goes from the third to the second level. Could you see this line in the absorption spectrum? Why?

# Objectives

· describe the shortcomings of the Bohr model.
· describe the quantum model of the atom.
· describe a laser and the properties of laser light; display an understanding of the operation of the laser.

FIGURE 28–15. These plots show the probability of finding the electron in a hydrogen atom at any given location. The denser the points, the higher the probability of finding the electron.

# 28.2 THE PRESENT MODEL OF THE ATOM

The **Bohr model** of the atom was a major contribution to the understanding of the structure of the atom. In addition to calculating the emission spectrum, Bohr and his students were able to calculate the ionization energy of a hydrogen atom. The ionization energy of an atom is the energy needed to free an electron completely from an atom. The calculated value was in good agreement with experimental data. Using spectrographic data for many elements, they were able to determine the energy levels of the elements, even though they could not predict these levels as they could the levels of hydrogen. The Bohr model also provided an explanation of some of the chemical properties of the elements. The idea that atoms have electron arrangements unique to each element is the foundation of much of our knowledge of chemical reactions and bonding.

The postulates Bohr made, however, could not be explained on the basis of known physics. Electromagnetism required that accelerated particles radiate energy, causing the rapid collapse of the atom. In addition, the reason for the quantization of angular momentum was not known. How could Bohr's work be put on a firm foundation?

## A Quantum Model of the Atom

The first hint to the solution of these problems was provided by de Broglie. As you recall from Chapter 27, he proposed that particles have wave properties just as light waves have particle properties. The wavelength of a particle with momentum $mv$ is given by $\lambda = h/mv$. Therefore, the angular momentum is given by $mvr = hr/\lambda$. The Bohr quantization condition, $mvr = nh/2\pi$, can be written as

$$\frac{hr}{\lambda} = \frac{nh}{2\pi}$$

or

$$n\lambda = 2\pi r.$$

FIGURE 28–16. The exact location of these moving cars cannot be pinpointed. Likewise, only the most probable location of an electron can be determined.

Note that the circumference of the Bohr orbit, $2\pi r$, is equal to a whole number multiple, $n$, of the wavelength of the electron, $\lambda$.

In 1926, the German physicist Erwin Schroedinger (1887–1961) used de Broglie's wave model to create a quantum theory of the atom based on waves. Further work by Werner Heisenberg, Wolfgang Pauli, Max Born, and others developed this theory into a complete description of the atom. The theory does not provide a simple planetary picture of an atom as in the Bohr model. In particular, the radius of the electron orbit is not like the radius of the orbit of a planet about the sun. The wave-particle nature of matter means that it is impossible to know both the position and momentum of an electron at the same time. Thus, the modern **quantum model** of the atom predicts only the *probability* that an electron is at a specific location. The most probable distance of the electron from the nucleus in hydrogen is found to be the same as the radius of the Bohr orbit. The probability that the electron is at any radius can be calculated, and a three-dimensional plot can be constructed that shows regions of equal probability. The region in which there is a high probability of finding the electron is called the **electron cloud**. Figure 28–15 shows a slice through the cloud for the two lowest states of hydrogen.

Even though the quantum model of the atom is difficult to visualize, **quantum mechanics**, which uses this model, has been extremely successful in predicting many details of the structure of the atom. These details are very difficult to calculate exactly for all but the simplest atoms. It takes large computers to make highly accurate approximations for the heavier atoms. Quantum mechanics also allows the structure of many molecules to be calculated, allowing chemists to determine the arrangement of atoms in the molecules. Guided by quantum mechanics, chemists have been able to create new and useful molecules not otherwise available.

Quantum mechanics also allows calculations of the details of the emission and absorption of light by atoms. As a result of this theory, a new source of light has been developed.

Schroedinger created a quantum theory of the atom based on Bohr's atomic model and de Broglie's wave model.

The quantum model of the atom predicts the probability of finding the electron at a specific location.

## POCKET LAB

### BRIGHT LINES

Turn on a gas discharge tube power supply attached to a gas tube so that the tube glows. **CAUTION:** *Do not touch any exposed metal when the power supply is turned on. Dangerous high voltages are present. Always turn off the power supply before changing gas tubes.* Turn off the room lights. Describe the colour. Now look through a diffraction grating at the tube. Make a sketch of the results. Repeat the activity with a different gas tube. Explain the differences.

FIGURE 28–17. Waves of incoherent
light (a) and coherent light (b).

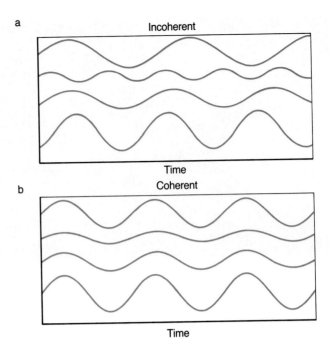

a

Incoherent

Time

b

Coherent

Time

## Lasers

Light is emitted by an incandescent source at many wavelengths and
in all directions. Light produced by an atomic gas consists of only a few
different wavelengths, but is also emitted in all directions. The light
waves emitted by atoms at one end of a discharge tube are not necessarily in step with the waves from the other end. That is, the waves are
not necessarily all at the same point in their cycle, Figure 28–17. Some
will be in step, others out of step. Such light is called incoherent.

Light is emitted by atoms that have been excited. So far we have
discussed two ways in which atoms can be excited, thermal excitation
and electron collision. Atoms can also be excited by collisions with
photons of exactly the right energy.

What happens when an atom is in an excited state? After a very short
time, it normally returns to the ground state, giving off a photon of the
same energy that it had absorbed. This is called spontaneous emission.
In 1917, Einstein considered what would happen to an atom already in

Ordinary light sources emit waves of
different wavelengths that are not in
step with each other.

Einstein predicted that when an atom in
an excited state is struck by a photon
with the correct energy, the atom is
stimulated to emit another photon.

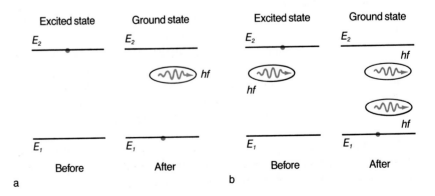

FIGURE 28–18. The spontaneous
emission of a photon with energy $hf$
when an electron in a atom drops
from an excited state $E_2$ to the
ground state $E_1$ (a). The stimulated
emission of a photon when an
excited atom is struck by a photon
with energy $hf$ (b). In both (a) and (b)
$hf = E_2 - E_1$.

FIGURE 28–19. A laser produces a beam of coherent light.

an excited state that is struck by another photon of the same energy as the original photon. He showed that the atom will emit a photon (of the same energy) and go to a lower state. The photon that caused, or stimulated, the emission will not be affected. This process is called **stimulated emission**. The two photons leaving the atom will not only have the same wavelength, they will also be in step, Figure 28–18b.

Either of the two photons can now strike other excited atoms, producing additional photons that are in step with the original photons. This process can continue, producing an avalanche of photons, all of the same wavelength and having their maxima and minima at the same times. To get this process to happen, certain conditions must be met. First, of course, there must be other atoms in the excited state. Second, the photons must be collected so that they strike the excited atoms. A device that fulfills both these conditions was invented in 1959 and is called a **laser**. The word laser is an acronym. It stands for **L**ight **A**mplification by **S**timulated **E**mission of **R**adiation. An atom that emits light when stimulated in a laser is said to *lase*.

The atoms in a laser can be put into the excited state, or pumped, in different ways. An intense flash of light with a wavelength shorter (more energetic) than that of the laser can pump the atoms. The more energetic photons produced by the flash collide with and excite the lasing atoms. One atom decays to a lower energy state, starting the avalanche. As a result, a brief flash or pulse of laser light is emitted. Alternatively, a continuous electric discharge like that in a neon sign can be used to put atoms in the excited state. The laser light resulting from this process is continuous rather than pulsed. The helium-neon lasers often seen in science classrooms, Figure 28–19, are continuous lasers. An electric discharge excites the helium atoms. They collide with the neon atoms, pumping them to an excited state causing them to lase.

Photons produced by stimulated emission are all in step, that is, they are coherent.

A laser contains atoms that have been put into their excited states. It has mirrors that reflect light emitted by the atoms so more atoms are stimulated to emit.

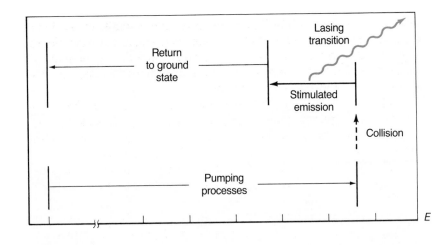

FIGURE 28–20. A photon striking an atom in the excited state stimulates it to make a transition to a lower state and emit a second coherent photon.

The photons emitted by the atoms are collected by placing the glass tube containing the atoms between two parallel mirrors. One mirror reflects all the light hitting it while the other allows about 1% to pass through. When a photon strikes an atom in the excited state, it stimulates the atom to make a transition to the lower state. Thus, two photons leave the atom. These photons can strike other atoms and produce more photons starting the avalanche. Photons that are directed toward the ends will be reflected back into the gas by the mirrors. Some of the photons will exit the tube through the partially reflecting mirror, producing the laser beam.

Laser light is highly directional because of the parallel mirrors. The light beam is very small, typically about 0.5 mm in diameter, so the light is very intense. The light is all one wavelength, or monochromatic, because the transition of electrons between only one pair of energy levels in one type of atom is involved. Finally, laser light is coherent because all the stimulated photons are emitted in step with the photons that struck the atoms.

Laser light is directional, monochromatic, intense, and coherent.

Table 28–1

| Common Lasers | | |
|---|---|---|
| **Medium** | **Wavelength (nm)** | **Type** |
| Nitrogen | 337 (UV) | Pulsed |
| Helium-cadmium | 441.6 | Continuous |
| Argon ion | 476.5, 488.0 | Continuous |
| Krypton ion | 524.5 | Continuous |
| Neon | 632.8 | Continuous |
| Ruby | 694.3 | Pulsed |
| Gallium arsenide | 840-930 (IR) | Continuous |
| Neodynium | 1040 (IR) | Pulsed |
| Carbon dioxide | 10 600 (IR) | Continuous |

(The wavelength of gallium arsenide depends on temperature.)

Many substances, solids, liquids, or gases, can be made to lase in this way. Most produce laser light at only one wavelength. For example, red is produced by a neon laser, blue by argon, and green by helium-cadmium. The light from some lasers, on the other hand, can be tuned, or adjusted, over a range of wavelengths.

All lasers are very inefficient. No more than 1% of the electrical energy delivered to the laser is converted to light energy. Despite this inefficiency, the unique properties of laser light have led to many applications. The laser beam is narrow and highly directional. It does not spread out over long distances. Surveyors use laser beams for this reason. A laser beam is used to check the straightness of long tunnels or pipes.

Laser light can be directed into a tiny glass fibre. The fibre uses total internal reflection to transmit light over many kilometres with little loss. The laser is switched on and off rapidly, transmitting information through the fibre. In many cities, optical fibres are replacing copper wires for the transmission of telephone calls, computer data, and even television pictures.

The single wavelength of light emitted by lasers makes lasers valuable in spectroscopy. The laser light is used to excite other atoms. The atoms then return to the ground state, emitting characteristic spectra. Samples with extremely small numbers of atoms can be analysed in this way. In fact, single atoms have been detected by means of laser excitation and have even been held almost motionless by laser beams!

Holograms are made possible by the coherent nature of laser light. A hologram, Figure 28–21, is a photographic recording of the phase as well as the intensity of the light. Holograms form realistic three-dimensional images and can be used in industry to study the vibration of sensitive parts.

Holograms use the coherent nature of laser light.

**FIGURE 28–21. When a hologram is made on film, a laser beam is split in two parts by a half-silvered mirror. Interference occurs on the film as the direct laser light meets laser light reflected off an object. The interference of both beams of light allows the film to record both intensity and phase of light from the object.**

The high power of lasers is used in cutting and welding metal as well as surgery.

The concentrated power of laser light is used in a variety of ways. In medicine, lasers can be used to repair the retina in an eye. Lasers can also be used in surgery in place of a knife to cut flesh with little loss of blood. In industry, lasers are used to cut steel and to weld materials together. In the future, lasers may produce nuclear fusion for an almost inexhaustible energy source.

# Physics and technology

## SCANNING TUNNELING MICROSCOPE

A powerful new instrument, the scanning tunnelling microscope (STM), produces pictures of the arrangements of atoms on solid surfaces. With it, scientists can even see bonds between atoms.

An STM uses a very sharp metal "finger" which is brought near, but not touching, the surface to be examined. Because the point of the finger and the surface are not touching, they are insulated from each other. But if a small voltage is applied, some electrons flow (tunnel) across the gap between the surface and the point as a result of the wave nature of electrons. The number of electrons that cross the gap depends on how close the point is to the surface. In this way, the STM maps out the "hills and valleys" of a surface. Each hill is a single atom and each valley is the space between neighboring atoms. STMs have been used to image the surfaces of various metals, semiconductors, and biological systems including viruses, biomembranes, and DNA molecules.

One of the intriguing features of an STM is that, under carefully controlled conditions, it can actually be used to move individual atoms into desired patterns.

· What practical applications might arise from the ability of the STM to manipulate individual atoms in a controlled manner?

# CONCEPT REVIEW

**2.1** Which of the lasers in Table 28–1 emits the reddest (visible) light? Which emits in the blue?

**2.2** Why could red light not be used to pump a green laser?

**2.3** Why does the Bohr model conflict with the uncertainty principle while the quantum model does not?

**2.4** Critical Thinking: Suppose the electron cloud were to get so small that the atom were almost the size of the nucleus. Use the uncertainty principle to explain why this would take a tremendous amount of energy.

# CHAPTER
# 28 REVIEW

## SUMMARY

### 28.1 The Bohr Model

· Ernest Rutherford directed positively-charged, high-speed alpha particles at thin metal foils. By studying the paths of the reflected particles, he showed that atoms are mostly empty space with a tiny, massive, positively-charged nucleus at the centre.

· The spectra produced by atoms of an element can be used to identify that element.

· If white light passes through a gas, the gas absorbs the same wavelengths it would emit if excited. If light leaving the gas goes through a prism, an absorption spectrum is seen.

· In the model of the atom developed by Niels Bohr, the electrons are allowed to have only certain energy levels.

· In the Bohr model, electrons can make transitions between energy levels. As they do, they emit or absorb electromagnetic radiation.

· The frequency and wavelength of the absorbed and emitted radiation can be calculated using the Bohr model. The calculations agree with experiments.

### 28.2 The Present Model of the Atom

· The quantum mechanical model of the atom cannot be visualized easily. Only the probability that an electron is at a specific location can be calculated.

· Quantum mechanics is extremely successful in calculating the properties of atoms, molecules, and solids.

· Lasers produce light that is directional, powerful, monochromatic, and coherent. Each property gives the laser useful applications.

## KEY TERMS

| | |
|---|---|
| alpha (α) particles | excited state |
| nuclear model | quantum number |
| emission spectrum | Bohr model |
| spectroscope | quantum model |
| absorption spectrum | electron cloud |
| quantized | quantum mechanics |
| energy levels | stimulated emission |
| ground state | laser |

## REVIEWING CONCEPTS

1. Describe how Rutherford determined that the positive charge in an atom is concentrated in a tiny region rather than spread throughout the atom.

2. How does the Bohr model explain why the absorption spectrum of hydrogen contains exactly the same frequencies as its emission spectrum?

3. What are some of the problems with a planetary model of the atom?

4. What three assumptions did Bohr make in developing his model of the atom?
5. How does the Bohr model account for the spectra emitted by atoms?
6. A laboratory laser has a power of only 0.8 mW (8 × 10$^{-4}$ W). Why does it seem stronger than the light of a 100-W lamp?
7. A device like a laser, that emits microwave radiation, is called a maser. What words are likely to make up this acronym?
8. What properties of the laser led to its use in light shows?

# APPLYING CONCEPTS

1. The northern lights are the result of high energy particles coming from the sun striking atoms high in Earth's atmosphere. If you looked at the light through a spectrometer, would you expect to see a continuous or line spectrum? Explain.
2. If white light were emitted from Earth's surface and observed by someone in space, would its spectrum be continuous? Explain.
3. Suppose you wanted to explain quantization to a younger brother or sister. Would you use money or water as an example? Explain.
4. A photon with an energy of 6.2 eV enters a mercury atom in the ground state. Will it be absorbed by the atom? See Figure 28–23. Explain.

5. A certain atom has energy levels, Figure 28–24. If an electron can make transitions between any two levels, how many spectral lines can the atom emit? Which transition gives the photon with the highest energy?

**FIGURE 28–24. Use with Applying Concepts 5.**

6. A photon is emitted when an electron drops through energy levels within an excited hydrogen atom. What is the maximum energy the photon can have? If this same amount of energy were given to an electron in ground state in a hydrogen atom, what would happen?
7. When electrons fall from higher energy levels to the third energy level within hydrogen atoms, are the photons emitted infrared, visible, or ultraviolet light? Explain.
8. Compare the quantum mechanical theory of the atom with the Bohr model.
9. Does a laser that emits red light, green light, or blue light produce photons with the highest energy?

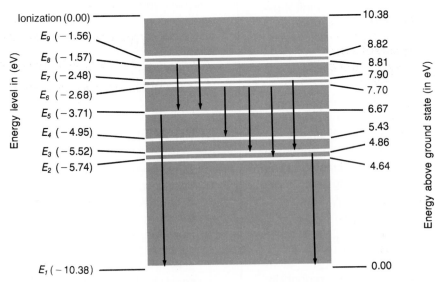

**FIGURE 28–23. Use with Applying Concepts 4 and Problems 3, 4, and 5.**

# PROBLEMS

## 28.1 The Bohr Model

1. The diameter of hydrogen nucleus is $2.5 \times 10^{-15}$ m; the distance between the nucleus and the first electron is about $5 \times 10^{-9}$ m. If you use a baseball to represent the nucleus, how far away would the electron be?
2. A mercury atom drops from 8.82 eV to 6.67 eV above its ground state.
   a. What is the energy of the photon emitted by the mercury atom?
   b. What is the frequency of the photon?
   See Figure 28–23 for Problems 3, 4, and 5.
3. A mercury atom is in an excited state when its energy level is 6.67 eV above the ground state. A photon of energy 2.15 eV strikes the mercury atom and is absorbed by it. To what energy level is the mercury atom raised?
4. A mercury atom is in an excited state at the $E_6$ energy level.
   a. How much energy would be needed to ionize the atom?
   b. How much energy would be released if the electron dropped down to the $E_2$ energy level instead?
5. A mercury atom is in an excited state that has an energy of $-4.95$ eV. It absorbs a photon that raises it to the next higher energy level.
   a. What is the energy of the photon?
   b. What is the photon's frequency?
6. A photon with an energy of 14.0 eV enters a hydrogen atom in the ground state and ionizes it. With what kinetic energy will the electron be ejected from the atom?
7. Calculate the radius of the orbital associated with the energy levels $E_5$ and $E_6$ of the hydrogen atom.
8. What energies are associated with hydrogen atom energy levels $E_2$, $E_3$, $E_4$, $E_5$, and $E_6$?
9. Using the values calculated in Problem 8, calculate the following energy differences for a hydrogen atom.
   a. $E_6 - E_5$   c. $E_4 - E_2$   e. $E_5 - E_3$
   b. $E_6 - E_3$   d. $E_5 - E_2$
10. Use the values from Problem 9 to determine the frequencies of the photons emitted when an electron in a hydrogen atom makes the level changes listed.
11. Determine the wavelengths of the photons of the frequencies calculated in Problem 10.
12. Determine the frequency and wavelength of the photon emitted when an electron drops
    a. from $E_3$ to $E_2$ in an excited hydrogen atom.
    b. from $E_4$ to $E_3$ in an excited hydrogen atom.
13. What is the difference between the energies of the $E_4$ and $E_1$ energy levels of the hydrogen atom?
► 14. By what amount does the mass of a hydrogen atom decrease when its electron makes a down transition from $E_4$ to $E_1$, in an excited hydrogen atom?
► 15. From what energy level did an electron fall if it emits a photon of $9.38 \times 10^{-8}$ m wavelength when it reaches ground state within a hydrogen atom?
► 16. For a hydrogen atom in the $n = 3$ Bohr orbital, find
    a. the radius of the orbital.
    b. the electric force acting on the electron.
    c. the centripetal acceleration of the electron.
    d. the orbital speed of the electron. Compare this speed with the speed of light.
17. A hydrogen atom has its electron in the $n = 2$ level.
    a. If a photon with a wavelength of 332 nm strikes the atom, show that the atom will be ionized.
    b. When the atom is ionized, assume the electron receives the excess energy from the ionization. What will be the kinetic energy of the electron in joules?
► 18. How many orders of magnitude larger is the electrical force between the electron and proton in a hydrogen atom than the gravitational force between them?

## 28.2 The Present Model of the Atom

► 19. Gallium arsenide lasers are used in CD (compact disk) players. If the temperature is chosen so the laser emits at 840 nm, what is the difference in eV between the two lasing energy levels?
► 20. The carbon dioxide laser emits very high power infrared radiation. What is the energy difference in eV between the two lasing energy levels?

# THINKING PHYSIC-LY

Often, posters that look rather dull under ordinary light glow brilliantly under black (UV) light. How is this effect achieved?

# CHAPTER
# 29

# Solid State Electronics

## ◀ The Inside Dope

How are conductors, resistors, diodes, and transistors that are the size of a human hair created on this crystal of pure silicon?

In our society we use electronic devices every day. From transistor radios and televisions to microcomputer-controlled microwave ovens and CD players, the results of solid-state physics and electrical engineering surround us. In the 1950s, the pencil-eraser sized transistor began to replace the much larger vacuum tube that had given birth to the field of electronics in the 1920s. In the 1960s, engineers found ways of putting many individual transistors on a single crystal of silicon. This integrated circuit, or microchip, was the key invention leading to today's technologies. Currently, circuits containing thousands of transistors are about the same size and cost as a single early transistor. Thus, designers can put systems as complex as a computer on your wrist.

## √ Concept Check

The following terms or concepts from earlier chapters are important for a good understanding of this chapter. If you are not familiar with them, you should review them before studying this chapter.
· conductors and insulators, Chapter 20
· current, potential difference, resistance, Chapter 22
· quantum theory, Chapter 27
· atomic structure, Chapter 28

# Objectives

- describe electron motion in conductors as the result of a partially-filled band of allowed energy levels.
- understand that electrons in metals have a very fast random motion, and that current flow results from a slow drift velocity when a potential difference is applied.
- describe insulators as having electrons bound to atoms, requiring more energy to move than is available.
- recognize that conduction in semiconductors is usually the result of doping with small numbers of impurity atoms.
- describe n-type semiconductors as conducting by means of free electrons and p-type semiconductors as conducting by means of "holes."

Each electron in a solid must have its own energy level. These individual levels are very close together in a band.

**FIGURE 29–1. The splitting of atomic energy levels when 2 hydrogen atoms are brought together (a); where 4 hydrogen atoms are brought together (b); and the formation of an energy band when many hydrogen atoms are brought together (c).**

# 29.1 CONDUCTION IN SOLIDS

Electronic devices depend not only on natural conductors and insulators, but even more on materials designed and produced by many scientists and engineers working together. We start our brief investigation into electronics by examining how materials conduct electricity.

## Band Theory of Solids

We have previously divided materials into electrical conductors and insulators. In conductors, electrical charges can move easily, but in insulators, charges remain where they are placed. On the microscopic level, how does a conductor differ from an insulator?

As you learned in Chapter 13, crystalline solids consist of atoms bound together in regular arrangements. From Chapters 27 and 28, you know that an atom consists of a heavy, positively-charged nucleus, surrounded by a cloud of light, negatively-charged electrons. Atoms can have only certain specific energies. This means that energy changes must also be in specific amounts—energy is said to be quantized. The allowed atomic energies are called energy levels. Under most conditions, atoms are in their lowest possible energy level. The lowest energy level is said to be filled, and the other levels are empty.

Suppose we could construct a solid by assembling atoms together, one by one. We start with all the atoms in their lowest energy states. If two of the atoms are now brought together, the electric field of each atom affects the other atom, changing its energy levels. The energy levels of one atom are raised slightly, while those of the other are lowered, Figure 29–1a. There are two atoms, and there are two different sets of energy levels. Now consider what happens when many atoms are brought closely together, as in a solid. No two atoms can have exactly the same energy levels. There are now so many energy levels that they can no longer be identified as unique levels. Rather, the levels are spread into broad **bands**, Figure 29–1c. The bands are separated by values of energy that electrons are not allowed to have. These energies are called **forbidden gaps**. Electrical conduction in solids explained in terms of these bands is called the **band theory**.

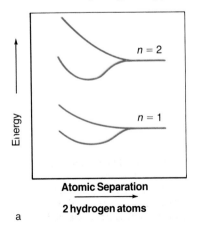

Atomic Separation
2 hydrogen atoms

a

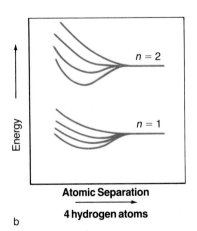

Atomic Separation
4 hydrogen atoms

b

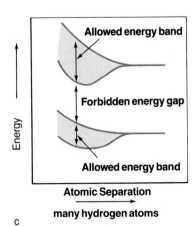

Atomic Separation
many hydrogen atoms

c

Recall that any system will adjust itself until its energy is minimized. In a solid, electrons settle into states of lowest energy. No two electrons can have the same energy. In some materials there are more spaces in the lowest band than there are electrons to fill them. Empty states remain, Figure 29–2. Materials with partially-filled bands are conductors.

In conductors, the lowest band is only partially filled.

## Conductors

Why do materials with partially-filled bands, such as the metals aluminum and copper, conduct electricity? When a potential difference is placed across a material, the resulting electric field exerts a force on the charged particles. They accelerate, the field does work on them, and they gain energy. But their energy can increase only if there is a higher energy level into which they can move. If the bands are only partially filled, then there are available energy levels only slightly higher than their present levels. As a result, the electrons can gain energy from the field and move from one atom to the next, or "conduct electricity."

In a conductor, the higher energy level is only a little above the normal level.

The free electrons in conductors act like atoms in an ordinary gas or water molecules in the sea. They move rapidly about in a random way, changing directions when they collide with the cores of the atoms. If an electric field is put across a length of wire, there will be a net force pushing the electrons to one end. Their overall motion is not greatly changed, however. As shown in Figure 29–3, they continue to move rapidly (speeds of $10^6$ m/s in random directions, but now they also drift very slowly ($10^{-5}$ m/s or less) toward the positive end of the wire. This model of conductors is called the **electron gas model.** If the temperature is increased, the electron speeds increase, but they collide more frequently with atomic cores. Thus, the conductivity of metals is reduced as the temperature rises. Conductivity is the reciprocal of resistivity. As conductivity is reduced, the material's resistance rises.

Electrons in a conductor have very high random speeds like atoms in a gas.

$\Delta V$

$-$     $+$

FIGURE 29–3. Electron motion in a conductor. The electrons move rapidly and randomly. If a field is applied across the wire, the electrons drift toward one end.

### The Free-Electron Density in a Conductor

If each copper atom contributes one electron, how many free electrons exist in 1 cm³ of copper? The density of copper is 8.96 g/cm³. Copper's atomic mass is 63.54 g/mol and Avogadro's number is $6.02 \times 10^{23}$ atoms/mol.

**Given:** Copper: **Unknown:** free electrons/cm³
1 free electron/atom
atomic mass, $M = 63.54$ g/mol
density, $\rho = 8.96$ g/cm³
Avogadro's number, $A_v = 6.02 \times 10^{23}$ atoms/mol

**Solution:** By dimensional analysis,

$$\frac{\text{free e}^-}{\text{cm}^3 \text{ Cu}}$$

$$= \left(\frac{1 \text{ free e}^-}{1 \text{ atom}}\right)\left(\frac{6.02 \times 10^{23} \text{ atoms}}{1 \text{ mol}}\right)\left(\frac{1 \text{ mol Cu}}{63.54 \text{ g Cu}}\right)\left(\frac{8.96 \text{ g}}{1 \text{ cm}^3 \text{ Cu}}\right)$$

$$= 8.49 \times 10^{22} \text{ free e}^-/\text{cm}^3 \text{ Cu}$$

## Practice Problem

1. Zinc, density 7.13 g/cm³, atomic mass 65.37 g/mol, has two free electrons per atom. How many free electrons are there in each cubic centimetre of zinc?

## Insulators

We have discussed the properties of materials with partially-filled energy bands. In some materials, all energy levels in the lowest band are filled. The next lowest available level is in the higher band. An electron must either gain a very large amount of energy or none at all. If an electric field is put across such a material, the electrons cannot gain enough energy to reach the next available energy level. Thus, the electrons remain on their "home" atoms. The filled band is called the valence band because, in chemical terms, the electrons are the valence electrons of the atoms. Such a material is an insulator; charges remain in place. Examples are sulfur, common table salt, and glass.

In insulators, all levels in the lowest band, the valence band, are filled.

An electric field cannot normally give an electron enough energy to reach the conduction band in insulators.

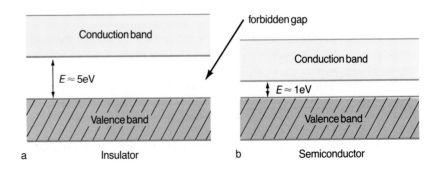

**FIGURE 29-4. Valence and conduction bands in an insulator (a) and in a semiconductor (b). Notice that the forbidden gap is wider in (a) than in (b).**

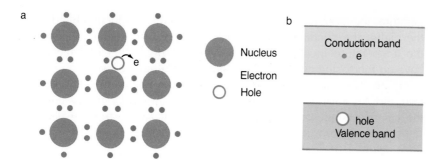

FIGURE 29–5. Some electrons in semiconductors have enough thermal energy to break free and wander through the crystal as shown in the crystal structure (a) and band (b).

If electrons are to move from atom to atom, that is, to conduct electricity, they will have to be given more energy than available from the electric field. The energy levels electrons would have to be in if they were to move are in a band called the **conduction band**, Figure 29–4.

How much energy would an electron need to gain to reach the next empty level? Recall from Chapter 27 that an electron volt (eV) is a convenient energy unit when discussing energy changes in atomic systems.

$$1 \text{ eV} = 1.6 \times 10^{-19} \text{ J}$$

One electron volt is $1.6 \times 10^{-19}$ J of energy.

In an insulator, the lowest energy level in the *conduction* band is between 5 and 10 eV above the highest energy level in the *valence* band, Figure 29–4a. There is a 5 to 10-eV gap of energies that no electrons can have. Of course, electrons have some kinetic energy as a result of their thermal energy. But the average thermal energy of electrons at room temperature is only 0.025 eV, hardly enough to jump the forbidden gap. If an electric field is placed across an insulator, almost no electrons gain enough energy to reach the conduction band, so no current flows. That is, electrons in an insulator must be given a large amount of energy if they are to be pulled free from one atom and moved to the next. As a result, the electrons in an insulator remain in place, and the material does not conduct electricity.

The forbidden gap in insulators is 5 to 10 eV wide.

## Semiconductors

Electrons can move more freely in semiconductors than in insulators, but not as easily as in conductors, Figure 29–4b. Thus, semiconductors have very high resistance. How does the microscopic structure of semiconductors explain this? Atoms of the most common semiconductors, silicon (Si) and germanium (Ge), each have four valence electrons. These four electrons are involved in binding the atoms together into the solid crystal. As a result, they are held, or bound, to an individual atom. The valence electrons form a filled band, as in an insulator, but the forbidden gap between the valence and conduction bands is much smaller. Not much energy is needed to pull one of the electrons from a silicon atom and put it into the conduction band, Figure 29–5. Indeed, the gap is so small that some electrons reach the conduction band due to their thermal energy. That is, the random motion of atoms and electrons gives some electrons enough energy to break free of their "home" atoms and wander around the silicon crystal. If an electric field is applied, these electrons can move through the solid. The higher the tem-

Semiconductors are usually made of atoms with four valence electrons.

The forbidden gap in semiconductors is only approximately 1 eV wide.

perature, the more electrons are able to reach the conduction band, and the higher the conductivity. This is the opposite in metals, where, as the temperature increases, conductivity is reduced because electrons have an increasing number of collisions with atomic cores.

An atom from which an electron has broken free is missing an electron and is said to contain a hole. A **hole** is an empty energy level in the valence band. It has a positive charge. If an electron breaks free from another atom, it can land on a hole, becoming bound to an atom once again. This process can also be seen as the hole and free electron recombining, eliminating each other. The electron, however, left behind a hole on its previous atom. Thus, as in a game of musical chairs, the negatively-charged, free electrons move in one direction and the positively-charged holes move in the other. The energy of the electrons is in the conduction band while the holes have energies in the valence band. Pure semiconductors that conduct as a result of thermally freed electrons and holes are called **intrinsic semiconductors**. Because so few electrons or holes are available to carry charge, conduction in intrinsic semiconductors is very small; their resistance is very large.

## Example Problem

### The Fraction of Free Electrons in an Intrinsic Semiconductor

Find the fraction of atoms that has free electrons in silicon. At room temperature, thermal energy frees $1 \times 10^{13}$ e$^-$/cm$^3$ in pure silicon. The density of silicon is 2.33 g/cm$^3$ and the atomic mass of silicon is 28.09 g/mol. **a.** How many silicon atoms are there in 1 cm$^3$? **b.** What is the fraction of silicon atoms that have free electrons? That is, what is the ratio of free e$^-$/cm$^3$ to atoms/cm$^3$ in silicon?

**Given:** silicon: density, $\rho = 2.33$ g/cm$^3$
atomic mass, $M = 28.09$ g/mol
free e$^-$/cm$^3$ = $1 \times 10^3$ e$^-$/cm$^3$
Avogadro's number, $A_v = 6.02 \times 10^{23}$ atoms/mol

**Unknowns: a.** Si atoms/cm$^3$
**b.** free e$^-$/atom Si

**Solution:**
**a.** By dimensional analysis,

$$\left(\frac{2.33\,\text{g}}{1\,\text{cm}^3}\right)\left(\frac{1\,\text{mol}}{28.09\,\text{g Si}}\right)\left(\frac{6.02 \times 10^{23}\,\text{atoms}}{1\,\text{mol}}\right)$$
$$= 4.99 \times 10^{22}\,\text{atoms/cm}^3$$

**b.** $\dfrac{\text{free e}^-}{\text{atom Si}} = \left(\dfrac{1 \times 10^{13}\,\text{free e}^-}{\text{cm}^3}\right)\left(\dfrac{1\,\text{cm}^3}{4.99 \times 10^{22}\,\text{atoms Si}}\right)$
$= 2 \times 10^{-10}$ (fraction of Si atoms with free electrons)
or $5 \times 10^9$ atoms of Si for every free e$^-$

Thus, there are many fewer free electrons in an intrinsic semiconductor than in a metal like copper.

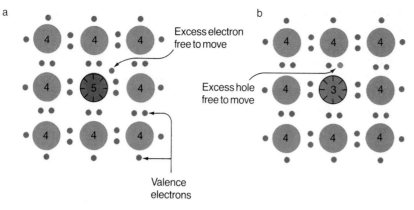

a

Excess electron
free to move

Valence
electrons

Arsenic donor

b

Excess hole
free to move

Gallium acceptor

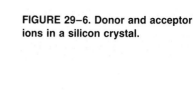

FIGURE 29–6. Donor and acceptor ions in a silicon crystal.

## Practice Problem

**2.** In pure germanium, density 5.23 g/cm$^3$, atomic mass 72.6 g/mol, there are $2 \times 10^{16}$ free electrons/cm$^3$ at room temperature. How many free electrons are there per atom?

## Doped Semiconductors

While conductivity does not depend only on the number of free electrons, a material with fewer than one free electron per million atoms can't conduct electricity well. To make a practical device, the conductivity of semiconductors must be increased greatly. This can be done by adding certain other atoms, or impurities, creating **extrinsic semiconductors**. Impurity atoms, often called **dopants**, increase conductivity by adding either electrons or holes. A few dopant atoms replace silicon atoms in the crystal. Arsenic (As) atoms that have five valence electrons can be used, Figure 29–6a. Four of the five electrons bind to neighboring silicon atoms. The fifth electron is not needed in bonding and so can move relatively freely. Another way to say this is that the energy of this **donor electron** is so close to the conduction band that thermal energy can easily remove it from the impurity atom, putting an electron in the conduction band, Figure 29–7a. A semiconductor that conducts by means of electrons is called an **n-type semiconductor** because conduction is by means of negatively-charged particles.

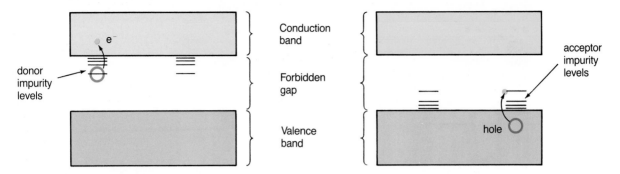

**FIGURE 29–7. Donor and acceptor energy levels in a semiconductor.**

# F. Y. I.

Electronic calculators can solve problems which the man who made them cannot solve; but no government-subsidized commission of engineers and physicists could create a worm.
—Joseph Wood Krutch
"March,"
*The Twelve Seasons*

A gallium (Ga) atom has only three valence electrons. If a gallium atom replaces a silicon atom, one binding electron is missing, Figure 29–6b. That is, the gallium atom creates a hole. Only thermal energy is needed to excite electrons from the valence band into this hole, creating a hole on a silicon atom that is free to move. The gallium atom is called an **electron acceptor**. A semiconductor that conducts by means of holes is called a **p-type semiconductor**. Conduction is the result of the motion of positively-charged holes in the valence band, Figure 29–7b. Whether p-type or n-type, the semiconductor is still neutral. Adding dopant atoms of either type does not add any net charge to the semiconductor. If there are free electrons, then there are the same number of positively-charged atoms. When a semiconductor conducts electricity by means of holes, there is a corresponding number of negatively-charged atoms.

Silicon is doped by putting a silicon crystal in a vacuum with a sample of the impurity. The impurity material is heated to vaporize it, and the atoms condense on the cold silicon. The silicon is gently warmed so the impurities diffuse into the material. Only a few impurity atoms per million silicon atoms are needed to increase the conductivity by a factor of 1000 or more. Thus, the electrical properties of the semiconductor can be chosen by carefully controlling the number of impurity atoms. Finally, a thin layer of aluminum or gold is evaporated on the crystal and a wire is welded to the conductor. The wire allows the user to put current into and bring it out of the doped silicon.

The electrical conductivity of both intrinsic and extrinsic semiconductors is sensitive to both temperature and light. An increase in temperature allows more electrons to reach the conduction band. Thus, the conductivity increases; the resistance decreases. One semiconductor device, the thermistor, is specially designed so its resistance depends very strongly on temperature. Thus, the thermistor can be used as a sensitive thermometer.

Other useful applications of semiconductors depend on their light sensitivity. When light falls on a semiconductor, the light can excite electrons from the valence band to the conduction band just as light excites atoms. Thus, the resistance decreases as the light intensity increases. Materials such as silicon and cadmium sulphide are used as light-dependent resistors in cameras and light meters.

# Example Problem

## The Conductivity of Doped Silicon

Silicon is doped with arsenic so that one in every $10^6$ Si atoms is replaced by an As atom. Assume that each As atom donates one electron to the conduction band. **a.** What is the density of free electrons in this extrinsic semiconductor? **b.** By what ratio is this density greater than that of intrinsic silicon of the Example Problem on page 600? **c.** Is conduction mainly by the thermally-freed electrons of the intrinsic silicon or by the arsenic-donated electrons?

**Given:** As atom density = 1 As atom /$10^6$ Si atom

free $e^-$/As atom = 1 free $e^-$/As atom

Si atom/$cm^3$ = $4.99 \times 10^{22}$ Si atoms /$cm^3$

free $e^-$/$cm^3$ in intrinsic Si = $1 \times 10^{13}$/$cm^3$

**Unknowns: a.** As-donated free $e^-$/$cm^3$

**b.** ratio of result **a** to $1 \times 10^{13}$/$cm^3$

**Solution: a.** By dimensional analysis,

$$\frac{\text{free } e^-}{cm^3} = \left(\frac{1 \text{ free } e^-}{1 \text{ As atom}}\right)\left(\frac{1 \text{ As atom}}{1 \times 10^6 \text{ Si atom}}\right)\left(\frac{4.99 \times 10^{22} \text{ Si atoms}}{1 \ cm^3}\right)$$

$$= 4.99 \times 10^{16} \text{ free } e^-/cm^3.$$

**b.** Ratio is

$$\frac{4.99 \times 10^{16} \text{ free } e^-/cm^3 \text{ in doped Si}}{1 \times 10^{13} \text{ free } e^-/cm^3 \text{ in pure Si}} = 4.99 \times 10^3$$

**c.** Since there are 5000 arsenic-donated electrons for every intrinsic one, conduction is mainly by the arsenic-donated ones.

# Practice Problem

**3.** If you wanted to have $5 \times 10^3$ as many electrons from As doping as thermally-free electrons in the germanium semiconductor described in Practice Problem 2, how many As atoms should there be per Ge atom?

........................

# CONCEPT REVIEW

**1.1** In which type of material, conductor, semiconductor, or insulator, are electrons more likely to remain with the same atom?

**1.2** Magnesium oxide has a forbidden gap of 8 eV. Is this material a conductor, insulator, or semiconductor?

**1.3** You are designing an integrated circuit using a single crystal of silicon. You want to have a region with relatively good insulating properties. Should you dope this region or leave it an intrinsic semiconductor?

**1.4** Critical Thinking: If the temperature increases, the number of free electrons in an intrinsic semiconductor increases. For example, raising the temperature by 10°C doubles the number of free electrons. Which is likely to have a conductivity that depends more on temperature, an intrinsic or doped semiconductor? Explain.

# PHYSICS LAB : The Stoplight

## Purpose

To investigate light emitting diodes (LEDs) by constructing a stoplight circuit.

## Materials

· 0 - 12 V variable power supply
· red LED
· green LED
· bi-colour LED
· wires
· 470-Ω resistor
· voltmeter

## Procedure

1. Put the bi-colour LED off to the side.
2. Connect a series circuit with the power supply, the resistor, and the coloured LEDs to light them both. Do not bypass or omit the resistor with an LED. Always have the resistor between an LED and one side of the power supply.
3. Reverse the direction of the current in the circuit and note the result. Measure the voltage across an LED.
4. Design a circuit so that changing the direction of the current will change the colour that lights up.
5. Test your circuit.

## Observations and Data

1. What voltage was needed to light the LEDs?
2. Describe what happened when the current was reversed in Procedure 3.

## Analysis

1. Make a drawing to show your stoplight circuit [red on (green off), then green on (red off)].
2. Explain why your stoplight circuit works.

## Applications

1. Design and conduct experiments to discover what type of LED the bi-colour LED is. Remember to leave the resistor connected to the power supply.

to LEDs

Stoplight

Variable Power Supply

# 29.2 ELECTRONIC DEVICES

Today's electronic instruments use many semiconductor devices, usually combined on "chips" of semiconducting silicon a few millimetres on a side. The chips contain not only regions of doped silicon that act as wires or resistors, but areas where two or three differently doped regions are in contact, forming diodes and transistors. In these devices, current and voltage vary in ways much more complex than described by Ohm's law. Because the variation is not linear, the devices can change current from AC to DC and amplify voltages. The integrated circuit contains several thousand diodes and transistors, connected together on a single chip, to perform the complex functions demanded by radios, televisions, tape and CD players, and microcomputers.

**Objectives**

- **understand why diodes conduct charges in one direction only.**
- **describe how diodes can be used to produce current that flows in one direction only.**
- **recognize how a transistor is constructed and how it can amplify or increase voltage changes.**

## Diodes

The simplest semiconductor device is the diode. A **diode** consists of joined regions of p-type and n-type semiconductors. Rather than joining two separate pieces of doped silicon, a single sample of intrinsic silicon is treated first with a p-dopant, then with an n-dopant. Metal contacts are coated on each region so wires can be attached, Figure 29–8. The boundary between the p-type and n-type regions is called the junction. Thus, the resulting device is called a **pn-junction diode**.

The holes and electrons in the p- and n-regions are affected by the junction. There are forces on the free charge carriers in the two regions near the junction. The free electrons on the n-side are attracted to the positive holes on the p-side. The electrons readily move into the p-side and recombine with the holes. Holes from the p-side similarly move into the n-side where they recombine with electrons. As a result of this flow, the n-side has a net positive charge, the p-side a net negative charge. These charges produce forces in the opposite direction that stop further movement of charge carriers. The region around the junction is left with neither holes nor free electrons. This area, depleted of charge carriers, is called the **depletion layer**. Because it has no charge carriers, it is a poor conductor of electricity. Thus, a junction diode consists of relatively good conductors at the ends surrounding a poor conductor.

A diode consists of adjacent n- and p-type semiconductors.

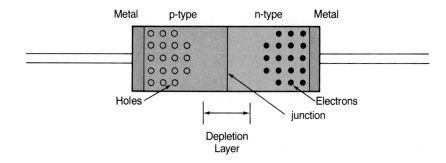

FIGURE 29–8. A junction diode showing the depletion layer.

**FIGURE 29–9. A reverse-biased diode (a); a forward-biased diode (b).**

When a diode is connected into a circuit in the way it is in Figure 29–9a, both the free electrons in the n-type semiconductor and the holes in the p-type semiconductor are attracted toward the battery. The width of the depletion layer is increased and no charge carriers meet. Almost no current flows through the diode—it acts like a very large resistor, almost an insulator. The diode is a **reverse-biased diode**.

If the battery is connected in the opposite direction, Figure 29–9b, charge carriers are pushed toward the junction. If the voltage of the battery is large enough, 0.6 V for a silicon diode, electrons reach the p-end and fill the holes. The depletion layer is eliminated and a current flows. The battery continues to supply electrons for the n-end. It removes electrons from the p-end, which is the same as supplying holes. With further increases in voltage from the battery, the current increases. The diode is a **forward-biased diode**.

Figure 29–10 shows the current through a silicon diode as a function of voltage. If the applied voltage is negative, the reverse-biased diode acts like a very high resistance; only a tiny current flows (about $10^{-11}$ A for a silicon diode). If the voltage is positive, the diode is forward-biased and acts like a small resistance, but not, however, one that obeys Ohm's law. One major use of a diode is to convert AC voltage to a voltage that has only one polarity. When a diode is used in a circuit such as that in Figure 29–12, it is called a rectifier. The arrow in the symbol for the diode shows the direction of conventional current flow.

A diode with its n-type end connected to the positive battery terminal is reverse-biased. Almost no current flows.

Diodes can convert AC voltage to voltage with only one polarity.

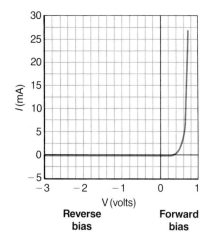

**FIGURE 29–10. Current-voltage characteristics for a silicon junction diode.**

## Example Problem

### A Diode in a Simple Circuit

A silicon diode, whose I/V characteristics are shown in Figure 29–10, is connected to a battery through a 470-$\Omega$ resistor. The battery forward-biases the diode and its voltage is adjusted until the diode current is 12 mA. **a.** Draw a schematic diagram of the circuit. **b.** What is the battery voltage?

**Given:** graph of $V_d$ versus $I$,  **Unknown:** battery voltage, $V$
$R = 470 \ \Omega$  **Basic equation:** $V = V_d + IR$

**Solution:** At $I = 12$ mA, $V_d = 0.7$ V (from the graph)
$V = V_d + IR = 0.7$ V $+ (470 \ \Omega )(1.2 \times 10^{-2}$ A$) = 6.3$ V.

FIGURE 29–11. Light-emitting diodes (LEDs) are doped diodes that emit light when they are forward-biased.

## Practice Problems

**4.** What battery voltage would be needed to have a current of 2.5 mA in the diode above?

▶ **5.** A Ge diode has a voltage drop of 0.4 V when 12 mA flows through it. If the same 470-Ω resistor is used, what battery voltage is needed?

Diodes can do more than provide one-way paths for current. Diodes made from combinations of gallium and aluminum with arsenic and phosphorus emit light when they are forward-biased. When electrons reach the holes in the junction, they recombine and release the excess energy at the wavelengths of light. These diodes are called light-emitting diodes, or LEDs. Certain semiconductor crystals can be cut with parallel faces so the light waves reflect back and forth in the crystal. The result is a diode laser that emits a narrow beam of coherent, monochromatic light or infrared radiation. Diode lasers are used in CD players and supermarket bar-code scanners. They are compact, powerful light sources.

Both CD players and supermarket scanners must detect the laser light reflected from the CD or bar-code. Diodes can detect light as well as emit it. A reverse-biased pn-junction diode is usually used as a light detector. Light falling on the junction creates pairs of electrons and holes. These are pulled toward the ends of the diode, resulting in a current flow that depends on the light intensity.

LEDs and semiconductor lasers are diodes that emit light.

## POCKET LAB

### RED LIGHT

Make a series circuit with the power supply, 470-Ω resistor, and the red LED. Connect the short lead of the LED to the negative side of the power supply. Attach the other lead to the resistor. Hook the remaining resistor lead to the positive of the power supply. Slowly increase the voltage until the LED glows. Note the voltage setting on the power supply. What would happen if you reverse the direction of current? Why? Try it. Explain what happened.

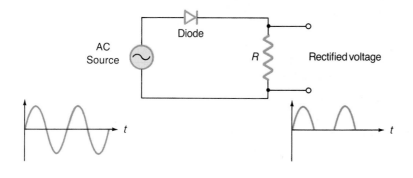

**FIGURE 29–12. A diode used as a rectifier in a circuit.**

# Physics and society

## COMPUTER VIRUSES— DANGEROUS ENEMIES OR FRIENDLY HAZARDS?

**M**any solid state components are found in computers. The micro computers that we use at home or in school are the devices that we most depend upon to do vital things for us.

PCs, school, and office computers can be afflicted by computer viruses. A computer virus is a piece of software that modifies other programs in such a way as to include a part of itself on the other programs. Most computer viruses invade PCs on a floppy disk brought to the PC. The floppy disk is said to be "infected." The hard disk, or hard drive, of a computer then becomes infected by the floppy disk.

Some computer viruses have been called "friendly." For example, in 1987 a German student developed a program that sent a Christmas message over a German computer network.

This virus typed out a greeting on a person's printer and then forwarded a copy of itself to everyone on that person's mailing list. Because of the way computers are linked in networks, the virus linked up to IBM's international network within hours. The IBM company quickly took steps to safeguard its network link with passwords so that such an event could not happen again.

Other computer viruses are definitely "unfriendly."

Computer viruses may affect specific kinds of computers, such as Apple Macintosh computers or Commodore Amiga computers. One computer virus affecting Macintosh computers may have originated here in Canada and then made its way into a computer game. Whoever used the game picked up the computer virus without knowing it.

Most of the computer viruses have affected home computers and small businesses up to now. Computer users have to be careful about using someone else's software or getting programs from unknown sources. Also, it is necessary to keep clean back-ups of system files in case the system becomes infected by using an infected floppy disk.

Engineers have developed detection kits for tracking down and safeguarding against computer viruses. There are also "antivirus" programs, which eradicate existing viruses. An antivirus program may catch one strain of computer virus but not other strains. Also, there may be more dangerous viruses on the way. Security consultants even warn that there are possibilities for blackmail or sabotage.

## DEVELOPING A VIEWPOINT

Read about computer viruses and come to class with answers to the following questions.

1. In your opinion, should friendly computer viruses be tolerated? Why or why not?

2. Suppose that an unfriendly computer virus was produced that could destroy all the data in the computers at your bank. How could your bank safeguard its financial data against such a virus?

3. In what ways could computer viruses be used as a weapon?

## SUGGESTED READINGS

Greenberg, Ross M. "Know Thy Viral Enemy." *Byte* 14, 275–280, June 1989.

Kerr, Susan. "A Secret No More." *Datamation* 35 (13), 53–55, July 1, 1989.

Marshall, Eliot. "The Scourge of Computer Viruses." *Science* 240, 113–134, April 8, 1988.

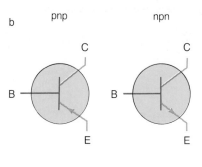

B = base    C = collector    E = emitter

**FIGURE 29–13. A pnp and an npn transistor (a); their circuit symbols (b).**

# Transistors and Integrated Circuits

A junction transistor consists of a region of one type of doped semiconductor sandwiched between layers of the opposite type. An **npn transistor** consists of n-type semiconductors surrounding a thin p-type layer. If the region in the centre is n-type, then the device is called a **pnp transistor**. In either case, the central layer is called the **base**. The two surrounding regions are the **emitter** and the **collector**. The schematic symbols for the two transistor types are shown in Figure 29–13. The arrow is on the emitter and shows the direction of conventional current flow.

The operation of an npn transistor can be described using Figure 29–14. The pn-junctions in the transistor can be thought of as two back-to-back diodes. The battery on the right keeps the potential difference between collector and emitter, $V_{CE}$, positive. The base-collector diode is reverse-biased, so no current flows. The battery on the left is connected so that the base is more positive than the emitter. That is, the base-emitter diode is forward-biased. Conventional current flows in the direction of the arrow from the base into the emitter. Thus, electrons flow from the emitter into the base. But the base layer is very thin, often less than $10^{-6}$ m wide. As a result, most of the electrons pass through the base to the collector. The current through the collector, $I_C$, is much larger than the current through the base, $I_B$. The collector current causes a voltage drop across resistor $R_C$. Small changes in the voltage on the base produce large changes in the collector current, and thus changes in the voltage drop across $R_C$. As a result, the transistor amplifies small voltage changes into much larger changes. A pnp transistor works the same way, except the potentials of both batteries are reversed and holes carry the current in the transistor. The energy for amplification comes from battery $V_c$.

Transistors are used as amplifiers in almost every electronic instrument. In a tape player, the small voltage variations from the voltage induced in a coil by magnetized regions on the tape are amplified to move the speaker coil. In computers, small currents in the base-emitter circuits can turn on or turn off large currents in the collector-emitter circuits. Several transistors can be connected together to perform logic operations or to add numbers together. In this case, they act as fast switches, not amplifiers.

A transistor consists of three alternating n- and p-type layers called the collector, base, and emitter.

A small current through the base-emitter junction causes a large current from the collector to the emitter.

**FIGURE 29–14. A transistor amplifying circuit.**

a

b

An integrated circuit is constructed on a slice of a single crystal of silicon.

A single exposure to dopants produces resistors. Two exposures result in diodes, three in transistors.

An integrated circuit, or a microchip, consists of thousands of transistors, diodes, resistors, and conductors each no more than a few micrometres across. All these components can be made by doping silicon in the proper way. A microchip starts with an extremely pure single crystal of silicon, 10 cm in diameter and 0.5 m long. It is sliced by a diamond-coated saw into wafers less than 1 mm thick. The circuit is then built layer by layer on the surface of this wafer. By a photographic process, most of the wafer's surface is convered by a protective layer, with a pattern of selected areas left uncovered so it can be doped appropriately. The wafer is placed in a chamber out of which almost all the air has been pumped. Vapours of a dopant such as arsenic enter the machine, doping the wafer in the unprotected regions. By controlling the amount of exposure, the engineer can control the conductivity of the exposed regions of the chip. This process creates resistors, as well as one of the two layers of a diode or one of the three layers of a transistor. The protective layer is removed, and another one with a different pattern of exposed areas is applied. Now the wafer is exposed to another dopant, often gallium, producing pn junctions. If a third layer is added, npn transistors are formed. The wafer may also be exposed to oxygen to produce areas of silicon dioxide insulation. A layer exposed to aluminum vapours can produce a pattern of thin conducting pathways between the resistors, diodes, and transistors. Hundreds of identical circuits, usually called chips, are produced on a single 10-cm diameter wafer at one time. The chips are then sliced apart and tested, have wires attached, and are mounted in a plastic protective body. They are sold for a few dollars or even less.

Semiconductor electronics illustrates how the sciences and engineering work together. Physicists gain an understanding of the motion of electrons and holes in semiconductors. Physicists and chemists together learn how to add precisely-controlled amounts of impurities to extremely pure silicon. Engineers develop means of mass producing chips containing thousands of miniaturized diodes and transistors. Together their efforts have revolutionized our world.

# CONCEPT REVIEW

**2.1** Compare the resistance of a pn-junction diode when it is forward-biased to when it is reverse-biased.

**2.2** Does a light-emitting diode produce light no matter which battery terminal is connected to the p-end of the diode? If not, which terminal should be connected to make the diode light?

**2.3** If the diode of Figure 29–10 is forward-biased by a battery and a series resistor so that more than about 10 mA of current flows, the voltage drop is always about 0.7 V. If the battery voltage is increased by one volt,
   **a.** does the voltage across the diode or the voltage across the resistor increase? by how much?
   **b.** does the current through the resistor increase? by how much?

**2.4 Critical Thinking:** Could you replace an npn transistor with two separate diodes with their p-terminals connected together? Explain.

# CHAPTER
# 29 REVIEW

## SUMMARY

### 29.1 Conduction in Solids

· Electrical conduction in materials is explained by the band theory of solids.
· Electrons can have only certain values of energy called allowed energy levels.
· In solids, the allowed energy levels are spread into broad bands. The bands are separated by values of energies that electrons may not have called the forbidden gap.
· In conductors, electrons can move because the band of allowed energy levels is only partially filled.
· Electrons in metals have a very fast random motion. A potential difference across the metal causes a very slow drift of the electrons.
· In insulators, electrons are bound to atoms. More energy is needed to move them than is available.
· Conduction in semiconductors is usually the result of doping pure crystals with small numbers of impurity atoms.
· N-type semiconductors conduct by means of free electrons, while in p-type semiconductors, conduction is by means of "holes."

### 29.2 Electronic Devices

· Diodes conduct charges in one direction only and can be used to produce current that flows in one direction only.
· A transistor is constructed of three alternate layers of n- and p-type semiconductors and can amplify or increase voltage changes.

## KEY TERMS

| | |
|---|---|
| bands | p-type semiconductor |
| forbidden gaps | diode |
| band theory | pn-junction diode |
| electron gas model | depletion layer |
| conduction band | reverse-biased diode |
| hole | forward-biased diode |
| intrinsic semiconductor | npn transistor |
| extrinsic semiconductor | pnp transistor |
| dopants | base |
| donor electron | emitter |
| n-type semiconductor | collector |
| electron acceptor | |

# REVIEWING CONCEPTS

1. How do the energy levels in a crystal of an element differ from the energy levels in a single atom of that element?
2. Why does heating a semiconductor increase its conductivity?
3. What is the main current carrier in a p-type semiconductor?
4. An ohmmeter is an instrument that places a potential difference across a device to be tested, measures the current flow, and displays the resistance of the device. If you connect an ohmmeter across a diode, will the current you measure depend on which end of the diode was connected to the positive terminal of the ohmmeter? Explain.
5. What is the significance of the arrowhead at the emitter in a transistor circuit symbol?
6. Redraw Figure 29–14 as a pnp transistor.

# APPLYING CONCEPTS

1. The resistance of graphite decreases as the temperature rises. Does graphite conduct electricity like copper or like silicon?
2. Which of the following materials would make a better insulator: one with a forbidden gap 8 eV wide, 3 eV wide, or one with no gap?
3. In which of the three materials in the previous problem would it be most difficult to remove an electron from an atom?
4. How does the size of the gap between the conduction band and the next lower energy band determine whether a solid will be a semiconductor or an insulator?
5. Which would make a better insulator, an extrinsic or an intrinsic semiconductor? Explain.
6. Silicon is doped with phosphorus. Will the dopant atoms be donors or acceptors? Will the semiconductor conduct with holes or electrons?
7. Doping silicon with gallium produces a p-type semiconductor. Why are there holes mainly on silicon atoms rather than on the gallium atoms that caused the holes to be produced?
8. Carol uses an ohmmeter to measure the resistance of a pn-junction diode. Would the meter show a higher resistance when the diode is forward-biased or reverse-biased?

9. If the ohmmeter in the previous problem shows the lower resistance, is the ohmmeter lead connected to the arrow side of the diode at a higher or lower potential than the lead connected to the other side?
10. If you dope pure germanium with gallium alone, do you produce a resistor, a diode, or a transistor?

# PROBLEMS

## 29.1 Conduction in Solids

1. The forbidden gap in silicon is 1.1 eV. Electromagnetic waves striking the silicon cause electrons to move from the valence band to the conduction band. What is the longest wavelength of radiation that could excite an electron in this way?

    Chapter 27 gives $E = \dfrac{1240 \text{ eV·nm}}{\lambda}$, where the energy is in eV and the wavelength in nm.
2. A light-emitting diode (LED) produces green light with a wavelength of 550 nm when an electron moves from the conduction band to the valence band. Find the width of the forbidden gap in eV in this diode.
3. How many free electrons exist in 1 cm³ of sodium? Its density is 0.971 g/cm³, atomic mass is 22.99 g/mol, and there is one free electron per atom.
4. At a temperature of 0°C, thermal energy frees $1.1 \times 10^{12}$ e⁻/cm³ in pure silicon. The density of silicon is 2.33 g/cm³ and the atomic mass of silicon is 28.09 g/mol. What is the fraction of atoms that have free electrons?
▶ 5. Use a periodic table to determine which of the following elements could be added to germanium to make a p-type semiconductor: B, C, N, P, Si, Al, Ge, Ga, As, In, Sn, Sb.
▶ 6. Which of the elements listed in the previous problem would produce an n-type semiconductor?

## 29.2 Electronic Devices

▶ 7. Which element or elements could be used as the second dopant when making a diode, if the first dopant was boron?

**8.** The potential drop across a glowing LED is about 1.2 V. In Figure 29–16, the potential drop across the resistor is the difference between the battery voltage and LED potential drop, 6.0 V − 1.2 V = 4.8 V. What is the current through **a.** the LED? **b.** the resistor?

**FIGURE 29–16. Use with Problems 8 and 9.**

**9.** Jon wanted to raise the current through the LED in the previous problem to 30 mA so that it would glow brighter. Assume that the potential drop across the LED is still 1.2 V. What resistor should be used?

**FIGURE 29–17. Use with Problem 10.**

**10.** Figure 29–17 shows a battery, diode, and bulb connected in series so that the bulb lights. Note that the diode is forward-biased. Describe whether the bulb in each of the pictured circuits is lighted.

**11.** For each pictured circuit, tell whether lamp L₁, lamp L₂, both, or neither, is lighted.

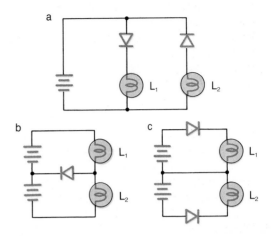

**12.** Draw a circuit having one 6.0-V battery, two LEDs, and two resistors. One LED should have a current of 30 mA, the other 20 mA.

**13.** A silicon diode whose $I/V$ characteristics are shown in Figure 29–10 is connected to a battery through a 270-$\Omega$ resistor. The battery forward-biases the diode and its voltage is adjusted until the diode current is 15 mA. What is the battery voltage?

**14.** What bulbs are lighted in the circuit of Figure 29–18 when
   **a.** switch 1 is closed and switch 2 is open?
   **b.** switch 2 is closed and switch 1 is open?

**FIGURE 29–18. Use with Problem 14.**

## THINKING PHYSIC-LY

A silicon solar cell consists of a thin, about 0.5 μm, n-type layer formed over a p-type base. Suggest a reason for the exposed layer being so thin that most of the light will penetrate the layer and be absorbed by atoms in or very near the pn junction.

# CHAPTER
# 30 : The Nucleus

## ◀ Phantom Tracks

In the highlighted box are two particles moving in opposite spiral paths. The curvatures are about the same, so their momenta must be equal. What might cause this pair of paths?

Rutherford not only established the existence of the nucleus, but he did some of the early experiments to discover its structure. Modern accelerators and detectors have given physicists the ability to study nuclei and the particles that compose them with much greater precision. The chapter-opening photo shows trails of subatomic particles moving to the left in a bubble chamber. These charged particles are bent by a magnetic field. The direction of the curve shows their charge. The faster they are moving, the less the bend. Thus their momentum can be determined as well. We will see how this and other tools have enlarged our knowledge of the ultimate building-blocks of matter.

## √ Concept Check

The following terms or concepts from earlier chapters are important for a good understanding of this chapter. If you are not familiar with them, you should review them before studying this chapter.
· conservation of energy, Chapter 11
· electric force on charged particles, Chapter 20
· magnetic force on charged particle, Chapter 24
· Rutherford scattering, structure of the atom, Chapter 24

- **define atomic number and mass number; find the charge and mass of a nucleus.**
- **define an isotope and a nuclide; calculate the number of neutrons, protons, and electrons in an isotope.**
- **describe three modes of radioactive decay; explain the changes in atomic number or mass number for each mode; write equations for the three forms of radioactive decay.**
- **define half-life; calculate the amount of material and its activity remaining after a given number of half-lives.**

# 30.1 RADIOACTIVITY

After the discovery of radioactivity by Becquerel in 1896, many scientists studied this new phenomenon. In Canada, Ernest Rutherford and Frederick Soddy discovered that uranium atoms were changed, or transmuted, to other atoms. The French scientists Marie and Pierre Curie discovered the new elements polonium and radium in samples of radioactive uranium. One of the first results of radioactivity studies was an understanding of the composition of the atomic nucleus.

## Description of the Nucleus

Rutherford's analysis of his scattering experiments predicted that the number of α particles deflected through a given angle should be proportional to the square of the charge of the nucleus of the atom. At that time, only the mass of an atom was known. The number of electrons, and thus the charge of the nucleus, was unknown.

Rutherford and his co-workers experimented with sheets of carbon, aluminum, and gold. In each case, the charge of the nucleus was found to be roughly half the atomic mass times the elementary unit of charge. Since each electron carries one elementary charge, the number of electrons in an atom is equal to roughly half the atomic mass number. The carbon nucleus has a charge of 6, so the carbon atom must contain 6 electrons. Using a similar argument, aluminum contains 13 electrons and gold 79 electrons.

The atom is neutral, so the nucleus must contain positive charge. The **proton** is the name given to the nucleus of the hydrogen atom. The proton is positively charged with one unit of elementary charge. Its mass is approximately one **atomic mass unit**, u. The number of protons in a nucleus, which, in a neutral atom, is equal to the number of electrons surrounding the nucleus, is called the atom's **atomic number**, $Z$. All atoms of a given element contain the same number of protons. Thus carbon always has 6 protons and aluminum 13. Their atomic numbers are $Z = 6$ for carbon and $Z = 13$ for aluminum.

Protons are the positively-charged particles in a nucleus.

The atomic number is the number of protons in the nucleus.

**FIGURE 30–1. Many countries have issued commemorative stamps documenting the history of radioactivity.**

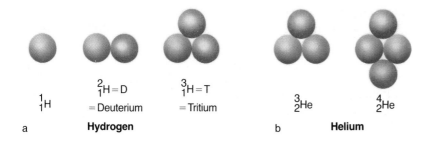

The mass of the carbon atom, however, is the mass of 12 protons, not 6. To account for the excess mass in the nucleus, Rutherford postulated the existence of a neutral particle with a mass of a proton. In 1932 James Chadwick, a student of Rutherford, demonstrated the existence of this particle, called the neutron. A **neutron** is a particle with no charge and with a mass almost equal to that of the proton.

The nucleus of every atom except hydrogen contains both neutrons and protons. The sum of the numbers of protons and neutrons is equal to the **mass number**, $A$. The mass of the nucleus is approximately equal to the mass number, $A$, multiplied by the atomic mass unit (u), $1.66 \times 10^{-27}$ kg. The mass of the nucleus in atomic mass units is approximately equal to the atomic mass number. The mass number of carbon is 12, while that of aluminum is 27. Elements with 20 or fewer protons have roughly equal numbers of protons and neutrons. Heavier elements, however, contain more neutrons than protons.

How large is the nucleus? Rutherford had found that the nucleus is a very small body in the centre of the atom. Today it is known that the nucleus is almost spherical and has a diameter ranging from 2.6 fm ($2.6 \times 10^{-15}$ m) in hydrogen to 16 fm in uranium.

## Isotopes

Careful measurements of the mass of boron atoms consistently yielded 10.8 u. If, as was thought, the nucleus is made up of protons and neutrons, each with a mass of approximately 1 u, then the total mass of any atom should be near a whole number.

The puzzle of atomic masses that were not integral numbers of atomic mass units was solved with the mass spectrometer. The mass spectrometer demonstrated that an element could have atoms with different masses. For example, when analysing a pure sample of neon, not one, but two spots appeared on the film of the spectrometer. The two spots were produced by neon atoms of different masses. One variety of neon atom was found to have a mass of 20 u, the second type a mass of 22 u. All neon atoms have 10 protons in the nucleus and 10 electrons in the atom. One kind of neon atom, however, has 10 neutrons in its nucleus, while the other has 12 neutrons. The two kinds of atoms are called **isotopes** of neon. The nucleus of an isotope is called a **nuclide**. All nuclides of an element have the same number of protons, but different numbers of neutrons, Figure 30–2. All isotopes of an element have the same number of electrons around the nucleus and behave the same chemically.

Neutrons are uncharged particles in the nucleus.

The mass number is the sum of the numbers of protons and neutrons in a nucleus.

Atoms with the same atomic number but different mass numbers are called isotopes.

# POCKET LAB

## BACKGROUND RADIATION

Place a Geiger counter on the lab table far away from any sources of radiation. Turn the counter on and record the number of counts for a three-minute interval. Tape a piece of paper around the tube and repeat the measurements. Did the count go down? What type of radiation could the counter be receiving? Explain.

The measured mass of neon gas is 20.183 u. This figure is now understood to be the average mass of the naturally occurring isotopes of neon. Thus, while the mass of an individual atom of neon is close to a whole number of mass units, the atomic mass of an average sample of neon atoms is not. Most elements have many isotopic forms that occur naturally. The mass of the isotope of carbon, $^{12}_{6}C$, is now used to define the mass unit. One u is defined to be 1/12 the mass of the $^{12}_{6}C$ isotope.

A special method of notation is used to describe an isotope. A subscript representing the atomic number, $Z$, is written to the lower left of the symbol for the element. A superscript written to the upper left of the symbol is the mass number, $A$. This notation takes the form $^{A}_{Z}X$, where X is any element. For example, the two isotopes of neon, with atomic number 10, are written as $^{20}_{10}Ne$ and $^{22}_{10}Ne$.

## Practice Problems

1. An isotope of oxygen has a mass number of 15. The atomic number of oxygen is 8. How many neutrons are in the nuclei of this isotope?
2. Three isotopes of uranium have mass numbers of 234, 235, and 238 respectively. The atomic number of uranium is 92. How many neutrons are in the nuclei of each of these isotopes?
3. How many neutrons are in an atom of the mercury isotope $^{200}_{80}Hg$?
▶ 4. Write the symbols for the three isotopes of hydrogen in Figure 30–2 with 0, 1, and 2 neutrons in the nucleus.

## Radioactive Decay

Nuclei that decay are radioactive.

In 1896 Henri Becquerel was working with compounds containing the element uranium. To his surprise, he found that photographic plates covered to keep out light, became fogged, or partially exposed, when these uranium compounds were anywhere near the plates. This fogging suggested that some kind of ray had passed through the plate coverings. Several materials other than uranium or its compounds were also found to emit these penetrating rays. Materials that emit this kind of radiation are said to be **radioactive** and to undergo **radioactive decay**.

In 1899 Rutherford discovered that uranium compounds produce three different kinds of radiation. He separated the radiations according to their penetrating ability and named them α (alpha), β (beta), and γ (gamma) radiation.

The decay of nuclei can produce α-, β-, or γ-particles.

The α radiation can be stopped by a thick sheet of paper. Rutherford later showed that an α particle is the nucleus of a helium atom, $^{4}_{2}He$. Beta particles were later identified as high-speed electrons. Six millimetres of aluminum are needed to stop most β particles. Several centimetres of lead are required to stop γ rays, which proved to be high-energy photons. Alpha particles and γ rays are emitted with a specific energy that depends on the radioactive isotope. Beta particles, however, are emitted with a wide range of energies.

The emission of an α particle is a process called **α decay**. Since α particles contain protons and neutrons, they must come from the nucleus of an atom. The nucleus that results from α decay will have a mass and charge different from those of the original nucleus. A change in nuclear charge means that the element has been changed, or transmuted, into a different element. The mass number, $A$, of an α particle,

Radioactive substance

Vacuum container

Photographic plate

−

+

Electrically charged plates

α

γ

β

**FIGURE 30–3.** Alpha, beta, and gamma emissions behave differently in an electric field. Alpha and beta particles are deflected because of their charge.

$^4_2$He, is four, so the mass number, $A$, of the decaying nucleus is reduced by four. The atomic number, $Z$, of $^4_2$He is two, and therefore the atomic number of the nucleus, the number of protons, is reduced by two. For example, when $^{238}_{92}$U emits an α particle, the atomic number, $Z$, changes from 92 to 90. From Table D–5 of the Appendix, we find that $Z = 90$ is thorium. The mass number of the nucleus is $A = 238 - 4 = 234$. A thorium isotope, $^{234}_{90}$Th, is formed. The uranium isotope has been transmuted into thorium.

Beta particles are negative electrons emitted by the nucleus. Since the mass of an electron is a tiny fraction of an atomic mass unit, the atomic mass of a nucleus that undergoes **β decay** is changed only a tiny amount. The mass number is unchanged. The nucleus contains no electrons. Rather, β decay occurs when a neutron is changed to a proton within the nucleus. An unseen neutrino accompanies each β decay. Neutrinos will be discussed later. The number of protons, and thus the atomic number, is increased by one. For example, the isotope $^{234}_{90}$Th, produced by the α decay of $^{238}_{92}$U, is unstable and emits a β particle. The $^{234}_{90}$Th then becomes a protactinium isotope, $^{234}_{91}$Pa.

Gamma radiation results from the redistribution of the charge within the nucleus. The γ ray is a high energy photon. Neither the mass number nor the atomic number is changed when a nucleus emits a γ ray in **γ decay**.

Radioactive elements often go through a series of successive decays, or **transmutations**, until they form a stable nucleus. For example, $^{238}_{92}$U undergoes fourteen separate transmutations before the stable lead isotope $^{206}_{82}$Pb is produced.

## Nuclear Reactions and Equations

A **nuclear reaction** occurs whenever the number of neutrons or protons in a nucleus changes. Just as in chemical reactions, some nuclear reactions occur with a release of energy; others occur only when energy is added to a nucleus.

One form of nuclear reaction is the emission of particles by radioactive nuclei. The reaction releases excess energy in the form of the kinetic energy of the emitted particles.

In α decay, the nucleus loses two charge units and four mass units.

β particles are high speed electrons.

In β-decay, the atomic number is increased by one while the mass number is not changed.

In gamma decay, neither the atomic number nor the mass number is changed.

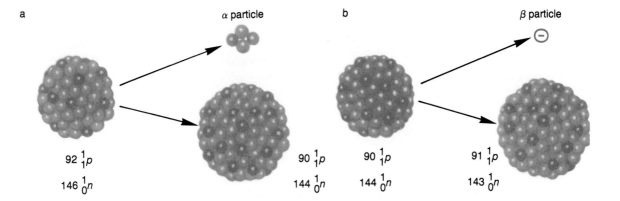

a

α particle

$92 \, {}^1_1 p$

$146 \, {}^1_0 n$

$90 \, {}^1_1 p$

$144 \, {}^1_0 n$

b

β particle

$90 \, {}^1_1 p$

$144 \, {}^1_0 n$

$91 \, {}^1_1 p$

$143 \, {}^1_0 n$

**FIGURE 30–4. The emission of an alpha particle (a) by uranium-238 results in the formation of thorium-234. The emission of a beta particle (b) by thorium-234 results in the formation of protactinium-234.**

When writing nuclear equations, be sure the atomic numbers and mass numbers are the same before and after the reaction.

While nuclear reactions can be described in words, or in pictures, such as Figure 30–4a, they can be written more easily in equation form. The symbols used for the nuclei in nuclear equations make the calculation of atomic number and mass number in nuclear reactions simpler. For example, the word equation for the change of uranium to thorium due to α decay is: uranium 238 yields thorium 234 plus an α particle. The nuclear equation for this reaction is

$${}^{238}_{92}U \rightarrow {}^{234}_{90}Th + {}^4_2He.$$

No nuclear particles are destroyed during the nuclear reaction. Thus, the sum of the superscripts on the right side of the equation must equal the sum of the superscripts on the left side of the equation. The sum of the superscripts on both sides of the equation is 238. Electric charge is also conserved. Thus, the sum of the subscripts on the right is equal to the sum of the subscripts on the left.

## Example Problem

### Nuclear Equations—Alpha Decay

Write the nuclear equation for the transmutation of a radioactive radium isotope, ${}^{226}_{88}Ra$, into a radon isotope, ${}^{222}_{86}Rn$, by the emission of an α particle.

**Solution:** ${}^{226}_{88}Ra \rightarrow {}^{222}_{86}Rn + {}^4_2He$

Since a β particle is a negative electron, it is represented by the symbol ${}^{\;\;0}_{-1}e$. This indicates that the electron has one negative charge and an atomic mass number of zero. The transmutation of a thorium atom by the emission of a β particle is shown in Figure 30–4b. Its equation is

$${}^{234}_{90}Th \rightarrow {}^{234}_{91}Pa + {}^{\;\;0}_{-1}e + {}^0_0\bar{\nu}$$

The symbol ${}^0_0\bar{\nu}$ represents an antineutrino that is emitted with the β particle. The sum of the superscripts on the right side of the equation equals the sum of the superscripts on the left side of the equation. Also, the sum of the subscripts on the right side of the equation equals the sum of the subscripts on the left side of the equation.

# Example Problem

## Nuclear Equations—Beta Decay

Write the nuclear equation for the transmutation of a radioactive lead isotope, $^{209}_{82}Pb$, into a bismuth isotope, $^{209}_{83}Bi$, by the emission of a β particle and an antineutrino.

**Solution:** $^{209}_{82}Pb \rightarrow\ ^{209}_{83}Bi\ +\ ^{\ 0}_{-1}e\ +\ ^{0}_{0}\overline{\nu}$

# Practice Problems

5. Write the nuclear equation for the transmutation of a radioactive uranium isotope, $^{234}_{92}U$, into a thorium isotope, $^{230}_{90}Th$, by the emission of an α particle.

6. Write the nuclear equation for the transmutation of a radioactive thorium isotope, $^{230}_{90}Th$, into a radioactive radium isotope, $^{226}_{88}Ra$, by the emission of an α particle.

7. Write the nuclear equation for the transmutation of a radioactive radium isotope, $^{226}_{88}Ra$, into a radon isotope, $^{222}_{86}Rn$, by the emission of an α particle.

▶ 8. A radioactive lead isotope, $^{214}_{82}Pb$, can change to a radioactive bismuth isotope, $^{214}_{83}Bi$, by the emission of a β particle and an antineutrino. Write the nuclear equation.

# Half-Life

The time required for half of the atoms in any given quantity of a radioactive isotope to decay is the **half-life** of that element. Each particular isotope has its own half-life. For example, the half-life of radium isotope $^{226}_{88}Ra$ is 1600 years. That is, in 1600 years, half of a given quantity of $^{226}_{88}Ra$ decays into another element. In a second 1600 years, half of the remaining sample will have decayed. Only one fourth of the original amount will remain after 3200 years.

In a time interval equal to one half-life, half the mass of the radioactive element decays.

**Table 30–1**

| Half-Life of Selected Isotopes | | | |
|---|---|---|---|
| Element | Isotope | Half-life | Radiation produced |
| hydrogen | $^{3}_{1}H$ | 12.3 a | β |
| carbon | $^{14}_{6}C$ | 5730 a | β |
| iodine | $^{131}_{53}I$ | 80.7 d | β |
| lead | $^{212}_{82}Pb$ | 10.6 h | β |
| polonium | $^{194}_{84}Po$ | 0.7 s | α |
| polonium | $^{210}_{84}Po$ | 138 d | α |
| uranium | $^{227}_{92}U$ | 1.1 min | α |
| uranium | $^{235}_{92}U$ | $7.1 \times 10^8$ a | α |
| uranium | $^{238}_{92}U$ | $4.51 \times 10^9$ a | α |
| plutonium | $^{236}_{94}Pu$ | 2.85 a | α |
| plutonium | $^{242}_{94}Pu$ | $3.79 \times 10^5$ a | α |

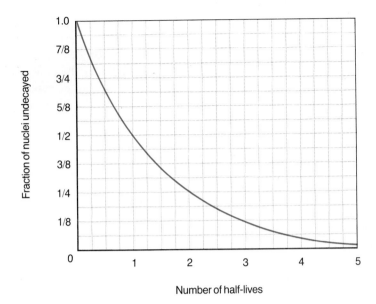

**Remaining nuclei as a Function of Time**

The decay rate, or number of decays per second, of a radioactive substance is called its **activity**. Activity is proportional to the number of radioactive atoms present. Therefore, the activity of a particular sample is also reduced by one half in one half-life. Consider $^{131}_{53}I$ with a half-life of 8.07d. If the activity of a certain sample is $8 \times 10^5$ decays per second when the $^{131}_{53}I$ is produced, 8.07 d later its activity will be $4 \times 10^5$ decays per second. After another 8.07 d, its activity will be $2 \times 10^5$ decays per second. The SI unit for decays per second is a Bequerel, Bq.

*Activity, or decays per second, is proportional to the number of radioactive atoms.*

## Practice Problems

*These problems require the use of Figure 30–5 and Table 30–1.*

**9.** A sample of 1.0 g of tritium, $^3_1H$, is produced. What will be the mass of tritium remaining after 24.6 years?

**10.** The isotope $^{238}_{93}NP$ has a half-life of 2.0 d. If 4.0 g are produced on Monday, what will be the mass of neptunium remaining on Tuesday of the next week?

**11.** A sample of $^{210}_{84}Po$ is purchased for a physics class on September 1. Its activity is $2 \times 10^6$ decays per second. The sample is used in an experiment on June 1. What activity can be expected?

▶ **12.** Tritium, $^3_1H$, was once used in some watches to produce a fluorescent glow so the watch could be read in the dark. If the brightness of the glow is proportional to the activity of the tritium, what would be the brightness of the watch, in comparison to its original brightness, when the watch is six years old?

# PHYSICS LAB : Heads Up

## Purpose

To formulate a model of radioactive decay.

## Materials

· 20 pennies
· graph paper

## Procedure

1. Set up a data table as shown below. Turn the pennies so that they are all heads. In this simulation, a heads indicates that the nucleus has not decayed.
2. Flip each coin separately and separate the heads and tails.
3. Record the number of heads on your data sheet. Remove the pennies that came up tails.
4. Flip all remaining coins and separate the heads and tails. Count the number of heads and record the value.
5. Repeat steps 2–4 one more time.
6. Share your data with four other students and copy their data onto your data sheet.

## Observations and Data

Data Table
Student 1 2 3 4 5 Total

Beginning
Number 20 20 20 20 20 100

After
Trial 1

After
Trial 2

After
Trial 3

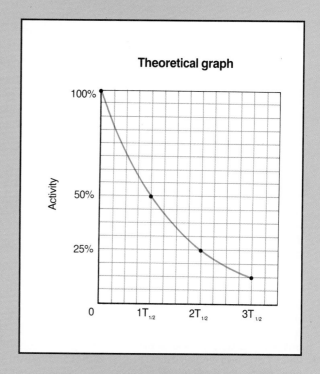

1. Did each person have the same number of heads after each trial?
2. Is the number of heads close to what you expected?

## Analysis

1. Total the number of heads remaining for each trial. Make a graph of the number of heads (vertical) versus the trial (horizontal).
2. Compare your results to the theoretical graph shown in the lab.

## Applications

1. Laws mandate that hospitals keep radioactive materials for 10 half-lives before disposing of them. Calculate the fraction of the original activity left at the end of 10 half-lives.

# CONCEPT REVIEW

**1.1** Consider the pairs of nuclei: first, $^{12}_6C$ and $^{13}_6C$; second, $^{11}_5B$ and $^{12}_6C$. In which way is the first pair like the second? In which way are they different?

**1.2** How can an electron be expelled from a nucleus in $\beta$ decay if the nucleus has no electrons?

**1.3** Use Figure 30–5 and Table 30–1 to estimate in how many days a sample of $^{131}_{53}I$ would have 3/8 its original activity.

**1.4 Critical Thinking:** An $\alpha$ emitter is used in smoke detectors. The emitter is mounted on one plate of a capacitor, and the $\alpha$ particles strike the other plate. As a result there is a potential difference across the plates. Explain and predict which plate has the more positive potential.

## Objectives

· balance nuclear equations showing the result of nuclear reactions.

· describe the operation of linear accelerators and synchrotrons and the operation of different particle detectors.

· define the two families of fundamental particles; explain the difference between particles and force carriers.

· define antiparticles; calculate the energy of $\gamma$ rays emitted when particles annihilate with their antiparticles.

· describe the quark content of the proton and neutron; understand the place of additional quark and lepton families in the quark model.

Rutherford used $\alpha$ particles to cause nuclear reactions.

# 30.2 THE BUILDING BLOCKS OF MATTER

Why are some isotopes radioactive while others are stable? What holds the nucleus together against the repulsive force of the charged protons? These questions and many more motivated many of the best physicists to study the nucleus. The tiny size of the nucleus meant that new tools had to be developed for this study. Studies of nuclei have also led to an understanding of the structure of the particles found in the nucleus, the proton and the neutron, and the nature of the forces that hold the nucleus together.

## Nuclear Bombardment

The first tool used was the result of radioactivity. Rutherford bombarded many elements with $\alpha$ particles, using them to cause a nuclear reaction. For example, when nitrogen gas was bombarded, Rutherford noted that high energy protons were emitted from the gas. A proton has a charge of one, while an $\alpha$ particle has a charge of two. Rutherford hypothesized that the nitrogen had been artificially transmuted by the $\alpha$ particles. The unknown results of the transmutation can be written $^A_ZX$, and the nuclear reaction can be written

$$^4_2He + {}^{14}_7N \rightarrow {}^1_1H + {}^A_ZX.$$

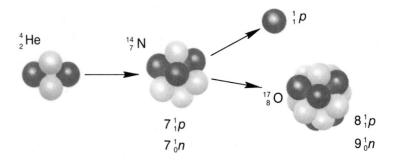

$^4_2He \qquad {}^{14}_7N \qquad {}^1_1p$

$7\,{}^1_1p \qquad\qquad {}^{17}_8O$

$7\,{}^1_0n \qquad\qquad 8\,{}^1_1p$

$\qquad\qquad\qquad 9\,{}^1_0n$

**FIGURE 30–6. Production of oxygen-17 from the artificial transmutation of nitrogen.**

b

Simple arithmetic shows that the atomic number of the unknown isotope is $Z = 2 + 7 - 1 = 8$. The mass number is $A = 4 + 14 - 1 = 17$. From Appendix Table D–5, the isotope must be $^{17}_{8}O$, Figure 30–6. The identity of the $^{17}_{8}O$ isotope was confirmed with a mass spectrometer several years later.

Bombarding $^{9}_{4}Be$ with $\alpha$ particles produced a radiation more penetrating than any previously discovered. In 1932, Irene Curie (daughter of Marie and Pierre Curie) and her husband, Frederic Joliot, discovered that high speed protons were expelled from paraffin wax that was exposed to this new radiation from beryllium. In the same year, James Chadwick showed that the particles emitted from beryllium were uncharged, but had approximately the same mass as protons. That is, the beryllium emitted the particle Rutherford had theorized must be in the nucleus, the neutron. The reaction can be written using the symbol for the neutron, $^{1}_{0}n$.

$$^{4}_{2}He + ^{9}_{4}Be \rightarrow ^{12}_{6}C + ^{1}_{0}n$$

Neutrons, being uncharged, are not repelled by the nucleus. As a result, neutrons are often used to bombard nuclei.

Free neutrons can be produced in a nuclear reaction.

Alpha particles are useful in producing nuclear reactions. Alphas from radioactive materials, however, have fixed energies. In addition, sources that emit a large number of particles per second are difficult to produce. Thus methods of artificially accelerating particles to high energies are needed. Energies of several million electron volts are required to produce nuclear reactions. Several types of particle accelerators have been developed. The linear accelerator, cyclotron, and the synchrotron are the accelerator types in greatest use today.

Accelerators give more flexibility in producing nuclear reactions.

## Linear Accelerators

A **linear accelerator** consists of a series of hollow tubes within a long evacuated chamber. The tubes are connected to a source of high frequency alternating voltage, Figure 30–7b. Protons are produced in an ion source similar to that described in Chapter 26. When the first tube has a negative potential, protons are accelerated into it. There is no electric field within the tube, so the proton moves at constant velocity. The length of the tube and the frequency of the voltage are adjusted so that when the protons have reached the far end of the tube, the poten-

Alternating voltages accelerate charged particles along a straight line in a linear accelerator.

**FIGURE 30–8. The synchrotron is a circular accelerator. Magnets are used to control the path and acceleration of the particles (a). Fermi Laboratory's synchrotron has a diameter of 2 km (b).**

tial of the second tube is negative with respect to that of the first. The resulting electric field in the gap between the tubes accelerates the protons into the second tube. This process continues, with the protons receiving an acceleration between each pair of tubes. The energy of the protons is increased by $10^5$ eV with each acceleration. The proton rides along the crest of an electric field wave much as a surfboard moves on the ocean. At the end of the accelerator, the protons can have energies of many millions or billions of electron volts.

Linear accelerators can be used with both electrons and protons. The largest linear accelerator is at Stanford University in California. It is 3.3 km long and accelerates electrons to energies of 20 GeV ($2.0 \times 10^{10}$ eV).

## The Synchrotron

An accelerator may be made smaller by using a magnetic field to bend the path of the particles into a circle. In a device known as a **synchrotron**, the bending magnets are separated by accelerating regions. In the straight regions, high frequency alternating voltage accelerates the particles. The strength of the magnetic field and the length of the path are chosen so that the particles reach the location of the alternating electric field precisely when the field's polarity will accelerate them. One of the largest synchrotrons in operation is at the Fermi National Accelerator Laboratory near Chicago, Figure 30–8. Protons there reach energies of 1 TeV ($1.0 \times 10^{12}$ eV). The Superconducting Super Collider (SSC), presently under construction near Dallas, Texas, is a synchrotron with two particle beams traveling around an 88-km ring in opposite directions. The beams will collide in several interaction regions and the results studied.

A synchrotron uses magnetic fields to bend charged particles into circular paths.

Particles that ionize matter can be detected by several means.

## Particle Detectors

Photographic films become "fogged," or exposed, when α particles, β particles, or γ rays strike them. Thus, photographic film can be used to detect these particles and rays. Many other devices are used to detect charged particles and γ rays. Most of these devices make use of the fact that a collision with a high speed particle will remove electrons from atoms. That is, the high speed particles ionize the matter that they bombard. In addition, some substances fluoresce when exposed to certain types of radiation. Thus, fluorescent substances can be used to detect radiation.

In the **Geiger-Mueller tube**, particles ionize gas atoms, Figure 30–9. The tube contains a gas at low pressure (10 kPa). At one end of the tube is a very thin "window" through which charged particles or gamma rays pass. Inside the tube is a copper cylinder with a negative charge. A rigid wire with a positive charge runs down the centre of this cylinder. The voltage across the wire and cylinder is kept just below the point at which a spontaneous discharge, or spark, occurs. When a charged particle or gamma ray enters the tube, it ionizes a gas atom between the copper cylinder and the wire. The positive ion produced is accelerated toward the copper cylinder by the potential difference. The electron is accelerated toward the positive wire. As these new particles move toward the electrodes, they strike other atoms and form even more ions in their path.

Thus an avalanche of charged particles is created and a pulse of current flows through the tube. The current causes a potential difference across a resistor in the circuit. The voltage is amplified and registers the arrival of a particle by advancing a counter or producing an audible signal, such as a click. The potential difference across the resistor lowers the voltage across the tube so that the current flow stops. Thus the tube is ready for the beginning of a new avalanche when another particle or gamma ray enters it.

A device once used to detect particles was the **Wilson cloud chamber**. The chamber contains an area supersaturated with water vapour or ethanol vapour. When charged particles travel through the chamber, leaving a trail of ions in their paths, the vapour tends to condense into small droplets on the ions. In this way, visible trails of droplets, or fog, are formed. The **bubble chamber** was similar, except that trails of small vapour droplets formed in a liquid held just above the boiling point.

Modern experiments use **spark chambers** that are like giant Geiger-Mueller tubes. Plates several metres in size are separated by a few centimetres. The gap is filled with a low-pressure gas. A discharge is pro-

In a cloud chamber, particles create tracks of condensed vapour.

In a bubble chamber, trails of bubbles show paths of particles.

A spark chamber uses computers to analyse the trail of ions left by the particles.

FIGURE 30–9. Gamma rays from a radioactive source ionize the low pressure gas in the tube, allowing a pulse of current to flow between the central wire and the copper tube.

30.2 The Building-Blocks of Matter **627**

duced in the path of a particle passing through the chamber. A computer locates the discharge and records its position for later analysis. Neutral particles do not produce discharges, and thus do not leave tracks. The laws of conservation of energy and momentum in collisions can be used to tell if any neutral particles were produced. Other detectors measure the energy of the particles. The entire array of detectors used in high energy accelerator experiments, such as that in Figure 30–10, can be many metres in size, with a mass of 9 Mt or more, and cost tens of millions of dollars.

Neutral particles cannot be detected directly. The laws of conservation of momentum and energy are used to find their paths.

# F.Y.I.

The atom is still the smallest amount of an element that retains the properties of that element.

## The Fundamental Particles

The atom was once thought to be the smallest particle into which matter could be divided. Then Rutherford found that the atom had a nucleus surrounded by electrons. After the proton was discovered, it was also thought to be indivisible. Experiments have been done that bombard protons with other protons or electrons accelerated by accelerators to very high energies. The results of these experiments show that the proton is composed of yet smaller bodies. The neutron also appears to be composed of smaller bodies.

Physicists now believe that the particles out of which all matter is made are grouped into two families, quarks and leptons. **Quarks** make up protons and neutrons. **Leptons** are particles, like the electron and neutrino. In addition to quarks and leptons, there are also particles that carry, or transmit, forces between particles. The photon is the carrier of the electromagnetic force. Eight particles, called **gluons**, carry the strong force that binds quarks into protons and the protons and neutrons into nuclei. Three particles, the **weak bosons**, are involved in the weak interaction, which operates in beta decay. The **graviton** is the name given to the yet-undetected carrier of the gravitational force. These particles are summarized in Tables 30–2 and 30–3. Charges are given in units of the electron charge and masses are stated as energy equivalents,

Other particles like the photon carry, or transmit, forces.

All matter is composed of quarks and leptons.

Table 30–2

| Quarks | | | | Leptons | | | |
|---|---|---|---|---|---|---|---|
| Name | Symbol | Mass | Charge | Name | Symbol | Mass | Charge |
| down | $d$ | 330 MeV | $-1/3$ e | electron | $e$ | 0.511 MeV | $-e$ |
| up | $u$ | 330 MeV | $2/3$ e | neutrino | $\nu_e$ | 0 | 0 |

**Table 30–3**

| Force carriers | | | | |
|---|---|---|---|---|
| Force | Name | Symbol | Mass | Charge |
| Electromagnetic | photon | $\gamma$ | 0 | 0 |
| Weak | weak boson | $W^+$ | 80.6 GeV | $+e$ |
|  |  | $W^-$ | 80.6 GeV | $-e$ |
|  |  | $Z^0$ | 91.2 GeV | 0 |
| Strong | gluon (8) | $g$ | 0 | 0 |
| Gravitational | graviton (?) | $G$ | 0 | 0 |

given by Einstein's famous formula, $E = mc^2$. The energy unit, the electron volt, was defined in Chapter 27. The energy equivalent of these particles is much larger, and so are shown in MeV (mega-electron volts, or $10^6$ eV) and GeV (giga-electron volts, or $10^9$ eV).

Each quark and each lepton also has its **antiparticle.** The antiparticles are identical with the particles except they have the opposite charge. When a particle and its antiparticle collide, they annihilate each other and are transformed into photons, or lighter particle-antiparticle pairs and energy, Figure 30–11. The total number of quarks and the total number of leptons in the universe are constant. That is, quarks and leptons are created or destroyed only in particle-antiparticle pairs. The number of charge carriers is not conserved; the total charge, however, is conserved. Gravitons, photons, gluons, and weak bosons can be created or destroyed if there is enough energy. After exploring the production and annihilation of antiparticles, we will return to the quark and lepton theory of matter.

Quarks and leptons cannot be created or destroyed individually, only in particle-antiparticle pairs.

## Particles and Antiparticles

The $\alpha$ particles and $\gamma$ rays emitted by radioactive nuclei have single energies that depend on the decaying nucleus. For example, the energy of the $\alpha$ particle emitted by $^{234}_{90}$Th is always 4.2 MeV. Beta particles, however, are emitted with a wide range of energies. One might expect the energy of the $\beta$ particles to be equal to the difference between the energy of the nucleus before decay and the energy of the nucleus produced by the decay. In fact, the wide range of energies of electrons emitted during $\beta$ decay suggested to Niels Bohr that energy might not be conserved in nuclear reactions. Wolfgang Pauli in 1931 and Enrico Fermi in 1934 suggested that an unseen neutral particle was emitted with the $\beta$ particle. Named the **neutrino** ("little neutral one" in Italian) by Fermi, the particle (actually an antineutrino) was not directly observed until 1956.

In a stable nucleus, the neutron does not decay. A free neutron, or one in an unstable nucleus, can decay by emitting a $\beta$ particle. Sharing the outgoing energy with the $\beta$ particle is an antineutrino ($^0_0\overline{\nu}$). The antineutrino has zero mass and is uncharged, but like the photon, it carries momentum and energy. The neutron decay equation is written

$$^1_0 n \rightarrow {}^1_1 p + {}^0_{-1}e + {}^0_0\overline{\nu}.$$

A neutron decay is accompanied by emission of an antineutrino.

**FIGURE 30–11. The collision of a positron and an electron results in gamma ray production.**

When an isotope decays by emission of a **positron** (antielectron), a process like β decay occurs. A proton within the nucleus changes into a neutron with the emission of a positron ($_{1}^{0}e$) and a neutrino ($_{0}^{0}\nu$). The decay reaction is written

$$_{1}^{1}p \rightarrow \, _{0}^{1}n + \, _{1}^{0}e + \, _{0}^{0}\nu.$$

The decay of neutrons into protons and protons into neutrons cannot be explained by the strong force. The existence of β decay indicates there must be another force or interaction, called the weak interaction, acting in the nucleus.

The positron is an example of an antiparticle, or a particle of antimatter. When a positron and an electron collide, the two can annihilate each other, resulting in energy in the form of γ rays. Matter is converted directly into energy. The amount of energy can be calculated using Einstein's equation for the energy equivalent of mass

$$E = mc^2.$$

The mass of the electron is $9.11 \times 10^{-31}$ kg. The mass of the positron is the same. Therefore, the energy equivalent of the positron and the electron together is

$$
\begin{aligned}
E &= 2(9.11 \times 10^{-31} \text{ kg})(3.00 \times 10^{8} \text{ m/s})^2 \\
&= (1.64 \times 10^{-13} \text{ J})(1 \text{ eV}/1.60 \times 10^{-19} \text{ J}) \\
&= 1.02 \times 10^{6} \text{ eV or } 1.02 \text{ MeV}.
\end{aligned}
$$

When a positron and an electron at rest annihilate each other, the sum of the energies of the γ rays emitted is 1.02 MeV.

The inverse of annihilation can also occur. That is, energy can be converted directly into matter. If a γ ray with at least 1.02 MeV energy passes close by a nucleus, a positron and electron pair can be produced. This is called **pair production**. Reactions like $\gamma \rightarrow e^{-}$ or $\gamma \rightarrow e^{+}$, however, cannot occur because such an event would violate the law of conservation of charge. Matter and antimatter particles must always be produced in pairs.

When an electron and positron annihilate, gamma rays are produced with total energy equal to the rest energy of the two particles.

# F.Y.I.

The electromagnetic attraction of an electron and a positron is $42 \times 10^{41}$ times stronger than their gravitational attraction.

—Isaac Asimov's *Book of Facts*

The production of a positron-electron pair is shown in the chapter-opening bubble chamber photograph. A magnetic field around the bubble chamber causes the oppositely-charged particles to curve in opposite directions. The γ ray that produced the pair produced no track. If the energy of the γ ray is larger than 1.02 MeV, the excess energy goes into kinetic energy of the positron and electron. The positron soon collides with another electron and they are both annihilated, resulting in the production of two or three γ rays with a total energy of 1.02 MeV.

Antiprotons can also be created. An antiproton has a mass equal to that of the proton but is negatively charged. Protons have 1836 times as much mass as electrons. The energy needed to create proton-antiproton pairs is comparably larger. The first proton-antiproton pair was produced and observed at Berkeley, California in 1955.

## Practice Problem

**13.** The mass of a proton is $1.67 \times 10^{-27}$ kg.
   **a.** Find the energy equivalent of the proton's mass in joules.
   **b.** Convert this value to eV.
   **c.** Find the smallest total γ ray energy that could result in a proton-antiproton pair.

## The Quark Model of Nucleons

The quark model describes the proton and the neutron as an assembly of quarks. The nucleons are each made up of three quarks. The proton has two up quarks (charge $+2/3$ e) and one down quark (charge $-1/3$ e). A proton is described as $p = (uud)$. The charge on the proton is the sum of the charges of the three quarks, $(2/3 + 2/3 + -1/3)e = +e$. The neutron is made up of one up quark and two down quarks, $n = (udd)$. The charge of the neutron is zero, $(2/3 + -1/3 + -1/3)e = 0$.

Individual quarks cannot be observed because the strong force that holds them together becomes larger as the quarks are pulled farther apart. In this sense, the strong force acts like the force of a spring. It is unlike the electric force, which becomes weaker as charged particles are moved farther apart. In the quark model, the strong force is the result of the emission and absorption of gluons that carry the force.

The weak interaction involves three force carriers: $W^+$, $W^-$, and $Z^0$ bosons. The weak interaction exhibits itself in beta decay, the decay of a neutron into a proton, electron, and antineutrino. As was shown before, only one quark in the neutron and the proton is different. Beta decay occurs in two steps. First, one $d$ quark in a neutron changes to a $u$ quark with the emission of a $W^-$ boson,

$$d \rightarrow u + W^-.$$

Then the $W^-$ boson decays into an electron and an antineutrino,

$$W^- \rightarrow e^- + \bar{\nu}.$$

Similarly, in the decay of a proton, a neutron and a $W^+$ boson are emitted. The weak boson then decays into a positron and a neutrino.

The emission of a $Z^0$ boson is not accompanied by a change from one quark to another. The $Z^0$ boson produces an interaction between

**Phantom Tracks**

Gamma rays of sufficient energy can produce particle-antiparticle pairs.

**FIGURE 30–13. Characteristic sizes of the structures of matter, given in metres, from the smallest "living" thing, a virus. It is not yet known whether quarks are measurable and have some internal structure, or whether they are really point-like objects.**

$10^{-7}$ m

Virus

$10^{-9}$ m

Molecule

$10^{-10}$ m

Atom

$10^{-14}$ m

Nucleus

$10^{-15}$ m

Proton

Quark

?

# Physics and society

## A DAILY DOSE OF RADON

The radioactive isotopes $^{226}_{88}$Ra (radium) and $^{222}_{86}$Rn (radon) are two elements formed in the series of radioactive elements as uranium decays to a stable form of lead.

Radon occurs in trace amounts in various rocks throughout Earth's crust. As radium decays, it produces gaseous radon. Radon is present in high concentrations in soils containing shale, granite, phosphate, and pitchblende. Radon moves out of the soil and into air, water, and buildings. Radon gas moves into houses through cracks in floors or walls, or any opening around water or gas pipes and drains. Radon mixes with the air in houses and is then inhaled by the occupants.

Within the last decade, serious concerns have arisen over the health effects of radon on the general population.

Health problems from radon are due mainly to its decay products, which are chemically active and become attached to particles in the air. If these particles are inhaled, they become deposited in the bronchi.

In outdoor air, radon is usually diluted and poses no health hazard. In a tightly-closed house, however, radon concentrations can build up to dangerous levels. Average indoor concentrations may be from five to ten times greater than average outdoor concentrations. Because radon is colourless and odourless, and causes no acute health effects, it is undetectable without special testing equipment. Reliable radon monitoring devices are widely available.

If radioactivity from radon is found to be present in a house at unacceptable levels, there are ways to reduce a person's exposure. Simply opening windows in basements can help. Sealing cracks and plugging up openings in floors yield only low to moderate reductions in radon. Most radon gas is drawn into a house by slight reductions in air pressure caused by air being driven from the house by such things as clothes dryers, fireplaces, exhaust-only fans, and by the chimney, or stack, effect. The stack effect occurs as warm air rises, moves out through openings at the top of the house, and draws air into the lower part of the structure. This effect can be counteracted by installation of a sub-slab venting system. In this method, a fan and pipe system is used to reverse the pressure difference between the soil and the house by continuously pumping out air from below the substructure. Such a system can bring about huge reductions in indoor radon concentrations.

## DEVELOPING A VIEWPOINT

1. Scientists do not agree on the risks associated with radon exposure. Some think estimates of deaths from radon-induced lung cancer are too high. Others believe that the radon poses an extremely serious long-term threat to health.

Study recent references on radon in houses. Come to class prepared to discuss the following questions.
1. What are the risks of living with radon and the pros and cons of using expensive methods to decrease radon concentrations? 2. Find out what you can about the type of soil on which your school is built. Predict whether your school will have a low, moderate, or high radon concentration. 3. Obtain radon testing equipment and measure the radon concentration. How well did you predict the outcome?

## SUGGESTED READINGS

Cole, Leonard A. "Much Ado About Radon." *The Sciences,* January/February 1990, pp. 19–23.
Moeller, Dade W. Moeller. "Radon Zapper." *Popular Science,* 235 (4), October 1989, pp. 78–80.

the nucleons and the electrons in atoms that is similar to, but much weaker than, the electromagnetic force holding the atom together. The interaction was first detected in 1979. The $W^+$, $W^-$, and $Z^0$ bosons were first observed directly in 1983.

The force between charged particles, the electromagnetic interaction, is carried by photons in much the same way as weak bosons carry the weak force. The electric force acts over a long range because the photon has zero mass, while the weak force acts over short distances because the $W$ and $Z$ bosons are so relatively massive. The mathematical structures of the theories of the weak interaction and electromagnetic interaction, however, are similar. In the high energy collisions produced in accelerators, the electromagnetic and weak interactions have the same strength and range.

Astrophysical theories of supernovae indicate that during massive stellar explosions, the two interactions are identical. Present theories of the origin of the universe suggest that the two forces were identical during the early moments in the life of the cosmos as well. For this reason, the electromagnetic and weak forces are said to be unified by this theory into a single force, called the electroweak force.

Bombardment of particles at high energies creates many particles of medium and large mass that have very short lifetimes. Some of these particles are combinations of two or three $u$ or $d$ quarks or a quark-antiquark pair. Particles composed of quark-antiquark pairs are called **mesons;** those composed of three quarks are called **baryons.** Combinations of the $u$ and $d$ quarks, however, cannot account for all the particles produced. Combinations of three other quarks are necessary to form all known baryons and mesons. A fourth additional quark, the top quark, has not been found, but the theories that work very well predict its existence. Two additional pairs of leptons are also produced in high energy collisions. The additional quarks and leptons are listed in Table 30–4. No one knows why there are six quarks and six leptons or if there are still other undiscovered particles. One reason for building the Superconducting Super Collider is to attempt to answer this question.

**FIGURE 30–14. A battery of devices is waiting to detect the decay of a proton in a water molecule in this subterranean lake.**

A total of six quarks and six leptons are needed to account for all particles produced by high-energy accelerators.

**Table 30–4**

| Additional Quarks | | | |
|---|---|---|---|
| Name | Symbol | Mass | Charge |
| strange | $s$ | 510 MeV | $-1/3\ e$ |
| charm | $c$ | 1.6 GeV | $+2/3\ e$ |
| bottom | $b$ | 5.2 GeV | $-1/3\ e$ |
| top | $t$ | >100 GeV | $+2/3\ e$ |

| Additional Leptons | | | |
|---|---|---|---|
| Name | Symbol | Mass | Charge |
| muon | $\mu$ | 105 MeV | $-e$ |
| muon neutrino | $\nu_\mu$ | 0 | 0 |
| tau | $\tau$ | 1.8 GeV | $-e$ |
| tau neutrino | $\nu_\tau$ | 0 | 0 |

# F. Y. I.

If I could remember the names of all these particles, I'd be a botanist.

Enrico Fermi

In the same way that the electromagnetic and weak forces were unified into the electroweak force during the 1970s, physicists are presently trying to create a Grand Unified Theory that includes the strong force as well. Work is still incomplete. One prediction of current theories is that the proton should not exist forever, but decay into leptons and photons. The proton half-life should be $10^{31}$ years. Experiments to test this prediction took data continuously for three years, but found no decays. Theories are being revised and new experiments planned. A fully unified theory that includes gravitation requires even more work.

The field of physics that studies these particles is called elementary particle physics. The field is very exciting because new discoveries occur almost every week. Each new discovery seems to raise as many questions as it answers.

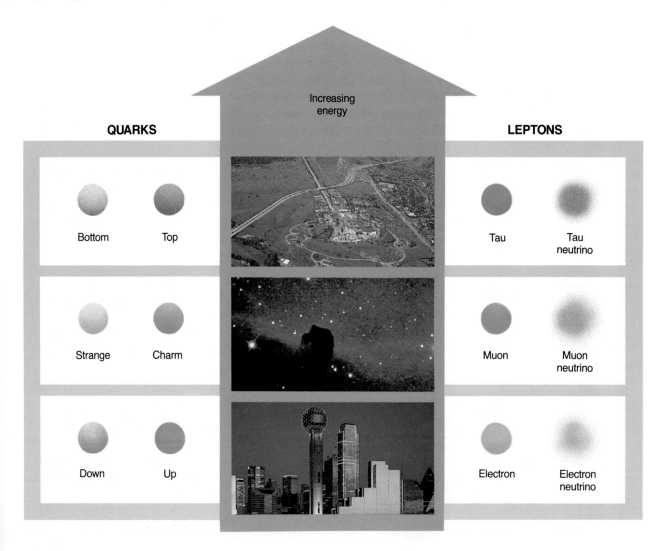

**FIGURE 30–15. The known quarks and leptons are divided into three families. The everyday world is made from particles in the bottom family. Particles in the middle group are found in cosmic rays and are routinely produced in particle accelerators. Particles in the top families are believed to have existed briefly during the earliest moments of the Big Bang and are created in high-energy collisions.**

## CONCEPT REVIEW

**2.1** Why would it require a more energetic proton than a neutron to produce a nuclear reaction?

**2.2** Protons in the FermiLab accelerator, Figure 30–8, move counter-clockwise. In what direction is the magnetic field of the bending magnets?

**2.3** Figure 30–12 shows the collision of an antiproton coming from the bottom of the photo with a proton in the liquid-hydrogen bubble chamber. The track moving upward and leaving the right-hand edge of the photo is a negatively-charged "pion." What is the charge of the particles producing the spirals seen in many locations?

**2.4** Critical Thinking: Write an equation for beta decay in which you write the quarks comprising both the neutron and the proton. Include both steps in the decay.

# CHAPTER
# 30 REVIEW

## SUMMARY

### 30.1 Radioactivity

· The number of protons in a nucleus is given by the atomic number.
· The sum of the numbers of protons and neutrons in a nucleus is equal to the mass number.
· Atoms having nuclei with the same number of protons but different numbers of neutrons are called isotopes.
· An unstable nucleus undergoes radioactive decay, transmuting into another element.
· Radioactive decay produces three kinds of particles. Alpha ($\alpha$) particles are helium nuclei; beta ($\beta$) particles are high speed electrons; and gamma ($\gamma$) rays are high energy photons.

### 30.2 The Building Blocks of Matter

· In nuclear reactions, the sum of the mass number, $A$, and the total charge is not changed.
· The half-life of a radioactive isotope is the time required for half of the nuclei to decay.
· The number of decays of a particle per second, the activity, is also reduced by a factor of two in a time equal to the half-life.

· Bombardment of nuclei by protons, neutrons, alpha particles, electrons, gamma rays, or other nuclei can produce a nuclear reaction.
· Linear accelerators and synchrotrons produce the high energy protons and electrons.
· The Geiger counter and other particle detectors use the ionization of charged particles passing through matter.
· In beta decay, an uncharged, massless antineutrino is emitted with the electron.
· A positron (antimatter electron) and a neutrino are emitted by radioactive nuclei in a process called positron decay.
· When antimatter and matter combine, all mass is converted into energy or lighter matter-antimatter particle pairs.
· By pair production, energy is transformed into a matter-antimatter particle pair.
· The weak interaction, or weak force, operates in beta decay. The strong force binds the nucleus together.
· Protons and neutrons, together called nucleons, are composed of still smaller particles called quarks.
· All matter appears to be made up of two families of particles, quarks and leptons.

# KEY TERMS

proton
atomic mass unit
atomic number
neutron
mass number
isotope
nuclide
radioactive
radioactive decay
$\alpha$ decay
$\beta$ decay
$\gamma$ decay
transmutation
nuclear reaction
half-life
activity
linear accelerator

synchrotron
Geiger-Mueller tube
Wilson cloud
    chamber
bubble chamber
spark chamber
quark
lepton
gluon
weak boson
graviton
antiparticle
neutrino
positron
pair production
meson
baryon

# REVIEWING CONCEPTS

1. What is the symbol for the atomic mass unit?
2. Define the term *transmutation* as used in nuclear physics and give an example.
3. What are the common names for an $\alpha$ particle, $\beta$ particle, and $\gamma$ radiation?
4. What happens to the atomic number and mass number of a nucleus that emits an alpha particle?
5. What happens to the atomic number and mass number of a nucleus that emits a beta particle?
6. What two quantities must always be conserved in any nuclear equation?
7. Why would a linear accelerator not work with a neutron?
8. Explain how a scintillation counter detects gamma rays and high-speed charged particles.
9. In which of the four interactions (strong, weak, electromagnetic, gravitational) does the following particle take part?
   **a.** electron  **b.** proton  **c.** neutrino
10. What happens to the atomic number and mass number of a nucleus that emits a positron?
11. Give the symbol, mass, and charge of the following particles.
   **a.** proton  **c.** positron  **e.** $\alpha$ particle
   **b.** neutron  **d.** electron

# APPLYING CONCEPTS

1. Which are generally more unstable, small or large nuclei?
2. Which isotope has the greater number of neutrons, uranium-235 or uranium-238?
3. Which is usually larger, $A$ or $Z$? Explain.
4. Which is most like an X ray, alpha particles, beta particles, or gamma radiation?
5. Could a deuteron, $^2_1H$, decay via alpha decay? Explain.
6. Which will give a higher reading on a radiation detector: equal amounts of a radioactive substance that has a short half-life or a radioactive substance that has a long half-life?
7. Why is carbon dating useful in establishing the age of campfires but not the age of a set of knight's armor?
8. What would happen if a meteorite made of antiprotons, antineutrons, and positrons landed on Earth?

# PROBLEMS

## 30.1 Radioactivity

1. An atom of an isotope of magnesium has an atomic mass of about 24 u. The atomic number of magnesium is 12. How many neutrons are in the nucleus of this atom?
2. An atom of an isotope of nitrogen has an atomic mass of about 15 u. The atomic number of nitrogen is 7. How many neutrons are in the nucleus of this isotope?
3. List the number of neutrons in an atom of each of these isotopes.
   **a.** $^{112}_{48}Cd$  **c.** $^{208}_{83}Bi$  **e.** $^1_1H$
   **b.** $^{209}_{83}Bi$  **d.** $^{80}_{35}Br$  **f.** $^{40}_{18}Ar$
4. Find the symbol for the elements that are shown by the following symbols, where X replaces the symbol for the element.
   **a.** $^{18}_9X$  **b.** $^{241}_{95}X$  **c.** $^{21}_{10}X$  **d.** $^7_3X$
5. A radioactive bismuth isotope, $^{214}_{83}Bi$, emits a $\beta$ particle. Write the complete nuclear equation, showing the element formed.
6. A radioactive polonium isotope, $^{210}_{84}Po$, emits an $\alpha$ particle. Write the complete nuclear equation, showing the element formed.
7. An unstable chromium isotope, $^{56}_{24}Cr$, emits a $\beta$ particle. Write a complete equation, showing the element formed.

8. During a reaction, two deuterons, $^2_1$H, combine to form a helium isotope, $^3_2$He. What other particle is produced?

9. On the sun, the nuclei of four ordinary hydrogen atoms combine to form a helium isotope, $^4_2$He. What type of particles are missing from the following equation for this reaction?

$$4^1_1\text{H} \rightarrow {}^4_2\text{He} + ?$$

10. Write a complete nuclear equation for the transmutation of a uranium isotope, $^{227}_{92}$U, into a thorium isotope, $^{223}_{90}$Th.

▶ 11. $^{238}_{92}$U decays by $\alpha$ emission and two successive $\beta$ emissions back into uranium again. Show the three nuclear decay equations and predict the atomic mass number of the uranium formed.

12. In an accident in a research laboratory, a radioactive isotope with a half-life of three days is spilled. As a result, the radiation is eight times the maximum permissible amount. How long must workers wait before they can enter the room?

13. If the half-life of an isotope is two years, what fraction of the isotope remains after six years?

14. The half-life of strontium-90 is 28 years. After 280 years, how would the intensity of a sample of strontium-90 compare to the original intensity of the sample?

▶ 15. A Geiger counter registers an initial reading of 3200 counts, measuring a radioactive substance and 100 counts 30 h later. What is the half-life of this substance?

▶ 16. A 14-g sample of $^{14}_6$C contains Avogadro's number, $6.02 \times 10^{23}$, nuclei. A 5.0 g-sample of $^{14}_6$C will have how many nondecayed nuclei after 11 460 years?

▶ 17. A 1.00-$\mu$g sample of a radioactive material contains $6.0 \times 10^{14}$ nuclei. After 48 h, 0.25 $\mu$g of the material remains.
   a. What is the half-life of the material?
   b. How could one determine the activity of the sample at 24 h using this information?

**30.2 The Building Blocks of Matter**

▶ 18. The synchrotron at FermiLab has a diameter of 2.0 km. Protons circling in it move at approximately the speed of light.
   a. How long does it take a proton to complete one revolution?

b. The protons enter the ring at an energy of 8.0 GeV. They gain 2.5 MeV each revolution. How many revolutions must they travel before they reach 400 GeV energy?
   c. How long does it take the protons to be accelerated to 400 GeV?
   d. How far do the protons travel during this acceleration?

19. What would be the charge of a particle composed of three *u* quarks?

20. The charge of an antiquark is opposite that of a quark. A pion is composed of a *u* quark and an *anti-d* quark. What would be the charge of this pion?

21. Find the charges of the following pions made of
   a. *u* and *anti-u* quark pair.
   b. *d* and *anti-u* quarks.
   c. *d* and *anti-d* quarks.

 USING A GRAPHING CALCULATOR

An archaeological expedition in Jerusalem finds three wooden bowls, each in a different part of the city. An analysis of the levels of carbon-14 reveals that the three bowls have 90%, 75%, and 60% of the carbon-14 one would expect to find in a similar bowl made today. The equation for the decay of carbon-14 is $y = 100 \cdot 2^{(-x/5730)}$, where $y$ is the percentage of carbon-14 remaining and $x$ is the age of the object in years. Graph this equation on a graphing calculator with axes scaled from 0 to 5000 years and from 100% to 50%. Trace along the equation to find the age of the three objects.

THINKING PHYSIC-LY

Why is a sample of radioactive material always a little warmer than its surrounding?

# CHAPTER
# 31

# Nuclear Applications

. . . . . . . . . . . . . . . .

◀ Shock Waves

One of the more familiar photos of a nuclear reactor is this picture of a bundle of uranium-filled fuel rods in water. What causes the blue glow surrounding the assembly?

## Chapter Outline

**31.1 HOLDING THE NUCLEUS TOGETHER**
· The Strong Nuclear Force
· Binding Energy of the Nucleus

**31.2 USING NUCLEAR ENERGY**
· Artificial Radioactivity
· Nuclear Fission
· Nuclear Reactors
· Nuclear Fusion
· Controlled Fusion

Few areas of physics are in the news more than nuclear physics. Whether it is nuclear weapons, the storage of waste from medical applications, or nuclear power reactors such as the one shown in the photograph, it seems nuclear physics is always in the news. Unfortunately, most of the publicity is negative. Seldom interviewed are people whose lives have been saved by nuclear medicine or people who can breathe more easily because of the lack of pollution from coal-burning electrical plants. An informed citizen must understand some of the science and technology before forming an opinion.

## ✓ Concept Check

The following terms or concepts from earlier chapters are important for a good understanding of this chapter. If you are not familiar with them, you should review them before studying this chapter.
· nuclear reaction; nuclear particles, Chapter 30

639

# 31.1 HOLDING THE NUCLEUS TOGETHER

The negatively-charged electrons that surround the positively-charged nucleus of an atom are held in place by the attractive electric force. The nucleus consists of positively-charged protons and neutral neutrons. The repulsive electric force between the protons might be expected to cause them to fly apart. This does not happen because an even stronger attractive force exists within the nucleus.

## The Strong Nuclear Force

The force that overcomes the mutual repulsion of the charged protons is called the **strong nuclear force**. The strong force acts between protons and neutrons that are very close together, as they are in a nucleus. The range of the strong force is very short, only about the radius of a proton, $1.3 \times 10^{-15}$ m. It is attractive and is of the same strength between protons and protons, protons and neutrons, and neutrons and neutrons. As a result of this equivalence, both neutrons and protons are called **nucleons**.

The strong force acts the same between neutrons and protons or between protons and protons or neutrons and neutrons.

The strong force holds the nucleons in the nucleus. If a nucleon were to be pulled out of a nucleus, work would have to be done to overcome the attractive force. Doing work adds energy to the system. Thus, the assembled nucleus has less energy than the separate protons and neutrons that make it up. The difference is the **binding energy** of the nucleus. Thus, the binding energy is negative.

## Binding Energy of the Nucleus

The binding energy of a nucleus is proportional to the difference between the mass of the nucleus and the masses of the nucleons from which it is assembled.

Binding energy can be expressed in the form of an equivalent amount of mass, according to the equation $E = mc^2$. The unit of mass used in nuclear physics is the atomic mass unit, u. One atomic mass unit is 1/12 the mass of the $^{12}_{6}C$ nucleus.

Because energy has to be added to take a nucleus apart, the mass of the assembled nucleus is less than the sum of the masses of the nucleons that compose it. For example, the helium nucleus, $^{4}_{2}He$, consists of 2 protons and 2 neutrons. The mass of a proton is 1.007825 u. The mass of a neutron is 1.008665 u. The mass of the nucleons that make up the helium nucleus is equal to the sum of the masses of the two protons and the two neutrons. Thus, if it weren't for the binding energy, the mass of the nucleus would be 4.032980 u. Careful measurement, however, shows the mass of a helium nucleus is only 4.002603 u. The mass of the helium nucleus is less than the mass of its constituent parts by 0.0030377 u. The difference, 0.0030377 u is called the **mass defect.** The binding energy can be calculated from the experimentally-determined mass defect by using $E = mc^2$ to compute the energy equivalent of the missing mass.

# F.Y.I.

**Binding energy versus A**

FIGURE 31–1. A graph of the binding energy per nucleon.

Masses are normally measured in atomic mass units. It will be useful, then, to determine the energy equivalent of 1 u (1.6605 × 10⁻²⁷ kg). The most convenient unit of energy to use is the electron volt. To five significant digits,

$$E = mc^2$$
$$= (1.6605 \times 10^{-27} \text{ kg})(2.9979 \times 10^8 \text{ m/s})^2$$
$$= (14.923 \times 10^{-11} \text{ J})(1 \text{ eV}/1.6022 \times 10^{-19} \text{ J})$$
$$= 9.3149 \times 10^8 \text{ eV}$$
$$E = 931.49 \text{ MeV}.$$

A useful relationship is shown by the graph of binding energy per nucleon in Figure 31–1.

The energy equivalent of one atomic mass unit is 931.5 MeV.

## Example Problem

### Calculating Mass Defect and Nuclear Binding Energy

The mass of a proton is 1.007825 u. The mass of a neutron is 1.008665 u. The mass of the nucleus of the radioactive hydrogen isotope tritium, $_1^3H$, is 3.016049 u. **a.** What is the nuclear mass defect of this isotope? **b.** What is the binding energy of tritium?

**Solution:**

**a.** As indicated by the superscript and subscript in the symbol for tritium, its nucleus contains 1 proton and 2 neutrons.

$$\begin{aligned}
\text{mass of 1 proton} &= 1.007825 \text{ u} \\
\text{mass of 2 neutrons} = (2)(1.008665 \text{ u}) &= 2.017330 \text{ u} \\
\text{total mass of nucleons} &= 3.025155 \text{ u} \\
\text{mass of tritium nucleus} &= 3.016049 \text{ u} \\
\text{less total mass of nucleons} &= -3.025155 \text{ u} \\
\text{mass defect} &= -0.009106 \text{ u}
\end{aligned}$$

**b.** Since 1 u is equivalent to 931.49 MeV, the binding energy of the tritium nucleus can be calculated.
binding energy of $_1^3H$ nucleus,
$$E = (-0.009106 \text{ u})(931.49 \text{ MeV/u})$$
$$= -8.482 \text{ MeV}$$

**POCKET LAB**

**BINDING ENERGY**

Particles within the nucleus are strongly bonded. Place two disk magnets together to represent a proton and neutron within a nucleus. Slowly pull them apart. Feel how the force changes with separation. Describe how this analogy could be extended for a nucleus that contains several protons and neutrons.

# Practice Problems

*Use these values in the following problems:* mass of proton = 1.007825 u; mass of neutron = 1.008665 u; 1 u = 931.49 MeV.

1. The carbon isotope, $^{12}_{6}C$, has a nuclear mass of 12.0000 u.
   a. Calculate its mass defect.
   b. Calculate its binding energy in MeV.
2. The isotope of hydrogen that contains 1 proton and 1 neutron is called deuterium. The mass of its nucleus is 2.0140 u.
   a. What is its mass defect?
   b. What is the binding energy of deuterium in MeV?
3. A nitrogen isotope, $^{15}_{7}N$, has 7 protons and 8 neutrons. Its nucleus has a mass of 15.00011 u.
   a. Calculate the mass defect of this nucleus.
   b. Calculate the binding energy of the nucleus.
▶ 4. An oxygen isotope, $^{16}_{8}O$, has a nuclear mass of 15.99491 u.
   a. What is the mass defect of this isotope?
   b. What is the binding energy of its nucleus?

Iron-56 has the most negative binding energy per nucleon.

When you worked the Practice Problems you found that the heavier nuclei were bound more strongly than lighter nuclei. Except for a few nuclei, the binding energy per nucleon becomes more negative as A increases to a value of 56, iron, Fe. $^{56}_{26}Fe$ is the most tightly bound nucleus. Nuclei larger than iron are less strongly bound.

A nuclear reaction will occur naturally if energy is released by the reaction. Energy will be released if the nucleus that results from the reaction is more tightly bound than the original nucleus. When a heavy nucleus, such as $^{238}_{92}U$, decays by releasing an alpha particle, the binding energy per nucleon of the resulting $^{234}_{90}Th$ is larger than that of the uranium. The excess energy of the $^{238}_{92}U$ nucleus is transferred into the kinetic energy of the alpha particle. At low atomic numbers, reactions that add nucleons to a nucleus make the binding energy of the nucleus more negative. Thus the energy of the larger nucleus is less than the sum of the energies of the two smaller ones. Energy is released when the reaction occurs. In the sun and other stars, the production of heavier nuclei like helium and carbon from hydrogen releases energy that eventually becomes the electromagnetic radiation by which we see the stars.

**FIGURE 31–2. The strawberries in the two cartons are identical except that those in the carton on the left have been treated with gamma radiation to destroy the bacteria causing spoilage.**

# CONCEPT REVIEW

**1.1** When tritium, $_1^3H$, decays, it emits a β particle and becomes $_2^3He$. Which nucleus would you expect to have a more negative binding energy?

**1.2** Which of the two nuclei above would have the larger mass defect?

**1.3** The range of the strong force is so short that only nucleons that touch each other feel the force. Use this fact to explain why in very large nuclei the repulsive electric force can overcome the strong attractive force and make the nucleus unstable.

**1.4** **Critical Thinking:** In old stars, not only are helium and carbon produced by joining more tightly-bound nuclei, but so are oxygen (Z = 8) and silicon (Z = 14). What would be the atomic number of the heaviest nucleus that could be formed this way? Explain.

# 31.2 USING NUCLEAR ENERGY

**O**bjectives

- **define artificially produced radioactive isotopes; describe their medical uses; solve nuclear equations involving the formation and decay of radioactive isotopes.**
- **define nuclear fission and a chain reaction; understand the source of energy in fission.**
- **describe the operation of one or more types of nuclear reactors; understand the formation of plutonium in a reactor.**
- **describe the fusion process and the formation of helium in the sun.**
- **describe two approaches to controlled nuclear fusion.**

**I**n no other area of physics has basic knowledge led to applications as quickly as in the field of nuclear physics. The medical use of the radioactive element radium began within 20 years of its discovery. Proton accelerators were tested for medical applications less than one year after being invented. In the case of nuclear fission, the military application was under development before the basic physics was even known. Peaceful applications followed in less than 10 years. The question of the uses of nuclear science in our society is an important one for all citizens today.

## Artificial Radioactivity

Marie and Pierre Curie had noted as early as 1899 that substances placed close to radioactive uranium became radioactive themselves. In 1934, Irene Joliot-Curie and Frederic Joliot bombarded aluminum with alpha particles, producing neutrons by the reaction

$$_2^4He + _{13}^{27}Al \rightarrow _{15}^{30}P + _0^1n.$$

In addition to neutrons, the Curies found another particle coming from the aluminum, a positively-charged electron, or positron. The positron, a particle with the same mass as the electron but with a positive charge, had been discovered two years earlier by American Carl Anderson. The most interesting result of the Curies' experiment was that positrons continued to be emitted after the alpha bombardment stopped. The positrons were found to come from the phosphorus isotope $_{15}^{30}P$. The Curies had produced a radioactive isotope not previously known.

Radioactive isotopes can be formed from stable isotopes by bombardment with alpha particles, protons, neutrons, electrons, or gamma rays. The resulting unstable nuclei emit radiation until they are transmuted into stable isotopes. The radioactive nuclei may emit alpha, beta, and gamma radiation as well as positrons.

Radioactive isotopes not found in nature can be produced by bombarding nuclei.

FIGURE 31–3. PET scanner results.

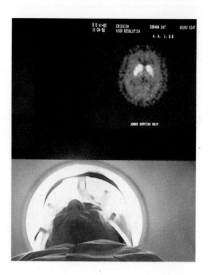

Tracer isotopes allow doctors to follow the path of molecules through the body.

## MEDICINE CONNECTION ▶

A PET scanner makes a three-dimensional map of the distribution of decaying nuclei in the body.

Ionizing radiation can destroy cells.

Artificially produced radioactive isotopes have many uses, especially in medicine. In many medical applications, patients are given radioactive isotopes that are absorbed by specific parts of the body. The detection of the decay products of these isotopes allows doctors to trace the movement of the isotopes, and of the molecules to which they are attached, through the body. For that reason, these isotopes are called tracer isotopes. Iodine, for example, is primarily used in the thyroid gland. A patient is given an iodine compound containing radioactive $^{131}_{53}I$. The iodine concentrates in the thyroid gland. A physician uses a Geiger-Mueller counter to monitor the activity of $^{131}_{53}I$ in the region of the thyroid. The amount of iodine taken up by this gland is a measure of its ability to function.

A new instrument, the Positron Emission Tomography Scanner, or PET scanner, Figure 31–3, uses isotopes that emit positrons. Such an isotope is included in a solution injected into the patient's body. In the body, the isotope decays, releasing a positron. The positron annihilates an electron, emitting two gamma rays. The PET scanner detects the gammas and pinpoints the location of the positron-emitting isotope. A computer is then used to make a three-dimensional map of the isotope distribution. By this means, details such as the use of nutrients in particular regions of the brain can be traced. For example, if a person in a PET scanner were solving a physics problem, more nutrients would flow to the part of the brain being used to solve the problem. The decay of the positrons in this part of the brain would increase, and the PET scanner could map this area.

Another use of radioactivity in medicine is the destruction of cells. Often gamma rays from the isotope $^{60}_{27}Co$ are used to treat cancer patients. The ionizing radiation produced by radioactive iodine can be used to destroy cells in a diseased thyroid gland, with minimal harm to the rest of the body. Another method of reducing damage to healthy cells is to use unstable particles produced by particle accelerators like the synchrotron. These unstable particles pass through body tissue without doing damage. When they decay, however, the emitted particles destroy cells. The physician adjusts the accelerator so the particles decay only in the cancerous tissue.

# Practice Problems

5. Use Table D–5 of the Appendix to complete the following nuclear equations.

a. $^{14}_{6}C \rightarrow ? + _{-1}^{0}e$

b. $^{55}_{24}Cr \rightarrow ? + _{-1}^{0}e$

6. Write the nuclear equation for the transmutation of a uranium isotope, $^{238}_{92}U$, into a thorium isotope, $^{234}_{90}Th$, by emission of an alpha particle.

7. A radioactive polonium isotope, $^{214}_{84}Po$, undergoes alpha decay and becomes lead. Write the nuclear equation.

▶ 8. Write the nuclear equations for the beta decay of these isotopes.

a. $^{210}_{82}Pb$   b. $^{210}_{83}Bi$   c. $^{234}_{90}Th$   d. $^{239}_{93}Np$

## Nuclear Fission

The possibility of obtaining useful forms of energy from nuclear reactions was discussed in the 1930s. The most promising results came from bombarding substances with neutrons. In Italy, in 1934, Enrico Fermi and Emilio Segré produced many new radioactive isotopes by bombarding uranium with neutrons. They believed they had formed new elements with atomic numbers larger than 92, that of uranium.

German chemists Otto Hahn and Fritz Strassmann made careful chemical studies of the results of bombardment of uranium by neutrons. In 1939, their analyses showed that the resulting atoms acted chemically like barium. The two chemists could not understand how barium, with an atomic number of 56, could be produced from uranium. One week later, Lise Meitner and Otto Frisch proposed that the neutrons had

Fission is the splitting of a nucleus into two or more fragments of roughly equal size. It is accompanied by the release of a large amount of energy.

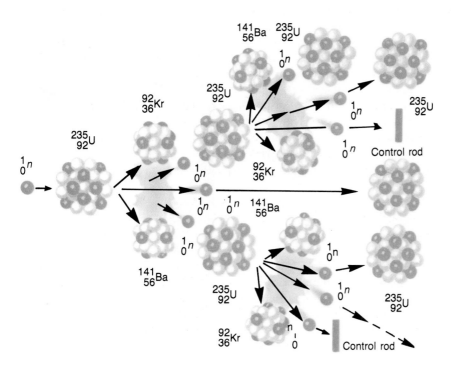

**FIGURE 31–4. The nuclear fission chain reaction of uranium-235 takes place in the core of a nuclear reactor.**

# Physics and society

## NUCLEAR WASTE DISPOSAL

Uranium fuel rods used to power nuclear reactors are useful for about 18 months before they must be replaced. In addition, some experts believe that entire nuclear facilities must be dismantled or sealed up after about 30 years due to high levels of radioactivity and resulting structural damage.

Although radiation has many useful applications, such as the treatment of cancer, it must be carefully monitored. Exposure to too much radiation can result in the destruction of body cells and eventual death. Unfortunately, all the materials in nuclear waste are still extremely radioactive and cannot be discarded using conventional waste disposal methods.

In Canada, approximately 1800 t of used fuel are produced every year. By 1989, about 14 000 t of used fuel had been accumulated in Canada — enough to fill an Olympic-sized swimming pool. This sounds like a lot of waste material, but it is quite small compared to the large amount of energy derived from it. (One 25-kg bundle of fuel can produce as much energy as 400 t of coal.)

So far, there is only one way to deal with nuclear waste. Used fuel is stored at nuclear reactor storage facilities (resembling large swimming pools). Liquid radioactive waste can be "vitrified" or turned into glass, result-ing in a solid that minimizes the chance of releasing radioactivity into the environment. The safety of these solids is now being tested. If proven safe, they would be stored underground in giant vaults. As you might expect, however, governments at all levels are hesitant to compete for the seemingly lucrative right to become nuclear waste disposal sites because of health and environmental concerns.

The original concept for nuclear power was that scientists would be able to devise a way to reprocess spent fuel, chemically separating it into uranium, plutonium, and waste fission products, with the uranium going back into the fuel cycle. It was also assumed that modern technology would soon devise ways to dispose of the small amount of spent fuel that could not be reprocessed.

Fuel reprocessing technology, however, has not kept up with nuclear waste production, and countries around the world are faced with the problem of storing spent fuel until a more permanent solution is developed.

Those countries involved in the use of nuclear energy face a difficult problem in the disposal of nuclear waste. They must decide whether or not the problems of nuclear energy outweigh the benefits.

## DEVELOPING A VIEWPOINT

Read further concerning nuclear waste disposal. Come to class prepared to discuss the following questions.

1. If ice cubes can be melted, vaporized, condensed, and refrozen into ice cubes, why can't we simply find a way to turn nuclear waste back into the raw material from which it was processed?
2. What are the pros and cons of sending nuclear waste into space?

## SUGGESTED READINGS

Wolf, Häfele, "Energy from Nuclear Power," *Scientific American*, September 1990, p. 144.
George E. Brown, Jr. "U.S. Nuclear Waste Policy: Flawed but Feasible," *Environment*, Vol 29 (No. 8) October 1987, pp. 6–7.
Atomic Energy of Canada Limited, Managing Canada's Nuclear Fuel Wastes, 1989.

caused a division of the uranium into two smaller nuclei, with a large release of energy. A division of a nucleus into two or more fragments is called **fission.** The possibility that fission could be not only a source of energy, but an explosive weapon, was immediately realized by many scientists.

The uranium isotope $^{235}_{92}U$ undergoes fission when bombarded with neutrons. The elements barium and krypton are typical results of fission, Figure 31–4. The reaction is

$$^{1}_{0}n + {}^{235}_{92}U \rightarrow {}^{92}_{36}Kr + {}^{141}_{56}Ba + 3\,{}^{1}_{0}n + 200\ \text{MeV}.$$

The energy released by each fission can be found by calculating the masses of the atoms on each side of the equation. In the uranium-235 reaction, the total mass on the right side of the equation is 0.215 u smaller than that on the left. The energy equivalent of this mass is 3.21 $\times\ 10^{-11}$ J, or 200 MeV. This energy is transferred to the kinetic energy of the products of the fission.

Once the fission process is started, the neutron needed to cause the fission of additional $^{235}_{92}U$ nuclei can be one of the three neutrons produced by an earlier fission. If one or more of the neutrons causes a fission, that fission releases three more neutrons, each of which can cause more fission. This process is called a **chain reaction.**

## Nuclear Reactors

Most of the neutrons released by the fission of $^{235}_{92}U$ atoms are moving at high speed and are unable to cause the fission of another $^{235}_{92}U$ atom. In addition, naturally occurring uranium consists of less than 1% $^{235}_{92}U$ and more than 99% $^{238}_{92}U$. When a $^{238}_{92}U$ nucleus absorbs a fast neutron, it does not undergo fission, but becomes a new isotope, $^{239}_{92}U$. The absorption of neutrons by $^{238}_{92}U$ keeps most of the neutrons from reaching the fissionable $^{235}_{92}U$ atoms.

Fermi suggested that a chain reaction would occur if the uranium were broken up into small pieces and placed in a material that can slow down, or moderate, the fast neutrons. When a neutron collides with a light atom, it transfers momentum and energy to the atom. In this way, the neutron loses energy. The **moderator** creates many slow neutrons, which are more likely to be absorbed by $^{235}_{92}U$ than by $^{238}_{92}U$. The larger number of slow neutrons greatly increases the probability that a neutron released by a fissioning $^{235}_{92}U$ nucleus will cause another $^{235}_{92}U$ nucleus to fission. If there is enough $^{235}_{92}U$ in the sample, a chain reaction can occur.

The lightest atom, hydrogen, would be an ideal moderator. Fast neutrons, however, cause a nuclear reaction with normal hydrogen nuclei, $^{1}_{1}H$. For this reason, when Fermi produced the first controlled chain reaction on December 2, 1942, he used graphite (carbon) as a moderator.

Heavy water, in which the hydrogen, $^{1}_{1}H$, is replaced by the isotope deuterium, $^{2}_{1}H$, does not absorb fast neutrons. As a result, heavy water is used as a moderator with natural uranium in the Canadian CANDU reactors.

Ordinary water can be used as a moderator if the number of $^{235}_{92}U$ nuclei in the uranium sample is increased. The process that increases the number of fissionable nuclei is called enrichment. Enrichment of

In a chain reaction, neutrons released by one fission induce other fissions.

A slow neutron is more effective in causing fission than is a fast neutron.

## F. Y. I.

The CANDU reactor gets its name from **CAN**ada (its place of design), **D**euterium oxide (heavy water), and **U**ranium (the fuel).

**FIGURE 31–5.** In a nuclear power plant, the thermal energy released in nuclear reactions is converted to electric energy. The nuclear reactor shown here is a pressurized water reactor. The Canadian-made CANDU reactor differs mainly in the use of heavy water as the moderator and coolant, and natural uranium (as opposed to enriched uranium).

a

uranium is difficult and requires large, expensive equipment. The United States produces enriched uranium for most of the nuclear reactors in the western world.

A common type of nuclear reactor used around the world, the pressurized water reactor, contains about 200 t of uranium sealed in hundreds of metal rods. The rods are immersed in water. Water not only is the moderator, but also transfers thermal energy away from the fissioning uranium. Between the uranium rods are placed rods of cadmium metal. Cadmium absorbs neutrons easily. The cadmium rods are moved in and out of the reactor to control the rate of the chain reaction. Thus the rods are called **control rods**. When the control rods are inserted completely into the reactor, they absorb enough neutrons to prevent the chain reaction. As they are removed from the reactor, the rate of energy release increases.

Energy released by the fission heats the water surrounding the uranium rods. The water itself doesn't boil because it is under high pressure, which increases its boiling temperature. As shown in Figure 31–5, this water is pumped to a heat exchanger, where it causes other water to boil, producing steam that turns turbines. The turbines are connected to generators that produce electrical energy.

Some of the fission energy goes into kinetic energy of electrons and neutrons, giving them speeds near the speed of light in vacuum. When these particles enter the water, they exceed the speed of light in the water. As a result, a blue glow is emitted when fuel rods are placed in water. The glow is called the Cerenkov effect. It is not the result of radioactivity in the water; radioactive objects do not emit a blue glow.

Fission of $^{235}_{92}$U nuclei produces Kr, Ba, and other atoms in the fuel rod. Most of these atoms are radioactive. About one every 18 months, some of the uranium fuel rods must be replaced. The old rods can no longer be used in the reactor, but they are still extremely radioactive and must be stored in safe locations. Research is now being done on methods of

Shock Waves ▶

safe, permanent storage of these radioactive waste products. Among the products of fission is an isotope of plutonium, $^{239}_{94}Pu$. This isotope is fissionable when it absorbs neutrons and can also be used in nuclear weapons. It is also very toxic. As a result, plutonium-containing materials are all stored in safe, temporary locations, never in "waste dumps." There is hope that in the future this fissionable isotope might be removed from radioactive waste and recycled to fuel other reactors.

The world's supply of uranium is limited. If nuclear reactors are used to supply a large fraction of the world's energy, uranium will become scarce. Even though the plutonium produced by normal reactors might be recovered to fuel other reactors, there is still a net loss of fuel. In order to extend the supply of uranium, **breeder reactors** have been developed. When a reactor contains both plutonium and $^{238}_{92}U$, the plutonium will undergo fission just as $^{235}_{92}U$ does. Many of the free nuetrons from the fission are absorbed by the $^{238}_{92}U$ to produce additional $^{239}_{94}Pu$. For every two plutonium atoms that undergo fission, three new ones are formed. More fissionable fuel can be recovered from this reactor than was originally present. Breeder reactors are operating only in France, but research is underway elsewhere.

## Nuclear Fusion

In nuclear **fusion**, nuclei with small masses combine to form a nucleus with a larger mass, Figure 31–6. In the process energy is released. The larger nucleus is more tightly bound, Figure 31–1, so its mass is less than the sum of the masses of the smaller nuclei. A typical example of fusion is the process that occurs in the sun. Four hydrogen nuclei (protons) fuse in several steps to form one helium nucleus. The mass of the four protons is greater than the mass of the helium nucleus that is produced. The energy equivalent of this mass difference is transferred to the kinetic energy of the resultant particles. The energy released by the fusion of one helium nucleus is 25 MeV. In comparison, the energy released when one dynamite molecule reacts chemically is about 20 eV, almost one million times smaller.

Fusion in the sun is believed to occur in steps. The most important process is expected to be the proton-proton chain.

$$^1_1H + {}^1_1H \rightarrow {}^2_1H + {}^0_{+1}e + {}^0_0\nu$$
$$^1_1H + {}^2_1H \rightarrow {}^3_2He$$
$$^3_2He + {}^3_2He \rightarrow {}^4_2He + 2\,{}^1_1H$$

The first two reactions must occur twice in order to produce the two $^3_2He$ particles needed for the final reaction. The net result is that four protons produce one $^4_2He$, two positrons, and two neutrinos.

Fusion is the union of small nuclei to form larger ones. It is accompanied by the release of a large amount of energy.

Fusion in the sun converts four protons to one helium nucleus.

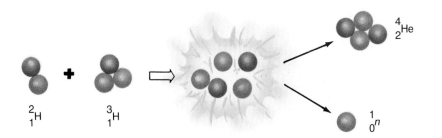

FIGURE 31–6. The fusion of deuterium and tritium produces helium. Protons are blue and neutrons are red in the figure.

# PHYSICS LAB : Hot Stuff

## Purpose

To measure the local power output from the nearest continuous running fusion reaction.

## Materials

- photocell
- voltmeter
- ammeter
- electrical leads
- ruler

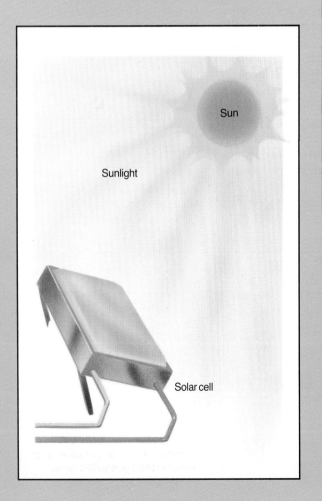

## Procedure

1. With no load attached, measure the voltage output of a solar cell when the cell is outdoors and directly facing the sun.
2. Measure the current from the solar cell when the cell is outdoors and directly facing the sun.
3. Measure the length and width of the solar cell and determine its surface area.
4. Remeasure the voltage and current when the sunlight passes through a window.

## Observations and Data

1. Record your voltage and current readings for outdoor and indoor readings.

## Analysis

1. Calculate the power, IV, for the solar cell outdoors and indoors. What percentage of power did the window stop?
2. Calculate the amount of power that could be produced by a cell that had an area of 1.0 m².
3. The sun supplies about 1000 W of power per square metre to the earth. Calculate the efficiency of your solar cell.

## Applications

1. Suppose that you installed 15 m² of solar cells on your roof. How much power could they produce?

The repulsive force between the charged nuclei requires the fusing nuclei to have high energies. Thus, fusion reactions take place only when the nuclei have large amounts of thermal energy. For this reason, fusion reactions are often called **thermonuclear reactions**. The proton-proton chain requires temperatures of about $2 \times 10^7$ K, temperatures found in the centre of the sun. Fusion reactions also occur in a "hydrogen," or thermonuclear, bomb. In this device, the high temperature necessary to produce the fusion reaction is produced by exploding a uranium, or "atomic," bomb.

## Controlled Fusion

Could the huge energy available from fusion be used safely on Earth? Safe energy requires control of the fusion reaction. One reaction that might produce **controlled fusion** is

$$\,^2_1H + \,^3_1H \rightarrow \,^4_2He + \,^1_0n + 17.6 \text{ MeV}.$$

Deuterium, $\,^2_1H$, is available in large quantities in seawater, and tritium, $\,^3_1H$, is easily produced from deuterium. Therefore, controlled fusion would give the world an almost limitless source of energy. In order to control fusion, however, some very difficult problems must be solved.

Fusion reactions require that the atoms be raised to temperatures of millions of degrees. No material we now have can withstand temperatures even as high as 5000 K. In addition, the atoms would be cooled if they touched confining material. Magnetic fields, however, can confine charged particles. Energy is added to the atoms, stripping away electrons and forming separated plasmas of electrons and ions. A sudden increase in the magnetic field will compress the plasma, raising its temperature. Electromagnetic fields and fast moving neutral atoms can also increase the energy of the plasma. Using this technique, hydrogen nuclei have been fused into helium. The energy released by the reaction becomes the kinetic energy of the neutron and helium ion. This energy would be used to heat some other material, possibly liquified lithium. The lithium, in turn, would boil water, producing steam to turn electric generators.

**FIGURE 31–7. The Tokamak is an experimental controlled fusion reactor.**

a

b

FIGURE 31–8. In laser confinement, pellets containing deuterium and tritium are imploded by many giant lasers, producing helium and large amounts of thermal energy (a). Electrical discharges are visible on the surface of the water covering the Particle Beam Fusion Accelerator II when a pulse of ions is fired (b).

Laser beams are used to implode tiny glass spheres containing liquified deuterium and tritium. The compression creates temperatures high enough to produce fusion.

A useful reactor must produce more energy than it consumes. So far, the energy produced by fusion has been only a tiny fraction of the energy required to create and hold the plasma. The confinement of plasma is a very difficult problem because instabilities in the magnetic field allow the plasma to escape. One of the most promising fusion reactors under development is the Tokamak reactor, Figure 31–7. The Tokamak provides a doughnut-shaped magnetic field in which the plasma is confined. Research has led to the confinement of larger amounts of plasma for longer periods of time. The next large Tokamak built should produce as much energy as it consumes.

A second approach to controlled fusion is called **inertial confinement fusion**. Deuterium and tritium are liquified under high pressure and confined in tiny glass spheres. Multiple laser beams, Figure 31–8a, are directed at the spheres. The energy deposited by the lasers causes forces that make the pellets implode, squeezing their contents. The tremendous compression of the hydrogen that results raises the temperature to levels needed for fusion.

## Practice Problems

**9. a.** Calculate the mass defect for the deuterium-tritium fusion reaction used in the Tokamak, $^2_1H + {}^3_1H \rightarrow {}^4_2He + {}^1_0n$.

  **b.** Find the energy equivalent of the mass defect.

▶ **10.** Calculate the energy released for the overall reaction in the sun where four protons produce one $^4_2He$, two positrons, and two neutrinos.

**2.1** What happens to the energy released in a fusion reaction in the sun?

**2.2** One fusion reaction involves two deuterium nuclei. A deuterium molecule contains two deuterium atoms. Why doesn't this molecule undergo fusion?

**2.3** How does a breeder reactor differ from a normal one?

**2.4** Critical Thinking: Fusion powers the sun. The temperatures are hottest, and the number of fusion reactions greatest, in the centre of the sun. What confines the fusion reaction?

# CHAPTER
# 31 REVIEW

## SUMMARY

### 31.1 Holding the Nucleus Together

· The strong force binds the nucleus together.

· The energy released in a nuclear reaction can be calculated by finding the mass defect, the difference in mass of the particles before and after the reaction.

· The binding energy is the energy equivalent of the mass defect.

### 31.2 Using Nuclear Energy

· Bombardment can produce radioactive isotopes not found in nature. These are called artificial radioactive nuclei and are often used in medicine.

· In nuclear fission, the uranium nucleus is split into two smaller nuclei with a release of neutrons and energy.

· Nuclear reactors use the energy released in fission to generate electrical energy.

· The fusion of hydrogen nuclei into a helium nucleus releases the energy that causes stars to shine.

· Development of a process for controlling fusion for use on Earth might provide large amounts of energy safely.

## KEY TERMS

| | |
|---|---|
| strong nuclear force | control rod |
| nucleon | breeder reactor |
| binding energy | fusion |
| mass defect | thermonuclear |
| fission | reaction |
| chain reaction | controlled fusion |
| moderator | inertial confinement |
| | fusion |

## REVIEWING CONCEPTS

**1.** What force inside a nucleus acts to tear the nucleus apart? What force inside the nucleus acts in a way to hold the nucleus together?

**2.** Define the mass defect of a nucleus. To what is it related?

**3.** List three medical uses of radioactivity.

**4.** What sequence of events must occur for a chain reaction to take place?

**5.** In a fission reaction, binding energy is converted into thermal energy. Objects with thermal energy have random kinetic energy. What objects have kinetic energy after fission?

**6.** A newspaper claims that scientists have been able to cause iron nuclei to undergo fission. Is the claim likely to be true? Explain.

7. What role does a moderator play in a fission reactor?

8. The reactor at the Chernobyl power station that exploded and burned used blocks of graphite. What was the purpose of the graphite blocks?

9. Breeder reactors generate more fuel than they consume. Is this a violation of the law of conservation of energy? Explain.

10. Scientists think Jupiter might have become a star, but temperatures inside the planet are too low. Why must stars have a very high internal temperature?

11. Fission and fusion are opposite processes. How can each release energy?

12. What two processes are being studied to control the fusion process?

# APPLYING CONCEPTS

1. What is the relationship between the average binding energy per nucleon and the degree of stability of a nucleus?

2. Use the graph of binding energy per nucleon to determine if the reaction $^2_1H + ^1_1H \rightarrow ^3_2He$ is energetically possible.

3. Give an example of a naturally and an artificially produced radioactive isotope. Explain the difference.

4. In a nuclear reactor, water that passes through the core of the reactor flows through one loop while the water that produces steam for the turbines flows through a second loop. Why are there two loops?

5. The fission of a uranium nucleus and the fusion of four hydrogen nuclei both produce energy.
   a. Which produces more energy?
   b. Does the fission of 1 kg of uranium nuclei or the fusion of 1 kg of deuterium produce more energy?
   c. Why are your answers to parts a and b different?

6. Explain how it might be possible for some fission reactors to produce more fissionable fuel than they consume. What are such reactors called?

7. What is the difference between the fission process in an atomic bomb and in a reactor?

8. Why might a fusion reactor be safer than a fission reactor?

# PROBLEMS

## 31.1 Holding the Nucleus Together

1. A carbon isotope, $^{13}_6C$, has a nuclear mass of 13.00335 u.
   a. What is the mass defect of this isotope?
   b. What is the binding energy of its nucleus?

2. A nitrogen isotope, $^{14}_7N$, has a nuclear mass of approximately 14.00307 u.
   a. What is the mass defect of the nucleus?
   b. What is the binding energy of this nucleus?
   c. What is the binding energy per nucleon?

3. A nitrogen isotope, $^{12}_7N$, has a nuclear mass of 12.0188 u.
   a. What is the binding energy per nucleon?
   b. Does it require more energy to separate a nucleon from a $^{14}_7N$ nucleus or from a $^{12}_7N$ nucleus? Refer to the previous problem.

4. The two positively-charged protons in a helium nucleus are separated by about $2.0 \times 10^{-15}$ m. Use Coulomb's law to find the electric force of repulsion between the two protons. The result will give you an indication of the strength of the strong nuclear force.

▶ 5. A $^{232}_{92}U$ nucleus, mass = 232.0372 u, decays to $^{228}_{90}Th$, mass = 228.0287 u, by emitting an α particle, mass = 4.0026 u, with a kinetic energy of 5.3 MeV. What must be the kinetic energy of the recoiling thorium nucleus?

▶ 6. The binding energy for $^4_2He$ is 28.3 MeV. Calculate the mass of a helium nucleus in atomic mass units.

## 31.2 Using Nuclear Energy

7. The radioactive nucleus indicated in each equation disintegrates by emitting a positron. Complete each nuclear equation.
   a. $^{21}_{11}Na \rightarrow ? ^0_1e + ?$
   b. $^{49}_{24}Cr \rightarrow ? ^0_1e + ?$

8. Complete the nuclear equations for these transmutations.
   a. $^{30}_{15}P \rightarrow ? + ^0_1e + ?$
   b. $^{205}_{82}Pb \rightarrow ? + ^0_1e + ?$

9. A mercury isotope, $^{200}_{80}Hg$, is bombarded with deuterons, $^2_1H$. The mercury nucleus absorbs the deuteron and then emits an α particle.

a. What element is formed by this reaction?

b. Write the nuclear equation for the reaction.

10. When bombarded by protons, a lithium isotope, $_3^7Li$, absorbs a proton and then ejects two $\alpha$ particles. Write the nuclear equation for this reaction.

11. Each of the nuclei given below can absorb an $\alpha$ particle, assuming that no secondary particles are emitted by the nucleus. Complete each equation.

a. $_7^{14}N + _2^4He \rightarrow$ ?

b. $_{13}^{27}Al + _2^4He \rightarrow$ ?

12. In each of these reactions, a neutron is absorbed by a nucleus. The nucleus then emits a proton. Complete the equations.

a. $_{29}^{65}Cu + _0^1n \rightarrow$ ? $+ _1^1H$

b. $_7^{14}N + _0^1n \rightarrow$ ? $+ _1^1H$

13. When a boron isotope, $_5^{10}B$, is bombarded with neutrons, it absorbs a neutron and then emits an $\alpha$ particle.

a. What element is also formed?

b. Write the nuclear equation for this reaction.

14. When a boron isotope, $_5^{11}B$, is bombarded with protons, it absorbs a proton and emits a neutron.

a. What element is formed?

b. Write the nuclear equation for this reaction.

c. The isotope formed is radioactive, decaying by emitting a positron. Write the complete nuclear equation for this reaction.

▶ 15. The isotope most commonly used in PET scanners is $_9^{18}F$.

a. What element is formed by the positron emission of this element?

b. Write the equation for this reaction.

c. The half-life of $_9^{18}F$ is 110 min. A solution containing 10.0 mg of this isotope is injected into a patient at 8:00 A.M. How much remains at 3:30 P.M.?

▶ 16. The basements of many homes contain the rock granite or are built over granite. Granite contains small amounts of radioactive uranium and thorium. Uranium-238 goes through a series of decays before reaching a stable lead isotope. $_{92}^{238}U$ emits an $\alpha$, leaving an isotope that decays by emitting a $\beta$. The next decay is again a $\beta$, followed by three $\alpha$ decays. The result is the gas radon that can seep into the basement. Write the equations for these decays.

▶ 17. The first atomic bomb released $1.0 \times 10^{14}$ J of energy. What was the mass of the uranium-

235 that was fissioned to produce this energy?

18. Complete the following fission reaction.
$_{94}^{239}Pu + _0^1n \rightarrow _{52}^{137}Te +$ ? $+ 3_0^1n$

19. Complete the following fission reaction.
$_{92}^{235}U + _0^1n \rightarrow _{36}^{92}Kr +$ ? $+ 3_0^1n$

20. Plutonium is formed in two steps. First U-238 absorbs a neutron which then becomes unstable U-239. The U-239 emits a $\beta$ particle forming a new element and this new element emits a second $\beta$ particle forming plutonium. Complete the following reaction. $_{92}^{238}U + _0^1n \rightarrow _{92}^{239}U \rightarrow$

21. Complete each of the following fusion reactions.

a. $_1^2H + _1^2H \rightarrow$ ? $+ _0^1n$

b. $_1^2H + _1^2H \rightarrow$ ? $+ _1^1H$

c. $_1^2H + _1^3H \rightarrow$ ? $+ _0^1n$

▶ 22. One fusion reaction is $_1^2H + _1^2H \rightarrow _2^4He$.

a. What energy is released in this reaction?

b. Deuterium exists as a diatomic, two-atom molecule. One mole of deuterium contains $6.02 \times 10^{23}$ molecules. Find the amount of energy released, in joules, in the fusion of 1 mol of deuterium molecules.

c. When 1 mol of deuterium burns, it releases $2.9 \times 10^6$ J. How many moles of deuterium molecules would have to burn to release just the energy released by the fusion of 1 mol of deuterium molecules?

▶ 23. The energy released in the fission of one atom of $_{92}^{235}U$ is $2.00 \times 10^2$ MeV. One mole of uranium atoms, $6.02 \times 10^{23}$ atoms, has a mass of 0.235 kg.

a. How many atoms are in 1.00 kg of $_{92}^{235}U$?

b. How much energy would be released if all of the atoms in 1.00 kg of $_{92}^{235}U$ underwent fission?

c. A typical large nuclear reactor produces fission energy at a rate of 3600 MW. How many kilograms of $_{92}^{235}U$ are used each second?

d. How much $_{92}^{235}U$ would be used in one year?

# THINKING PHYSIC-LY

If a uranium nucleus were to split into three pieces of approximately the same size instead of two, would more or less energy be released?

*There are no Practice Problems in Chapter 1.*

## Chapter 2

**1. a.** $5.8 \times 10^3$ m
   **b.** $4.5 \times 10^5$ m
   **c.** $3.02 \times 10^8$ m
   **d.** $8.6 \times 10^{10}$ m

**2. a.** $5.08 \times 10^{-4}$ kg
   **b.** $4.5 \times 10^{-7}$ kg
   **c.** $3.600 \times 10^{-3}$ kg
   **d.** $4 \times 10^{-3}$ kg

**3. a.** $3 \times 10^8$ s
   **b.** $1.86 \times 10^5$ s
   **c.** $9.3 \times 10^7$ s

**4. a.** $(1.1 \text{ cm})\dfrac{(1 \times 10^{-2} \text{ m})}{(1 \text{ cm})} = 1.1 \times 10^{-2}$ m

   **b.** $(76.2 \text{ pm})\dfrac{(1 \times 10^{-12} \text{ m})}{(1 \text{ pm})} = 76.2 \times 10^{-12}$ m

   $\qquad\qquad\qquad = 7.62 \times 10^{-11}$ m

   **c.** $(2.1 \text{ km})\dfrac{(1 \times 10^3 \text{ m})}{(1 \text{ km})} = 2.1 \times 10^3$ m

   **d.** $(0.123 \text{ Mm})\dfrac{(1 \times 10^6 \text{ m})}{(1 \text{ Mm})} = 0.123 \times 10^6$ m

   $\qquad\qquad\qquad = 1.23 \times 10^5$ m

**5. a.** $1 \text{ kg} = 1 \times 10^3 \text{ g}$ so $147 \text{ g}\left[\dfrac{1 \text{ kg}}{1 \times 10^3 \text{ g}}\right]$

   $\qquad = 147 \times 10^{-3}$ kg
   $\qquad = 1.47 \times 10^{-1}$ kg

   **b.** $1 \text{ μg} = 1 \times 10^{-6} \text{ g}$ and $1 \text{ kg}$
   $\qquad = 1 \times 10^3 \text{ g}$ so

   $11 \text{ μg}\left[\dfrac{1 \times 10^{-6} \text{ g}}{1 \text{ μg}}\right]\left[\dfrac{1 \text{ kg}}{1 \times 10^3 \text{ g}}\right]$

   $\qquad = 11 \times 10^{-6} \times 10^{-3}$ kg
   $\qquad = 1.1 \times 10^{-8}$ kg

   **c.** $7.23 \text{ Mg}\left[\dfrac{1 \times 10^6 \text{ g}}{1 \text{ Mg}}\right]\left[\dfrac{1 \text{ kg}}{1 \times 10^3 \text{ g}}\right]$

   $\qquad = 7.23 \times 10^3$ kg

   **d.** $478 \text{ mg}\left[\dfrac{1 \times 10^{-3} \text{ g}}{1 \text{ mg}}\right]\left[\dfrac{1 \text{ kg}}{1 \times 10^3 \text{ g}}\right]$

   $\qquad = 4.78 \times 10^{-4}$ kg

**6. a.** $8 \times 10^{-7}$ kg
   **b.** $7 \times 10^{-3}$ kg
   **c.** $3.96 \times 10^{-19}$ kg
   **d.** $4.6 \times 10^{-12}$ kg

**7. a.** $2 \times 10^{-8}$ m$^2$
   **b.** $-1.52 \times 10^{-11}$ m$^2$
   **c.** $3.0 \times 10^{-9}$ m$^2$
   **d.** $0.46 \times 10^{-18}$ m$^2 = 4.6 \times 10^{-19}$ m$^2$

**8. a.** $5.0 \times 10^{-7}$ mg $+ 4 \times 10^{-8}$ mg
   $\qquad = 5.0 \times 10^{-7}$ mg $+ 0.4 \times 10^{-7}$ mg
   $\qquad = 5.4 \times 10^{-7}$ mg
   **b.** $6.0 \times 10^{-3}$ mg $+ 2 \times 10^{-4}$ mg
   $\qquad = 6.0 \times 10^{-3}$ mg $+ 0.2 \times 10^{-3}$ mg
   $\qquad = 6.2 \times 10^{-3}$ mg
   **c.** $3.0 \times 10^{-2}$ pg $- 2 \times 10^{-6}$ ng
   $\qquad = 3.0 \times 10^{-2} \times 10^{-12}$ g $- 2 \times 10^{-6} \times 10^{-9}$ g
   $\qquad = 3.0 \times 10^{-14}$ g $- 0.2 \times 10^{-14}$ g
   $\qquad = 2.8 \times 10^{-14}$ g
   **d.** $8.2 \text{ km} - 3 \times 10^2$ m
   $\qquad = 8.2 \times 10^3 \text{ m} - 0.3 \times 10^3$ m
   $\qquad = 7.9 \times 10^3$ m

**9. a.** $(2 \times 10^4 \text{ m})(4 \times 10^8 \text{ m}) = 8 \times 10^{4+8}$ m$^2$
   $\qquad\qquad\qquad\qquad\qquad = 8 \times 10^{12}$ m$^2$
   **b.** $(3 \times 10^4 \text{ m})(2 \times 10^6 \text{ m}) = 6 \times 10^{4+6}$ m$^2$
   $\qquad\qquad\qquad\qquad\qquad = 6 \times 10^{10}$ m$^2$
   **c.** $(6 \times 10^{-4} \text{ m})(5 \times 10^{-8} \text{ m}) = 30 \times 10^{-4-8}$ m$^2$
   $\qquad\qquad\qquad\qquad\qquad = 3 \times 10^{-11}$ m$^2$
   **d.** $(2.50 \times 10^{-7} \text{ m})(2.50 \times 10^{16} \text{ m})$
   $\qquad = 6.25 \times 10^{-7+16}$ m$^2$
   $\qquad = 6.25 \times 10^9$ m$^2$

**10. a.** $\dfrac{6 \times 10^8 \text{ kg}}{2 \times 10^4 \text{ m}^3} = 3 \times 10^{8-4}$ kg/m$^3$

   $\qquad\qquad\qquad = 3 \times 10^4$ kg/m$^3$

   **b.** $\dfrac{6 \times 10^8 \text{ kg}}{2 \times 10^{-4} \text{ m}^3} = 3 \times 10^{8-(-4)}$ kg/m$^3$

   $\qquad\qquad\qquad = 3 \times 10^{12}$ kg/m$^3$

   **c.** $\dfrac{6 \times 10^{-8} \text{ m}}{2 \times 10^4 \text{ s}} = 3 \times 10^{-8-4}$ m/s

   $\qquad\qquad\qquad = 3 \times 10^{-12}$ m/s

   **d.** $\dfrac{6 \times 10^{-8} \text{ m}}{2 \times 10^{-4} \text{ s}} = 3 \times 10^{-8-(-4)}$ m/s

   $\qquad\qquad\qquad = 3 \times 10^{-4}$ m/s

**11. a.** $\dfrac{(3 \times 10^4 \text{ kg})(4 \times 10^4 \text{ m})}{6 \times 10^4 \text{ s}} = \dfrac{12 \times 10^{4+4} \text{ kg·m}}{6 \times 10^4 \text{ s}}$

$\qquad = 2 \times 10^{8-4} \text{ kg·m/s}$
$\qquad = 2 \times 10^4 \text{ kg·m/s}$

The evaluation may be done in several other ways. For example,

$\dfrac{(3 \times 10^4 \text{ kg})(4 \times 10^4 \text{ m})}{6 \times 10^4 \text{ s}}$

$= (0.5 \times 10^{4-4} \text{ kg/s})(4 \times 10^4 \text{ m})$
$= (0.5 \text{ kg/s})(5 \times 10^4 \text{ m}) = 2 \times 10^4 \text{ kg·m/s}.$

**b.** $\dfrac{(2.5 \times 10^6 \text{ kg})(6 \times 10^4 \text{ m})}{5 \times 10^{-2}\text{s}^2}$

$= \dfrac{15 \times 10^{6+4} \text{ kg·m}}{5 \times 10^{-2}\text{s}^2}$

$= 3 \times 10^{10-(-2)} \text{ kg·m/s}^2$
$= 3 \times 10^{12} \text{ kg·m/s}^2$

**12. a.** 4 **b.** 3 **c.** 2
  **d.** 4 **e.** 2 **f.** 3

**13. a.** 2 **b.** 4 **c.** 4
  **d.** 3 **e.** 4 **f.** 3

**14.** 26.3 cm (rounded from 26.281 cm)

**15. a.** 2.5 g (rounded from 2.536 g)
  **b.** 475 m (rounded from 474.5832 m)

**16. a.** $3.0 \times 10^2$ cm² (the result 301.3 cm² expressed to two significant digits. Note that the expression in the form 300 cm² would not indicate how many of the digits are significant.)
  **b.** 13.6 km² (the result 13.597335 expressed to three significant digits)

**17. a.** 2.73 cm/s (the result 2.726045 . . . cm/s expressed to three significant digits)
  **b.** 0.253 cm/s (the result 0.253354 . . . cm/s expressed to three significant digits)

**18.** $mx + b = y, \ b = y - mx$

**19. a.** $vt = d, \ v = \dfrac{d}{t}$

  **b.** $t = \dfrac{d}{v}, \ tv = d, \ v = \dfrac{d}{t}$

  **c.** $\dfrac{v^2}{2d} = a, \ v^2 = 2ad, \ v = \pm\sqrt{2ad}$

  **d.** $\dfrac{v}{a} = \dfrac{b}{c}, \ v = \dfrac{ab}{c}$

**20. a.** $\dfrac{E}{s} = f, \ E = fs$

**b.** $\dfrac{2E}{v^2} = m, \ 2E = mv^2, \ E = \dfrac{mv^2}{2}$

**c.** $\dfrac{E}{c^2} = m, \ E = mc^2$

**21.** $v_0^2 + 2ad = v^2, \ 2ad = v^2 - v_0^2, \ d = \dfrac{(v^2 - v_0^2)}{2a}$

**22. a.** $at = v - v_0; \ a = \dfrac{v - v_0}{t}$

  **b.** $\dfrac{1}{2}at^2 = y - v_0t; \ a = \dfrac{2(y - v_0t)}{t^2}$

  **c.** $2ay = v^2 - v_0^2; \ a = \dfrac{v^2 - v_0^2}{2y}$

  **d.** $v = \sqrt{2as}; \ v^2 = 2as; \ a = \dfrac{v^2}{2s}$

**23. a.** $A = (0.2 \text{ cm})(30 \text{ cm}) = 6 \text{ cm}^2$
  **b.** $P = 0.25 \text{ m} + 0.25 \text{ m} + 2.00 \text{ m} + 2.00 \text{ m}$
  $= 4.50 \text{ m}$

**24. a.** incorrect since area has units $m^2$ and (length)(width)(height) has units $m^3$

  **b.** correct since $\dfrac{\text{distance}}{\text{speed}}$ has units $\dfrac{m}{(m/s)} = s$

  **c.** incorrect since (speed)(time)² has units $(m/s)(s)^2 = m·s$

# Chapter 3

**1.** $\vec{v}_{\text{AVE}} = \dfrac{\Delta \vec{d}}{\Delta t} = (1.00 \times 10^2 \text{ m})/(12.20 \text{ s})$

$\qquad = 8.20 \text{ m/s}$
(8.20 m/s)(1 km/1000 m)(3600 s/1 h)
$\qquad = 29.5 \text{ km/h}$
or (8.20 m/s)(3600 s/h)/(1000 m/km)
$\qquad = 29.5 \text{ km/h}$

**2.** $\vec{v}_{\text{AVE}} = \dfrac{\Delta \vec{d}}{\Delta t} = (13 \text{ km})/2.0 \text{ h}$

$\qquad = 6.5 \text{ km/h};$
(6.5 km/h)(1 h/3600 s)(1000 m/1 km)
$\qquad = 1.8 \text{ m/s}$
or (6.5 km/h)(1000 m/km)/(3600 s/h) = 1.8 m/s

**3.** Slowest between 0.0 and 1.0 s (0 m/s). Fastest between 3.0 and 4.0 s (15 m/s).

**4.** $\vec{v}_{AVE} = (\vec{d}_2 - \vec{d}_1)/(t_2 - t_1)$
$= (35\ m - 30\ m)/(2.0\ s - 0.0\ s)$
$= 2.5\ m/s$

**5.** Using $\vec{d} = \vec{v}t$ with $\vec{v} = 10\ m/s$:

| $t$ | $\vec{d}$ |
|---|---|
| $1\ h = 3600\ s$ | $3.6 \times 10^4\ m$ |
| $1\ min = 60\ s$ | $6.0 \times 10^2\ m$ |
| $1\ s$ | $10\ m$ |
| $1\ ms = 10^{-3}\ s$ | $10 \times 10^{-3}\ m = 10\ mm$ |
| $1\ \mu s = 10^{-6}\ s$ | $10 \times 10^{-6}\ m = 10\ \mu m$ |
| $1\ ns = 10^{-9}\ s$ | $10 \times 10^{-9}\ m = 10\ nm$ |

**6. a.** $\vec{v} = \dfrac{\vec{d}}{t}$, so $t = \dfrac{\vec{d}}{\vec{v}} = (1620.0\ m)/(36.0\ m/s)$
$= 45.0\ s$

**b.** $\vec{v} = (36.0\ m/s)(1\ km/1000\ m)(3600\ s/1\ h)$
$= 130\ km/h$

**7.** $\vec{v}_{AVE} = (\vec{d}_2 - \vec{d}_1)/(t_2 - t_1)$ with $t_2 - t_1 = 2.5\ h$
$\vec{d}_2 = \vec{d}_1 + \vec{v}_{AVE}(t_2 - t_1)$
$= 17\ km + (94\ km/h)(2.5\ h)$
$= 252\ km$ west of school

**8. a.** Same displacement, but position is
$-17\ km + 235\ km = 218\ km$ west of school.

**b.** $\Delta t = \dfrac{\Delta \vec{d}}{\vec{v}_{AVE}} = (17\ km)/(94\ km/h) = 11\ min$, so
$t = 1{:}11$ P.M.

**9. a.** Starting at High St., walking east at a constant velocity.
**b.** Starts west of High St., walking east at slower constant velocity.
**c.** Walks west from High St., first fast, but slowing to a stop.
**d.** Starts east of High St., walking west at constant velocity.

**10.**

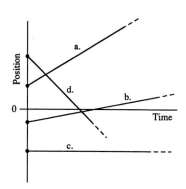

**11. a.** $\vec{v}_{AVE} = \dfrac{\Delta \vec{d}}{\Delta t} = \dfrac{+5\ m}{2\ s} = 2.5\ m/s$

**b.** $\vec{v}_{AVE} = \dfrac{\Delta \vec{d}}{\Delta t} = \dfrac{0\ m}{4\ s} = 0\ m/s$

**c.** $\vec{v}_{AVE} = \dfrac{\Delta \vec{d}}{\Delta t} = \dfrac{-15\ m}{4\ s} = -3.75\ m/s$

**d.** $\vec{v}_{AVE} = \dfrac{\Delta \vec{d}}{\Delta t} = \dfrac{+5\ m}{4\ s} = 1.25\ m/s$

**12.**

**13.**

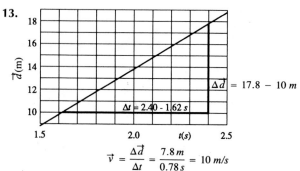

$\Delta \vec{d} = 17.8 - 10\ m$

$\Delta t = 2.40 - 1.62\ s$

$\vec{v} = \dfrac{\Delta \vec{d}}{\Delta t} = \dfrac{7.8\ m}{0.78\ s} = 10\ m/s$

14. **a.** Move to right at constant velocity.
    **b.** Moves to right from rest at constantly increasing velocity.
    **c.** Has an initial non-zero velocity to the right and continues to move to right at constantly increasing velocity.

15. **a.** 10 m/s
    **b.** 20 m/s
    **c.** 30 m/s

16. Each second it increases 10 m/s.

17.

18. **a.**

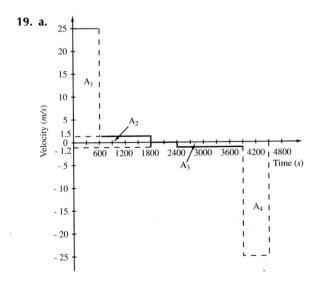

    **b.** Area is (75 km/h)(4 h) = 300 km, the displacement in that time.
    **c.** Find total area under curve for all three segments of trip, which is
    300 km + 0 km + (−225 km) = 75 km.

19. **a.**

Displacement to station
    = (1.5 m/s)(20.0 min)(60 s/min)
    = 1800 m.
Time for walk back to car
    = (1800 m)/(1.2 m/s)
    = 1500 s.

**b.**

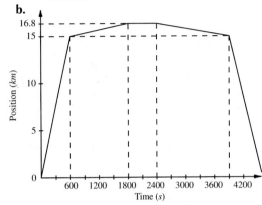

From the graph in part **a**, the changes in position are
$\Delta \vec{d}_1 = A_1 = $ (25 m/s)(600 s)
    = 15 000 m = 15 km
$\Delta \vec{d}_2 = A_2 = $ (1.5 m/s)(1200 s)
    = 1800 m = 1.8 km
$\Delta \vec{d}_3 = A_3 = $ (−1.2 m/s)(1500 s)
    = −1800 m = −1.8 km
$\Delta \vec{d}_4 = A_4 = $ (−25 m/s)(600 s)
    = −15 000 m = −15 km

20. If $\vec{v}_B = \vec{v}_A + \vec{v}_{BA}$, where $\vec{v}_A$, $\vec{v}_B$ are velocities relative to Earth and $\vec{v}_{BA}$ is the velocity of B relative to A, then $\vec{v}_{BA} = \vec{v}_B = \vec{v}_A$.
    **a.** $\vec{v}_{tc} = \vec{v}_t - \vec{v}_c = $ 105 km/h − 92 km/h
        = 13 km/h
    **b.** $\vec{v}_{ct} = \vec{v}_c - \vec{v}_t = $ 92 km/h − 105 km/h
        = −13 km/h

21. The relative speed is (3.5 m)/(1.8 s) = 1.9 m/s
    = 7.0 km/h, so its speed is 102 km/h.

# Chapter 4

1. $\vec{a} = \dfrac{\Delta \vec{v}}{\Delta t} = $ (36 m/s − 4.0 m/s)/(4.0 s) = 8.0 m/s²

2. $\vec{a} = (\vec{v}_2 - \vec{v}_1)/(t_2 - t_1) = $ (15 m/s − 36 m/s)/(3.0 s)
                = −7.0 m/s²

3. $\vec{a} = (\vec{v}_2 - \vec{v}_1)/(t_2 - t_1)$
    = (4.5 m/s − (−3.0 m/s))/(2.5 s)
    = 3.0 m/s²

**4. a.** $\vec{a}_{AVE} = (\vec{v}_2 - \vec{v}_1)/(t_2 - t_1)$
$= (0 \text{ m/s} - 25 \text{ m/s})/(3.0 \text{ s})$
$= -8.3 \text{ m/s}^2$
**b.** half as great $(-4.2 \text{ m/s}^2)$

**5.** Starting from rest, it accelerates to 10 m/s in the first 5 s. It remains at this speed for 10 s, before slowing to 4 m/s over the last 5 s.

**6. a.** 5 to 15 s and 21 to 28 s
**b.** 0 to 6 s
**c.** 15 to 20 s, 28 s to 40 s
**d.** 16 to 19 s

**7. a.** 2 m/s$^2$
**b.** 1 m/s$^2$
**c.** $-1.2$ m/s$^2$
**d.** 0 m/s$^2$

**8. a.** 10

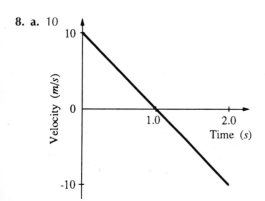

**b.** $\vec{v}_{AVE} = \dfrac{\Delta \vec{v}}{\Delta t} = (-10 \text{ m/s} - 10 \text{ m/s})/(2 \text{ s})$
$= -10 \text{ m/s}^2$

**c.** the same, $-10$ m/s$^2$

**9. a.** $\vec{v}_f = \vec{v}_i + \vec{a}t = 2.0 \text{ m/s} + (-0.50 \text{ m/s}^2)(2.0 \text{ s})$
$= 1.0 \text{ m/s}$
**b.** $\vec{v}_f = \vec{v}_i + \vec{a}t = 2.0 \text{ m/s} + (-0.50 \text{ m/s}^2)(6.0 \text{ s})$
$= -1.0 \text{ m/s}$
**c.** The ball velocity simply decreased in the first case. In the second case, the ball slowed to a stop and then began rolling down the hill.

**10.** $\vec{a} = (3.5 \text{ m/s}^2)(1 \text{ km}/1000 \text{ m})(3600 \text{ s}/1 \text{ h})$
$= 12.6 \text{ (km/h)/s}$
$\vec{v}_f = \vec{v}_i + \vec{a}t = 30 \text{ km/h} + (12.6 \text{ (km/h)/s})(6.8 \text{ s})$
$= 30 \text{ km/h} + 86 \text{ km/h} = 116 \text{ km/h}$

**11.** $\vec{v}_f = \vec{v}_i + \vec{a}t$, so $t = (\vec{v}_f - \vec{v}_i)/\vec{a}$
$= (28 \text{ m/s} - 0 \text{ m/s})/(5.5 \text{ m/s}^2)$
$= 5.1 \text{ s}$

**12.** $\vec{v}_f = \vec{v}_i + \vec{a}t$, so
$t = (\vec{v}_f - \vec{v}_i)/\vec{a}$
$= (3 \text{ m/s} - 22 \text{ m/s})/(-2.1 \text{ m/s}^2)$
$= 9.0 \text{ s}$

**13.** $\vec{d} = \dfrac{1}{2}(\vec{v}_f + \vec{v}_i)t = \dfrac{1}{2}(22 \text{ m/s} + 44 \text{ m/s})(11 \text{ s})$
$= 3.6 \times 10^2 \text{ m}$

**14.** $\vec{d} = \dfrac{1}{2}(\vec{v}_f + \vec{v}_i)t = \dfrac{1}{2}(132 \text{ m/s} + 88 \text{ m/s})(15 \text{ s})$
$= 1.7 \times 10^3 \text{ m}$

**15.** $\vec{d} = \dfrac{1}{2}(\vec{v}_f + \vec{v}_i)t$, so
$t = 2\vec{d}/(\vec{v}_f + \vec{v}_i)$
$= 2(125 \text{ m})/(25 \text{ m/s} + 15 \text{ m/s})$
$= 6.3 \text{ s}$

**16.** $\vec{d} = \dfrac{1}{2}(\vec{v}_f + \vec{v}_i)t$, so
$\vec{v}_i = 2\vec{d}/t - \vec{v}_f$
$= 2(19 \text{ m})/(4.5 \text{ s}) - 7.5 \text{ m/s}$
$= 0.94 \text{ m/s}$

**17.** $\vec{d} = \vec{v}_i t + \dfrac{1}{2}\vec{a}t^2$
$= (0 \text{ m/s})(30.0 \text{ s}) + \dfrac{1}{2}(3.00 \text{ m/s}^2)(30.0 \text{ s})^2$
$= 0 \text{ m} + 1350 \text{ m} = 1.35 \times 10^3 \text{ m}$

**18.** Using $\vec{d} = \vec{v}_i t + \dfrac{1}{2}\vec{a}t^2$ with $\vec{v}_i = 0$,
$\vec{a} = 2\vec{d}/t^2 = 2(110 \text{ m})/(5.0 \text{ s})^2 = 8.8 \text{ m/s}^2$.

**19. a.** $\vec{a} = (\vec{v}_2 - \vec{v}_1)/(t_2 - t_1)$
$= (0 \text{ m/s} - 22 \text{ m/s})/(2.0 \text{ s})$
$= -11 \text{ m/s}^2$

**b.** $\vec{d} = \vec{v}_i t + \dfrac{1}{2}\vec{a}t^2$
$= (22 \text{ m/s})(2.0 \text{ s}) + \dfrac{1}{2}(-11 \text{ m/s}^2)(2.0 \text{ s})^2$
$= 44 \text{ m} - 22 \text{ m} = 22 \text{ m}$

**20.** $\vec{d} = \vec{v}_i t + \dfrac{1}{2}\vec{a}t^2$
$= (4.5 \text{ m/s})(12 \text{ s}) + \dfrac{1}{2}(0.40 \text{ m/s}^2)(12 \text{ s})^2$
$= 54 \text{ m} + 29 \text{ m} = 83 \text{ m}$

21. $\vec{v}_f^2 = \vec{v}_i^2 + 2\vec{a}\vec{d}$
$= (21 \text{ m/s})^2 + 2(3.0 \text{ m/s}^2)(535 \text{ m})$
$= 3651 \text{ m}^2/\text{s}^2$
$\vec{v}_f = 60 \text{ m/s}$

22. $\vec{v}_f^2 = \vec{v}_i^2 + 2\vec{a}\vec{d}$, so
$\vec{v}_i^2 = \vec{v}_f^2 + 2\vec{a}\vec{d}$
$= (0 \text{ m/s})^2 - 2(-8.0 \text{ m/s}^2)(484 \text{ m})$
$= 7744 \text{ m}^2/\text{s}^2$
$\vec{v}_i = 88 \text{ m/s}$

23. Using $\vec{v}_f^2 = \vec{v}_i^2 + 2\vec{a}\vec{d}$ with
$\vec{v}_i = 101 \text{ km/h} = 28.1 \text{ m/s}$ and $\vec{v}_f = 0$,
$\vec{d} = (\vec{v}_f^2 - \vec{v}_i^2)/2\vec{a}$
$= ((0 \text{ m/s})^2 - (28.1 \text{ m/s})^2)/2(-300 \text{ m/s}^2)$
$= 1.32 \text{ m}.$

24. Convert speeds to m/s.
$\vec{v}_i = -6.9 \text{ m/s}, \vec{v}_f = 9.7 \text{ m/s},$
$\vec{d} = (\vec{v}_f^2 - \vec{v}_i^2)/2\vec{a}$, so
$\vec{a} = (\vec{v}_f^2 - \vec{v}_i^2)/2\vec{d}$
$= ((9.7 \text{ m/s})^2 - (-6.9 \text{ m/s})^2)/2(3.2 \text{ m})$
$= 7.3 \text{ m/s}^2.$

25. **a.** $\vec{v}_f = \vec{v}_i + \vec{g}t$
$= 0 \text{ m/s} + (-9.80 \text{ m/s}^2)(4.0 \text{ s})$
$\vec{v}_i = -39 \text{ m/s, downward}$

   **b.** $\vec{d} = \vec{v}_i t + \dfrac{1}{2}\vec{g}t^2$
$= 0 + \dfrac{1}{2}(-9.80 \text{ m/s}^2)(4.0 \text{ s})^2$
$= \dfrac{1}{2}(-9.81 \text{ m/s}^2)(16 \text{ s}^2)$
$\vec{d} = -78 \text{ m, downward}$

26. Using $\vec{d} = \dfrac{1}{2}\vec{g}t^2$, the reaction time can be calculated
from $t = \sqrt{2\dfrac{\vec{d}}{\vec{g}}}$

27. $\vec{d} = \vec{v}_i t + \dfrac{1}{2}\vec{g}t^2 = 0 + \dfrac{1}{2}(-9.80 \text{ m/s}^2)(0.50 \text{ s})^2$
$= -1.2 \text{ m}$

28. $\vec{v}_f = \vec{v}_i + \vec{a}t = 1210 \text{ m/s} + (-150 \text{ m/s}^2)(8.68 \text{ s})$
$= 1210 \text{ m/s} - 1300 \text{ m/s}$
$= -90 \text{ m/s}$
Spacecraft slows to a stop then reverses motion.

29. **a.** Using $\vec{d} = \vec{v}_i t + \dfrac{1}{2}\vec{g}t^2$ with $\vec{v}_i = 0$,
$t = \sqrt{\dfrac{2\vec{d}}{\vec{g}}} = \sqrt{2(-1.0 \text{ m})/(-9.80 \text{ m/s}^2)} = 0.45 \text{ s}.$

   **b.** $\vec{v}_f = \vec{v}_i + \vec{g}t = 0 \text{ m/s} + (-9.80 \text{ m/s}^2)(0.45 \text{ s})$
$= -4.4 \text{ m/s}$

30. **a.** $\vec{v}_i = 0 \text{ m/s, so}$
$\vec{v}_f = \vec{g}t = (0.2)(9.80 \text{ m/s}^2)(2.0 \text{ s}) = 3.9 \text{ m/s}$

   **b.** $\vec{d} = \dfrac{1}{2}\vec{a}t^2 = \dfrac{1}{2}(0.2)(9.8 \text{ m/s}^2)(4.0 \text{ s})^2 = 16 \text{ m}$

31. **a.** Since $\vec{v}_f = 0$ at high point, $\vec{v}_f = \vec{v}_i + \vec{g}t$
becomes $t = -\vec{v}_i/\vec{g}$
$= -(27 \text{ m/s})/(-9.80 \text{ m/s}^2)$
$= 2.8 \text{ s}$

   **b.** $\vec{d} = \vec{v}_i t + \dfrac{1}{2}\vec{g}t^2$
$= (27 \text{ m/s})(2.8 \text{ s}) + \dfrac{1}{2}(-9.80 \text{ m/s}^2)(2.8 \text{ s})^2$
$= 75.6 \text{ m} - 38.4 \text{ m} = 37 \text{ m}$

32. **a.** 46 m/(min · s) can be interpreted as a speed change of either 46 m/min each second or 46 m/s each minute.

   **b.** $\vec{v}_f = \vec{v}_i + \vec{a}t$
$= 0 \text{ m/min} + (46 \text{ m/min/s})(2.0 \text{ s})$
$= 92 \text{ m/min}$

   **c.** Velocities before 2.0 s are given by $\vec{v}_f = \vec{a}t$; velocities after are 92 m/min.

| t (s) | $\vec{v}_f$ (m/min) |
|-------|---------------------|
| 0.5 | 23 |
| 1.0 | 46 |
| 1.5 | 69 |
| 2.0 | 92 |
| 3.0 | 92 |
| 4.0 | 92 |
| 5.0 | 92 |

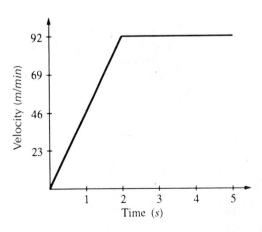

**d.** For first 2 seconds $\vec{d} = \frac{1}{2}\vec{a}t^2$, where

$\vec{a} = (46\ \text{m/min/s})(1\ \text{min/60 s}) = 0.767\ \text{m/s}^2$
and after 2 seconds it continues to rise
$(92\ \text{m/min})(1/60\ \text{min}) = 1.5\ \text{m}$ each second.

| $t$ (s) | $\vec{d}$ (m) |
|---------|---------------|
| 1.0 | 0.4 |
| 2.0 | 1.5 |
| 3.0 | 3.0 |
| 4.0 | 4.5 |
| 5.0 | 6.0 |

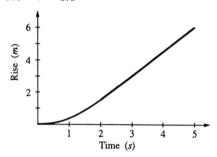

**Chapter 5**

**1.** $m = \dfrac{\vec{F}}{\vec{a}} = \dfrac{+140\ \text{N}}{+19\ \text{m/s}^2} = 7.4\ \text{kg}$

**2.** $\vec{F} = m\vec{a} = (275\ \text{kg})(-4.50\ \text{m/s}^2)$
$= -1.24 \times 10^3\ \text{N}$
The negative sign of the acceleration slowing down the motor bike tells us that the motor bike has a velocity in the positive direction. The negative sign on the force indicates that it is directed opposite to the motor bike velocity.

**3.** Given: $\vec{v}_i = 105\ \text{km/h} = 29.2\ \text{m/s}$,
$\vec{v}_f = 0$, $\vec{d} = 53\ \text{m}$,
$\vec{a} = \dfrac{(\vec{v}_f^2 - \vec{v}_i^2)}{2\vec{d}} = -8.0\ \text{m/s}^2$
$\vec{F} = m\vec{a} = (1225\ \text{kg})(-8.0\ \text{m/s}^2) = -9.8 \times 10^3\ \text{N}$
The force is directed opposite to the car motion and is provided by the road surface pushing against the car tires.

**4. a.** $\vec{a} = \dfrac{\vec{F}}{m} = \dfrac{(+1.2 \times 10^{-4}\ \text{N})}{(7.0 \times 10^{-5}\ \text{kg})} = +1.7\ \text{m/s}^2$

**b.** The upward force being given as a positive number means that the downward motion of the spider is represented as a negative velocity. The positive acceleration is opposed to this negative velocity and gives rise to a slowing down of the spider.

**5. a.** $\vec{W} = m\vec{g} = (0.113\ \text{kg})(9.8\ \text{m/s}^2) = 1.11\ \text{N}$
**b.** $\vec{W} = m\vec{g} = (108\ \text{kg})(9.80\ \text{m/s}^2)$
$= 1.06 \times 10^3\ \text{N}$
**c.** $\vec{W} = m\vec{g} = (870\ \text{kg})(9.80\ \text{m/s}^2)$
$= 8.50 \times 10^3\ \text{N}$

**6. a.** $m = \dfrac{\vec{W}}{\vec{g}} = \dfrac{98\ \text{N}}{9.80\ \text{m/s}^2} = 10\ \text{kg}$

**b.** $m = \dfrac{\vec{W}}{\vec{g}} = \dfrac{80\ \text{N}}{9.80\ \text{m/s}^2} = 8.2\ \text{kg}$

**c.** $m = \dfrac{\vec{W}}{\vec{g}} = \dfrac{0.98\ \text{N}}{9.80\ \text{m/s}^2} = 0.10\ \text{kg}$

**7.** 20 N, upward

**8. a.** $\vec{W} = m\vec{g} = (75\ \text{kg})(9.80\ \text{m/s}^2) = 7.4 \times 10^2\ \text{N}$
**b.** $\vec{W} = m\vec{g} = (75\ \text{kg})(3.8\ \text{m/s}^2) = 2.9 \times 10^2\ \text{N}$

**c.** $\vec{g} = \dfrac{\vec{W}}{m} = \dfrac{683\ \text{N}}{75\ \text{kg}} = 9.1\ \text{m/s}^2$

**9. a.** 625 N, upward
**b.** 675 N
**c.** Since $\vec{F}_{\text{father on Joe}} + \vec{F}_{\text{scale on Joe}} = \vec{F}_{\text{W Joe}}$.
$\vec{F}_{\text{scale on Joe}} = W_{\text{Joe}} - \vec{F}_{\text{father on Joe}}$
$= 625\ \text{N} - 72\ \text{N} = 553\ \text{N}$, upward.

**10. a.** $\vec{F}_f = \mu\vec{F}_N$ with $\vec{F}_N = \vec{W}$, so

$\mu = \dfrac{\vec{F}_f}{\vec{F}_N} = \dfrac{36\ \text{N}}{52\ \text{N}} = 0.69$

**b.** The force must equal the friction force.
$\vec{F}_f = \mu\vec{F}_N = \mu(\vec{W} + \vec{W}_1)$
$= (0.12)(52\ \text{N} + 650\ \text{N}) = 84\ \text{N}$

**11. a.** $\vec{F}_f = \mu\vec{F}_N$ where $\vec{F}_N = \vec{W} = m\vec{g}$, so
$\vec{F}_f = -(0.50)(750\ \text{kg})(9.80\ \text{m/s}^2)$
$= -3.7 \times 10^3\ \text{N}$
The negative sign has been used to indicate that the friction force is opposite the car velocity.

**b.** $\vec{a} = \dfrac{\vec{F}_f}{m} = \dfrac{(-3.7 \times 10^3\ \text{N})}{750\ \text{kg}} = -4.9\ \text{m/s}^2$
directed opposite car velocity and constant because $F_f$ is constant
**c.** $\vec{v}_f^2 = \vec{v}_i^2 + 2\vec{a}\vec{d}$, so
$\vec{d} = \dfrac{(\vec{v}_f^2 - \vec{v}_i^2)}{2\vec{a}} = \dfrac{(0 - (30\ \text{m/s})^2)}{-9.8\ \text{m/s}^2}$
$= 92\ \text{m}$

**12.** larger, since $\vec{F}_f$ is proportional to $\mu$; shorter distance since, from the solution to Practice Problem 11, $\vec{d}$ is inversely proportional to $a$, and $a$ is proportional to $\vec{F}_f$

**13. a.** $m = \dfrac{\vec{W}}{\vec{g}} = \dfrac{49\,\text{N}}{9.80\,\text{m/s}^2} = 5.0\,\text{kg}$

**b.** $m\vec{a} = \vec{F}_\text{net} = \vec{F}_\text{appl} + \vec{W} = 69\,\text{N} + (-49\,\text{N})$
$\qquad = 20\,\text{N}$

So, $\vec{a} = \dfrac{\vec{F}_\text{net}}{m} = \dfrac{20\,\text{N}}{5.0\,\text{kg}}$
$\qquad = 4.0\,\text{m/s}^2$

**14. a.** $m = \dfrac{\vec{W}}{\vec{g}} = \dfrac{14.7\,\text{N}}{9.80\,\text{m/s}^2} = 1.50\,\text{kg}$

**b.** $m\vec{a} = \vec{F}_\text{net} = \vec{F}_\text{appl} + \vec{W}$
$\qquad = 10.2\,\text{N} + (-14.7\,\text{N})$
$\qquad = -4.50\,\text{N}$

Thus, $\vec{a} = \dfrac{\vec{F}_\text{net}}{m} = \dfrac{-4.50\,\text{N}}{1.5\,\text{kg}} = -3.00\,\text{m/s}^2$

**15. a.** $\vec{W} = m\vec{g} = (2 \times 10^6\,\text{kg})(9.80\,\text{m/s}^2)$
$\qquad = 20 \times 10^6\,\text{N}$

**b.** $m\vec{a} = \vec{F}_\text{net} = \vec{F}_\text{appl} + \vec{W}$
$\qquad = 30 \times 10^6\,\text{N} + (-20 \times 10^6\,\text{N})$
$\qquad = 10 \times 10^6\,\text{N}$

Thus, $\vec{a} = \dfrac{\vec{F}_\text{net}}{m} = \dfrac{(10 \times 10^6\,\text{N})}{(2 \times 10^6\,\text{kg})} = 5.0\,\text{m/s}^2$

**c.** $\vec{v} = \vec{a}t = (13\,\text{m/s}^2)(600\,\text{s})$
$\qquad = 7.8 \times 10^3\,\text{m/s} = 7.8\,\text{km/s}$

**d.** It would increase.

$\vec{a} = \dfrac{\vec{F}}{m}\vec{F}$ is constant, $m$ decreases, so $\vec{a}$

increases.

**16.** $\vec{F}_\text{net} = m\vec{a} = (1354\,\text{kg})(3.0\,\text{m/s}^2) = 4.1 \times 10^3\,\text{N}$
$\vec{F}_\text{net} = \vec{F}_\text{appl} + \vec{F}_\text{drag}$, so
$\vec{F}_\text{appl} = \vec{F}_\text{net} - \vec{F}_\text{drag}$
$\qquad = 4.1 \times 10^3\,\text{N} - (-280\,\text{N}) = 4.4 \times 10^3\,\text{N}$

# Chapter 6

**1. a.** 11 km + 11 km = 22 km
**b.** 16 km

**2.** 207 N, 53°, north of east

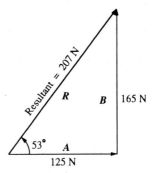

**3. a.** 13 km + 18 km + 3 km = 34 km
**b.** 21 km, 61°, north of east

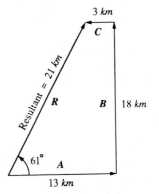

**4. a.** 18 m/s, 29°, north of east

**b.** $t = \dfrac{\vec{d}}{\vec{v}_E} = \dfrac{136\,\text{m}}{16\,\text{m/s}} = 8.5\,\text{s}$

**c.** $\vec{d} = \vec{v}_N t = (9.0\,\text{m/s})(8.5\,\text{s}) = 77\,\text{m}$

**5.** 130 km/h, 21°, north of east

**6.** 434 N, 11.5°, south of east

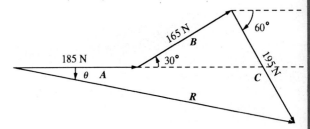

**7.** $\vec{F}^2_R = \vec{F}^2_A + \vec{F}^2_B$

$\vec{F}_R = \sqrt{(55\,N)^2 + (110\,N)^2} = 120\,N$

$\tan \theta = \dfrac{110}{55} = 2.0$

$\theta = 63°$

**8. a.** $\vec{v}_R = \sqrt{(8.5\,m/s)^2 + (3.8\,m/s)^2} = 9.3\,m/s$

$\tan \theta = \dfrac{3.8}{8.5} = 0.45, \theta = 24°$

$\vec{v}_R = 9.3\,m/s$ at $24°$

**b.** $t = \dfrac{\vec{d}}{\vec{v}} = \dfrac{110\,m}{8.5\,m/s} = 13\,s$

**9. a.** $\vec{v}_R = \sqrt{(3.8\,m/s)^2 + (2.2\,m/s)^2} = 4.4\,m/s$

$\tan \theta = \dfrac{2.2}{3.8} = 0.58, \theta = 30°$

$\vec{v}_R = 4.4\,m/s$ at $30°$

**b.** $t = \dfrac{\vec{d}}{\vec{v}} = \dfrac{41\,m}{3.8\,m/s} = 11\,s$

**c.** $\vec{d} = \vec{v}t = (2.2\,m/s)(11\,s) = 24\,m$

**10.** $\vec{v}_R = \sqrt{(152\,km/h)^2 + (42\,km/h)^2} = 160\,km/h$

$\tan \theta = \dfrac{42}{152} = 0.276$

$\theta = 15°$

$\theta_R = 125° + 15° = 140°$

$\vec{v}_R = 160\,km/h$ at $140°$

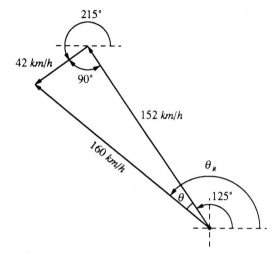

**11.** $\vec{F}_h = (75\,N) \cos 60° = 37.5\,N$

**12.**

$\theta = 180° - 149° = 31°$

**a.** $\vec{v}_{90} = \vec{v} \sin \theta = (525\,km/h) \sin 31°$
$= 270\,km/h$

**b.** $\vec{v}_{180} = -\vec{v} \cos \theta = -(525\,km/h) \cos 31°$
$= -450\,km/h$

**13. a.** $\vec{F}_h = (72\,N) \cos 60° = 36\,N$

**b.** $\vec{F}_h = (72\,N) \cos 40° = 55\,N$

**c.** $\vec{F}_h = (72\,N) \cos 30° = 62\,N$

**14.** $\theta = 360° - 305° = 55°$ south of east

east $-$ west component $= (14.7\,km) \cos 55°$
$= 8.43\,km$, east

north $-$ south component $= (14.7\,km) \sin 55°$
$= 12.0\,km$, south

**15.** $\vec{F}_{1x} = (12.0\ \text{N})\cos 10.0° = 11.8\ \text{N}$
$\vec{F}_{1y} = (12.0\ \text{N})\sin 10.0° = 2.0\ \text{N}$
$\vec{F}_{2x} = (14.0\ \text{N})\cos 310.0° = 9.0\ \text{N}$
$\vec{F}_{2y} = (14.0\ \text{N})\sin 310.0° = -10.7\ \text{N}$,
where $\cos 310.0° = \cos(-50.0°) = \cos 50.0°$
$\quad\quad\quad \sin 310.0° = \sin(-50.0°) = -\sin 50.0°$

$\vec{F}_{net} = \sqrt{(\vec{F}_{1x} + \vec{F}_{2x})^2 + (\vec{F}_{1y} + \vec{F}_{2y})^2}$

$\vec{F} = \sqrt{(11.8\ \text{N} + 9.0\ \text{N})^2 + (2.0\ \text{N} - 10.7\ \text{N})^2}$

$\vec{F} = \sqrt{(20.8\ \text{N})^2 + (-8.7\ \text{N})^2} = 22.5\ \text{N}$

$\tan\theta = \dfrac{\vec{F}_y}{\vec{F}_x} = \dfrac{-8.7\ \text{N}}{20.8\ \text{N}} = -0.418$

$\theta = -22.7°$ or $337.3°$

**16.** $\vec{F}_{1x} = (15\ \text{N})\cos 65.0° = 6.3\ \text{N}$
$\vec{F}_{1y} = (15\ \text{N})\sin 65.0° = 13.6\ \text{N}$
$\vec{F}_{2x} = (16\ \text{N})\cos 135° = -11.3\ \text{N}$
$\vec{F}_{2y} = (16\ \text{N})\sin 135° = 11.3\ \text{N}$
$\vec{F}_{3x} = (11\ \text{N})\cos 195° = -10.6\ \text{N}$
$\vec{F}_{3y} = (11\ \text{N})\sin 195° = -2.8\ \text{N}$
$\vec{F}_x = \vec{F}_{1x} + \vec{F}_{2x} + \vec{F}_{3x}$
$\quad = 6.3\ \text{N} + (-11.3\ \text{N}) + (-10.6\ \text{N})$
$\quad = -15.6\ \text{N}$
$\vec{F}_y = \vec{F}_{1y} + \vec{F}_{2y} + \vec{F}_{3y}$
$\quad = 13.6\ \text{N} + 11.3\ \text{N} + (-2.8\ \text{N}) = 22.1\ \text{N}$
$\vec{F}_{net} = \sqrt{\vec{F}_x^2 + \vec{F}_y^2}$
$\quad = \sqrt{(-15.6\ \text{N})^2 + (22.1\ \text{N})^2} = 27.1\ \text{N}$

$\tan\theta = \dfrac{\vec{F}_y}{\vec{F}_x} = \dfrac{22.1\ \text{N}}{-15.6\ \text{N}} = -1.42$

Since, from signs of $\vec{F}_x$ and $\vec{F}_y$, $\theta$ is in second quadrant, angle $\theta = 180° - 54.8° = 125°$.

**17.** 55 N, due east

**18.**

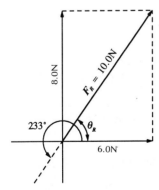

**a.** $\vec{F}_R = \sqrt{(6.0\ \text{N})^2 + (8.0\ \text{N})^2}$
$\quad\quad = 10.0\ \text{N}$

$\tan\theta_R = \dfrac{8.0}{6.0} = 1.33$

$\theta_R = 53°$

$\vec{F}_R = 10.0\ \text{N at } 53°$

**b.** $\vec{F}_E = 10.0\ \text{N at } 53° + 180° = 233°$

**19.**

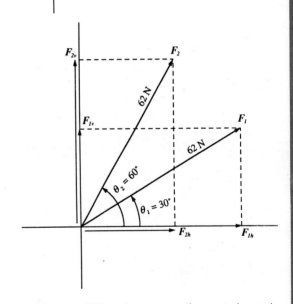

**a.** Vector addition is most easily carried out by using the method of addition by components. The first step in this method is the resolution of the given vectors into their horizontal and vertical components.

$\vec{F}_{1h} = \vec{F}_1 \cos\theta_1 = (62\ \text{N})\cos 30° = 54\ \text{N}$
$\vec{F}_{1v} = \vec{F}_1 \sin\theta_1 = (62\ \text{N})\sin 30° = 31\ \text{N}$

$\vec{F}_{2h} = \vec{F}_2 \cos\theta_2 = (62\ \text{N})\cos 60° = 31\ \text{N}$
$\vec{F}_{2v} = \vec{F}_2 \sin\theta_2 = (62\ \text{N})\sin 60° = 54\ \text{N}$

At this point, the two original vectors have been replaced by four components, vectors that are much easier to add. The horizontal and vertical components of the resultant vector are found by simple addition.

$\vec{F}_{Rh} = \vec{F}_{1h} + \vec{F}_{2h} = 54\ \text{N} + 31\ \text{N} = 85\ \text{N}$
$\vec{F}_{Rv} = \vec{F}_{1v} + \vec{F}_{2v} = 31\ \text{N} + 54\ \text{N} = 85\ \text{N}$

The magnitude and direction of the resultant vector are found by the usual method.

$$\vec{F}_R = \sqrt{(\vec{F}_{Rh})^2 + (\vec{F}_{Rv})^2}$$
$$= \sqrt{(85\ N)^2 + (85\ N)^2}$$
$$= 120\ N$$
$$\tan\theta_R = \frac{\vec{F}_{Rv}}{\vec{F}_{Rh}} = \frac{85\ N}{85\ N} = 1,\ \theta_R = 45°$$
$$\vec{F}_R = 120\ N\ \text{at}\ 45°$$

**b.** $\vec{F}_E = 120\ N,\ 225°$

**20.**

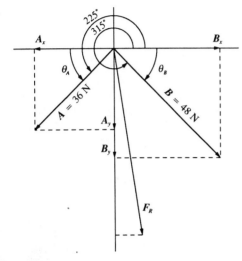

$$\theta_A = 225° - 180° = 45°$$
$$\theta_B = 360° - 315° = 45°$$
$$\vec{A}_x = -\vec{A}\cos\theta_A = -(36\ N)\cos 45° = -25\ N$$
$$\vec{A}_y = -\vec{A}\sin\theta_A = (-36\ N)\sin 45° = -25\ N$$
$$\vec{B}_x = \vec{B}\cos\theta_B = (48\ N)\cos 45° = 34\ N$$
$$\vec{B}_y = -\vec{B}\sin\theta_B = -(48\ N)\sin 45° = -34\ N$$
$$\vec{F}_x = \vec{A}_x + \vec{B}_x = -25\ N + 34\ N = 9\ N$$
$$\vec{F}_y = \vec{A}_y + \vec{B}_y = -25\ N - 34\ N = -59\ N$$
$$\vec{F}_R = \sqrt{\vec{F}_x^2 + \vec{F}_y^2} = \sqrt{(-9\ N)^2 + (-59\ N)^2}$$
$$= 60\ N$$
$$\tan\theta_R = \frac{9}{59} = 0.153,\ \theta = 9°$$
$$\theta_R = 270° + 9° = 279°$$
$$\vec{F}_R = 60\ N\ \text{at}\ 279°$$
$$\vec{F}_E = 60\ N$$
$$\theta_E = 279° - 180° = 99°$$

**21.** Following the method of the Example Problem, the vertical component of the force exerted by each rope must support half of the sign weight.

$$\vec{A}_v = \vec{B}_v = \frac{168\ N}{2} = 84\ \dot{N}$$

$$\frac{\vec{A}_v}{\sin 42°} = \vec{A} = \frac{84\ N}{\sin 42°} = 126\ N$$

$$\vec{B} = \vec{A} = 126\ N$$

**22.** Since $\vec{A}_v = \vec{A}\sin\theta$, and $\vec{A}_v = 84\ N$

and $\vec{A} = 575\ N$,
$$\sin\theta = \frac{84}{575} = 0.146$$
$$\theta = 8.4°.$$

**23. a.** $\vec{F}_\perp = (562\ N)\cos 66° = 229\ N$
$\vec{F}_\parallel = (562\ N)\sin 66° = 513\ N$

**b.** The perpendicular force is less and the parallel force is greater on the 66° incline than in the case of the 30° incline.

**24. a.** $\vec{F}_\parallel = (1.2 \times 10^4\ N)\sin 36° = 7.1 \times 10^3\ N$
**b.** $\vec{F}_\perp = (1.2 \times 10^4\ N)\cos 36° = 9.7 \times 10^3\ N$

**25. a.** $\vec{a} = \dfrac{\vec{F}}{m} = \dfrac{\vec{F}_\parallel}{m} = \dfrac{m\vec{g}\sin\theta}{m}$

$\vec{g}\sin\theta = 5.8\ m/s^2$

**b.** $\vec{v}^2 = 2\vec{a}\vec{d} = 2(5.8\ m/s^2)(30\ m)$, so
$\vec{v} = 19\ m/s$

**c.** No. A sprinter can run about 10 m/s.

**26.** $\vec{F}_\parallel = \vec{W}\sin\theta$, where we find $\theta$ from tan
$\theta = (1.00\ m)/(3.50\ m) = 0.286$, so $\theta = 16.0°$.
$\vec{W} = (71.0\ kg)(9.80\ m/s^2) = 969\ N$,
so $\vec{F}_\parallel = 191\ N$

## Chapter 7

**1. a.** Since $\vec{v}_y = 0$, $\vec{y} = \vec{v}_y t + \frac{1}{2}\vec{g}t^2$ becomes

$$\vec{y} = \frac{1}{2}\vec{g}t^2,\ \text{or}$$

$$t^2 = \frac{2\vec{y}}{\vec{g}} = \frac{2(-78.4\ m)}{-9.80\ m/s^2} = 16.0\ s^2,$$

$$t = \sqrt{16.0\ s^2} = 4.00\ s.$$

**b.** $\vec{x} = \vec{v}_x t = (5.0\ m/s)(4.00\ s) = 20\ m$

**c.** $\vec{v}_x = 5.0\ m/s$. This is the same as the initial horizontal speed because the acceleration of gravity influences only the vertical motion. For the vertical component, use $\vec{v}_f = \vec{v}_i + \vec{g}t$ with $\vec{v}_f = \vec{v}_y$ and $\vec{v}_i$, the initial vertical component of velocity zero. At $t = 4.00\ s$, $\vec{v}_y = \vec{g}t = (-9.80\ m/s^2)(4.00\ s) = -39.2\ m/s$.

**2. a.** (a) no change; 4.00 s
(b) twice the previous distance; 40 m
(c) $\vec{v}_x$ doubles; 10 m/s
no change in $\vec{v}_y$; $-39.2\ m/s$

**b.** (a) increases by $\sqrt{2}$, since $t = \sqrt{\dfrac{2\vec{y}}{\vec{g}}}$ and

$\vec{y}$ doubles; 5.66 s

(b) increases by $\sqrt{2}$, since $t$ increases by $\sqrt{2}$; 28 m

(c) no change in $\vec{v}_x$; 5.0 m/s
$\vec{v}_y$ increases by $\sqrt{2}$, since $t$ increases by $\sqrt{2}$; $-55.4$ m/s

**3.** Since $\vec{v}_y = 0$, $\vec{y} = \dfrac{1}{2}\vec{g}t^2$ and the time to reach the

ground is

$$t = \sqrt{\frac{2\vec{y}}{\vec{g}}} = \sqrt{\frac{2(-0.950\,\text{m})}{-9.80\,\text{m/s}}} = 0.440\,\text{s}.$$

From $\vec{x} = \vec{v}_x t$,

$$\vec{v}_x = \frac{\vec{x}}{t} = \frac{0.352\,\text{m}}{0.440\,\text{s}} = 0.800\,\text{m/s}.$$

**4.** Following the method of Practice Problem 3,

**a.** $t = \sqrt{\dfrac{2\vec{y}}{\vec{g}}} = \sqrt{\dfrac{2(-43.9\,\text{m})}{-9.80\,\text{m/s}^2}} = 2.99\,\text{s}.$

**b.** $\vec{v}_x = \dfrac{\vec{x}}{t} = \dfrac{87.7\,\text{m}}{2.99\,\text{s}} = 29.3\,\text{m/s}$

$= 29.3\,\text{m/s}\left[\dfrac{1\,\text{km}}{1000\,\text{m}}\right]\left[\dfrac{3600\,\text{s}}{1\,\text{h}}\right]$

$= 105\,\text{km/h}$

**c.** $\vec{g} = -9.80\,\text{m/s}^2$ at all times.

**5. a.** $\vec{v}_x = \vec{v}_i \cos\theta = (27.0\,\text{m/s})\cos 30.0°$
$= 23.4\,\text{m/s}$
$\vec{v}_y = \vec{v}_i \sin\theta = (27.0\,\text{m/s})\sin 30.0°$
$= 13.5\,\text{m/s}$

When it lands, $\vec{y} = \vec{v}_y t + \dfrac{1}{2}\vec{g}t^2 = 0$.

Therefore,

$t = \dfrac{-2\vec{v}_y}{\vec{g}} = \dfrac{-2(13.5\,\text{m/s})}{-9.8\,\text{m/s}^2} = 2.76\,\text{s}.$

**b.** $\vec{x} = \vec{v}_x t = (23.4\,\text{m/s})(2.76\,\text{s}) = 64.6\,\text{m}$

**c.** Maximum height occurs at half the "long time," or 1.38 s. Thus,

$\vec{y} = \vec{v}_y t + \dfrac{1}{2}\vec{g}t^2$

$= (13.5\,\text{m/s})(1.38\,\text{s})$

$\quad + \dfrac{1}{2}(-9.80\,\text{m/s}^2)(1.38\,\text{s})^2$

$= 18.6\,\text{m} - 9.3\,\text{m} = 9.3\,\text{m}.$

**6.** Following the method of Practice Problem 5,

**a.** $\vec{v}_x = \vec{v}_i \cos\theta = (27.0\,\text{m/s})\cos 60.0°$
$= 13.5\,\text{m/s}$
$\vec{v}_y = \vec{v}_i \sin\theta = (27.0\,\text{m/s})\sin 60.0°$
$= 23.4\,\text{m/s}$

$t = \dfrac{-2\vec{v}_y}{\vec{g}} = \dfrac{-2(23.4\,\text{m/s})}{-9.80\,\text{m/s}^2} = 4.78\,\text{s}.$

**b.** $\vec{x} = \vec{v}_x t = (13.5\,\text{m/s})(4.78\,\text{s}) = 64.5\,\text{m}$

**c.** at $t = \dfrac{1}{2}(4.78\,\text{s}) = 2.39\,\text{s}$,

$\vec{y} = \vec{v}_y t + \dfrac{1}{2}\vec{g}t^2$

$= (23.4\,\text{m/s})(2.39\,\text{s})$

$\quad + \dfrac{1}{2}(-9.80\,\text{m/s}^2)(2.39\,\text{s})^2 = 27.9\,\text{m}.$

**7.** For two projectiles with the same initial velocity and complementary launch angles, the projectile with the higher trajectory has the longest flight time and the greatest maximum height. The ranges are the same.

**8. a.** $\vec{v}_y = 0$ and $\vec{y} = -17.0\,\text{m} = $ ground level.

Therefore, $\vec{y} = \vec{v}_y t = \dfrac{1}{2}\vec{g}t^2$ becomes

$\vec{y} = \dfrac{1}{2}\vec{g}t^2$ or $t = \sqrt{\dfrac{2\vec{y}}{\vec{g}}} = \sqrt{\dfrac{2(-17.0\,\text{m})}{-9.80\,\text{m/s}^2}}$

$= 1.86\,\text{s}.$

**b.** $\vec{v}_x = 7.0\,\text{m/s}$, so $\vec{x} = \vec{v}_x t = (7.0\,\text{m/s})(1.86\,\text{s})$
$= 13\,\text{m}$

**c.** Now $\vec{v}_y = 8.5\,\text{m/s}$ and $\vec{y} = \vec{v}_y t + \dfrac{1}{2}\vec{g}t^2$

becomes $-17.0\,\text{m} = (8.5\,\text{m/s})t$

$\quad\quad\quad\quad + \dfrac{1}{2}(-9.80\,\text{m/s})t^2,$

or $(4.90\,\text{m/s}^2)t^2 - (8.5\,\text{m/s})t - 17.0\,\text{m} = 0$.
Using the quadratic formula to solve for $t$,

$t = \dfrac{8.5\,\text{m/s} \pm \sqrt{(8.5\,\text{m/s})^2 - 4(4.90\,\text{m/s}^2)(-17.0\,\text{m})}}{2(4.90\,\text{m/s})^2}$

$= \dfrac{-8.50\,\text{m/s} \pm 20.1\,\text{m/s}}{9.80\,\text{m/s}^2}.$

Choosing the $+$ sign to make flight time positive $t = 2.92\,\text{s}.$

**d.** $\vec{v}_x = 7.0\,\text{m/s}$, so $\vec{x} = \vec{v}_x t = (7.0\,\text{m/s})(2.92\,\text{s})$
$= 20\,\text{m}$

**9. a.** Since $r$ and $T$ remain the same,

$\vec{v} = \dfrac{2\pi r}{T}$ and $\vec{a} = \dfrac{\vec{v}^2}{r}$ remain the same. The new

value of the mass is $m' = 2m$. The new force is $\vec{F}' = m'\vec{a} = 2m\vec{a} = 2\vec{F}$, double the original force.

**b.** The new radius is $r' = 2r$, so the new velocity is $\vec{v}' = \dfrac{2\pi r'}{T} = \dfrac{2\pi(2r)}{T} = 2\vec{v}$, twice the original velocity. The new acceleration is

$$\vec{a}' = \frac{(\vec{v}')^2}{r'} = \frac{(2\vec{v})^2}{2r} = 2\vec{a}, \text{ twice the original.}$$

The new force is $\vec{F}' = m\vec{a}' = m(2\vec{a}) = 2\vec{F}$, twice the original.

**c.** new velocity, $\vec{v}' = \dfrac{2\pi r}{T'} = \dfrac{2\pi r}{\left[\dfrac{1}{2}T\right]} = 2\vec{v}$, twice the original;

new acceleration, $\vec{a}' = \dfrac{(\vec{v}')^2}{r} = \dfrac{(2\vec{v})^2}{r} = 4\vec{a}$, four times original;

new force, $\vec{F}' = m\vec{a}' = m(4\vec{a}) = 4F$, four times original

**10. a.** $\vec{a}_c = \dfrac{\vec{v}^2}{r} = \dfrac{(8.8 \text{ m/s})^2}{25 \text{ m}} = 3.1 \text{ m/s}^2$

**b.** the track friction force acting on the runner's shoes

**11. a.** $\vec{a}_c = \dfrac{\vec{v}^2}{r} = \dfrac{(32 \text{ m/s})^2}{56 \text{ m}} = 18 \text{ m/s}^2$

**b.** Recall $\vec{F}_f = \mu \vec{F}_N$. The friction force must supply the centripetal force so $\vec{F}_f = m\vec{a}_c$. The normal force is $\vec{F}_N = -\vec{W} = -m\vec{g}$. The coefficient of friction must be at least

$$\mu = \frac{\vec{F}_f}{\vec{F}_N} = \frac{m\vec{a}_c}{-m\vec{g}} = \frac{\vec{a}_c}{-\vec{g}} = \frac{18 \text{ m/s}^2}{-(-9.80 \text{ m/s}^2)} = 1.8.$$

**12. a.**

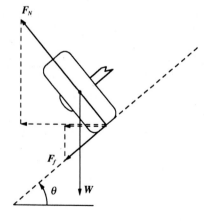

**b.** the horizontal component of the normal force and the horizontal component of the friction force; These component forces, $\vec{F}_N \sin\theta$ and $\vec{F}_f \cos\theta$ are shown by dotted lines in the figure.

**13.** From $T = 2\pi\sqrt{\dfrac{1}{\vec{g}}}$, we obtain

$$l = \frac{\vec{g}T^2}{4\pi^2} = \frac{(9.80 \text{ m/s}^2)(1.00 \text{ s})^2}{4\pi^2} = 0.248 \text{ m.}$$

**14.** From $T = 2\pi\sqrt{\dfrac{1}{\vec{g}}}$, we obtain

$$\vec{g} = \frac{4\pi^2 l}{T^2} = \frac{4\pi^2(0.65 \text{ m})}{(2.85 \text{ s})^2} = 3.3 \text{ m/s}^2.$$

# Chapter 8

**1.** $\left[\dfrac{T_a}{T_E}\right]^2 = \left[\dfrac{r_a}{r_E}\right]^3$ with $r_a = 2r_E$.

Thus, $T_a^2 = \left[\dfrac{r_a}{r_E}\right]^3 T_E^2$

$$= \left[\frac{2r_E}{r_E}\right]^3 (1 \text{ a})^2 = 8 \text{ a}^2, \; T_a = 2.8 \text{ a}$$

**2.** $\left[\dfrac{T_M}{T_E}\right] = \left[\dfrac{r_M}{r_E}\right]^3$, with $r_M = 1.52r_E$.

Thus, $T_M^2 = \left[\dfrac{r_M}{r_E}\right]^3 T_E^2 = \left[\dfrac{1.52r_E}{r_E}\right]^3 (365 \text{ d})^2$

$$= 4.679 \times 10^5 \text{ d}^2, \; T_M = 684 \text{ d}$$

**3.** $\left[\dfrac{T_s}{T_m}\right]^2 = \left[\dfrac{r_s}{r_m}\right]^3, \; T_s^2 = \left[\dfrac{r_s}{r_m}\right]^3 T_m^2$

$$= \left[\frac{6.70 \times 10^3 \text{ km}}{3.90 \times 10^5 \text{ km}}\right]^3 (27.3 \text{ d})^2$$

$$= 3.779 \times 10^{-3} \text{ d}^2, \; T_s$$
$$= 6.15 \times 10^{-2} \text{ d} = 88.5 \text{ min}$$

**4.** $\left[\dfrac{T_s}{T_m}\right]^2 = \left[\dfrac{r_s}{r_m}\right]^3$, so $r_s^3 = r_m^3 \left[\dfrac{T_s}{T_m}\right]^2$

$$= (3.90 \times 10^5 \text{ km})^3 \left[\frac{1.00}{27.3}\right]^2$$

$$= 7.96 \times 10^{13} \text{ km}^3, \text{ so } r_s = 4.30 \times 10^4 \text{ km}$$

**5. a.** $v = \sqrt{\dfrac{GM_E}{r}}$, with $r = r_E + 150$ km

$$r = 6.37 \times 10^6 \text{ m} + 0.150 \times 10^6 \text{ m}$$
$$= 6.52 \times 10^6 \text{ m}$$

$$v = \sqrt{\frac{(6.67 \times 10^{-11})(5.98 \times 10^{24})}{6.52 \times 10^6}} = 7.82 \times 10^3 \text{ m/s}$$

**b.** $T = 2\pi\sqrt{\dfrac{r^3}{GM_E}}$

$= 2\pi\sqrt{\dfrac{(6.52 \times 10^6 \text{ m})^3}{(6.67 \times 10^{-11} \text{ Nm}^2/\text{kg}^2)(5.98 \times 10^{24} \text{ kg})}}$

$= 5.24 \times 10^3 \text{ s} = 87.3 \text{ min}$

**6. a.** $v = \sqrt{\dfrac{GM_m}{r}}$, with $r = r_m + 265 \text{ km}$

$= 2.43 \times 10^6 \text{ m} + 0.265 \times 10^6 \text{ m}$

$= 2.70 \times 10^6 \text{ m}$

$v = \sqrt{\dfrac{(6.67 \times 10^{-11} \text{ Nm}^2/\text{kg}^2)(3.2 \times 10^{23} \text{ kg})}{2.70 \times 10^6 \text{ m}}}$

$= 2.8 \times 10^3 \text{ m/s}$

**b.** $T = 2\pi\sqrt{\dfrac{r^3}{GM_m}}$

$= 2\pi\sqrt{\dfrac{(2.70 \times 10^6 \text{ m})^3}{(6.67 \times 10^{-11} \text{ Nm}^2/\text{kg}^2)(3.2 \times 10^{23} \text{ kg})}}$

$= 6.03 \times 10^3 \text{ s} = 1.0 \times 10^2 \text{ min}$

**7. a.** $v = \sqrt{\dfrac{GM}{r}}$, where here $M$ is the mass of the sun.

$v = \sqrt{\dfrac{(6.67 \times 10^{-11} \text{ Nm}^2/\text{kg}^2)(1.991 \times 10^{30} \text{ kg})}{(5.80 \times 10^{10} \text{ m})}}$

$= 4.79 \times 10^4 \text{ m/s}$

**b.** $v = \sqrt{\dfrac{(6.67 \times 10^{-11} \text{ Nm}^2/\text{kg}^2)(1.991 \times 10^{30} \text{ kg})}{(1.427 \times 10^{12} \text{ m})}}$

$= 9.65 \times 10^3 \text{ m/s}$, about 1/5 as fast as Mercury

**8. a.** Using $T = 2\pi\sqrt{\dfrac{r^3}{GM}}$, with

$T = 2.5 \times 10^8 y = 7.9 \times 10^{15} \text{ s}$

$M = \dfrac{4\pi^2 r^3}{GT^2}$

$= \dfrac{4\pi^2(2.2 \times 10^{20} \text{ m})^3}{(6.67 \times 10^{-11} \text{ Nm}^2/\text{kg}^2)(7.9 \times 10^{15} \text{ s})^2}$

$= 1.0 \times 10^{41} \text{ kg}$

**b.** number of stars $= \dfrac{\text{total galaxy mass}}{\text{mass per star}}$

$= \dfrac{1.0 \times 10^{41} \text{ kg}}{2.0 \times 10^{30} \text{ kg}}$

$= 5.0 \times 10^{10}$

**c.** $v = \sqrt{\dfrac{GM}{r}}$

$= \sqrt{\dfrac{(6.67 \times 10^{-11} \text{ Nm}^2/\text{kg}^2)(1.0 \times 10^{41} \text{ kg})}{2.2 \times 10^{20} \text{ m}}}$

$= 1.7 \times 10^5 \text{ m/s} = 6.1 \times 10^5 \text{ km/h}$

# Chapter 9

**1. a.** $100 \text{ km/h} = 27.8 \text{ m/s}$,

$\vec{p} = m\vec{v} = (725 \text{ kg})(27.8 \text{ m/s})$

$= 2.02 \times 10^4 \text{ kg} \cdot \text{m/s}$

**b.** $\vec{v} = \vec{p}/m = \dfrac{(2.02 \times 10^4 \text{ kg} \cdot \text{m/s})}{(2175 \text{ kg})}$

$= 9.29 \text{ m/s} = 33.4 \text{ km/h}$

**2. a.** $\Delta\vec{p} = m(\vec{v}_f - \vec{v}_i)$

$= (250 \text{ kg})(28.0 \text{ m/s} - 6.0 \text{ m/s})$

$= 5.50 \times 10^3 \text{ kg} \cdot \text{m/s}$

**b.** $\vec{F} = \Delta\vec{p}/\Delta t = \dfrac{(5.50 \times 10^3 \text{ kg} \cdot \text{m/s})}{(60.0 \text{ s})} = 91.7 \text{ N}$

**3. a.** $m = \vec{W}/g = \dfrac{(15\,680 \text{ N})}{(9.80 \text{ m/s}^2)} = 1.60 \times 10^3 \text{ kg}$

**b.** $\vec{p}_i = mv_i = (1600 \text{ kg})(20.0 \text{ m/s})$

$= 3.20 \times 10^4 \text{ kg} \cdot \text{m/s}$

**c.** $\Delta\vec{p} = \vec{p}_f - \vec{p}_i = 0 - 3.20 \times 10^4 \text{ kg} \cdot \text{m/s}$

$= -3.20 \times 10^4 \text{ kg} \cdot \text{m/s}$

**d.** $\vec{F}\Delta t = \Delta\vec{p},\ \Delta t = \Delta\vec{p}/\vec{F}$

$= \dfrac{(-3.20 \times 10^4 \text{ kg} \cdot \text{m/s})}{(-6.40 \times 10^2 \text{ N})}$

$= 50.0 \text{ s}$

**4. a.** The area under the curve is 52.5 squares. Each square represents 0.100 N·s, so the impulse is

$\vec{F}\Delta T = \text{Area}$

$= (52.5 \text{ squares})(0.100 \text{ N} \cdot \text{s/square})$

$= 5.25 \text{ N} \cdot \text{s}.$

**b.** $\Delta\vec{p} = m\Delta\vec{v}$ with $\Delta\vec{p} = \vec{F}\Delta t$, so

$\Delta\vec{v} = \dfrac{\Delta\vec{p}}{m} = \dfrac{\vec{F}\Delta t}{m} = \dfrac{(5.25 \text{ N} \cdot \text{s})}{(2.4 \text{ kg})} = 2.2 \text{ m/s}$

**5.** $\vec{p}_h + \vec{p}_g = \vec{p}_h' + \vec{p}_g'$ or $m_h\vec{v}_h + m_g\vec{v}_g$

$= m_h\vec{v}_h' + m_g\vec{v}_g'$

Since $\vec{v}_g = 0$, $m_h\vec{v}_h = (m_h + m_h)\vec{v}'$

where $\vec{v}' = \vec{v}_h' = \vec{v}_g'$ is the common final speed of goalie and puck.

$\vec{v}' = \dfrac{m_h\vec{v}_h}{(m_h + m_g)}$

$= (0.105 \text{ kg})(48 \text{ m/s})(0.105 \text{ kg} + 75 \text{ kg})$

$= 0.067 \text{ m/s}$

**6.** $m_b\vec{v}_b + m_w\vec{v}_w = (m_b + m_w)\vec{v}'$ where $\vec{v}'$ is the common final velocity of bullet and wooden block. Since $\vec{v}_w = 0$, $\vec{v}_b = (m_b + m_w)\vec{v}'/m_b$

$$= \frac{(0.035\,\text{kg} + 5.0\,\text{kg})(8.6\,\text{m/s})}{(0.035\,\text{kg})}$$

$$= 1.2 \times 10^3 \text{ m/s}$$

**7.** $m_b\vec{v}_b + m_w\vec{v}_w = m_b\vec{v}_b' + m_w\vec{v}_w'$ with $\vec{v}_w = 0$

$$\vec{v}_w' = \frac{(m_b\vec{v}_b - m_b\vec{v}_b')}{m_w} = \frac{m_b(\vec{v}_b(\vec{v}_b'))}{m_w}$$

$$= \frac{(0.035\,\text{kg})(475\,\text{m/s} - 275\,\text{m/s})}{(2.5\,\text{kg})}$$

$$= 2.8 \text{ m/s}$$

**8.** $m_A\vec{v}_A + m_B\vec{v}_B = m_A\vec{v}_A' + m_B\vec{v}_B'$, so $\vec{v}_B'$

$$= \frac{(m_A\vec{v}_A + m_B\vec{v}_B - m_A\vec{v}_A')}{m_B}$$

$$= [(0.50\,\text{kg})(6.0\,\text{m/s}) + (1.00\,\text{kg})(-12.0\,\text{m/s})$$
$$- (0.50\,\text{kg})(-14\,\text{m/s})]/(1.00\,\text{kg})$$

$$= -2.0 \text{ m/s}$$

**9.** $\vec{p}_r + \vec{p}_f = \vec{p}_r' + \vec{p}_f'$, where $\vec{p}_r + \vec{p}_f = 0$.
If the initial mass of the rocket (including fuel) is $m_r = 4.00$ kg, then the final mass of the rocket is
$m_r' = 4.00$ kg $- 0.050$ kg $= 3.95$ kg.
$0 = m_r'\vec{v}_r' + m_f\vec{v}_f'$,

$$v_r' = \frac{-m_f\vec{v}_f'}{m_r'}$$

$$= \frac{-(0.050\,\text{kg})(-625\,\text{m/s})}{(3.95\,\text{kg})}$$

$$= 7.91 \text{ m/s}$$

**10.** $\vec{p}_A + \vec{p}_B = \vec{p}_A' + \vec{p}_B'$ with $\vec{p}_A + \vec{p}_B = 0$,
$m_B\vec{v}_B' = -m_A\vec{v}_A'$,

$$\text{so } \vec{v}_B' = \frac{-m_A\vec{v}_A}{m_B} = \frac{-(1.5\,\text{kg})(-27\,\text{cm/s})}{(4.5\,\text{kg})}$$

$$= 9.0 \text{ cm/s, or } 9.0 \text{ cm/s to the right.}$$

**11.** $\vec{p}_A + \vec{p}_B = \vec{p}_A' + \vec{p}_B'$ with $\vec{p}_A + \vec{p}_B = 0$,

$$m_A\vec{v}_A' = -m_B\vec{v}_B', \text{ so } \vec{v}_B' = \frac{-m_A\vec{v}_A'}{m_B}$$

$$= \frac{-(80.0\,\text{kg})(4.0\,\text{m/s})}{(110\,\text{kg})}$$

$$= -2.9 \text{ m/s, or } 2.9 \text{ m/s in the opposite direction.}$$

**12. a.** Both the cannon and the ball fall to the ground in the same time from the same height. In that fall time, the ball moves 215 m, the cannon an unknown displacement we will call $x$.

Now $t = \dfrac{\vec{d}}{\vec{v}}$, so $\dfrac{(215\,\text{m})}{v_{\text{ball}}} = \dfrac{x}{\vec{v}_{\text{cannon}}}$,

so $x = \left[\dfrac{\vec{v}_{\text{cannon}}}{\vec{v}_{\text{ball}}}\right](215\,\text{m})$

related by conservation of momentum;
$(4.5\,\text{kg})\vec{v}_{\text{ball}} = -(225\,\text{kg})\vec{v}_{\text{cannon}}$, so

$$\left[\frac{\vec{v}_{\text{cannon}}}{\vec{v}_{\text{ball}}}\right] = \frac{(4.5\,\text{kg})}{(225\,\text{kg})}.$$

Thus, $x = \left[\dfrac{4.5}{225}\right](215 \text{ m}) = 4.3$ m.

**b.** While on top, the cannon moves with no friction, and its velocity doesn't change, so it can take any amount of time to reach the back edge.

**13.**

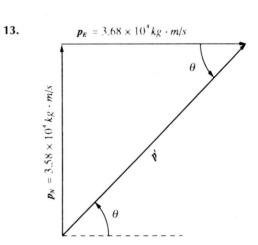

$$\vec{p}_N = \vec{p}_E = \vec{p}' \text{ (vector sum)}$$

$$\vec{p}_N = m_N\vec{v}_N = (1325\,\text{kg})(27.0\,\text{m/s})$$
$$= 3.58 \times 10^4 \text{ kg·m/s}$$

$$\vec{p}_E = m_E\vec{v}_E = (2165\,\text{kg})(17.0\,\text{m/s})$$
$$= 3.68 \times 10^4 \text{ kg·m/s}$$

$$\tan\theta = \frac{\vec{p}_N}{\vec{p}_E} = \frac{3.58 \times 10^4 \text{ kg·m/s}}{3.68 \times 10^4 \text{ kg·m/s}} = 0.973,$$

$$\theta = 44.2°, \text{ north of east}$$

$$(\vec{p}')^2 = (\vec{p}_N)^2 + (\vec{p}_E)^2$$
$$= (3.58 \times 10^4 \text{ kg·m/s})^2$$
$$+ (3.68 \times 10^4 \text{ kg·m/s})^2$$
$$= 2.64 \times 10^9 \text{ kg}^2 \text{ m}^2/\text{s}^2,$$

$$\vec{p}' = 5.13 \times 10^4 \text{ kg·m/s}$$

$$\vec{p}' = m'\vec{v}' = (m_N + m_E)\vec{v}',$$

$$\vec{v}' = \frac{p'}{(m_N + m_E)}$$

$$= \frac{(5.13 \times 10^4 \text{ kg·m/s})}{(1325\,\text{kg} + 2165\,\text{kg})}$$

$$= 14.7 \text{ m/s}$$

**14.**

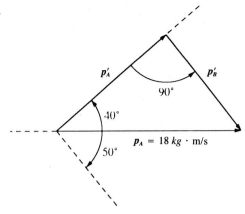

a. $\vec{p}_A + \vec{p}_B = \vec{p}'_A + \vec{p}'_B$ (vector sum)
with $\vec{p}_B = 0$
$\vec{p}_A = m_A\vec{v}_A = (6.0\ kg)(3.0\ m/s) = 18\ kg\cdot m/s$
$\vec{p}'_A = \vec{p}_A\cos 40° = (18\ kg\cdot m/s)\cos 40°$
$\quad = 14\ kg\cdot m/s$
$\vec{p}'_B = \vec{p}_A\sin 40° = (18\ kg\cdot m/s)\sin 40°$
$\quad = 12\ kg\cdot m/s$

b. $\vec{p}'_A = m_A\vec{v}'_A,$
$\vec{v}'_A = \dfrac{\vec{p}'_A}{m_A} = \dfrac{(14\ kg\cdot m/s)}{(6.0\ kg)}$
$\quad = 2.3\ m/s, 40°\ to\ left$
$\vec{p}'_B = m_B\vec{v}'_B,$
$\vec{v}'_B = \dfrac{\vec{p}'_B}{m_B} = \dfrac{(12\ kg\cdot m/s)}{(6.0\ kg)}$
$\quad = 2.0\ m/s, 50°\ to\ right$

**15.**

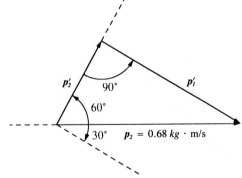

$\vec{p}_1 + \vec{p}_2 = \vec{p}'_1 + \vec{p}'_2$ (vector sum) with $p_1 = 0$
$m_1 \quad = m_2 = m = 0.17\ kg$
$\vec{p}_2 \quad = m_2\vec{v}_2 = (0.17\ kg)(4.0\ m/s) = 0.68\ kg\cdot m/s$
$\vec{p}'_1 \quad = \vec{p}_2\sin 60°, mv'_1 = m\vec{v}_2\sin 60°,$
$\vec{v}'_1 \quad = \vec{v}_2\sin 60° = (4.0\ m/s)\sin 60°$
$\quad = 3.5\ m/s, 30°\ to\ right$
$\vec{p}'_2 \quad = \vec{p}_2\cos 60°, mv'_2 = m\vec{v}_2\cos 60°,$
$\vec{v}'_2 \quad = \vec{v}_2\cos 60° = (4.0\ m/s)\cos 60°$
$\quad = 2.0\ m/s, 60°\ to\ left$

## Chapter 10

**1. a.** $W = Fd = (825\ N)(35\ m) = 2.9 \times 10^4\ J$
  **b.** The work doubles; when displacement remains the same, work is directly proportional to force.

**2.** $W = Fd = (34\ N)(15\ m) = 510\ J$

**3.** $W = Fd = mgd = (583\ kg)(9.80\ m/s^2)(1.2\ m)$
$\quad = 6.9 \times 10^3\ J$

**4.** Both do the same amount of work. Only the height lifted and the vertical force exerted count.

**5.** Both the force and displacement are in the same direction, so
$W = Fd = (25\ N)(3.5\ m) = 88\ J.$

**6. a.** Since gravity acts vertically, only the vertical displacement needs to be considered.
$\quad W = Fd = (215\ N)(4.20\ m) = 903\ J$
  **b.** Force is upward, but vertical displacement is downward, so
$\quad W = Fd\cos\theta = Fd\cos 180°$
$\quad\quad = (215\ N)(4.20\ m)(-1) = -903\ J.$

**7.** $W = Fd\cos\theta = (628\ N)(15.0\ m)(\cos 46.0°)$
$\quad = 6.54 \times 10^3\ J$

**8. a.** Displacement in direction of force is 4.0 m,
so $W = (85\ N)(4.0\ m) = 340\ J.$
  **b.** Displacement in direction of force is $-3.0$ m, so
$W = (93\ N)(-3.0\ m) = -279\ J$ (work done against gravity).
  **c.** $W = \mu F_N d$
$$= 0.20\left[85\ N \cdot \frac{3}{5} + 93\ N \cdot \frac{4}{5}\right]5.0\ m$$
$$= 1.3 \times 10^2\ J$$

**9.** $P = \dfrac{W}{t} = \dfrac{Fd}{t} = \dfrac{(575\ N)(20.0\ m)}{10.0\ m}$
$\quad = 1.15 \times 10^3\ W = 1.15\ kW$

**10. a.** $W = mgd = (750\ kg)(9.80\ m/s^2)(8.2\ m)$
$\quad = 6.0 \times 10^2\ J$
  **b.** $W = Fd + 6.0 \times 10^2\ J$
$\quad = (645\ N)(8.2\ m) + 6.0 \times 10^2\ J$
$\quad = 5.9 \times 10^3\ J$
  **c.** $P = \dfrac{W}{t} = \dfrac{5.9 \times 10^3\ J}{(30\ min)(60\ s/min)}$
$\quad = 3.3\ W$

**11.** $P = \dfrac{W}{t}$, and $W = Fd$,

so $F = \dfrac{Pt}{d} = \dfrac{(65 \times 10^3 \text{ W})(35.0 \text{ s})}{17.5 \text{ m}}$

$= 1.3 \times 10^5 \text{ N}$

**12. a.** forward: force of road on cart; rearward: force of air on car; These forces are equal in magnitude when the car moves with constant speed.

**b.** Car exerts a rearward force on road and a forward force on air.

**c.** $P = \dfrac{W}{t}$ and $W = Fd$, so $P = \dfrac{Fd}{t}$,

so $F = \dfrac{Pt}{d} = \dfrac{P}{v}$

For sports car,

$F = \dfrac{35 \times 10^3 \text{ W}}{29.2 \text{ m/s}} = 1.2 \times 10^3 \text{ N}$;

for other,

$F = \dfrac{65 \times 10^3 \text{ W}}{29.2 \text{ m/s}} = 2.2 \times 10^3 \text{ N}$.

**d.** from the chemical energy in the gasoline

**13. a.** $IMA = \dfrac{d_e}{d_r} = \dfrac{20 \text{ cm}}{5.0 \text{ cm}} = 4.0$

**b.** $MA = \dfrac{F_r}{F_e} = \dfrac{1.9 \times 10^4 \text{ N}}{9.8 \times 10^3 \text{ N}} = 1.9$

**c.** Efficiency $= \left[\dfrac{MA}{IMA}\right] \times 100\%$

$= \left[\dfrac{1.9}{4.0}\right] \times 100\% = 48\%$

**14. a.** $MA = \dfrac{F_r}{F_e} = \dfrac{225 \text{ N}}{129 \text{ N}} = 1.74$

**b.** Efficiency $= \left[\dfrac{MA}{IMA}\right] \times 100\%$, where

$IMA = \dfrac{d_e}{d_r} = \dfrac{33.0 \text{ m}}{16.5 \text{ m}} = 2.00$, so

efficiency $= \dfrac{1.74}{2.00} \times 100\% = 87\%$

**15.** eff $= \dfrac{W_o}{W_i} \times 100\% = \dfrac{F_r d_r}{F_e d_e} \times 100\%$, so

$d_e = \dfrac{F_r d_r (100\%)}{F_e (\text{eff})}$

$= \dfrac{(125 \times 10^3 \text{ N})(0.13 \text{ m})(100\%)}{(225 \text{ N})(88.7\%)}$

$= 0.81 \text{ m}$

**16.** $IMA = \dfrac{8.00 \text{ cm}}{35.6 \text{ cm}} = 0.224$

$MA = (95\%)\dfrac{0.224}{100\%} = 0.214 \text{ (both doubled)}$

The force exerted by the distance the chain moved, $d_e$, would also be doubled to 3.14 cm.

# Chapter 11

**1. a.** 50 km/h is 14 m/s, so

$E_k = \dfrac{1}{2}mv^2 = \dfrac{1}{2}(750 \text{ kg})(14 \text{ m/s})^2$

$= 7.4 \times 10^4 \text{ J}$

**b.** $W = \Delta E_k = E_{kf} - E_{ki}$
$= 0.74 \times 10^5 \text{ J} - 2.94 \times 10^5 \text{ J}$
$= -2.20 \times 10^5 \text{ J}$

**c.** $W = \Delta E_k = 0 - 7.4 \times 10^4 \text{ J}$
$= -7.4 \times 10^4 \text{ J}$

**d.** $W = Fd$, so distance is proportional to work. The ratio is $(-2.2 \times 10^5 \text{ J})/(-7.4 \times 10^4 \text{ J}) = 3$. It takes three times the distance to slow the car to half its speed than it does to a complete stop.

**2. a.** $E_k = \dfrac{1}{2}mv^2 = \dfrac{1}{2}(0.00420 \text{ kg})(965 \text{ m/s})^2$

$= 1.96 \times 10^3 \text{ J}$

**b.** $W = \Delta E_k = 1.96 \times 10^3 \text{ J}$

**c.** $W = Fd$, so
$F = E_W/d = (1.96 \times 10^3 \text{ J})/(0.75 \text{ m})$
$= 2.6 \times 10^3 \text{ N}$

**d.** $F = E_W/d = E_k/d = (1.96 \times 10^3 \text{ J})/(0.015 \text{ m})$
$= 1.3 \times 10^5 \text{ N}$

**3. a.** $E_k = \dfrac{1}{2}mv^2$

$= \dfrac{1}{2}(7.85 \times 10^{11} \text{ kg})(2.5 \times 10^4 \text{ m/s})^2$

$= 2.5 \times 10^{20} \text{ J}$

**4. a.** Since $W = \Delta E_k = \dfrac{1}{2}mv^2$, then $v = \sqrt{2W/m}$.

If $W' = \dfrac{1}{2}W$,

$v' = \sqrt{2W'/m}$

$= \sqrt{2\left(\dfrac{1}{2}W\right)/m} = \sqrt{\dfrac{1}{2}}\,v$

$= (0.707)(100 \text{ km/h}) = 71 \text{ km/h}$

**b.** If $W' = 2W$,
$v' = \sqrt{2}\,(100 \text{ km/h})$
$= 140 \text{ km/h}$

**5.** $E_p = mgh$. At the edge,
$$E_p = (90 \text{ kg})(9.8 \text{ m/s}^2)(+45 \text{ m})$$
$$= +4.0 \times 10^4 \text{ J}.$$

At bottom,
$$E_p = (90 \text{ kg})(9.8 \text{ m/s}^2)(+45 \text{ m} - 85 \text{ m})$$
$$= -3.5 \times 10^4 \text{ J}.$$

**6. a.** $E_p = mgh = (50.0 \text{ kg})(9.80 \text{ m/s}^2)(400 \text{ m})$
$$= 1.96 \times 10^5 \text{ J}$$
**b.** $\Delta E_p = mgh_f - mgh_i = mg(h_f - h_i)$
$$= (50.0 \text{ kg})(9.80 \text{ m/s}^2)(200 \text{ m} - 400 \text{ m})$$
$$= -9.80 \times 10^4 \text{ J}$$

**7. a.** $W = Fd = Fh = (630 \text{ N})(5.0 \text{ m}) = 3200 \text{ J}$
**b.** $\Delta E_p = (mg)h = (630 \text{ N})(5.0 \text{ m}) = 3200 \text{ J}$
The increase in gravitational potential energy is equal to the work done.
**c.** Directly from the work done by the person. Indirectly from the chemical energy stored in the person's body.

**8. a.**

$$h = (2.5 \text{ m})(1 - \cos \theta) = 0.73 \text{ m}$$
$$E_p = mgh = (7.26 \text{ kg})(9.80 \text{ m/s}^2)(0.73 \text{ m})$$
$$= 52 \text{ J}$$
**b.** the height of the ball when the rope was vertical

**9. a.** $E_k = \frac{1}{2}mv^2$
$$= \frac{1}{2}(85 \text{ kg})(8.5 \text{ m/s})^2 = 3.1 \times 10^3 \text{ J}$$
**b.** $E_{ki} + E_{pi} = E_{kf} + E_{pf}$
$$\frac{1}{2}mv^2 + 0 = 0 + mgh$$
$$h = v^2/2g = (8.5 \text{ m/s})^2/(2)(9.8 \text{ m/s}^2) = 3.7 \text{ m}$$
**c.** No. It cancels because both $E_k$ and $E_p$ are proportional to $m$.

**10. a.** $E_{ki} + E_{pi} = E_{kf} + E_{pf}$
$$0 + mgh = \frac{1}{2}mv^2 + 0$$
$$v^2 = 2gh = 2(9.8 \text{ m/s}^2)(4.0 \text{ m}) = 78.4 \text{ m}^2/\text{s}^2$$
$$v = 8.9 \text{ m/s}$$
**b.** No
**c.** No

**11. a.** $E_{ki} + E_{pi} = E_{kf} + E_{pf}$
$$0 + mgh = \frac{1}{2}mv^2 + 0$$
$$v^2 = 2gh = 2(9.8 \text{ m/s}^2)(45 \text{ m}) = 880 \text{ m}^2/\text{s}^2$$
$$v = 30 \text{ m/s}$$
**b.** $E_{ki} + E_{pi} = E_{kf} + E_{pf}$
$$0 + mgh_i = \frac{1}{2}mv^2 + mgh_f$$
$$v^2 = 2g(h_i - h_f)$$
$$= 2(9.8 \text{ m/s}^2)(45 \text{ m} - 40 \text{ m}) = 98 \text{ m}^2/\text{s}^2$$
$$v = 10 \text{ m/s}$$

**12. a.** The system Earth, bike, and rider remains the same but now the energy involved is not mechanical energy alone. The rider must be considered as having stored energy, some of which is converted to mechanical energy.
**b.** Energy came from chemical potential energy stored in the rider's body.

**13. a.** From conservation of momentum,
$$m\vec{v} = (m + M)\vec{V}, \text{ so}$$
$$\vec{V} = m\vec{v}/(m + M)$$
$$= \frac{(0.002 \text{ kg})(538 \text{ m/s})}{(0.002 \text{ kg} + 0.250 \text{ kg})} = 4.27 \text{ m/s}.$$
**b.** $E_{ki} = \frac{1}{2}mv^2 = \frac{1}{2}(0.002 \text{ kg})(538 \text{ m/s})^2 = 289 \text{ J}$
**c.** $E_{kf} = \frac{1}{2}(m + M)V^2$
$$= \frac{1}{2}(0.002 \text{ kg} + 0.250 \text{ kg})(4.27 \text{ m/s})^2$$
$$= 2.30 \text{ J}$$
**d.** $\Delta E_k = E_{ki} - E_{kf} = 289 \text{ J} - 2 \text{ J} = 287 \text{ J}$
**e.** $\% E_k \text{ lost} = (\Delta E_k/E_{ki}) \times 100$
$$= (287 \text{ J}/298 \text{ J}) \times 100$$
$$= 99.3\%$$

**14.** Conservation of momentum, $mv = (m + M)V$, or
$$v = (m + M)V/m$$
$$= (0.008 \text{ kg} + 9.00 \text{ kg})(0.10 \text{ m/s})/(0.008 \text{ kg})$$
$$= 1.1 \times 10^2 \text{ m/s}.$$

**15.** We have conservation of momentum
$mv + MV = mv' + MV'$ and conservation of energy $\frac{1}{2}mv^2 + \frac{1}{2}MV^2 = \frac{1}{2}mv'^2 + \frac{1}{2}MV'^2$ where $m$, $v$, $v'$ refer to bullet, $M$, $V$, $V'$ to Superman, and $V = 0$. $v'$ may be eliminated from these equations by solving the momentum equation for $v' = (mv - MV')/m$ and substituting this into the energy equation $mv^2 = mv'^2 + MV'^2$. This gives a quadratic equation for $V'$ which, in factored form, is $MV'[(M + m)V' - 2mv] = 0$. We are not interested in the

solution $V' = 0$ which corresponds to the case where the bullet does not hit Superman. We want the other,

$$V' = 2mv/(M + m) = \frac{2(0.0042 \text{ kg})(835 \text{ m/s})}{(104 \text{ kg} + 0.0042 \text{ kg})}$$

$$= 6.7 \times 10^{-2} \text{ m/s}.$$

16. Only momentum is conserved in the inelastic dart-target collision, so $mv_i + MV_i = (m + M)V_f$ where $V_i = 0$, since the target is initially at rest and $V_f$ is the common velocity just after impact. As the dart-target combination swings upward, energy is conserved, so $\Delta PE = \Delta KE$ or, at the top of the swing, $(m + M)gh = \frac{1}{2}(m + M)V_f^2$. Solving this for $V_f$ and inserting into the momentum equation gives

$$v_i = (m + M)\sqrt{2gh}/m$$

$$= \frac{(0.025 \text{ kg} + 0.73 \text{ kg})\sqrt{2(9.8 \text{ m/s}^2)(0.12 \text{ m})}}{(0.025 \text{ kg})}$$

$$= 46 \text{ m/s}.$$

# Chapter 12

1. **a.** $K = °C + 273 = 0 + 273 = 273 \text{ K}$
   **b.** $°C = K - 273 = 0 - 273 = -273°C$
   **c.** $K = °C + 273 = 273 + 273 = 546 \text{ K}$
   **d.** $°C = K - 273 = 273 - 273 = 0°C$

2. **a.** $K = 27°C + 273 = 300 \text{ K}$
   **b.** $K = 560°C + 273 = 833 \text{ K}$
   **c.** $K = -184°C + 273 = 89 \text{ K}$
   **d.** impossible temperature — below absolute zero

3. **a.** $°C = 110 - 273 = -163°C$
   **b.** $°C = 22 - 273 = -251°C$
   **c.** $°C = 402 - 273 = 129°C$
   **d.** $°C = 323 - 273 = 50°C$

4. Answers will vary:
   **a.** 20 to 22°C, 293 – 295 K
   **b.** 4°C, 277 K
   **c.** 30°C, 303 K
   **d.** –18°C, 255 K

5. $Q = mc\Delta T$
   $= (0.0600 \text{ kg})(385 \text{ J/kg} \cdot \text{K})(80.0°C - 20.0°C)$
   $= 1.39 \times 10^3 \text{ J}$

6. $Q = mc\Delta T$
   $= (38 \text{ kg})(130 \text{ J/kg} \cdot \text{K})(180°C - (-26°C))$
   $= 1.0 \times 10^6 \text{ J}$

7. **a.** $Q = mc\Delta T$
   $\Delta T = Q/mc$
   $$= \frac{(836 \times 10^3 \text{ J})}{(20.0 \text{ kg})(4180 \text{ J/kg} \cdot \text{K})}$$
   $= 10.0°C$

   **b.** Using $1 \text{ L} = 1000 \text{ cm}^3$, the mass of methanol required is
   $DV = (0.80 \text{ g/cm}^3)(20 \text{ L})(1000 \text{ cm}^3/\text{L})$
   $= 16 000 \text{ g or } 16 \text{ kg.}$
   $$\Delta T = Q/mc = \frac{(836 \times 10^3 \text{ J})}{(16 \text{ kg})(2450 \text{ J/kg} \cdot \text{K})}$$
   $= 21°C$

   **c.** Water is the better coolant since its temperature increase is less than half that of methanol when absorbing the same amount of heat.

8. **a.** Iron: $Q = mc\Delta T$
   $= (0.565 \text{ kg})(450 \text{ J/kg} \cdot \text{K})(100°C - 20°C)$
   $= 2.0 \times 10^4 \text{ J}$

   **b.** Water: $Q = mc\Delta T$, so
   $$m = Q/c\Delta T = \frac{(2.0 \times 10^4 \text{ J})}{(4180 \text{ J/kg} \cdot \text{K})(20°C)}$$
   $= 0.24 \text{ kg}$

9. $m_A c_A(T_f - T_{A,i}) + m_B c_B(T_f - T_{B,i}) = 0$
   Since $m_A = m_B$ and $c_A = c_B$, there is cancellation in this particular case so that
   $$T_f = \frac{(T_{A,i} + T_{B,i})}{2} = \frac{(80.0° + 10.0°C)}{2} = 45.0°C.$$

10. $m_a c_a(T_f - T_{a,i}) + m_w c_w(T_f - T_{w,i}) = 0$
    Since, in this particular case, $m_a = m_w$, the masses cancel and
    $$T_f = \frac{c_a T_{a,i} + c_w T_{w,i}}{c_a + c_w}$$
    $$= \frac{(2450 \text{ J/kg} \cdot \text{C}°)(16.0°C) + (4180 \text{ J/kg} \cdot \text{C}°)(85.0°C)}{2450 \text{ J/kg} \cdot \text{C}° + 4180 \text{ J/kg} \cdot \text{C}°}$$
    $= 59.5°C.$

11. $m_b c_b(T_f - T_{b,i}) + m_w c_w(T_f - T_{w,i}) = 0$
    $$T_f = \frac{m_b c_b T_{b,i} + m_w c_w T_{w,i}}{m_b c_b + m_w c_w}$$
    $$= \frac{(0.100 \text{ kg})(376 \text{ J/kg} \cdot \text{C}°)(90.0°C) + (0.200 \text{ kg})(4180 \text{ J/kg} \cdot \text{C}°)(20.0°C)}{(0.100 \text{ kg})(376 \text{ J/kg} \cdot \text{C}°) + (0.200 \text{ kg})(4180 \text{ J/kg} \cdot \text{C}°)}$$
    $= 23.0°C$

12. $m_a c_a(T_f - T_{a,i}) + m_w c_w(T_f - T_{w,i}) = 0$
Since $m_a = m_w$, the masses cancel and

$c_a = -c_w(T_f - T_{wi})/(T_f - T_{a,i})$

$= \dfrac{-(4180 \text{ J/kg} \cdot \text{K})(25°C - 10°C)}{(25°C - 100°C)} = 8.4 \times 10^2 \text{ J/kg} \cdot \text{K.}$

13. To warm the ice to 0°C, $Q_w$
$= mc\Delta T = (0.100 \text{ kg})(2060 \text{ J/kg} \cdot \text{C°})(0 - (-20.0°C))$
$= 4120 \text{ J.}$
To melt the ice, $Q_m = mH_f$
$= (0.100 \text{ kg})(3.34 \times 10^5 \text{ J/kg}) = 3.34 \times 10^4 \text{ J.}$
Total heat required $= Q_w + Q_m$
$= 0.41 \times 10^4 + 3.34 \times 10^4 \text{ J} = 3.75 \times 10^4 \text{ J.}$

14. To heat the water from 60°C to 100°C:
$Q = mc\Delta T = (0.200 \text{ kg})(4180 \text{ J/kg} \cdot \text{C°})(40°C)$
$= 0.334 \times 10^5 \text{ J}$
To change the water to steam:
$Q = mH_v = (0.200 \text{ kg})(2.26 \times 10^6 \text{ J/kg})$
$= 4.52 \times 10^5 \text{ J}$
To heat the steam from 100°C to 140°C:
$Q = mc\Delta T = (0.200 \text{ kg})(2020 \text{ J/kg} \cdot \text{C°})(40°C)$
$= 0.162 \times 10^5 \text{ J}$
$Q_{total} = 5.02 \times 10^5 \text{ J}$

15. Warm ice from −30°C to 0°C:
$Q = mc\Delta T = (0.300 \text{ kg})(2060 \text{ J/kg} \cdot \text{C°})(30.0°C)$
$= 0.185 \times 10^5 \text{ J}$
Melt ice:
$Q = mH_f = (0.300 \text{ kg})(3.34 \times 10^5 \text{ J/kg})$
$= 1.00 \times 10^5 \text{ J}$
Heat water 0°C to 100°C:
$Q = mc\Delta T = (0.300 \text{ kg})(4180 \text{ J/kg} \cdot \text{C°})(100°C)$
$= 1.25 \times 10^5 \text{ J}$
Vaporize water:
$Q = mH_v = (0.300 \text{ kg})(2.26 \times 10^6 \text{ J/kg})$
$= 6.78 \times 10^5 \text{ J}$
Heat steam 100°C to 130°C:
$Q = mc\Delta T = (0.300 \text{ kg})(2020 \text{ J/kg} \cdot \text{C°})(30°C)$
$= 0.18 \times 10^5 \text{ J}$
$Q_{total} = 9.40 \times 10^5 \text{ J}$

16. **a.** To freeze, lead must absorb
$Q = -mH_f = -(0.175 \text{ kg})(2.04 \times 10^4 \text{ J/kg})$
$= -3.57 \times 10^3 \text{ J.}$
This will heat the water.

$\Delta T = Q/mc = \dfrac{(3.57 \times 10^3 \text{ J})}{(0.055 \text{ kg})(4180 \text{ J/kg} \cdot \text{K})}$

$= 16°C \text{ to } 36°C$

**b.** Now, $T_f = \dfrac{(m_A c_A T_{A,i} + m_B c_B T_{B,i})}{(m_A c_A + m_B c_B)}$

$= \dfrac{(0.175 \text{ kg})(130 \text{ J/kg} \cdot \text{K})(327°C) + (0.55 \text{ kg})(4180 \text{ J/kg} \cdot \text{K})(35.5°C)}{(0.175 \text{ kg})(130 \text{ J/kg} \cdot \text{K}) + (0.055 \text{ kg})(4180 \text{ J/kg} \cdot \text{K})}$

$= 62°C$

# Chapter 13

1. $p = F/A$, so
$F = pA = (1.0 \times 10^5 \text{ Pa})(1.52 \text{ m})(0.76 \text{ m})$
$= 1.2 \times 10^5 \text{ N}$

2. $F = mg = (925 \text{ kg})(9.80 \text{ m/s}^2) = 9.07 \times 10^3 \text{ N}$
$A = 4(0.12 \text{ m})(0.18 \text{ m}) = 0.0864 \text{ m}^2$
$p = F/A = (9.07 \times 10^3 \text{ N})/(0.0864 \text{ m}^2)$
$= 1.0 \times 10^5 \text{ Pa}$

3. $F = (11.8 \text{ gm/cm}^3)(10^{-3} \text{ kg/g})(5.0 \text{ cm})(10 \text{ cm}) \times$
$(20 \text{ cm})(9.8 \text{ m/s}^2)$
$= 116 \text{ N}$
$A = (0.05 \text{ m})(0.10 \text{ m}) = 0.005 \text{ m}^2$
$p = F/A = (116 \text{ N})/(0.005 \text{ m}^2) = 23 \text{ kPa}$

4. $F_{net} = F_{outside} - F_{inside}$
$= (p_{outside} - p_{inside})A$
$= (0.85 \times 10^5 \text{ Pa} - 1.00 \times 10^5 \text{ Pa}) \times$
$(1.82 \text{ m})(0.91 \text{ m})$
$= -2.5 \times 10^4 \text{ N (toward the outside)}$

5. $F_1/A_1 = F_2/A_2$ with $A_2 = 0.400 \text{ m}^2$, since the circular area is proportional to the diameter squared and the original diameter has been doubled.
$F_2 = A_2 F_1/A_1 = (0.400 \text{ m}^2)(20.0 \text{ N})/(0.0500 \text{ m}^2)$
$= 160 \text{ N}$

6. $F_1/A_1 = F_2/A_2$
$F_1 = F_2 A_1/A_2$
$= (1600 \text{ N})(72 \text{ cm}^2)/(1440 \text{ cm}^2) = 80 \text{ N}$

7. $F_{weight} = F_{buoyant} = \rho_{water} Vg$
$V = F_{weight}/\rho_{water} g$
$= (600 \text{ N})/(1000 \text{ kg/m}^3)(9.8 \text{ m/s}^2)$
$= 0.06 \text{ m}^3.$
This volume does not include that portion of her head that is above the water.

8. $T + F_{buoyant} = \vec{W}$
$T = \vec{W} - F_{buoyant} = \vec{W} - \rho_{water} Vg$
$= 1250 \text{ N} - (1000 \text{ kg/m}^3)(0.083 \text{ m}^3)(9.8 \text{ m/s}^2)$
$= 4.4 \times 10^2 \text{ N}$

9. $\Delta L = \alpha L_i \Delta T = (25 \times 10^{-6} \text{ °C}^{-1})(3.66 \text{ m})(67°C)$
$= 6.1 \times 10^{-3} \text{ m, or 6.1 mm}$

10. $L_f = L_i + \alpha L_i(T - T_i) = (11.5 \text{ m})$
$+ (11 \times 10^{-6} \text{ °C}^{-1})(11.5 \text{ m})(1221°C - 22°C)$
$= 11.7 \text{ m}$

11. **a.** For water, $\beta = 210 \times 10^{-6} \text{ °C}^{-1}$, so $\Delta V = \beta V \Delta T$
$= (354 \text{ mL})(210 \times 10^{-6} \text{ °C}^{-1})(30.1°C)$
$= 2.24 \text{ mL}$

**b.** For Al $\beta = 75 \times 10^{-6}\,°C^{-1}$, so

$$\Delta V = \beta V \Delta T$$
$$= (354\ mL)(75 \times 10^{-6}\,°C^{-1})(30.1°C)$$
$$= 0.80\ mL$$

**c.** The difference will spill.

$2.24\ mL - 0.80\ mL = 1.44\ mL$

**12. a.** $V = V_i + \beta V_i(T - T_i)$

$$= 45\ 725\ L + (950 \times 10^{-6}\,°C^{-1})(45\ 725\ L) \times$$
$$(-18.0°C - 32.0°C)$$
$$= 45\ 725\ L - 2170\ L$$
$$= 43\ 555\ L = 43\ 560\ L$$

**b.** Its volume has decreased because of temperature change.

# Chapter 14

**1. a.** $v = d/t = (515\ m)/(1.5\ s) = 343\ m/s$
  **b.** $T = 1/f = 1/(436\ Hz) = 2.29 \times 10^{-3}\ s$
    $= 2.29\ ms$
  **c.** $\lambda = v/f = (343\ m/s)/(436\ Hz) = 0.787\ m$

**2. a.** $v = d/t = (685\ m)/(2.0\ s) = 343\ m/s$
  **b.** $f = v/\lambda = (342\ m/s)/(0.750\ m) = 457\ Hz$
  **c.** $T = 1/f = 1/(456\ Hz) = 2.19 \times 10^{-3}\ s$
    $= 2.19\ ms$

**3.** $\lambda = v/f = (3.00 \times 10^8\ m/s)/(99.5 \times 10^6\ Hz)$
    $= 3.02\ m$

**4. a.** $\lambda = (580\ nm)(1 \times 10^{-9}\ m/nm)$
    $= 5.8 \times 10^{-7}\ m$
  **b.** $f = v/\lambda = (3.0 \times 10^8\ m/s)/(5.8 \times 10^{-7}\ m)$
    $= 5.2 \times 10^{14}\ Hz$

**5. a.** The pulse is partially reflected, partially transmitted.
  **b.** Erect, since reflection is from a less dense medium.
  **c.** It is almost totally reflected from the wall.
  **d.** Inverted, since reflection is from a more dense medium.

**6.** Pulse inversion means rigid boundary: attached to wall.

**7.** at a lower frequency because wavelength varies inversely with frequency

**8. a.** The pulse is partially reflected, partially transmitted.

**b.** Inverted, since reflection is from a more dense medium.
  **c.** It is almost totally reflected from the wall.
  **d.** Inverted, since reflection is from a more dense medium.

# Chapter 15

**1.** $v = \lambda f$, so $\lambda = \dfrac{v}{f} = \dfrac{1435\ m/s}{261.6\ Hz} = 5.485\ m$

**2.** $v = \lambda f$, so $f = \dfrac{v}{\lambda} = \dfrac{343\ m/s}{0.667\ m} = 514\ Hz$

**3.** From $v = \lambda f$, the largest wavelength is

$$\lambda = \frac{v}{f} = \frac{343\ m/s}{20\ Hz} = 17\ m;\ \text{the smallest is}$$

$$\lambda = \frac{v}{f} = \frac{343\ m/s}{16\ 000\ Hz} = 0.021\ m.$$

**4.** Woofer diameter 38 cm,
$f = v/\lambda = (343\ m/s)/(0.38\ m) = 0.90\ kHz$
Tweeter diameter 7.6 cm,
$f = v/\lambda = (343\ m/s)/(0.076\ m) = 4.5\ kHz$

**5.** Resonance spacing is $\lambda/2$, so using $v = \lambda f$, the

resonance spacing is $\dfrac{\lambda}{2} = \dfrac{v}{2f}$

$$= \frac{343\ m/s}{2(440\ Hz)} = 0.390\ m.$$

**6.** Resonance spacing $= \dfrac{\lambda}{2} = 1.10\ m$, so $\lambda = 2.20\ m$

and $v = f\lambda = (440\ Hz)(2.20\ m) = 968\ m/s$.

**7.** From the previous Example Problem, $v = 347\ m/s$ at 27°C and the resonance spacing gives

$\dfrac{\lambda}{2} = 0.392\ m$ or $\lambda = 0.784\ m$. Using $v = \lambda f$,

$$f = \frac{v}{\lambda} = \frac{347\ m/s}{(0.784\ m)} = 443\ Hz.$$

**8.** $l = \lambda/4$, $v = \lambda f$, so
$f = v/4l = (343\ m/s)/(4 \times 0.03\ m) = 2.9\ kHz$

**9.** The lowest resonant frequency of an open pipe corresponds to the wavelength $\lambda_1$, where

$\dfrac{\lambda_1}{2} = L = $ length of pipe. Further resonances are spaced $\dfrac{\lambda}{2}$ apart giving the series of resonant

wavelengths $L = \dfrac{\lambda_1}{2}, \ 2\left(\dfrac{\lambda_2}{2}\right), \ 3\left(\dfrac{\lambda_3}{2}\right), \ \ldots.$

**a.** $\lambda_1 = 2L = 2(2.65 \text{ m}) = 5.30$ m, so that the lowest frequency is

$$f_1 = \dfrac{v}{\lambda_1} = \dfrac{343 \text{ m/s}}{5.30 \text{ m}} = 64.7 \text{ Hz}.$$

**b.** $f_2 = \dfrac{v}{\lambda_2} = \dfrac{v}{L} = \dfrac{343 \text{ m/s}}{2.65 \text{ m}} = 129$ Hz

$$f_3 = \dfrac{v}{\lambda_3} = \dfrac{3v}{2L} = \dfrac{3(343 \text{ m/s})}{2(2.65 \text{ m})} = 194 \text{ Hz}$$

**10.** The lowest resonant frequency corresponds to the

wavelength given by $\dfrac{\lambda}{2} = L$, the length of the pipe.

$$\lambda = 2L = 2(0.65 \text{ m}) = 1.30 \text{ m, so } f = \dfrac{v}{\lambda}$$

$$= \dfrac{343 \text{ m/s}}{1.30 \text{ m}} = 260 \text{ Hz}$$

Since the saxophone is an open pipe, $\lambda_{max} = 2 \times$ (pipe length) $= 2(0.65 \text{ m}) = 1.30$ m. $f_{min} = v/\lambda_{max} = (343 \text{ m/s})/(1.30 \text{ m}) = 260$ Hz

**11.** Beat frequency $= |f_2 - f_1|$
$$= |333 \text{ Hz} - 330 \text{ Hz}|$$
$$= 3 \text{ Hz}$$

**12.** The frequency of the second fork could be either $f_2 = f_1 + f_{beat} = 349 \text{ Hz} + 3 \text{ Hz} = 352$ Hz or $f_2 = f_1 - f_{beat} = 349 \text{ Hz} - 3 \text{ Hz} = 346$ Hz.

# Chapter 16

**1.** $c = \lambda f$, so
$$f = c/\lambda = (3.00 \times 10^8 \text{ m/s})/(556 \times 10^{-9} \text{ m})$$
$$= 5.40 \times 10^{14} \text{ Hz}$$

**2.** $d = ct = (3.00 \times 10^8 \text{ m/s})(1.0 \times 10^{-9} \text{ s})$
$$= 0.30 \text{ m}$$

**3. a.** $d = ct = (3.00 \times 10^8 \text{ m/s})(6.0 \times 10^{-15} \text{ s})$
$$= 1.8 \times 10^{-6} \text{ m}$$

**b.** Number of wavelengths $= \dfrac{\text{pulse length}}{\lambda_{violet}}$

$$= \dfrac{1.8 \times 10^{-6} \text{ m}}{4.0 \times 10^{-7} \text{ m}}$$

$$= 4.5$$

**4.** $d = ct = (299\ 792\ 458 \text{ m/s})(1/2)(2.562 \text{ s})$
$$= 3.840 \times 10^8 \text{ m}$$

**5.** $v = d/t = (3.0 \times 10^{11} \text{ m})/(16 \text{ min})(60 \text{ s/m})$
$$= 3.1 \times 10^8 \text{ m/s}$$

**6.** $\dfrac{E_{after}}{E_{before}} = \dfrac{P/4\pi d_{after}^2}{P/4\pi d_{before}^2} = \dfrac{d_{before}^2}{d_{after}^2} = \dfrac{(30 \text{ cm})^2}{(90 \text{ cm})^2} = \dfrac{1}{9}$

**7.** $E = \dfrac{P}{4\pi d^2} = \dfrac{2275 \text{ lm}}{4\pi(3.0 \text{ m})^2} = 20 \text{ lx}$

**8.** Illuminance of a 150-W bulb
$P = 2275, d = 0.5, 0.75 \ldots 5$

$$E(d) = \dfrac{P}{4\pi d^2}$$

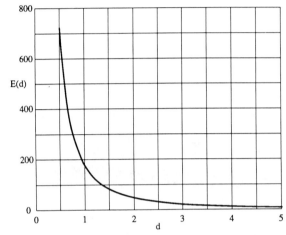

**9.** $P = 4\pi I = 4\pi(64 \text{ cd}) = 256\pi \text{ lm,}$

so $E = \dfrac{P}{4\pi d^2} = \dfrac{256\pi \text{ lm}}{4\pi(3.0 \text{ m})^2} = 7.1 \text{ lx}$

**10.** From $E = \dfrac{P}{4\pi d^2}$,

$$P = 4\pi d^2 E = 3\pi(4.0 \text{ m})^2(2.0 \times 10^1 \text{ lx})$$
$$= 1280\pi \text{ lm,}$$

so $I = \dfrac{P}{4\pi} = \dfrac{1280\pi \text{ lm}}{4\pi} = 320 \text{ cd}$

# Chapter 17

**1.** Assume the light is incident from air.
From $n_i \sin \theta_i = n_r \sin \theta_r$,

$$\sin \theta_r = \dfrac{n_i \sin \theta_i}{n_r} = \dfrac{(1.00) \sin 45.0°}{1.52}$$
$$= 0.465, \text{ or } \theta_r = 27.7°.$$

**2.** $n_i \sin \theta_i = n_r \sin \theta_r$ so,

$$\sin \theta_r = \dfrac{n_i \sin \theta_i}{n_r} = \dfrac{(1.00) \sin 30.0°}{1.33} = 0.376,$$

or $\theta_r = 22.1°$

**3. a.** Assume the light is incident from air.
$n_i \sin \theta_i = n_r \sin \theta_r$ gives

$$\sin \theta_r = \frac{n_i \sin \theta_i}{n_r} = \frac{(1.00) \sin 45.0°}{2.42} = 0.292,$$

or $\theta_r = 17.0°$

**b.** Diamond bends the light more.

**4.** $n_1 \sin \theta_1 = n_2 \sin \theta_2$, so
$n_2 = n_1 \sin \theta_1/\sin \theta_2 = (1.33)(0.515)/(0.454) = 1.5$

**5. a.** $v_{ethanol} = \dfrac{c}{n_{ethanol}} = \dfrac{3.00 \times 10^8 \text{ m/s}}{1.36}$
$= 2.21 \times 10^8 \text{ m/s}$

**b.** $v_{quartz} = \dfrac{c}{n_{quartz}} = \dfrac{3.00 \times 10^8 \text{ m/s}}{1.54}$
$= 1.95 \times 10^8 \text{ m/s}$

**c.** $v_{flint \ glass} = \dfrac{c}{n_{flint \ glass}} = \dfrac{3.00 \times 10^8 \text{ m/s}}{1.61}$
$= 1.86 \times 10^8 \text{ m/s}$

**6.** $n = \dfrac{c}{v} = \dfrac{3.00 \times 10^8 \text{ m/s}}{2.00 \times 10^8 \text{ m/s}} = 1.50$

**7.** $n = 1.5$, so $v = \dfrac{c}{n} = \dfrac{3.00 \times 10^8 \text{ m/s}}{1.5}$
$= 2.0 \times 10^8 \text{ m/s}$

**8.** $t = d/v = dn/c$
$\Delta t = d(n_{air} - n_{vacuum})/c$
$= d(1.0003 - 1.0000)/3.00 \times 10^8 \text{ m/s}$
$= d(1 \times 10^{-12} \text{ s/m})$
Thus, $d = \Delta t/(1 \times 10^{-12} \text{ s/m})$
$= 1 \times 10^{-8} \text{ s}/1 \times 10^{-12} \text{ s/m}$
$= 10^4 \text{ m} = 10 \text{ km}.$

## Chapter 18

**1.**

**2. a.**

**b.** $\dfrac{1}{f} = \dfrac{1}{d_o} + \dfrac{1}{d_i}$, so
$d_i = d_o f/(d_o - f)$
$= (10 \text{ cm})(6.0 \text{ cm})/(10 \text{ cm} - 6.0 \text{ cm})$
$= 15 \text{ cm}$

**c.** $m = -d_i/d_o = -(15 \text{ cm})/(10.0 \text{ cm}) = -1.5$

**d.** $m = h_i/h_o$, so
$h_i = mh_o = (-1.5)(3.0 \text{ mm}) = -4.5 \text{ mm}$

**3.** $f = r/2 = (20.0 \text{ cm})/2 = 10.0 \text{ cm}$,
$1/d_o + 1/d_i = 1/f$, so
$d_o = fd_i/(d_i - f)$
$= (10.0 \text{ cm})(30.0 \text{ cm})/(30.0 \text{ cm} - 10.0 \text{ cm})$
$= 15.0 \text{ cm}$

**4.** If $d_o = d_i$, then $1/f = 2/d_o$, or $f = \dfrac{1}{2}d_o$

Now, $r = 2f = d_o = 25 \text{ cm}$

**5.** $f = r/2 = (12.0 \text{ cm})/2 = 6.0 \text{ cm}$
$1/d_o + 1/d_i = 1/f$, so
$d_i = fd_o/(d_o - f)$
$= (6.0 \text{ cm})(4.0 \text{ cm})/(4.0 \text{ cm} - 6.0 \text{ cm})$
$= -12 \text{ cm}$

**6. a.** $1/d_o + 1/d_i = 1/f$, so
$d_i = fd_o/(d_o - f)$
$= (9.0 \text{ cm})(6.0 \text{ cm})/(6.0 \text{ cm} - 9.0 \text{ cm})$
$= -18 \text{ cm}$

**b.** $m = h_i/h_o = -d_i/d_o = -(-18 \text{ cm})/(6.0 \text{ cm})$
$= +3.0$, so
$h_i = mh_o = (3.0)(15 \text{ mm}) = 45 \text{ mm}$

**7. a.** $1/d_o + 1/d_i = 1/f$, so
$d_i = fd_o/(d_o - f)$
$= (16.0 \text{ cm})(10.0 \text{ cm})/(10.0 \text{ cm} - 16.0 \text{ cm})$
$= -27 \text{ cm}$

**b.** $m = h_i/h_o = -d_i/d_o$
$= -(-27 \text{ cm})/(10.0 \text{ cm}) = +2.7$, so
$h_i = mh_o = (2.7)(4.0 \text{ cm}) = 11 \text{ cm}$

**8.** $m = -d_i/d_o = 3$, so
$d_i = -75 \text{ cm}$
$1/f = 1/d_o + 1/d_i$, so
$f = d_o d_i/(d_o + d_i)$
$= (25 \text{ cm})(-75 \text{ cm})/(25 \text{ cm} + (-75 \text{ cm}))$
$= 37.5 \text{ cm}$ and $r = 2f = 75 \text{ cm}$

**9. a.**

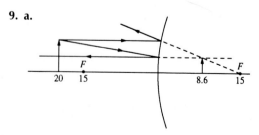

**b.** $1/d_o + 1/d_i = 1/f$, so
$$d_i = fd_o/(d_o - f)$$
$$= \frac{(-15.0 \text{ cm})(20.0 \text{ cm})}{(20.0 \text{ cm} - (-15.0 \text{ cm}))}$$
$$= -8.57 \text{ cm}$$

**10. a.** $1/d_o + 1/d_i = 1/f$, so
$$d_i = fd_o/(d_o - f)$$
$$= \frac{(-12 \text{ cm})(60.0 \text{ cm})}{(60.0 \text{ cm} - (-12 \text{ cm}))}$$
$$= -10 \text{ cm}$$
**b.** $m = h_i/h_o = -d_i/d_o$
$$= -(-10 \text{ cm})/(60.0 \text{ cm}) = +0.17, \text{ so}$$
$$h_i = mh_o = (0.17)(6.0 \text{ cm}) = 1.0 \text{ cm}$$

**11.** $1/d_o + 1/d_i = 1/f$, so
$$d_i = fd_o/(d_o - f)$$
$$= (-0.40 \text{ m})(6.0 \text{ m})/(6.0 \text{ m} - (-0.40 \text{ m}))$$
$$= -0.38 \text{ m}$$

**12.** $1/f = 1/d_o + 1/d_i$, so $f = d_od_i/(d_o + d_i)$ and $m = -d_i/d_o$, so $d_o = -d_i/m$.
Since $d_i = -24 \text{ cm}$ and $m = 0.75$,
$$d_o = \frac{-(-24 \text{ cm})}{0.75} = 32 \text{ cm and}$$
$$f = \frac{(32 \text{ cm})(-24 \text{ cm})}{32 \text{ cm} + (-24 \text{ cm})} = -96 \text{ cm}.$$

**13.**

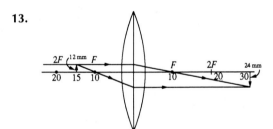

**14.** $1/d_o + 1/d_i = 1/f$, so
$$d_i = fd_o/(d_o - f)$$
$$= (5.5 \text{ cm})(8.5 \text{ cm})/(8.5 \text{ cm} - 5.5 \text{ cm})$$
$$= 16 \text{ cm}$$
$$h_i = -d_ih_o/d_o = -(16 \text{ cm})(2.25 \text{ mm})/(8.5 \text{ cm})$$
$$= -4.2 \text{ mm}$$

**15.** $1/d_o + 1/d_i = 1/f$ with $d_o = d_i$, since $m = -d_i/d_o$ and $m = -1$. Therefore,
$2/d_o = 1/f$, $d_o = d_i = 2f = 50 \text{ mm}$.

**16.** $m = -d_i/d_o$,
so $d_i = -md_o = -(-2)(7.0 \text{ cm}) = 14 \text{ cm}$
$1/f = 1/d_o + 1/d_i$, so
$$f = d_od_i/(d_o + d_i)$$
$$= (7.0 \text{ cm})(14 \text{ cm})/(7.0 \text{ cm} + 14 \text{ cm})$$
$$= 4.7 \text{ cm}$$

**17.** $1/d_o + 1/d_i = 1/f$, so
$$d_i = fd_o/(d_o - f)$$
$$= (20.0 \text{ cm})(6.0 \text{ cm})/(6.0 \text{ cm} - 20.0 \text{ cm})$$
$$= -8.6 \text{ cm}$$

**18. a.** $1/d_o + 1/d_i = 1/f$, so
$$d_i = fd_o/(d_o - f)$$
$$= (12 \text{ cm})(3.4 \text{ cm})/(3.4 \text{ cm} - 12 \text{ cm})$$
$$= -4.7 \text{ cm}$$
**b.** $h_i = -h_od_i/d_o$
$$= -(2.0 \text{ cm})(-4.7 \text{ cm})/(3.4 \text{ cm})$$
$$= 2.8 \text{ cm}$$

**19.** $m = -d_i/d_o$, so
$$d_i = -md_o = -(4.0)(3.5 \text{ cm}) = -14 \text{ cm}$$
$1/f = 1/d_o + 1/d_i$, so
$$f = d_od_i/(d_o + d_i)$$
$$= (3.5 \text{ cm})(-14 \text{ cm})/(3.5 \text{ cm} + (-14 \text{ cm}))$$
$$= 4.7 \text{ cm}$$

**20.** From Figure 18–17, you can increase image size by making $(d_o - f)$ as small as possible. Thus, increase $d_o$ until it is almost $f$, which is the limit.

## Chapter 19

**1.** $\lambda = xd/L$
$$= (13.2 \times 10^{-3} \text{ m})(1.90 \times 10^{-5} \text{ m})/(0.600 \text{ m})$$
$$= 4.18 \times 10^{-7} \text{ m}$$
$$= 418 \text{ nm}$$

**2.** $x = \lambda L/d$
$$= (5.96 \times 10^{-7} \text{ m})(0.600 \text{ m})/(1.90 \times 10^{-5} \text{ m})$$
$$= 0.0188 \text{ m}$$
$$= 18.8 \text{ mm}$$

**3.** $d = \lambda L/x$
$$= (6.328 \times 10^{-7} \text{ m})/(1.000 \text{ m})(65.5 \times 10^{-3} \text{ m})$$
$$= 9.66 \times 10^{-6} \text{ m}$$

**4.** $\lambda = xd/L$
$$= (55.8 \times 10^{-3} \text{ m})(9.66 \times 10^{-6} \text{ m})/(1.000 \text{ m})$$
$$= 5.39 \times 10^{-7} \text{ m}$$
$$= 539 \text{ nm}$$

**5.** $x = \lambda L/w$
$$= (5.46 \times 10^{-7} \text{ m})(0.75 \text{ m})/(9.5 \times 10^{-5} \text{ m})$$
$$= 4.3 \times 10^{-3} \text{ m}$$
$$= 4.3 \text{ mm}$$

**6.** $w = \dfrac{\lambda L}{x}$

$\quad = (6.328 \times 10^{-7} \text{ m})(1.15 \text{ m})/(7.5 \times 10^{-3} \text{ m})$

$\quad = 9.7 \times 10^{-5} \text{ m}$

**7.** $\lambda = \dfrac{wx}{L}$

$\quad = (2.95 \times 10^{-5} \text{ m})(1.20 \times 10^{-2} \text{ m})/(0.600 \text{ m})$

$\quad = 5.90 \times 10^{-7} \text{ m}$

$\quad = 590 \text{ nm}$

**8. a.** Red, because central peak width is proportional to wavelength.

   **b.** Width $= 2x = 2\lambda L/w$

    for blue,

$$2x = \frac{2(4.41 \times 10^{-7} \text{ m})(1.00 \text{ m})}{(5.0 \times 10^{-5} \text{ m})}$$

$\quad\quad = 18 \text{ mm}$

    for red,

$$2x = \frac{2(6.22 \times 10^{-7} \text{ m})(1.00 \text{ m})}{(5.0 \times 10^{-5} \text{ m})}$$

$\quad\quad = 25 \text{ mm}$

## Chapter 20

**1.** $F = \dfrac{kqq'}{d^2}$

$\quad = \dfrac{(9.0 \times 10^9 \text{ N} \cdot \text{m}^2/\text{C}^2)(6.0 \times 10^{-6} \text{ C})(6.0 \times 10^{-6} \text{ C})}{(0.5 \text{ m})^2}$

$\quad = 1.3 \text{ N}$

**2.** $F = \dfrac{kqq'}{d^2}$

$\quad = \dfrac{(9.0 \times 10^9 \text{ N} \cdot \text{m}^2/\text{C}^2)(-2.0 \times 10^{-4} \text{ C})(8.0 \times 10^{-4} \text{ C})}{(0.30 \text{ m})^2}$

$\quad = -1.6 \times 10^4 \text{ N}$

**3.** $F = \dfrac{kqq'}{d^2}$

$\quad q' = \dfrac{Fd^2}{Kq}$

$\quad\quad = \dfrac{(65 \text{ N})(0.05 \text{ m})^2}{(9.0 \times 10^9 \text{ N} \cdot \text{m}^2/\text{C}^2)(6.0 \times 10^{-6} \text{ C})}$

$\quad\quad = 3.0 \times 10^{-6} \text{ C}$

**4.**

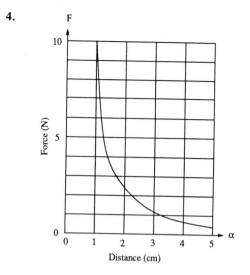

**5.** Magnitudes of all forces remain the same. The direction changes to 42° above the $-x$ axis, or 138°.

## Chapter 21

**1.** $\vec{E} = \dfrac{\vec{F}}{q'} = \dfrac{0.060 \text{ N}}{2.0 \times 10^{-8} \text{ C}}$

$\quad\quad = 3.0 \times 10^6 \text{ N/C}$, directed to the left

**2.** $\vec{E} = \dfrac{\vec{F}}{q'} = \dfrac{2.5 \times 10^{-4} \text{ N}}{5.0 \times 10^{-4} \text{ C}} = 0.50 \text{ N/C}$

**3.** $F_2/F_1 = (Kqq'/d_2{}^2)/(Kqq'/d_1{}^2)$

$\quad\quad = (d_1/d_2)^2$ with $d_2 = 2d_1$

$\quad F_2 = (d_1/d_2)^2 F_1 = (d_1/2d_1)^2(2.5 \times 10^{-4} \text{ N})$

$\quad\quad = 6.3 \times 10^{-5} \text{ N}$

**4. a.** No. The force on the 2.0 μC charge would be twice that on the 1.0 μC charge.

   **b.** Yes. You would divide the force by the strength of the test charge, so the results would be the same.

**5.** $V = Ed = (8000 \text{ N/C})(0.05 \text{ m}) = 400 \text{ J/C}$

$\quad\quad = 4 \times 10^2 \text{ V}$

**6.** $V = Ed$

$\quad E = \dfrac{V}{d} = \dfrac{500 \text{ V}}{0.02 \text{ m}} = 2.5 \times 10^4 \text{ N/C}$

**7.** $V = Ed = (2.50 \times 10^3 \text{ N/C})(0.500 \text{ m})$

$\quad\quad = 1.25 \times 10^3 \text{ V}$

**8.** $W = qV = (5.0 \text{ C})(1.5 \text{ V}) = 7.5 \text{ J}$

**9. a.** Gravitational force (weight), downward; frictional force of air, upward

**b.** The two are equal in magnitude.

**10. a.** $\vec{F} = \vec{E}q$

$$q = \frac{\vec{F}}{\vec{E}} = \frac{1.9 \times 10^{-15}\,N}{6.0 \times 10^3\,N/C} = 3.2 \times 10^{-19}\,C$$

**b.** # electrons $= \dfrac{q}{q_e} = \dfrac{3.2 \times 10^{-19}\,C}{1.6 \times 10^{-19}\,C/electron}$

$= 2$ electrons

**11. a.** $\vec{F} = \vec{E}q$

$$q = \frac{\vec{F}}{\vec{E}} = \frac{6.4 \times 10^{-13}\,N}{4.0 \times 10^6\,N/C} = 1.6 \times 10^{-19}\,C$$

**b.** # electrons $= \dfrac{q}{1.6 \times 10^{-19}\,C/electron}$

$= 1$ electron

**12.** $\vec{E} = \dfrac{\vec{F}}{q} = \dfrac{6.4 \times 10^{-13}\,N}{(4)(1.6 \times 10^{-19}\,C)} = 1.0 \times 10^6\,N/C$

**13.** $q = CV = 27\ \mu F(25\ V) = 6.8 \times 10^{-4}\,C$

**14.** $q = CV$, so the larger capacitor has a greater charge.
$q = 1.0 \times 10^{-4}\,C$

**15.** $V = q/C$, so the smaller capacitor has the larger potential difference.
$V = (2.5 \times 10^{-4}\,C)/(3.3 \times 10^{-6}\,F) = 76\,V$

**16.** $q = CV$, so $\Delta q = C\Delta V$;
$\Delta q = (2.2\ \mu F)(15.0\ V - 6.0\ V) = 2.0 \times 10^{-5}\,C$

# Chapter 22

**1.** $P = VI = (120\ V)(0.5\ A) = 60\ J/s = 60\ W$

**2.** $P = VI = (12\ V)(2.0\ A) = 24\ W$

**3.** $P = VI,\ I = \dfrac{P}{V} = \dfrac{75\ W}{120\ V} = 0.63\ A$

**4.** $P = VI = (12\ V)(210\ A) = 2500\ W$
In 10 s, $E = Pt = (2500\ J/s)(10\ s)$
$= 25\ 000\ J = 2.5 \times 10^4\,J.$

**5.** $I = \dfrac{V}{R} = \dfrac{12\ V}{30\ \Omega} = 0.40\ A$

**6.** $V = IR = (3.8\ A)(32\ \Omega) = 120\ V$

**7.** $R = \dfrac{V}{I} = \dfrac{3\ V}{2 \times 10^{-4}\,A} = 1.5 \times 10^4\ \Omega$

$= 2 \times 10^4\ \Omega$

**8. a.** $R = \dfrac{V}{I} = \dfrac{120\ V}{0.5\ A} = 240\ \Omega = 200\ \Omega$

**b.** $P = VI = (120\ V)(0.5\ A) = 60\ W$

**9. a.** $I = P/V = (75\ W)/(120\ V) = 0.63\ A$

**b.** $R = V/I = 120\ V/0.63\ A = 190\ \Omega$

**10. a.** The new value of the current is
$0.63\ A/2 = 0.315\ A$, so
$V = IR = (0.315\ A)(190\ \Omega) = 60\ V.$

**b.** The total resistance of the circuit is now
$R_{total} = V/I = (120\ V)/(0.315\ A) = 380\ \Omega.$
Therefore, $R_{res} = R_{total} - R_{lamp}$
$= 380\ \Omega - 190\ \Omega = 190\ \Omega.$

**c.** $P = VI = (60\ V)(0.315\ A) = 19\ W$

**11.** $I = \dfrac{V}{R} = \dfrac{60\ V}{12.5\ \Omega} = 4.8\ A$

**12.** $R = V/I = (4.5\ V)/(0.090\ A) = 50\ \Omega$

**13.** Both circuits will take the form

Since the ammeter resistance is assumed zero, the voltmeter readings will be
Practice Problem 11   60 V.
Practice Problem 12   4.5 V.

**14. a.** $I = V/R = (120\ V)/(15\ \Omega) = 8.0\ A$

**b.** $E = I^2Rt = (8.0\ A)^2(15\ \Omega)(30.0\ s)$
$= 2.9 \times 10^4\,J$

**c.** $2.9 \times 10^4\,J$, since all electrical energy is converted to thermal energy.

**15. a.** $I = V/R = (60\ V)/(30\ \Omega) = 2.0\ A$

**b.** $E = I^2Rt = (2.0\ A)^2(30\ \Omega)(5\ min)(60\ s/min)$
$= 3.6 \times 10^4\,J$

**16. a.** $E = (0.200)(100.0 \text{ J/s})(60.0 \text{ s})$
    $= 1.20 \times 10^3 \text{ J}$
**b.** $E = (0.800)(100.0 \text{ J/s})(60.0 \text{ s})$
    $= 4.80 \times 10^3 \text{ J}$

**17. a.** $I = V/R = (220 \text{ V})/(11 \ \Omega) = 20 \text{ A}$
**b.** $E = I^2Rt = (20 \text{ A})^2(11 \ \Omega)(30.0 \text{ s})$
    $= 1.3 \times 10^5 \text{ J}$
**c.** $Q = mC\Delta T$ with $Q = 0.70 \ E$
    $\Delta T = 0.70 \ E/mC$

    $= \dfrac{(0.70)(1.3 \times 10^5 \text{ J})}{(1.20 \text{ kg})(4180 \text{ J/kg} \cdot {}^\circ\text{C})} = 18{}^\circ\text{C}$

**18. a.** $P = IV = (15.0 \text{ A})(120 \text{ V})$
    $= 1800 \text{ W} = 1.80 \text{ kW}$
**b.** $E = Pt = (1.8 \text{ kW})(5 \text{ h/day})(30 \text{ days})$
    $= 270 \text{ kWh}$
**c.** Cost $= (0.11 \text{ \$/kWh})(270 \text{ kWh}) = \$29.70$

**19. a.** $I = \dfrac{V}{R} = \dfrac{(115 \text{ V})}{(12\ 000 \ \Omega)} = 9.6 \times 10^{-3} \text{ A}$

**b.** $P = VI = (115 \text{ V})(9.6 \times 10^{-3} \text{ A}) = 1.10 \text{ W}$
**c.** Cost $= (1.10 \times 10^{-3} \text{ kW})(\$0.09/\text{kWh}) \times$
    $(30 \text{ days})(24 \text{ h/day}) = \$0.07$

# Chapter 23

**1. a.** $R = R_1 + R_2 + R_3$
    $= 20 \ \Omega + 20 \ \Omega + 20 \ \Omega$
    $= 60 \ \Omega$
**b.** $I = V/R = (120 \text{ V})/(60 \ \Omega) = 2.0 \text{ A}$

**2. a.** $R = 10 \ \Omega + 15 \ \Omega + 5 \ \Omega = 30 \ \Omega$
**b.** $I = V/R = (90 \text{ V})/(30 \ \Omega) = 3.0 \text{ A}$

**3. a.** It will increase.
**b.** $I = V/R$, so it will decrease.
**c.** No. It does not depend on the resistance.

**4. a.** $R = V/I = (120 \text{ V})/(0.06 \text{ A}) = 2000 \ \Omega$
**b.** $2000 \ \Omega/10 = 200 \ \Omega$

**5. a.** $R = 20.0 \ \Omega + 30.0 \ \Omega = 50.0 \ \Omega$
**b.** $I = V/R = (120 \text{ V})/(50.0 \ \Omega) = 2.40 \text{ A}$
**c.** $V = IR$. Across 20.0 -$\Omega$ resistor,
    $V = (2.40 \text{ A})(20.0 \ \Omega) = 48.0 \text{ V}$
    Across 30.0 -$\Omega$ resistor,
    $V = (2.40 \text{ A})(30.0 \ \Omega) = 72.0 \text{ V}.$
**d.** $V = 48.0 \text{ V} + 72.0 \text{ V} = 120 \text{ V}$

**6. a.** $R = 3.0 \text{ k}\Omega + 5.0 \text{ k}\Omega + 4.0 \text{ k}\Omega = 12.0 \text{ k}\Omega$
**b.** $I = V/R = (12 \text{ V})/(12.0 \text{ k}\Omega)$
    $= 1.0 \text{ mA} = 1.0 \times 10^{-3} \text{ A}$
**c.** $V = IR$,
    so $V = 3.0 \text{ V}, 5.0 \text{ V},$ and $4.0 \text{ V}$
**d.** $V = 3.0 \text{ V} + 5.0 \text{ V} + 4.0 \text{ V}$
    $= 12.0 \text{ V}$

**7.** $V_2 = VR_2/(R_1 + R_2)$
    $= (45 \text{ V})(235 \text{ k}\Omega)/(475 \text{ k}\Omega + 235 \text{ k}\Omega) = 15 \text{ V}$

**8. a.** $V_2 = VR_2/(R_1 + R_2)$
    $= (9.0 \text{ V})(475 \ \Omega)/(500 \ \Omega + 475 \ \Omega)$
    $= 4.4 \text{ V}$
**b.** $V_2 = VR_2/(R_1 + R_2)$
    $= (9.0 \text{ V})(4.0 \text{ k}\Omega)/(0.50 \text{ k}\Omega + 4.0 \text{ k}\Omega)$
    $= 8.0 \text{ V}$
**c.** $V_2 = VR_2/(R_1 + R_2)$

    $= \dfrac{(9.0 \text{ V})(4.0 \times 10^5 \ \Omega)}{(0.005 \times 10^5 \ \Omega + 4.0 \times 10^5 \ \Omega)}$

    $= 9.0 \text{ V}$

**9. a.** $1/R = 1/R_1 + 1/R_2 + 1/R_3$
    $= 3/15 \ \Omega, R = 5.0 \ \Omega$
**b.** $I = V/R = (30 \text{ V})/(5.0 \ \Omega) = 6.0 \text{ A}$
**c.** $I = V/R = (30 \text{ V})/(15.0 \ \Omega) = 2.0 \text{ A}$

**10. a.** $1/R = 1/15.0 \ \Omega + 1/12.0 \ \Omega$, so
    $R = 6.67 \ \Omega$
**b.** $I = V/R = (15.0 \text{V})/(6.67 \ \Omega) = 2.25 \text{ A}$
**c.** $I = V/R$
    $= (15.0 \text{V})/(15.0 \ \Omega)$
    $= 1.00 \text{ A},$
    $(15.0 \text{ V})/(12.0 \ \Omega)$
    $= 1.25 \text{ A}$

**11. a.** $1/R = 1/120.0 \ \Omega + 1/60.0 \ \Omega + 1/40.0 \ \Omega,$
    $R = 20.0 \ \Omega$
**b.** $I = V/R$
    $= (12.0 \text{ V})/(20.0 \ \Omega)$
    $= 0.600 \text{ A}$
**c.** $I = V/R$
    $= (12.0 \text{ V})/(120.0 \ \Omega)$
    $= 0.100 \text{ A},$
    $(12.0 \text{ V})/(60.0 \ \Omega)$
    $= 0.200 \text{ A},$
    $(12.0 \text{ V})/(40.0 \ \Omega)$
    $= 0.300 \text{ A}$

**12. a.** smaller
**b.** gets larger
**c.** No. It remains the same. Currents are independent.

**13. a.**

**b.** $\dfrac{1}{R} = \dfrac{1}{60\ \Omega} + \dfrac{1}{60\ \Omega} = \dfrac{2}{60\ \Omega}$

$R = \dfrac{60\ \Omega}{2} = 30\ \Omega$

**c.** $R_{\text{eff}} = 30\ \Omega + 30\ \Omega = 60\ \Omega$

**d.** $I = \dfrac{V}{R} = \dfrac{120\ V}{60\ \Omega} = 2.0\ A$

**e.** $V_3 = IR_3 = (2.0)(30\ \Omega) = 60\ V$

**f.** $V = IR = (2.0\ A)(30\ \Omega) = 60\ V$

**g.** $I = \dfrac{V}{R_1} = \dfrac{V}{R_2} = \dfrac{60\ V}{60\ \Omega} = 1.0\ A$

**14. a.**

**b.** $\dfrac{1}{R} = \dfrac{1}{15\ \Omega} + \dfrac{1}{15\ \Omega} + \dfrac{1}{15\ \Omega} = \dfrac{3}{15\ \Omega}$

$R = \dfrac{15\ \Omega}{3} = 5.0\ \Omega$

**c.** $R_{\text{eff}} = 5\ \Omega + 10\ \Omega = 15\ \Omega$

**d.** $I = \dfrac{V}{R_{\text{eff}}} = \dfrac{45\ V}{15\ \Omega} = 3.0\ A$

**e.** $V = IR = (3.0\ A)(10\ \Omega) = 30\ V$

**15.** Series: $68\ \Omega + 68\ \Omega + 68\ \Omega = 204\ \Omega$
Parallel: $68\ \Omega/3 = 23\ \Omega$
Series parallel: $68\ \Omega + 68\ \Omega/2 = 102\ \Omega$

# Chapter 24

**1. a.** repulsive      **b.** attractive

**2.** south, north, south, north

**3.** The top face of the disk is the N-pole, so the direction of the field is up out of the N-pole.

**4.** the bottom (the point)

**5. a.** from south to north      **b.** west

**6.** Since magnetic field strength varies inversely with the distance from the wire, it will be
**a.** half as strong.
**b.** one-third as strong.

**7.** It will point toward the top of the page.

**8.** the pointed end

**9.** $F = BIL$,

$B = \dfrac{F}{IL} = \dfrac{0.04\ N}{(2.0\ A)(0.10\ m)} = 0.2\ T$

**10.** $F = BIL = (0.40\ N/A \cdot m)(8.0\ A)(0.50\ m)$
$= 1.6\ N$

**11.** $B = \dfrac{F}{IL} = \dfrac{0.60\ N}{(6.0\ A)(0.75\ m)} = 0.13\ T$

**12.** $F = BIL$, $F = $ weight of wire

$B = \dfrac{F}{IL} = \dfrac{0.35\ N}{(6.0\ A)(0.40\ m)} = 0.15\ T$

**13.** $F = Bqv$
$= (0.50\ T)(1.6 \times 10^{-19}\ C)(4.0 \times 10^6\ m/s)$
$= 3.2 \times 10^{-13}\ N$

**14.** $F = Bqv$
$= (9.0 \times 10^{-2}\ T)\ (2)\ (1.6 \times 10^{-19}\ C)$
$(3.0 \times 10^4\ m/s)$
$= 8.6 \times 10^{-16}\ N$

**15.** $F = Bqv$
$= (4.0 \times 10^{-2}\ T)(3)(1.6 \times 10^{-19}\ C)$
$(9.0 \times 10^6\ m/s)$
$= 1.7 \times 10^{-13}\ N$

**16.** $F = Bqv$
$= (5.0 \times 10^{-2}\ T)(2)(1.6 \times 10^{-19}\ C)$
$(4.0 \times 10^{-2}\ m/s)$
$= 6.4 \times 10^{-22}\ N$

# Chapter 25

**1. a.** $EMF = BLv$
$= (0.4\ N/A \cdot m)(0.5\ m)(20\ m/s) = 4\ V$

**b.** $I = \dfrac{V}{R} = \dfrac{4\ V}{6.0\ \Omega} = 0.7\ A$

**2.** $EMF = BLv$
$= (5.0 \times 10^{-5}\ T)(25\ m)(125\ m/s) = 0.16\ V$

**3.** Using the right-hand rule, the north pole is at the bottom.

**4. a.** $EMF = BLv = (1.0\ T)(30.0\ m)(2.0\ m/s)$
$= 60\ V$

   **b.** $I = \dfrac{V}{R} = \dfrac{60\ V}{15.0\ \Omega} = 4.0\ A$

**5. a.** $V_{eff} = (0.707)V_{max} = (0.707)(170\ V) = 120\ V$
   **b.** $I_{eff} = (0.707)I_{max} = (0.707)(0.70\ A) = 0.49\ A$

   **c.** $R = \dfrac{V_{eff}}{I_{eff}} = \dfrac{120\ V}{0.49\ A} = 240\ \Omega$

**6. a.** $V_{max} = \dfrac{V_{eff}}{0.707} = \dfrac{117\ V}{0.707} = 165\ V$

   **b.** $I_{max} = \dfrac{I_{eff}}{0.707} = \dfrac{5.5\ A}{0.707} = 7.8\ A$

**7. a.** $V_{eff} = (0.707)V_{max} = (0.707)(425\ V) = 300\ V$ or $3.00 \times 10^2\ V$
   **b.** $I_{eff} = V_{eff}/R = (300\ V)/(5.0 \times 10^2\ \Omega) = 0.60\ A$

**8.** Since $P = V_{eff}I_{eff} = (0.707\ V_{max})(0.707\ I_{max})$

$$= \dfrac{1}{2}\ P_{max},$$

$P_{max} = 2P = 2(100\ W)$
$= 200\ W$

**9. a.** $\dfrac{V_s}{V_p} = \dfrac{N_s}{N_p}$

$V_s = \dfrac{V_pN_s}{N_p} = \dfrac{(7200\ V)(125)}{7500}$
$= 120\ V$

   **b.** $V_pI_p = V_sI_s$

$I_p = \dfrac{V_sI_s}{V_p} = \dfrac{(120\ V)(36\ A)}{7200\ V}$
$= 0.60\ A$

**10. a.** $V_s = \dfrac{V_pN_s}{N_p} = \dfrac{(3600\ V)(500)}{15\ 000} = 120\ V$

   **b.** $I_s = \dfrac{V_pI_p}{V_s} = \dfrac{(3600\ V)(3.0\ A)}{120\ V} = 90\ A$

**11. a.** $\dfrac{V_p}{V_s} = \dfrac{N_p}{N_s}$

$V_s = \dfrac{V_pN_s}{N_p} = \dfrac{(120\ V)(15\ 000)}{500} = 3.60 \times 10^3\ V$

   **b.** $V_pI_p = V_sI_s$

$I_p = \dfrac{V_sI_s}{V_p} = \dfrac{(3600\ V)(3.0\ A)}{120\ V} = 90\ A$

   **c.** $V_pI_p = (120\ V)(90\ A) = 1.1 \times 10^4\ W$
$V_sI_s = (3600\ V)(3.0\ A) = 1.1 \times 10^4\ W$

**12. a.** $V_s = \dfrac{V_pN_s}{N_p} = \dfrac{(60.0\ V)(90\ 000)}{300} = 1.80 \times 10^4\ V$

   **b.** $I_p = \dfrac{V_sI_s}{V_p}$

$= \dfrac{(1.80 \times 10^4\ V)(0.50\ A)}{60.0\ V}$

$= 1.5 \times 10^2\ A$

# Chapter 26

**1.** $Bqv = Eq,$

$$v = \dfrac{E}{B} = \dfrac{4.5 \times 10^3\ N/C}{0.6\ T} = 8 \times 10^3\ m/s$$

**2.** $Bqv = \dfrac{mv^2}{r},$

$$r = \dfrac{mv}{Bq} = \dfrac{(1.7 \times 10^{-27}\ kg)(7.5 \times 10^3\ m/s)}{(0.6\ T)(1.6 \times 10^{-19}\ C)}$$
$$= 1 \times 10^{-4}\ m$$

**3.** $Bqv = Eq,$

$$v = \dfrac{E}{B} = \dfrac{3.0 \times 10^3\ N/C}{6.0 \times 10^{-2}\ T} = 5.0 \times 10^4\ m/s$$

**4.** $Bqv = \dfrac{mv^2}{r},$

$$r = \dfrac{mv}{Bq} = \dfrac{(9.11 \times 10^{-31}\ kg)(5.0 \times 10^4\ m/s)}{(6.0 \times 10^{-2}\ T)(1.6 \times 10^{-19}\ C)}$$
$$= 4.7 \times 10^{-6}\ m$$

**5. a.** $Bqv = Eq,$

$$v = \dfrac{E}{B} = \dfrac{6.0 \times 10^2\ N/C}{1.5 \times 10^{-3}\ T} = 4.0 \times 10^5\ m/s$$

   **b.** $Bqv = \dfrac{mv^2}{r},$

$$m = \dfrac{Bqr}{v} = \dfrac{(0.18\ T)(1.6 \times 10^{-19}\ C)(0.165\ m)}{4.0 \times 10^5\ m/s}$$
$$= 1.2 \times 10^{-26}\ kg$$

**6.** $m = \dfrac{B^2r^2q}{2V}$

$$= \dfrac{(5.0 \times 10^{-2}\ T)^2(0.106\ m)^2(2)(1.6 \times 10^{-19}\ C)}{2(66.0\ V)}$$

$$= 6.8 \times 10^{-26}\ kg$$

**7.** $m = B^2r^2q/2V$

$$= \dfrac{(7.2 \times 10^{-2}\ T)^2(0.085\ m)^2(1.6 \times 10^{-19}\ C)}{2(110\ V)}$$

$$= 2.7 \times 10^{-26}\ kg$$

**8.** Use $r = \frac{1}{B}\sqrt{\frac{2Vm}{q}}$ to find the ratio of radii of the two isotopes. If M represents number of proton masses, then $\frac{r_{22}}{r_{20}} = \sqrt{\frac{M_{22}}{M_{20}}}$, so $r_{22} = r_{20}(22/20)^{1/2} = 0.056$ m. Separation then is $2(0.056 \text{ m} - 0.053 \text{ m}) = 6$ mm.

# Chapter 27

**1.** $E_k = -qV_0 = -(-1.6 \times 10^{-19} \text{ C})(3.2 \text{ J/C})$
$= 5.1 \times 10^{-19}$ J

**2.** $E_k = -qV_0 = \frac{-(-1.6 \times 10^{-19} \text{ C})(5.7 \text{ J/C})}{(1.6 \times 10^{-19} \text{ J/eV})}$
$= 5.7$ eV

**3. a.** $c = f_0\lambda$
$f_0 = \frac{c}{\lambda} = \frac{3.00 \times 10^8 \text{ m/s}}{310 \times 10^{-9} \text{ m}} = 9.68 \times 10^{14}$ Hz

**b.** $hf_0 = (6.6 \times 10^{-34} \text{ J/Hz})(9.67 \times 10^{14} \text{ Hz})$
$= (6.4 \times 10^{-19} \text{ J})(1 \text{ eV}/1.6 \times 10^{-19} \text{ J})$
$= 4.0$ eV

**c.** $E_{k \text{ max}} = \frac{hc}{\lambda} - hf_0$
$= \frac{(6.6 \times 10^{-34} \text{ J/Hz})(3.00 \times 10^8 \text{ m/s})(1 \text{ eV}/1.6 \times 10^{-19} \text{ J})}{240 \times 10^{-9} \text{ m}} - 4.0 \text{ eV}$
$= 5.2 \text{ eV} - 4.0 \text{ eV} = 1.2$ eV

**4. a.** $E = \text{work function} = hf_0 = \frac{1240 \text{ eV} \cdot \text{nm}}{\lambda_0}$ where $\lambda_0$ has units of nm and $E$ has units of eV.
$\lambda_0 = (1240 \text{ eV} \cdot \text{nm})/E$
$= (1240 \text{ eV} \cdot \text{nm})/(1.96 \text{ eV}) = 633$ nm

**b.** $E_{k \text{ max}} = hf - hf_0 = E_{\text{photon}} - hf_0$
$= (1240 \text{ eV} \cdot \text{nm})/\lambda - hf_0$
$= (1240 \text{ eV} \cdot \text{nm})/(425 \text{ nm}) - 1.96 \text{ eV}$
$= 2.92 \text{ eV} - 1.96 \text{ eV} = 0.96$ eV

**5. a.** $\frac{1}{2}mv^2 = qV_0$,
$v^2 = 2qV_0/m$
$= 2(1.60 \times 10^{-19} \text{ C})(250 \text{ J/C})/(9.11 \times 10^{-31} \text{ kg})$
$= 8.78 \times 10^{13} \text{ m}^2/\text{s}^2$
$v = 9.4 \times 10^6$ m/s

**b.** $\lambda = h/mv$
$= (6.6 \times 10^{-34} \text{ J} \cdot \text{s})/(9.11 \times 10^{-31} \text{ kg}) \times (9.4 \times 10^6 \text{ m/s})$
$= 7.7 \times 10^{-11}$ m

**6. a.** $\lambda = \frac{h}{mv}$
$= \frac{6.6 \times 10^{-34} \text{ J} \cdot \text{s}}{(7.0 \text{ kg})(8.5 \text{ m/s})} = 1.1 \times 10^{-35}$ m

**b.** The wavelength is too small to show observable effects.

**7. a.** $p = \frac{h}{\lambda} = \frac{6.6 \times 10^{-34} \text{ J} \cdot \text{s}}{5.0 \times 10^{-12} \text{ m}}$
$= 1.3 \times 10^{-22} \text{ kg} \cdot \text{m/s}$

**b.** Its momentum is too small to affect objects of ordinary size.

**8. a.** They have momentum and energy, and they show wave behavior.

**b.** An electron has mass and charge, a photon does not.

# Chapter 28

**1.** Four times as large since orbit radius is proportional to $n^2$, when $n$ is the integer labelling the level.

**2.** $r_n = n^2k$, where $k = 5.3 \times 10^{-11}$ m
$r_2 = (2)^2(5.3 \times 10^{-11} \text{ m}) = 2.1 \times 10^{-10}$ m
$r_3 = (3)^2(5.3 \times 10^{-11} \text{ m}) = 4.8 \times 10^{-10}$ m
$r_4 = (4)^2(5.3 \times 10^{-11} \text{ m}) = 8.5 \times 10^{-10}$ m

**3.** $E_n = \frac{-13.6 \text{ eV}}{n^2}$
$E_2 = \frac{-13.6 \text{ eV}}{(2)^2} = -3.4$ eV
$E_3 = \frac{-13.6 \text{ eV}}{(3)^2} = -1.5$ eV
$E_4 = \frac{-13.6 \text{ eV}}{(4)^2} = -0.85$ eV

**4.** Using the results of Practice Exercise 3,
$E_3 - E_2 = (-1.5 \text{ eV}) - (-3.4 \text{ eV}) = 1.9$ eV
$E_4 - E_3 = (-0.85 \text{ eV}) - (-1.5 \text{ eV}) = 0.7$ eV

# Chapter 29

**1.** free $e^-/\text{cm}^3$
$= \frac{(2 \text{ e}^-/\text{atom})(6.02 \times 10^{23} \text{ atoms/mole})(7.13 \text{ g/cm}^3)}{(65.37 \text{ g/mole})}$
$= 1.31 \times 10^{23}$ free $e^-/\text{cm}^3$

**2.** atoms/cm³

$$= \frac{(6.02 \times 10^{23} \text{ atoms/mol})(5.23 \text{ g/cm}^3)}{(72.6 \text{ g/mol})}$$

$$= 4.34 \times 10^{22} \text{ atoms/cm}^3$$

$$\text{free } e^-/\text{atom} = \frac{(2 \times 10^{16} \text{ free } e^-/\text{cm}^3)}{(4.34 \times 10^{22} \text{ atoms/cm}^3)}$$

$$= 5 \times 10^{-7}$$

**3.** There were $5 \times 10^{-7}$ free $e^-$/Ge atoms, so we need $5 \times 10^3$ as many As dopant atoms, or $2 \times 10^{-3}$ As atoms/Ge atoms.

**4.** At $I = 2.5$ mA, $V_d = 0.6$ V, so
$$V = V_d + IR$$
$$= 0.6 \text{ V} + (2.5 \times 10^{-3} \text{ A})(470 \ \Omega) = 1.8 \text{ V}.$$

**5.** $V = V_d + IR$
$$= 0.4 \text{ V} + (1.2 \times 10^{-2} \text{ A})(470 \ \Omega) = 6.0 \text{ V}$$

# Chapter 30

**1.** $A - Z = 15 - 8 = 7$ neutrons

**2.** $A - Z$ = neutrons
$234 - 92 = 142$ neutrons
$235 - 92 = 143$ neutrons
$238 - 92 = 146$ neutrons

**3.** $A - Z = 200 - 80 = 120$ neutrons

**4.** $^1_1\text{H}, \ ^2_1\text{H}, \ ^3_1\text{H}$

**5.** $^{234}_{92}\text{U} \rightarrow \ ^{230}_{90}\text{Th} + \ ^4_2\text{He}$

**6.** $^{230}_{90}\text{Th} \rightarrow \ ^{226}_{88}\text{Ra} + \ ^4_2\text{He}$

**7.** $^{226}_{88}\text{Ra} \rightarrow \ ^{222}_{86}\text{Rn} + \ ^4_2\text{He}$

**8.** $^{214}_{82}\text{Pb} \rightarrow \ ^{214}_{83}\text{Bi} + \ ^0_{-1}e + \ ^0_0\bar{v}$

**9.** 24.6 years = 2(12.3 years) which is 2 half-lives.

Since $\frac{1}{2} \times \frac{1}{2} = \frac{1}{4}$, there will be

$(1.0 \text{ g})\left(\dfrac{1}{4}\right) = 0.25$ g remaining.

**10.** Amount remaining = (original amount $\left(\dfrac{1}{2}\right)^N$,

where $N$ is the number of half-lives elapsed.
Since $N = 8$ d/2.0 d = 4,

amount remaining $= (4.0 \text{ g}) \left(\dfrac{1}{2}\right)^4 = 0.25$ g

**11.** The half-life of $^{220}_{84}\text{Po}$ is 138 d.
There are 273 d or about 2 half-lives between September 1 and June 1.
So the activity is

$$= \left(2 \times 10^6 \frac{\text{decays}}{\text{s}}\right)\left(\frac{1}{2}\right)\left(\frac{1}{2}\right) = 5 \times 10^5 \frac{\text{decays}}{\text{s}}$$

**12.** From Table 30−1, 6 years is approximately 0.5 half-life for tritium. Since Figure 30−5 indicates that approximately $\dfrac{11}{16}$ of the original nuclei remain after 0.5 half-life, the brightness will be about $\dfrac{11}{16}$ of the original.

**13. a.** $E = mc^2$
$$= (1.67 \times 10^{-27} \text{ kg})(3.00 \times 10^8 \text{ m/s})^2$$
$$= 1.50 \times 10^{-10} \text{ J}$$

**b.** $E = \dfrac{1.50 \times 10^{-10} \text{ J}}{1.60 \times 10^{-19} \text{ J/eV}}$

$$= 9.38 \times 10^8 \text{ eV}$$
$$= 938 \text{ MeV}$$

**c.** The pair will be (2)(938 MeV) = 1.88 GeV.

# Chapter 31

**1. a.**

| | |
|---|---:|
| 6 protons = (6)(1.007825 u) = | 6.046950 u |
| 6 neutrons = (6)(1.008665 u) = | 6.051990 u |
| total | 12.098940 u |
| mass of carbon nucleus | −12.000000 u |
| mass defect | −0.098940 u |

**b.** −(0.098940 u)(931.49 MeV/u) = −92.162 MeV

**2. a.**

| | |
|---|---:|
| 1 proton = | 0.007825 u |
| 1 neutron = | 1.008665 u |
| | 2.016490 u |
| mass of deuterium nucleus = | −2.0140 u |
| mass defect | −0.0025 u |

**b.** −(0.0025 u)(931.49 MeV/u) = −2.3 MeV

**3. a.**

| | |
|---|---:|
| 7 protons = 7(1.007825 u) = | 7.054775 u |
| 8 neutrons = 8(1.008665 u) = | 8.069320 u |
| total | 15.124095 u |
| mass of nitrogen nucleus | −15.00011 u |
| mass defect | −0.123985 u |
| | −0.12399 u |

**b.** −(0.12399 u)(931.49 MeV/u) = −115.50 MeV

**4. a.**

$$
\begin{array}{lrr}
\text{8 protons} = 8(1.007825\ \text{u}) = & 8.062600\ \text{u} \\
\text{8 neutrons} = 8(1.008665\ \text{u}) = & \underline{8.069320}\ \text{u} \\
\text{total} & 16.131920\ \text{u} \\
\text{mass of oxygen nucleus} & \underline{-15.99491}\ \ \text{u} \\
\text{mass defect} & -0.13701\ \text{u}
\end{array}
$$

**b.** $-(0.13701\ \text{u})(931.49\ \text{MeV/u}) = -127.62\ \text{MeV}$

**5. a.** $^{14}_{6}\text{C} \rightarrow {}^{14}_{7}\text{N} + {}^{\ \ 0}_{-1}\text{e}$
**b.** $^{55}_{24}\text{Cr} \rightarrow {}^{55}_{25}\text{Mn} + {}^{\ \ 0}_{-1}\text{e}$

**6. a.** $^{238}_{92}\text{U} \rightarrow {}^{234}_{90}\text{Th} + {}^{4}_{2}\text{He}$

**7.** $^{214}_{84}\text{Po} \rightarrow {}^{210}_{82}\text{Pb} + {}^{4}_{2}\text{He}$

**8. a.** $^{210}_{82}\text{Pb} \rightarrow {}^{210}_{83}\text{Bi} + {}^{\ \ 0}_{-1}\text{e}$
**b.** $^{210}_{83}\text{Bi} \rightarrow {}^{210}_{84}\text{Po} + {}^{\ \ 0}_{-1}\text{e}$
**c.** $^{234}_{90}\text{Th} \rightarrow {}^{234}_{91}\text{Pa} + {}^{\ \ 0}_{-1}\text{e}$
**d.** $^{239}_{93}\text{Np} \rightarrow {}^{239}_{94}\text{Pu} + {}^{\ \ 0}_{-1}\text{e}$

**9. a.** Input masses $2.014102\ \text{u} + 3.016049\ \text{u}$
$= 5.030151\ \text{u}$
Output masses $4.002603\ \text{u} + 1.008665\ \text{u}$
$= 5.011268\ \text{u}$
Difference is $-0.018883\ \text{u}$
**b.** $-(0.018883\ \text{u})(931.49\ \text{MeV/u}) = -17.589\ \text{MeV}$

**10.** Positron mass

$$
= (9.109 \times 10^{-31}\ \text{kg})\left(\frac{1\ \text{u}}{1.661 \times 10^{-27}\ \text{kg}}\right)
$$

$= 0.000548\ \text{u}$
Input mass: 4 protons $= 4(1.007825\ \text{u})$
$= 4.031300\ \text{u}$

Output mass:
$^{4}_{2}\text{He}$ + 2 positrons $= 4.002603\ \text{u} + 2(0.000548\ \text{u})$
$= 4.003699$

Mass difference $= 0.027601\ \text{u}$
Energy released $= (0.027601\ \text{u})(931.49\ \text{MeV/u})$
$= 25.710\ \text{MeV}$

# Appendix B
## Supplemental Problems

*There are no supplemental problems for Chapter 1.*

## Chapter 2

1. Express the following numbers in scientific notation.
   a. 810 000 g
   b. 0.000634 g
   c. 60 000 000 g
   d. 0.0000010 g

2. Convert each of the following time measurements to its equivalent in seconds.
   a. 58 ns
   b. 0.046 Gs
   c. 9270 ms
   d. 12.3 ks

3. Solve the following problems. Express your answers in scientific notation.
   a. $6.2 \times 10^{-4}$ m + $5.7 \times 10^{-3}$ m
   b. $8.7 \times 10^{8}$ km − $3.4 \times 10^{7}$ km
   c. $(9.21 \times 10^{-5}$ cm$)$ $(1.83 \times 10^{8}$ cm$)$
   d. $(2.63 \times 10^{-6}$ m$)$ ÷ $(4.08 \times 10^{6}$ s$)$

4. State the number of significant digits in the following measurements.
   a. 3218 kg
   b. 60.080 kg
   c. 801 kg
   d. 0.000534 kg

5. State the number of significant digits in the following measurements.
   a. $5.60 \times 10^{8}$ m
   b. $3.0005 \times 10^{-6}$ m
   c. $8.0 \times 10^{10}$ m
   d. $9.204 \times 10^{-3}$ m

6. Add or subtract as indicated and state the answer with the correct number of significant digits.
   a. 85.26 g + 4.7 g
   b. 1.07 km + 0.608 km
   c. 186.4 kg − 57.83 kg
   d. 60.08 s − 12.2 s

7. Multiply or divide as indicated using significant digits correctly.
   a. $(5 \times 10^{8}$ m$)$ $(4.2 \times 10^{7}$ m$)$
   b. $(1.67 \times 10^{-2}$ km$)$ $(8.5 \times 10^{-6}$ km$)$
   c. $(2.6 \times 10^{4}$ kg$)$ ÷ $(9.4 \times 10^{3}$ m³$)$
   d. $(6.3 \times 10^{-1}$ m$)$ ÷ $(3.8 \times 10^{2}$ s$)$

8. A rectangular room is 8.7 m by 2.41 m.
   a. What length of baseboard molding must be purchased to go around the perimeter of the floor?
   b. What area must be covered if floor tiles are laid?

▶ 9. The following data table was established showing the total distances an object fell during various lengths of time.

| Time (s) | Distance (m) |
|----------|--------------|
| 1.0 | 5 |
| 2.0 | 20 |
| 3.0 | 44 |
| 4.0 | 78 |
| 5.0 | 123 |

   a. Plot distance vs time from the values given in the table and draw a curve that best fits all points.
   b. Describe the resulting curve.
   c. According to the graph, what is the relationship between distance and time for a free-falling object?

▶ 10. The total distance a lab cart travels during specified lengths of time is given in the following table.

| Time (s) | Distance (m) |
|----------|--------------|
| 1.0 | 0.32 |
| 2.0 | 0.60 |
| 3.0 | 0.95 |
| 4.0 | 1.18 |
| 5.0 | 1.45 |

   a. Plot distance vs time from the values given in the table and draw the curve that best fits all points.
   b. Describe the resulting curve.
   c. According to the graph, what type of relationship exists between the total distance traveled by the lab cart and the time?
   d. What is the slope of this graph?
   e. Write an equation relating distance and time for this data.

11. Solve the equation

$$F = \frac{mv^2}{r}$$

   a. for $m$.　　b. for $r$.　　c. for $v$.

▶ 12. Solve the equation for $d_o$.

$$\frac{1}{f} = \frac{1}{d_o} + \frac{1}{d_i}$$

**13.** A cube has an edge of length 5.2 cm.
  **a.** Find its surface area.
  **b.** Find its volume.

**14.** A truck is traveling at a constant velocity of 70 km/h. Convert the velocity to m/s.

**15.** The density of gold is 19.3 g/cm³. A gold washer has an outside radius of 4.3 cm and an inside radius of 2.1 cm. Its thickness is 0.14 cm. What is the mass of the washer?

## Chapter 3 _____

**1.** Bob walks 80 m and then he walks 125 m.
  **a.** What is Bob's displacement if he walks east both times?
  **b.** What is Bob's displacement if he walks east then west?
  **c.** What distance does Bob walk in each case?

**2.** A cross-country runner runs 5.0 km east along the course, then turns around and runs 5.0 km west along the same path. She returns to the starting point in 40 min. What is her average speed? her average velocity?

**3.** 0.30 s after seeing a puff of smoke rise from the starter's pistol, the sound of the firing of the pistol is heard by the track timer 100 m away. What is the velocity of sound?

▶ **4.** The radius of the tires on a particular vehicle is 0.62 m. If the tires are rotating 5 times per second, what is the velocity of the vehicle?

**5.** A bullet is fired with a speed of 720.0 m/s.
  **a.** What time is required for the bullet to strike a target 324 m away?
  **b.** What is the velocity in km/h?

**6.** Light travels at $3.0 \times 10^8$ m/s. How many seconds go by from the moment the starter's pistol is shot until the smoke is seen by the track timer 100 m away?

▶ **7.** You drive your car from home at an average velocity of 80 km/h for 3 h. Halfway to your destination, you develop some engine problems, and for 5 h you nurse the car the rest of the way. What is your average velocity for the entire trip?

▶ **8.** The total distance a ball is off the ground when thrown vertically is given for each second of flight by the following table.

| Time (s) | Distance (m) |
|---|---|
| 0.0 | 0.0 |
| 1.0 | 24.5 |
| 2.0 | 39.2 |
| 3.0 | 44.1 |
| 4.0 | 39.2 |
| 5.0 | 24.5 |
| 6.0 | 0.0 |

  **a.** Draw a position-time graph of the motion of the ball.
  **b.** How far off the ground is the ball at the end of 0.5 s? When would the ball again be this distance from the ground?

**9.** Use the following position-time graph to find how far the object travels between
  **a.** $t = 0$ s and $t = 5$ s.
  **b.** $t = 5$ s and $t = 10$ s.
  **c.** $t = 10$ s and $t = 15$ s.
  **d.** $t = 15$ s and $t = 20$ s.
  **e.** $t = 0$ s and $t = 20$ s.

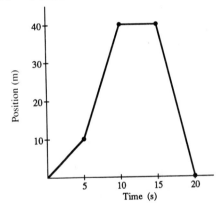

**10.** Use the position-time graph from problem 9 to find the object's velocity between
  **a.** $t = 0$ s and $t = 5$ s.
  **b.** $t = 5$ s and $t = 10$ s.
  **c.** $t = 10$ s and $t = 15$ s.
  **d.** $t = 15$ s and $t = 20$ s.

**11.** Two cars are headed in the same direction; one travelling 60 km/h is 20 km ahead of the other travelling 80 km/h.
  **a.** Draw a position-time graph showing the motion of the cars.
  **b.** Use your graph to find the time when the faster car overtakes the slower one.

**12.** Use your graph from Problem 8 to calculate the ball's instantaneous velocity at
  **a.** $t = 2$ s.    **b.** $t = 3$ s.    **c.** $t = 4$ s.

**13.** A plane flies in a straight line at a constant velocity of +75 m/s. Assume that it is at the reference point when the clock reads $t = 0$.

    **a.** Construct a table showing the position or displacement of the plane at the end of each second for a 10-s period.

    **b.** Use the data from the table to plot a position-time graph.

    **c.** Show that the slope of the line is the velocity of the plane. Use at least two different sets of points along the line.

    **d.** Plot a velocity-time graph of the plane's motion for the first 6 s of the 10-s interval.

    **e.** From the velocity-time graph, find the displacement of the plane between the second and the sixth period.

**14.** Mary jogs for 15 min at 240 m/min, walks the next 10 min at 90 m/min, rests for 5 min, and jogs back to where she started at −180 m/min.

    **a.** Plot a velocity-time graph for Mary's exercise run.

    **b.** Find the area under the curve for the first 15 min. What does this represent?

    **c.** What is the total distance travelled by Mary?

    **d.** What is Mary's displacement from start to finish?

**15.** Car A is travelling at 85 km/h while car B is at 60 km/h. What is the relative velocity of car A to car B

    **a.** if they both are travelling in the same direction?

    **b.** if they are headed towards each other?

# Chapter 4

**1.** From the moment a 40 m/s fastball touches the catcher's mitt until it is completely stopped takes 0.012 s. Calculate the average acceleration of the ball as it is being caught.

**2.** The following velocity-time graph describes a familiar motion of a car traveling during rush-hour traffic.

    **a.** Describe the car's motion from $t = 0$ s to $t = 4$ s.

    **b.** Describe the car's motion from $t = 4$ s to $t = 6$ s.

    **c.** What is the average acceleration for the first 4 s?

    **d.** What is the average acceleration from $t = 4$ s to $t = 6$ s?

**3.** Given the following table:

| Time (s) | Velocity (m/s) |
|----------|----------------|
| 0.0 | 0.0 |
| 1.0 | 5.0 |
| 2.0 | 20.0 |
| 3.0 | 45.0 |
| 4.0 | 80.0 |

    **a.** Plot a velocity-time graph for this motion.

    **b.** Is this motion constant velocity? uniform acceleration?

    **c.** Calculate the instantaneous acceleration at $t = 3.0$ s.

**4.** Top-fuel drag racers are able to uniformly accelerate at 12.5 m/s² from rest to 100 m/s before crossing the finish line. How much time elapses during the run?

**5.** A race car accelerates from rest at +7.5 m/s² for 4.5 s. How fast will it be going at the end of that time?

**6.** A race car starts from rest and is accelerated uniformly to +41 m/s in 8.0 s. What is the car's displacement?

**7.** A jet plane travelling at +88 m/s lands on a runway and comes to rest in 11 s.

    **a.** Calculate its uniform acceleration.

    **b.** Calculate the displacement it travels.

**8.** A bullet accelerates at $6.8 \times 10^4$ m/s² from rest as it travels the 0.80 m of the rifle barrel.

    **a.** How long was the bullet in the barrel?

    **b.** What velocity does the bullet have as it leaves the barrel?

**9.** A car travelling at 14 m/s encounters a patch of ice and takes 5.0 s to stop.

    **a.** What is the car's acceleration?

    **b.** How far does it travel before stopping?

**10.** A motorcycle travelling at 16 m/s accelerates at a constant rate of 4.0 m/s² over 50 m. What is its final velocity?

**11.** A hockey player skating at 18 m/s comes to a complete stop in 2.0 m. What is the acceleration of the hockey player?

**12.** Police find skid marks 60 m long on a highway showing where a car made an emergency stop. Assuming that the acceleration was −10 m/s² (about the maximum for dry pavement), how fast was the car going? Was the car exceeding the 80 km/h speed limit?

**13.** An accelerating lab cart passes through two photo gate timers 3.0 m apart in 4.2 s. The velocity of the cart at the second timer is 1.2 m/s.
 **a.** What is the cart's velocity at the first gate?
 **b.** What is the acceleration?

**14.** A camera is accidentally dropped from the edge of a cliff and 6.0 s later hits the bottom.
 **a.** How fast was it going just before it hit?
 **b.** How high is the cliff?

▶ **15.** A rock is thrown vertically with a velocity of 20 m/s from the edge of a bridge 42 m above a river. How long does the rock stay in the air?

▶ **16.** A platform diver jumps vertically with a velocity of 4.2 m/s. The diver enters the water 2.5 s later. How high is the platform above the water?

# Chapter 5

**1.** A towrope is used to pull a 1750-kg car, giving it an acceleration of 1.35 m/s$^2$. What force does the rope exert?

**2.** A racing car undergoes a uniform acceleration of 4.00 m/s$^2$. If the net force causing the acceleration is $3.00 \times 10^3$ N, what is the mass of the car?

▶ **3.** A 5.2-kg bowling ball is accelerated from rest to a velocity of 12 m/s as the bowler covers 5.0 m of approach before releasing the ball. What force is exerted on the ball during this time?

▶ **4.** A high jumper, falling at 4.0 m/s, lands on a foam pit and comes to rest, compressing the pit 0.40 m. If the pit is able to exert an average force of 1200 N on the high jumper in breaking the fall, what is the jumper's mass?

**5.** When a 20-kg child steps off a 3.0-kg stationary skateboard with an acceleration of 0.50 m/s$^2$, with what acceleration will the skateboard travel in the opposite direction?

**6.** On Planet X, a 50-kg barbell can be lifted by only exerting a force of 180 N.
 **a.** What is the acceleration of gravity on Planet X?
 **b.** If the same barbell is lifted on Earth, what minimal force is needed?

**7.** A proton has a mass of $1.672 \times 10^{-27}$ kg. What is its weight?

**8.** A force of 20 N accelerates a 9.0-kg wagon at 2.0 m/s$^2$ along the sidewalk.
 **a.** How large is the frictional force?
 **b.** What is the coefficient of friction?

**9.** A 2.0-kg brick has a sliding coefficient of friction of 0.38. What force must be applied to the brick for it to move at a constant velocity?

**10.** In bench pressing 100 kg, a weight lifter applies a force of 1040 N. How large is the upward acceleration of the weights during the lift?

▶ **11.** An elevator that weighs $3.0 \times 10^3$ N is accelerated upward at 1.0 m/s$^2$. What force does the cable exert to give it this acceleration?

▶ **12.** A person weighing 490 N stands on a scale in an elevator.
 **a.** What does the scale read when the elevator is at rest?
 **b.** What is the reading on the scale when the elevator rises at a constant velocity?
 **c.** The elevator slows down at $-2.2$ m/s$^2$ as it reaches the desired floor. What does the scale read?
 **d.** The elevator descends, accelerating at $-2.7$ m/s$^2$. What does the scale read?
 **e.** What does the scale read when the elevator descends at a constant velocity?
 **f.** Suppose the cable snapped and the elevator fell freely. What would the scale read?

▶ **13.** A 10.0-kg mass, $m_1$, on a frictionless table is accelerated by a 5.0-kg mass, $m_2$, hanging over the edge of the table. What is the acceleration of the mass along the table?

# Chapter 6

**1.** Find $\theta$ if
 **a.** $\tan \theta = 9.5143$.
 **b.** $\sin \theta = .4540$.
 **c.** $\cos \theta = .8192$.
 **d.** $\tan \theta = .1405$.
 **e.** $\sin \theta = .7547$.
 **f.** $\cos \theta = .9781$.

**2.** Find the value of:
 **a.** $\tan 28°$.
 **b.** $\sin 86°$.
 **c.** $\cos 2°$.
 **d.** $\tan 58°$.
 **e.** $\sin 40°$.
 **f.** $\cos 71°$.

3. Solve for all sides and all angles for the following right triangles.

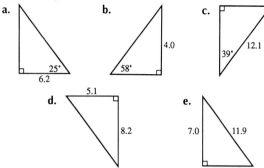

a.

b.

4.0

58°

c.

39°

12.1

25°

6.2

d.

5.1

8.2

e.

7.0

11.9

4. An 80-N and a 60-N force act concurrently on a point. Find the magnitude of the vector sum if the forces pull
   a. in the same direction.
   b. in opposite directions.
   c. at a right angle to each other.

▶ 5. You head downstream on a river in an outboard. The current is flowing at a rate of 1.50 m/s. After 30.0 min, you find that you have traveled 24.3 km. How long will it take you to travel back upstream to your original point of departure?

6. One force of 60 N and a second of 30 N act on an object at point **P**. Graphically add the vectors and find the magnitude of the resultant when the angle between them is as follows.
   a. 0° b. 30° c. 45° d. 60° e. 90° f. 180°

7. You walk 30 m south and 30 m east. Draw and add vectors representing these two displacements.

8. A plane flying at 90° at $1.00 \times 10^2$ m/s is blown toward 180° at $5.0 \times 10^1$ m/s by a strong wind. Find the plane's resultant velocity and direction.

9. In tackling a running back from the opposing team, a defensive lineman exerts a force of 500 N at 180°, while a linebacker simultaneously applies a force of 650 N at 270°. What is the resultant force on the ball carrier?

▶ 10. A person rides in a freight car 15 m long and 3.0 m wide. The car is moving east at 2.5 m/s. Exploring the surroundings, he walks from corner A to corner B in 20.0 s; then from corner B to corner C in 5.0 s as shown. With the aid of a vector diagram, compute his displacement relative to the ground.

C

3.0 m

East

B

15.0 m

A

11. A plane travels on a heading of 40.0° for a displacement of $3.00 \times 10^2$ km. How far north and how far east does the plane travel?

12. A water skier is towed by a speedboat. The skier moves to one side of the boat in such a way that the tow rope forms an angle of 55° with the direction of the boat. The tension on the rope is 350 N. What would be the tension on the rope if the skier were directly behind the boat?

13. What are the x and y components of a velocity vector of magnitude 100 km/h and direction of 240°?

14. Wendy pushes a lawn spreader across a lawn by applying a force of 95 N along the handle that makes an angle of 60.0° with the horizontal.
   a. What are the horizontal and vertical components of the force?
   b. The handle is lowered so it makes an angle of 30.0° with the horizontal. Now what are the horizontal and vertical components of the force?

▶ 15. A brick layer applies a force of 100 N to each of two handles of a wheelbarrow. Its mass is 20 kg and it is loaded with 30 bricks, each of mass 1.5 kg. The handles of the wheelbarrow are 30° from the horizontal and the coefficient of friction is 0.20. What initial acceleration is given the wheelbarrow?

16. Two 15-N forces act concurrently on point **P**. Find the magnitude of their resultant when the angle between them is
   a. 0.0°. b. 30.0°. c. 90.0°. d. 120.0°. e. 180.0°.

▶ 17. You are a pilot on an aircraft carrier. You must fly to another aircraft carrier, now 1450 km at 45° of your position, moving at 56 km/h due east. The wind is blowing from the south at 72 km/h. Calculate the heading and air speed needed to reach the carrier 2.5 h after you take off. **Hint:** Draw a displacement vector diagram.

▶ 18. A 33-N force acting at 90° and a 44-N force acting at 60° act concurrently on point **P**. What is the magnitude and direction of a third force that produces equilibrium at point **P**?

▶ 19. A person weighs 612 N. If the person sits in the middle of a hammock that is 3.0 m long and sags 1.0 m below the points of support, what force would be exerted by each of the two hammock ropes?

▶ 20. A bell ringer decides to use a bowling ball to ring the bell. He hangs the 7.3-kg ball from the end of a 2.0 m long rope. He attaches another rope to the ball to pull the ball back, and pulls it horizontally until the ball has moved 0.60 m away from the vertical. How much force must he apply?

▶ **21.** A mass, $M$, starts from rest and slides down the frictionless incline, Figure 6–19. As it leaves the incline, its speed is 24 m/s.
  **a.** What is the acceleration of the mass while on the incline?
  **b.** What is the length of the incline?
  **c.** How long does it take the mass to reach the floor after it leaves the top of the incline?

# Chapter 7

**1.** A ball falls from rest from a height of 490 m.
  **a.** How long does it remain in the air?
  **b.** If the ball has a horizontal velocity of $2.00 \times 10^2$ m/s when it begins its fall, what horizontal displacement will it have?

▶ **2.** An archer stands 40.0 m from the target. If the arrow is shot horizontally with a velocity of 90.0 m/s, how far above the bull's-eye must he aim to compensate for gravity pulling his arrow downward?

**3.** A bridge is 176.4 m above a river. If a lead-weighted fishing line is thrown from the bridge with a horizontal velocity of 22.0 m/s, how far has it moved horizontally when it hits the water?

**4.** A beach ball, moving with a speed of $+1.27$ m/s, rolls off a pier and hits the water 0.75 m from the end of the pier. How high above the water is the pier?

**5.** Pete has a tendency to drop his bowling ball on his release. Instead of having the ball on the floor at the completion of his swing, Pete lets go with the ball 0.35 m above the floor. If he throws it horizontally with a velocity of 6.3 m/s, what distance does it travel before you hear a "thud"?

**6.** A discus is released at an angle of 45° and a velocity of 24.0 m/s.
  **a.** How long does it stay in the air?
  **b.** What horizontal displacement does it travel?

▶ **7.** A shot put is released with a velocity of 12 m/s and stays in the air for 2.0 s.
  **a.** At what angle with the horizontal was it released?
  **b.** What horizontal displacement did it travel?

▶ **8.** A football is kicked at 45° and travels 82 m before hitting the ground.
  **a.** What was its initial velocity?
  **b.** How long was it in the air?
  **c.** How high did it go?

**9.** A golf ball is hit with a velocity of 24.5 m/s at 35.0° above the horizontal. Find
  **a.** the range of the ball.
  **b.** the maximum height of the ball.

▶ **10.** A carnival clown rides a motorcycle down a ramp and around a "loop-the-loop." If the loop has a radius of 18 m, what is the slowest speed the rider can have at the top of the loop to avoid falling? **Hint:** At this slowest speed, at the top of the loop, the clown's weight is equal to the centripetal force.

▶ **11.** A 75-kg pilot flies a plane in a loop. At the top of the loop, where the plane is completely upside-down for an instant, the pilot hangs freely in the seat and does not push against the seat belt. The airspeed indicator reads 120 m/s. What is the radius of the plane's loop?

▶ **12.** A 2.0-kg object is attached to a 1.5 m long string and swung in a vertical circle at a constant speed of 12 m/s.
  **a.** What is the tension in the string when the object is at the bottom of its path?
  **b.** What is the tension in the string when the object is at the top of its path?

**13.** A 60.0-kg speed skater with a velocity of 18.0 m/s comes into a curve of 20.0-m radius. How much friction must be exerted between the skates and ice to negotiate the curve?

**14.** A 20.0-kg child wishes to balance on a seesaw with a child of 32.0 kg. If the smaller child sits 3.2 m from the pivot, where must the larger child sit?

**15.** A pendulum has a length of 1.00 m.
  **a.** What is its period on Earth?
  **b.** What is its period on the moon where the acceleration due to gravity is 1.67 m/s²?

**16.** The period of an object oscillating on a spring is

$$T = 2\pi\sqrt{\frac{m}{k}},$$

where $m$ is the mass of the object and $k$ is the spring constant which indicates the force necessary to produce a unit elongation of the spring. The period of a simple pendulum is

$$T = 2\pi\sqrt{\frac{l}{|g|}}.$$

a. What mass will produce a 1.0-s period of oscillation if it is attached to a spring with a spring constant of 4.0 N/m?

b. What length pendulum will produce a period of 1.0 s?

c. How would the harmonic oscillator and the pendulum have to be modified in order to produce 1.0-s periods on the surface of the moon where $g$ is 1.6 m/s²?

## Chapter 8

**1.** Comet Halley returns every 76 years. Find the average distance of the comet from the sun.

**2.** Area is measured in m², so the rate at which area is swept out by a planet or satellite is measured in m²/s.

a. How fast is area swept out by Earth in its orbit about the sun? See table 8–1.

b. How fast is area swept out by the moon in its orbit about Earth? Use $3.9 \times 10^8$ m as the average distance between the Earth and the moon, and 27.3 days as the moon's period.

**3.** You wish to launch a satellite that will remain above the same spot on Earth's surface. This means the satellite must have a period of exactly one day. Calculate the radius of the circular orbit this satellite must have. **Hint:** The moon also circles Earth and both the moon and the satellite will obey Kepler's third law. The moon is $3.8 \times 10^8$ m from Earth and its period is 27.33 days.

**4.** The mass of an electron is $9.1 \times 10^{-31}$ kg. The mass of a proton is $1.7 \times 10^{-27}$ kg. They are about $1.0 \times 10^{-10}$ m apart in a hydrogen atom. What gravitational force exists between the proton and the electron of a hydrogen atom?

**5.** Two 1.00-kg masses have their centres 1.00 m apart. What is the force of attraction between them?

**6.** Two satellites of equal mass are put into orbit 30 m apart. The gravitational force between them is $2.0 \times 10^{-7}$ N.

a. What is the mass of each satellite?

b. What is the initial acceleration given to each satellite by the gravitational force?

**7.** Two large spheres are suspended close to each other. Their centres are 4.0 m apart. One sphere weighs $9.8 \times 10^2$ N. The other sphere has a weight of $1.96 \times 10^2$ N. What is the gravitational force between them?

**8.** If the centres of Earth and the moon are $3.9 \times 10^8$ m apart, the gravitational force between them is about $1.9 \times 10^{20}$ N. What is the approximate mass of the moon?

**9. a.** What is the gravitational force between two spherical 8.00-kg masses that are 5.0 m apart?

**b.** What is the gravitational force between them when they are $5.0 \times 10^1$ m apart?

**10.** A satellite is placed in a circular orbit with a radius of $1.0 \times 10^7$ m a period of $9.9 \times 10^3$ s. Calculate the mass of Earth. **Hint:** Gravity supplies the needed centripetal force for such a satellite. Scientists have actually measured the mass of Earth this way.

**11.** If you weigh 637 N on Earth's surface, how much would you weigh on the planet Mars? (Mars has a mass of $6.37 \times 10^{23}$ kg and a radius of $3.43 \times 10^6$ m.)

**12.** Using Newton's variation of Kepler's third law and information from Table 8–1, calculate the period of Earth's moon if the radius of orbit was twice the actual value of $3.9 \times 10^8$ m.

**13.** Use the data from Table 8–1 to find the speed and period of a satellite that would orbit Mars 175 km above its surface.

**14.** What would be the value of $g$, acceleration of gravity, if Earth's mass was double its actual value, but its radius remained the same? If the radius was doubled, but the mass remained the same? If both the mass and radius were doubled?

**15.** What would be the strength of Earth's gravitational field at a point where an 80.0-kg astronaut would experience a 25% reduction in weight?

**16.** On the surface of the moon, a 91.0-kg physics teacher weighs only 145.6 N. What is the value of the moon's gravitational field at its surface?

# Chapter 9

1. Jim strikes a 0.058-kg golf ball with a force of 272 N and gives it a velocity of 62.0 m/s. How long was the club in contact with the ball?

2. A force of 186 N acts on a 7.3-kg bowling ball for 0.40 s.
   a. What is the bowling ball's change in momentum?
   b. What is its change in velocity?

3. A 5500-kg freight truck accelerates from 4.2 m/s to 7.8 m/s in 15.0 s by applying a constant force.
   a. What change in momentum occurs?
   b. How large of a force is exerted?

▶ 4. In running a ballistics test at the police department, officer Spears fires a 6.0-g bullet at 350 m/s into a container that stops it in 0.30 m. What average force stops the bullet?

5. A 0.24-kg volleyball approaches Jennifer with a velocity of 3.8 m/s. Jennifer bumps the ball giving it a velocity of −2.4 m/s. What average force did she apply if the interaction time between her hands and the ball is 0.025 s?

6. A 0.145-kg baseball is pitched at 42 m/s. The batter hits it horizontally to the pitcher at 58 m/s.
   a. Find the change in momentum of the ball.
   b. If the ball and bat were in contact $4.6 \times 10^{-4}$ s, what would be the average force while they touched?

7. A 550-kg car travelling at 24.0 m/s collides head-on with a 680-kg pick-up truck. Both vehicles come to a complete stop upon impact.
   a. What is the momentum of the car before collision?
   b. What is the change in the car's momentum?
   c. What is the change in the truck's momentum?
   d. What is the velocity of the truck before collision?

8. A truck weighs four times as much as a car. If the truck coasts into the car at 12 km/h and they stick together, what is their final velocity?

9. A 50.0-g projectile is launched with a horizontal velocity of 647 m/s from a 4.65-kg launcher moving in the same direction at 2.00 m/s. What is the velocity of the launcher after the projectile is launched?

10. Two lab carts are pushed together with a spring mechanism compressed between them. Upon release, the 5.0-kg cart repels one way with a velocity of 0.12 m/s while the 2.0-kg cart goes in the opposite direction. What velocity does it have?

▶ 11. A 12.0-g rubber bullet travels at a velocity of 150 m/s, hits a stationary 8.5-kg concrete block resting on a frictionless surface, and ricochets in the opposite direction with a velocity of −100 m/s. How fast will the concrete block be moving?

12. A 6500-kg freight car travelling at 2.5 m/s collides with an 8000-kg stationary freight car. If they interlock upon collision, find their velocity.

▶ 13. Tim, mass 42.00 kg, is riding a skateboard, mass 2.00 kg, travelling at 1.20 m/s. Tim jumps off and the skateboard stops dead in its tracks. In what direction and with what velocity did he jump?

▶ 14. A cue ball, mass 0.16 kg, rolling at 4.0 m/s, hits a stationary eight-ball of similar mass. If the cue ball travels 45° above its original path, and the eight-ball at 45° below, what is the velocity of each after collision?

▶ 15. Two opposing hockey players, one of mass 82.0 kg skating north at 6.0 m/s and the other of mass 70.0 kg skating east at 3.0 m/s, collide and become tangled.
   a. Draw a vector momentum diagram of the collision.
   b. In what direction and with what velocity do they move after collision?

# Chapter 10

1. After scoring a touchdown, an 84.0-kg wide receiver celebrates by leaping 120 cm off the ground. How much work was done in the celebration?

2. During a tug-of-war, Team A does $2.20 \times 10^5$ J of work in pulling Team B 8.00 m. What force was Team A exerting?

3. To keep a car travelling at a constant velocity, 551 N of force is needed to overcome frictional forces. How much work is done against friction by the car in travelling a distance of 161 km?

4. A weightlifter raises a 180-kg barbell to a height of 1.95 m. How much work was done by the weightlifter in lifting the barbells?

▶ 5. A wagon is pulled by a force of 38.0 N on the handle at an angle of 42° with the horizontal. If the wagon is pulled in a circle of radius 25.0 m, how much work is done?

**6.** A 185-kg refrigerator is loaded into a moving van by pushing it up a 10.0-m ramp at an angle of inclination of 11°. How much work is done?

**7.** A lawn mower is pushed with a force of 88.0 N along a handle that makes an angle of 41° with the horizontal. How much work is done in pushing the mower 1.2 km in mowing the yard?

**8.** A 17.0-kg crate is to be pulled a distance of 20.0 m requiring 1210 J of work being done. If the job is done by attaching a rope and pulling with a force of 75.0 N, at what angle is the rope held?

**9.** An elevator lifts a total mass of $1.1 \times 10^3$ kg, a distance of 40.0 m in 12.5 s. How much power does the elevator demonstrate?

**10.** A cyclist exerts a force of 15.0 N in riding a bike 251 m in 30.0 s. What is the cyclist's power?

**11.** A 120-kg lawn tractor goes up a 21° incline of 12.0 m in 2.5 s. What power is shown by the tractor?

**12.** What power does a pump develop to lift 35 L of water per minute from a depth of 110 m? (A litre of water has a mass of 1.00 kg.)

**13.** A force of 1.4 N is exerted through a distance of 40.0 cm on a rope in a pulley system to lift a 0.50-kg mass 10.0 cm.
  **a.** Calculate the *MA*.
  **b.** Calculate the *IMA*.
  **c.** What is the efficiency of the pulley system?

**14.** A student exerts a force of 250 N through a distance of 1.6 m on a lever in lifting a 150-kg crate. If the efficiency of the lever is 90%, how far is the crate lifted?

**15.** Karen pedals a bicycle with a gear radius of 5.00 cm and a wheel radius of 38.6 cm. What length of chain must be pulled through to make the wheel revolve once?

## Chapter 11

**1.** Calculate the kinetic energy of a proton, mass $1.67 \times 10^{-27}$ kg, traveling at $5.20 \times 10^7$ m/s.

**2.** What is the kinetic energy of a 3.2-kg pike swimming at 2.7 km/h?

**3.** A force of 30.0 N pushes a 1.5-kg cart, initially at rest, a distance of 2.8 m along a frictionless surface.
  **a.** Find the work done on the cart.
  **b.** What is its change in kinetic energy?
  **c.** What is the cart's final velocity?

**4.** A bike and rider, 82.0-kg combined mass, are travelling at 4.2 m/s. A constant force of − 140 N is applied by the brakes in stopping the bike. What braking distance is needed?

**5.** A 712-kg car is travelling at 5.6 m/s when a force acts on it for 8.4 s, changing its velocity to 10.2 m/s.
  **a.** What is the change in kinetic energy of the car?
  **b.** How far did the car move while the force acted?
  **c.** How large is the force?

**6.** Five identical 0.85-kg books of 2.50-cm thickness are each laying flat on a table. Calculate the gain in potential energy of the system if they are stacked one on top of the other.

**7.** Each step of a ladder increases one's vertical height 40 cm. If a 90.0-kg painter climbs 8 steps of the ladder, what is the increase in potential energy?

**8.** A 0.25-kg ball is dropped from a height of 3.2 m and bounces to a height of 2.4 m. What is its loss in potential energy?

**9.** A 0.18-kg ball is placed on a compressed spring on the floor. The spring exerts an average force of 2.8 N through a distance of 15 cm as it shoots the ball upward. How high will the ball travel above the release spring?

**10.** A force of 14.0 N is applied to a 1.5-kg cart as it travels 2.6 m along an inclined plane. What is the angle of inclination of the plane?

**11.** A 15.0-kg model plane flies horizontally at a constant speed of 12.5 m/s.
  **a.** Calculate its kinetic energy.
  **b.** The plane goes into a dive and levels off 20.4 m closer to Earth. How much potential energy does it lose during the dive? Assume no additional drag.
  **c.** How much kinetic energy does the plane gain during the dive?
  **d.** What is its new kinetic energy?
  **e.** What is its new horizontal velocity?

**12.** A 1200-kg car starts from rest and accelerates to 72 km/h in 20.0 s. Friction exerts an average force of 450 N on the car during this time.
  **a.** What is the net work done on the car?
  **b.** How far does the car move during its acceleration?
  **c.** What is the net force exerted on the car during this time?
  **d.** What is the forward force exerted on the car as a result of the engine, power train, and wheels pushing backward on the road?

▶ **13.** In an electronics factory, small cabinets slide down a 30.0° incline a distance of 16.0 m to reach the next assembly stage. The cabinets have a mass of 10.0 kg each.
  **a.** Calculate the speed each cabinet would acquire if the incline were frictionless.
  **b.** What kinetic energy would a cabinet have under such circumstances?

▶ **14.** An average force of 8.2 N is used to pull a 0.40-kg rock, stretching a sling shot 43 cm. The rock is shot downward from a bridge 18 m above a stream. What will be the velocity of the rock just before it enters the water?

▶ **15.** A 15-g bullet is fired horizontally into a 3.000-kg block of wood suspended by a long cord. The bullet sticks in the block. Compute the velocity of the bullet if the impact causes the block to swing 10 cm above its initial level.

# Chapter 12

**1.** The boiling point of liquid chlorine is −34.60°C. Find this temperature in Kelvin.

**2.** Fluorine has a melting point of 50.28 K. Find this temperature in degrees Celsius.

**3.** Five kilograms of ice cubes are moved from the freezing compartment of a refrigerator into a home freezer. The refrigerator's freezing compartment is kept at −4.0°C. The home freezer is kept at −17°C. How much heat does the freezer's cooling system remove from the ice cubes?

**4.** How much heat must be added to 124 g of brass at 12.5°C to raise its temperature to 97.0°C?

**5.** $2.8 \times 10^5$ J of thermal energy are added to a sample of water and its temperature changes from 293 K to 308 K. What is the mass of the water?

**6.** 1420 J of thermal energy are added to a 100.0-g block of carbon at −20.0°C. What final temperature will the carbon reach?

**7.** A gold brick, mass 10.5 kg, requires $2.08 \times 10^4$ J of heat to change its temperature from 35.0°C to 50.0°C. What is the specific heat of gold?

▶ **8.** An $8.00 \times 10^2$-g block of lead is heated in boiling water, 100.0°C, until the block's temperature is the same as the water's. The lead is then removed from the boiling water and dropped into $2.50 \times 10^2$ g of cool water at 12.2°C. After a short time, the temperature of both lead and water is 20.0°C.
  **a.** How much heat is gained by the cool water?
  **b.** On the basis of these measurements, what is the specific heat of lead?

▶ **9.** 250.0 g of copper at 100.0°C are placed in a cup containing 325.0 g of water at 20.0°C. Assume no heat loss to the surroundings. What is the final temperature of the copper and water?

▶ **10.** A $4.00 \times 10^2$-g sample of methanol at 30.0°C is mixed with a $2.00 \times 10^2$-g sample of water at 0.0°C. Assume no heat loss to the surroundings. What is the final temperature of the mixture?

**11.** How much heat is needed to change 50.0 g of water at 80.0°C to steam at 110°C?

▶ **12.** The specific heat of mercury is 140 J/kg · C°. Its heat of vaporization is $3.06 \times 10^5$ J/kg. How much heat is needed to heat 1.0 kg of mercury metal from 10.0°C to its boiling point and vaporize it completely? The boiling point of mercury is 357°C.

▶ **13.** 30.0 g of −3.0°C ice is placed in a cup containing 104.0 g of water at 62.0°C. All the ice melts. Find the final temperature of the mixture. Assume no heat loss to the surroundings.

▶ **14.** Water flows over a falls 125.0 m high. If the potential energy of the water is all converted to thermal energy, calculate the temperature difference between the water at the top and the bottom of the falls.

▶ **15.** During the game, the metabolism of basketball players often increases by as much as 30.0 W. How much perspiration must a player vaporize per hour to dissipate this extra thermal energy?

# Chapter 13

1. How tall must a column of mercury, $\rho = 1.36 \times 10^4$ kg/m$^3$, be to exert a pressure equal to the atmosphere?

2. A dog, whose paw has an area of 12.0 cm$^2$, has a mass of 8.0 kg. What average pressure does the dog exert while standing?

3. A crate, whose bottom surface is 50.4 cm by 28.3 cm, exerts a pressure of $2.50 \times 10^3$ Pa on the floor. What is the mass of the crate?

▶ 4. The dimensions of a waterbed are 2.13 m by 1.52 m by 0.38 m. If the frame has a mass of 91.0 kg and the mattress is filled with water, what pressure does the bed exert on the floor?

▶ 5. A rectangular block of tin, $\rho = 7.29 \times 10^3$ kg/m$^3$, has dimensions of 5.00 cm by 8.50 cm by 2.25 cm. What pressure does it exert on a table top if it is laying on its side of
   a. greatest surface area?
   b. smallest surface area?

6. A rowboat, mass 42.0 kg, is floating on a lake.
   a. What is the size of the buoyant force?
   b. What is the volume of the submerged part of the boat?

7. A hydraulic lift has a large piston of 20.00-cm diameter and a small piston of 5.00-cm diameter. What is the mechanical advantage of the lift?

8. A lever on a hydraulic system gives a mechanical advantage of 5.00. The cross-sectional area of the small piston is 0.0400 m$^2$, and that of the large piston is 0.280 m$^2$. If a force of 25.0 N is exerted on the lever, what is the force given by the larger piston?

▶ 9. A piece of metal weighs 75.0 N in air and 60.0 N in water. What is the density of the metal?

▶ 10. A river barge with vertical sides is 20.0 m long and 10.0 m wide. It floats 3.00 m out of the water when empty. When loaded with coals the water is only 1.00 m from the top. What is the weight of the load of coal?

11. What is the change in the length of a 15.0-m steel rail as it is cooled from 1535°C to 20°C?

12. A concrete sidewalk section 8.000 m by 1.000 m by 0.100 m at exactly 0°C will expand to what volume at 35°C?

13. An air-filled balloon of 15.0-cm radius at 11°C is heated to 121°C. What change in volume occurs?

▶ 14. A circular, pyrex watch glass of 10.0-cm diameter at 21°C is heated to 501°C. What change will be found in the circumference of the glass?

▶ 15. A 200.0-cm copper wire and a 201-cm platinum wire are both at exactly 0°C. At what temperature will they both be of equal length?

# Chapter 14

1. A periodic transverse wave that has a frequency of 10.0 Hz, travels along a string. The distance between a crest and either adjacent trough is 2.50 m. What is its wavelength?

2. A wave generator produces 16.0 pulses in 4.00 s.
   a. What is its period?
   b. What is its frequency?

3. A wave generator produces 22.5 pulses in 5.50 s.
   a. What is its period?
   b. What is its frequency?

4. What is the speed of a periodic wave disturbance that has a frequency of 2.50 Hz and a wavelength of 0.600 m?

5. One pulse is generated every 0.100 s in a tank of water. What is the speed of propagation of the wave if the wavelength of the surface wave is 3.30 cm?

▶ 6. Five pulses are generated every 0.100 s in a tank of water. What is the speed of propagation of the wave if the wavelength of the surface wave is 1.20 cm?

▶ 7. A periodic longitudinal wave that has a frequency of 20.0 Hz travels along a coil spring. If the distance between successive compressions is 0.400 m, what is the speed of the wave?

8. What is the wavelength of a water wave that has a frequency of 2.50 Hz and a speed of 4.0 m/s?

9. The speed of a transverse wave in a string is 15.0 m/s. If a source produces a disturbance that has a frequency of 5.00 Hz, what is its wavelength?

10. The speed of a transverse wave in a string is 15.0 m/s. If a source produces a disturbance that has a wavelength of 1.25 m, what is the frequency of the wave?

**11.** A wave has an angle of incidence of 24°. What is the angle of reflection?

# Chapter 15_____

**1.** The echo of a ship's fog horn, reflected from an iceberg, is heard 5.0 s after the horn is sounded. How far away is the iceberg?

**2.** What is the speed of sound that has a frequency of 250 Hz and a wavelength of 0.600 m?

**3.** A sound wave has a frequency of 2000 Hz and travels along a steel rod. If the distance between successive compressions is 0.400 m, what is the speed of the wave?

**4.** What is the wavelength of a sound wave that has a frequency of 250 Hz and a speed of 400 m/s?

**5.** What is the wavelength of sound that has a frequency of 539.8 Hz?

**6.** What is the wavelength of sound that has a frequency of 320.0 Hz?

▶ **7.** A stone is dropped into a mine shaft 250.0 m deep. How many seconds pass before the stone is heard to strike the bottom of the shaft?

▶ **8.** A rifle is shot in a valley formed between two parallel mountains. The echo from one mountain is heard after 2.00 s and from the other mountain 2.00 s later. What is the width of the valley?

▶ **9.** Sam, a train engineer, blows a whistle that has a frequency of $4.0 \times 10^2$ Hz as the train approaches a station. If the speed of the train is 25 m/s, what frequency will be heard by a person at the station?

▶ **10.** Jane is on a train that is travelling at 95 km/h. The train passes a factory whose whistle is blowing at 288 Hz. What frequency does Jane hear as the train approaches the factory?

**11.** What is the sound level of a sound that has a sound pressure one tenth of 90 dB?

**12.** What is the sound level of a sound that has a sound pressure ten times 90 dB?

**13.** A tuning fork produces a resonance with a closed tube 19.0 cm long. What is the lowest possible frequency of the tuning fork?

**14.** How do the frequencies of notes that are an octave apart compare?

**15.** Two tuning forks of 320 Hz and 324 Hz are sounded simultaneously. What frequency of sound will the listener hear?

**16.** How many beats will be heard each second when a string with a frequency of 288 Hz is plucked simultaneously with another string that has a frequency of 296 Hz?

**17.** A tuning fork has a frequency of 440 Hz. If another tuning fork of slightly lower pitch is sounded at the same time, 5.0 beats per second are produced. What is the frequency of the second tuning fork?

# Chapter 16_____

**1.** The wavelength of blue light is about $4.5 \times 10^{-7}$ m. Convert this to nm.

**2.** As a spacecraft passes directly over Cape Kennedy, radar pulses are transmitted toward the craft and are then reflected back toward the ground. If the total time interval was $3.00 \times 10^{-3}$ s, how far above the ground was the spacecraft when it passed over Cape Kennedy?

**3.** It takes 4.0 years for light from a star to reach Earth. How far away is this star from Earth?

**4.** The planet Venus is sometimes a very bright object in the night sky. Venus is $4.1 \times 10^{10}$ m away from Earth when it is closest to Earth. How long would we have to wait for a radar signal to return from Venus and be detected?

**5.** The distance from Earth to the moon is about $3.8 \times 10^8$ m. A beam of light is sent to the moon and, after it reflects, returns to Earth. How long did it take to make the round trip?

**6.** A baseball fan in a ball park is 101 m away from the batter's box when the batter hits the ball. How long after the batter hits the ball does the fan see it occur?

**7.** A radio station on the AM band has an assigned frequency of 825 kHz (kilohertz). What is the wavelength of the station?

**8.** A short-wave, HAM, radio operator uses the 5-m band. On what frequency does the HAM operate?

9. Find the illumination 8.0 m below a 405-lm lamp.

10. Two lamps illuminate a screen equally. The first lamp has an intensity of 12.5 cd and is 3.0 m from the screen. The second lamp is 9.0 m from the screen. What is its intensity?

11. A 15-cd point source lamp and a 45-cd point source lamp provide equal illuminations on a wall. If the 45-cd lamp is 12 m away from the wall, how far from the wall is the 15-cd lamp?

12. What is the name given to the electromagnetic radiation that has a wavelength slightly longer than visible light?

13. What is the name given to the electromagnetic radiation that has a wavelength slightly shorter than visible light?

14. If a black object absorbs all light ray incident on it, how can we see it?

15. What is the appearance of a red dress in a closed room illuminated only by green light?

16. A shirt that is the colour of a primary colour is illuminated with the component of that primary colour. What colour do you see?

# Chapter 17

1. A ray of light strikes a mirror at an angle of incidence of 28°. What is the angle of reflection?

2. A ray of light passes from an unknown substance into air. If the angle in the unknown substance is 35.0° and the angle in air is 52.0°, what is the index of refraction of the unknown substance?

3. A ray of light has an angle of incidence of 25.0° upon the surface of a piece of quartz. What is the angle of refraction?

4. A beam of light passes from water into polyethylene, index of refraction = 1.50. If the angle in water is 57.5°, what is the angle in polyethylene?

5. Dave makes some hydrogen sulphide, index of refraction = 1.000644. If Karen measures an angle of 85.000000° in the hydrogen sulphide, what angle will Karen measure in air if the index of refraction of air is 1.0002926?

6. Sue submerged some ice in water and shined a laser beam through the water and into the ice. Sue found the angle in ice was larger than the angle in water. Which material has a larger index of refraction?

7. A ray of light enters a triangular crown glass prism perpendicular to one face and it emerges from an adjacent side. If the two adjacent sides meet at a 30.0° angle, what is the angle the light ray has in the air when it comes out?

8. Make a drawing, to scale, of the side of an aquarium in which the water is 12.0 cm deep. From a single point on the bottom, draw two lines upward, one vertical and the other 5.0° from the vertical. Let these two lines represent two light rays that start from the same point on the bottom of the tank. Compute the directions the refracted rays will travel above the surface of the water. Draw in these rays and continue them backward into the tank until they intersect. At what depth does the bottom of the tank appear to be if you look into the water? Divide the apparent depth into the true depth and compare it to the index of refraction.

9. Find the speed of light in water.

10. Find the speed of light in antimony trioxide if it has an index of refraction of 2.35.

11. The speed of light in a special piece of glass is $1.75 \times 10^8$ m/s. What is its index of refraction?

12. Glenn gently pours some acetic acid, index of refraction = 1.37, onto some antimony trioxide, index of refraction = 2.35. What angle will Glenn find in the acetic acid if the angle in the antimony trioxide is 42.0°?

13. Steve finds that a plastic has a critical angle of 40.0°. What is the index of refraction of the plastic?

14. Kathy decides to find the critical angle of arsenic trioxide, index of refraction = 2.01, which is very toxic. What angle did Kathy find?

15. A light source is in a cylindrical container of carbon dichloride, index of refraction = 1.500. The light source sends a ray of light parallel to the bottom of the container at a 45.0° angle from the radius to the circumference. What will the path of the light ray be?

16. With a square block of glass, index of refraction = 1.50, it is impossible, when looking into one side, to see out of an adjacent side of the square block of

glass. It appears to be a mirror. Use your knowledge of geometry and critical angles to show that this is true.

17. The index of refraction for red light in arsenic trioxide is 2.010, while the index of refraction for blue light is 2.023. Find the difference between the angles of refraction if white light is incident at an angle of 65.0°.

18. The index of refraction for red light in a diamond is 2.410, while the index of refraction for blue light is 2.450. Find the difference in the speed of light in diamond.

# Chapter 18_____

1. Sally's face is 75 cm in front of a plane mirror. Where is the image of Sally's face?

2. A concave mirror has a focal length of 10.0 cm. What is its radius of curvature?

3. Light from a distant star is collected by a concave mirror that has a radius of curvature of 150 cm. How far from the mirror is the image of the star?

4. An object is placed 25.0 cm away from a concave mirror that has a focal length of 5.00 cm. Where is the image located?

5. An object and its image as seen in a concave mirror are the same height when the object is 48.4 cm from the mirror. What is the focal length of the mirror?

6. An object placed 50.0 cm from a concave mirror gives a real image 33.3 cm from the mirror. If the image is 28.4 cm high, what is the height of the object?

7. An object, 15.8 cm high, is located 87.6 cm from a concave mirror that has a focal length of 17.0 cm.
   a. Where is the image located?
   b. How high is the image?

▶ 8. The image of the moon is formed by a concave mirror whose radius of curvature is 4.20 m at a time when the moon's distance is $3.80 \times 10^5$ km. What is the diameter of the image of the moon if the diameter of the moon is 3480 km?

9. A shaving mirror has a radius of curvature of 30.0 cm. When a face is 10.0 cm away from the mirror, what is the magnification of the mirror?

10. A convex mirror has a focal length of −16 cm. How far behind the mirror does the image of a person 3.0 m away appear?

11. How far behind the surface of a convex mirror, focal length of −6.0 cm, does a car 10.0 m from the mirror appear?

12. A converging lens has a focal length of 25.5 cm. If it is placed 72.5 cm from an object, at what distance from the lens will the image be?

13. If an object is 10.0 cm from a converging lens that has a focal length of 5.00 cm, how far from the lens will the image be?

14. The focal length of a lens in a box camera is 10.0 cm. The fixed distance between the lens and the film is 11.0 cm. If an object is clearly focused on the film, how far must the object be from the lens?

15. An object 3.0 cm tall is placed 22 cm in front of a converging lens. A real image is formed 11 cm from the lens. What is the size of the image?

▶ 16. An object 3.0 cm tall is placed 20 cm in front of a converging lens. A real image is formed 10 cm from the lens. What is the focal length of the lens?

▶ 17. What is the focal length of the lens in your eye when you read a book that is 35.0 cm from your eye? The distance from the lens to the retina is 0.19 mm.

▶ 18. When an object 5.0 cm tall is placed 12 cm from a converging lens, an image is formed on the same side of the lens as the object but the image is 61 cm away from the lens. What is the focal length of the lens?

▶ 19. When an object 5.0 cm tall is placed 12 cm from a converging lens, an image is formed on the same side of the lens as the object but the image is 61 cm away from the lens. What is the size of the image?

# Chapter 19_____

1. Monochromatic light passes through two slits that are 0.0300 cm apart and it falls on a screen 120 cm away. The first-order image is 0.160 cm from the middle of the center band. What is the wavelength of the light used?

2. Green light passes through a double slit for which $d = 0.20$ mm and it falls on a screen 2.00 m away. The first-order image is at 0.50 cm. What is the wavelength of the light?

3. Yellow light that has a wavelength of $6.00 \times 10^2$ nm passes through two narrow slits that are 0.200 mm apart. An interference pattern is produced on a screen 180 cm away. What is the location of the first-order image?

4. Violet light that has a wavelength of $4.00 \times 10^2$ nm passes through two slits that are 0.0100 cm apart. How far away must the screen be so the first-order image is at 0.300 cm?

▶ 5. Two radio transmitters are 25.0 m apart and each one sends out a radio wave with a wavelength of 10.0 m. The two radio towers act exactly like a double-slit source for light. How far from the central band is the first-order image if you are 15.0 km away? (Yes, this really happens. Radio stations can and do fade in and out as you cross the nodals and the antinodals.)

6. Monochromatic light passes through a single slit, 0.500 mm wide, and falls on a screen 1.0 m away. If the distance from the centre of the pattern to the first band is 2.6 mm, what is the wavelength of the light?

7. Red light that has a wavelength of $7.50 \times 10^2$ nm passes through a single slit that is 0.1350 mm wide. How far away from the screen must the slit be if the first dark band is 0.9000 cm away from the central bright band?

8. Microwaves with a wavelength of 3.5 cm pass through a single slit 0.85 cm wide and fall on a screen 91 cm away. What is the distance to the first-order band?

▶ 9. Radio waves that are emitted by two adjacent radio transmitters behave like light waves coming from a double slit. If two transmitters, 1500 m apart, each send out radio waves with a wavelength of 150 m, what is the diffraction angle?

10. What is the average distance between the lines of a diffraction grating if the number of lines per millimetre is 425?

11. A transmission grating with $5.85 \times 10^3$ lines/cm is illuminated by monochromatic light that has a wavelength of 492 nm. What is the diffraction angle for the first-order image?

12. Monochromatic light illuminates a transmission grating having 5900 lines/cm. The diffraction angle for a first-order image is 18.0°. What is the wavelength of the light in nanometres?

13. A transmission grating, $5.80 \times 10^3$ lines/cm, is illuminated by a monochromatic light source that has a wavelength of 495 nm. How far from the centre line is the first-order image if the distance to the grating is 1.25 m?

14. A pinhole camera uses a 1.5-mm hole instead of a lens to form an image. What is the resolution of this camera for green light, 545-nm wavelength, if the film is 6.0 cm behind the pinhole?

## Chapter 20

1. Two charges, $q_1$ and $q_2$, are separated by a distance, $d$, and exert a force on each other. What new force will exist if $d$ is doubled?

2. Two charges, $q_1$ and $q_2$, are separated by a distance, $d$, and exert a force on each other. What new force will exist if $q_1$ and $q_2$ are both doubled?

3. Two identical point charges are separated by a distance of 3.0 cm and they repel each other with a force of $4.0 \times 10^{-5}$ N. What is the new force if the distance between the point charges is doubled?

▶ 4. An electric force of $2.5 \times 10^{-4}$ N acts between two small equally-charged spheres which are 2.0 cm apart. Calculate the force acting between the spheres if the charge on one of the spheres is doubled and the spheres move to a 5.0-cm separation.

5. How many electrons would be required to have a total charge of 1.00 C on a sphere?

6. If two identical charges, 1.000 C each, are separated by a distance of 1.00 km, what is the force between them?

7. Two point charges are separated by 10.0 cm. If one charge is $+20.00$ μC and the other is $-6.00$ μC, what is the force between them?

8. The two point charges in the previous problem are allowed to touch each other and are again separated by 10.00 cm. Now what is the force between them?

9. Determine the electrostatic force of attraction between a proton and an electron that are separated by $5.00 \times 10^2$ nm.

10. Find the force between two charged spheres 1.25 cm apart if the charge on one sphere is 2.50 μC and the charge on the other sphere is $1.75 \times 10^{-8}$ C.

11. Two identical point charges are 3.00 cm apart. Find the charge on each of them if the force of repulsion is $4.00 \times 10^{-7}$ N.

12. A charge of $4.0 \times 10^{-5}$ C is attracted by a second charge with a force of 350 N when the separation is 10.0 cm. Calculate the size of the second charge.

▶ 13. Three particles are placed on a straight line. The left particle has a charge of $+4.6 \times 10^{-6}$ C, the middle particle has a charge of $-2.3 \times 10^{-6}$ C, and the right particle has a charge of $-2.3 \times 10^{-6}$ C. The left particle is 12 cm from the middle particle and the right particle is 24 cm from the middle particle. Find the total force on the middle particle.

▶ 14. The left particle in the problem above is moved directly above the middle particle, still 12 cm away. Find the force on the middle particle.

# Chapter 21

1. How strong would an electric field have to be to produce a force of 1.00 N if the charge was $1.000 \times 10^3$ μC?

2. A positive charge of 7.0 mC experiences a $5.6 \times 10^{-2}$-N force when placed in an electric field. What is the size of the electric field intensity?

3. A positive test charge of $6.5 \times 10^{-6}$ C experiences a force of $4.5 \times 10^{-5}$ N. What is the magnitude of the electric field intensity?

4. A charge experiences a force of $3.0 \times 10^{-3}$ N in an electric field of intensity 2.0 N/C. What is the magnitude of the charge?

5. What is the size of the force on an electron when the electron is in a uniform electric field that has an intensity of $1.000 \times 10^3$ N/C?

6. Sketch the electric field lines around a $-1.0$-μC charge.

7. It takes 8.00 mJ to move a charge of 4.00 μC from point **A** to point **C** in an electric field. What is the potential difference between the two points?

8. How much work is required to move a positive charge of 2.5 μC between two points that have a potential difference of 60 V?

▶ 9. A cloud has a potential difference relative to a tree of $9.00 \times 10^2$ MV. During a lighting storm, a charge of $1.00 \times 10^2$ C travels through this potential difference. How much work is done on this charge?

10. A constant electric field of 750 N/C is between a set of parallel plates. What is the potential difference between the parallel plates if they are 1.5 cm apart?

11. A spark will jump between two people if the electric field exceeds $4.0 \times 10^6$ V/m. You shuffle across a rug and a spark jumps when you put your finger 0.15 cm from another person's arm. Calculate the potential difference between your body and the other person's arm.

12. A potential difference of 0.90 V exists from one side to the other side of a cell membrane that is 5.0 nm thick. What is the electric field across the membrane?

▶ 13. An oil drop having a charge of $8.0 \times 10^{-19}$ C is suspended between two charged parallel plates. The plates are separated by a distance of 8.0 mm, and there is a potential difference of 1200 V between the plates. What is the weight of the suspended oil drop?

14. A capacitor accumulates 4.0 μC on each plate when the potential difference between the plates is 100 V. What is the capacitance of the capacitor?

15. What is the voltage across a capacitor with a charge of 6.0 μC and a capacitance 7.0 pF?

16. How large is the charge accumulated on one of the plates of a 30-μF capacitor when the potential difference between the plates is 120 V?

# Chapter 22

1. How many amperes of current flow in a wire through which $1.00 \times 10^{18}$ electrons pass per second?

2. A current of 5.00 A flowed in a copper wire for 20.0 s. How many coulombs of charge passed through the wire in this time?

3. What power is supplied to a motor that operates on a 120-V line and draws 1.50 A of current?

4. An electric lamp is connected to a 110-V source. If the current through the lamp is 0.75 A, what is the power consumption of the lamp?

5. A lamp is labeled 6.0 V and 12 W.
   a. What current flows through the lamp when it is operating?
   b. How much energy is supplied to the lamp in $1.000 \times 10^3$ s?

6. A current of 3.00 A flows through a resistor when it is connected to a 12.0-V battery. What is the resistance of the resistor?

7. A small lamp is designed to draw a current of $3.00 \times 10^2$ mA in a 6.00-V circuit. What is the resistance of the lamp?

8. What potential difference is required if you want a current of 8.00 mA in a load having a resistance of 50.0 Ω?

9. In common metals, resistance increases as the temperature increases. An electric toaster has a resistance of 12.0 Ω when hot.
   a. What current will flow through it when it is connected to 125 V?
   b. When the toaster is first turned on, will the current be more or less than during operation?

10. The resistance of a lamp is 230 Ω. The voltage is 115 V when the lamp is turned on.
    a. What is the current in the lamp?
    b. If the voltage rises to 120 V, what is the current?

11. What should the resistance of the lamp in part **a** of the previous problem be if the lamp is to draw the same current, but in a 230-V circuit?

12. A 110-W lamp draws 0.909 A. What is the lamp's resistance?

13. Each coil in a resistance box is capable of dissipating heat at the rate of 4.00 W. What is the maximum current that should be allowed across a coil to avoid overheating if the coil has a resistance of
    a. 2.00 Ω.
    b. 20.0 Ω.

▶ 14. What is the power supplied to a lamp that is operated by a battery having a 12-V potential difference across its terminals when the resistance of the lamp is 6.0 Ω?

15. How much does it cost to run a 2.00-W clock for one year (365.25 d) if it costs 3.53 cents/kW · h?

▶ 16. A small electric furnace that expends 2.00 kW of power is connected across a potential difference of 120 V.
    a. What is the current in the circuit?
    b. What is the resistance of the furnace?
    c. What is the cost of operating the furnace for 24.0 h at 7.00 ¢/kW · h?

# Chapter 23

1. The load across a 50.0-V battery consists of a series combination of two lamps with resistances of 125 Ω and 225 Ω.
   a. Find the total resistance of the circuit.
   b. Find the current in the circuit.
   c. Find the potential difference across the 125-Ω lamp.

2. The load across a 12-V battery consists of a series combination of three resistances that are 15 Ω, 21 Ω, and 24 Ω respectively.
   a. Draw the circuit diagram.
   b. What is the total resistance of the load?
   c. What is the magnitude of the circuit current?

3. The load across a 12-V battery consists of a series combination of three resistances $R_1$, $R_2$, and $R_3$. $R_1$ is 210 Ω, $R_2$ is 350 Ω, and $R_3$ is 120 Ω.
   a. Find the equivalent resistance of the circuit.
   b. Find the current in the circuit.
   c. Find the potential difference across $R_3$.

▶ 4. The load across a 40-V battery consists of a series combination of three resistances $R_1$, $R_2$, and $R_3$. $R_1$ is 240 Ω, and $R_3$ is 120 Ω. The potential difference across $R_1$ is 24 V.
    a. Find the current in the circuit.
    b. Find the equivalent resistance of the circuit.
    c. Find the resistance of $R_2$.

▶ 5. Pete is designing a voltage divider using a 12.0-V battery and a 100-Ω resistor as $R_2$. What resistor should be used as $R_1$ if the output voltage is 4.75 V?

6. Two resistances, one 12 Ω and the other 18 Ω, are connected in parallel. What is the equivalent resistance of the parallel combination?

7. Three resistances of 12 Ω each are connected in parallel. What is the equivalent resistance?

▶ 8. Two resistances, one 62 Ω and the other 88 Ω, are connected in parallel. The resistors are then connected to a 12-V battery.
   a. What is the equivalent resistance of the parallel combination?
   b. What is the current through each resistor?

▶ 9. A 35-Ω, 55-Ω, and 85-Ω resistor are connected in parallel. The resistors are then connected to a 35-V battery.
   a. What is the equivalent resistance of the parallel combination?
   b. What is the current through each resistor?

10. A 110-V household circuit that contains an 1800-W microwave, a 1000-W toaster, and an 800-W coffee maker is connected to a 20-A fuse. Will the fuse melt if the microwave and the coffee maker are both on?

11. Resistors $R_1$, $R_2$, and $R_3$ have resistances of 15.0 Ω, 9.0 Ω, and 8.0 Ω respectively. $R_1$ and $R_2$ are connected in series, and their combination is in parallel with $R_3$ to form a load across a 6.0-V battery.
   a. Draw the circuit diagram.
   b. What is the total resistance of the load?
   c. What is the magnitude of the circuit current?
   d. What is the current in $R_3$?
   e. What is the potential difference across $R_2$?

12. A 15.0-Ω resistor is connected in series to a 120-V generator and two 10.0-Ω resistors that are connected in parallel to each other.
   a. Draw the circuit diagram.
   b. What is the total resistance of the load?
   c. What is the magnitude of the circuit current?
   d. What is the current in one of the 10.0-Ω resistors?
   e. What is the potential difference across the 15.0-Ω resistor?

13. How would you change the resistance of a voltmeter to allow the voltmeter to measure a larger potential difference?

14. How would you change the shunt in an ammeter to allow the ammeter to measure a larger current?

▶ 15. An ohmmeter is made by connecting a 6.0-V battery in series with an adjustable resistor and an ideal ammeter. The ammeter deflects full-scale with a current

of 1.0 mA. The two leads are touched together and the resistance is adjusted so 1.0-mA current flows.
   a. What is the resistance of the adjustable resistor?
   b. The leads are now connected to an unknown resistance. What external resistance would produce a reading of 0.50 mA, half full-scale?
   c. What external resistance would produce a reading of 0.25 mA, quarter-scale?
   d. What external resistance would produce a reading of 0.75 mA, three-quarter full-scale?

# Chapter 24

1. Assume the current in the wire shown in Figure 24–28 goes in the opposite direction. Copy the wire segment and sketch the new magnetic field the current generated.

2. Assume the current shown in Figure 24–29 goes into the page instead of out of the page. Copy the figure with the new current and sketch the magnetic field.

3. What happens to the strength of a magnetic field around a wire if the current in the wire is doubled?

4. What happens to the magnetic field inside the coil of Figure 24–30 if the current shown was reversed?

5. What is the direction of the force on a current carrying wire in a magnetic field if the current is toward the left on a page and the magnetic field is down the page?

6. A 0.25 m long wire is carrying a 1.25 A current while the wire is perpendicular to a 0.35-T magnetic field. What is the force on the wire?

7. A 3.0 cm long wire lies perpendicular to a magnetic field with a magnetic induction of 0.40 T. Calculate the force on the wire if the current in the wire is 5.0 A.

8. What is the force on a 3.5 m long wire that is carrying a 12-A current if the wire is perpendicular to Earth's magnetic field?

9. A wire, 0.50 m long, is put into a uniform magnetic field. The force exerted upon the wire when the current in the wire is 20 A is 3.0 N. What is the magnetic induction of the field acting upon the wire?

10. What is the size of the current in a 35 cm long wire that is perpendicular to a magnetic field of 0.085 T if the force on the wire is 125 mN?

**11.** A galvanometer has a full-scale deflection when the current is 50.0 μA. If the galvanometer has a resistance of 1.0 kΩ, what should the resistance of the multiplier resistor be to make a voltmeter with a full-scale deflection of 30.0 V?

**12.** A charged particle is moving to the right in a magnetic field whose direction is up the page. Show by diagram the direction of the force exerted by the magnetic field upon the particle if the particle is a positive proton.

**13.** An electron beam moving horizontally away from you is deflected toward the right after passing through a certain region of space that contains a constant magnetic field. What is the direction of the magnetic field?

**14.** A beam of electrons moving left at $3.0 \times 10^7$ m/s passes at right angles to a uniform magnetic field that is down and in which the magnetic induction is $2.0 \times 10^{-4}$ T. What force acts upon each electron in the beam?

**15.** The electrons in a beam in a cathode ray tube are moving horizontally at $5.0 \times 10^7$ m/s and pass through a vertical magnetic field of $3.5 \times 10^{-3}$ T. What size force acts on each of the electrons in the beam?

**16.** An ion of oxygen having 2 elementary negative electric charges is moving at right angles to a uniform magnetic field for which B = 0.30 T. If its velocity is $2.0 \times 10^7$ m/s, what force is acting on the ion?

# Chapter 25 _____

**1.** A north-south wire is moved toward the east through a magnetic field that is pointing down, into Earth. What is the direction of the induced current?

**2.** A wire, 1.0 m long, is moved at right angles to Earth's magnetic field where the magnetic induction is $5.0 \times 10^{-5}$ T at a speed of 4.0 m/s. What is the EMF induced in the wire?

**3.** An EMF of 2.0 mV is induced in a wire 0.10 m long when it is moving perpendicularly across a uniform magnetic field at a velocity of 4.0 m/s. What is the magnetic induction of the field?

**4.** With what speed must a 0.20-m long wire cut across a magnetic field for which B is 2.5 T if it is to have an EMF of 10 V induced in it?

**5.** At what speed must a wire conductor 50 cm long be moved at right angles to a magnetic field of induction 0.20 T to induce an EMF of 1.0 V in it?

**6.** A wire, 0.40 m long, cuts perpendicularly across a magnetic field for which B is 2.0 T at a velocity of 8.0 m/s.
  **a.** What EMF is induced in the wire?
  **b.** If the wire is in a circuit having a resistance of 6.4 Ω, what is the size of the current through the wire?

▶ **7.** A coil of wire, which has a total length of 7.50 m, is moved perpendicular to Earth's magnetic field at 5.50 m/s. What is the size of the current in the wire if the total resistance of the wire is $5.0 \times 10^{-2}$ mΩ?

**8.** A house lighting circuit is rated at 120 V. What is the maximum voltage that can be expected from this circuit?

**9.** A toaster draws 2.5 A of alternating current. What is the maximum current that this toaster can draw?

**10.** The insulation of a capacitor will break down if the instantaneous voltage exceeds 575 V. What is the largest effective alternating voltage that may be applied to the capacitor?

**11.** A magnetic circuit breaker will open its circuit if the instantaneous current reaches 21.25 A. What is the largest effective current the circuit will carry?

▶ **12.** The peak value of the alternating voltage applied to a 144 -Ω resistor is $1.00 \times 10^2$ V. What power must the resistor be able to handle?

▶ **13.** Steve drops a magnet, S-pole down, through a vertical copper pipe.
  **a.** What is the direction of the induced current in the copper pipe as the bottom of the magnet passes?
  **b.** The induced current produces a magnetic field. What is the direction of the induced magnetic field?

**14.** The electricity received at an electrical substation has a potential difference of 240 000 V. What should the ratio of the turns of the step-down transformer be to have an output of 440 V?

▶ **15.** The CRT in a television uses a step-up transformer to change 120 V to 48 000 V. The secondary side of the transformer has 20 000 turns and an output of 1.0 mA.
  **a.** How many turns does the primary side have?
  **b.** What is the input current?

# Chapter 26

1. A beam of electrons travels through a set of crossed electric and magnetic fields. What is the speed of the electrons if the magnetic field is 85 mT and the electric field is $6.5 \times 10^4$ N/C?

2. Electrons, moving at $8.5 \times 10^7$ m/s, pass through crossed magnetic and electric fields undeflected. What is the size of the magnetic field if the electric field is $4.0 \times 10^4$ N/C?

3. What effect does increasing the magnetic induction of the field have on the radius of the particle's path for a given particle moving at a fixed speed?

4. An electron is moving at $2.0 \times 10^8$ m/s in a constant magnetic field. How strong should the magnetic field be to keep the electron moving in a circle of radius 0.50 m?

5. A positively-charged ion, having 2 elementary charges and a velocity of $5.0 \times 10^7$ m/s, is moving across a magnetic field for which $B = 4.0$ T. If the mass of the ion is $6.8 \times 10^{-27}$ kg, what is the radius of the circular path it travels?

6. A beam of electrons, moving at $2.0 \times 10^8$ m/s, passes at right angles to a uniform magnetic field of 41 mT. What is the radius of the circular path in which this beam will travel through the magnetic field?

7. An unknown particle is accelerated by a potential difference of 150 V. The particle then enters a magnetic field of 50.0 mT, and follows a curved path with a radius of 9.80 cm. What is the ratio of $q/m$?

8. A beam of doubly-ionized oxygen atoms is accelerated by a potential difference of 232 V. The oxygen then enters a magnetic field of 75.0 mT, and follows a curved path with a radius of 8.3 cm. What is the mass of the oxygen atom?

9. If the atomic mass unit is equal to $1.67 \times 10^{-27}$ kg, how many atomic mass units are in the oxygen atom in the previous problem?

10. A hydrogen ion is accelerated through an accelerating potential of $1.00 \times 10^2$ V and then through a magnetic field of 50.0 mT to standardize the mass spectrometer. What is the radius of curvature if the mass of the ion is $1.67 \times 10^{-27}$ kg?

▶ 11. What is the change in the radius of curvature if a doubly-ionized neon atom, mass = $3.34 \times 10^{-26}$ kg, is sent through the mass spectrometer in the previous problem?

12. Microwaves for a microwave oven are produced in a special tube, the klystron tube, which has a microwave antenna attached to it. What length antenna would produce 3.0-cm microwaves?

13. An FM radio station broadcasts on a frequency of 94.5 MHz. What is the antenna length that would give the best reception for this radio station?

# Chapter 27

1. Consider an incandescent light bulb on a dimmer control. What happens to the colour of the light given off by the bulb as the dimmer control is turned down?

2. What would the change in frequency of the vibration of an atom be according to Planck's theory if it gave off $5.44 \times 10^{-19}$ J? Assume n = 1.

3. What is the maximum kinetic energy of photoelectrons ejected from the metal that has a stopping potential of 3.8 V?

4. The stopping potential needed to return all the electrons ejected from a metal is 7.3 V. What is the maximum kinetic energy of the electrons in J?

5. What is the potential difference needed to stop photoelectrons that have a maximum kinetic energy of $8.0 \times 10^{-19}$ J?

6. The threshold frequency of a certain metal is $8.0 \times 10^{14}$ Hz. What is the work function of the metal?

7. If light with a frequency of $1.6 \times 10^{15}$ Hz falls on the metal in the previous problem, what is the maximum kinetic energy of the photoelectrons?

8. The threshold frequency of a certain metal is $3.00 \times 10^{14}$ Hz. What is the maximum kinetic energy of the ejected photoelectrons when the metal is illuminated by light with a wavelength of 650 nm?

9. What is the momentum of a photon of violet light that has a wavelength of $4.00 \times 10^2$ nm?

10. What is the momentum of a photon of red light that has a wavelength of $7.00 \times 10^2$ nm?

11. What is the wavelength associated with an electron moving at $3.0 \times 10^6$ m/s?

12. What velocity would an electron need to have a wavelength of $3.0 \times 10^{-10}$ m associated with it?

▶13. An electron is accelerated across a potential difference of $5.0 \times 10^3$ V in the CRT of a television.
   a. What is the velocity of the electron if it started from rest?
   b. What is the wavelength associated with the electron?

# Chapter 28

1 A calcium atom drops from 5.16 eV above the ground state to 2.93 eV above the ground state. What is the frequency of the photon emitted by the atom?

2. A calcium atom is in an excited state when the energy level is 2.93 eV, $E_2$, above the ground state. A photon of energy 1.20 eV strikes the calcium atom and is absorbed by it. To what energy level is the calcium atom raised? Refer to diagram below.

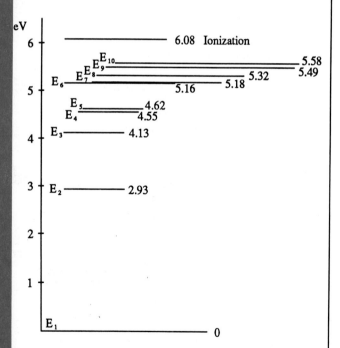

Energy Level Diagram for Calcium Atom

3. A calcium atom is in an excited state at the $E_6$ energy level. How much energy is released when the atom dropped down to the $E_2$ energy level?

▶4. A photon of orange light, wavelength of 600 nm, enters a calcium atom in the $E_6$ excited state and ionizes the atom. What kinetic energy will the electron have as it is ejected from the atom?

5. Calculate the radius of the orbital associated with the energy level $E_4$ of the hydrogen atom.

6. Calculate the energy associated with the $E_7$ and the $E_2$ energy levels of the hydrogen atom.

7. Calculate the difference in energy levels in the previous problems.

8. What frequency photon is emitted from the hydrogen atom when the atom releases the energy found in the previous problem?

# Chapter 29

1. An LED, light-emitting diode, produces infrared radiation wavelength, 800 nm, when an electron jumps from the conduction band to the valence band. Find the energy width of the forbidden gap in this diode.

2. How many free electrons exist in 1.00 cm$^3$ of lithium? Its density is 0.534 gm/cm$^3$, atomic mass is 6.941 g/mol, and there is one free electron per atom.

3. The voltage drop across a diode is 0.70 V when it is connected in series to a 210-$\Omega$ resistor and a battery, and there is a 11-mA current. If the LED has an equivalent resistance of 70 $\Omega$, what potential difference must be supplied by the battery?

4. What resistor would replace the 210-$\Omega$ resistor in the previous problem if the current was changed to 30 mA?

5. What would the new current in the previous problem be if the leads on the battery were reversed?

# Chapter 30

1. What particles, and how many of each, make up an atom of $^{109}_{47}$Ag?

2. A calcium ion has 20 protons and 20 neutrons. Write its isotopic symbol.

3. What is the isotopic symbol of a zinc atom composed of 30 protons and 34 neutrons?

**4.** Write the complete nuclear equation for the alpha decay of $^{210}_{84}\text{Po}$.

**5.** Write the complete nuclear equation for the beta decay of $^{14}_{6}\text{C}$.

**6.** Complete the nuclear reaction:
$^{225}_{89}\text{Ac} \rightarrow {}^{4}_{2}\text{He} +$

**7.** Complete the nuclear reaction:
$^{227}_{88}\text{Ra} \rightarrow {}^{0}_{-1}\text{e} +$

▶ **8.** Complete the nuclear reaction:
$^{65}_{29}\text{Cu} + {}^{1}_{0}\text{n} \rightarrow \underline{\qquad} \rightarrow {}^{1}_{1}\text{p} +$

▶ **9.** Complete the nuclear equation:
$^{235}_{92}\text{U} + {}^{1}_{0}\text{n} \rightarrow {}^{96}_{40}\text{Zr} + 3({}^{1}_{0}\text{n}) +$

**10.** An isotope has a half-life of 3.0 d. What percent of the original material will be left after
 **a.** 6.0 d?
 **b.** 9.0 d?
 **c.** 12 d?

**11.** $^{211}_{86}\text{Rn}$ has a half-life of 15 h. What fraction of a sample would be left after 60 h?

▶ **12.** $^{209}_{84}\text{Po}$ has a half-life of 103 years. How long would it take for a 100-g sample to decay so only 3.1 g of Po-209 was left?

▶ **13.** The positron, $_{+1}^{0}\text{e}$, is the antiparticle to the electron and is the particle ejected from the nucleus in some nuclear reactions. Complete the nuclear reaction:
$^{17}_{9}\text{F} \rightarrow {}^{0}_{+1}\text{e} +$

▶ **14.** Complete the nuclear reaction: $^{22}_{11}\text{Na} \rightarrow {}^{0}_{+1}\text{e} +$

**15.** Find the charge of a $\pi^+$ meson made of a $u$ and *anti-d* quark pair.

**16.** Baryons are particles that are made of three quarks. Find the charge on each of the following baryons.
 **a.** neutron; $d, d, u$ quark triplet
 **b.** antiproton; *anti-u, anti-u, anti-d* quark triplet

## Chapter 31

**1.** The carbon isotope, $^{12}_{6}\text{C}$, has a nuclear mass of 12.000 000 u.
 **a.** What is the mass defect of this isotope?
 **b.** What is the binding energy of its nucleus?

**2.** The sulphur isotope, $^{32}_{16}\text{S}$, has a nuclear mass of 31.972 07 u.
 **a.** What is the mass defect of this isotope?
 **b.** What is the binding energy of its nucleus?

**3.** The sodium isotope, $^{22}_{11}\text{Na}$, has a nuclear mass of 21.994 434 u.
 **a.** What is the mass defect of this isotope?
 **b.** What is the binding energy of its nucleus?
 **c.** What is the binding energy per nucleon?

▶ **4.** The binding energy for $^{7}_{3}\text{Li}$ is 39.25 MeV. Calculate the mass of the lithium-7 nucleus in atomic mass units.

**5.** Write the complete nuclear equation for the positron decay of $^{132}_{55}\text{Cs}$.

**6.** Complete the nuclear reaction:
$^{14}_{7}\text{N} + {}^{1}_{0}\text{n} \rightarrow \underline{\qquad} \rightarrow {}^{1}_{1}\text{p} +$

**7.** Complete the nuclear reaction:
$^{65}_{29}\text{Cu} + {}^{1}_{0}\text{n} \rightarrow \underline{\qquad} \rightarrow {}^{1}_{1}\text{p} +$

**8.** When a magnesium isotope, $^{24}_{12}\text{Mg}$, is bombarded with neutrons, it absorbs a neutron and then emits a proton. Write the complete nuclear equation for this reaction.

▶ **9.** When oxygen-17 is bombarded by neutrons, it absorbs a neutron and then emits an alpha particle. The resulting nucleus is unstable and it will emit a beta particle. Write the complete nuclear equation for this reaction.

**10.** Complete the following fission reaction:
$^{239}_{94}\text{Pu} + {}^{1}_{0}\text{n} \rightarrow {}^{137}_{52}\text{Te} + 3({}^{1}_{0}\text{n})$

**11.** Complete the following fission reaction:
$^{233}_{92}\text{U} + {}^{1}_{0}\text{n} \rightarrow {}^{134}_{55}\text{Cs} + 2({}^{1}_{0}\text{n}) +$

**12.** Complete the following fission reaction:
$^{235}_{92}\text{U} + {}^{1}_{0}\text{n} \rightarrow {}^{90}_{38}\text{Sr} + 10({}^{1}_{0}\text{n}) +$

▶ **13.** Strontium-90 has a mass of 89.907 747 u, xenon-136 has a mass of 135.907 221 u, and uranium-235 has a mass of 235.043 915 u.
 **a.** Compute the mass defect in the previous problem.
 **b.** Compute the amount of energy released.

▶ **14.** One of the simplest fusion reactions involves the production of deuterium, $^{2}_{1}\text{H}$ (2.014 102 u), from a neutron and a proton. Write the complete fusion reaction and find the amount of energy released.

**15.** The fusion reactions most likely to succeed in a fusion reactor are listed below. Complete each fusion reaction.
 **a.** $^{2}_{1}\text{H} + {}^{2}_{1}\text{H} \rightarrow {}^{3}_{1}\text{H} +$
 **b.** $^{2}_{1}\text{H} + {}^{2}_{1}\text{H} \rightarrow {}^{3}_{2}\text{He} +$
 **c.** $^{2}_{1}\text{H} + {}^{3}_{1}\text{H} \rightarrow {}^{4}_{2}\text{He} +$
 **d.** $^{3}_{1}\text{H} + {}^{3}_{1}\text{H} \rightarrow {}^{4}_{2}\text{He} + 2$

# Appendix B Continued
## Answers to Supplemental Problems

### Chapter 1
*No supplemental problems*

### Chapter 2

1. **a.** $8.1 \times 10^5$ g
   **b.** $6.34 \times 10^{-4}$ g
   **c.** $6 \times 10^7$ g
   **d.** $1.0 \times 10^{-6}$ g

2. **a.** $5.8 \times 10^{-8}$ s
   **b.** $4.6 \times 10^7$ s
   **c.** 9.27 s
   **d.** $1.23 \times 10^4$ s

3. **a.** $6.32 \times 10^{-3}$ s
   **b.** $8.36 \times 10^8$ km
   **c.** $1.69 \times 10^4$ cm$^2$
   **d.** $6.45 \times 10^{-13}$ m/s

4. **a.** 4
   **b.** 5
   **c.** 3
   **d.** 3

5. **a.** 3
   **b.** 5
   **c.** 2
   **d.** 4

6. **a.** 90.0 g
   **b.** 1.68 km
   **c.** 128.6 kg
   **d.** 47.9 s

7. **a.** $2 \times 10^{16}$ m$^2$
   **b.** $1.4 \times 10^{-7}$ km$^2$
   **c.** 2.8 kg/m$^3$
   **d.** $1.7 \times 10^{-3}$ m/s

8. **a.** 22.2 m
   **b.** 21 m$^2$

9. **c.** $d = 5t^2$

10. **d.** 0.30 m/s
    **e.** $d = 0.30t$

11. **a.** $m = \dfrac{Fr}{v^2}$
    **b.** $r = \dfrac{mv^2}{F}$
    **c.** $v = \sqrt{\dfrac{Fr}{m}}$

12. $d_0 = \dfrac{d_i f}{d_i - f}$

13. **a.** 160 cm$^2$
    **b.** 140 cm$^2$

### Chapter 3

1. **a.** 205 m
   **b.** −45 m
   **c.** 205 m

2. 15 km/h; 0

3. 330 m/s

4. 20 m/s

5. **a.** 0.450 s
   **b.** 2592 km/h

6. $3.3 \times 10^{-7}$ s

7. 60 km/h

8. **b.** 13.5 m, 5.5 s

9. **a.** 10 m
   **b.** 30 m
   **c.** 0 m
   **d.** −40 m
   **e.** 80 m distance, but no displacement

10. **a.** 2 m/s
    **b.** 6 m/s
    **c.** 0 m/s
    **d.** −8 m/s

11. **b.** 1 h

12. **a.** ≈ 10 m/s
    **b.** 0 m/s
    **c.** ≈ −10 m/s

13. **c.** 75 m/s
    **e.** 300 m

14. **b.** 3600 m
    **c.** 9000 m
    **d.** 0 m

15. **a.** 25 km/h
    **b.** 145 km/h

### Chapter 4

1. $-3.3 \times 10^3$ m/s$^2$

2. **a.** constant velocity = 10 m/s
   **b.** slows to $v = 0$ m/s
   **c.** 0 m/s$^2$
   **d.** −5 m/s$^2$

3. **c.** ≈ 30 m/s$^2$

4. 8.00 s

5. 34 m/s

6. 160 m

7. **a.** −8.0 m/s$^2$
   **b.** 480 m

8. **a.** $4.9 \times 10^{-3}$ s
   **b.** $3.3 \times 10^2$ m/s

9. **a.** 2.8 m/s$^2$
   **b.** 35 m

10. 26 m/s

11. −81 m/s$^2$

12. 35 m/s = 130 km/h

13. **a.** 0.23 m/s
    **b.** 0.24 m/s$^2$

14. **a.** 59 m/s
    **b.** $1.8 \times 10^2$ m

15. 5.6 s

16. −20 m

### Chapter 5

1. $2.36 \times 10^3$ N in direction of acceleration

2. 750 kg

3. 75 N

4. 60 kg

5. 3.3 m/s$^2$

6. **a.** 3.6 m/s$^2$
   **b.** $4.9 \times 10^2$ N

7. $1.6 \times 10^{-26}$ N

8. **a.** 2 N
   **b.** 0.02

9. 7.4 N

10. 0.60 m/s$^2$

11. $3.3 \times 10^3$ N

12. **a.** 490 N
    **b.** 490 N
    **c.** $3.8 \times 10^2$ N
    **d.** $3.6 \times 10^2$ N
    **e.** 490 N
    **f.** 0

13. $3.3$ m/s$^2$

## Chapter 6

1. **a.** $\theta = 84.000°$
   **b.** $\theta = 27.00°$
   **c.** $\theta = 35.00°$
   **d.** $\theta = 7.998°$
   **e.** $\theta = 49.00°$
   **f.** $\theta = 12.01°$

2. **a.** 0.53
   **b.** 1.0
   **c.** 1
   **d.** 1.6
   **e.** 0.64
   **f.** 0.33

4. **a.** 140 N
   **b.** 20 N
   **c.** 100 N

5. 38.5 min

6. **a.** 90 N
   **b.** 87 N
   **c.** 84 N
   **d.** 79 N
   **e.** 67 N
   **f.** 30 N

7. $R = 42$ m, $315°$

8. $V = 112$ m/s, $117°$

9. $F = 820$ N, $232°$

10. $R = 48.1$ m, $3.6°$ north of east

11. $1.93 \times 10^2$ km, north
    $2.30 \times 10^2$ km, east

12. 200 N

13. $V_x = -50.0$ km/h,
    $V_y = -86.6$ km/h

14. **a.** horizontal = 48 N;
    vertical = 82 N
    **b.** horizontal = 82 N;
    vertical = 48 N

15. $0.71$ m/s$^2$

16. **a.** 30 N
    **b.** 29 N

c. 21 N
d. 15 N
e. 0 N

17. 580 km/h, 54° east of north

18. 74 N, 253°

19. 460 N

20. 22 N

21. **a.** $4.9$ m/s$^2$
    **b.** 59 m
    **c.** 1 s

## Chapter 7

1. **a.** 10.0 s
   **b.** $2.00 \times 10^3$ m

2. 0.966 m

3. 132 m

4. 1.7 m

5. 1.7 m

6. **a.** 3.46 s
   **b.** 58.8 m

7. **a.** 55°
   **b.** 14 m

8. **a.** 28 m/s
   **b.** 4.1 s
   **c.** 20 m

9. **a.** 57.9 m
   **b.** 10.2 m

10. 13 m/s

11. $1.5 \times 10^3$ m

12. **a.** $2.1 \times 10^2$ N
    **b.** $1.7 \times 10^2$ N

13. 972 N

14. 2.0 m

15. **a.** 2.01 s
    **b.** 4.86 s

16. **a.** 0.10 kg
    **b.** 0.25 m
    **c.** shorten pendulum to 4.1 cm

## Chapter 8

1. $2.7 \times 10^{12}$ m

2. **a.** $2.21 \times 10^{15}$ m$^2$/s
   **b.** $2.0 \times 10^{11}$ m$^2$/s

3. $4.2 \times 10^7$ m

4. $1.0 \times 10^{-47}$ N

5. $6.67 \times 10^{-11}$ N

6. **a.** $1.6 \times 10^3$ kg
   **b.** $1.3 \times 10^{-10}$ m/s$^2$

7. $8.3 \times 10^{-9}$ N

8. $7.2 \times 10^{22}$ kg

9. **a.** $1.7 \times 10^{-10}$ N
   **b.** $1.7 \times 10^{-12}$ N

10. $6.0 \times 10^{24}$ kg

11. 235 N

12. 79 days

13. $V = 3.47 \times 10^3$ m/s;
    $T = 6.45 \times 10^3$ s or 1.79 h

14. $19.6$ m/s$^2$; $2.45$ m/s$^2$; $4.9$ m/s$^2$

15. $7.35$ m/s$^2$

16. $1.60$ m/s$^2$

## Chapter 9

1. 0.013 s

2. **a.** 74 N · s
   **b.** $1.0 \times 10^1$ m/s

3. **a.** $2.0 \times 10^4$ kg · m/s
   **b.** $1.3 \times 10^3$ N

4. $-1.2 \times 10^3$ N

5. $-6.0 \times 10^1$ N

6. **a.** $-14.5$ kg · m/s
   **b.** $-3.2 \times 10^4$ N

7. **a.** $1.32 \times 10^4$ kg · m/s
   **b.** $-1.32 \times 10^4$ kg · m/s
   **c.** $1.32 \times 10^4$ kg · m/s
   **d.** $-19.4$ m/s

8. 9.6 km/h

9. $-4.94$ m/s

10. 0.30 m/s

11. 0.35 m/s

12. 1.1 m/s

13. 1.26 in direction of riding

14. 2.8 m/s

15. **b.** 3.5 m/s; 67°

# Chapter 10

1. 988 J
2. $2.75 \times 10^4$ N
3. $8.87 \times 10^7$ J
4. $3.44 \times 10^3$ J
5. $4.4 \times 10^3$ J
6. $3.4 \times 10^3$ J
7. $8.0 \times 10^4$ J
8. 36.2°
9. $3.4 \times 10^4$ W
10. 126 W
11. $2.04 \times 10^3$ W
12. 0.63 kW
13. **a.** 3.5
    **b.** 4.00
    **c.** 88%
14. 0.24 m
15. 31.5 cm

# Chapter 11

1. $2.26 \times 10^{-12}$ J
2. 0.90 J
3. **a.** 84 J
   **b.** 84 J
   **c.** 11 m/s
4. 5.2 m
5. **a.** $2.6 \times 10^4$ J
   **b.** 66 m
   **c.** $3.9 \times 10^2$ N
6. 2.1 J
7. $2.8 \times 10^3$ J
8. −2.0 J
9. 0.24 m
10. 72°
11. **a.** $1.17 \times 10^3$ J
    **b.** $3.00 \times 10^3$ J
    **c.** $3.00 \times 10^3$ J
    **d.** $4.17 \times 10^3$ J
    **e.** 23.6 m/s
12. **a.** $2.4 \times 10^5$ J
    **b.** $2.0 \times 10^2$ m
    **c.** $1.2 \times 10^3$ N
    **d.** $1.7 \times 10^3$ N

13. **a.** 12.5 m/s
    **b.** 781 J
14. 19 m/s
15. $2.8 \times 10^2$ m/s

# Chapter 12

1. 238.55 K
2. −222.87°C
3. $1.3 \times 10^5$ J removed
4. $3.94 \times 10^3$ J
5. 4.6 kg
6. 0°C
7. 132 J/kg · K
8. **a.** $8.2 \times 10^3$ J
   **b.** $1.3 \times 10^2$ J/kg · K
9. 25.2°C
10. $T_f = 16.2$°C
11. $1.18 \times 10^5$ J
12. $3.6 \times 10^5$ J
13. 30.0°C
14. 0.29°C
15. 47.8 g

# Chapter 13

1. 0.760 m
2. $1.6 \times 10^4$ Pa
3. 36.5 kg
4. $4.0 \times 10^3$ Pa
5. **a.** $1.61 \times 10^3$ Pa
   **b.** $6.07 \times 10^3$ Pa
6. **a.** 412 N
   **b.** $4.20 \times 10^{-2}$ m$^3$
7. 16.0
8. 875 N
9. $5.00 \times 10^3$ kg/m$^3$
10. $3.92 \times 10^6$ N
11. $-2.7 \times 10^{-1}$ m
12. 0.801 m$^3$
13. $5.3 \times 10^3$ cm$^3$
14. $4.5 \times 10^{-2}$ cm

15. 719°C

# Chapter 14

1. 5.00 m
2. **a.** 0.250 s
   **b.** 4.00 Hz
3. **a.** 0.244 s
   **b.** 4.10 Hz
4. 1.50 m/s
5. 0.330 m/s
6. 0.600 m/s
7. 8.00 m/s
8. 1.6 m
9. 3.00 m
10. 12.0 Hz
11. 24°

# Chapter 15

1. $8.6 \times 10^2$ m
2. 150 m/s
3. 800 m/s
4. 1.60 m
5. 0.635 m
6. 1.07 s
7. 7.87 s
8. 1030 m
9. 430 Hz
10. 310 Hz
11. 70 dB
12. 110 dB
13. 451 Hz
15. 4 Hz
16. 8 beats/s
17. 435 Hz

# Chapter 16

1. $4.5 \times 10^2$ nm
2. $4.50 \times 10^5$ m
3. $3.8 \times 10^{16}$ m

**4.** $2.7 \times 10^2$ s

**5.** 2.5 s

**6.** $3.37 \times 10^{-7}$ s

**7.** 364 m

**8.** 60 MHz

**9.** 0.50 lx

**10.** $1.1 \times 10^2$ cd

**11.** 6.9 m

## Chapter 17

**1.** 28°

**2.** 1.37

**3.** 15.9°

**4.** 48.4°

**5.** 85.23560°

**7.** 49.5°

**8.** apparent interception of rays at 9.0 cm below surface; apparent depth/ true depth = 0.75

**9.** $2.26 \times 10^8$ m/s

**10.** $1.28 \times 10^8$ m/s

**11.** 1.71

**13.** 1.56

**14.** 29.8°

**17.** 0.20

**18.** $2.0 \times 10^6$ m/s

## Chapter 18

**1.** 75 cm behind mirror

**2.** 20.0 cm

**3.** 75.0 cm

**4.** 6.25 cm in front of mirror

**5.** 24.2 cm

**6.** 42.6 cm

**7.** **a.** 21.1 cm
**b.** −3.81 cm; inverted

**8.** −1.92 cm; inverted

**9.** 3.0

**10.** −0.15 m

**11.** −0.060 m

**12.** 39.3 cm

**13.** 10 cm

**14.** $1.1 \times 10^2$ cm

**15.** −1.5 cm; inverted

**16.** 6.7 cm

**17.** 0.19 mm

**18.** 15 cm

**19.** 25 cm; erect

## Chapter 19

**1.** $4.00 \times 10^2$ nm

**2.** $5.0 \times 10^2$ nm

**3.** 5.40 mm

**4.** 0.750 m

**5.** 6.00 km

**6.** $1.3 \times 10^{-6}$ m

**7.** 1.62 m

**8.** 3.7 m

**9.** 5.7°

**10.** $2.35 \times 10^{-3}$ mm/line

**11.** 16.7°

**12.** 524 nm

**13.** 0.360 m

**14.** $2.18 \times 10^{-5}$ m

## Chapter 20

**1.** $F/4$

**2.** $4F$

**3.** $1.0 \times 10^{-5}$ N

**4.** $8.0 \times 10^{-5}$ N

**5.** $6.25 \times 10^{18}$ electrons

**6.** $+9.0 \times 10^3$ N

**7.** $-1.1 \times 10^2$ N; the force is attractive

**8.** +44N; away

**9.** $-9.2 \times 10^{-16}$ N

**10.** +2.5 N

**11.** $\pm 2.0 + 10^{-10}$ C

**12.** $-9.7 \times 10^{-6}$ C

**13.** 7.4 N to the left

**14.** 6.7 N at 7.2° to the left of vertical

## Chapter 21

**1.** $1.00 \times 10^3$ N/C

**2.** 8.0 N/C

**3.** 6.9 N/C

**4.** 1.5 mC

**5.** $-1.60 \times 10^{-16}$ N

**7.** $2.00 \times 10^3$ V

**8.** 0.15 mJ

**9.** $9.00 \times 10^{10}$ J

**10.** 11 V

**11.** $6.0 \times 10^3$ V

**12.** $1.8 \times 10^8$ V/m

**13.** $1.2 \times 10^{-13}$ N

**14.** 40 μF

**15.** $8.6 \times 10^5$ V

**16.** 3.6 mC

## Chapter 22

**1.** 0.160 A

**2.** $1.00 \times 10^2$ C

**3.** 180 W

**4.** 83 W

**5.** **a.** 2.0 A
**b.** 12 kJ

**6.** 4.00 Ω

**7.** 20.0 Ω

**8.** 0.400 V

**9.** **a.** 10.4 A

**10.** **a.** 0.500 A
**b.** 0.522 A

**11.** 460 Ω

**12.** 133 Ω

**13.** **a.** 1.41 A
**b.** 0.447 A

**14.** 24 W

**15.** 62 cents/year

**16. a.** 16.7 A
 **b.** 7.19 Ω

 **c.** $3.36

## Chapter 23 _____

**1. a.** 350 Ω
 **b.** 0.143 A
 **c.** 17.9 V

**2. b.** 60 Ω
 **c.** 0.20 A

**3. a.** 680 Ω
 **b.** 18 mA
 **c.** 2.2 V

**4. a.** 0.10 A
 **b.** 400 Ω
 **c.** 40 Ω

**5.** 153 Ω

**6.** 7.2 Ω

**7.** 4.0 Ω

**8. a.** 36 Ω
 **b.** 0.19 A
 **c.** 0.14 A

**9. a.** 17 Ω
 **b.** $I_1 = 1.0$ A; $I_2 = 0.64$ A;
 $I_3 = 0.41$ A

**11. b.** 6.0 Ω
 **c.** 1.0 A
 **d.** 0.75 A
 **e.** 2.3 V

**12. b.** 20.0Ω
 **c.** 6.00 A
 **d.** 3.00 A
 **e.** 90.0 V

**15. a.** $6.0 \times 10^3$ Ω
 **b.** $6 \times 10^3$ Ω
 **c.** $1.8 \times 10^4$ Ω
 **d.** $2.0 \times 10^3$ Ω

## Chapter 24 _____

**6.** 0.11 N

**7.** 0.060 N

**8.** 21 mN

**9.** 0.30 T

**10.** 4.2 A

**11.** 599 kΩ

**14.** $9.6 \times 10^{-16}$ N into the page

**15.** $2.8 \times 10^{-14}$ N

**16.** $1.9 \times 10^{-12}$ N

## Chapter 25 _____

**2.** 0.20 mV

**3.** 5.0 mT

**4.** 20 m/s

**5.** 10 m/s

**6. a.** 6.4 V
 **b.** 1.0 A

**7.** 41 mA

**8.** 170 V

**9.** 3.5 A

**10.** 406 V

**11.** 15.0 A

**12.** 69.4 Ω

**14.** 1 to 545

**15. a.** 50 turns
 **b.** 0.40 A

## Chapter 26 _____

**1.** $7.6 \times 10^5$ m/s

**2.** 0.47 mT

**4.** 2.3 mT

**5.** 0.27 m

**6.** 2.8 cm

**7.** $1.25 \times 10^7$ C/kg

**8.** $2.7 \times 10^{-26}$ kg

**9.** 16 u

**10.** 2.89 cm

**11.** 6.25 cm

**12.** 0.75 cm

**13.** 0.794 m

## Chapter 27 _____

**2.** $8.21 \times 10^{14}$ Hz

**3.** 3.8 eV

**4.** $1.2 \times 10^{-18}$ J

**5.** 5.0 V

**6.** $5.3 \times 10^{-19}$ J

**7.** $5.3 \times 10^{-19}$ J

**8.** $1.07 \times 10^{-19}$ J

**9.** $1.66 \times 10^{-27}$ kg · m/s

**10.** $9.47 \times 10^{-28}$ kg · m/s

**11.** 0.24 nm

**12.** $2.4 \times 10^6$ m/s

**13. a.** $4.2 \times 10^7$ m/s
 **b.** 0.017 nm

## Chapter 28 _____

**1.** $5.38 \times 10^{14}$ Hz

**2.** $E_3$

**3.** 2.23 eV

**4.** 1.15 eV

**5.** 0.848 nm

**6.** $E_1 = -0.278$ eV
 $E_2 = -3.40$ eV

**7.** 3.12 eV

**8.** $7.53 \times 10^{14}$ Hz

## Chapter 29 _____

**1.** 1.55 eV

**2.** $4.63 \times 10^{22}$ e⁻/cm³

**3.** 3.1 V

**4.** 20 Ω

**5.** 0

## Chapter 30 _____

**1.** 47 electrons, 47 protons, 62 neutrons

**2.** $^{40}_{20}$Ca

**3.** $^{64}_{30}$Zn

**4.** $^{210}_{84}$Bi $\rightarrow$ $^{4}_{2}$He + $^{206}_{82}$Pb

**5.** $^{14}_{6}$C $\rightarrow$ $^{0}_{-1}$e + $^{14}_{7}$N + $^{0}_{0}\bar{v}$

**6.** $^{225}_{89}$Ac $\rightarrow$ $^{4}_{2}$He + $^{221}_{87}$Fr

**7.** $^{227}_{88}$Ra $\rightarrow$ $^{0}_{-1}$e + $^{227}_{89}$Ac

**8.** $^{65}_{29}$Cu + $^{1}_{0}$n $\rightarrow$ $^{66}_{29}$Cu $\rightarrow$ $^{1}_{1}$p + $^{65}_{28}$Ni

**9.** $^{235}_{92}$U + $^{1}_{0}$n $\rightarrow$ $^{96}_{40}$Zr + 3($^{1}_{0}$n) + $^{137}_{52}$Te

**10. a.** 25% is left
 **b.** 12.5 % is left
 **c.** 6.3 % is left

**11.** 1/16 is left

**12.** 5 half-lives, or 515 years

**13.** $^0_1e + ^{17}_8O + ^0_0v$

**14.** $^0_1e + ^{22}_{10}Ne + ^0_0v$

**15.** +1

**16. a.** 0
 **b.** −1

# Chapter 31 ─────────

**1. a.** 0.098 940 u
 **b.** 92.16 MeV

**2. a.** 0.291 77 u
 **b.** 271.8 MeV

**3. a.** 0.186 96 u
 **b.** 174.2 MeV
 **c.** 7.916 MeV/nucleon

**4.** 7.01600 U

**5.** $^{132}_{55}Cs \rightarrow ^0_1e + ^{133}_{54}Xe + ^0_0v$

**6.** $^{15}_7N \rightarrow ^1_1p + ^{14}_6C$

**7.** $^{66}_{29}Cu \rightarrow ^1_1p + ^{65}_{28}Ni$

**8.** $^{24}_{12}Mg + ^1_0n \rightarrow ^{25}_{12}Mg \rightarrow ^1_1p + ^{24}_{11}Na$

**9.** $^{17}_8O + ^1_0n \rightarrow ^{18}_8O \rightarrow ^4_2He + ^{14}_6C \rightarrow$ $^0_{-1}e + ^{14}_7N + ^{0-}_0v$

**10.** $^{137}_{52}Te + 3(^1_0n) + ^{100}_{42}Mo$

**11.** $^{134}_{55}Cs + 2(^1_0n) + ^{98}_{37}Rb$

**12.** $^{90}_{38}Sr + 10(^1_0n) + ^{136}_{54}Xe$

**13. a.** 0.15096
 **b.** 140.6 MeV

**14.** $^1_1p + ^1_0n \rightarrow ^2_1H$ 2.224 MeV

**15. a.** $^2_1H + ^2_1H \rightarrow ^3_1H + ^1_1H$
 **b.** $^2_1H + ^2_1H \rightarrow ^3_2H + ^1_0n$
 **c.** $^2_1H + ^3_1H \rightarrow ^4_2H + ^1_0n$
 **d.** $^3_1H + ^3_1H \rightarrow ^4_2H_2 + 2(^1_0n)$

# Appendix B Continued
## Numerical Answers to Text Questions

## Chapter 1
*No numerical answers*

## Chapter 2
**Concept Review**

**p.19**
**1.1** $1.574 \times 10^8$

**p.26**
**2.3** Between 181.5 and 182.5 cm

**p.31**
**3.2** Between 12 and 13 m/s

**p.34**
**4.3** $S = 20T$

**Applying Concepts**

**p.36**
**2a.** Approx. 1 cm

**2b.** Approx. 0.1 mm

**2c.** Approx. 3 m

**2d.** Approx. 1 km

**p.37**

**9.** Zero

## Chapter 3
**Concept Review**

**p.49**
**1.4b** 171 numbers/min

**Applying Concepts**

**p.58**
**9a.** At 1.4 s and 8.2 s

**9b.** Car A

**9c.** At 4s

**p.61**
**Using a Graphing Calculator**

**19.7** m/s

## Chapter 4
*No numerical answers*

## Chapter 5
**Reviewing Concepts**

**p.104**
**5.** 3.0 kg

## Chapter 6
**Concept Review**

**p.113**
**1.3** 700 N and 100 N

**p.120**
**2.1** 5 N

**Applying Concepts**

**p.128**
**1.** 10 mm

**2.** 15 N

**3.** Largest: 7 N; smallest: 1 N

**9.** Zero

**p.129**
**12a.** 45°

**12b.** 0°

**12c.** 90°

## Chapter 7
**Applying Concepts**

**p.151**
**1.** −20 m/s

**4.** 6.0 s

**p.153**
**Using a Graphing Calculator**

45 m above the ground

## Chapter 8
**Concept Review**

**p.170**
**2.1** 1.6 N/kg

**Applying Concepts**

**p.171**
**2.** Force becomes 1/4 as strong

**4.** Ratio is halved

**9.** $(1/4)g$

**10.** *g* would double

**11.** 3 times Earth's *g*

**12.** It will double

**p.173**
**Using a Graphing Calculator**

9.77 m/s$^2$; 9.73 m/s$^2$; 9.46 m/s$^2$; 9.18 m/s$^2$

## Chapter 9
*No numerical answers*

## Chapter 10
**Concept Review**

**p.211**
**2.3a** 2 J

**2.3b** 2 J

## Chapter 11
**Applying Concepts**

**p.237**
**11.** 50 J

**13.** Speed is larger by a ratio of 1.414:1

## Chapter 12
**Applying Concepts**

**p.262**
**2a.** −40°C = −40°F

**2b.** 574K = 574°F

## Chapter 13
**Concept Review**
**p.277**

**1.1b** Force is 1.67 times more on the larger box

## Chapter 14

*No numerical answers*

## Chapter 15
**Concept Review**

**p.312**
**1.4** By a factor of 300

**Applying Concepts**

**p.325**
**7.** 100 times greater

**8.** 10

**p.327**
**Using a Graphing Calculator**

Amplitude = 1.41;
wavelength = 360

## Chapter 16
**Concept Review**

**p.336**
**1.1** 9 km

**1.4** 0.71 m

**p.342**
**2.4** $\lambda/2$

**Reviewing Concepts**

**p.343**
**2.** 400 nm to 700 nm

**Applying Concepts**

**p.344**
**3.** 1/4 as bright

**4.** 1/4 as bright

## Chapter 17
**Applying Concepts**

**p.363**
**5a.** 19.2°

**5b.** 30.0°

## Chapter 18

**p.389**
**Using a Graphing Calculator**

At 5 cm, 7.5 cm; at 10 cm, 15.2 cm;
at 13 cm, 38 cm; at 17 cm, 37 cm;
at 20 cm, 14.4 cm; at 30 cm,
5.0 cm; at 50 cm, 2.1 cm

## Chapter 19

*No numerical answers*

## Chapter 20
**Applying Concepts**

**p.422**
**12.** 16 times the original force

## Chapter 21

*No numerical answers*

## Chapter 22
**Reviewing Concepts**

**p.464**
**4.** $6.25 \times 10^{18}$

**Applying Concepts**

**p.465**
**8.** With 1.5-V battery, $R = 3.3 \times 10^4$ $\Omega$; with 3.0-V battery, $R = 120$ $\Omega$

## Chapter 23

*No numerical answers*

## Chapter 24

*No numerical answers*

## Chapter 25

*No numerical answers*

## Chapter 26
**Reviewing Concepts**

**p.552**
**1.** Mass = $9.11 \times 10^{-31}$ kg; charge = $-1.60 \times 10^{-19}$ C

## Chapter 27
**Concept Review**

**p.569**
**2.4** Approx. 50 nm

**Applying Concepts**

**p.570**
**1.** Approx. 7-fold increase

**7.** Approx. $10^{33}$-fold difference

## Chapter 28
**Applying Concepts**

**p.592**
**6.** Maximum energy = 13.6 eV

## Chapter 29

*No numerical answers*

## Chapter 30
**Concept Review**

**p.624**
**1.3** 113 days

**Applying Concepts**

**p.636**
**2.** Uranium-238, with 146 neutrons

**p.637**
**Using a Graphing Calculator**

850, 2400 and 4200 years old, respectively

## Chapter 31

*No numerical answers*

**Chapter 3** Describing Motion: Velocity

$$\vec{v}_{AVE} = \frac{\Delta \vec{d}}{\Delta t}$$

**Chapter 4** Acceleration

$$\vec{a}_{AVE} = \frac{\Delta \vec{v}}{\Delta t}$$
$$\vec{v}_f = \vec{v}_i + \vec{a}t$$
$$\vec{d} = \frac{1}{2}(\vec{v}_f + \vec{v}_i)t$$
$$\vec{d} = \vec{v}_i t + \frac{1}{2}\vec{a}t^2$$
$$\vec{v}_f^2 = \vec{v}_i^2 + 2\vec{a}\vec{d}$$

**Chapter 5** Forces

$$\vec{F} = m\vec{a}$$
$$\vec{FW} = m\vec{g}$$
$$\vec{F}_f = \mu \vec{F}_N$$

**Chapter 6** Vectors

$$\vec{F}_v = \vec{F}\sin\theta \qquad \vec{F}_h = \vec{F}\cos\theta$$
$$\vec{F}^2 = \vec{F}_h^2 + \vec{F}_v^2$$

**Chapter 7** Motion in Two Dimensions

$$\vec{x} = \vec{x}_x t \qquad \vec{y} = \vec{v}_y t + \frac{1}{2}\vec{g}t^2$$
$$\vec{a}_c = \frac{\vec{v}^2}{r} \qquad T = 2\pi\sqrt{\frac{l}{|g|}}$$

**Chapter 8** Universal Gravitation

$$F = G\frac{m_1 m_2}{d^2}$$

**Chapter 9** Momentum and Its Conservation

$$\vec{p} = m\vec{v}$$
$$\vec{F}\Delta t = \Delta \vec{p}$$
$$\vec{p}_A + \vec{p}_B = \vec{p}'_A + \vec{p}'_B$$

**Chapter 10** Work, Energy, and Simple Machines

$$W = Fd$$
$$P = \frac{W}{t} \qquad MA = \frac{F_r}{F_e}$$

$$IMA = \frac{d_e}{d_r}$$
$$efficiency = \frac{W_o}{W_i} \times 100\%$$

**Chapter 11** Energy

$$E_k = \frac{1}{2}mv^2$$
$$W = \Delta E_k$$
$$E_p = mgh$$
$$E_{ki} + E_{pi} = E_{kf} + E_{pf}$$

**Chapter 12** Thermal Energy

$$Q = mc\Delta T$$
$$Q = mH_f$$
$$Q = mH_v$$

**Chapter 13** States of Matter

$$p = \frac{F}{A} \qquad \frac{F_1}{A_1} = \frac{F_2}{A_2}$$

**Chapter 14** Waves and Energy Transfer

$$v = \lambda f$$

**Chapter 16** Light

$$E = \frac{P}{4\pi d^2}$$

**Chapter 17** Reflection and Refraction

$$n_i \sin\theta_i = n_r \sin\theta_r$$
$$n = \frac{c}{v}$$

**Chapter 18** Mirrors and Lenses

$$\frac{1}{f} = \frac{1}{d_i} + \frac{1}{d_o}$$
$$m = \frac{h_i}{h_o} = -\frac{d_i}{d_o}$$

**Chapter 19** Diffraction and Interference of Light

$$\lambda = \frac{xd}{L} = d\sin\theta$$

**Chapter 20** Static Electricity

$$F = \frac{Kqq'}{d^2}$$

**Chapter 21** Electric Fields

$$E = \frac{F}{q'} \qquad \Delta V = \frac{\Delta PE}{q'}$$
$$C = \frac{q}{V}$$

**Chapter 22** Current Electricity

$$R = \frac{V}{I} \qquad P = VI$$

**Chapter 23** Series and Parallel Circuits

$$R_{eq} = R_1 + R_2 + R_3$$
$$\frac{1}{R_{eq}} = \frac{1}{R_1} + \frac{1}{R_2} + \frac{1}{R_3}$$

**Chapter 24** Magnetic Fields

$$B = \frac{F}{IL} \qquad F = Bqv$$

**Chapter 25** Electromagnetic Induction

$$EMF = BLv \qquad I_{eff} = 0.707 I_{max}$$
$$V_{eff} = 0.707 V_{max}$$
$$\frac{V_s}{V_p} = \frac{N_s}{N_p}$$

**Chapter 26** Electric and Magnetic Fields

$$\frac{q}{m} = \frac{v}{Br} \qquad \frac{q}{m} = \frac{2V}{B^2 r^2}$$

**Chapter 27** Quantum Theory

$$E = nhf \qquad KE = hf - hf_o$$
$$p = \frac{h}{\lambda}$$

**Chapter 28** The Atom

$$r_n = \frac{h^2}{4\pi^2 Kmq^2}n^2$$
$$E_n = \frac{-2\pi^2 K^2 mq^4}{h^2} \cdot \frac{1}{n^2}$$
$$hf = \Delta E$$

**Chapter 31** Nuclear Applications

$$E = mc^2$$

# Appendix D
## Tables

### TABLE D–1
#### SI Base Units

| Measurement | Unit | Symbol |
|---|---|---|
| length | metre | m |
| mass | kilogram | kg |
| time | second | s |
| electric current | ampere | A |
| temperature | kelvin | K |
| amount of substance | mole | mol |
| intensity of light | candela | cd |

### TABLE D–2
#### SI Prefixes

| Prefix | | Multiplication Factor | Prefix | | Multiplication Factor |
|---|---|---|---|---|---|
| exa | E | $1\ 000\ 000\ 000\ 000\ 000\ 000 = 10^{18}$ | deci | d | $0.1 = 10^{-1}$ |
| peta | P | $1\ 000\ 000\ 000\ 000\ 000 = 10^{15}$ | centi | c | $0.01 = 10^{-2}$ |
| tera | T | $1\ 000\ 000\ 000\ 000 = 10^{12}$ | milli | m | $0.001 = 10^{-3}$ |
| giga | G | $1\ 000\ 000\ 000 = 10^{9}$ | micro | μ | $0.000\ 001 = 10^{-6}$ |
| mega | M | $1\ 000\ 000 = 10^{6}$ | nano | n | $0.000\ 000\ 001 = 10^{-9}$ |
| kilo | k | $1\ 000 = 10^{3}$ | pico | p | $0.000\ 000\ 000\ 001 = 10^{-12}$ |
| hecto | h | $100 = 10^{2}$ | femto | f | $0.000\ 000\ 000\ 000\ 001 = 10^{-15}$ |
| deka | da | $10 = 10^{1}$ | atto | a | $0.000\ 000\ 000\ 000\ 000\ 001 = 10^{-18}$ |

### TABLE D–3
#### Units with Special Names Derived from SI Base Units

| Measurement | Unit | Symbol | Expressed in Base Units |
|---|---|---|---|
| energy, work | joule | J | $kg \cdot m^2/s^2$ |
| force | newton | N | $kg \cdot m/s^2$ |
| frequency | hertz | Hz | $1/s$ |
| illuminance | lux | lx | $m^{-2} \cdot cd$ |
| luminous flux | lumen | lm | cd |
| potential difference | volt | V | $kg \cdot m^2/A \cdot s^3$ |
| power | watt | W | $kg \cdot m^2/s^3$ |
| pressure | pascal | Pa | $kg/m \cdot s^2$ |
| quantity of electric charge | coulomb | C | $A \cdot s$ |
| resistance | ohm | Ω | $m^2 \cdot kg/s^3 \cdot A^2$ |
| magnetic field strength | tesla | T | $kg \cdot s^{-2} \cdot A^{-1}$ |
| capacitance | farad | F | $A^2 \cdot s^4/kg \cdot m^2$ |

# TABLE D–4
## Reference Data: Physical Constants, Conversion Factors, Useful Equations

## Physical Constants

Absolute zero temperature: $0 \text{ K} = -273.15°C$

Acceleration due to gravity at sea level: $9.801 \text{ m/s}^2$

Avogadro's number: $N_A = 6.022 \times 10^{23}$ particles/mol

Charge of an electron: $e = -1.6022 \times 10^{-19}$ C

Constant in Coulomb's law: $K = 8.988 \times 10^9 \text{ N} \cdot \text{m}^3/\text{C}^2$

Gravitational constant: $G = 6.673 \times 10^{-11} \text{ N} \cdot \text{m}^2/\text{kg}^2$

Mass of electron: $m_e = 9.109 \times 10^{-31}$ kg

Mass of a proton: $m_p = 1.673 \times 10^{-27}$ kg

Planck's constant: $h = 6.626 \times 10^{-34} \text{ J/Hz} = 4.136 \times 10^{-15} \text{ eV} \cdot \text{s}$

Speed of light in a vacuum: $c = 2.99792458 \times 10^8$ m/s (exact)

## Conversion Factors

1 atomic mass unit $= 1.661 \times 10^{-27} \text{ kg} = 931.5 \text{ MeV/c}^2$

1 electronvolt $= 1.602 \times 10^{-19}$ J

1 joule $= 1 \text{ N} \cdot \text{m}$

1 joule $= 1 \text{ V} \cdot \text{C}$

1 coulomb $= 6.242 \times 10^{18}$ elementary charge units

## Useful Equations

Quadratic equation: A quadratic equation may be reduced to the form

$$ax^2 + bx + c = 0$$

then
$$x = \frac{-b \pm \sqrt{b^2 - 4ac}}{2a}$$

Remember that the sign immediately preceding the coefficient is carried with the coefficient in solving for the two values of x.

Circumference of a circle: $C = 2\pi r$ or $C = \pi d$

Area of a circle: $A = \pi r^2$

Volume of a cylinder: $V = \pi r^2 h$

Surface area of a sphere: $A = 4\pi r^2$

Volume of a sphere: $V = \dfrac{4\pi r^3}{3}$

# TABLE D–5
## International Atomic Masses

| Element | Symbol | Atomic number | Atomic mass | Element | Symbol | Atomic number | Atomic mass |
|---|---|---|---|---|---|---|---|
| Actinium | Ac | 89 | 227.02777* | Neodymium | Nd | 60 | 144.24 |
| Aluminum | Al | 13 | 26.98154 | Neon | Ne | 10 | 20.179 |
| Americium | Am | 95 | 243.06139* | Neptunium | Np | 93 | 237.04819 |
| Antimony | Sb | 51 | 121.75 | Nickel | Ni | 28 | 58.70 |
| Argon | Ar | 18 | 39.948 | Niobium | Nb | 41 | 92.9064 |
| Arsenic | As | 33 | 74.9216 | Nitrogen | N | 7 | 14.0067 |
| Astatine | At | 85 | 209.98704* | Nobelium | No | 102 | 255.093* |
| Barium | Ba | 56 | 137.33 | Osmium | Os | 76 | 190.2 |
| Berkelium | Bk | 97 | 247.07032* | Oxygen | O | 8 | 15.9994 |
| Beryllium | Be | 4 | 9.01218 | Palladium | Pd | 46 | 106.4 |
| Bismuth | Bi | 83 | 208.9804 | Phosphorus | P | 15 | 30.97376 |
| Boron | B | 5 | 10.81 | Platinum | Pt | 78 | 195.09 |
| Bromine | Br | 35 | 79.904 | Plutonium | Pu | 94 | 244.06424* |
| Cadmium | Cd | 48 | 112.41 | Polonium | Po | 84 | 208.98244* |
| Calcium | Ca | 20 | 40.08 | Potassium | K | 19 | 39.0983 |
| Californium | Cf | 98 | 251.07961* | Praseodymium | Pr | 59 | 140.9077 |
| Carbon | C | 6 | 12.011 | Promethium | Pm | 61 | 144.91279* |
| Cerium | Ce | 58 | 140.12 | Protactinium | Pa | 91 | 231.03590* |
| Cesium | Cs | 55 | 132.9054 | Radium | Ra | 88 | 226.0254 |
| Chlorine | Cl | 17 | 35.453 | Radon | Rn | 86 | 222* |
| Chromium | Cr | 24 | 51.996 | Rhenium | Re | 75 | 186.207 |
| Cobalt | Co | 27 | 58.9332 | Rhodium | Rh | 45 | 102.9055 |
| Copper | Cu | 29 | 63.546 | Rubidium | Rb | 37 | 85.4678 |
| Curium | Cm | 96 | 247.07038* | Ruthenium | Ru | 44 | 101.07 |
| Dysprosium | Dy | 66 | 162.50 | Samarium | Sm | 62 | 150.4 |
| Einsteinium | Es | 99 | 254.08805* | Scandium | Sc | 21 | 44.9559 |
| Erbium | Er | 68 | 167.26 | Selenium | Se | 34 | 78.96 |
| Europium | Eu | 63 | 151.96 | Silicon | Si | 14 | 28.0855 |
| Fermium | Fm | 100 | 257.09515* | Silver | Ag | 47 | 107.868 |
| Fluorine | F | 9 | 18.998403 | Sodium | Na | 11 | 22.98977 |
| Francium | Fr | 87 | 223.01976* | Strontium | Sr | 38 | 87.62 |
| Gadolinium | Gd | 64 | 157.25 | Sulfur | S | 16 | 32.06 |
| Gallium | Ga | 31 | 69.72 | Tantalum | Ta | 73 | 180.9479 |
| Germanium | Ge | 32 | 72.59 | Technetium | Tc | 43 | 96.90639* |
| Gold | Au | 79 | 196.9665 | Tellurium | Te | 52 | 127.60 |
| Hafnium | Hf | 72 | 178.49 | Terbium | Tb | 65 | 158.9254 |
| Helium | He | 2 | 4.00260 | Thallium | Tl | 81 | 204.37 |
| Holmium | Ho | 67 | 164.9304 | Thorium | Th | 90 | 232.0381 |
| Hydrogen | H | 1 | 1.0079 | Thulium | Tm | 69 | 168.9342 |
| Indium | In | 49 | 114.82 | Tin | Sn | 50 | 118.69 |
| Iodine | I | 53 | 126.9045 | Titanium | Ti | 22 | 47.90 |
| Iridium | Ir | 77 | 192.22 | Tungsten | W | 74 | 183.85 |
| Iron | Fe | 26 | 55.847 | Uranium | U | 92 | 238.029 |
| Krypton | Kr | 36 | 83.80 | Vanadium | V | 23 | 50.9414 |
| Lanthanum | La | 57 | 138.9055 | Xenon | Xe | 54 | 131.30 |
| Lawrencium | Lr | 103 | 256.099* | Ytterbium | Yb | 70 | 173.04 |
| Lead | Pb | 82 | 207.2 | Yttrium | Y | 39 | 88.9059 |
| Lithium | Li | 3 | 6.941 | Zinc | Zn | 30 | 65.38 |
| Lutetium | Lu | 71 | 174.97 | Zirconium | Zr | 40 | 91.22 |
| Magnesium | Mg | 12 | 24.305 | Element 104† | | 104 | 257* |
| Manganese | Mn | 25 | 54.9380 | Element 105† | | 105 | 260* |
| Mendelevium | Md | 101 | 258* | Element 106† | | 106 | 263* |
| Mercury | Hg | 80 | 200.59 | Element 107† | | 107 | 258* |
| Molybdenum | Mo | 42 | 95.94 | Element 108† | | 108 | 265* |
| | | | | Element 109† | | 109 | 266* |

*The mass of the isotope with the longest known half-life.

†Names for elements 104 and 105 have not yet been approved by the IUPAC. The USSR has proposed Kurchatovium (Ku) for element 104 and Bohrium (Bh) for element 105. The United States has proposed Rutherfordium (Rf) for element 104 and Hahnium (Ha) for element 105.

# TABLE D–6  Trigonometric Functions

| Angle | sin | cos | tan | Angle | sin | cos | tan |
|---|---|---|---|---|---|---|---|
| 0° | .0000 | 1.0000 | .0000 | 45° | .7071 | .7071 | 1.0000 |
| 1° | .0175 | .9998 | .0175 | 46° | .7193 | .6947 | 1.0355 |
| 2° | .0349 | .9994 | .0349 | 47° | .7314 | .6820 | 1.0724 |
| 3° | .0523 | .9986 | .0524 | 48° | .7431 | .6691 | 1.1106 |
| 4° | .0698 | .9976 | .0699 | 49° | .7547 | .6561 | 1.1504 |
| 5° | .0872 | .9962 | .0875 | 50° | .7660 | .6428 | 1.1918 |
| 6° | .1045 | .9945 | .1051 | 51° | .7771 | .6293 | 1.2349 |
| 7° | .1219 | .9925 | .1228 | 52° | .7880 | .6157 | 1.2799 |
| 8° | .1392 | .9903 | .1405 | 53° | .7986 | .6018 | 1.3270 |
| 9° | .1564 | .9877 | .1584 | 54° | .8090 | .5878 | 1.3764 |
| 10° | .1736 | .9848 | .1763 | 55° | .8192 | .5736 | 1.4281 |
| 11° | .1908 | .9816 | .1944 | 56° | .8290 | .5592 | 1.4826 |
| 12° | .2079 | .9781 | .2126 | 57° | .8387 | .5446 | 1.5399 |
| 13° | .2250 | .9744 | .2309 | 58° | .8480 | .5299 | 1.6003 |
| 14° | .2419 | .9703 | .2493 | 59° | .8572 | .5150 | 1.6643 |
| 15° | .2588 | .9659 | .2679 | 60° | .8660 | .5000 | 1.7321 |
| 16° | .2756 | .9613 | .2867 | 61° | .8746 | .4848 | 1.8040 |
| 17° | .2924 | .9563 | .3057 | 62° | .8829 | .4695 | 1.8807 |
| 18° | .3090 | .9511 | .3249 | 63° | .8910 | .4540 | 1.9626 |
| 19° | .3256 | .9455 | .3443 | 64° | .8988 | .4384 | 2.0503 |
| 20° | .3420 | .9397 | .3640 | 65° | .9063 | .4226 | 2.1445 |
| 21° | .3584 | .9336 | .3839 | 66° | .9135 | .4067 | 2.2460 |
| 22° | .3746 | .9272 | .4040 | 67° | .9205 | .3907 | 2.3559 |
| 23° | .3907 | .9205 | .4245 | 68° | .9272 | .3746 | 2.4751 |
| 24° | .4067 | .9135 | .4452 | 69° | .9336 | .3584 | 2.6051 |
| 25° | .4226 | .9063 | .4663 | 70° | .9397 | .3420 | 2.7475 |
| 26° | .4384 | .8988 | .4877 | 71° | .9455 | .3256 | 2.9042 |
| 27° | .4540 | .8910 | .5095 | 72° | .9511 | .3090 | 3.0777 |
| 28° | .4695 | .8829 | .5317 | 73° | .9563 | .2924 | 3.2709 |
| 29° | .4848 | .8746 | .5543 | 74° | .9613 | .2756 | 3.4874 |
| 30° | .5000 | .8660 | .5774 | 75° | .9659 | .2588 | 3.7321 |
| 31° | .5150 | .8572 | .6009 | 76° | .9703 | .2419 | 4.0108 |
| 32° | .5299 | .8480 | .6249 | 77° | .9744 | .2250 | 4.3315 |
| 33° | .5446 | .8387 | .6494 | 78° | .9781 | .2079 | 4.7046 |
| 34° | .5592 | .8290 | .6745 | 79° | .9816 | .1908 | 5.1446 |
| 35° | .5736 | .8192 | .7002 | 80° | .9848 | .1736 | 5.6713 |
| 36° | .5878 | .8090 | .7265 | 81° | .9877 | .1564 | 6.3138 |
| 37° | .6018 | .7986 | .7536 | 82° | .9903 | .1392 | 7.1154 |
| 38° | .6157 | .7880 | .7813 | 83° | .9925 | .1219 | 8.1443 |
| 39° | .6293 | .7771 | .8098 | 84° | .9945 | .1045 | 9.5144 |
| 40° | .6428 | .7660 | .8391 | 85° | .9962 | .0872 | 11.4301 |
| 41° | .6561 | .7547 | .8693 | 86° | .9976 | .0698 | 14.3007 |
| 42° | .6691 | .7431 | .9004 | 87° | .9986 | .0523 | 19.0811 |
| 43° | .6820 | .7314 | .9325 | 88° | .9994 | .0349 | 28.6363 |
| 44° | .6947 | .7193 | .9657 | 89° | .9998 | .0175 | 57.2900 |
| 45° | .7071 | .7071 | 1.0000 | 90° | 1.0000 | .0000 | ∞ |

# TABLE D–7
## Safety Symbols

**DISPOSAL ALERT**
This symbol appears when care must be taken to dispose of materials properly.

**LASER SAFETY**
This symbol appears when care must be taken to avoid staring directly into the laser beam or at bright reflections.

**BIOLOGICAL HAZARD**
This symbol appears when there is danger involving bacteria, fungi, or protists.

**RADIOACTIVE SAFETY**
This symbol appears when radioactive materials are used.

**OPEN FLAME ALERT**
This symbol appears when use of an open flame could cause a fire or an explosion.

**CLOTHING PROTECTION SAFETY**
This symbol appears when substances used could stain or burn clothing.

**THERMAL SAFETY**
This symbol appears as a reminder to use caution when handling hot objects.

**FIRE SAFETY**
This symbol appears when care should be taken around open flames.

**SHARP OBJECT SAFETY**
This symbol appears when a danger of cuts or punctures caused by the use of sharp objects exists.

**EXPLOSION SAFETY**
This symbol appears when the misuse of chemicals could cause an explosion.

**FUME SAFETY**
This symbol appears when chemicals or chemical reactions could cause dangerous fumes.

**EYE SAFETY**
This symbol appears when a danger to the eyes exists. Safety goggles should be worn when this symbol appears

**ELECTRICAL SAFETY**
This symbol appears when care should be taken when using electrical equipment

**POISON SAFETY**
This symbol appears when poisonous substances are used.

**PLANT SAFETY**
This symbol appears when poisonous plants or plants with thorns are handled.

**CHEMICAL SAFETY**
This symbol appears when chemicals used can cause burns or are poisonous if absorbed through the skin.

# Appendix E
## Laws of Cosines and Sines

### E:1 Law of Cosines

To use the trigonometry of the right triangle, two of the sides of a triangle must be perpendicular. That is, you must have a right triangle. But sometimes you will need to work with a triangle that is not a right triangle. The law of cosines applies to all triangles. Consider the two triangles shown in Figure E-1. They are not right triangles. When angle C is known, the lengths of the sides obey the following relationship.

$$c^2 = a^2 + b^2 - 2ab \cos C$$

If $a$, $b$, and angle C are known, the length of side $c$ is

$$c = \sqrt{a^2 + b^2 - 2ab \cos C}.$$

In triangle 1 of Figure E-1, the length of side a is 4.00 cm, side b is 5.00 cm, and angle C is 60.0°. Substituting the values in the equation, side c is obtained. Substituting the appropriate values yields

$$a^2 = (4.0 \text{ cm})^2 = 16.0 \text{ cm}^2$$

$$b^2 = (5.0 \text{ cm})^2 = 25.0 \text{ cm}^2$$

$$2ab \cos \theta = 2(4.00 \text{ cm})(5.00 \text{ cm})(\cos 60.0°)$$
$$= 2(4.00 \text{ cm})(5.00 \text{ cm})(0.500)$$
$$2ab \cos \theta = 20.0 \text{ cm}^2.$$

Therefore,

$$c = \sqrt{a^2 + b^2 - 2ab \cos \theta}$$
$$= \sqrt{16.0 \text{ cm}^2 + 25.0 \text{ cm}^2 - 20.0 \text{ cm}^2}$$
$$= \sqrt{21.0 \text{ cm}^2}$$
$$c = 4.58 \text{ cm}$$

If angle C is larger than 90°, its cosine is negative and is numerically equal to the cosine of its supplement. In triangle 2, Figure E-1, angle C is 120.0°. Therefore, its cosine is the negative of the cosine of (180.0° − 120.0°) or 60.0°. The cosine of 60.0° is 0.500. Thus, the cosine of 120.0° is −0.500.

### E:2 Law of Sines

Just as the law of cosines applies to all triangles, the law of sines also applies to all triangles. The relationship is

$$\frac{a}{\sin A} = \frac{b}{\sin B} = \frac{c}{\sin C}.$$

Using the values for triangle 1 shown in Figure E-1, angle A can be calculated by the law of sines.

$$\frac{a}{\sin A} = \frac{c}{\sin C}$$

$$\sin A = \frac{a}{c} \sin C$$

$$\sin A = \frac{4.00 \text{ cm}}{4.58 \text{ cm}} \sin (60.0°)$$

$$= \frac{(4.00 \text{ cm})(0.867)}{(4.58 \text{ cm})}$$

$$= 0.757$$

$$A = 49.2°$$

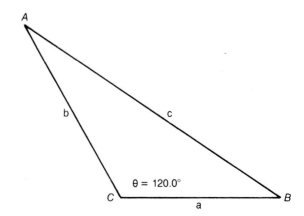

**FIGURE E-1.**

724

# Appendix F
## Physics Nobel Laureates

**1901 Wilhelm Roentgen**
discovered X rays

**1902 Hendrik A. Lorentz**
predicted the Zeeman effect

**1902 Pieter Zeeman**
discovered the Zeeman effect, the splitting of spectral lines in magnetic fields

**1903 Antoine-Henri Becquerel**
discovered radioactivity

**1903 Pierre and Marie Curie**
studied radioactivity

**1904 Lord Rayleigh**
studied the density of gases and discovered argon

**1905 Philipp Lenard**
studied cathode rays and electrons

**1906 J. J. Thomson**
studied electrical discharge through gases and discovered the electron

**1907 Albert A. Michelson**
invented optical instruments and measured the speed of light

**1908 Gabriel Lippmann**
made the first colour photographic plate, using interference methods

**1909 Guglielmo Marconi and Carl Ferdinand Braun**
developed wireless telegraphy

**1910 Johannes D. van der Waals**
studied the equation of state for gases and liquids

**1911 Wilhelm Wien**
discovered Wien's law giving the peak of a blackbody spectrum

**1912 Nils Dalén**
invented automatic gas regulators for lighthouses

**1913 Heike Kamerlingh Onnes**
discovered superconductivity and liquefied helium

**1914 Max T. F. von Laue**
studied X rays from their diffraction by crystals, showing that X rays are electromagnetic waves

**1915 William Henry Bragg and William Lawrence Bragg**, (his son)
studied the diffraction of X rays in crystals

**1917 Charles Barkla**
studied atoms by X-ray scattering

**1918 Max Planck**
discovered energy quanta

**1919 Johannes Stark**
discovered the Stark effect, the splitting of spectral lines in electric fields

**1920 Charles-Édouard Guillaume**
discovered invar, a nickel-steel alloy with low coefficient of expansion

**1921 Albert Einstein**
explained the photoelectric effect and honoured for his service to theoretical physics

**1922 Niels Bohr**
model of the atom and its radiation

**1923 Robert A. Millikan**
measured the charge on an electron and studied the photoelectric effect experimentally

**1924 Karl M. G. Siegbahn**
X-ray spectroscopy

**1925 James Franck and Gustav Hertz**
discovered the Franck-Hertz effect in electron-atom collisions

**1926 Jean-Baptiste Perrin**
studied Brownian motion to validate the discontinuous structure of matter and measure the size of atoms

**1927 Arthur Holly Compton**
discovered the Compton effect on X rays, and how they change in wavelength when they collide with matter

**1927 Charles T. R. Wilson**
invented the cloud chamber, used to study charged particles

**1928 Owen W. Richardson**
studied the thermionic effect and electrons emitted by hot metals

**1929 Louis Victor de Broglie**
discovered the wave nature of electrons

**1930 Chandrasekhara Venkata Raman**
studied Raman scattering, the scattering of light by atoms and molecules with a change in wavelength

**1932 Werner Heisenberg**
created quantum mechanics

**1933 Erwin Schrödinger and Paul A. M. Dirac**
developed wave mechanics and relativistic quantum mechanics

**1935 James Chadwick**
discovered the neutron

**1936 Carl D. Anderson**
discovered the positron in particular and antimatter in general

**1936 Victor F. Hess**
discovered cosmic rays

**1937 Clinton Davisson and George Thomson**
discovered the diffraction of electrons by crystals, confirming de Broglie's hypothesis

**1938 Enrico Fermi**
produced transuranic radioactive elements by neutron irradiation

**1939 Ernest O. Lawrence**
invented the cyclotron

**1943 Otto Stern**

developed molecular-beam studies and used them to discover the magnetic element of the proton

**1944 Isidor I. Rabi**

discovered nuclear magnetic resonance in atomic and molecular beams

**1945 Wolfgang Pauli**

discovered the exclusion principle

**1946 Percy W. Bridgman**

studied physics at high pressures

**1947 Edward V. Appleton**

studied the ionosphere

**1948 Patrick M. S. Blackett**

studied nuclear physics with cloud-chamber photographs of cosmic-ray interactions

**1949 Hideki Yukawa**

predicted the existence of mesons

**1950 Cecil F. Powell**

developed the method of studying cosmic rays with photographic emulsions and discovered new mesons

**1951 John D. Cockcroft** and **Ernest T. S. Walton**

transmuted nuclei in an accelerator

**1952 Felix Bloch** and **Edward Mills Purcell**

discovered nuclear magnetic resonance in liquids and gases

**1953 Frits Zernike**

invented the phase-contrast microscope

**1954 Max Born**

interpreted the wave function as a probability

**1954 Walther Bothe**

developed the coincidence method to study subatomic particles

**1955 Willis E. Lamb, Jr.**

discovered the Lamb shift in the hydrogen spectrum

**1955 Polykarp Kusch**

determined the magnetic moment of the electron

**1956 John Bardeen, Walter H. Brattain,** and **William Shockley**

invented the transistor

**1957 T.-D. Lee** and **C.-N. Yang**

predicted that parity is not conserved in beta decay

**1958 Pavel A. Cerenkov**

discovered Cerenkov radiation

**1958 Ilya M. Frank** and **Igor Tamm**

interpreted Cerenkov radiation

**1959 Emilio G. Segre** and **Owen Chamberlain**

discovered the antiproton

**1960 Donald A. Glaser**

invented the bubble chamber to study elementary particles

**1961 Robert Hofstadter**

discovered internal structure in protons and neutrons

**1961 Rudolf L. Mössbauer**

discovered the Mössbauer effect of recoilless gamma-ray emission

**1962 Lev Davidovich Landau**

studied liquid helium and other condensed matter theoretically

**1963 Eugene P. Wigner**

applied symmetry principles to elementary-particle theory

**1963 Maria Goeppert Mayer** and **J. Hans D. Jensen**

studied the shell model of nuclei

**1964 Charles H. Townes, Nikolai G. Basov,** and **Alexander M. Prokhorov**

developed masers and lasers

**1965 Sin-itiro Tomonaga, Julian S. Schwinger,** and **Richard P. Feynman**

developed quantum electrodynamics

**1966 Alfred Kastler**

optical methods of studying atomic energy levels

**1967 Hans Albrecht Bethe**

discovered the routes of energy production in stars

**1968 Luis W. Alvarez**

discovered resonance states of elementary particles

**1969 Murray Gell-Mann**

classified elementary particles

**1970 Hannes Alfvén**

developed magnetohydrodynamic theory

**1970 Louis Eugène Félix Néel**

discovered antiferromagnetism and ferrimagnetism

**1971 Dennis Gabor**

developed holography

**1972 John Bardeen, Leon N. Cooper,** and **John Robert Schrieffer**

explained superconductivity

**1973 Leo Esaki**

discovered tunnelling in semiconductors

**1973 Ivar Giaever**

discovered tunnelling in superconductors

**1973 Brian D. Josephson**

predicted the Josephson effect

**1974 Anthony Hewish**

discovered pulsars

**1974 Martin Ryle**

developed radio interferometry

**1975 Aage N. Bohr, Ben R. Mottelson,** and **James Rainwater**

discovered why some nuclei take asymmetric shapes

**1976 Burton Richter** and **Samuel C. C. Ting**

discovered the J/psi particle, the first charmed particle

**1977 John H. Van Vleck, Nevill F. Mott,** and **Philip W. Anderson**

studied solids in terms of quantum mechanics

**1978 Arno A. Penzias** and **Robert W. Wilson**

discovered the cosmic background radiation

**1978 Pyotr Kapitsa**
studies of liquid helium

**1979 Sheldon L. Glashow, Abdus Salam,** and **Steven Weinberg**
developed theory that unified the weak and electromagnetic forces

**1980 Val Fitch** and **James W. Cronin**
discovered **CP** (charge-parity) violation

**1981 Nicolaas Bloembergen** and **Arthur L. Schawlow**
developed laser spectroscopy

**1981 Kai M. Siegbahn**
developed high-resolution electron spectroscopy

**1982 Kenneth G. Wilson**
developed a method of constructing theories of phase transitions to analyse critical phenomena

**1983 William A. Fowler**
theoretical studies of astrophysical nucleosynthesis

**1983 Subramanyan Chandrasekhar**
studied physical processes of importance to stellar structure and evolution, including the prediction of white dwarf stars

**1984 Carlo Rubbia**
discovered the **W** and **Z** particles

**1984 Simon van der Meer**
developed the method of stochastic cooling of the CERN beam that allowed the discovery

**1985 Klaus von Klitzing**
quantized Hall effect, relating to conductivity in the presence of a magnetic field

**1986 Ernst Ruska**
invented the electron microscope

**1986 Gerd Binning** and **Heinrich Rohrer**
invented the scanning-tunnelling electron microscope

**1987 J. Georg Bednorz** and **Karl Alex Müller**
discovered high temperature superconductivity

**1988 Leon M. Lederman, Melvin Schwartz,** and **Jack Steinberger**
the development of a new tool for studying the weak nuclear force, which affects the radioactive decay of atoms

**1989 Norman Ramsay**
development of techniques for studying the structure of atoms, the hydrogen atom and hydrogen maser, and the development of the cesium atomic clock

**1989 Hans Dehmelt** and **Wolfgang Paul**
development of the ion-trap method for separating charged particles, especially the electron and ions

**1990 Richard E. Taylor, Jerome I. Friedman,** and **Henry W. Kendall**
"deep inelastic scattering" experiments that showed the quark structures of the proton and neutron

# Glossary

*The numbers in parentheses refer to the page on which the term is introduced.*

## A

**absolute zero** (246): Lowest possible temperature at which gas would have zero volume.

**absorption spectrum** (577): Spectrum of electromagnetic radiation absorbed by matter when radiation of all frequencies is passed through it.

**acceleration** (64): Change in velocity divided by time interval over which it occurred.

**accuracy** (22): Closeness of a measurement to the standard value of that quantity.

**achromatic lens** (384): Lens for which all light colours have the same focal length.

**action-reaction forces** (92): Pair of forces involved in an interaction that are equal in magnitude and opposite in direction.

**activity** (622): Number of decays per second of a radioactive substance.

**adhesion** (275): Force of attraction between two unlike materials.

**air resistance** (102): Force of air on objects moving through it.

**alpha decay** (618): Process in which a nucleus emits an alpha particle.

**alpha particle** (574): Positively-charged particles consisting of two protons and two neutrons emitted by radioactive materials.

**ammeter** (485): Device to measure electrical current.

**amorphous solid** (278): Solids that have no long-range order; no crystal structure.

**ampere (A)** (450): Unit of electric current. One ampere is the flow of one coulomb of charge per second.

**amplitude** (145): In any periodic motion, the maximum displacement from equilibrium.

**angle of incidence** (299): Angle between direction of motion of waves and a line perpendicular to surface the waves are striking.

**angle of reflection** (299): Angle between direction of motion of waves and a line perpendicular to surface the waves are reflected from.

**angle of refraction** (300): Angle between direction of motion of waves and a line perpendicular to surface the waves have been refracted from.

**angular momentum** (179): Quantity of rotational motion. For a rotating object, product of moment of inertia and angular velocity.

**annihilation** (629): Process in which a particle and its antiparticle are converted into energy.

**antenna** (544): Device used to receive or transmit electromagnetic waves.

**antineutrino** (620): Subatomic particle with no charge or mass emitted in beta decay.

**antinode** (298): Point of maximum displacement of two superimposed waves.

**Archimedes' principle** (270): Object immersed in a fluid has an upward force equal to the weight of the fluid displaced by the object.

**artificial radioactivity** (643): Radioactive isotope not found in nature.

**atomic mass unit (u)** (616): Unit of mass equal to $1/12$ the atomic mass of the carbon-12 nucleus.

**atomic number (Z)** (616): Number of protons in the nucleus of the atom.

**average acceleration** (64): Acceleration measured over a finite time interval.

**average velocity** (44): Velocity measured over a finite time interval.

## B

**back-EMF** (524): Potential difference across a conductor caused by change in magnetic flux.

**band theory** (596): Theory explaining electrical conduction in solids.

**baryon** (633): Subatomic particle composed of three quarks. Interacts with the strong nuclear force.

**battery** (448): Device that converts chemical to electrical energy consisting of two dissimilar conductors and an electrolyte.

**beat** (320): Slow oscillation in amplitude of a complex wave.

**Bernoulli's principle** (273): When a fixed quantity of fluid flows, the pressure is decreased when the flow velocity increases.

**beta decay** (619): Radioactive decay process in which an electron or positron and neutrino is emitted from a nucleus.

**beta particle** (619): High speed electron emitted by a radioactive nucleus in beta decay.

**binding energy** (640): Negative of the amount of energy needed to separate a nucleus into individual nucleons.

**boiling point** (253): Temperature at which a substance, under normal atmospheric pressure, changes from a liquid to a vapour state.

**breeder reactor** (649): Nuclear reactor that converts nonfissionable nuclei to fissionable nuclei while producing energy.

**bubble chamber** (627): Instrument containing superheated liquid in which the path of ionizing particles is made visible as trails of tiny bubbles.

**buoyant force** (270): Upward force on an object immersed in fluid.

## C

**calorimeter** (250): Device that isolates objects to measure temperature changes due to heat flow.

**candela (cd)** (335): Unit of luminous intensity.

**capacitance** (441): Ratio of charge stored per increase in potential difference.

**capacitor** (441): Electrical device used to store charge and energy in the electric field.

**capillary action** (275): Rise of liquid in narrow tube due to surface tension.

**Carnot efficiency** (258): Ideal efficiency of heat engine or refrigerator working between two constant temperatures.

**centripetal acceleration** (143): Acceleration toward centre of circular motion.

**centripetal force** (144): Force that causes centripetal acceleration.

**chain reaction** (647): Nuclear reaction in which neutrons are produced that can cause further reactions.

**charged** (408): Object that has an unbalance of positive and negative electrical charges.

**charging by conduction** (414): Process of charging by touching neutral object to a charged object.

**charging by induction** (414): Process of charging by bringing neutral object near charged object, then removing part of resulting separated charge.

**chromatic aberration** (383): Variation in focal length of lens with wavelength of light.

**circular motion** (142): Motion with constant radius of curvature caused by acceleration being perpendicular to velocity.

**clock reading** (43): Time between event and a reference time, usually zero.

**closed, isolated system** (180): Collection of objects such that neither matter nor energy can enter or leave the collection.

**closed-pipe resonator** (315): Cylindrical tube with one end closed and a sound source at other end.

**coefficient of friction ($\mu$)** (97): Ratio of frictional force and the normal force between two surfaces.

**coefficient of linear expansion** (281): Change in length divided by original length and by temperature change.

**coefficient of volume expansion** (281): Change in volume divided by original volume and by temperature change.

**coherent waves** (392): Waves in which all are in step; are in phase.

**cohesive force** (274): Attractive force between similar substances.

**complementary colour** (339): Two colours that, when added, produce white light. Two pigments that, when combined, produce black.

**compound machine** (207): Machine consisting of two or more simple machines.

**Compton effect** (563): Interaction of photons, usually X rays, with electrons in matter resulting in increased wavelength of X rays and kinetic energy of electrons.

**concave lens** (378): Lens thinner in centre than edges; a diverging lens.

**concave mirror** (370): Converging mirror, one with centre of curvature on reflecting side of mirror.

**conduction band** (599): Energies of charge carriers in a solid such that the carriers are free to move.

**conductor** (411): Materials (electrical) through which charged particles move readily; (heat) or heat flow readily.

**conserved properties** (180): Property (like energy or momentum) that is the same before and after an interaction.

**consonance** (321): Two or more sounds that, when heard together, sound pleasant.

**constant acceleration** (69): Acceleration that does not change in time.

**constant velocity** (47): Velocity that does not change in time.

**constructive interference** (297): Superposition of waves resulting in a combined wave with amplitude larger than the component waves.

**convection** (243): Heat transfer by means of motion of fluid.

**conventional current** (450): Motion of positive electrical current.

**converging lens** (378): Lens that causes light rays to converge; usually a convex lens.

**convex lens** (378): Lens that is thicker in centre than at edges.

**convex mirror** (376): Diverging mirror. Centre of curvature is on side opposite reflecting side of mirror.

**cosine** (113): The ratio of the adjacent side and the hypotenuse.

**coulomb (C)** (417): Unit of electrical charge. Charge caused by flow of one ampere for one second.

**crest of wave** (290): High point of wave motion.

**critical angle** (357): Minimum angle of incidence that produces total internal reflection.

**crystal lattice** (278): Structure of solid consisting of regular arrangement of atoms.

# D

**de Broglie wavelength** (566): Length of de Broglie wave of particle; Planck's constant divided by momentum of particle.

**decibel (dB)** (311): Unit of sound level.

**dependent variable** (27): Variable that responds to change in manipulated variable.

**derived units** (15): Unit of a quantity that consists of combination of fundamental units.

**destructive interference** (297): Superposition of waves resulting in a combined wave with zero amplitude.

**diffraction** (301): Bending of waves around object in their path.

**diffraction grating** (400): Material containing many parallel lines very closely spaced that produces a light spectrum by interference.

**diffuse reflection** (348): Reflection of light into many directions by rough object.

**dimensional analysis** (45): Checking a derived equation by making sure dimensions are the same on both sides.

**diode** (605): Electrical device permitting only one way current flow.

**dispersion of light** (360): Variation with wavelength of speed of light through matter resulting in separation of light into spectrum.

**displacement (d)** (43): Change in position. A vector quantity.

**dissonance** (321): Two or more sounds that, when heard together, sound unpleasant.

**distance** (42): The separation between two points. A scalar quantity.

**diverging lens** (378): Lens that causes light rays to spread apart or diverge; usually a concave lens.

**dopants** (601): Small quantities of material added to semiconductor to increase electrical conduction.

**Doppler shift** (309): Change in wavelength due to relative motion of source and detector.

**dynamics** (87): Study of motion of particles acted on by forces.

# E

**effective current (AC)** (520): DC current that would produce the same heating effects.

**effective voltage (AC)** (520): DC potential difference that would produce the same heating effects.

**efficiency** (206): Ratio of output work (or energy) to input work (or energy).

**effort force** (205): Force exerted on a machine.

**elastic collision** (231): Interaction between two objects in which the total energy is the same before and after the interaction.

**elasticity** (279): Ability of object to return to original shape after deforming forces are removed.

**electric charge pump** (449): Device, often battery or generator, that increases potential of electric charges.

**electric circuit** (449): Continuous path through which electric charges can flow.

**electric current** (450): Flow of charged particles.

**electric field** (426): Property of space around a charged object that causes forces on other charged objects.

**electric field lines** (428): Lines representing the direction of electric field.

**electric field strength** (426): Ratio of force exerted by field on a tiny test charge to that charge.

**electric generator** (518): Device converting mechanical energy to electrical energy.

**electric potential** (432): Ratio of electric potential energy to charge.

**electric potential difference** (432): Difference in electric potential between two points.

**electric potential energy** (432): Energy of a charged body in an electric field.

**electromagnet** (498): Device that uses an electric current to produce a concentrated magnetic field.

**electromagnetic force** (88): One of fundamental forces due to electric charges, both static and moving.

**electromagnetic induction** (516): Production of electric field or current due to change in magnetic flux.

**electromagnetic radiation** (547): Energy carried by electromagnetic waves through space.

**electromagnetic waves** (288): Wave consisting of oscillating electric and magnetic fields that move at speed of light through space.

**electromotive force (EMF)** (517): Potential difference produced by electromagnetic induction.

**electron** (410): Subatomic particle of small mass and negative charge found in every atom.

**electron cloud** (585): Region of high probability of finding an electron around an atom.

**electron diffraction** (566): Effects on electrons due to wave-like interference of electrons with matter.

**electron gas model** (597): Description of current flow through conductors.

**electroscope** (414): Device to detect electric charges.

**electrostatics** (408): Study of properties and results of electric charges at rest.

**electroweak force** (633): Unification of electromagnetic and weak forces.

**elementary charge** (418): Magnitude of the charge of an electron, $1.602 \times 10^{-19}$ C.

**emission spectrum** (575): Spectrum produced by radiation from excited atoms.

**energy** (201): Non-material property capable of causing changes in matter.

**energy levels** (581): Amounts of energy an electron in an atom may have.

**entropy** (258): Measure of disorder in a system; ratio of heat added to temperature.

**equilibrant force** (121): Force needed to bring an object into translational equilibrium.

**equilibrium** (121): (translational) Condition in which net force on object is zero. (rotational) Condition in which net torque on object is zero.

**equivalent resistance** (471): Single resistance that could replace several resistors.

**evaporation** (276): Change from liquid to vapour state.

**excited state** (581): Energy level of atom higher than ground state.

**external forces** (186): Forces exerted from outside a system.

**extrinsic semiconductor** (601): Semiconductor in which conduction is primarily the result of added impurities (dopants).

# F

**factor-label method** (45): Dimensional analysis.

**farad (f)** (441): Unit of capacitance. One coulomb per volt.

**ferromagnetic materials** (499): Materials in which large internal magnetic fields are generated by cooperative action of electrons.

**first harmonic** (321): In music, the fundamental frequency.

**first law of thermodynamics** (256): Change in internal or thermal energy is equal to heat added and work done on system. Same as law of conservation of energy.

**fluid** (266): Material that flows, i.e. liquids, gases, and plasmas.

**focal length** (371): Distance from the focal point to the cetre of a lens or vertex of a mirror.

**focal point** (370): Location at which rays parallel to the optical axis of an ideal mirror or lens converge to a point.

**forbidden gap** (596): Energy values that electrons in a semiconductor or insulator may not have.

**force** (88): Agent that results in accelerating or deforming an object.

**frame of reference** (42): Coordinate system used to define motion.

**Fraunhofer lines** (578): Absorption lines in the sun's spectrum due to gases in the solar atmosphere.

**frequency** (290): Number of occurrences per unit time.

**friction** (96): Force opposing relative motion of two objects that are in contact.

**fundamental particles** (628): Those particles (i.e. quarks and leptons) of which all matter is composed.

**fundamental tone** (321): Lowest frequency sound produced by a musical instrument.

**fundamental units** (14): Set of units on which a measurement system is based (i.e. metre, second, kilogram, ampere, candela).

**fuse** (480): Metal safety device in an electric circuit that melts to stop current flow when current is too large.

**fusion** (253): Combination of two nuclei into one with release of energy.

# G

**galvanometer** (505): Device used to measure very small currents.

**gamma decay** (619): Process by which a nucleus emits a gamma ray.

**gamma particle** (619): High energy photon (very high frequency electromagnetic wave) emitted by a radioactive nucleus.

**gas** (266): State of matter that expands to fill container.

**Geiger-Mueller tube** (627): Device used to detect radiation using its ability to ionize matter.

**general theory of relativity** (169): Explanation of gravity and accelerated motion invented by Einstein.

**gluon** (628): Carrier of the strong nuclear force.

**grand unified theories (GUTs)** (88): Theories being developed that unify the strong and electroweak forces into one force.

**gravitational field** (168): Distortion of space due to the presence of a mass.

**gravitational force** (88): Attraction between two objects due to their mass.

**gravitational mass** (96): Ratio of gravitational force to object's acceleration.

**gravitational potential energy** (223): Change of energy of object when moved in a gravitational field.

**graviton** (628): Particle that carries the gravitational force. Not yet observed.

**ground state** (581): Lowest energy level of an electron in an atom.

**grounding** (439): Process of connecting a charged object to Earth to remove object's unbalanced charge.

# H

**half-life** (621): Length of time for half of a sample of radioactive material to decay.

**harmonics** (321): Frequencies produced by musical instrument that are multiples of fundamental tone.

**heat (Q)** (247): Quantity of energy transferred from one object to another because of a difference in temperature.

**heat engine** (256): Device that converts thermal energy to mechanical energy.

**heat of fusion** (253): Quantity of energy needed to change a unit mass of a substance from solid to liquid state at the melting point.

**heat of vaporization** (253): Quantity of energy needed to change a unit mass of a substance from liquid to gaseous state at the boiling point.

**heavy water** (647): Deuterium oxide used mainly in CANDU nuclear reactors.

**Heisenberg uncertainty principle** (568): The more accurately one determines the position of a particle, the less accurately the momentum can be known, and vice versa.

**hertz (Hz)** (290): Unit of frequency equal to one event or cycle per second.

**hole** (600): Absence of an electron in a semiconductor.

**Hooke's law** (147): Deformation of an object is proportional to force causing it.

**Huygens' wavelets** (392): Model of spreading of waves in which each point on wavefront is source of circular or spherical waves.

**hydraulic system** (268): Machines using fluids to transmit energy.

**hyperbola** (31): Mathematical curve that describes an inverse relationship between two variables.

**hypotenuse** (113): Side opposite the right angle in a triangle.

# I

**ideal mechanical advantage (IMA)** (206): In simple machine, the ratio of effort distance to resistance distance.

**illuminance** (333): Rate at which electromagnetic wave energy falls on a surface.

**illuminated object** (368): Object on which light falls.

**image** (368): Reproduction of object formed with lenses or mirrors.

**impulse** (177): Product of force and time interval over which it acts.

**impulse-momentum theorem** (177): Impulse given to an object is equal to its change in momentum.

**incandescent body** (556): Object that emits light because of its high temperature.

**incident wave** (295): Wave that strikes a boundary where it is either reflected or refracted.

**incoherent light** (586): Light consisting of waves that are not in step (not coherent).

**independent variable** (27): Variable that is manipulated or changed in an experiment.

**index of refraction** (350): Ratio of the speed of light in vacuum to its speed in a material.

**inelastic collision** (231): Collision in which some of the kinetic energy is changed into another form.

**inertia** (90): Tendency of object not to change its motion.

**inertial mass** (96): Ratio of net force exerted on object to its acceleration.

**initial velocity** (69): Velocity of object at time $t = 0$.

**instantaneous acceleration** (67): Acceleration at a specific time; slope of tangent to velocity-time graph.

**instantaneous position** (43): Position of object at specific time.

**instantaneous velocity** (53): Slope of the tangent to position-time graph.

**insulator** (411): Material through which the flow of electrical charge carriers or heat is greatly reduced.

**interference fringes** (392): Pattern of dark and light bands from interference of light waves.

**interference of waves** (297): Displacements of two or more waves, producing either larger or smaller waves.

**internal forces** (186): Forces between objects within a system.

**intrinsic semiconductor** (600): Semiconductor in which conduction is by charges due to host material, not impurities (of extrinsic semiconductor).

**inverse relationship** (31): Mathematical relationship between two variables, $x$ and $y$, summarized by the equation $xy = k$, where $k$ is a constant.

**ionizing radiation** (644): Particles or waves that can remove electrons from atoms, molecules, or atoms in a solid.

**isolated system** (180): A collection of objects not acted upon by external forces into which energy neither enters nor leaves.

**isotope** (617): Atomic nuclei having same number of protons but different numbers of neutrons.

# J

**joule (J)** (198): SI unit of energy (or work or heat) equal to one newton-metre.

**Joule heating** (460): Increase in temperature of electrical conductor due to conversion of electrical to thermal energy.

# K

**Kelvin temperature scale** (246): Scale with 0 K = absolute zero and 273.16 K = triple point of water.

**Kepler's laws** (157): Three laws of motion of bodies attracted together by the gravitational force.

**kilogram (kg)** (15): SI unit of mass.

**kilowatt hour (kW·h)** (462): Amount of energy equal to $3.6 \times 10^6$ J. Usually used in electrical measurement.

**kinematics** (87): Study of motion of objects without regard to the causes of this motion.

**kinetic energy** (218): Energy of object due to its motion.

**kinetic-molecular theory** (242): Description of matter as being made up of extremely small particles in constant motion.

# L

**laser** (587): Devise that produces coherent light by stimulated emission of radiation.

**laser-induced fusion** (652): Proposed method of creating nuclear fusion by using heating caused by intense laser beams to squeeze matter together.

**law of conservation of energy** (227): In a closed, isolated system, the total energy does not change.

**law of conservation of momentum** (183): In a closed, isolated system, the total momentum is constant.

**law of reflection** (299): Angle of incidence of a wave is equal to the angle of reflection.

**law of universal gravitation** (164): Gravitational force between two objects depends directly on the product of their masses and inversely on the square of their separation.

**lens** (378): Optical device designed to converge or diverge light.

**lens equation** (381): *See mirror equation.*

**Lenz's law** (523): Magnetic field generated by an induced current opposes the change in field that caused the current.

**lepton** (628): Particle (like electron) that interacts with other particles only by the electroweak and gravitational interactions.

**lever arm** (146): Component of the displacement of the force from the axis of rotation in the direction perpendicular to the force.

**light** (330): Electromagnetic radiation with wavelengths between 400 and 700 nm that is visible.

**linear accelerator** (625): Device to accelerate subatomic particles by applying successive electric fields.

**linear relationship** (29): Relationship between two variables, $x$ and $y$, summarized by the equation $y = ax + b$, where $a$ and $b$ are constant.

**linear restoring force** (147): Force in direction toward equilibrium position that depends linearly on distance from that position.

**liquid** (274): Materials that have fixed volume but whose shape depends on the container.

**lodestone** (491): Naturally occurring magnetic rock.

**longitudinal waves** (288): Wave in which direction of disturbance is the same as the direction of travel of wave.

**loudness** (310): Physiological measure of amplitude on a sound wave; heard loudness depends on pitch and tone colour as well as amplitude.

**lumen (lm)** (333): Unit of luminous flux.

**luminance intensity** (338): Measure of light emitted by source in candelas; luminous flux divided by $4\pi$.

**luminous flux** (333): Flow of light from source measured in lumens.

**luminous object** (368): Object that emits light, as opposed to one that reflects light.

**lux (lx)** (333): Unit of luminous flux; one lumen per square metre.

# M

**machine** (205): Device that changes force needed to do work.

**magnetic field** (494): Space around a magnet throughout which magnetic force exists.

**magnification** (373): Ratio of size of an optical image to the size of the object.

**manipulated variable** (27): Variable that the experimenter can change.

**mass defect** (640): Mass equivalent of the binding energy; $m = E/c^2$.

**mass number (A)** (617): Number of nucleons (protons plus neutrons) in the nucleus of an atom.

**mass spectrometer** (539): Device used to measure the mass of atoms or molecules.

**matter wave** (288): Wave-like properties of particles such as electrons.

**mechanical advantage (MA)** (205): Ratio of resistance force to effort force in a machine.

**mechanical energy** (227): Sum of potential and kinetic energy.

**mechanical resonance** (149): Condition at which natural oscillation frequency equals frequency of driving force; amplitude of oscillatory motion at a maximum.

**mechanical wave** (288): Wave consisting of periodic motion of matter; e.g. sound wave or water wave as opposed to electromagnetic wave.

**melting point** (253): Temperature at which substance changes from solid to liquid state.

**meson** (633): Medium mass subatomic particle consisting of combination of a quark and antiquark.

**metre (m)** (14): SI unit of length.

**mirror equation** (373): $1/d_o + 1/d_i = 1/f$, where $d_o$ is object distance, $d_i$ is image distance, $f$ is focal length.

**moderator** (647): Material used to decrease speed of neutrons in nuclear reactor.

**momentum** (176): Product of object's mass and velocity.

**monochromatic light** (392): Light of a single wavelength.

**mutual inductance** (526): Measures the amount of overlap between the magnetic flux produced in one coil and that which passes through a second coil, thus the amount of *EMF* induced in a secondary coil by the varying flux in the primary coil.

**myopia** (384): Defect of eye, commonly called nearsightedness, in which distant objects focus in front of the retina.

# N

**n-type semiconductor** (601): Semiconductor in which current is carried by electrons.

**net force** (89): Vector sum of forces on object.

**neutral** (410): Object that has no net electric charge.

**neutrino** (629): Chargeless, massless, subatomic particle emitted with beta particles; type of lepton.

**neutron** (617): Subatomic particle with no charge and mass slightly greater than that of proton; type of nucleon.

**newton (N)** (91): SI unit of force.

**Newton's laws of motion** (89, 90, 92): Laws relating force and acceleration.

**node** (298): Point where disturbances caused by two or more waves result in no displacement.

**normal** (299): Perpendicular to plane of interest.

**normal force** (97): Force perpendicular to surface.

**nuclear equation** (620): Equation representing a nuclear reaction.

**nuclear fission** (647): Reaction in which large nucleus splits into two parts, often approximately equal in mass.

**nuclear fusion** (649): Reaction in which two nuclei are combined into one.

**nuclear reaction** (619): Reaction involving the strong force in which the number of protons or neutrons in a nucleus changes.

**nuclear reactor** (647): Device in which nuclear fusion is used to generate electricity.

**nuclear transmutation** (619): Change of one nucleus into another as the result of a nuclear reaction.

**nucleon** (640): Either a proton or a neutron.

**nuclide** (617): Nucleus of an isotope.

# O

**object (optics)** (368): Source of diverging light rays: either luminous or illuminated.

**octave** (311): Interval between two frequencies with a ratio of two to one.

**ohm (Ω)** (452): SI unit of resistance; one volt per ampere.

**Ohm's law** (452): Resistance of object is constant, independent of voltage across it.

**opaque** (336): Material that does not transmit light.

**open-pipe resonator** (318): Cylindrical tube with both ends closed and a sound source at one end.

# P

**p-type semiconductor** (602): Semiconductor in which conduction is the result of motion of holes.

**pair production** (630): Formation of particle and antiparticle from gamma rays.

**parabolic mirror** (371): Mirror the shape of a paraboloid of revolution that has no spherical aberration.

**parallel circuit** (475): Circuit in which there are two or more paths for current flow.

**parallel connection** (455): Connection of two or more electrical devices between two points to provide more than one current path.

**pascal (Pa)** (267): SI unit of pressure; one newton per square metre.

**Pascal's principle** (268): Pressure applied to a fluid is transmitted undiminished throughout it.

**period (T)** (143, 147): Time needed to repeat one complete cycle of motion.

**periodic motion** (141): Motion that repeats itself at regular intervals of time.

**photoelectric effect** (558): Ejection of electrons from surface of metal exposed to electromagnetic radiation.

**photon** (558): Quantum of electromagnetic waves; particle aspect of these waves.

**photovoltaic cell** (448): Device that converts electromagnetic radiation (light) into electrical energy.

**physics** (4): Study of matter and energy and their relationships.

**piezoelectricity** (549): Electric potential produced by deforming material.

**pigment** (339): Coloured material that absorbs certain colours and transmits or reflects others.

**pitch** (310): Perceived sound characteristic equivalent to frequency.

**Planck's constant ($h$)** (558): ratio of energy of photon to its frequency.

**plane mirror** (368): Flat, smooth surface that reflects light regularly (specularly).

**plasma** (276): State of matter in which atoms are separated into electrons and positive ions or bare nuclei.

**point object** (42): Object idealized as so small to be located at only one position.

**polarized light** (342): Light in which electric fields are all in same plane.

**position** (42): Separation between object and a reference point.

**position-time graph** (48): Graph of object's motion that shows how its position depends on clock reading, or time.

**positron** (630): Antiparticle equivalent of electron.

**potential difference** (432): Difference in electric potential between two points.

**potential energy** (218): Energy of object due to its position or state.

**potentiometer** (453): Electrical device with variable resistance; rheostat.

**power** (202): Rate of doing work; rate of energy conversion.

**precision** (21): Degree of exactness in a measurement.

**pressure** (266): Force per unit area.

**primary coil** (526): Transformer coil that, when connected to voltage source, creates varying magnetic flux.

**primary light colours** (338): Red, green, or blue light.

**primary pigment** (339): Yellow, cyan, or magenta pigment.

**principal axis** (370): Line connecting center of curvature of spherical mirror with its geometric vertex. Line perpendicular to plane of lens passing through its center.

**principle of superposition** (297): Displacement due to two or more forces is equal to vector sum of forces.

**projectiles** (134): Motion of objects given initial velocity that then move only under force of gravity.

**proton** (616): Subatomic particle with positive charge that is nucleus of hydrogen atom.

# Q

**quantized** (580): A quantity that cannot be divided into smaller and smaller increments forever, for which there exists a minimum, quantum increment.

**quantum mechanics** (585): Study of properties of matter using its wave properties.

**quantum model of atom** (585): Atomic model in which only probability of locating electron is known.

**quantum number** (582): Integer ratio of energy to its quantum increment.

**quark** (628): Basic building block of protons, neutrons, other baryons, and mesons.

**quark model** (631): Model in which all particles that interact via the strong interaction are composed of two or three quarks.

# R

**radiation** (243): Electromagnetic waves that carry energy.

**radioactive decay** (618): Spontaneous change of unstable nuclei into other nuclei.

**radioactive materials** (618): Materials that undergo radioactive decay.

**range of projectile** (137): Horizontal distance between launch point of projectile and where it returns to launch height.

**ray model of light** (330): Light may be represented by straight line along direction of motion.

**ray optics** (330): Study of light using ray model.

**Rayleigh criterion** (401): Two optical images are separable if central bright spot of one image falls on first dark band of second.

**real image** (371): Optical image at which rays from object converge.

**receiver** (550): Device that detects electromagnetic waves.

**reference level** (223): Location at which potential energy is chosen to be zero.

**reference point** (42): Zero location in a coordinate system or frame of reference.

**refraction** (348): Change in direction of light ray when passing from one medium to another.

**refractive index** (351): Ratio of speed of light in vacuum to that in the medium.

**resistance** (451): Ratio of potential difference across device to current through it.

**resistance force** (205): Force exerted by a machine.

**resistor** (452): Device designed to have a specific resistance.

**responding variable** (27): Variable that changes as result of change in manipulated variable.

**rest energy** (229): Energy due to mass of object; $E = mc^2$.

**resultant** (110): Vector sum of two or more vectors.

**right-hand rules** (497, 498, 502): Used to find force on current or moving particle in magnetic field; used to find direction of magnetic field caused by current or of induced *EMF*.

**Rutherford's model of atom** (575): Nuclear model of atom; essentially all mass in compact, positively-charged object at center, surrounded by electrons.

# S

**scalar** (42): Quantity, like distance, that has only a magnitude, or size.

**schematic diagram** (454): Representation of electric circuit using symbols.

**scientific notation** (15): Numbers expressed in form $M \times 10^n$, where $1 < M < 10$, and $n$ is an integer.

**scintillation** (574): Flash of light emitted when substance is struck by radiation.

**second (s)** (14): SI unit of time.

**second law of thermodynamics** (258): Heat flow only from region of high temperature to region of lower temperature.

**secondary coil** (526): Transformer coil in which varying *EMF* is induced.

**secondary light colours** (338): Yellow, cyan, or magenta light.

**secondary pigment** (339): Red, green, or blue pigment.

**self-inductance** (525): Induced *EMF* produced in coil by changing current.

**semiconductor** (599): Material in which electrical conduction is smaller than that in a conductor, but more than in an insulator.

**series circuit** (470): Circuit in which electrical current flows through each component, one after another.

**series connection** (455): Arrangement of electrical devices so that there is only one path through which current can flow.

**short circuit** (481): Low resistance connection between two points, often accidental.

**SI** (14): Internationally agreed-upon method of using the metric system of measurement.

**significant digit** (22): Reliable digits reported in a measurement.

**simple harmonic motion** (147): Motion caused by linear restoring force that has a period independent of amplitude of motion.

**simple machine** (205): Machine consisting of only one lever, inclined plane, wedge, screw, pulley, or wheel and axle.

**sine** (113): The ratio of the opposite side and the hypotenuse.

**sliding friction** (97): Force between two surfaces in relative motion.

**slope** (29): Ratio of the vertical separation, or rise to the horizontal separation, or run.

**solid** (278): State of matter with fixed volume and shape.

**sound level** (311): Quantity measuring logarithm of sound intensity in decibels.

**spark chamber** (627): Device used to detect path of charged subatomic particles by a spark that jumps along path of ionization created in a gas.

**specific heat** (247): Thermal energy needed to change temperature of unit mass of substance one kelvin.

**spectroscope** (576): Device used to study spectrum of material.

**spectrum** (337): Collection of wavelengths in electromagnetic spectrum.

**speed (v)** (51): Ratio of distance traveled to time interval.

**speed of light** (332): In vacuum, $2.9979458 \times 10^8$ m/s.

**spherical aberration** (371): Inability of spherical mirror to focus all parallel rays to a single point.

**standing wave** (316): Wave with stationary nodes.

**static friction** (96): Force that opposes start of motion between two surfaces.

**step-down transformer** (526): Transformer with output voltage smaller than input voltage.

**step-up transformer** (526): Transformer with output voltage larger than input voltage.

**stimulated emission** (587): Emission of photon from excited atom caused by impact of photon of same energy.

**strong nuclear force** (88): Force of very short range that holds neutrons and protons in nucleus together.

**superconductor** (452): Electrical conductor that has no resistance and low temperatures.

**surface wave** (289): Wave on surface of liquid with characteristics of both longitudinal and transverse waves.

**symmetry** (75): Property that is now changed when operation or reference frame is changed.

**synchrotron** (626): Device to accelerate particles in which particles move in circular path.

**system** (180): Defined collection of objects.

# T

**tangent** (113): The ratio of the opposite side and the adjacent side.

**temperature** (244): Measure of hotness of object on a quantitative scale. In gases, proportional to average kinetic energy of molecules.

**terminal velocity** (102): Velocity of falling object reached when force of air resistance equals weight.

**test charge** (426): Charge used, in principle, to measure electric field.

**thermal energy** (243): Internal energy. Sum of kinetic and potential energy of random motion of particles making up object.

**thermal equilibrium** (244): State between two or more bodies where temperatures do not change.

**thermal expansion** (279): Increase in length or volume of object due to change in temperature.

**thermometer** (244): Device used to measure temperature.

**thermonuclear reaction** (651): Nuclear fusion.

**thin-film interference** (340): Light interference caused by reflection from both front and rear surface of thin layer of liquid or solid.

**timbre** (320): Sound quality or tone colour; spectrum of sound frequencies that produce a complex wave.

**time interval ($\Delta t$)** (43): Difference in time between two clock readings.

**Tokamak** (652): Type of fusion reactor.

**tone colour** (320): Timbre or tone quality.

**torque ($\tau$)** (146): Product of force and the lever arm.

**trajectory** (134): The path followed by projectile.

**transformer** (526): Device to transfer energy from one electrical circuit to another by means of mutual inductance between two coils.

**transistor** (609): Semiconductor device that controls large current by means of small voltage changes.

**translucent** (336): Material transmitting light but distorting its path.

**transmutation** (619): Nuclear change from one element to another.

**transparent** (336): Material transmitting light without distorting directions of rays.

**transverse wave** (288): Wave in which disturbance is perpendicular to direction of travel of wave.

**traveling wave** (289): Moving, periodic disturbance in a medium or field.

**trigonometry** (113): Branch of math that deals with the relationships among angles and sides of triangles.

**trough of wave** (290): Low point of wave motion, where displacement is most negative.

# U

**uniform acceleration** (69): constant acceleration.

**uniform circular motion** (142): Motion in a circle of constant radius with constant speed.

# V

**valence band** (598): In a solid, the range of energies of electrons that are bound to atoms.

**vector quantity** (110): Quantity having both magnitude (size) and direction.

**vector resolution** (116): Process of finding the effective value of a component in a given direction.

**velocity (v)** (51): Ratio of change in position to time interval over which change takes place.

**velocity-time graph** (54): Plot of velocity of object as a function of time.

**virtual image** (368): Point from which light rays appear to diverge without actually doing so.

**viscous fluid** (278): Fluid that creates force that opposes motion of objects through it. The force is proportional to object's speed.

**volatile liquid** (276): Liquid that is easily vaporized.

# W

**watt (W)** (202): Unit of power, one joule per second.

**wavelength ($\lambda$)** (290): Distance between corresponding points on two successive waves.

**wave pulse** (289): Single disturbance moving through a medium or field.

**weak boson** (628): Particle that carries or transmits the weak interaction or force.

**weak interaction** (631): Force involved in beta decay of the neutron and atomic nuclei; one aspect of the electroweak force.

**weight** (94): Force of gravity on an object.

**weightlessness** (166): Object in freefall, on which only the gravitational force acts.

**Wilson cloud chamber** (627): Chamber containing supersaturated vapour through which ionizing radiation leaves trails of visible droplets.

**work** (198): Product of force and displacement in the direction of the force.

**work function** (560): Energy needed to remove an electron from metal.

**work-energy theorem** (220): Work done on object is equal to the change in its kinetic energy.

# X

**X ray** (551): High-energy photons; high-frequency, short-wavelength electromagnetic waves.

# Index

# H

**Hahn,** Otto, 645
**Half-life,** 621
**Half-life and activity,** 621
**Half-life of selected isotopes (Table),** 621
**Harmonic,** 321
**Heat,** specific (C), 247; unit of (J), 247
**Heat (Q),** 247
**Heat engine,** 256
**Heat of fusion ($H_f$),** 253
**Heat pump,** 257
**Heat transfer,** 248
**Heat of vaporization ($H_v$),** 253
**Heating,** joule, 460
**Heats of fusion of common substances (Table),** 254
**Heats of vaporization of common substances (Table),** 254
**Heavy water,** 647
**Heisenberg,** Werner, 585
**Heisenberg uncertainty principle,** 568
**Helmholtz,** Hermann, 314
**Help Wanted,** Actuary, 32; Air traffic controller, 74; Aircraft mechanic, 95; Audiologist, 299; Auto mechanic, 46; Broadcast technician, 322; Chiropractor, 207; Civil Engineer, 136; Computer programmer, 567; Computer-aided drafter, 394; Electric power plant operator, 477; Electrician, 520; Electronic equipment repairer, 493; Geologist, 587; HVAC technician, 255; Materials Engineer, 282; Meteorologist, 541; Nuclear engineer, 617; Optician, 374; Optometrist, 355; Photographer, 341; Physicist, 5; Pilot, 162; Podiatrist, 185; Radiologic technologist, 649; Recreational therapist, 229; Surveyor, 125; Systems analyst, 600; Telecommunications worker, 418; Vending machine repairer, 434; Welder, 459
**Henry,** Joseph, 516
**Hertz,** Heinrich, 544
**Holes,** 600; conduction by, 600
**Hologram,** 589
**Hooke,** Robert, 310
**Hooke's law,** 147
**Hubble Space Telescope aberration,** 371
**Human body resistance,** 454
**Huygens,** Christiaan, 392
**Huygens' wavelets,** 392
**Hydraulic system,** 268, 269
**Hydrogen, visible spectrum of,** 578; energy levels, 582; orbital radii, 582
**Hyperbola,** 31
**Hyperopia,** 385

# I

**Ideal fluid,** 268
**Ideal mechanical advantage (IMA),** 206
**Illuminance (E),** 333

**Illuminated body,** 333; object, 368
**Illumination of surface,** calculating, 335
**IMA,** ideal mechanical advantage, 206
**Image,** 368; colour convention, 374; distance ($d_i$), 368; location of, 368; real, 371; real from concave mirror, 372; real formed by convex lens, 380; virtual, 368; virtual formed by concave lens, 383; virtual formed by concave mirror, 375; virtual formed by convex lens, 382; virtual formed by convex mirror, 376
**Impulse,** 177
**Impulse-momentum theorem,** 177
**Incandescent body,** 556; power emitted by, 556; spectrum of, 556
**Incidence,** angle of, 299
**Incident wave,** 295
**Inclined plane,** motion on, 123; with friction, 123
**Incoherent light,** 586
**Independence of vector quantities,** 112
**Independent variable,** 27
**Index of refraction (n),** 350; (Table), 353
**Induced current flow,** direction of, 516
**Inductance,** mutual, 526; self, 525
**Induction,** charging by, 414; electromagnetic, 516; Faraday's discovery of, 516; magnetic, 503
**Inelastic collision,** 231
**Inertia,** 90
**Inertial confinement fusion,** 652
**Inertial mass (m),** 95
**Initial velocity ($v_i$),** 69
**Instantaneous acceleration (a),** 67
**Instantaneous position,** 43
**Instantaneous velocity,** 53
**Insulator,** 411, 598; forbidden gap in, 599
**Integrated circuit manufacture,** 610
**Intensity,** luminous, 333
**Interference,** constructive, 297; destructive, 297; thin-film, 340
**Interference fringes,** 392
**Interference pattern,** two-slit, 392; from grating, 400
**Interference of waves,** 297
**Internal combustion engine,** 241
**Internal forces,** 186
**International System of Units (SI),** 14
**Intrinsic semiconductor,** 600
**Inverse relationship,** 31
**Inverse square law,** 161
**Ionizing radiation,** 644
**Ions,** charge-to-mass ratio of, 536
**Iron core in electromagnet,** 499
**Iron filing,** 494
**Isotopes,** 539, 617; half-life of selected (Table), 621

# J

**Joliot,** Frederick, 625
**Joule,** James Prescott, 198, 230
**Joule (J),** 198, 201; unit of heat, 247
**Joule heating,** 460

# K

**Kamerlingh Onnes,** Heike, 6
**Kelvin (K),** 246
**Kelvin scale,** 246
**Kepler,** Johannes, 156
**Kepler's laws,** 157
**Kilogram (kg),** 15
**Kilowatt hour (kW·h),** 462
**Kinematics,** 87
**Kinetic energies,** Typical (Table), 221
**Kinetic energy,** 218; of photoelectron, 558
**Kinetic-molecular theory,** 242

# L

**Laboratory,** Ball and Car Race, 70; Bending of Light, 352; The Car Race, 50; Charges, Energy, Voltage, 430; Circuits, 479; Down the Hill, 225; Electric Motor, 501; Elevator Ride, 98; The Explosion, 182; Float or Sink?, 271; Getting Straight, 38; Heads Up, 623; Heating Up, 249; Homemade Mass Spectrometer, 543; Hot Stuff, 650; Mystery Cans, 456; The Orbit, 158; The Paper River, 114; The Paper Tower, 10; Photoelectric Steel Balls, 562; The Pick Up, 522; Pinhole Camera, 334; Seeing Is Believing, 379; Shots in the Dark, 579; The Softball Throw, 140; Speed of Sound, 313; The Stoplight, 604; Wavelengths of Colours, 399; Waves on a Snakey, 292; What's the Charge?, 412; Your Power, 204
**Lamp,** fluorescent, spectrum of, 361
**Laser,** 587; common (Table), 588; continuous, 587; pulsed, 587; in surgery, 590
**Laser diode,** 607
**Laser-induced fusion,** 652
**Law(s),** conservation of energy, 227; conservation of momentum, 183; Hooke's, 147; inverse square, 161; Kepler's, 157; Lenz's, 523; Newton's first, 89; Newton's second, 90; Newton's third, 92; Newton's universal gravitation, 162, 163; Ohm's, 452; of reflection, 299; Snell's, 350; of thermodynamics, first, 256; of thermodynamics, second, 258
**LED,** 607
**Length,** unit of (m), 14
**Lens,** 378; achromatic, 384; concave, 378; contact, 385; converging, 378; convex, 378; diverging, 378; focal length of (f), 380; focal point of, 380; real image formed by convex, 380; resolving power of, 402; virtual image formed by concave, 383; virtual image formed by convex, 382
**Lens equation,** 381
**Lens and mirror colors convention,** 369
**Lens sign convention,** 381
**Lenz,** H.F.E., 523

# Photo Credits